D0108787

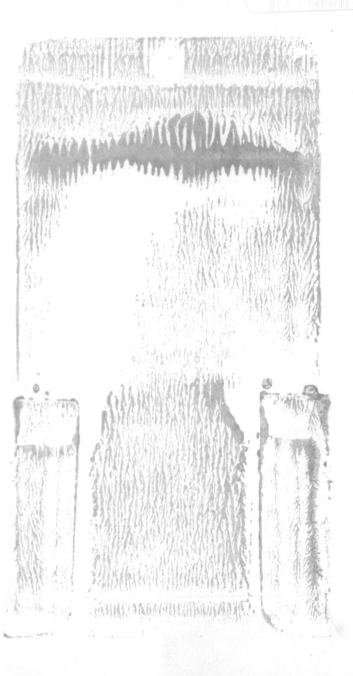

BASIC PROCESSES OF GASEOUS ELECTRONICS

(*photograph H. Raether*)

CLOUD TRACK PICTURE OF A SINGLE ELECTRON AVALANCHE

LEONARD B. LOEB

BASIC PROCESSES OF GASEOUS ELECTRONICS

UNIVERSITY OF CALIFORNIA PRESS
BERKELEY AND LOS ANGELES · 1961

Second edition, revised
Second printing
University of California Press
Berkeley and Los Angeles, California
Cambridge University Press
London, England
Copyright, 1955, by
The Regents of the University of California
L. C. Catalog Card No.: 55-5196
Printed in the United States of America
Designed by John B. Goetz

This book is humbly dedicated to that group of capable and enthusiastic young physicists, theoretical and experimental, with their fine appreciation of modern atomic physics and kinetic theory, who have, during and since World War II, in America, England, Germany, and Italy, rejuvenated the field of study previously called the Discharge of Electricity in Gases, and now more properly called Gaseous Electronics.

PREFACE

The author published a book in 1939, entitled *Fundamental Processes of Electrical Discharge in Gases*. Except for the last two chapters dealing with glow and arc discharges, it presented a comprehensive, up-to-date review of the field, based on actual experimental acquaintance with the various subjects treated. This was the result of many years' work by the author and his students. Such a critical review was then urgently needed, since the accumulated and often conflicting researches and theory of nearly forty years, carried out with techniques ranging from those of the most primitive type to the improved techniques and atomic theory of the nineteen-thirties, had been adopted and used *indiscriminately* by various workers without analysis. Several earlier books written on the subject had either been compilations of past work, or were somewhat specialized monographs, presenting the methods and theories of some school of workers in a more restricted sphere.

Two somewhat more timely compilations then existing require separate mention. One of these was the excellent review of limited scope by K. T. Compton and I. Langmuir in *Reviews of Modern Physics* of 1930-1931. The other was a more unified treatment of the whole subject, based on sound atomic theory as of 1930, written by A. von Engel and M. Steenbeck in two volumes that were published in 1931 and 1934. The latter books were basically not critical of the subject material. The kinetic theory there used was relatively primitive, and was presented without indicating its weakness. The worst defect of the books was their lack of proper references and coverage of the literature. The author's book in 1939 thus filled a particular need.

Fifteen years have passed since *Fundamental Processes* appeared. During those years, a major war has accelerated technical advance to the point where new tools and methods, such as microwave techniques, square pulsed potentials of short duration, improved vacuum techniques, and high-speed oscilloscopes have permitted developments that were previously impossible. In the same period have appeared certain major theoretical and experimental contributions to the subject. Many of these lie in generalizations of the methods of Chapman and

Cowling to the analysis of electron-energy distributions in gases to include microwave fields and carriers of all masses at all energies; a unification of methods and techniques, with consequent much better agreement in the conclusions drawn.

There has been a mature mathematical physical analysis of the generalized recombination problem by G. Jaffé, which has clarified past controversies and placed the subject on a sound basis. There has also appeared an excellent summary of certain aspects of the breakdown problems as developed before 1939 in the famous Philips Research Laboratory at Eindhoven by M. J. Druyvesteyn and F. M. Penning, published in *Reviews of Modern Physics* in 1940. The streamer theory of the mechanism of the electric spark, with all of its implications, especially in connection with photoionization in gases, was completed in this period, and newer techniques were applied to establish its reality and limitations. Again, the fast Geiger counter anode mechanism and the photoelectrically conditioned burst-pulse corona were analyzed in detail during this period.

Another significant advance lay in the summary and unification of the researches of J. S. Townsend, V. A. Bailey, and their school, published in *The Behaviour of Slow Electrons in Gases*, by R. H. Healey and J. W. Reed in 1941. Later researches, notably by L. G. H. Huxley, introduced improvements in techniques and analysis of the Townsend measurements, thus bringing them more into line with the methods of other workers.

Probably most important of all in the current rebirth of this field of study was the invasion during the war and afterward by a group of brilliant, modern young physicists, both theoretical and experimental, who were well trained in the kinetic theory of nonequilibrium gases, modern atomic theory, and modern laboratory techniques. It should also be added that in this country during the past several years, the workers in this field have tightened the bonds of common scientific interest through an annual convention, entitled the "Conference on Gaseous Electronics," for the discussion of common problems. This has resulted in far better co-operation, co-ordination of work, and avoidance of duplication and polemics, thus further accelerating progress. Under these happy auspices, the advances made in the last ten years merit incorporation into the somewhat clarified and organized body of knowledge which was striven for in the author's *Fundamental Processes*. It is his hope that in the present book the first step will have been made toward achieving this goal.

Obviously, the problem could not have been solved by writing a new edition of the earlier work. The old book laid many ghosts of the past which require no comment today. Furthermore, the new material is so extensive that it must be approached *de novo* in many instances. In order to be of value, the present work must serve not only for use in instruction in the subject, but, even more, for the benefit of the engineer or physicist who is not conversant with the field of gaseous electronics, there must be a simplified phenomenological or kinetic-theoretical introduction to each topic, as there was in the earlier book. Then, on the basis of experimental findings and later theoretical development, there will be presented the more esoteric advances. Obviously, it is impossible to include in detail the elaborate mathematical physical analyses, but enough of the analytical approach can be given to indicate the physics underlying the main trend of the study, together with its logical conclusions.

Considerable emphasis is placed on laying the proper, simplified physical foundation, in order that the later more complicated and subtle implications of seemingly simple theory may be anticipated and understood. As indicated by the table of contents, the general chapter topics covered in *Fundamental Processes* will be followed. However, the chapter on recombination has been moved to a later section of the book, being logically preceded by that on the formation of negative ions. Some chapters of a more classical nature, such as chapters II and VII, have not been altered materially, as there has been little to add. Others, such as those on ionic-drift velocities, electron-drift velocities, energy distributions, electron attachment, recombination, and the first and second Townsend coefficients, have been radically changed.

The re-evaluation of many of the accumulated measurements has made it possible to present reliable tables of needed data for the use of workers in the field. Owing to the rapid advances that have been made and the free exchange of information between the various workers, this book contains much recent material and detail, some of which has not as yet been published, or is currently being published in abbreviated form. In presenting some of this advanced and highly technical material, the author acknowledges with thanks the expert contributions from his coauthors. These are Prof. Sanborn C. Brown, who wrote on microwave studies of recombination; Dr. Gregory H. Wannier, who wrote on the theory of ion mobility; Dr. Julius P. Molnar, for his contribution on metastable action; and Dr. John A. Hornbeck, for his contribution on dynamic time studies of the second coefficient. The last three named, together with Dr. H. D. Hagstrum, belonged to the excellent research group in the Bell Telephone Laboratories, which made such great advances from 1947 to 1952 under the direction of

A. D. White. Their helpful co-operation is here gratefully acknowledged.

In presenting this book to the reader, the author hopes that it will serve as a useful text and reference book for all those interested in working with or in gaseous electronics. In particular, it is hoped that the material here presented will lay the foundation for a second book by the author and for books by some of his colleagues and co-workers that will deal more directly with the various breakdown processes.

L. B. L.

Berkeley, California
February, 1955

ACKNOWLEDGMENTS

The writing of this monograph has extended over a period of five years, entailing many revisions and alterations owing to the rapid advances made in the years following World War II. A considerable share of the support of the basic research in the field of gaseous electronics, especially in university research laboratories, accrues to the credit of the Office of Naval Research. Had it not been for the generous support and encouragement given by this far-seeing organization, many of the outstanding advances recorded in this book would still require to be made in the face of competition with more popular fields of modern research.

Not only has much of the advance made in the author's understanding come from the research of the many ONR-supported projects in other institutions as well as in his own laboratory, but the Office of Naval Research has actively encouraged and aided him in the preparation of the present work in ways too numerous to mention. He is especially indebted to his ONR grant for assistance in the typing of the manuscript, in its many revisions, in the augmenting of his reference index file, and in the preparation of some of the revised drawings and prints. It is thus with thanks that he acknowledges the assistance of the Office of Naval Research, which has made this comprehensive summary of an important basic area of modern physical research available to industry, colleges, and to his many co-workers throughout the world.

As indicated in the preface, the author is greatly indebted to his coauthors, Prof. S. C. Brown, Dr. G. H. Wannier, Dr. J. P. Molnar, and Dr. J. A. Hornbeck. Much inspiration and help have come to him through his frequent discussions with a number of gaseous electronic enthusiasts, Dr. T. R. Holstein, Dr. M. A. Biondi, Dr. A. V. Phelps, Dr. A. O. McCoubrey, Dr. L. J. Varnerin, Jr., and many other members of the research group of Dr. Dan Alpert at Westinghouse Research, whose notable contributions to the field have made writing this book a genuine pleasure.

The author's thanks are due to Dr. Holstein, Prof. W. P. Allis, and Prof. H. Margenau for their constructive criticism of chapter I, and especially to Prof. Margenau for the investigation and subsequent solution of many controversial issues through the work of his research students. His appreciation is also extended to Dr. H. D. Hagstrum and Dr. G. H. Wannier of the Bell Telephone Laboratories, as well as to Prof. R. N. Varney of the Bell Telephone Laboratories and the Washington University of St. Louis, for making available their detailed data on secondary electron liberation and ion-drift velocities in advance of publication.

His indebtedness to Prof. W. P. Dyke, Dr. Willard H. Bennett, and Dr. A. Doehring, as well as to his former students, Professors L. H. Fisher, R. Geballe, and G. L. Weissler, for their many contributions and discussions, must be recorded. Thanks are also due to Prof. D. R. Bates, of Queen's University, Belfast, for his co-operation in the chapter on recombination in 1950.

The author is also grateful to Prof. R. B. Holt, formerly of Harvard, and to Doctors L. Malter and E. O. Johnson of R.C.A. Laboratories, for discussions on the use of probes, and to Dr. Harry J. White of the Research Corporation, for his many useful discussions.

Into a very special class of contributors to whatever success this book enjoys, fall the names of Dr. E. E. Dodd, Dr. W. B. Kunkel, Dr. A. W. Overhauser, and Dr. R. J. Wijsman, gifted young theoretical physicists, all of whom were the author's former students. Their correct and valuable solutions of many small but important intricate problems may be found throughout the book, most of them not having found their way into print elsewhere.

The author is especially indebted to Mrs. Betty P. Hurd, M.A. in Physics, for many of the drawings. He must also acknowledge his thanks to his several part- and full-time secretaries, the Misses Ruth Johnson, Czerna A. Flanagan, Edna Palmeter, Mrs. Muriel Alan, and Mrs. Nancy Jaster, without whose help over the years this book could never have been written. Finally, he is most grateful to Mr. Grant V. Wallace, editor, for his many hours of painstaking and conscientious work in preparing the manuscript for press.

TABLE OF CONTENTS

Chapter I

IONIC MOBILITIES

PART ONE

§1. Introduction.

In December of 1895 the scientific world was electrified by Roentgen's announcement of the discovery of X-rays. One very important property of these mysterious rays was that in passing through gases which were normally recognized as good insulators, they rendered them conducting in a measure that made conduction currents in gases open to quantitative study. With this new tool, J. J. Thomson and his brilliant group of young investigators at the Cavendish Laboratory, including notably Ernest Rutherford and J. S. Townsend, at once set to work to study the properties of the conductivity produced. It was soon established that the conductivity produced by the rays decayed with time after radiation ceased; that the conductivity could be filtered out by means of glass wool, or metal tubes of small diameter; and that the conductivity was produced by electrical carriers of both signs which moved in electrical fields with reasonably high velocities. The velocities were first measured roughly by Thomson and Rutherford, and were found to be proportional to the electrical field strength and of the order of one to two cm/sec per volt/cm.

The disappearance in time of these carriers was ascribed to recombination of the positive and negative carriers present in the volume, and to diffusion of these carriers from the gas to the walls. In analogy to the conduction in solution, these carriers were called gaseous ions. It was suspected that the positive and negative carriers in gases had different velocities in the same field, but it remained for J. Zeleny (1), by means of careful experiments in air, to evaluate these with any accuracy—a feat accomplished by 1899. Meanwhile, the recombination of ions was studied by numerous investigators in the years immediately following, probably the outstanding investigations being those of P. Langevin. Among other notable early studies were those of Townsend on the coefficient of diffusion of the ions. These studies, combined with mobility measurements, did

1

much to establish the fact that the charge of gaseous ions was predominantly that of the univalent ions in solutions.

Thus, it was early established that in some fashion X-rays separated normally neutral gaseous molecules into positive and negative carriers called *ions*, having a single ionic charge and moving with a velocity $v = kX$ in an electrical field of strength X. The quantity k was called the *mobility* of the ion, which was recognized as a constant for the gas in question. It was also observed that the mobility k was inversely proportional to pressure p at constant temperature, and more generally that it was inversely proportional to the gaseous density ρ. Thus it may be written that

$$k = K \left(\frac{760}{p} \right)_T = K \frac{\rho_0}{\rho} ,$$

with ρ_0 the density at n.t.p. and K the reduced mobility or the mobility constant.

§2. Nature of the Problem of Mobility Measurement.

In retrospect, it is today amazing that the workers of the earlier years, with their inadequate instrumentation and insufficient knowledge of atomic processes, should have achieved the progress that they did. In order to appreciate the problems involved in mobility measurement, it is best to outline the pitfalls and difficulties of the problem and then to indicate the solutions proposed. It may as well be pointed out that considerations similar to these apply equally to many other measurements of gaseous carriers to be presented; therefore, they may be summarized at this point, once and for all.
A. *The Production of Ions.*

Ions are created by the following processes:

1. Subjecting a gas to X-rays or rapidly moving high-energy particles produces positive and negative ions in the volume of the gas. With X-rays the primary particle occasionally ejected from the atoms is a very fast, energetic electron. This fast electron, in common with all rapidly moving electrified bodies, produces occasional secondary ion pairs along its trajectory. The theory of the production of secondary electron-ion pairs by this mechanism is now fairly well understood. The primary electron paths are more or less tortuous, and ions are created in somewhat sparsely spaced pairs. Heavy, rapidly moving charged particles that ionize, such as α particles, give paths that are exceptionally straight, with great initial local densities of ions along the path axis. Heavy-particle ionization can be con-

tained within rather sharply defined beams, but initially it is thus seriously anisotropic in space. Electron and X-ray ionization yields beams with very poorly defined edges because of the tortuous primary electron paths. While their ionization is more isotropic in density distribution on a macroscale, it is still inhomogeneous on a microscale until diffusion has been active for some time. In the volume, equal numbers of free electrons and positively charged atomic, or molecular, entities are produced. Occasionally, certain polar molecules can be ionized by electron impact into positive and negative ions. These occurrences are very rare, and usually ionization of a gas by electrons yields electrons and positive ions. If the X-ray beams strike the walls or electrodes, an excess of electrons may be produced, since owing to the density of atoms the X-radiation liberates electrons from solids rather effectively. By the judicious use of fields, ions of one sign can be drawn out and studied.

2. Gaseous discharges, such as sparks, arcs, or glows, create ions in the volume of the gas. In the sparks, the ionization is usually exceedingly dense along a narrow path. For the arcs and glows, usually at low pressure, considerable volumes of densely ionized and excited gas are produced. These are called "plasmas." They have about equal numbers of positive ions and electrons, except near bounding surfaces, electrodes, or walls. A new, fairly homogeneous source of ions and electrons of considerable density is achieved by the ultrahigh-frequency breakdown of the gas in a volume, using microwave techniques. High carrier densities and considerable uniformity of distribution can be produced in a whole volume within sharply defined time intervals by this technique, which is now frequently used for ion studies. These ions can be drawn out by appropriate fields and studied.

3. Photoelectric or thermionic emission from surfaces liberates free electrons into gases. The current liberated depends on the field and gas pressure, owing to back diffusion and/or space-charge effects. Thermionic liberations, by virtue of the required heating, introduce density gradients into the gas not open to exact evaluation. These must be circumvented in measurements.

4. Certain heated substances, Kunsman catalysts, some fused salts or glasses, and certain oxides on electrode surfaces will liberate positive ions of sorts appropriate to their composition at relatively low temperatures. Emission from such ion sources is space-charge limited. They also introduce temperature gradients into the gas near their point of origin. Similar ions can be obtained by shooting beams of alkali atoms at hot, gas-free W or Pt filaments,

if the work function of the metal is greater than the ionization potential of the atoms. Some heated salts and glasses on negative electrodes emit negative ions into the gas.

5. Ions of unique sign appropriate to the gas and in considerable numbers can be obtained by using positive or negative point or wire corona discharge in a gas.

6. Ions can be created by chemical actions and in flames, but these sources are not good for basic studies owing to the complex conditions and effects of temperature variations.

7. Ions can be produced in a gas in small numbers by ultraviolet illumination with photons of short wave length appropriate to the gas. Under some conditions such illumination also produces nucleation of the gas with neutral particles. These nuclei, picking up small primary ions, yield large or Langevin ions. Similar ions as well as small ions can be created by the spraying or bubbling of liquids.

The foregoing list given comprises all of the known ion-producing mechanisms.

B. *Factors Imposing Limitations on Measurement.*

It will be seen at once that the listed methods of obtaining ions for study introduce the following limitations into the designs of apparatus for ion-mobility measurements.

1. It will be noted that while the methods of ion formation always yield massive positive ions which are initially charged atoms or molecules, there are very few processes that *initially* create formed negative ions in a gas. The initial negative carriers in gases are thus usually all electrons which are torn out of the gas molecules or surfaces. This probably applies even in flames. Thus, if negative ions are to be studied, these must later form by electron attachment to atoms or molecules. Unless time is given for such formation, there will appear electronic carriers, or carriers that are electronic part of the way and ionic for the remainder. Therefore, one must always be careful to have' *negative ions formed* before study. Negative ions can be formed directly by emission from some heated salts, bombardment of surfaces at grazing incidence by appropriate energetic positive ions, and occasionally by dissociation of molecules; e.g., the creation of H^- ions from H_2O-contaminated discharges. Yields are not great, and many of these ions are negative atomic ions. They are not commonly encountered.

2. As random thermal velocities are of the order of 10^4 cm/sec and distances traversed between collisions with molecules are of the order of 10^{-5} cm or less at n.t.p., ions make some 10^9 collisions with molecules per second. Thus, in a millisecond an ion on the

average will meet an impurity present to one part in 10⁶.[1] Gases as usually prepared and stored, especially in metal vessels, are pure to no better than one part in 10⁴. With impurities, and even with some gases in the absence of impurities, the following changes can occur in encounters of the initial ions (positive or negative) with molecules.

a) Positive ions will exchange charges with neutral atoms or molecules of lower ionizing potential (Kallmann-Rosen effect). The probability is greater, the nearer the ionizing potentials are together. With argon ions in argon, it may reach close to unity. With mercury gauges and diffusion pumps, Hg vapor is present to a pressure of 10^{-3} mm at 300° K. unless special precautions are taken. Thus, even in 760 mm pressure of air, Hg is present to better than one part in 10⁶. Hence, in a millisecond there is a good chance that initially created ions like O_2^+, H_2^+, etc., will have changed to Hg^+. Increase in mass of the ion of this order materially affects ionic properties. The impurity could also well be a large organic molecule from stopcock grease vapors which change ionic properties even more drastically. Interference due to change of charge in ionic studies can only be prevented by using ions such as the alkali or alkaline earth series, having lower ionizing potentials than any gas or common impurity present.

b) By the same token (see under *a*), any multiply charged positive ion will quickly steal an electron from a neutral atom to give two singly charged ions, even in pure gases. Above 1 mm pressure doubly charged ions will not persist much over 10^{-4} sec.

c) Initial electronic carriers will sooner or later attach to some molecule or foreign molecule to form negative ions of unknown character unless the gas used has a strong affinity for electrons. Whether the Kallmann-Rosen effect occurs for negative ions is not known from experiment. It must be possible where a Cl_2 molecule meets an ion of O_2^-, since the energy balance is strongly in favor of a change to Cl^- and a Cl atom and O_2 molecule.

d) While in general, forces between ions and molecules in the gas are not such as to favor attachment of a gas molecule to the ion, this is not always true. It appears that at low temperatures, especially with smaller ions and larger polarizable molecules, attachment of one or more molecules can occur. At higher temperatures

---

[1]The purest gas studied so far was He obtained by superfluid leakage of liquid He into a chamber cleaned by Alpert vacuum techniques. The purity here conservatively claimed by M. A. Biondi (74) was one part impurity in 10⁹.

this is less likely, but strongly polar molecules will attach to smaller ions either permanently as a complex ion, or they will repeatedly attach and dissociate, thus changing mobilities. Much recent information (32), (75), indicates that with inert gases, molecular ions are formed from excited atoms in single impact with neutral atoms, or from atomic ions in triple impact with neutral atoms, according to the relations

$$A* \text{ at } (E_i - 1.5 \ ev) + A \rightarrow A_2^+ + e$$

and

$$A^+ + 2A \rightarrow A_2^+ + A \ .$$

Certain gases have a charge-specific affinity for ions; e.g., positive ions with RNH_2 or CN, and negative ions with ROH. It is clear, then, that with the magnitude of the collision frequency and the chance of varied impurities, the ions, positive and negative, can change their nature by addition or exchange in addition products not once but possibly two or three times in 10^{-1} sec of study. Such changes can sometimes be controlled, depending on the duration of measurement and the use of purposefully added gases, while usually they are uncontrolled in longer intervals where purity remains uncertain. This requires that if known ions are to be studied, the measurements must be made within less than a millisecond on reasonably pure gases to prevent change.

3. Ideally, in order that mobilities may be measured accurately, the ions must start from a clearly defined surface or plane and be received as a group with a sharply defined boundary at the detecting plate. Achievement of such conditions is exceedingly difficult. X-ray ionization beams from the viewpoint of boundaries are very poor. Temperature and density gradients at hot cathodes or anodes, as well as the delay of electron attachment to negative ion formation for photoelectrons, are detrimental to such boundaries. Ions may be drawn from plasmas or bulk ionized gases by means of slits, grids, or gauzes. This requires an auxiliary field for extraction behind the gauze which penetrates through the gauze into the measuring side of the field. While the contributed addition of the penetrating fields may be small, the important action is the effect that gauze and fields have on the plane of departure of the carriers let through (2). If the field on the measuring side is alternating and high or low compared to the extracting field, the ions at the beginning of the accelerative phase may be in a plane respectively well behind or well in front of the gauze plane. Furthermore, the boundaries

will be very ill defined. Only two or three of the existing methods of mobility measurement really insure clean-cut edges for all kinds of ions or circumvent lack of definition.

4. Diffusion of ions is ever present. This diffusive motion is superposed on the field-imposed velocities. Thus, owing to diffusion, originally clean-cut surfaces of ionization will broaden, tail off, and blur by diffusion. For ions at n.t.p. the effect is normally small for intervals of 10^{-1} second or less. For electrons the interval must be 10^{-3} or less to prevent trouble. In any case, where diffusion intervenes, its presence must be expected and corrections should be made. One expedient is to vary distances traversed and choose corresponding points on the observed current-potential or current-time curves.

5. The measurements must be made with accurately known and clearly defined electrostatic fields. Field uniformity must be maintained, and distorting fields must be scrupulously avoided by use of guard rings, etc.; a condition frequently lost sight of. Contact potentials must be avoided, eliminated, or corrected. Account must be taken of all secondary falls of potential across auxiliary condensers. Floating conductors and ill-defined screening must be avoided. All insulating surfaces, glass container walls, supports, etc., which can acquire charges from ions or otherwise, must be effectively screened by gauzes or adequate coatings, for such electrostatic influences can completely vitiate measurements.

6. Gases, in order to maintain any degree of purity, must be carefully prepared and handled in outgassed glass vessels. Electrodes must be outgassed by induction heating, or most effectively by appropriate ion bombardment. All foreign vapors, such as those from organic insulators, stopcock greases, and diffusion pumps, must be frozen out and avoided. "Getters" may be employed in some gases to remove liberated impurities, or else contacts with freezing-out traps must be maintained. The new Westinghouse Alpert metal valves (76) may make such precautions unnecessary in the future.

7. In many cases currents are very small. This requires that insulation be of a high order. Leakage losses are usually slight with well-dried gases inside outgassed glass or quartz systems. More serious losses occur over the outsides of the vessels. Often background losses caused by natural ionization, as well as by electrostatic inductive effects, can be canceled out by use of appropriate dummy chambers with reversed polarity.

8. Finally, the question of resolution arises. Many mobility methods

give only the rise of current caused by the arrival of the ion block with edges blurred by diffusion at the collecting electrode. This yields resolution only by graphic differentiation of the current-potential or similar observed curves between variables. Methods using thin slabs of ions of initially well-defined boundaries will give more or less peaked curves with mobilities differing by more than 10% clearly resolved. Such methods are to be preferred to others.

9. Mobility measurements must consist in essence of a measurement of the time T to cross a given distance x under a given uniform field X. It is a matter of convenience or expediency whether distance x is fixed for a fixed field X and time T varied, whether time is fixed and field varied, or whether time and field are fixed and distance x is varied. Each has its use, depending on the tools at hand and purpose of the experiment, and all combinations have been used. Sometimes one variable, such as distance x, can be changed to calibrate the systems in absolute measure, and thereafter X or T can be varied.

10. Before the development of pulse techniques, it became essential in shorter time intervals to use sinusoidal oscillations of potential or field. These present some difficulties when it comes to biasing the potentials to avoid the effects of diffusion. Such fields are very bad where mobility varies with field strength, as is the case for electrons or for ions at low pressures, and thus they should only be used as triggering pulses on shutters. Fortunately, marked improvements are possible today over methods of the past, especially in the use of techniques with pulses of square wave form, short duration, and variable repeat rate. Certainly, electron- and ion-mobility studies of high precision are now possible if care is taken and such accuracy is desired.

§ 3. Summary of the Useful Experimental Methods.

In the presentation of actual methods of measurement, it is proposed to discuss in detail only six, using as examples the latest developments of these. There are many other measurements and principles, involving such things as the electrical wind in corona discharge; ion currents and potentials in various systems, including coaxial cylinders; observations on the operation of Geiger counters, etc.; determination of diffusion coefficients;[2] as well as various combinations of more direct conventional techniques (3). A book could appropriately be written on the subject. As the reader is in-

---

[2]Some of the indirect methods will be discussed at other more appropriate points.

terested first in evaluating mobilities accurately in a given regime of age, gas, pressure, etc., he desires to acquire only such methods as can most profitably be used for his purpose. Other than in satisfying an academic interest, there is today little merit in most of the methods omitted, so far as the reader is concerned. Therefore, only direct methods of proven worth will be presented, covering the various contingencies. It should further be noted that these are mainly the procedures that have yielded the decisive results discussed. The six methods follow.

a) The air-blast method of Erikson (4). This is presented because it gives the most flexible apparatus for studying *relative* values of mobilities of ions from normal to very large ones as a function of age from 10^{-3} second to tens of seconds. Purity control in such methods is poor. Accuracy of measurement in absolute values is not possible. Resolution can be made very good. It is the only method suitable for certain types of studies. All types of ion generation can be used.

b) The Bradbury (5) modification of the Tyndall-Grindley (6) method, using an alternating potential of complicated form and flashed X-ray ionization. It is thus limited to the ions produced by X-ray ionization in the volume of the gas. This rules out the study of negative ions in nonelectron-attaching gases. Electrons must be removed by a special potential flash in the cycle. The complicated potential cycle probably cannot be achieved by other than mechanical commutators, and thus the method is limited to ions measured over 10^{-4} second down to seconds of age. It can be applied to ions in the purest gases. It is subject to the contaminations produced by X-ray ionization in gases where reactive gases are present. Its geometrically well-defined ion boundaries lead to sharply peaked curves of high resolving power which yield absolute values of the mobilities, limited only by the blurring produced by diffusion.

c) The most flexible of all methods for precision work over ages probably now ranging from 10^{-6} sec on down, is the Tyndall-Powell four-gauze electrical shutter method (7). It has high resolving power and yields mobilities down to 1% of accuracy. It can be calibrated to yield absolute mobilities. It can be applied to ions of all origins, and allows of ions being studied after colliding in a drift space as well as to rather newly formed ions. It can be used with gaseous mixtures on known ions, and is susceptible of use with the most highly purified gases. Its design is complicated and it requires time to set up. Application of modern pulse techniques offers unlimited possibilities for improvement of this method (77).

d) Another method of precision is the Bradbury-Nielsen (8) electrical shutter method, applicable to carriers however produced. It has been used primarily for the direct measurement of electron mobilities. It is especially adaptable to high-velocity measurements and to carriers of various ages. Its general applicability is about the same as that of the Tyndall-Powell four-gauze method, from which it differs only by replacing the gauze shutters with the Loeb electron or ion filters. Its resolving power is not so good as that of the latter method, nor is its precision so high, even though it yields absolute values. How much it can be improved by the use of modern pulse techniques cannot be conjectured.

e) An effective method is the magnetic-deflection method of J. S. Townsend, initially limited to studies of low pressures on electrons (9).[3] Later adapted for use with positive ions by Hershey, it extended mobility studies down to the limits of pressures where failure of ions to attain equilibrium with the field makes the word "mobility" meaningless. It can be used for carriers from all sources, but is limited to lower pressures for all ionic carriers unless uniform high magnetic fields in kilogauss over volumes of tens of centimeters on a side are available. Its resolving power is low, and it must be used for carriers of unique mobility. It yields only average values. Its accuracy is not so high as that of the Tyndall-Powell or Bradbury-Nielsen methods, which perhaps can now be developed to supersede it, even for ions at low pressures.

f) Very recently, the use of pulsed discharges and fast oscillographs has yielded directly measured values of the mobility at high fields and low pressures that were previously inaccessible. This work was a by-product of other studies, and is reported in detail at another point. Extension of such techniques is possible, and should lead to precision results.

§ 4. The Erikson Air-Blast Method (4).

The method uses a long tube of rectangular cross section, having its plane surfaces, top, *A*, and bottom, *B*, made of metal sheets placed *D* cm apart, shown in figure 1.1. The width of the tube is immaterial. Its other sides must be insulating, and of such nature as not to contaminate the gas. For example, they could be of plate glass and slightly conducting. The length of the tube must be suited to the problem, but it must be long compared to *D*. The lower plate

---

[3]The method has been improved in recent years by L. G. H. Huxley (9) for study of electron mobilities. A modification of this method has been developed by V. A. Bailey for electron mobilities. Precision is not high, but results confirm others in general.

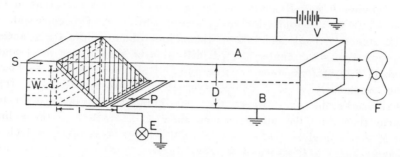

Fig. 1.1. Schematic diagram of the Erikson air-blast tube.

may be made mobile along the length of the tube by rack and pinion to enable its critical section P to be moved up and down the length of the tube. The critical section consists of a transverse slot in the lower plate B, into which is inserted a narrow, insulated strip P, with a minimum clearance from the edges of slot. The width of P critically determines the resolving power of the device, but it must be large enough to receive adequate ions. By means of a fan F, gas is circulated, if need be, in a continuous system with purifiers, through the long tube at a uniform velocity. The uniform distribution of flow across the tube can be assisted by having at the entrance end a series of horizontal vanes W. Of the vanes, the uppermost one with the plane of plate A delimits a critical volume S. Uniformly through the vertical cross section of this volume S are run or created the ions to be measured. The distance between the top vane and the plane of A is critical for the resolving power of the device. The distance d from the center of this space S to B is the important distance in measurement. The narrower the ionization space S consistent with an adequate supply of ions, the higher the resolving power. Ions can be introduced into S by placing ionizing agents on the top or bottom of the space, or by ionizing gas in an auxiliary volume and flowing it into the upstream end of S. This could be done through a delay line if it were desired to age the ions. The plate B is grounded and A is raised to suitable potentials by means of the battery V. Electrode P is connected to an electrometer.

Ions leave the orifice of S and are carried downstream by the supposedly uniform gas stream at a velocity u. Meanwhile, the field $X = V/D$ is driving the ions at a uniform velocity from A toward B. The collector at P is downstream at distance l from the front face of W and S. With uniform fields and velocities, the slab of ionized gas from S proceeds along the shaded area in the figure.

By moving B and P upstream, by increasing u or by decreasing V, the width of the ionized slab is swept across P. The current to P will rise to a peak and fall as the center plane of the ionized slab sweeps across the center of P. If diffusion is absent, and the ionization in S is uniform, then the rise and fall of current should be linear and graphically yield a sharp, symmetrical isosceles triangle. The peak marks the point where the ions cross the distance d in the same time t as the stream moves them a distance l to the center of P. Accordingly, $vt/ut = kX_0t/ut = d/l$. Since $X_0 = V_0/D$, it follows that $kV_0/uD = d/l$, so that $k = (D/V_0)\,(d/l)\,u$.

Usually, it is not convenient to vary u. This quantity is set at a fixed value consistent with the timing desired. It should not be so high as to cause marked turbulence. The uniformity of u down the tube can be studied and observed by smoke particles introduced between the vanes of W. Usually again l is set at a suitable value, but may be changed to assist in covering a large range of values. The peaks will be narrower, the larger the ratio d/l. Accuracy requires l to be large enough. Thus, it is most convenient and usual to vary V in practice. The nature of the curves obtained is shown in figure

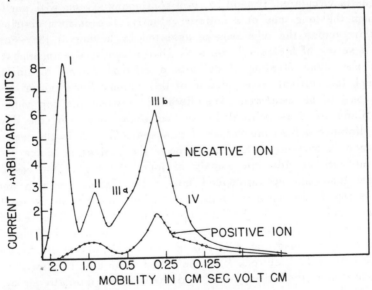

Fig. 1.2. Ion-current peaks relative to air ion mobility scale, as observed by Seville Chapman for ions created by spraying water, using the Erikson tube. The tube was calibrated on known ions to give the scale shown. Note that negative ions show three and possibly four mobilities, while positive ions show three peaks. The resolving power is clearly indicated.

1.2. These results were obtained by Seville Chapman (4) on ions obtained by spraying of pure water. In these measurements, Chapman actually studied mobilities ranging from 1.5 to 10^{-5} cm/sec per volt/cm.

§ 5. The Bradbury Modification of the Tyndall-Grindley Method (5).

In principle this method, using a source of ionization producing ions in the gas, attempts to get a clearly defined boundary of the ionized slab to give a sharply defined time in crossing from one plate to the other. This is achieved by creating the ions in a thin plane parallel slab $F\,G$ of gas as shown in figure 1.3. This slab is placed parallel to the two plates A and B of the plane parallel electrode system quite close to the high-potential plate B, and far removed from the collecting or measuring plate A. By exposing the ionized slab $F\,G$ to a reversed field for a short time, about half the ions in the $F\,G$ are dragged out to plate B before the collecting field is applied. The ion slab, which survives collection and crosses to A, the collecting plate, thus has at its lower face a sharply defined surface of ionization. The advent of such a surface at the collecting electrode A gives a sharp current change when conditions are right. The way in which this change can be achieved is as follows: X-rays from a fairly distant source pass through a slot in a lead plate forming a plane flat slab $F\,G$ of thickness t and upper edge F, a distance d_F above the electrode B. This beam is flashed on for a short time βT by means of an open sector in a lead-armored commutator disc. Here β represents a small fraction of the total time T of one revolution. In practice, β is of the order of magnitude of 0.04 (T). It must be long enough to give appreciable ionization for measurement and

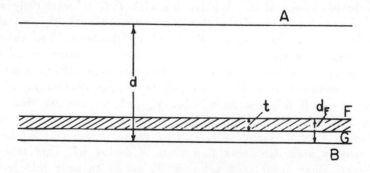

Fig. 1.3. Diagram accompanying the discussion of the principle of Bradbury's modification of the Tyndall-Grindley method.

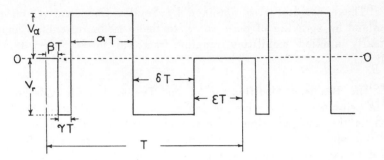

Fig. 1.4. Potential cycle used in the Tyndall-Grindley method.

to permit the slab to be uniformly ionized. The actual potential
cycle applied is shown in figure 1.4.

As noted, the cycle begins with the interval βT governing the
X-ray flash, at which time the potential on plate B is 0. It is then
followed by an interval γT, during which B is at such a potential
as to draw toward itself the ions of the sign to be studied. The
magnitude of this potential V_r is such that in combination with the
duration of the time γT it will draw the slab $F\ G$ so that at least
the lower surface labeled G comes in contact with B, and perhaps
that some ions in $F\ G$ are drawn into B. The ions of opposing sign
are moved a small amount toward A. In gases where electrons do
not attach to give negative ions of a mobility comparable with that
of the positive ions, γT may have to be preceded by a phase of
short duration θT, and an appropriate positive potential V_θ on B
sufficient to draw *all free electrons* of a mobility of the order of
100 times that of the positive ions being studied to B and remove
them. The interval θT and the potential applied V_θ may be so small
that the movement of the positive ion slab $F\ G$ is practically zero.
The value of γ is small, and of the same order as β; i.e., about
0.04 for optimum results, as developed by Bradbury. The value of
γ and the potential amplitude V_r must be calculated in advance
in terms of the theory of the process, so as to give sufficient latitude
in the movement of $F\ G$ to get full resolution. Following γT the
potential on B reverses to a value V_α and remains at that value
for a time αT. The interval αT and V_α must be such in relation to
the width T of $F\ G$ and to V_r and γT as to insure that the ions of
the desired sign can cross from B to A during αT. This crossing,
moreover, must occur at a value of T, so as to have this longest
path of ions fall in the middle of the interval between the first and
last ions crossing. The values of αT, and of the succeeding intervals

δT and ϵT, were chosen by Bradbury to be about equal to 0.32 T. In practice V_r was made 10 to 20% greater than V_a. Actually, from the reasoning to follow, it is a simple matter to figure properly the values of γ, a, V_r, and V_a from the necessary width of $F\ G$ and $F\ B$. During aT, in the event that the ions of opposite sign, e.g., electrons, were not removed in θT, the ions of opposite sign will all be drawn to B and can be neglected in further considerations. The phase δT with a potential V_r draws residual ions that did not reach A during aT back to B, thus clearing the gap to prepare for the next cycle after a period ϵT, during which B is at 0 potential. The purpose of the cyclical arrangement using a commutator lies in sending successive batches of ions to yield an easily measured current to A. X-ray ionization is limited in density and βT is necessarily short, so that the few ions in the slab are multiplied by $N = 1/T$ per second, giving a relatively comfortable current to measure.

The theory of the method is as follows: The cycle may be regarded as keeping a, β, γ, δ, ϵ, and θ, as well as V_r and V_a and their corresponding fields X_r and X_a, constant, and only varying T. Starting with a large value of T, all ions will be swept to B until T is reduced to the point T_F, at which with a mobility k it follows that $kX_r\gamma T_F \lessgtr d_F$, or the distance $F\ B$. If, then, X_a and a have been correctly chosen, and the distance from B to A be designated as d, it will be assumed that $kX_a aT_F > d$, so that ions surviving capture by B during γT can reach A. At T_F, then, a current begins to be registered per cm^2 of A, which may be written as $i = ne(d_F - kX_r\gamma T)$. This consists of all the n ions per cm^3 which escape capture by B and now reach A. As T is still further decreased, and with a proper choice of values of fields and pulse lengths, a time T_0 will be reached, at which during aT all the ions that escaped capture at B just cease to be able to reach A. This occurs when $kX_a aT_0 = d$. This represents a peak in the value of i. After this, i is determined by the width of the surviving ions in $F\ G$ between the top F of the band, at $d - (d_F - kX_r\gamma T)$ from A, down to a distance $d_a = kX_a aT$ from A, which marks the lowest ion group toward B which can reach A in T with $T < T_0$. The current then is

$$i = ne\ [d_a - \{d - d_F - kX_r\ \gamma\ T\}] = ne\ [d_F + k(X_a a - X_r\ \gamma)\ T - d].$$

The current i thus decreases linearly with decrease in the time T to $T = T_a$, at which time the current i equals 0. At this point, solution of the equation for $i = 0$ evaluates T_a as $T_a = d - d_F/k\ (X_a a - X_r\gamma)$. It is seen that except for diffusion effects as T decreases, the current rises sharply at a well-defined time T_F and is linear with T

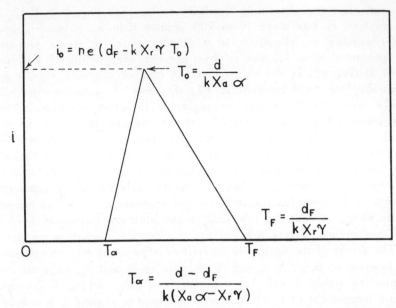

Fig. 1.5. Schematic plot of current against time in the Tyndall-Grindley method, as modified by Bradbury. Note that T_α for rise of current, peak value at T_0 and T_F, when the current is again zero, all yield values of the mobility. Note the relatively high resolution.

until T_0 is reached, as seen in figure 1.5. Thereafter it falls linearly with T to a sharp cutoff at T_α, but with a different slope from that above T_0. The resolving power depends on the interval $T_F \ T_\alpha$, which in turn depends on

$$\frac{d_F}{kX_r\gamma} - \frac{d - d_F}{k(X_a a - X_r \gamma)},$$

or on

$$(d_F X_a a - d X_r \gamma)k.$$

Actual curves observed by Bradbury for positive ions in pure N_2 at three ages given in seconds bear this out, as seen in figure 1.6. The resolving power is indicated by the appearance of two ions in H_2, shown in figure 1.7.

§6. The Four-Gauze Electrical Shutter Method of Tyndall and Powell (7).

In this method ions are created by any desired means in a first section $F \ I$ of the device of figure 1.8. They pass from this chamber by means of a field that removes positive or negative ions through the appropriate potential applied to the gauze I relative to F. Any

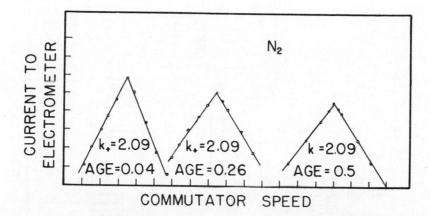

Fig. 1.6. Curves for ions in pure N_2 as a function of age, as revealed in Bradbury's work with the Tyndall-Grindley method.

temperature gradients ascribed to sources occur in this area, where they do not alter the measurement of mobilities and are amenable to some reduction by cooling. From the gauze l the ions pass into a drift space l G_1, which can be made as long or short as desired,

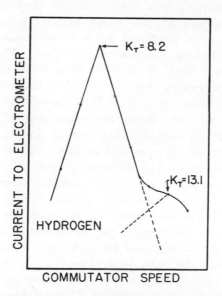

Fig. 1.7. Resolving power of the Bradbury modification of the Tyndall-Grindley method, as exemplified by the presence of two ions in H_2. The faster ion is one that is normally observed in very pure H_2 when ions are studied in short time intervals.

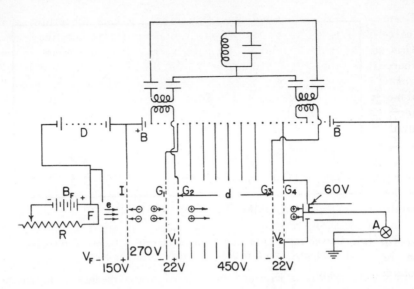

Fig. 1.8. Schematic diagram of the Tyndall-Powell four-gauze shutter method.

depending on whether it is desired to age ions or measure them shortly after formation. Ions then enter the first electrical shutter G_1 G_2. This consists of two plane parallel gauzes representing equipotential surfaces separated by a short distance only with a fixed suitable retarding potential V_1 on them. These gauzes are periodically pulsed with a suitable high-frequency potential of amplitude slightly greater than V_1, the frequency of which is continuously and smoothly variable. Thus ions from I G_1 can penetrate through G_1 G_2 only during the sharp peak of potential which exceeds the retarding bias V_1. Between G_2 and G_3, the two plane parallel gauzes accurately spaced d cm apart, exists the d.c. measuring field of strength X. The distance d may be varied by moving the left-hand assembly uniformly by external magnets. The plane parallel gauzes G_3 G_4, separated as are G_1 G_2, constitute the second shutter. These are biased by the same magnitude-retarding potential $V_2 = V_1$ on the ions. They are acted on by the same high frequency, a.c., as G_1 G_2, and are synchronized with that system. Beyond G_3 G_4 lies the collecting space G_4 E, in which the ions passing through G_3 G_4 during the open phase of the oscillations are driven to the collecting electrode E attached to the electrometer A.

In figure 1.8 the ions are produced by electron bombardment of gas molecules in the drift space I G_1. The electrons from the filament

F are speeded up to ionizing energy in F I, which is narrow, and ionize in I G_1. The potentials are arranged as for positive ions. This source could be replaced for positive alkali ions by a hot anode source using an alkali ion emitter in the place of F, or by a high-frequency glow discharge between electrodes placed in a vertical plane where F is placed in the diagram. The field F I would then serve as an extracting field, and I G_1 as a drift space, either for alkali ions or glow-discharge ions. Little imagination is needed to substitute any other convenient ion source. The fields, especially in G_2 G_3, are maintained uniform by having the region surrounded by equipotential vanes connected to a high-resistance tower. Recorded is the current to E as a function of either the frequency of the master oscillator or as a function of the distance d between G_2 and G_3.

In analyzing the results to be expected, the shutters G_1 G_2 and G_3 G_4, with their separation between gauzes of some 2 mm, must be regarded. There is undoubtedly interpenetration between the retarding fields G_1 G_2 and G_3 G_4 with the bordering fields F G_1, G_2 G_3, and G_4 E. These may in some measure be asymmetrical, so that at the instant when the ions can enter G_1 or G_3 at the phase when the impressed a.c. exceeds the bias, the entering ions do not start from the same planes in both shutters. Such delays may not be serious, and definitely will not seriously affect the peak of the current transmitted. The shutter G_1 G_2 begins to open at a time 0. It remains open, drawing ions in increasing measure over an interval $\Delta T/2$, while the a.c. rises to a peak. It continues to transmit with decreasing amplitude in the decline of the a.c. during another $\Delta T/2$. In this varying a.c. peak pulse of length ΔT the ions enter and cross the distance G_1 G_2 of the grids, the current pulse declining to 0 as the end of ΔT is approached. At this time, then, a sort of bell-shaped distribution of ion densities has passed through and lies in front of G_2. It then proceeds to cross to G_3, distant d cm under the field X.

If, on arrival of the front of this pulse at G_3, the time T_0 of one complete oscillation of the a.c. has elapsed since the beginning of ΔT at G_1, the slab will be transmitted through G_3 G_4, except for losses caused by diffusion. It will then find itself just outside of G_4 and will go to E. Thus, varying either T or d will give a series of fluctuating currents at E, possibly of rather asymmetrical form, with clearly defined peaks, but of similarity such that T or d corresponding to two equivalent points can readily be picked off of the curves with precision. As T is decreased or the frequency N is increased, the ions which just crossed at the lowest frequency or largest time T, will not get through again until a value of $T = T_2$ is reached in which $2T_2 = T_1$, and again not until $3T_3 = T_1$. By choosing the frequency of the observed current maxima N_1, N_2, and N_3, then, the time of T_0 traversing the distance can be found from $N_0 = N_1 = N_2/2 = N_3/3$, giving the time of crossing as $T_0 = 1/N_0$. If such a method is used, keeping the field X and distance d constant in G_2 G_3, the velocity of the ions is *not* d/T_0, because the reference point or peak of the ion group has traversed $d + \delta$, where δ is an equivalent length representing the time spent in crossing from G_3 to G_4 in the second shutter, times the velocity of the ion in the field of the grids. This correction is uncertain but constant under constant a.c. and d.c. fields. Thus, mobilities taken by varying the frequency are derived from $v = (d + \delta)/T_0$. These give *relative* values of the mobilities, and if $d \gg \delta$, the error because of δ is small.

For *absolute values* of mobility the procedure would be as follows: With X and T constant at T_0, the distance d can be increased. If

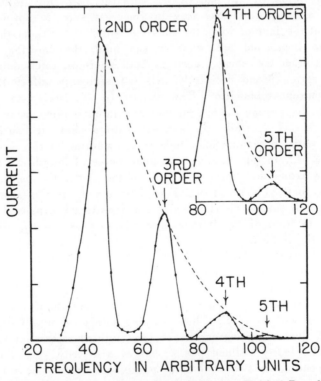

Fig. 1.9. Current-frequency curves as revealed by the Tyndall-Powell method. Note diminishing amplitudes from reduced open times of shutters.

a peak occurred at $d = x_0$ at T_0, then new peaks will occur at x_1, x_2, x_3, such that with constant v the distances are related by $v = (x_0 + \delta)/T_0 = (x_1 + \delta)/2T_0 = (x_2 + \delta)/3T_0$. From the relations between the measured values of x_0, x_1, x_2, and the resulting relations $2x_0 + 2\delta = x_1 + \delta$, $3x_1 + 3\delta = 2x_2 + 2\delta$, $x_1 - 2x_0 = \delta$, $2x_2 - 3x_1 = \delta$, the value of δ can be determined. With δ evaluated for a given set of conditions, correction can be made to give the true value of v by adding δ to x_0 and dividing by T_0. The Bristol group usually varied N or T and evaluated v and k in relative measure. Where absolute values were required, their apparatus was calibrated for these by determining δ. The technique used in which N or T is varied gives a series of peaks to which the Bristol group refers as "orders" of the ion-mobility spectrum. Figure 1.9 shows such a spectrum, as observed by Tyndall and Powell.

It is to be noted from the curves that the successive orders of the peaks with constant d and varying N decrease in amplitude, but that the peaks are clearly defined. This decrease results from the decrease in length of the ΔT, the open time of the shutters, with decreasing T, which reduces the current transmitted. The use of successive orders can assist in fixing T accurately, though one peak suffices. The successive peaks with d changing are constant in amplitude, since T is constant. These will decrease only as a result of diffusion, and are shown in figure 1.10. However, the increasing background current caused by diffusion and stray ions as d increases, is indicated. As will appear in chapter V, A. Doehring

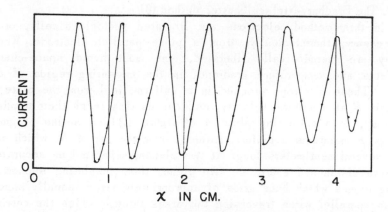

Fig. 1.10. Current-distance curves at constant fields, with x varied. Note that the peaks are all of equal amplitude here, but that the background caused by diffusion and stray ions is quite perceptible.

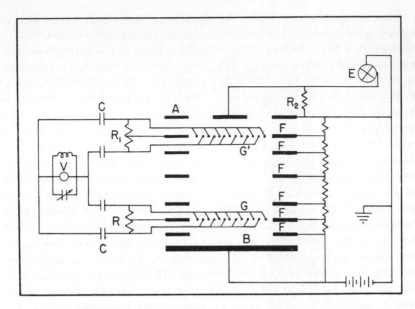

Fig. 1.11. The use of the Loeb electron filters as shutters for electron-velocity studies by Bradbury and Nielsen. Note that this method employs two shutters as in Tyndall and Powell's work, but the a.c. is transverse to the direction of ion motion.

(77) achieved beautiful results by using short-duration square wave pulses in applying the method to negative ions.

§7. The Bradbury-Nielsen Shutter Method (8).

In this method, electrons are liberated photoelectrically, or if necessary, thermionically, from a plane parallel electrode. Where they are thermionically liberated, one must avoid space-charge effects and temperature gradients in the measuring region of the gas. These electrons proceed in a uniform field from the plate of origin B at a uniform velocity, as soon as they reach their terminal energy, to a collecting plate A of figure 1.11. A series of guard rings F maintains a uniform gradient over the gap A B, which may be several centimeters long. At two planes, separated an accurately known distance d apart, are two plane, thin, insulating supporting ring frames which have grids of appropriately sized, equally spaced plane parallel wires traversing the areas through which the carriers run. The sets of wires on a given frame are insulated from each other and are alternately connected to the two sides of a high-frequency oscillator.

Such grids, connected to a high-frequency oscillator, were initially designed by the author as *electron filters* to capture electrons traversing them in a field normal to their plane, while permitting the more sluggish ions to pass through (10). It occurred to Bradbury to use the filters as electrical shutters for electrons. If the period of the high frequency, and its amplitude relative to the impressed driving field pulling electrons or ions through the gauzes are properly chosen, then the gauze will act as a shutter. Thus, except for a very short interval during each half cycle when the field between alternate wires of the gauze is zero, no ions or electrons will get through. Hence, the shutters which lie in equipotential planes in the field and which have zero potential between wires of the grid at the time they are open, open and close in synchronism through a master oscillator. Before and after the point of zero field, the horizontal fields between wires in the plane of the grid cause the electrons or ions to have lateral motions which usually lead to capture on the wires. The transverse fields will also influence electrons or ions which get through by imposing transverse oscillations on them for distances of several wire spacings above and below the gauze. In this fashion, the grids can somewhat alter the energy of the electrons in the field. If the distance d between the

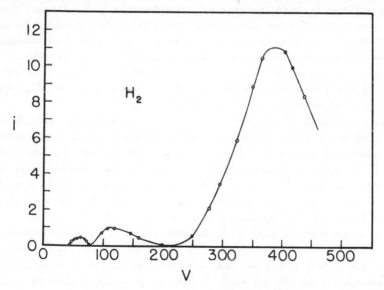

Fig. 1.12. Current-potential curves in the Bradbury-Nielsen electrical shutter method for electrons in H_2. Note the diminishing amplitude of the peaks as successive orders pass through.

planes of the two grids is large compared to the wire spacing, the disturbing effect of oscillations on the mobilities will be small. Thus, "interpenetration" or gauze effects will be at a minimum.

Symmetry of grid action reduces errors still further. By varying the frequency of the a.c. on the grid, or the imposed field X between A and B, the carriers, electrons, or ions, leaving the lower grid G during phases of zero field, will pass through grid G' if they traverse the space d between the gauzes in $T/2$, $2T/2$, $3T/2$ seconds. Here $T = 1/N$ is the period of the potential of high frequency N.

In figure 1.12 is shown a typical curve for electrons in H_2 as V, the potential between A and B increases. The distance d between grids was 5.93 cm. The grids were number 40 copper wires spaced 1 mm apart. The system used was all glass except for the mica grid frames. Because of the mica the chamber could be baked out only to 300° C. The high frequency used in the observations shown was 2.205×10^6 cycles/sec, with a potential between the grid wires of 40 volts. The pressure was 6.8 mm, and peaks were observed at 390, 119, and 62 volts. These were electrons that crossed in 1/2, 2/2, and 3/2 of a cycle. The velocities were 26.5, 13.2, and 8.84×10^5 cm/sec. Since the velocity of electrons getting across in 1/2 cycle was about three times that for electrons getting across in 3/2 cycles, the shutters were *effectively open*, as regards current transmittal, at least three times as long as for the slower ones. Since this effect occurred for two shutters, the total current as a function of potential was markedly greater for the fast than for the slow ones. Diffusion of the electrons is also responsible for some of the attenuation observed. The location of the peaks is possible to within 2% for carriers of unique mobility. The method is satisfactory for such carriers.

The operation of the shutters is open to theoretical calculation for carriers of unique velocities, and comparison between calculated and observed curves given by Bradbury and Nielsen for the case above is shown in figure 1.13. It is seen that the resolution is not so good as that of the Tyndall-Powell four-gauze method. If there is any doubt as to the absolute values yielded by the method, d could be varied for constant X and the values of $T/2$ corresponding to the same order of peak could be determined. This would eliminate any gauze errors. The mobility is given by $k = 2d^2/V_0 T$, with T the whole period. It has not been tried on ions, but there is no *a priori* reason why it should not work. It may be possible that some of the microwave or radar-pulsing techniques could be applied to this in some ranges. Thus, if the grids were biased with a fixed field, to be closed except when a neutralizing square wave pulse of short duration

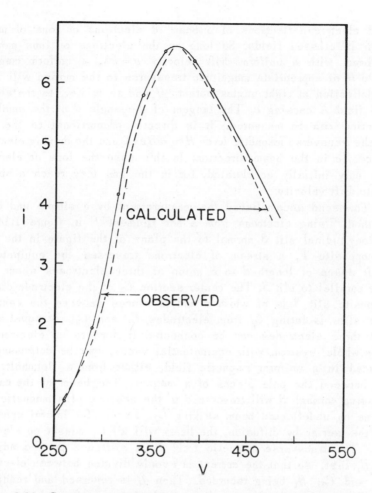

Fig. 1.13. Comparison of observed and calculated current-potential curves with the Bradbury-Nielsen shutter method, using Loeb electron filters as shutters. Note the rather broad peaks and poor resolution.

is applied at a constant-repeat frequency, it is possible that better results could be obtained, since distance d and field X can be conveniently measured. This system has the advantage over the four-gauze method of being somewhat more simple mechanically, except for the mica mounting of the grids, which can now no doubt be replaced by a heat-resistant insulator.

§8. The Townsend Magnetic-Deflection Method (9).

This method evaluates mobility by directly comparing the magnetic and electric deflections of a beam of electrons or ions of unique sign in crossed fields. So long as the electrons or ions move in a beam with a uniform drift velocity $v = kX$, a uniform magnetic field H of appropriate magnitude transverse to the motion will cause a deflection at right angles both to H and to v; i.e., to the electrical field X causing v. The tangent of the angle θ of the small deflection can be measured. It is directly proportional to the ratio of the transverse magnetic force $Hev = HekX$ and the driving electrical force Xe in the beam direction. In this case the ions or electrons are only initially accelerated, for in the gas they reach a steady-state drift velocity.

Townsend accomplished the measurement by a simple and direct method. Using electrons from a hot filament F in figure 1.14 and a longitudinal slit S normal to the plane of the figure in the plate B opposite F, a stream of electrons traverses the equipotential drift space of length d to a group of three electrodes whose axes are parallel to slit S. The center section C_2 of the electrode directly opposite slit S is of width a and is placed between the center of the slits isolating C_2 from electrodes C_1 and C_3, of equal width. All three electrodes can be connected in turn to an electrometer. The whole system, with equipotential vanes, can be outgassed and placed in a uniform magnetic field, either from a Helmholtz coil or between the pole pieces of a magnet. The beam of the carriers passing through S will traverse d in the absence of a magnetic field H as an undeflected beam striking C_2. Except for lateral spreading of the carrier by diffusion, the beam will all be caught on electrode C_2. The transverse magnetic field H is switched on and adjusted to H_1 first, so that the current is evenly divided between electrodes C_1 and C_2, H_1 being recorded. Then H is reversed and readjusted to H_2, so that the beam splits evenly between C_2 and C_3, and H_2 is recorded. Calling $\bar{H} = (H_1 + H_2)/2$, it follows at once that $\tan \theta = \theta = a/2d = f_a/f_0 = \bar{H}ev/Xe$, with f_a and f_0 the forces along the magnetic and electrical fields. Thus the velocity v is given by $v = Xa/H2d$, and the mobility k is given by $k = a/2d\bar{H}$. For electrons, Townsend observed that k was a function of X and p, or better X/p, so that there is, properly speaking, no sense to the term "mobility." The method is, therefore, ideally suited to the study of the variation of k with X/p, since X does not enter explicitly into the expression for k. It does enter into measurement in that it determines the value of v and hence the values of fields $\bar{H}$ needed, thus placing physical limits on the range of values of X/p and p that can be used. It is capable of giving *average* velocities only, and its resolving power is very poor.

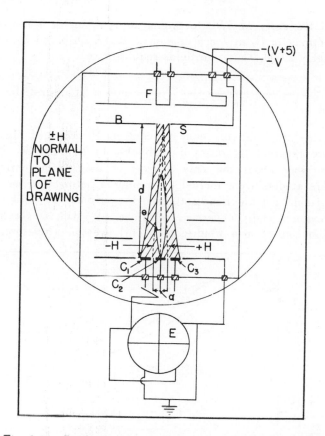

Fig. 1.14. Diagram of the apparatus used in the Townsend
magnetic-deflection method.

Regarding the mobility k, this is given, at least in theory, for
ions at low fields and constant temperature, by $k = K\ 760/p$, with
K the reduced mobility. Placing this in the relation deduced yields
$K = (p/760)\ (a/2dH)$. For use with values of K, expressed in cm/sec
per volt/cm, K must be divided by 10^8, since it is given in terms
of e.m.u. through the use of $\overline{H}$. From this relation may be derived
the limits of pressure over which the method can be used in any
given situation in terms of the permissible values of K and $\overline{H}$. In
most applications the values of $a/2$ range around 0.5 cm and d about
10 cm. Thus $p = 3.04 \times 10^{-4}\ K\overline{H}$. For ions where K is of the order
of 2, it is seen that $p = 6.08 \times 10^{-4}\ \overline{H}$, and that to work at appreciable
pressures, $\overline{H}$ must be large, uniform, and constant over a large volume,
of about $15 \times 15 \times 15$ cm. Thus A. V. Hershey (9) had to use values

of $\bar{H}$ of the order of 5,000 oersteds to work up to 3 mm pressure. For electrons in O_2 at 1 mm pressure, the K observed by Townsend was roughly 2,000. Thus, the fields required are

$$\bar{H} = \frac{1}{3.04 \times 10^{-4} \times 2,000} = \frac{1}{6.08 \times 10^{-1}} = 1.65 \text{ oersted.}$$

Such fields are relatively easy to control. However, if higher pressures are resorted to, $\bar{H}$ rapidly mounts. In Townsend's time, coil systems were about the only source of uniform magnetic fields. Thus, his studies were limited to pressures below 100 mm. Hershey had available the electromagnet from the original 10^6-volt cyclotron of Livingston and Henderson, with an 800-ampere electronically controlled current in a water-cooled coil system. Therefore, he was

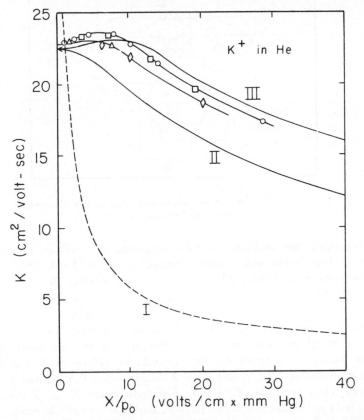

Fig. 1.15. Hershey's values of velocity of K^+ ions in He as a function of X/p, by the magnetic-deflection method.

able to command useful fields of the order of 5,000 oersteds. The method is thus limited. Low pressures, especially at high fields and with ions, raise problems as to whether the ions are in equilibrium with the field, and the same applies to electrons. The technique of the method in terms of modern laboratory practice was exhaustively studied by Hershey. He found that a lower pressure correction had to be made for such effects as the cycloidal character of the ion paths before terminal velocities were reached. This introduced a correction for the origin of the ion beam, which is not, as might be assumed, at the plane of the slit S. The corrections required and the full analysis and procedure can be found in Hershey's papers. The character of the mobility curves observed by Hershey is shown in figures 1.15, 1.16, 1.17, and 1.18.

Just preceding and during the last decade, Townsend and his

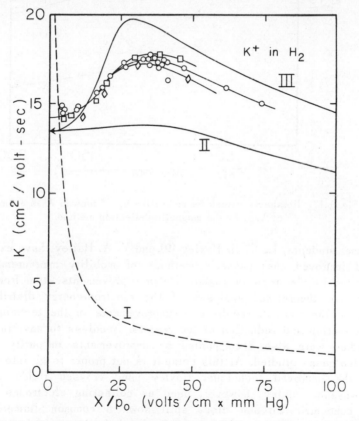

Fig. 1.16. Hershey's values for mobilities of K^+ ions in H_2 as a function of X/p, by the magnetic-deflection method.

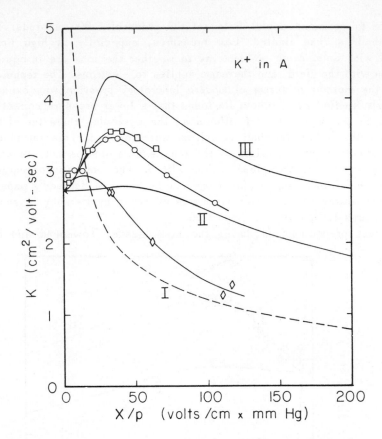

Fig. 1.17. Hershey's values for mobilities of K^+ ions in A as a function of X/p, by the magnetic-deflection method.

former students, L. G. H. Huxley (9) and V. A. Bailey, have extended and improved the magnetic methods of mobility measurement as applied to electrons in gases. These improvements stem from more accurate theoretical analyses of the electron-energy distributions and of the method, resulting in improvements in the techniques of observation and reduction of the results. Needless to say, the later studies were also accompanied by improvements in purity control of the gases studied. At this point it is not proper to go into details of the improved technique. Huxley used crossed fields, as did Townsend. Huxley, however, used as collecting electrodes a pair of concentric circular discs split down a common diameter. His electron beam came through a circular hole instead of through a slit. Recorded was the ratio of currents R_1 to the two semicircular

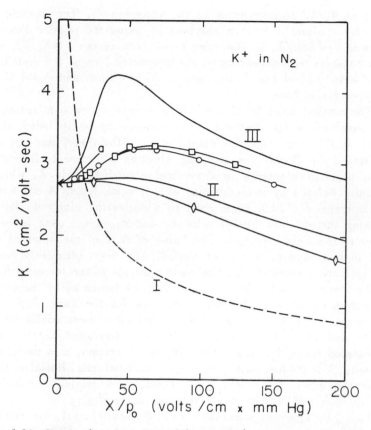

Fig. 1.18. Hershey's values for mobilities of K⁺ ions in N₂ as a function of X/p, by the magnetic-deflection method.

halves as a function of the magnetic field H. When H was off, the currents to the two halves were equal. When H was on, parallel to the transverse slot, the currents gave a ratio R_1 different from 0.5. This ratio was known to be a function of the electric field X, the length d of the beam, a corrected value η_1 of Townsend's factor η for electron temperatures, and the ratio of W_x and W_z, the relative drift velocities of electrons parallel to the electric field and in the direction of magnetic deflection. Needless to say, W_x and W_z depend on the fields X and H. The same apparatus was designed, by separate measurement, to yield the value of η through measuring the ratio of currents to the inner and outer concentric circular segments of the collector plate when the field H is zero. Calculated curves for R_1, plotted against $X(d/\eta_1)$, enabled the observer to pick out the correct ratio of W_x/W_z corresponding to the observed R_1. The desired drift velocity v along X is then obtained by using the regular Townsend relation $W = \delta\theta H/X$. In this case θ is given as $\tan\theta = W_x/W_z$, and δ is a constant term depending on the suspected form of the distribution law. It is 0.85 if the distribution is Maxwellian, and 0.943 if it is Druyvesteyn in form.

The method used by Bailey (9) is simple in its application, but too involved in its theoretical justification to be included at this point. In this approach, the method utilizes the theory and apparatus developed by Bailey for studying electron attachment. It consists of a beam of electrons in a vertical electrical field X, which is initially defined by a rectangular slit of some length 4 mm wide in a diaphragm E_s. This beam goes to a collecting electrode E_0 after passing through two further slits E_3 and E_1, d cm each below the other in the field direction. The value of d is of the order of 4 cm, and in later apparatus can be varied. The beam ultimately reaches the collecting electrode E_0. Elaborate analysis of the lateral diffusion of the electrons and of ions to E_3 and E_1, as indicated by the currents collected by each at different pressures for the same X/p, or by changing d, yields an evaluation of the attachment coefficient $a = hc/\lambda v$ and of η, the Townsend electron-temperature factor. In the expression for a, h is the probability of attachment, c is the electron velocity, λ is its free path, and v is its drift velocity. Initially, Bailey used the other data yielded by Townsend's original methods for evaluating v and λ, c being given by the value of η.

Later, by applying a magnetic field H parallel to X, the electrical field, the divergence of the electron beam due to diffusion was reduced, as indicated earlier by theoretical studies of Townsend and later by Huxley. This theory can be applied to the change in charge distribution produced by the field. The precise manner in which the theory can be applied to get the necessary data from measurement appears to be flexible, and different approaches may be used. Admittedly, the values of the velocity so obtained are subject to a certain percentage of error. Since some of this theory must be presented in later chapters, it is necessary only to indicate that the method is among the more modern ones in use, and to refer the reader to its full discussion in chapters III and V.

§ 9. The Measurement of Mobilities, with Pulse Techniques.

The development of pulsing circuits capable of yielding square wave pulses of controlled amplitude of the order of 1 microsecond and up in duration, and of suitable means of applying and measuring the pulses without distortion, together with the accessibility of fast-sweep oscilloscopes and suitable amplifying circuits during World War II, have opened up a series of new methods, some of which are capable of high accuracy. These methods may be subdivided into the two groups described below; (A), those applicable to ions; and (B), those applicable to electrons.

A. *Ion Mobilities.*

Several different methods have been worked out. (1) Using pulsed microwave breakdown and a measurement of ambipolar diffusion applying mostly to ions at very low X/p ratios. (2) Using uniform field geometry and a liberation of photoelectrons from a cathode by a flash of ultraviolet light of short (10^{-7} sec) duration. The electrons cross the gap to the anode in a very short time, ionizing cumulatively by electron impact in high fields. Thus is created a sheet of positive ions very near the anode, the advent of which at the cathode can readily be timed. (3) A similar technique, using coaxial cylindrical geometry with wire anode, and triggering the electrons by single and particle tracks accurately parallel to the anode and projected near the surface of the cathode cylinder. This yields mobilities at lower X/p. (4) A method by which the ions are generated in a space by a pulsed discharge, and are then admitted into a drift space through a grid. In this region, their time of flight to reach the recording electrode in the constant-drift field can be recorded on an oscilloscope. The method can be used where X/p is not too high.

1. Microwaves of adequate amplitude are caused to break down a gas in an outgassed vessel of appropriate shape. The discharge is maintained over an interval long enough to insure adequate ion concentrations and uniformity ($\sim 10^{-3}$ sec). The loss of electrons in time after a cooling-off and spatial homogenization period ($\sim 3 \times 10^{-3}$ sec) is measured by a microwave probing beam. This procedure for studying ions and electrons in gases was initiated shortly after World War II by S. C. Brown, in collaboration with W. P. Allis (29), at Massachusetts Institute of Technology, and was developed by them.

If pressures are sufficiently low to insure that the dominant carrier loss is by ambipolar diffusion of electrons and positive ions to the walls, the rate of loss of electrons in time yields the coefficient of ambipolar diffusion. As will be seen in chapters II and VI, where the details of the method and the underlying theory are presented, the coefficient of ambipolar diffusion leads to an evaluation of the ionic mobility, which in theory is certainly accurate to 2 or 3%. The method applies to electrons and ions at near-thermal energies. From the very careful studies of M. A. Biondi and S. C. Brown on inert gases, values of the ion mobilities in inert gases at low X/p were obtained. Unfortunately, mobility values of known ions, such as He^+ in He, which several observers have obtained by this method, have not been consistent in yielding the same value to better than 10%. Values appear high, possibly because of poor resolving power. Recent work by K. B. Persson (78) has also yielded good values of the mobility in very pure H_2 gas.

2. In the process of making analyses of the fast components of secondary processes in a Townsend discharge, J. A. Hornbeck (32), at the Bell Laboratories, developed the technique described below. The method, both theoretically and instrumentally, was still further developed by R. N. Varney (79), also at Bell Laboratories. It is capable of yielding an accuracy of perhaps 3%, and can be used over a range of X/p values extending from that for ionization by collision up to 1,000 or more. In this method, a pair of plane parallel electrodes yield a uniform constant field X across a gap length from 2 cm down, adequate to cause ionization by electron impact at the pressure of the gas whose ions are to be studied. Small perforations in the anode permit ultraviolet light from an external source admitted by a quartz window to strike the cathode without distorting the field. The ultraviolet light comes from a condensed discharge in which the duration of intense luminosity is of the order of 10^{-7} sec or less. The light from the triggering spark then liberates a slab of photoelectrons from the cathode, which proceed across the gap in time intervals of the order of 0.5% of the ion crossing time. As these electrons cross the gap they ionize cumulatively, producing a maximum of positive ions in a sheath some two ionizing free paths from the anode. The ions created so near the anode then proceed to cross the gap to the cathode. The spark giving the ultraviolet light pulse triggers the oscilloscope sweep.

The rather complicated current curve first analyzed by Hornbeck, and much more accurately investigated by Varney under varying conditions of X/p, yields a sharp discontinuity when the ions reach the cathode. The time length of the sweep from triggering to discontinuity yields a measure of the ion transit time. Repeated sweeps occur at the rate of 30 to 60 per second, and enable the oscilloscope patterns to be photographed and measured, since they are highly reproducible. The results of Hornbeck and Varney's studies will be reported later in this chapter.

In Hornbeck's early studies of the inert gas ions he observed double breaks in his curves, which he could only attribute to two ions of different mobility. To ascertain the accuracy of his conclusions he resorted to coaxial cylindrical geometry with anode wire. In this geometry, ionization is concentrated even more closely to the wire, and the crossing of the ions to the cathode cylinder yields even more strongly resolved peaks. However, he did not derive any quantitative theory.

3. In a study of the mechanisms active in coaxial cylindrical coronas with positive wire in A and in H_2, E. J. Lauer (80) developed, in the author's laboratory, a technique of observation which yielded ion mobilities good to 2% at relatively low X/p. E. Gatti, L. Colli, and U. Facchini (80) in an earlier study had utilized α particles fired nearly parallel to the axis of such a tube to trigger the corona. Lauer refined their techniques by using a well-outgassed borosilicate glass system with an Ni outer cylindrical cathode, a fine W wire anode, and projected single α particles closely parallel to the anode near the cathode surface. Using up to 600 mm of A gas, he observed the sequence of events by oscilloscope across a low resistance between the cathode cylinder and the ground. Once the 104 electrons from the α-particle track crossed, producing their positive ions very close to the anode, there was a large deflection when the electrons entered the anode. Then the arrival of the positive ion cloud at the Ni cathode liberated a shower of electrons, which crossed to the anode wire in a very short time and produced a new pulse of ionization. As potential was raised, a succession of secondary peaks was observed, corresponding to the successive crossing of the first, second, third, etc., groups of ions. Transit times between beginnings of successive peaks could be accurately measured. While the ion generation takes place at high X/p, the field over the major portion of the gap is very low. Thus, the ions cross at low X/p.

In the absence of secondary action, the absorption of the ion cloud by the cathode gives a small but clearly defined pip. Thus, the crossing time of ions can always be measured. Since the fields in the absence of much space charge are accurately known, the method enables accurate values of the mobility to be observed. Accuracy can well be 2% or better with a well-collimated α-particle beam. This method, because of the inhomogeneous field, cannot be used where mobility varies with field strength, as at high fields. It can be used to check the values of the variable drift velocities by integrating the velocities over the variable field, giving the computed time of flight as compared to the directly observed time.

4. Using a short-duration pulse (0.5 sec) of high amplitude between a grid cathode and plate anode of an ionization chamber, the gas can be broken down behind a grid and a positive ion sheath projected through the gauze. Shortly after the pulse, a weak retarding field is placed across the ionization chamber to insure that the initiating pulse be thin. Between the gauze and a collecting plate beyond, which is negatively charged, the ions traverse a uniform field-drift space where the X/p ratio is *below* values for appreciable ionization by electron impact. The ionizing pulse triggers the oscilloscope sweep which records the current drawn to the collector plate by induction resulting from the motion of the ions and by their arrival at the collector. While the contour of the front of the ion pulse, or perhaps better, the density contour of the ion sheath projected through the gauze screen, is distorted by diffusion and interpenetration of fields, so that the part of the current change at the collector due to ion collection is not sharply defined, it is still possible to make very accurate measurements if the length of the drift space d is changed from d_1 to d_2 at constant X/p. Then, the difference in time between corresponding points of ion arrival on the collector current-time curve divided into $d_1 - d_2$, yields an accurate value of the drift velocity. In this fashion L. M. Chanin and M. A. Biondi (81) have measured ion-drift velocities in the inert gases from very low values of X/p up to the values obtained by Hornbeck, using the pulsed technique of subsection 2 above, at high X/p. The results will be presented at a later point. Figure 1.19 shows current-time oscillograph traces for helium gas at two distances; $d_1 = 1.17$ cm, $d_2 = 1.54$ cm, $p = 4.35$ mm, $X/p = 5.2$ volts/cm per mm. Small pips are 10μ sec timing marks. The width of trace marks background. Note diffusive and grid-conditioned rounding. The sharp initial rise and fast decline are caused by the narrow pulse and back diffusion to the cathode while ions are near it. Note the two dips caused by He_2^+ and He^+ ions and the technique of using corresponding points. Before oscillographs yielded complete current-time traces it was hard to use this method.

B. *Electron Mobilities.*

Here various devices have been used. They are described at the end of chapter III, §6 (where they belong), since they involve various assumptions and theory not appropriate here. One method uses a thin, flashed X-ray pulse in plane parallel geometry in which the collected current as a function of time is observed oscilloscopically (83). By moving the ionization chamber relative to the beam of X-rays, the recorded currents as a function of time are temporally

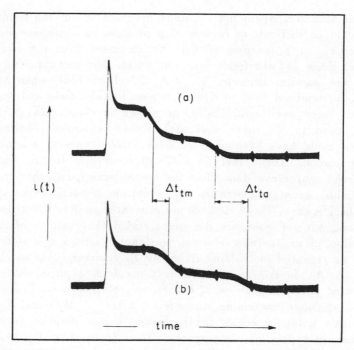

Fig. 1.19. Chanin and Biondi's current-time oscillogram for He gas: $d_1 = 1.17$ cm, trace (a), and $d_2 = 1.54$ cm, trace (b); $p = 4.35$ mm; $X/p = 5.2$. Dots on traces are 10 μ sec timing marks. Note slopes for He_2^+ and He^+.

displaced. Picking corresponding points on the different time curves for the different distances, Herreng (83) succeeded in obtaining electron mobilities in pure, clean A in good agreement with Nielsen. Attempts of D. E. Hudson, Klema and Allen (84), and Kirschner and Toffolo (84), using X-ray and α-particle ionization with improper pulse techniques and crude theory, yielded very poor data. In the first two studies of argon, this gas was soiled with up to 2% N_2 in one instance. At best, only 10% agreement with Nielsen's data in pure A was achieved by Kirschner and Toffolo. Lauer's technique, using single α-particle pulses in pure H_2 (80), where photoelectrons were liberated by the Ni cathode as a result of photons produced in the electron avalanches at the wire, gave clean-cut transit times for electrons across the gap. The values of electron-drift velocities from Nielsen's data, integrated across the gap from anode to cathode, gave calculated drift times agreeing to within 2% of Lauer's observed electron-transit times. Where the photons causing photoelectric liberation are delayed by secondary action in the gas, the method is not accurate. Again the electrons here are in varying fields, and it would be difficult to reverse this process and compute the drift velocities as a function of X/p for electrons from the integrated transit times and the fields known to exist. The technique was used in plane parallel geometry by J. A. Hornbeck (32), when he sent a 0.1-microsecond flash of light to trigger his electrons and measured transit times oscillographically, as shown in chapter IX, § 16. His data, good to 5%, agree well with Nielsen's values. Shorter light pulses could have been obtained from Trichel pulses in a negative point corona. These last for 0.03 microsecond. It will again be observed that these data came as by-products from other research at fields causing ionization by electron impact, especially in Hornbeck's case. These methods are presented in detail in chapter IX.

Last, but not least, are the direct visual observations of the progression of an ionizing electron avalanche across a uniform field gap, as revealed in ionizing fields by H. Raether (85), and chapter III, § 6 (A). In this case, photoelectrons from a plane cathode are liberated in gases such as A, H_2, N_2, air, etc., of a C. T. R. Wilson cloud chamber containing saturated vapors of H_2O and C_2H_5OH. A square pulse of known amplitude and known duration is applied to the plane parallel plate system. The electrons at the beginning of the pulse start avalanches lasting the time T of the pulse and advancing into the gas toward the anode. Some 1/100 of a second after the pulse is over, the cloud chamber is expanded adiabatically, and the clouds condensed on the avalanche tracks are photographed. The distances traversed in different fractions of a microsecond pulse duration can be measured and the velocity of advance inferred. In Raether's study, and in many other prewar studies, the amplitude and time duration of the pulses were not precisely known. One feature was the possibility of the voltage doubling on advent of the pulse on the chamber electrodes. The amplitude of the waves was not well known, and the waves were far from square. Today, radar studies have yielded far better knowledge of these pulse techniques, and the method is available in cases such as used in cloud chambers. The method is discussed in chapter III in connection with the measurement of drift velocities. The accuracy was *not* high, say at best 25%. The method gave the first information on the value of the drift velocity of avalanches in breakdown fields. These data were urgently needed.

With this, the part in which methods are discussed can be fittingly closed with the statement that if newer pulse techniques are applied to the precision techniques of the past, and if the precautions indicated earlier in the chapter are followed, we can today get both electron- and ion-drift velocities at low and high X/p to within 1% and better for all types of gases. Failure to observe the precautions will give unreliable results. Further, if a given observer's results fail to agree reasonably with the good data of the past, he should first check his method and his gaseous purity before he condemns the careful work of such investigators as Tyndall and Powell, Bradbury, or Nielsen, whose gases *were* very pure. It may be added that where data show that these results appear to be contrary to theory, care should be taken to ascertain that the ions believed to have been observed were in fact those to which theory applies. Mass-spectroscopic analysis was not made on the ions of the earlier careful observers.

PART TWO

§ 1. Introduction.

It seems logical to follow the description of the methods of measurement with a section detailing the results obtained. In view of the introductory remarks, efficiency of presentation makes it advisable to present the theory of ionic mobilities as a framework for discussion of the data. While the exact and powerful generalized methods of the kinetic theory are more generally familiar to present-day physicists than they were to those of the past, it is still preferable to initiate the discussion of the application of the theory in terms of the simple mechanistic approach, using average free paths, average velocities, and the assumption of equilibrium processes. Such treatments, despite their fallibility, have the virtue of making the basic analysis interpretable in terms of readily visualized physical processes. Thus, it will be the uniform policy of this text first to present the analysis in terms of the classical kinetic theory, and then to extend the discussion to the more accurate and esoteric analyses with their interpretation. The predictions derived from these theoretical analyses will be compared with the experimental findings, thus guiding the reader to the further analysis indicated by the deviations from theory, and so leading to a more perfect understanding. Orders of numerical magnitudes and concepts common to kinetic theory will be introduced on the way, to assist the readers of less specialized background.

§ 2. The Generic Classical Kinetic Analysis of Mobilities, Assuming Solid Elastic Spherical Molecules and Ions of Equal Mass.

Consider an ion of the dimensions of a single gaseous molecule of mass m and diameter σ, moving in a gas composed of identical molecules. The diameters are of the order of 2×10^{-8} cm or greater, and $m = 1.66 \times 10^{-24}$ M_0 grams where M_0 is the molecular weight of the molecules. The target or cross-sectional area of a molecule for collisions is thus $\pi\sigma^2$ or of the order of 12×10^{-16} cm^2. The ions here considered, therefore, differ from the surrounding molecules only by virtue of their electrical charge. This charge may be positive or negative and of a single electronic unit in magnitude; viz., $e = 4.802 \times 10^{-10}$ e.s.u. All forces of attraction between ions and molecules will be ignored at this juncture. The ions and molecules move with average molecular velocities $\bar{c}$ characteristic of their mass and temperature T in the gas. By elementary kinetic theory, $\bar{c} = 0.922 \, C = 0.922 \sqrt{3p/\rho}$, where p is the pressure, ρ is the density, and C is the root-mean-square, or computed, velocity.

Thermal equilibrium of molecular ions with gas molecules at the temperature T is assured under the conditions *usually* encountered in ion-mobility studies. It will here be useful to introduce the ratio X/p, field strength in volts/cm divided by pressure p in mm of Hg, which in general experimentally and theoretically governs the behavior of carriers in gases. Hereafter, this ratio will be freely used. It has experimentally been established that in inert gases below values of $X/p = 5$, and in other gases, such as H$_2$ and N$_2$ up to $X/p = 10$ to 20, the ion does not gain much energy from the electrical field. Thus, under conditions where most mobility studies are made, the random-heat motions of ions are nearly the same as those of the surrounding molecules, and it is possible to write that the kinetic energy $E = \tfrac{1}{2} mC^2 = 3/2 \, kT$ for the ions following kinetic theory.[4] Here k is the Boltzmann constant, or gas constant per atom, given by R_A/N_A, where R_A is the gas constant per mole, and N_A is the Avagadro number 6.023×10^{23} molecules per mole at 760 mm. Thus, while C is evaluated from the ratio of p and ρ, the energy of the molecules can be established relative to the absolute temperature T by means of the relation given. Here k has the value 1.38×10^{-16} erg per degree. From this it follows that $C = \sqrt{3kT/m}$, and thus that C is proportional to the square root of T and inversely proportional to the square root of m. The velocity of the N$_2$ molecule, molecular weight 28, at 273° K. is about 4.93×10^4 cm/sec. The

---

[4]For electrons these conditions rarely hold, and the average energy of the electrons in the field, and thus their "temperatures," will be higher than those of the surrounding gas molecules.

ionic and molecular trajectories are straight and executed at a velocity $\bar{c}$ until collision with some molecule causes them to alter direction.
The spherically considered ions and molecules collide elastically
on impact with their centers σ cm apart and scatter isotropically.
The target area of one molecule for the center of the ion is $\pi\sigma^2$ cm.
This leads to the conclusion that the ion or molecule on the average
will travel in a rectilinear path element of *mean* value L between
collisions. The value of L, the *mean free path*, is $L = 1/\sqrt{2}\pi\sigma^2 N$ cm.
In this, N is the number of molecules per cm^3, which, of course,
vastly outnumber the few ions being studied. As the mean free path
is inversely proportional to the numerical density of the molecules,
it is inversely proportional to the mass density ρ, and at constant
temperature it is inversely proportional to the pressure p of the
gas. The mean free path L is independent of T for constant N,
unless σ varies with T. At 760 mm and 0° C., N is equal to 2.687×10^{19} molecules/cm^3. The approximate data for σ given make L of
the order of 2.1×10^{-5} cm at 0° C. and 760 mm pressure. The time
to execute a free path t_L is thus about 4.27×10^{-10} second and
the collision frequency $z = 1/t_L = \bar{c}/L = 2.35 \times 10^9$ per second.
The molecular and ion paths are perfectly random in space, and
the path lengths are governed by pure chance. If n_0 molecules or
ions start out, the number n which have traversed a distance x without an impact is given by the expression

$$n = n_0 \; \epsilon^{-x/L} = n_0 \; \epsilon^{-\sqrt{2}\pi\sigma^2 Nx}.$$

This is an exponential curve with a monotonic decline. The average
free path L is thus the centroid of the free-path distribution curve,
and does not represent a probable value about which the free paths
cluster. It is, however, a convenient scale factor in analysis. Thus,
in a gas the ions and molecules pictured above have completely
random thermally conditioned paths diffusing away from their origin
isotropically in one direction or another as time goes on.

If now the ions in the gas are placed in an electrical field X
having a direction say along the x axis, the random motion is altered.
The ions of charge e in the field X experience at every instant a
force $f = Xe$ and an acceleration $a = Xe/m$ along the x direction.
Thus, during the times t_L between collisions, the ion is accelerated
in the x direction. On collision it changes its path and disperses
some of the energy it gained from the field. Since even the energy
XeL gained in the rare free path lying along x is small compared
to $\tfrac{1}{2}mC^2$, the general zigzagged random motion still prevails, but

with one difference. On each free path the ion has been accelerated along x toward the electrode of opposite sign to its charge. This superposes on the random motion a slight directed motion, *or drift*, along x, which, with the 10^9 impacts/sec, amounts on the average to a value of $\bar{v}_x$ in one second. Thus the average *drift velocity* $\bar{v}_x$ of the ion in the field may be used to describe its average motion in contrast to the *random velocity* $\bar{c}$ of molecular motion. To calculate the drift velocity $\bar{v}_x$, it is noted that in the collision interval t_L the ion moves a distance S_x in the field, superposed on the random motion. This distance is given by $S_x = \frac{1}{2}at_L^2 = \frac{1}{2}Xe/m\,t_L^2$. The average drift velocity is thus $\bar{v}_x = S_x/t_L = \frac{1}{2}Xe/m\,t_L = \frac{1}{2}(Xe/m)\,L/\bar{c}$. Since the mobility k is by definition $k = \bar{v}_x/X$, the ionic mobility becomes

$$k = \frac{1}{2}\frac{e}{m}\frac{L}{\bar{c}}.$$

This is the basic, or generic, *solid elastic ion-mobility expression,* which can by modification and suitable interpretations of L or $\bar{c}$, depending on conditions, orient the mechanistic thinking of the whole problem.

Even for the collision-process type of classical kinetic-theory analysis, the treatment just given yields only a crude approximation. It neglects persistence of directed velocity; it neglects the distributions of mean free paths and of velocities; and finally, it precludes considering the mobilities of ions among molecules of differing mass. There have been numerous solid elastic theories set up to correct for these deficiencies. Irrespective of rival claims, the author considers the expression derived by P. Langevin (11) on the basis of general and rigorous kinetic-theory analysis to be the most satisfactory expression.[5] Its acceptance by other physicists of the modern school confirms this choice. In any case, refinements in such a theory beyond those of Langevin are mostly irrelevant, as the general weaknesses of such a theory make further refinements of doubtful value.

The Langevin expression reads,

(1.1a) $$k = 0.815\,\frac{e}{M}\frac{L}{C}\sqrt{\frac{m + M}{m}},$$

with M the mass of the *gas molecules*, m that of the ions, and C the root-mean-square velocity of the gas molecules, in place of $\bar{c}$, the average velocity. Had $\bar{c}$ been used, the constant would have been 0.75 in place of 0.815. If the ions and molecules have different

---

[5]In its application to the collision of electrons with molecules, it is possible that the averaging of Langevin may not be correct (12). For ions it is probably the most satisfactory.

masses, care must be used in noting whether the C in the equation
refers to that of the molecules or the ions. Since C, the molecular
velocity, is related to C_i, that for the ions in equilibrium, by the
expression $C/C_i = \sqrt{m/M}$, equation 1.1a may be written in an *alternate
form:*

$$(1.1b) \qquad\qquad k = 0.815 \, \frac{e \, L}{m \, C_i} \, \sqrt{\frac{m + M}{M}} \, .$$

Equation 1.1a is in a convenient form for computation in ionic
studies, as it contains only absolute masses of the gas molecules
and their velocities. The frequently unknown mass m of the ions
in this relation appears only under the radical. Hence, unless $m < M$,
a rare occurrence, the unknown value of m influences k relatively
little. At a later point it will be very convenient, when $M >> m$, to
write this expression in the alternate form shown by equation 1.1b,
where the mass of the carrier m, and the random-carrier velocity
C_i, appear in the equation. The alternate form is especially useful
in cases where the carriers have random velocities differing from
those arising from equilibrium with the surrounding molecules, such
as occur for ions at high X/p or for electrons in general.

It is seen that the Langevin relation (1.1a) renders k, independent
of X, has it vary inversely as ρ, or at constant T as p through the
variation in L, has it vary directly with e, makes it vary inversely
proportional to $\sqrt{T}$ through C at constant density, makes it proportional to $\sqrt{M + m/mM}$, since C varies as $1/\sqrt{M}$. Experiment has
established the independence of k with X up to high values of X/p.
At higher values of X/p, the derivation given above does not apply,
as XeL approaches $\frac{1}{2}MC^2$ in value. Experiment has established the
inverse pressure, or density, rule over very large ranges of pressures. Experiments on known ions have tested the mass variation
and show it to be as given. However, the form of the law (1.1a) is
not different from that for other more correct theories; i.e., the correct
mass variation is universal. Like all solid elastic impact equations,
neglecting attractive forces between ion and molecule, the equation *incorrectly* predicts the temperature variation of mobility, and
in this case also the variation with charge e. The equation also
fails to include any variation of the mobility with the dielectric
constant D of the gas. The factor D is observed markedly to influence k in measurement on smaller ions when D is appreciable.

The most glaring failure of the simple theory at once came to
light when it was put to a quantitative test. If $m = M$, as in the
initial assumptions, then $k = 1.154 \, (e/m) \, (L/C)$, and placing the

values assumed into the equation, it yields for k in O_2 the value of 7.6 cm/sec per volt/cm. This is *more than three times* as great as the commonly accepted value for the mobility of the negative ion of 0.1 sec age in relatively clean, dry air. This value is 2.18 cm/sec per volt/cm. Similar differences between the motion of charged molecules in gases relative to uncharged molecules were early revealed by the values of the diffusion coefficients of ions. These were uniformly of the order of one-third to one-fifth those for equivalent molecules.

Regarding equation 1.1a for mobilities, it is clear that the only uncertain quantity capable of producing deviations by a factor of 3 to 5 must be in the value of the mean free path, $L = 1/\sqrt{2}\pi\sigma^2 N$, chosen. Here relatively small changes in the collision radius σ can cause large changes in L. Therefore, the obvious conclusion early drawn was that because of the electrostatic forces between ions and molecules, the ions were composed of several molecules of the gas, i.e., a cluster with $m = xM$; and that in consequence, σ was changed. Thus, for example, an approximate agreement between the calculated k for O_2 and the observed k would be achieved by an increase of the value of σ_M used of the order of $\sigma_m = 1.73 \sigma_M$.[6]

The indicated increase in *target area* $\pi\sigma^2$ for impacts between ions and molecules in consequence of the action of forces, is in fact the cause for the observation of reduced mobilities. It is, however, *naïve*, though perhaps natural, to assume that the *sole* action of the forces is to cause an increase from σ_M to σ_m, the correct value, by *attaching molecules to form a cluster of mass* $m = xM$. As is well known from viscosity and other studies in gases, forces entirely too small to cause appreciable clustering of molecules can deviate the otherwise rectilinear molecular trajectories so that collisions are more frequent than in the absence of forces. Hence; the actual collision diameter σ_0 *is increased to an apparent σ of larger value by force action without clustering.* Since such action materially affecting viscosity and its temperature variation occurs in gases where forces are weak, such action certainly cannot be neglected in mobility studies. Accordingly, a study must first be

---

[6]As seen in the generalized theory of Wannier in his part II (reviewed in § 11), for cases of nearly equal mass of ion and molecule under certain types of force interaction leading to a constant mean free path and nearly isotropic scattering, the conditions assumed for this hard sphere model are met. This occurs with change-of-charge attractive forces, and a cross section measured at high fields when the polarization forces are negligible can be used in the Langevin relation and yields satisfactory agreement.

made of ionic forces and their consequences. With this knowledge, the question of deviation of free paths versus clustering can be considered.

§3. **Forces between Ions and Molecules, and Cluster Formation.**
While the van der Waals forces between neutral, and in some cases electrically symmetrical, molecules and atoms are hard to visualize and evaluate theoretically, this is not the case with the forces between molecules and ions. The ion of charge e has an electrical field of strength $X = e/r^2$ about itself at a distance r. This field is of the order of 10^8 volts/cm at $r = 10^{-8}$ cm and 10^4 volts/cm at 10^{-6} cm. The distance 10^{-6} cm is about three times the average intermolecular distance and one-fifth the mean free path at 760 mm pressure. In fields of this order, all molecules experience a displacement of their electron clouds relative to the nuclei, so as to produce an electrical dipole of moment $\mu_i = el$ by effective separation of their centers of positive and negative charge. In addition to this, a molecule like NH_3, HCl, H_2O, etc., that, owing to its structure, already has a permanent electrical dipole moment μ_p, will, despite its thermal rotation, have an effective part of its permanent moment oriented by the molecular field X in such a sense as to add its quota to the effective polarization of the gas. Thus, there is an effective average moment $\bar{m} = \gamma X$ induced on the molecules by the ionic-force field at a distance r. Now a dipole of moment $\bar{m}$ at a distance r from a charge e with its axis aligned by the field X will experience an attractive force $f = 2\bar{m}e/r^3$, as is well known in analogy to the force of an isolated pole on a bar magnet of moment m distant r from its center. Thus, between ion and molecule, there is a force of attraction $f = 2\bar{m}e/r^3 = 2\gamma X e/r^3 = 2\gamma e^2/r^5$. The constant γ is the total effective molecular polarizability. It can be evaluated for the case of uniform weak fields in gases directly by measurement of the dielectric constant. If a uniform field X be applied across a volume of gas of dielectric constant D, the number of lines of force entering unit area placed normal to the flux is the dielectric induction $B = DX$. In analogy to similar relations in magnetics $B = DX = X + 4\pi I$, with I the intensity of induced electrification, $I = M/V$, the block moment of the material per unit volume. But $M/V = n\bar{m}/V$, where n is the number of molecules in V, and $\bar{m}$ is the moment of each molecule. Thus, $I = M/V = n\bar{m}/V = N\bar{m}$, where N is the number density of molecules. Further, $\bar{m} = \gamma X$, where γ is the polarizability. Thus, $DX = X + 4\pi N\bar{m}$ and $\bar{m} = \gamma X = (D-1)X/4\pi N$, so that $\gamma = (D-1)/4\pi N$. This makes the force f between molecule and ion

$$(1.2) \qquad f = \frac{2\gamma e^2}{r^5} = \frac{(D-1)e^2}{2\pi N r^5}.$$

This law of force is correct and accurate while r is sufficiently great, so that the field X is sensibly uniform over σ, and the forces are not too great, so that polarizing electron displacement is given by a linear relation at constant D.

While this force law is significant and will hereafter be freely used, it is often of greater convenience to know the potential energy of a polarized molecule in the field of the ion at a distance r. This potential energy is given by

$$(1.3) \qquad PE = \int_r^\infty f dr = -\frac{(D-1)e^2}{8\pi N r^4}.$$

With these data, it is possible to apply the values of quantities f and PE to the consideration of cluster ion formation. As a rough criterion for the stability of a cluster of molecules whose centers are distant r cm from the center of charge on the ion, it was logical, before the more critical thinking of the era of 1920, to set

$$(1.4) \qquad \frac{PE}{KE} = 1.$$

This in essence states that if the *average* ionic molecular impact occurs with a kinetic energy KE equal to the potential energy of a molecule in the cluster, there is an even chance that the molecule will be knocked off the cluster if it is there, or a molecule will stick and form a cluster if it was not there before. Hence, it was assumed that cluster ions were stable if $PE/KE>1$, and would not exist for any length of time if $PE/KE<1$.

Accordingly, the criterion for cluster ion formation was set as

$$(1.5) \qquad \frac{PE}{KE} = \frac{(D-1)e^2}{4\pi N r^4 M C^2} = \frac{(D-1)e^2}{12\pi p r^4} \gtrless 1.$$

Here p is the existing atmospheric pressure and r is the distance of the center of the clustered molecule from the center of the ion.

At a later date it became obvious that this criterion was faulty. Thermodynamic equilibrium between a molecule, or an ion, and its *dissociation* products essentially depends on a type of relation derived for thermal ionization in equilibrium by M. N. Saha. This expression includes not only the Boltzmann factor

$$\epsilon^{\frac{-PE}{KE}},$$

but other "entropy" factors which weight it heavily in favor of dissociation. This means that the *a priori probability of a state* must be included as a factor in the ratio of PE/KE in the condition for stability. Now the ion cluster is a "condensed" state with a relatively low entropy, while the dissociated single molecules, or ion and free molecules, constitute a "dispersed" state with a rather higher entropy, or statistical weight. Unless much is known of the specific nature of a given possible cluster and its constituents, the number of molecules, etc., it is impossible to evaluate even approximately the relative statistical weight factor g for dissociated and condensed states. It is accordingly necessary to set the criterion for cluster stability as $PE/gKE \gtrsim 1$. In this relation, the relative statistical weight g of the dispersed state may be greater than unity by a considerable margin. In a recent study, S. Bloom and H. Margenau (86) have made a study of this, using various force fields and assuming energy levels closely spaced enough to permit integration. With hard sphere repulsive models they essentially obtained results akin to those with $g=1$. With inverse twelfth-power repulsion this clustering was much reduced, and some of the values calculated agreed well with data of the Bristol group for Li^+ ions. Their findings will be considered at a later point. At this juncture it suffices to state that while the result of their calculation shows a reduction of the cluster size by a factor as large as 100 in, in some cases it is not capable of expressing the alteration by theory in terms of the somewhat naïvely conceived illustrative factor g. However, for convenience of discussion until the exact theory can be presented, it will be convenient to use the factor g; or better, to replace it by its reciprocal $\beta = 1/g$ with $0 < \beta < 1$, and use β as a multiplier into PE, e.g., $\beta PE/KE$, to express the stability condition $\beta PE/KE > 1$. Thus, the condition for stability of an ion cluster will henceforth be expressed as

$$(1.6) \qquad \beta PE/KE = \frac{PE}{gKE} \sim 1.$$

The significance of this criterion is as follows: When $\beta PE/KE \ll 1$, the ion will be unencumbered and will remain essentially monomolecular. When $\beta PE/KE \sim 1$, then molecules can attach. However, subsequent collisions may be sufficiently energetic to remove the attached molecules. Thus, as the charged molecule or ion moves through the gas, molecules will be picked up, attach, travel along for a distance, and be knocked off. The ion will thus have a mass, diameter, and hence mobility which changes continuously as it moves through the gas. It will on measurement exhibit an *average* mobility *intermediate between that for the attached and unattached* states. The value on the average varies continuously as the average period in the attached state becomes longer. This attached phase will increase in the measure that KE is reduced and $\beta PE/KE$ is increased. Thus, the observed average mobility will increase as the average kinetic energy of ions increases through increase in temperature or the ratio of X/p. Such a clustered ion could best be described by the term "labile cluster."[7] As $\beta PE/KE$ increases above unity, one molecule may permanently attach and increase the "effective" radius of the ion so that no more molecules *permanently* attach. However, no matter how much $\beta PE/KE$ exceeds unity, the cluster ion formed *will always add on molecules to the point of instability and yield a labile ion.* Strangely, it was never clearly recognized in the earlier days of the cluster theory that any cluster formation based on equation 1.5 would always lead to a labile cluster, the mobility of which would be continuously variable with temperature and X/p, and thus would be quite sensitive to such variables. Despite rather careful tests for such variations of mobility with T and X/p, the common ions studied universally gave negative results (49), (50). However, since the labile character of the clusters was not recognized, the significance of the failure to observe variations was not noted.

It is probably essential at this point to indicate another property of cluster formation that escaped consideration in the early days; i.e., when a cluster ion forms by addition of a molecule, especially addition of the first one, the *energy of the cluster formation,* or *heat of association,* must be dissipated. This can only happen through kinetic impacts with other molecules. Thus, the addition of the first molecule in cluster formation must require a three-body impact. Such impacts can be so rare that the rate of addition of molecules may be relatively slow compared to the collisions breaking up the addition product. Such action will thus further weight the scales against cluster formation. It will also result in the simultaneous appearance of clustered and unclustered ions side by side, even when $\beta PE/KE$ is somewhat greater than unity.

---

[7] It should be noted that mass-spectrographic analysis will *not* reveal the existence of labile clusters.

Ignoring these later considerations, it is instructive to proceed by setting $\beta = 1$ and considering what will happen, on the basis of equation 1.5, to an O_2^+ ion at n.t.p. in O_2 gas. Insertion of numerical values of accepted molecular constants with $r = \sigma$ makes the ratio $PE/KE = 3.1$. On the other hand, with $r = 2\sigma$, the ratio $PE/KE = 0.19$. This means that if the O_2 molecule is naïvely considered as a rigid sphere, the originally charged molecule O_2^+ could surround itself with a spherical shell of 12 equal spherical O_2 molecules at $r = \sigma$.[8] Here σ is the diameter of the molecule; i.e., the distance between centers at contact. The outer radius of such an ion then is $\sigma_m = 3\sigma/2$. Beyond this no more molecules could add, as $PE/KE < 1$. On the basis of the naïve conception, it was customary in the early twentieth century to regard the ion as a simple cluster with saturated forces. Then, from the solid elastic mobility equation 1.1a or its equivalent, and the observed value of the mobility k, it was natural to estimate the value of L, or better, of σ. Since solution of such an equation in most cases yielded other than integral half values for σ_m of the ion, the naïvely considered simple geometrical model of the addition product led to difficulties in interpretation. As time went on, the accumulated evidence appeared to argue decisively not only against the more naïve aspects of the cluster theory, but even more generally against labile clustering as here conceived. It is accordingly essential to regard both the force law and the criterion for stability more critically. Toward this end, certain weaknesses of the dielectric polarization theory will be listed in what follows.

a) First and foremost, labile clustering will occur only when $\beta PE/KE > 1$. The quantity β is likely to be small, and will be smaller as the number of molecules in the cluster is larger. Therefore, clustering may *not* be observed, even if $PE/KE > 1$, as for O_2^+ ions in O_2 today (79), and clusters (if formed) will remain small. The factor β is probably the most important item preventing clustering.

b) The value of D used in calculation is derived in bulk measurements of the gas in fields less than 10^4 volts/cm. Even when r is of the order of 10^{-6} cm, the ionic force fields exceed 10^4 volts/cm. The ionic fields when $r \sim \sigma$ may exceed 10^7 to 10^8 volts/cm. It

---

[8]Here again care must be taken in such considerations to note that molecules are essentially treated as points, and that while theoretically twelve spheres can be packed around one sphere and perhaps another layer packed outside of the first, our assumption of the point center, spherical symmetry and noninterference between molecules themselves is naïve. The steric hindrances and other intermolecular forces will presumably much reduce the number in a cluster.

is conceivable that in such fields the value of D and the linear polarizability assumed no longer apply. H. Margenau (23) states that the linear polarizability formula used should hold as long as $\frac{1}{2}aX^2$ is much less than the distance between molecular unperturbed levels. Since a is of the order of 10^{-24}, this requires the allowed values of the field X to be much less than 10^9 volts/cm, which is higher than the fields mentioned and indicates that serious errors are not caused by the fields.

c) At distances of $r = \sigma$, the field of the ion is highly divergent over the molecule. Thus, the polarizing field changes between the inner surface of the molecule at $r = \sigma/2$ by a factor of 9 in going to the outer surface of the molecule at $r = 3\sigma/2$. The fields acting are not the uniform fields given by the relation $(D - 1)\ e^2/2\pi N\sigma^5$. This is taken account of through an evaluation of the quadrupole moments, and leads to forces of the form b_1/r^7. In some cases computed by Margenau, it is less than but nearly as large as the uniform-field force. The discussion so far has been applied to the displacement polarizability. What the effect of such fields will be on the quantized orientation of the dipoles of polar molecules cannot be predicted, but judging from past experience the values will not be changed materially.

d) In addition to the simple dipole forces there are other forces, such as van der Waals forces and the forces caused by quadrupole and other moments of higher order noted above. According to Margenau (23) these inverse seventh-power forces can with little error be added to the dipole forces. In some systems Margenau has shown that the quadrupole forces caused by polarization of the ion are commensurate with the van der Waals forces, and that the higher-order force at suitably small distances σ may contribute nearly as much to the energy as the dipole forces. These forces depend on σ and on the combination of ions and molecules involved. Except for Margenau's calculations, they have been largely neglected, and in considerations of clustering they must be included in some cases. They will in general serve to increase the PE term.

e) In such configurations, with the forces and fields involved, the charged molecule or ion and its attached molecules certainly do not constitute the idealized concept of a central charged spherical core surrounded by 12 molecular marbles. There is nothing to prevent the redistribution of charges in the cluster and the formation of a new molecule in many combinations when centers are σ cm apart and fields are high. Furthermore, after what has been stated about other forces, it is not impossible that unlike the naïve model considered, there will be considerable interaction between the one or more attached molecules as well as between the ion and the molecules. These interactions may reduce the number of molecules which may be added, and weaken the binding forces which would be acting if the other molecules were absent. Behavior of this sort is frequently observed in organic chemical combination.

These questions have not been studied at all, but recent evidence appears to indicate that in He gas at a few mm pressure, He^+ ions in a triple impact with He atoms form stable He_2^+ molecular ions (31), (75).[9] These are by no means a labile cluster, but are true ionized molecules. Many polar molecules form charge-sensitive and very specific complex ions with ionized atoms of appropriate sign, which again are not clusters (44), (45). In these, the chemical bindings are altered and charges are redistributed.

f) As stated above, if the dipole forces lead to clusters, the clusters *are insensitive to the sign of the charge on the ion.* The clusters grow to a size where they are always *labile* ions that are sensitive to temperature and X/p, with mobilities varying as smooth, continuous functions of these variables. Such ions may also show reluctance to forming.

It may accordingly be concluded that the cluster theory and the forces acting are such that with the exception of the increase of forces by the addition of quadrupole and van der Waals forces, all factors act to reduce the tendency to labile cluster formation as derived from the theory. The considerations further indicate that when such clusters form, they will be labile clusters of *very few* added molecules which tend to form reluctantly. However, with the distances and forces involved, there is nothing in some cases to prevent very profound rearrangements of charges among the molecules, leading to the formation of new chemical compounds of considerable stability with saturated forces. These reactions will not be universal. They will be charge-specific, and will lead to fixed, charged, permanent compounds of stoichiometrical character, and not to labile clusters.

In consequence of these considerations, it is clear that the lowering of the mobility by a factor of 3 to 5 below that estimated by the simple theory of equation 1.1a for unclustered ions appears not to be accounted for on the theory of labile clustering by virtue of the dielectric forces of equation 1.2.

§ 4. The Action of Forces at a Distance, and the Small-Ion Concept.

From the preceding section it may be concluded that while limited

[9]The same action has been observed for Ne^+ ions in Ne and A^+ ions in A.

clustering can and does occur in some cases, in itself it can account neither for the observed mobilities nor for their behavior. Attention must thus be turned to the longer-range action of these same dielectric forces in order to round out the study. Recognition of the action of such forces in relation to mobilities came following the introduction of similar considerations to the study of the coefficient of viscosity in the kinetic theory of gases. Thus, it is not surprising to note that G. B. M. Sutherland (13), following his study of the effect of the van der Waals forces between molecules in decreasing molecular free paths and increasing target areas, should have applied these considerations to a study of L in the ionic-mobility equation. Almost simultaneously, E. M. Wellisch (13) in 1909 introduced the *small-ion theory* of ionic mobilities founded on similar considerations. On this view, ions are all *monomolecular*, but the collision cross section $\pi\sigma^2$ is increased beyond that of $\pi\sigma_0^2$ for molecular impacts by the deviations of the otherwise straight-line trajectories of the ions in consequence of attractive forces. The mathematical approach of both of these theories was that of the classical kinetic theory involving mean free paths and was, therefore, none too accurate. However, some years earlier, P. Langevin (14) had made a very exact and complete theoretical study of ionic mobilities, assuming solid elastic impacts of ions of collision radius σ with molecules (allowing σ to include clustered ions), and assuming further attractive forces between ions and molecules of the form of equation 1.2.

The method was the classical esoteric theoretical approach of Maxwell and Boltzmann, using force fields instead of the more naïve free-path considerations. The lengthy paper published in 1905 in *Annales de Chimie et de Physique* was far ahead of its time. It went practically unnoticed[10] for nearly twenty years, until rediscovered by H. R. Hassé (15). In the meantime, J. J. Thomson (16) had calculated the effect of the forces between ions and molecules in causing momentum loss to the ions in their motion in the field, whether through direct impact, or *momentum transfer without impact.*[11]

---

[10]The author was aware of the paper, and at an earlier period had thumbed through its many pages of calculation. Owing to the form of the resulting relations, he had failed to realize the importance of this work, and especially the point center of force equation to be discussed.

[11]It should be noted that Wellisch and Sutherland's theories take account of momentum loss *in impact only,* as the increased impacts are caused by increased target areas. Losses of momentum by interaction without impact were not considered. The application of these theories to solid elastic equation 1.1a for mobility leads to inconsistent results except in a very limited range of values. They will thus be ignored in what follows.

In 1924, this analysis was adapted by the author to yield an equation for ionic mobilities (17). The equation virtually assumed that the ions were point centers of charge, exerting forces on dielectric molecules through equation 1.2. Collisions occurred when these point centers had trajectories in the force fields such as to strike the target areas of the molecules $\pi \sigma_M{}^2$ in impacts with velocities along the line of centers. Otherwise, momentum was transferred to the molecules by the pull of the passing ion in the applied field.

The equation deduced was notable in that without any arbitrary assumptions, it predicted mobilities in gases of the right order of magnitude. What was better, it predicted far more accurately the observed behavior of mobilities with different variables than the original solid elastic cluster equation. In 1926, H. R. Hassé (15) pointed out that the author's equation was nothing other than a special case of Langevin's general treatment, derived on the assumption that the solid elastic collision radius was small compared to the target area for collision as caused by dielectric attractive forces. This special case of Langevin's theory was, in fact, identical with the Thomson-Loeb equation, except for the numerical constant, which was more rigorously deduced from the exact integrations of Langevin. The equation, as translated into convenient form by the author, reads

$$(1.7) \qquad k = \frac{0.235 \sqrt{\frac{m+M}{m}}}{\rho/\rho_0 \sqrt{(D-1)_0 M_0}} \quad \text{in cm/sec per volt/cm.}$$

Here ρ_0 and ρ are the gas densities at $0°$ C. 760 mm pressure, and under the experimental conditions. D is the dielectric constant of the gas as measured in bulk at ρ_0, and M_0 is the *molecular weight* of the gas in question. The masses m and M are the masses of ions and molecules, and the expression under that radical is therefore a dimensionless ratio. The usefulness of the equation is noted at once, for if m/M is known, k is at once given in standard units with no arbitrary assumptions as soon as ρ, D, and M_0 are given.[12] The striking fact at once noted was that equation 1.7, far more accurately than the solid elastic theory, gives values of ionic mobilities in keeping with observation. Differences in mobilities of positive and negative ions could be included by differences in m/M if these differences were known, as D is charge-insensitive. The

[12]Even if m and M are not known accurately, so long as $m > M$ the error is less than 40%. In most cases of observed ions, m is greater than M, so that the error caused by neglect is of the order of 10%. Where m is much less than M, as for Li^+ ions in Xe, the factor is important.

equation predicts the following ionic behavior: (1) The mobility
is independent of field strength X, except again at high X/p, as
is to be expected. (2) The mobility is proportional to $1/\rho$, as is
observed. (3) The mobility is independent of temperature at constant ρ. Experimentally, at constant ρ, the mobility in many instances
is *relatively insensitive* to temperature change except over large
ranges of temperature. (4) The mobility depends on

$$\sqrt{(M + m)/m}\Big/\sqrt{(D - 1)_0 M_0},$$

which, as noted, is in relatively good accord with observation. (5) The
mobility is independent of the ionic charge. This point has never
been put to experimental test, but is to be expected for a point center
of force theory. This independence should be remembered before any
high-mobility values of small ions observed are glibly ascribed to
doubly charged ions.

It is to be noted that this theory is the extreme antithesis to
that given by the previous solid elastic equation (1.1a), where impacts
only accounted for momentum exchange between ions and molecules.
It is, therefore, *like the solid elastic cluster theory, one-sided,
incomplete,* and thus accurately applicable only to a limited number
of cases. The rather more surprising features which it contains,
such as the independence of mobility on the random velocity, and
ion radius and charge, become clear from the following reasoning:
Thomson postulated that with attracting centers of force on an in-
verse-square law, either the trajectories of the point centers were
so bent as to lead to central impact and thus energy change, or the
ions moving past molecules at a sufficiently close encounter simply
transferred energy in the field direction by force interaction. Calculation of these energy exchanges led to an expression for the
ratio of E_f, the loss of energy per cm of the ion path under attractive-
force encounters relative to E_1, the loss of energy per cm of the
ion path with classical kinetic collisions only. The expression,
in the notation of this text, reads

$$E_f = E_1\left[0.98\left\{\frac{(D-1)e^2}{\pi N \sigma_0^4 M C^2}\right\}^{\frac{1}{2}}\right].$$

Since the reciprocal of the energy loss per cm is proportional
to the mean free path for energy loss, if follows that $\pi \sigma_f^2/\pi \sigma_0^2 =$
$L/L_f = E_f/E_L$. This defines a new mean free path with force acting

to replace the $L = 1/\pi \sigma_0^2 N$ of equation 1.1a. It at once follows that

$$k = \frac{0.815\,e}{MC\pi \sigma^2 N} \quad \frac{\sqrt{(M+m)/m}}{0.98 \left\{ \dfrac{(D-1)e^2}{\pi N \sigma_0^4 MC^2} \right\}^{\frac{1}{2}}} \quad .$$

This relation is quite revealing in that it shows that if the *energy free path* is considered, i.e., if energy exchange is used to define a "collision," the term in the denominator increasing collision rate by virtue of force action cancels out certain terms entering into the elastic-collision concept. Accordingly, as the charge on the ion increases, it increases the *pull of the field* on the ion, but likewise increases the *drag of the molecules* on the ion in exact proportion. Thus, the resulting Langevin point center of force equation (1.7) yields a mobility independent of charge e. In a like fashion the quantity $\pi \sigma_0^2$ and the quantity C are eliminated from the point center of force equation.

It should next be noted that the center of force theory and the energy-collision concept make the ratio of σ_f^2/σ_0^2 proportional to the square root of expression 1.4, which is virtually the ratio of potential to kinetic energy of the ion and molecule at a distance σ_0. That is $\sigma_f^2 = \sigma_0^2 \sqrt{PE/KE}$. It will be noted that to have a sensible reduction in mobility, with the energy-transfer relation it is necessary that $\sqrt{PE/KE}$ be large enough to give the observed general 3-fold reduction in k below the value deduced from equation 1.1a. Such an increase requires that $(D-1)$ be *large* and σ_0 correspondingly *small*. This requirement is another way of saying that the *action of the attractive forces must predominate over the physical-collision radius*. Thus, to give the required results, σ_0 and $(D-1)$ must be such as to give a ratio of PE/KE of the order of 9 and yet cause no clustering. This could occur if clustering depends on $\beta PE/KE$ with β small.

§ 5. Comparison of Limiting Theories with Experiment.

It is now of interest to compare the predictions of the various limiting theories with experiment. Until the study of mobilities of known alkali ions in pure gases, over time intervals so short as to preclude much alteration of the ions, there were no data at hand. Beginning in 1932, a group of physicists under A. M. Tyndall and C. F. Powell, at Bristol, England, perfected the four-gauze shutter method and began to collect data in a systematic fashion (7), (18).

The method was extensively tested by using what were supposed

TABLE 1.1

Mobilities of Alkali Ions in Gases, Bristol Data

K *in cm/sec per volt/cm,* 20° C. 760 mm

Gas	Li$^+$	Na$^+$	K$^+$	Rb$^+$	Cs$^+$	Ga$^+$	In$^+$	Tl$^+$
He	25.30	23.20	22.40	21.00	19.00	—	22.00	20.30
Ne	14.35	9.00	8.00	7.18	6.58	—	7.08	6.63
A	4.99	3.22	2.78	2.39	2.24	—	2.14	2.05
Kr	4.03	2.34	1.98	1.61	1.44	—	—	—
Xe	—	—	1.50	1.12	0.94	—	—	—
H$_2$	13.30	13.60	13.50	13.40	13.40	—	—	—
N$_2$	4.21	3.04	2.70	2.39	2.25	2.45	2.29	2.17

to be He$^+$ ions in He. All data were of such reliability, reproducibility, and consistency as to lead to great confidence in the method. They next studied mobilities of ions of Li$^+$, Na$^+$, K$^+$, Rb$^+$, and Cs$^+$, in the gases He, Ne, A, Kr, and Xe. At values of X/p in the lower brackets, where ionization by collision does not occur, the data for large ranges of X/p showed the reduced mobility K constant. These results further confirmed previous evidence that under ordinary circumstances the ions do *not* show the behavior characteristics of labile clusters. The values of the reduced mobilities K at 760 mm and 20° C. are shown in table 1.1.

The variation of mobility k with the ratio m/M in the gases A and He is shown in figures 1.20a and 1.20b. The points are the observed values cited in table 1.1, while the full lines represent the point center of force equation of Langevin. The agreement between theory and experiment in argon is striking. It was observed that in Ne and more so in He, as shown in figure 1.20b, the mobilities decrease more rapidly with increase in mass than the law predicts. The gases Ne and especially He have very low values of $(D-1)$. Impacts with ions of increasing $\sigma_0/2$ from Li$^+$ to Cs$^+$ will introduce larger and larger solid elastic collision radii. Hence for He with a very low $(D-1)$ the collisions, even with Na$^+$ ions, will cause marked deviations from the law. Above A gas the value of $(D-1)$ is so large that even the size of Rb$^+$ and Cs$^+$ causes no deviations. Thus, the solid elastic impact collisions are relatively important in He and Ne, but appear to be unimportant in A. The same is true in greater measure for Kr and Xe. A further proof of the validity of the point center of force theory for the gases of large D, lies in an experimental evaluation of the constant 0.235, given in the

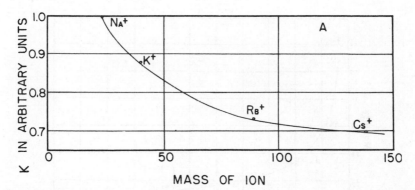

Fig. 1.20a. Tyndall and Powell's data for mobility of various alkali ions in A compared to the small-ion theory of Langevin. Note the good agreement when D is large.

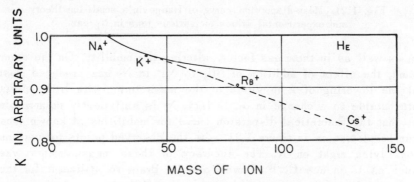

Fig. 1.20b. The same data as in 1.20a, but in He gas with low D. Note that the large ions Rb^+ and Cs^+ with large collision radii deviate badly from the small-ion law.

author's form of equation 1.7, which in Langevin's original paper takes the value of 0.51. The Bristol group, utilizing Langevin's equation, applied experimental values of k and determined the value of this constant for ions in A, Kr, and Xe as 0.54, 0.55, 0.56. This is remarkably close, in consideration of the assumptions involved in the theory. [13]

In these studies, apparent addition or clustering of an H_2O molecule to Na^+ in H_2 gas of low $(D-1)$ produced an increase in radius

[13] The rather striking agreement of this relation with some experimental data, despite its definite neglect of radii, becomes clear through reference to the generalized theory of carrier motion in gases by Wannier in his part II (reviewed in § 11). It is shown that where the elastic-impact radius is small and polarization forces are relatively high, at lower temperatures, the spiraling character of the orbits leads to a nearly isotropic scattering both at high and low fields. The force also satisfies the mean free-time requirement. Under such conditions the center of force theory is quite satisfactory.

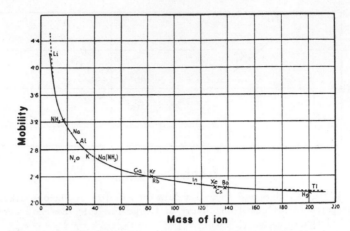

Fig. 1.21. Mass-dispersion curve of Langevin's small-ion theory
and experimental values for various ions in N_2 gas.

σ_0 as well as in the mass factor, altering the mobility. On the other
hand, the effect of addition of NH_3 to Na^+ in N_2 gas produced most
of the lowering of k in virtue of the mass term, with little effect
attributable to a change in σ_0. In fact, N_2 is sufficiently polarizable
so that the theoretical dispersion curve for mobilities of known ions
can be plotted as in figure 1.21, with the observed points for various
ions lying right on it. The accuracy of these measurements was
such as to induce C. F. Powell and L. Brata to utilize it for the
investigation of ions given off by hot bodies (18).

Deviations observed in values of the mobilities for N_2^+ ions in
N_2 were ascribed to change-of-charge, or Kallmann-Rosen effect
(19), as indicated in part one, section 2, of this chapter.[14] Similar
deviations occur for O_2^+ in O_2, He^+ in He, A^+ in A, Ne^+ in Ne, and H_2^+ in
H_2 for the same reason.[15] The Kallmann-Rosen action is further indicated when N_2 ions move in N_2 contaminated with Hg, where all the
positive ions observed show a mobility of 2.16, which is characteristic
of Hg^+ to within 1.5% (19). The presence of traces of H_2 in N_2 with a
discharge yielding the ions, gave N_2^+ and NH_3^+ ions, also indicating
charge transfer from the ionized H_2^+ to the sparse NH_3 molecules.

The limits of X/p at which the values of k in N_2 were constant
was determined for different ions (19). These are shown in figure
1.22. The increase in k is due essentially to the gain in energy

[14] Actually, the ions in N_2 are N_4^+ (79), and their reduced mobility is 2.49
cm^2/volt sec, which puts the value right on the curve.

[15] The ions in H_2 are probably for the most part H_3^+ above 10 mm pressure.

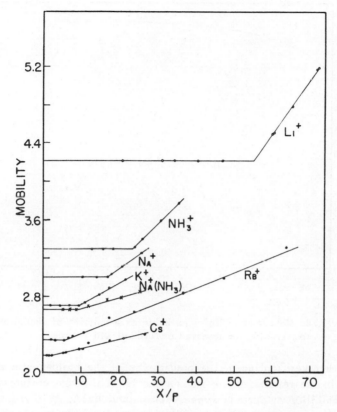

Fig. 1.22. Limiting values of X/p at which mobility ceases to be independent of X/p, as observed by the Bristol group.

of the ions in the field, such that their velocity reduces the importance of attractive forces and/or alters the size of the ion by knocking off attached molecules. A more detailed discussion of this effect will be given under the analysis of the more exact theories of ion mobilities.

In many instances it is difficult to interpret the observed behavior of the various ions, since both radii and forces must play some role. Thus it is likely that the Li^+ ion in N_2 is not an Li^+ ion, but an Li^+N_2 or other complex ion which requires a high X/p for breakup. Much more complete data in this region are given by the researches of A. V. Hershey by the Townsend method (9). It is to be noted that the value of X/p for increase in mobility of pure N_2^+ ions in N_2 gas occurs above an $X/p = 20$, which is consistent with the failure of the author and of Kia-Lok Yen (49) to observe such changes in air and H_2 at a much earlier date.

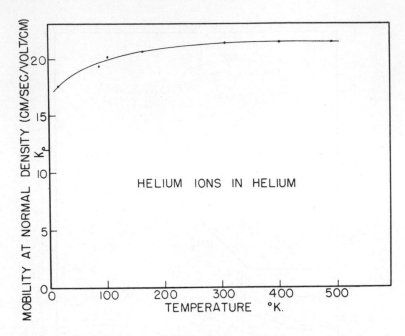

Fig. 1.23. Mobilities of He$^+$ ions in He as a function of absolute temperature, as observed by Tyndall and Pearce.

A further verification of the predictions of the point-center theory appears in the results of the measurements of the temperature variation of mobility in various gases, determined by A. M. Tyndall and A. F. Pearce, and by Pearce (20). Curves for He$^+$ ions in He, N$_2^+$ ions in N$_2$, Na$^+$ ions in He, and Cs$^+$ ions in He, are shown in figures 1.23, 1.24, and 1.25, at constant density. Later results of K. Hoselitz (21) for Li$^+$ in He, Na$^+$ in He, Cs$^+$ in He, K$^+$ in A, Rb$^+$ in Kr, and Cs$^+$ in Xe, are shown in figure 1.26. The actually observed values for constant density are given in tables 1.2 and 1.3.

The results in He and in N$_2$ are complicated, since the ions are not He$^+$ and N$_2^+$, but instead are He$_2^+$ and N$_4^+$.[16] In He with Cs$^+$ and Na$^+$, the variation of K_ρ is remarkably slight, considering that solid elastic collisions intervene to some extent. The same applies to Cs$^+$ in Xe, and in a smaller measure to Li$^+$ in He. The effect is striking for Cs$^+$ in Xe. There is little chance of clustering in these gases at lower temperatures. However, in the case of K$^+$ ions in

---

[16]The ions observed in He, Ne, and A are now known to have been He$_2^+$, Ne$_2^+$, and A$_2^+$. The variation of mobility for He$_2^+$ in He has been determined from theory by S. Geltman (88). The ion in N$_2$ is probably N$_4^+$ (79). Theory for this ion has not been developed.

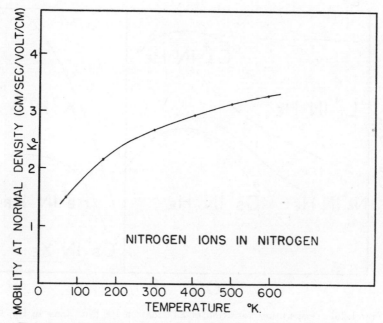

Fig. 1.24. Mobilities of N_2^+ ions in N_2 as a function of absolute temperature, as observed by Tyndall and Pearce.

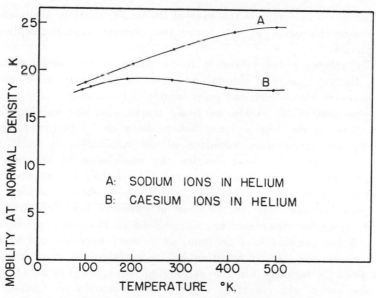

Fig. 1.25. Temperature variation of Na^+ and Cs^+ ions in He, as reported by Tyndall and Pearce.

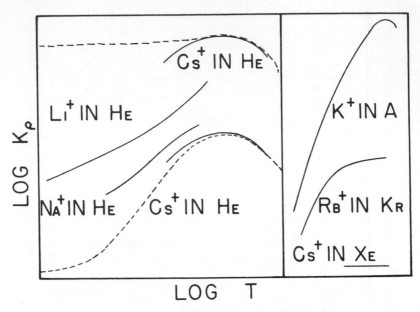

Fig. 1.26. Temperature variation of Li⁺ ions in He, Na⁺ ions in He, Cs⁺ ions in He, K⁺ ions in A, Rb⁺ ions in Kr, and Cs⁺ ions in Xe, as reported by Tyndall and Pearce and by Hoselitz.

A, and to a less extent in the case of Rb⁺ in Kr, there is a possibility of cluster formation at the lower temperatures which complicates the picture.

The following conclusion is to be drawn on the basis of these data: Barring change of charge and some cluster formation, it appears for gases of high D that the point center of force theory is unexpectedly successful. It yields not only proper absolute values of the mobilities of the known ions, but predicts the mobilities and the approximate temperature variation of the mobilities. It must, however, be remembered that despite the usefulness of the relation, it neglects the solid elastic impacts. The failure to include these effects will be of considerable significance where complex ions or small clusters form, in the case of gases of low dielectric constant, or at low temperatures, as well as in the study of negative ions. Where complex ions do form, as in many mixtures and in some pure gases, *the use of equation 1.7 to evaluate the mass m of the ion from the mobility via the dispersion curve, is just as incorrect as the use of the classical solid elastic equation to evaluate the ionic radius.* Under these conditions use of equation 1.7 will always yield values of the ionic mass, and hence an inferred cluster size

TABLE 1.2

Temperature Variation of Ion Mobilities in Gases
at Constant Density, Bristol Data

He$^+$ in He		N$_2$$^+$ in N$_2$	
Temp. °K.	K_ρ	Temp. °K.	K_ρ
480	21.4	587	3.19
399	21.4	500	3.11
291	21.4	407	2.94
169	21.0	292	2.67
90	20.3	169	2.15
77	19.3	90	1.62
20	17.6	77	1.56
—	—	65	1.46
—	—	—	—

Cs$^+$ in He		Na$^+$ in He	
Temp. °K.	K_ρ	Temp. °K.	K_ρ
79	17.5	92	18.5
92	18.0	195	20.9
195	19.2	290	22.8
290	18.9	405	24.0
392	18.1	477	24.6
492	17.4	—	—

TABLE 1.3

Temperature Variation of Alkali Ions in Inert Gases
at Constant Density, Bristol Data

Temp. °K.	Li$^+$ in He K_ρ	K$^+$ in A K_ρ	Rb$^+$ in Kr K_ρ	Cs$^+$ in Xe K_ρ
20.5	20.0	—	—	—
78.0	21.8	1.30	—	—
90.0	22.2	1.52	1.15	—
195.0	23.9	2.34	1.57	1.02
293.0	—	—	1.575	1.005
291.0	25.8	2.81	1.58	1.01
370.0	—	—	1.59	1.01
389.0	27.8	—	—	—
400.0	—	3.07	—	—
450.0	—	—	—	1.03
455.0	—	—	1.64	—
460.0	—	2.93	—	—
493.0	29.2	—	—	—

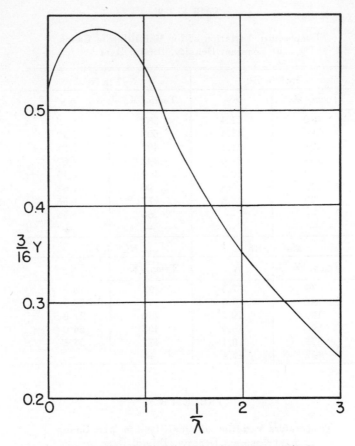

Fig. 1.27. Plot of Langevin's quantity $3/16Y$
as a function of the parameter $1/\lambda$.

materially higher than it really is from the nature of the sensitivity
of the equations to mass and collision-radius changes.

§ 6. Complete Ion-Mobility Theories.

It is now clear that the real understanding and prediction of ionic
mobilities will lie in the use of the full equations involving solid
elastic collisions as well as forces, or involving both attractive
and repulsive forces. It is also clear that such equations must be
derived from far more generalized theory than use of the simple
mean free-path concept. Of such theories, probably the best is that
evolved initially in 1905 by P. Langevin, following procedures of
Maxwell and Boltzmann. It was recomputed in part by H. R. Hassé

TABLE 1.4

Langevin Theory Coefficients

$1/\lambda$	$\dfrac{3}{16Y}$	$1/\lambda$	$\dfrac{3}{16Y}$
0.0	.5105	1.6	.4201
0.1	.5488	1.8	.3834
0.2	.5648	2.0	.3514
0.3	.5756	2.2	.3236
0.4	.5830	2.4	.2994
0.5	.5880	2.6	.2784
0.6	.5904	2.8	.2599
0.7	.5878	3.0	.2436
0.8	.5790	3.2	.2292
0.9	.5662	3.4	.2163
1.0	.5483	3.6	.2048
1.2	.5057	3.8	.1944
1.4	.4614	4.0	.1849

in 1926 (15), using the later considerations of Chapman and Enskog.[17] This theory assumes solid elastic impacts in consequence of repulsive forces and the inverse fifth-power attractive law of equation 1.2. The solution takes the form

$$(1.8) \qquad k = \frac{3}{16Y} \frac{0.462\sqrt{(M+m)/m}}{\rho/\rho_0 \sqrt{(D-1)_0 M_0}} = \frac{3}{16Y} \frac{\sqrt{(M+m)/m}}{\sqrt{(D-1)\rho}}.$$

This is seen to be similar to equation 1.7, except for the use of the term $3/16Y$, which is a function of a variable λ containing the effects of the integration over all classes of orbits involved in the solid elastic impacts. The relation between $3/16Y$ plotted as ordinates against $1/\lambda$ is shown in figure 1.27. The values, as recomputed by Hassé, are shown in table 1.4, where $3/16Y$ is tabulated against values of $1/\lambda$.

Here, $1/\lambda$ is given by

$$\frac{1}{\lambda} = \sqrt{\frac{8\pi N_0 \sigma^4 M C^2}{3(D-1)_0 e^2}} = \sqrt{\frac{8\pi \rho_0 \sigma^4}{(D-1)_0 e^2}} = \sqrt{\frac{KE}{PE}}.$$

[17]Solid elastic impacts as here used are impacts in which the molecules and ions are spheres of radii $\sigma_M/2$ and $\sigma_m/2$. The only forces acting are the inverse fifth-power attractive forces up to a distance between centers of ion and molecule of $(\sigma_m + \sigma_M)/2$. At this distance, repulsive forces of a high order, $-1/r^n$ with $n = \infty$ become active. The use of such forces of repulsion gives a lower value to the potential-distance curve than actually occurs.

TABLE 1.5

Hershey's Radii of Atoms and Ions

Radii in $\overset{\circ}{A}$ for the Atoms $\sigma_M/2$ and Ions $\sigma_m/2$

He	Ne	A	Kr	Xe	H_2	N_2
1.00	1.50	1.55	1.60	1.85	1.05	1.65
Li^+	Na^+	K^+	Rb^+	Cs	–	–
0.45	1.35	1.40	1.50	1.80	–	–

TABLE 1.6

Hershey's Values of Dielectric Constant

The Corresponding Values of D, Computed and Observed at $0°$ C. 760 mm

Values	He	Ne	A	Kr	Xe	H_2	N_2
Computed	1.000052	1.000106	1.00063	1.00091	1.00148	1.00028	1.00082
Observed	1.0000665	1.000123	1.000504	1.000708	1.00124	1.000252	1.000589

The value of σ here is the distance between centers of ion and molecule at impact, which can be taken as $\sigma = (\sigma_m + \sigma_M)/2$. The solution assumes that the ions remain in thermal equilibrium with the gas and that $\frac{1}{2}mC_i^2 = \frac{1}{2}MC^2 = (3/2)kT$. The value of the mobility k, it is seen, depends quite critically on the ratio of KE/PE. At a given set of values of T and D, it depends critically on the value of σ. Where σ^4 is negligible, relative to $(D-1)\,e^2/N_0\,MC^2$, it is clear that $1/\lambda = 0$ and $3/16Y = 0.5105$, making equation 1.8 the center of force theory of equation 1.7.

The use of this equation depends on having known values of σ. This, of course, becomes a major problem even for the unclustered ion, since atomic theory and experiment give only meager data. In the case of the complex ion with its asymmetry, the evaluation of σ_m becomes almost hopeless. Data for σ_M and σ_m from the van der Waals equation, or closest packing of the molecules, might be used. Data from viscosity give σ_M too large. Atomic data for alkali ions give values that may be too small. In evaluating the mobilities from Langevin's theory for alkali ions in various gases, extended to include the case where $\frac{1}{2}mC_i^2 > (3/2)kT$, A. V. Hershey derived values for $(D-1)$ and for σ, which are both in doubt, by adjusting these values to give the best experimental fit for the mobilities of various ions, Na^+, K^+, Rb^+, etc., in the different gases observed by the Bristol group at low values of X/p, where Langevin's theory applied (22). The values of $(D-1)$ so derived were not seriously different from the values observed in bulk, being smaller in He and Ne and larger in A, Kr, and N_2. The values for these quantities, as derived by Hershey, are given in table 1.5.

Hershey's values are mostly a little higher than those of table 1.6. The meaning of Hershey's adjustments is obscure. They result from an attempt to fit observed mobility curves, *assuming Langevin's equation to be accurate* and that $(D-1)$ is constant down to distances of the order of σ, but modified by divergence of field and failure of the displacement law at high fields. In the case of ion complexes, the device of Hershey's is the only way to estimate the average value of σ_m if D is known. Thus, the Langevin equation is in a peculiar position in that it is probably somewhat better than the accuracy of the data to be fed in to predict values of k. Probably its best function would, in general, be the inverse of predicting k, i.e., it would use k to predict σ_m and D.[18] It can be used in cases where D is reasonably well known to estimate σ_m from values of k. Here again care must be used, as k involves not only the value of $(\sigma_M + \sigma_m)/2 = \sigma$, but also a knowledge of m and M.[19] In this instance successive approximations could be used. Strictly, the adjustment for k to yield σ if D is known can only be done where m/M is known, as in the alkali ions.

In a paper, "On the Forces between Positive Ions and Neutral Molecules," H. Margenau (23), gives a table of values of minimum solid elastic radii for collision between alkali ions and some atoms and molecules. These represent the sum of gas-kinetic molecular radii and ionic radii at contact equal to $(\sigma_m + \sigma_M)/2$ as used here. The values were taken from V. M. Goldschmidt (24). They are listed in table 1.7.

---

[18]This use is analogous to the first use of equation 1.1a for evaluating the size of the cluster, except that in this case Langevin's theory is far more exact and sound. It must be noted that the classical theories fail where change-of-charge reactions occur, and wave mechanics only can give the correct answer. Thus, where exchange forces are important, Langevin's theory is not accurate. It is also faulty in that with such forces the quantity β for entropy effects is overestimated, leading to more clustering than observed.

[19]Caution must be used in any such study, which is valueless unless the nature of the ion is definitely known. This could apply for some of the alkali ions at adequate temperatures in some gases. Recent results indicate that in the inert gases, ions assumed to be He^+, Ne^+, and A^+ were really He_2^+, Ne_2^+, and A_2^+ (32).

TABLE 1.7

Goldschmidt Values of the Distance between Ionic
or Molecular Centers at Impact in Å

Gas	Li$^+$	Na$^+$	K$^+$	Rb$^+$	Cs$^+$
He	1.85	2.05	2.40	2.56	2.72
Ne	1.97	2.75	2.52	2.68	2.84
Ar	2.21	2.41	2.76	2.92	3.08
Kr	2.35	2.55	2.90	3.06	3.22
Xe	2.49	2.69	3.04	3.20	3.36
H$_2$	2.16	2.36	2.71	2.87	3.03
N$_2$	2.35	2.55	2.90	3.06	3.22
O$_2$	2.23	2.43	2.78	2.94	3.10
CO$_2$	2.39	2.59	2.94	3.10	3.26

The attractive forces follow the force and potential laws given by

$$f = +a/r^5 + b/r^7 + c/r^9$$

and

$$V = -A/r^4 - (B_1 + B_2)/r^6 - C/r^8$$

with

$$a = 4A, \ b = 6(B_1 + B_2), \text{ and } c = 8C.$$

The coefficient C is negligibly small, and at the radii mentioned in table 1.7 these last terms may be neglected. The inverse fourth-power potential term is obviously the interaction between ionic charge and the induced molecular dipole moment μ.

However, aside from producing a dipole moment in the molecule, the ion induces a quadrupole moment θ contributing to $1/r^6$ and higher moments contributing to C/r^8. Now while the dipole moment produces a force $\mu dX/dr$, where X is the ionic field at the molecule, the quadrupole moment produces an attraction $\theta d^2 X/dr^2$, and while μ is proportional to X, θ is proportional to dX/dr. Thus, since the Coulomb field X varies as e/r^2, the quadrupole moments will be attracted as b/r^7. Again the ion is not a point charge but is itself polarizable. While it cannot take on a permanent polarity in the absence of a static field, it undergoes instantaneous polarization more or less in phase with the rapidly rotating dipoles of the molecule. This yields an attraction similar to a van der Waals force. This force also shows a dependence on r^{-7}, and is comparable to the quadrupole force. This explains the two additive constants B_1 and B_2

TABLE 1.8

Margenau's Table of Potential Coefficients B_1 and B_2 for Alkali Ions
in Various Gases in Units of 10^{-60} erg cm^6

Gas	B_1	B_2				
		Li$^+$	Na$^+$	K$^+$	Rb$^+$	Cs$^+$
He	1.12	0.72	1.65	5.94	8.94	15.5
Ne	1.97	1.42	3.27	11.60	17.30	30.7
A	12.20	4.39	10.50	38.60	58.30	103.1
Kr	21.80	5.72	13.90	52.10	78.90	139.5
Xe	41.70	7.94	19.50	74.50	113.80	200.0
H_2	7.66	1.07	4.52	17.00	25.80	45.1
N_2	12.50	4.28	10.40	38.40	58.60	102.8
O_2	12.90	3.42	8.38	31.50	48.20	84.9
CO_2	26.70	6.96	16.80	62.60	95.40	167.0

in the inverse sixth-power attractive-energy term. Margenau calculated the quadrupole forces for a number of gases as coefficient B_1. The coefficient B_2 comes from the van der Waals type forces. Again the van der Waals forces between ion and molecules or atoms may be roughly calculated. This leads to the data in table 1.8, expressed in units of 10^{-60} erg cm^6.

It will be noted that for less polarizable gases with highly polarizable ions, such as Cs$^+$ in helium, the van der Waals forces far outweigh the quadrupole forces, while Li$^+$ ions in Xe have quadrupole forces far outweighing the van der Waals forces. The highest forces of this type in any case are those between Cs$^+$ ions in Xe, where the van der Waals forces outweigh the quadrupole forces by a factor of 5.

Margenau also calculated a table of values of the interaction energy V_{σ}, due to the addition of the polarization forces and the combined van der Waals and quadrupole forces for various combinations of gases and alkali ions at the closest distance of approach given by the collision radii of table 1.7. These are tabulated in table 1.9, with energy in units of 10^{-13} erg.

This table is of interest in that it yields a concept of the relative importance of the polarizability (left-hand column) and higher-order forces (right-hand column) at the critical distance σ_0. It is noted that the polarizability, i.e., the inverse fourth-power term in all cases, is greater than the van der Waals quadrupole term. For Cs$^+$, which is very polarizable, the two energies are nearly equal; 0.43 relative to 0.41×10^{-13} erg. For Li$^+$ in Xe, the inverse fourth-power

TABLE 1.9

Margenau's Table of Dipole and Quadrupole Energies at Critical Radii of
Table 1.7, for Alkali Ions in Various Gases in Units of 10^{-13} erg

Gas	Li^+	Na^+	K^+	Rb^+	Cs^+
He	2.02 + 0.46	1.34 + 0.37	0.71 + 0.37	0.55 + 0.35	0.43 + 0.41
Ne	2.98 + 0.58	2.02 + 0.50	1.11 + 0.53	0.87 + 0.52	0.69 + 0.62
A	7.81 + 1.42	5.57 + 1.16	3.22 + 1.14	2.57 + 1.14	2.10 + 1.36
Kr	9.31 + 1.65	6.68 + 1.30	4.02 + 1.25	3.23 + 1.23	2.66 + 1.45
Xe	12.00 + 2.09	8.83 + 1.62	5.38 + 1.48	4.37 + 1.43	3.63 + 1.69
H_2	4.29 + 0.94	3.01 + 0.71	1.73 + 0.62	1.37 + 0.60	1.11 + 0.68
N_2	6.58 + 1.00	4.72 + 0.83	2.83 + 0.86	2.28 + 0.88	1.88 + 1.04
O_2	7.28 + 1.33	5.20 + 1.04	3.03 + 0.97	2.42 + 0.95	1.96 + 1.10
CO_2	10.00 + 1.79	7.30 + 1.44	4.41 + 1.37	3.59 + 1.38	2.93 + 1.63

term is large (12×10^{-13} erg), and much greater than the higher-order
term, 2.09×10^{-13}. For Li^+ in He, where the field about the small
Li^+ ion is high, even in the feebly polarizable He the values of
lower- and higher-order energies are 2.02 and 0.46×10^{-13} erg respectively, and for Cs^+ in Xe the terms are 3.63 and 1.69×10^{-13} erg
respectively.

The data given are very useful for calculation, and help one to
understand the nature of these forces more accurately. They also
take account of the divergence of field strength over the molecular
diameter through the quadrupole moments.

During the past few years there have been some rather illuminating
examples of the validity of the solid elastic, the center of force,
and the Langevin theories. First, recent advances (to be described
at a later point) have given specific information as to the nature
of the ions in pure gases studied by the modern techniques indicated
above. Secondly, in the studies of drift velocities of inert gas and
some other ions in their own gases at high X/p, the theoretical
analyses of G. H. Wannier (32), (87) (to be given at a later point)
have led to some interesting findings. The theory of Wannier indicates that at an X/p such that the ion has an energy in excess of
that of the surrounding atoms, its drift velocity v is quite nicely
given by the expression

1.8a $v = 1.147 \, (aL)^{1/2},$

in which a is the acceleration of the ion Xe/m by the field and L
is its mean free path. This makes v proportional to $\sqrt{X/p}$ and k
proportional to $1/\sqrt{X/p}$. This relation applies so long as the molecules scatter the ions isotropically, and provided the collision cross

TABLE 1.10

Hard Sphere Elastic Ion-Atom Cross Sections for Exchange Forces
at High Energy, According to Hornbeck and Varney

Gas	Ion	Hard Sphere Ion-Atom $cm^2 \times 10^{16}$	Atom-Atom from Viscosity $cm^2 \times 10^{16}$	Ratio: $\dfrac{\text{Ion-Atom}}{\text{Atom-Atom}}$
He	He^+	54	15	3.6
Ne	Ne^+	65	21	3.1
A	A^+	134	42	3.2
Kr	Kr^+	157	59	3.2
Xe	Xe^+	192	67	3.9
O_2	O_2^+	79	–	–
N_2	N_2^+	123	–	–
CO	CO^+	145	–	–

section $\pi[(\sigma_m + \sigma_M)/2]^2$ is constant with velocity. At ion energies greater than the thermal energies $(3/2)kT$ of the ambient gas atoms, the action of the polarization forces is negligible. This is in agreement with the ion-mobility curves of A. V. Hershey (9) at high X/p, where for some ions the *increase* in mobility with ion energy can be seen before it is compensated by the decrease in mobility caused by the $k \propto 1/\sqrt{X/p}$ law. The assumptions of Wannier were found substantiated by Hornbeck's (32) values for the drift velocity v as a function of X/p for He^+, A^+, and Ne^+, and for Varney's (79) values for K^+, Xe^+, O_2^+, and N_2^+ in the parent gases, and for CO^+ in CO. It may be added that the character of the cross section evaluated from equation 1.8a is independent of the nature of the forces causing it. So long as isotropy and independence of velocity apply, it can yield a pure solid elastic spherical collision radius to be used with equation 1.1a for evaluating mobilities in cases such as exchange forces, where the collision cross section is dominated by other than the polarization forces active at low X/p.

On the basis of the studies of Hornbeck and Varney, the hard sphere, high-energy elastic repulsive force cross sections shown in table 1.10 are given in cm^2. For comparison there are given the atom-atom collision cross sections as derived from viscosity, as well as the ratios of the ion-atom to the atom-atom cross sections. It will be noted that owing to exchange forces, the ion-atom cross sections are about three times the atom-atom cross sections and are remarkably constant.

These cross sections may be compared with the data in table 1.7 by dividing by π and extracting the square root. Thus, in argon

TABLE 1.11

Computed and Observed Mobilities at Low X/p, Using Wannier's
Force Radii and by Langevin's Center of Force Equation

Gas	Ion	Wannier Radii	Langevin Force Equation	Observed by:		
				Tyndall and Powell	Chanin and Biondi	Hornbeck and Varney
He	He$^+$	13.40	—	—	11.20	10.20
He	He$_2^+$	—	18.20	21.60	20.00	18.00
Ne	Ne$^+$	4.86	—	—	4.20	4.40
Ne	Ne$_2^+$	—	6.21	6.30	6.50	6.30
A	A$^+$	1.67	—	—	1.65	1.63
A	A$_2^+$	—	2.09	1.93	2.60	1.94
Kr	Kr$^+$	1.01	—	1.01	0.93	0.90-0.95
Kr	Kr$_2^+$	—	1.18	—	1.20	1.10-1.20
Xe	Xe$^+$	0.77	—	0.77	0.63	0.60-0.65
Xe	Xe$_2^+$	—	0.74	—	0.80	0.67-0.77
O$_2$	O$_2^+$	2.78	2.75	—	—	2.25
N$_2$	N$_2^+$	2.17	2.80	—	—	—
N$_2$	N$_4^+$	—	2.42	2.49	—	2.49
CO	CO$^+$	1.58	2.19	—	—	1.60

$(\sigma_m + \sigma_M)/2$ for A$^+$ ions is effectively about 6.6×10^{-8} cm as a result of the exchange force compared to 2.76 for K$^+$ ions in A.

On this basis, Hornbeck and Wannier, as well as Varney, computed the mobilities of the various atomic ions in the gases at low energies, using the values of σ to evaluate the mean free path and equation 1.1a or a similar one. Wannier and Varney also computed the mobilities of the molecular ions of He to Xe, as well as molecular ions using the Langevin center of force equation 1.7. These computed values are compared with those from experiment in table 1.11, mobilities in cm^2/volt sec reduced to 0° C. and 760 mm.

It is seen that the Langevin solid elastic repulsive-force law equation with suitable radii yields reasonable agreement with observation, especially where exchange forces are active. For molecular ions with no exchange forces, the center of force small-ion Langevin equation 1.7 appears as satisfactory as the data available for insertion would lead one to expect.

In 1931, H. R. Hassé and W. R. Cook applied the methods used by Chapman and Lennard-Jones in the analysis of viscosity involving attractive and repulsive forces to the mobility problem (25). In the viscosity study they had used as the law of force, $f = +\mu\, r^{-5} - \lambda\, r^{-9}$ with some success in computing the temperature variation of the coefficient of viscosity for a number of gases. This was next applied to the calculation of ionic mobilities. In so doing, they assumed the inverse fifth-power attractive law. The coefficient μ' used was the *sum* of the $(D-1)e^2/2\pi N$ term for ionic attractions plus the equivalent coefficient, *assuming the van der Waals forces to be inverse fifth-power* attractive forces, having the constant which they derived from viscosity. The added terms in the case of H_2 represented 10% of the dielectric term and so produced no serious error. The repulsive-force constant λ' was that inferred from viscosity study. The equation they derived was

$$k = \frac{3}{16} \frac{e}{2\sqrt{\pi RT}} \left[\frac{M+m}{Mm} 2RT \right]^{\frac{1}{4}} \frac{(1+\epsilon)}{N_0 I(s)(\lambda')^{\frac{1}{4}}}.$$

If $m = M$, then k takes on the value

$$(1.9) \qquad k = \frac{3e}{16} \left(\frac{2}{\pi M} \right)^{\frac{1}{2}} \frac{1}{(2RT\lambda_1')^{\frac{1}{4}}} \frac{(1+\epsilon)}{N_0 I(s)},$$

with $\lambda_1' = \lambda'(M+m)/Mm$, and λ' the repulsive-force coefficient. The $1 + \epsilon$ is a correction factor derived by Chapman for elastic spheres, which lies between 1 and 1.015. For stated values of the quantity $s = 2RT\lambda'/(\mu')^2$, where μ' is the attractive-force coefficient, a table of values of the integrals involved has been computed, yielding the quantity $I(s)$ in the equation. The values of $I(s)$ for various values of s are given in table 1.12.

On this basis, Hassé and Cook calculated a number of ionic mobilities as indicated in table 1.13. This table gives computed values of mobilities assuming ions as indicated under "Ion Assumed," both by the Langevin theory and the Hassé-Cook theory. The observed values may apply to the ions indicated at the right. Exchange forces were not considered.

A few comments may be made about these data. It is first to be noted that there are no very great differences between the inverse ninth-power repulsive center of force theory values and the Langevin theory values. Such differences as there are reflect differences in effective radii stemming from use of different force laws. The repulsive law chosen by Hassé and Cook is probably too soft for all but A and N_2. The most appropriate law for H_2 is an inverse eleventh power, and that for He is more nearly an inverse fourteenth power. However, since ionic energies are low, the magnitude of the force law will not make much difference if the constants are properly

TABLE 1.12

Functions $I(s)$ in Terms of Argument s for the Hassé-Cook Theory

s	$I(s)$	s	$I(s)$	s	$I(s)$	s	$I(s)$
0.05	2.2584	0.55	0.3747	1.1	0.2866	2.2	0.2867
0.10	1.5619	0.60	0.3515	1.2	0.2848	2.4	0.2878
0.15	1.2496	0.65	0.3343	1.3	0.2839	2.6	0.2888
0.20	1.0431	0.70	0.3216	1.4	0.2836	2.8	0.2897
0.25	0.8634	0.75	0.3121	1.5	0.2836	3.0	0.2905
0.30	0.7129	0.80	0.3249	1.6	0.2838	3.2	0.2913
0.35	0.5971	0.85	0.2995	1.7	0.2842	3.4	0.2920
0.40	0.5121	0.90	0.2953	1.8	0.2846	3.6	0.2927
0.45	0.4508	0.95	0.2922	1.9	0.2852	3.8	0.2933
0.50	0.4067	1.00	0.2898	2.0	0.2857	4.0	0.2938

chosen, for these define the effective radii. If more appropriate repulsive-force laws were chosen with proper constants, the center of force theory might be superior to the Langevin theory. Since the use of higher repulsive forces causes considerable mathematical difficulty, the gain may not be worth the effort unless far better values of the constants are at hand.

The more important point to note, however, is that any attempt at a theoretical calculation or its comparison with experimental data requires that the nature of the ion studied must surely be known. Thus, as noted from the last column, present-day knowledge indicates that the assumed ion in computation in only two cases corresponds to the probable ion. Thus, the ion in air was certainly not an O_2^+ ion. O_2^+ ions in O_2 have recently been shown by Varney to have a reduced mobility of 2.25. Since O_2^+ ions in O_2 suffer from charge exchange, the value will be low compared to this theory. The inert gas ions were *not* monatomic, but molecular, and the ions in N_2 and H_2 were N_4^+ and probably H_3^+. With Na^+ in N_2 and H_2, both theories underestimated the mobility.

It is now clear that two problems remain to be clarified as a result of the studies of Hassé and Cook and the measurements of the Bristol group. These concern the inclusion of the exchange forces involved in the motion of the ions of atoms and molecules in their own gases, and a more satisfactory knowledge of the ions present. By sheer chance the clarification of both of these problems came in connection with the application of the quantum mechanics to the solution of the mobility problem for the case of He^+ ions in He, where charge exchange is frequent. It was in a sense the discrepancy in values

TABLE 1.13

Comparison of the Hassé-Cook Theory with the Langevin Theory,
and Experiment for Some Ions

Gas	Ion· Assumed	Langevin Elastic Spheres	Centers of Force	Observed Value (Bristol Data)	Probable Ion
Air	O_2^+	3.14	3.35	1.60	Hg^+
A	A^+	2.95	2.68	1.94	A_2^+
He	He^+	26.30	29.90	21.40	He_2^+
N_2	N_2^+	3.44	3.47	2.67	N_4^+
H_2	H_2^+	19.00	18.30	13.40	H_3^+
				14.70	
H_2	Na^+	10.75	10.20	13.60	Na^+
N_2	Na^+	2.72	2.22	3.04	Na^+

for He$^+$ ions in He, wave-mechanically computed, that furnished
the guiding clue to the apparently contradictory observations from
microwave breakdown study.

Before proceeding to these problems, attention must first be
called to an excellent paper by H. Margenau in 1941 (23), concerning
the attractive-force fields between ions and molecules. In this paper
Margenau went much farther than Hassé and Cook, since he examined
not only the inverse fifth-power dipole attractive forces, but also
the higher-order forces, such as quadrupole forces coming from the
polarization of the ion. The paper ignored the repulsive forces,
assuming solid elastic impacts. The interaction energies caused
by quadrupole interaction and van der Waals forces, which are of
the r^{-7} type, were computed for a number of ion-gas combinations.
The quadrupole forces outweigh the van der Waals forces for the
lighter ions, but this reverses for heavy ions. The total interaction
was computed at collision distances, and it was shown that while
in combinations like Li$^+$ in He, the dielectric forces of equation
1.2 predominate, for Cs$^+$ ions the two types of forces, dielectric
and interaction, are nearly equal. These forces can be combined
with solid elastic or repulsive center of force theories, and lead
to a slight improvement of the computed results. No proper calculations involving interactions, such as those entering into the Langevin
and Hassé-Cook studies, should be made without reference to this
important contribution.

From what has gone before, it is clear that future study requires
inclusion of exchange forces. Exchange forces are attractive or
repulsive. Repulsive exchange forces of the ϵ^{-ar} type are more accu-

rate than the inverse-power repulsive forces previously considered. The more important exchange forces so far neglected are the attractive ones which are manifested when electron transfer occurs, as in the Kallmann-Rosen effect. For the study of this interaction, recourse must be had to quantum mechanics in order to calculate the correct force law and to take account of the charge exchange. The first attempt in this direction was made in 1934 by Massey and Mohr, for He^+ ions in He, where change of charge is very frequent (26). They computed the mobility as 12 $cm^2/volt$ sec, while the accepted value was that of Tyndall and Powell, who had observed 21.4 $cm^2/volt$ sec. Massey and Mohr used the method of Pauling and Majorana, and later repeated the study with the method of Hylleraas with no change in the result (27). In 1944, R. Meyerott (under Margenau) repeated the study, using a method of Weinbaum with the same result (27). He concluded that the force law cannot be the cause of the apparent disagreement. H. Mott had suggested that Massey and Mohr might have overestimated the effect of exchange forces when they assumed that the mean period of electron exchange is small compared to the time of passage of the ion past the atom (27). This is equivalent to an overestimate of the range of interactions, and would lead to too low a value for the mobility. If this were so, calculation for a similar structure where the exchange effect is small should give a better result. To this end, Meyerott studied the Li^+ ion in He. Exchange forces are very small except at very short distances. Electron exchange cannot occur, as the ionization potential of Li is too low.

The calculation for this case was not too accurate. Had more correct functional data been available, Meyerott believed that the computed values for mobilities of Li^+ in He by wave mechanics would have agreed well with observation. The wave-mechanical method with adequate data should be good to 10%. Thus, Meyerott was induced to conclude that Massey and Mohr's value of 12 for the mobility of He^+ in He was of the correct order of magnitude. This meant that the observed value of 21.4 must be ascribed to another ion. From the character of the results with Li^+ in He, Meyerott was led to conclude that if the He used was pure, the mobility must be ascribed to some form of clustered or molecular ion, e.g., He_2^+. It thus appeared possible that Tyndall and Powell had observed the He_2^+ ion in He and that the He^+ ion in He actually has $k \sim 12$. This possibility is most interesting in that it presents the paradox of a larger ion having higher mobility.

The suggestion of Meyerott that the mobility of He^+ in He was of the order of 12 cm^2/volt sec, as calculated from exchange forces by Massey and Mohr, and that the mobility of 21.4 cm^2/volt sec observed by Tyndall and Powell in pure He was due to a molecular ion He$_2^+$, appears to have been well founded.

After World War II, microwave breakdown studies in very pure inert gases were first initiated by S. C. Brown (29) and W. P. Allis at Massachusetts Institute of Technology. The use of microwaves has the advantage that they yield quite uniform densities of ions of fairly high value over considerable volumes in very clean quartz cavities. There are no asymmetries such as those produced by currents, and no electrodes to contaminate the gas. The microwave breakdown process can be applied for times from 1 microsecond to milliseconds, yielding concentrations of ions ranging from 10^8 ions per cm^3 to 10^{12} ions per cm^3. The plasma of ions and electrons can then be left to itself and allowed to cool down. The change in electron density can be determined by characteristic properties of the plasma in the cavity, such as changes in resonant frequency, changes in the Q of the cavity, etc. The probing signals used to measure these changes are weak compared with the breakdown fields, and give correct values of electron density if ion densities are not too great. This cannot as yet be said of other devices, such as probes of the Langmuir type. The study of the physics of microwave breakdown and of the changes in the electron density in the plasma with time was theoretically facilitated by the remarkable analyses of W. P. Allis, of electronic and ionic carriers under a.c. fields. Soon other groups besides those at M.I.T. were applying the method, including the group of R. B. Holt (31) at Harvard. Especially important for the discussion to follow were the studies of M. A. Biondi and S. C. Brown (29), in association with Allis at M.I.T. These were later carried farther by Biondi (29) with the superb vacuum and purity control techniques for He developed by D. Alpert at Westinghouse Research. Together, with the help of T. Holstein and of A. V. Phelps (75), the whole problem was finally clarified. Active help in the interpretations came from quite a different series of studies carried on by J. A. Hornbeck and J. P. Molnar (32), of the Bell Telephone Research Laboratory. These workers were contemporaneously studying the secondary liberation of electrons from cathodes in uniform-field discharge gaps by a dynamic method using pulse techniques.

Biondi's observations follow: At pressures around and below 1 mm in pure He, the ionization in the plasma studied after some milliseconds, when electrons had gained thermal energies, decayed at a time rate indicating that the principal process of electron loss was by ambipolar diffusion, as discussed in chapter II. The coefficient of diffusion observed depends primarily on that of the positive ions. It is possible to determine the diffusion coefficient from the decline in electron densities. From this, by a well-known relation (2.4, discussed further in chapter II) that $k/D = Ne/p$, one can evaluate the reduced ion mobility K, since Ne is the Faraday constant per cm^3 and p is the gas pressure in mm. The value of K inferred for He ions in He was of the order of 13.7. At somewhat higher pressures, say from 10 mm up, the disappearance of the ions and electrons was largely due to a *recombination* of electron and ion. Now for the recombination of an electron and an He$^+$ ion, wave mechanics gives a coefficient of the order of 10^{-11} if electrons have near thermal velocities. The values observed by Biondi and Brown were 1.8×10^{-8}. This value can by no stretch of the imagination be ascribed to the classical recombination procedure. Analogous data with minor differences were observed for Ne and A gases.

In accounting for similarly large recombination magnitudes in the upper atmosphere, where electrons are certainly free, D. R. Bates (30) proposed that these were due to processes of the nature of

$$N_2^+ + e \rightarrow N^* + N + KE.$$

Such a process is called *dissociative recombination*, and ends in an excited atom and an unexcited atom, or one plus kinetic energy. The cross sections for such processes, which are the reverse of well-known photoelectric ionization processes observed below the long wave-length limit for atomic photoionization, can be expected to be large enough to give the coefficients of recombination observed. If so, the reaction removing electrons in He at higher pressures must have been of the type

$$He_2^+ + e \rightarrow He^* + He + KE.$$

Now molecules of He were at this time known to exist in the excited state from band spectra observed, and Tuxen had identified molecular ions He_2^+, Ne_2^+, and A_2^+ in mass-spectrographic studies of He, Ne, and A discharges (89).

However, Biondi and Brown's results were curious indeed, for in order to account for mobilities of 13.7 at low pressures and molecular recombination at high pressures, it must have been inferred that after 1,000 microseconds of ionization and perhaps some 1,000 more of cooling down of the gas, the preponderant ion at below 1 mm pressure in He was He$^+$, and that at above 10 mm the preponderant ion was He_2^+.

At about this time, J. A. Hornbeck (32), at the Bell Laboratories, was studying the ion pulses produced when electrons were triggered by a 0.1 microsecond photoelectrically active flash of radiation on the cathode. The photoelectrons progressed as ionizing avalanches in high fields to the anode. Arrived at the anode, the electrons left behind a rather dense group of positive ions. These proceeded to cross to the cathode on time scales 100 times greater than electron-transit times. Oscillographic analysis of the currents as a function of time indicated the presence of *two groups of ions* which crossed to the cathode from near the anode with different velocities. The velocities were evaluated as being nearly in the ratio of 2 to 1. Confirmation of the existence of the ions of two mobilities in pure He from these avalanches was obtained with a positive wire in a coaxial cylindrical system having a higher resolving power. The values of the mobilities of these ions in the fields of high X/p were not too significant. However, they converged as X/p was reduced, toward the values of 19.9 and 11 cm²/volt sec, reduced to 0° C. and 760 mm. The proportion of the faster to the slower ions in A lay near 0.5, but was less in He at the proper value of X/p for the maximum. The ratios declined at higher values of X/p.

Hornbeck and Molnar applied a mass spectrograph to the analysis of the ionic masses and found that the *fast ion* was He_2^+ and the other was He^+ (32).

Appearance-potential studies indicated that the He^+ ions came at all potentials above the ionization potential, and that He_2^+ came from excited states lying within 1.5 to 0.3 e.v. *below* the ionization potentials. More detailed recent studies showed that the molecular ions He_2^+ are formed from an excited He^* atom in single impacts with He atoms before the excited atom radiates. Hornbeck determined the ratio of the number of excited states produced per ion pair created by electron impacts at various values of X/p (32). These were 0.2 in He at $X/p = 14$ volts/cm × mm, 0.2 in Ne at $X/p = 15$, and 1 in A at $X/p = 30$. If τ is the mean lifetime of the excited state and σ is the cross section for the process, the values of $\tau\sigma = 0.5 \times 10^{-22}$ cm² sec in He, $\tau\sigma = 0.5 \times 10^{-22}$ cm² sec in Ne, and $\tau\sigma = 0.9 \times 10^{-22}$ cm² sec in A. This makes σ of the value of 10^{-16} cm² if τ is 10^{-6} sec, and gives a reasonable atomic-collision radius for such a process.

This discovery of two mobilities of He ions in He and the identification of the ions as He_2^+, K~19.9 cm²/volt sec, and He^+ K~12 cm²/volt sec, was quite encouraging, except that the mechanism of formation of He_2^+ discovered by Hornbeck was not one which would have given the results observed in Biondi's cooled microwave plasma.

It had been proposed by R. B. Holt (31) that the ions largely observed in the plasma of Biondi must have initially been He^+ ions, which at higher pressures formed He_2^+ in *a three-body collision process*. Such an explanation was also put forward by D. R. Bates in 1950 (30) when confronted with these observations. Bates calculated the necessary rate of conversion of He^+ to He_2^+ as of the order of 10^{-5} at 23 mm pressure. To establish this proposal required further work.

Before presenting the evidence, it is of interest to report another action discovered by Biondi (29), (74) in the He plasma. It was observed that at fairly low pressures (1 to 2 mm in He at about room temperature), the electron density of a plasma which had been built up during a discharge for several milliseconds began to increase after the discharge was cut off, rose to a maximum in about 1 millisecond, and then declined, eventually reaching a steady state. R. A. Johnson, B. T. McClure, and R. B. Holt (31), whose discharge had run only for 10 microseconds, did not observe the initial rise. Biondi later showed that the rise came from the interaction of two metastable atoms in the singlet S state, at 20.5 volts, to give an atomic ion, a neutral atom, and an electron, the energy being emitted as kinetic according to

$$He^{ms} + He^{ms} \rightarrow He^+ + He + e + KE.$$

The action was first postulated by R. Schade, and later by R. Buttner. It was also proposed by M. J. Druyvesteyn and F. M. Penning in 1940 (91). That the singlet state was involved was shown by irradiating with the 20,580 Å line that raises the state to a radiating $2P$ state. This reduced the initial rise of electron density. Use of the 10,830 Å triplet $2P$-$2S$ line proved ineffective, so that the triplet metastable atom was not involved.

An alternate reaction could have occurred, of the form

$$He^m + He^m \rightarrow He_2^+ + e,$$

leading to a molecular He_2^+ ion. This was in fact the reaction at first assumed. Since there was no evidence of molecular ions He_2^+ in the measurements, there was no molecular ion-forming reaction. The measurements were carried out at lower pressures where ambipolar diffusion was active. Thus, secondary production of He_2^+ by triple impacts was absent, and He_2^+ created by excited states had disappeared during the cooling-off period.

One question arises: Why does the metastable ionization, which gives only a fraction of the ionization *during* discharge, result in an increase in electron density after the ionizing field is removed? During discharge, in which 90% of the ionization is by electron impact and the rest by metastables, ionization balances diffusion loss of electrons and ions. During the afterglow, when no more primary ions are created by electron impact, the metastable production is the only source of ions. If the diffusion rate remained high and constant, the electron density would decline monotonically during the afterglow. Once discharge ceases, the electrons, which had some 3 volts of energy during discharge, quickly lose their initial energy by collisions in the gas and achieve thermal energies of 0.04 volt. This reduces the ambipolar-diffusion loss rate by a hundredfold. Thus, since the ionization rate has only decreased by a factor of 10, there will be an initial rise of electron density followed by a decline.

The very pure He (74) was obtained by superfluidity leakage, and the new vacuum techniques of the Westinghouse research group were used (76). In He and Ne the analyses gave the ambipolar-diffusion coefficient for the ions created to be those of He^+ and Ne^+. They also yielded the collision cross section for destruction of metastable atoms by collisions with atoms of their own species, or else by A or Hg atoms added as an impurity. They did not yield the cross section for formation of He^+ by collisions of He^{ms} atoms.

The values of the quantities derived are shown below.

Parent gas	$D_m p$(cm^2/sec)-(mm Hg)	σ_d(cm^2)	σ_i(cm^2) in:	
He	520 ± 20	9.6×10^{-21}	Argon	9.7×10^{-17}
			Mercury	1.4×10^{-14}
Ne	200 ± 20	8.9×10^{-20}	Argon	2.6×10^{-16}

It is seen that the cross sections for metastable destruction by collisions with their own atoms, either by raising them to a higher state or by allowing transitions to ground σ_d, are relatively small. The cross sections for ionization for A are quite high. In He they agree with Molnar's values. With Ne in A they are about one-tenth that estimated by Penning's group at an earlier date. The cross section for Hg atoms is very large, but makes plausible the assumption of A. D. MacDonald and S. C. Brown (92), that each He atom excited to a metastable state yields an Hg ion in the gas Heg, where the first inelastic impacts to the metastable states lead to ionization. The data are consistent with the better measurements by optical methods.

It was thus to be expected that initially the measurements of

Biondi and Brown should have shown quite an appreciable concentration of He_2^+ as well as He^+, had the ambipolar-diffusion measurements been carried out on the plasma *shortly* after ionization. However, Biondi and Brown used plasmas which had "cooled" down appreciably (2-3 milliseconds) for ambipolar studies. At the low pressures, the He_2^+ initially present would have diffused out, leaving largely He^+. Hence, the ambipolar-diffusion coefficients observed by them yielded the value of 13.7, which, within the accuracy of Massey and Mohr's theory, agrees with the computed value of 12 and with Hornbeck's extrapolated value of 11.

It was next required to show that at the higher pressures, first the recombination coefficient could be ascribed to the dissociative recombination of He_2^+, and next that at higher pressures it was possible to get He_2^+ from the He^+ existing by triple impacts. The first problem was solved by Biondi and Holstein (75) at Westinghouse. It was noted that the intensity of line radiation emitted in the afterglow of the plasma declined in proportion to the square of the electron-density decline in the gas, as for a recombination process. The spectra observed, from 3,700 to 7,200 Å, showed this radiation to consist of lines coming from states $n = 3$, 4, 5, 6, all lying at less than, or within, 1.5 e.v. of the atomic-ionization potential. Rough measurements indicated that for each electron lost one quantum of energy was emitted. This is consistent with the postulated relation

$$He_2^+ + e \rightarrow He^* + He + KE.$$

Similar results were observed in Ne, except that all lines originated in levels more than 0.85 e.v. below ionization potential. If the electron in Ne is captured into the ground-vibrational state of the Ne molecule, the energy of the final excited atom can be no more than the ionization potential E_i less D, the dissociation energy. This explains the spectra of Ne. For He, the value of D lies between 2.2 and 3.1 e.v. Thus, the highly excited states of 0.3 to 1.5 e.v. below E_i for He could only have ions from *very highly excited* vibrational molecular states of He_2^+. From the frequency of collision at the pressures used (10^7 to 10^8), then if dissociative recombination of highly excited He_2^+ is to give the spectra, these excited He_2^+ molecules must *survive* some 10^6 collisions before de-excitation. Some theoretical work by Holstein indicates that life of the He vibrational state at 0.3 volts below E_i is of the order of 10^5 collisions. On this basis, the dissociative recombination of He_2^+ can be reasonably considered as possible.

The matter was finally tested in a most ingenious fashion suggested by T. Holstein for the case of A, not He. For this purpose,

He and Ne containing small admixtures of around 0.1% A were used with low energy of excitation. The A atoms are ionized by the He and Ne metastable atoms, so that there are only atomic A^+ ions present, since there is too little A gas to form A_2^+. Pure A at 14 mm pressure gave a recombination decay that had a coefficient of 8.8×10^{-7} cm³/sec, which comes from A_2^+ and dissociative recombination. When He and A were mixed as indicated, decline of electron ionization at 7 mm was by ambipolar diffusion, giving the mobility of the A^+ ion in He from the diffusion coefficient as 22.4 cm²/volt sec. Comparison with the Bristol data for the mobility of Li^+, Na^+, K^+, and Rb^+ in He shows that this value of 22.4 cm² is within 0.2 cm²/volt sec of that for K^+ in He, as it should be, since no change-of-charge effects occur. Thus, the high recombination coefficient of 8.8×10^{-7} in A is definitely due to the A_2^+ ion. When A^+ ions only were present, decay was by ambipolar diffusion, with a loss by recombination of electrons with A^+ of the order 10^{-11} or less, if present at all.

Very recently, A. V. Phelps and S. C. Brown (75) have studied the composition of the ions diffusing to the walls after cutoff of a He discharge as a function of time and pressure, using a mass spectrometer. As the pressure of the He increased, the dominant ion in the afterglow was found to change from He^+ to He_2^+. The rate of conversion of He^+ to He_2^+ by triple impacts was estimated from the electron-density decay data to be about one-third the value estimated by Bates. This is remarkably good agreement, in view of the very sketchy data at his disposal.

These results indicate the following important facts: First, that the wave-mechanical theory is valid in predicting mobilities of positive ions in the presence of change-of-charge effects to better than 10% where sufficient data on force fields are at hand. Thus, predictions from such computations must be seriously considered at all times, and the method is established as the correct one to use. Secondly, it is established that molecular ions do exist in inert gases, and that because of the absence of Kallmann-Rosen change-of-charge action, the mobilities of such ions are *higher*, in fact nearly twice as high, as those of the atomic ions in inert gases, despite the doubling of the mass. Finally, the molecular ions are observed to be produced by at least two processes, both of them interesting in themselves. The molecular ions are not cluster ions, such as would result by dielectric induction, but are actually due to molecule formation. Here follow the processes, B representing one of the three inert gas atoms discussed.

(1) $B^* + B \rightarrow B_2^+ + e + KE$—energy B^* may be close to E_i.

(2) $B^m + B^m \rightarrow B^+ + e + KE$—goes by (3) to B_2^+ with some time delay.

(3) $B^+ + 2B \rightarrow B_2^+ + B + KE$.

The reaction (3) has been established for $K\overset{+}{r}$ and $X\overset{+}{e}$ by Varney, but yields are less (79). The ions B_2^+ and B^+ are removed by recombination with thermal electrons, as follows:

Dissociative recombination with—

(4) $e + B_2^+ \rightarrow B^* + B + KE$ $\alpha \sim 10^{-7}$.

If B^* is excited and nearer to E_i than the energy of dissociation for the ion, then the excited state comes from a long-lived excited state of B_2^+. This reaction is the inverse of action (1). It has recently been verified by M. A. Biondi, who observed the Doppler broadening coming from He* in the process (93):

(5) $e + B^+ \rightarrow B + h$ ν—radiative recombination with $\alpha \sim 10^{-11}$.

Another electron- and ion-loss process is by ambipolar diffusion to the walls. Evaluation of the ambipolar-diffusion coefficients gives fairly reliable values of the mobilities of the positive carriers, i.e., the positive ions. Earlier studies of Holt (31) and his associates have little bearing on this work, since in general they did not have their ionizing pulses on so as to build up concentrations over milliseconds, and their cooling-down periods were too short. Finally, it seems that at times they worked with very high electron densities, which ceased to yield reliable values of the density.

One other study, carried out by R. L. F. Boyd (33) in collaboration with D. R. Bates in London, contemporaneously with the work of Hornbeck and Molnar, yielded high observed ratios of He_2^+ to He^+ ions. These ranged up to 4.7 with a special mass spectrometer. The discharge was that of a hot cathode arc in He at pressures below 0.045 mm. The yields increased with pressure and current. The mechanisms of creation here are involved, since some He_2^+ comes from excited states, while probably very little comes from three-body collisions. The ratios could have been falsified by dispersion of He^+ ions from the beam through exchange-of-charge reactions. The work was well done, but work in an arc plasma is highly unsatisfactory compared to the beautiful direct studies in microwave plasma under much cleaner conditions, with no electrodes to soil the gas.

Recent researches have thus clarified the paradox concerning the classically observed mobilities and the wave-mechanical calculation of mobilities where charge exchange was present, by indicating that there were two possible ions present in the inert gases, atomic and molecular; that one of these predominated at higher pressures; the other, at lower pressures; and that the mechanism of creation could be one of two, the likelihood of which varied with pressure and time elapsed. It is clear, then, that at the high pressures and long time intervals, the Bristol group observed mobilities of the molecular ions He_2^+, Ne_2^+, and A_2^+, which are high. Recent work by R. N. Varney (79) with Kr and Xe indicates that the Bristol group observed largely the Kr^+ and Xe^+ at their higher pressures, as Kr_2^+ and Xe_2^+ are not formed in great quantity.

Further, it is not strange that the theoretical investigators, stimulated by these studies, should have proceeded to compute the values of the mobilities in Ne^+ and A^+, as well as to attempt the computation of values of the mobilities of the molecular ions in their own gases. These calculations came through the work of T. Holstein and his associates, and of S. Geltman (88); the latter in association first with Margenau and later with Holstein (34) and his associates. Geltman's work was preceded by a study made by S. H. Bloom and H. Margenau (86) a year earlier; this had been inspired by reading the early rough draft of the present chapter. Early in 1950, the chapter in its rough form was sent to Holstein, Margenau, and Allis for their comment. In fact, it was Holstein who first indicated the need for the statistical weight β in the clustering criterion. Noting the absence of such a factor in the literature, Margenau set Bloom to the task of evaluating the effect of the entropy term on clustering. This material was then available to Geltman when he undertook his study of the He_2^+ ion.

Contemporaneously with theoretical advances, various determinations of the mobilities of the ions were being carried forward with the newer pulsed techniques, as well as estimates from the ambipolar-diffusion coefficients in microwave breakdown. Thus, extrapolation of the mobilities of the atomic and molecular ions by Hornbeck's method to low X/p values was carried out by Hornbeck and Varney. Lauer, in the author's laboratory, got a value of the drift velocity at low X/p and high p in argon for the A_2^+ ion, and in H_2 for probably the H_3^+ ion. Finally, L. M. Chanin and M. A. Biondi made measurements of ions at relatively low X/p, using pulsed-discharge techniques for all of the inert gases. Varney also carried out studies on the gases O_2, N_2, and CO, while K. B. Persson (78) has recently given a value for ions in H_2 from ambipolar diffusion which agrees with Lauer's and the older, more classical values.

In carrying out their studies of mobilities at high X/p yielded by the Hornbeck method, data were obtained which were open to comparison with the generalized theory of G. H. Wannier covering the whole range of conditions applicable to ion-mobility studies. Actually, while data had been obtained by A. V. Hershey for alkali ions in inert gases H_2 and N_2 at high X/p, and he had applied a modified Langevin theory to the results, it was not until the work of Hornbeck in the inert gases, where exchange forces could be estimated, that Wannier's comprehensive theory was evolved. From this theory, it transpires that at high X/p a hard (68) elastic-collision cross section can be obtained. This, when inserted into the true solid elastic equation 1.1a at low X/p, should yield mobilities as indicated earlier.

Holstein (34) computed the mobilities for Ne^+ and A^+ in their own gases quantum-mechanically, in a fashion different from that of Massey and Mohr. The crucial factor in Holstein's calculation was the computation of the resonance, or charge-exchange, interaction component of the total ion-atom interaction. A new method was used, requiring solely a knowledge of the Hartree-Fock wave function of the outermost atomic shell. The resonance-interaction curves so obtained differed somewhat from those given by Massey and Mohr's perturbation treatment. The theory in its present form is strictly valid only for ions with angular momentum of zero. The error for the cases of Ne^+ and A^+ (ground state $^2P_{1/2}$ or $^2P_{3/2}$) was only of the order of 10% or less. The values obtained by Holstein are shown in table 1.15 (infra).

It is next of interest to consider the study by S. Bloom and H. Margenau (86) on ion-molecular forces and clustering. This study on the basis of force fields leads to an evaluation of the statistical weights of different states of motion of the ion-molecular system, which was indicated in section 3 to be determinative of cluster formation. In such a study, it is first essential to determine whether quantization must be taken into account when determining the statistical weights; if it does, the problem becomes very complex. Quantization is not essential if the spacing of the energy levels in the potential trough describing the interactions between ion and molecules is close. If there are only a *few* levels, then quantization is required; otherwise, classical statistics can be applied.

Computations with simplified potentials show that the vibrational levels are of the order of 50 in number for all interesting instances. For H_2 interacting with Li^+, there are but 10 levels, in view of the small mass of the system. The study, therefore, uses classical kinetic theory and simple, nonpolar gases. The first calculation is made using ion-attractive forces acting on the ion-induced dipole of the molecule. The molecules exhibit "hard sphere" repulsion. Using the ordinary dielectric forces of equation 1.2 and the Margenau solid elastic ionic and molecular radii (table 1.7), values for the cluster size as a function of temperature, computed for systems such as K^+-O_2, Li^+-H_2, show large clusters at room temperatures. In some cases these are in excess of those computed from the author's relation $PE/KE = 1$.

This result is due to the presence of the deep crevasse in the potential diagram of the hard sphere potential-separation diagram. Using an inverse twelfth-power repulsive law, such as is closely obeyed for H_2 and many other gases, the picture is radically altered. This law yields a far shallower potential minimum and leads to a reduction of the clustering by a factor greater than 100. The extreme value calculated is that for CO_2 about an Li^+ ion. It yields a cluster of 28 molecules as computed at 273° K. Oxygen at 273° K. has only 2 molecules in the cluster, while H_2 has no clustering at that temperature. The K^+ ion in O_2 would not cluster at 273° K. but near its condensation point would give a cluster of perhaps 2 molecules.

However, these calculations are incomplete, since they give the total number possible from the integration dealing with *clustering molecules treated as points.* Thus, interactions between the molecules of the cluster, i.e., molecule-molecule repulsions, are not included. In other words, no account has been taken of *steric exclusion.* Viewed from the authors' initial approach, if in the space considered the relations give a cluster of 28 molecules, but only 12 spherically conceived molecules can be packed around the one ion, then the cluster is limited to 12, irrespective of the calculation. A rough concept of the spatial distribution of the few molecules that cluster can be gained in the present calculation by stating that, roughly, 99% of the molecules that do cluster congregate within 3.2 Å of the ion.

The authors compare these calculations with the data of Munson and Hoselitz (28) for Li^+ and inert gases. The comparison is shown in table 1.14.

The pressures used by Munson and Hoselitz are not specifically given in each case, but they are not radically different from the pressure used by Margenau. Agreement is good for Li^+-A and Li^+-Xe. For Li^+-K, agreement requires that T be 225° K. to bring theory into line with observation. Otherwise stated, the pressure at 290° K. would have to be raised to 190 mm to bring agreement.

TABLE 1.14

Computation of Clustering by Bloom and Margenau,
Compared with Bristol Data

System	Temp. °K.	Expt. estimate of N	Theory at p = 19 mm Hg
Li$^+$-A	195	2	1.7
Li$^+$-Xe	290	2	2.3
Li$^+$-Kr	290	2	0.2
Li$^+$-Kr	225	—	2.0

The only possible comment is that the estimates of the number of molecules in the cluster, according to the Munson-Hoselitz experiments, are *not* of great significance. All that need be said is that clustering is observed to take place. On the other hand, the accuracy of the theory is questionable. It really suffices to indicate that the rough theoretical approach, using attractive and repulsive forces of the more correct form, conducted so as to include the *statistical weights*, bears out the earlier contention that in the study of clustering the statistical weight factor β must be included in the clustering criterion. This justifies the use of β in the more naively stated condition $\beta PE/KE > 1$ for cluster formation. It further shows that including this factor, the clustering observed is reasonably consistent with theory. The calculation also indicates that proper study yields a quantity $N\beta$ which, in principle, is more accurate than the naive calculation of layers of spherical molecules about the ion. However, in being more accurate, this suffers from the inaccuracy inherent in the omission of steric hindrance, which can be roughly included in the use of the more naive criterion $\beta PE/KE > 1$.

The calculations also approximately indicate agreement between the theoretical point at which clustering occurs as a function of pressure and temperature, and the observations of these occurrences by Munson and Hoselitz. It is believed that neither the interpretation of the number clustered from experiment nor the value computed by the theory, is of sufficient reliability to do more than give an order-of-magnitude agreement and an agreement as to the region of pressures, temperatures, and systems of ion and gas where this can occur. It must also be emphasized that *all such clusters are labile*, and that the value of mass and/or radius inferred from a mobility measurement applies to the average observed for a carrier that is probably gaining and shedding molecules, as the later theory of A. W. Overhauser (48) indicates. In any case, the result of this study

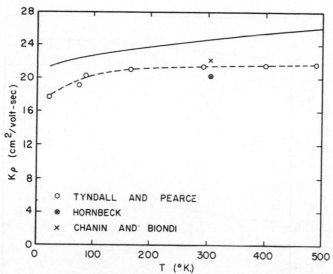

Fig. 1.28. Geltman's calculated mobility of He_2^+ ions in He at constant density as a function of temperature, using perturbation theory.

finally closes the chapter of futile controversy of an earlier era, and clarifies the modern interpretation. This is gratifying.

In 1952, S. Geltman, working with Margenau (88), and later with Holstein at Westinghouse, studied the mobility of He_2^+ ions in He. The forces between He_2^+ and He were calculated by perturbation theory. Determination of the scattering phase shifts yielded the momentum-transfer cross section as a function of collision energy. Use of the Chapman-Enskog theory of diffusion permitted calculation of the mobility as a function of temperature. The temperature variation of the mobility of He_2^+ from the measurements of Tyndall and Pearce was next analyzed by means of classical theories, yielding an effective potential for the He_2^+-He interaction.

Figure 1.28 shows the mobility of He_2^+ ions in He at constant density as a function of T, as the dashed curve with experimental points. The solid curve shows the calculation by Geltman's theory. Figure 1.29 shows a log-log plot of mobility against temperature. The experimental points are indicated by circles. The upper solid line is the best fit of the Langevin theory, assuming no clustering, but fitted to one experimental point. The dashed line is a correction to the solid line, taking clustering into account, and yields a reasonable fit. The lower solid line comes from the Hassé-Cook theory for arbitrary potential parameters. The clustering was taken into account by calculating the statistical size of the cluster by the methods

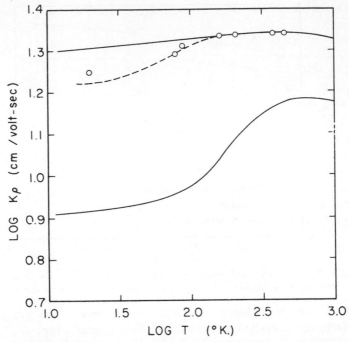

Fig. 1.29. Geltman's calculation for mobility of He_2^+ in He at constant density as a function of temperature, using Langevin theory and clustering.

of Margenau and Bloom. For potentials with the values assumed from a fit of Langevin's theory at 300° K., it was found that clustering sets in at 200° K. with a cluster of perhaps 20 atoms at 20° K. No measurements exist at this temperature. The clustering increases the effective ion mass and so lowers the mobility.

The discrepancy between the perturbation-theory curve of figure 1.28 and the observed curve below is not significantly related to the absolute value of 24.2 calculated as against the value 22 observed, but lies more in the fact that the calculated curve slopes, while the observed one is nearly constant. The difference is to be ascribed to the dissimilarity between the theoretically derived potential curve and that deduced from experiment, using Langevin's theory. If the experimentally derived curve gives a good representation of the true average potential between He_2^+ and He, the theoretical potential may be at fault for two possible reasons: the use of inexact wave functions in the perturbation calculation, or an improper method of averaging over orientation. The form of the average inferred potential, derived from experiment relative to the potential curves assumed for the two extreme orientations, indicates that the quantum-mechanical calculation of interaction was fairly good. This indicates that the method of averaging over orientations on the basis of slow rotation was not entirely valid.

It may be concluded from this study that with the present state of knowledge, methods are at hand which enable the mobilities and the essential elements needed for their evaluation to be calculated with satisfactory accuracy if desired. If the experimental data are accurate and adequate to enable the necessary constants to be evaluated, the Langevin theory indeed leads to quite satisfactory results. It is seen that with these methods, available corrections are possible, both for clustering and even charge exchange.

It is next of interest to assemble the data gathered from recent theory and experiment into a single table (1.15), wherein it is seen that overall, the theories appropriate to a given situation can usually yield values almost as good as experimental accuracy. It is particularly gratifying to note that the so-called classical values of the Bristol group are not erroneous, nor are they caused by impurity, as was asserted when the newer data first began to come in. In fact, the values when the ions are properly identified are remarkably good, and their precision at low X/p is probably superior to that of later observations. Certainly, their purity was adequate. It is seen, and will later be noted more specifically, that identification of the ion is paramount in interpreting mobility data.

§ 7. The Effect of Temperature on Mobilities.

Thanks to the Bristol school, some very good data are at hand on the variation of mobilities of certain ions now known in pure gases as a function of temperature. These comprise a study of He_2^+ ions in He, N_4^+ ions in N_2, Na^+ ions in He, Cs^+ ions in He, Li^+ in He, K^+ in A, Rb^+ in K, and Cs^+ in Xe. The curves have been given in figures 1.23, 1.24, 1.25, and 1.26, while the data have been given in tables 1.2 and 1.3, *supra*. In what follows, the variation of the mobility K_ρ at constant density will be considered. The solid elastic theory of mobility (equation 1.1a) predicts K_ρ to be proportional to $1/\sqrt{T}$. The Sutherland-Wellisch theory places K_ρ proportional to $1/\sqrt{T}(1 + b/T)$, both of which indicate a marked decrease in K_ρ with increase in T. The point center of force theory (equation 1.7) predicts K_ρ to be constant, independent of temperature. From what is known of viscosity as a function of temperature, it is clear that a proper analysis of the data will lead to a fairly good estimate of the repulsive- and attractive-force laws active, as shown by

TABLE 1.15

Comparison of Mobilities of Known Ions—from Several Sources, with Various Theories

Mobilities of Known Ions in cm^2 volt sec at 0°C 760 mm Hg

Gas	Ion	Hornbeck-Varney	Chanin-Biondi	Microwave Diffusion: Biondi-Persson	Others and Lauer	Tyndall-Powell	Solid Elastic Wannier Radii	Wave Mechanics: Massey-Mohr; Holstein	Langevin Equation 1.8; Geltman	Langevin Equation 1.7; Wannier-Varney
He	He_2^+	18.00	20.00	–	–	21.60	–	24.00	21.6	18.2
He	He^+	10.20	11.20	13.7	–	–	13.40	12.00	–	–
Ne	Ne_2^+	6.30	6.50	–	–	6.30	–	–	–	6.21
Ne	Ne^+	4.40	4.20	2.5	–	–	4.85	4.05	–	–
A	A_2^+	1.94	2.60	–	1.94	1.93	–	–	–	2.09
A	A^+	1.67	1.65	–	1.50+	–	1.67	1.70	–	–
Kr	Kr_2^+	1.10-1.20	1.20	–	–	1.01	–	–	–	1.18
Kr	Kr^+	0.90-0.95	0.93	–	–	–	1.01	–	–	–
Xe	Xe_2^+	0.67-0.77	0.80	–	–	0.77	–	–	–	0.74
Xe	Xe^+	0.60-0.65	0.63	–	–	–	0.77	–	–	–
O_2	O_2^+	2.25	–	–	–	–	2.78	–	–	2.75
N_2	N_2^+	–	–	–	–	–	2.17	–	–	2.80
N_2	N_4^+	2.49	–	–	–	2.49	–	–	–	2.42
CO	CO^+	1.60	–	–	–	–	1.58	–	–	2.19
H_2	H_3^+	–	–	13.0	13.40	–	–	–	–	–

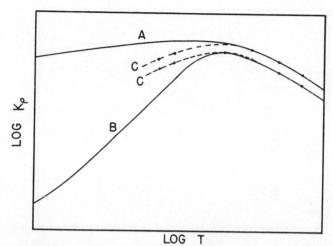

A: ELASTIC SPHERE MODEL   B: CENTER OF FORCE MODEL
C: EXPERIMENTAL RESULTS FOR CAESIUM IONS

Fig. 1.30a. Pearce's data for mobility of Cs^+ ions in He as a function of temperature, compared to Langevin's and to Hassé and Cook's theories. The A curve is for Langevin's theory; the B is for Hassé and Cook's inverse ninth-power repulsion. The observed curves are adjusted in absolute value to yield agreement at one point.

R. H. Fowler (82). From these the ionic-molecular forces can be applied to derive a fairly accurate equation of mobility.

Until very recently this procedure has not been resorted to, primarily because of the mathematical difficulties and lack of short-cut procedures. Instead, the Langevin theory (equation 1.8), with suitably chosen constants, and the Hassé-Cook center of force theory, with inverse fifth- and ninth-power forces, were applied to the results of A. F. Pearce on Cs^+ and Na^+ ions in He. The experimental results for Cs^+, adjusted to the observed curves at higher temperatures in curves C of figure 1.30a, are shown compared to the theoretical Langevin curve A and the theoretical center of force curve B in figure 1.30a. The results for Na^+ are shown in C of figure 1.30b, compared to the Langevin theory in curve A and the center of force curve B. It will at once be noted that where the two curves A and B do not follow experiment at lower temperatures, the two theories bracket the results. This could indicate that the solid elastic impacts with kinetic-theory radii impose too stringent a repulsive law, while the inverse ninth-power repulsive law is too soft a law. Actually, it is correct that repulsive forces are more

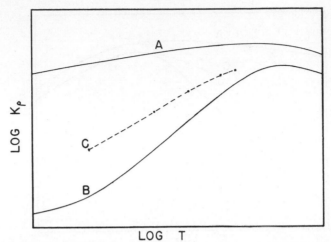

A: ELASTIC SPHERE MODEL   B: CENTER OF FORCE MODEL
C: EXPERIMENTAL RESULTS FOR SODIUM IONS

Fig. 1.30b. Pearce's data for mobility of Na^+ ions in He are shown by curve C. The full elastic solid theory of Langevin gives curve A. The inverse ninth-power repulsive theory of Hassé and Cook gives curve B. Note that the observed variation lies nicely between the two.

nearly of an inverse eleventh or even 14.6 power than an inverse ninth power. Strictly analogous results were obtained by A. V. Hershey in approximating his data on K^+ in various gases at high ion energy by the Langevin and the soft-repulsive law center of force theories, which bracketed observation.

No computations have been carried out for the case of the other alkali ions or N_2. However, S. Geltman recently made a study of the force laws, using the temperature variation observed for He_2^+ ions in He to evaluate the forces. From these data he achieved quite successful agreement for the variation of the mobility of He_2^+ ions in He with temperature, for temperatures above 170° K. Below this, correction for clustering was needed to handle the data. Using a rather rough theory of Bloom and Margenau to correct for clustering, the curves can be made to agree fairly well. The curves for Li^+ in He, K^+ in A, and Rb^+ in Kr (for which no calculation has been made) show definite evidence of clustering at low temperatures.

It can be concluded from what has been indicated that present theory is adequate to take account of the temperature variation of K_ρ. It would be desirable to get more extensive data on the variation of K_ρ with T for different ion-gas combinations amenable to wave-mechanical treatment, and through the variation to learn more about the force laws that are active.

§ 8. The Variation of Mobilities with X/p, and the Mobilities at High X/p.

With the naively considered cluster theory of the early nineteen-hundreds, it was anticipated that if sufficiently high fields could be achieved at a given pressure, the ion cluster would begin to break up, with a consequent increase of the mobility. Before the days of electron oscillator tubes, the author, after three years of work (49), overcame the formidable difficulties of achieving appropriately high values of alternating electrical field at adequate frequencies (104-105 c.p.s.) with relatively undamped oscillations. The ion mobilities were measured in air up to an X/p of 16 at about atmospheric pressure. To his surprise, the reduced mobility independent of X/p remained the same. This indicated that the ion cluster did not break up readily, as had been anticipated. After the author left, Kia-Lok Yen (49) who had initially assisted him, extended the work to H_2 with $X/p = 20$ with similar results.

No more work was done until that of J. H. Mitchell and K. E. W. Ridler (19), working in Tyndall's laboratory at Bristol in 1934. Here it was observed that above a certain value of X/p in N_2, the alkali ions showed a rather sharp increase in K at characteristic values of X/p, shown in figure 1.22. The increase for Cs^+ ions occurred at the lowest X/p of the order of 3. The value of X/p for the rise was 5 for Rb^+, 10 for K^+, 15 for Na^+, and 60 for Li^+, all in volts/cm per mm.

As reported, the break was sharp and the increase linear. It is probable that in actuality the break is gradual and the rise asymptotic at lower X/p, rounding off to a peak at higher values and then declining. This increase can be regarded as representing either a breakup of some complex ion cluster, or a reduction in attractive-force action which occurs as the energy of the ion caused by the field begins to exceed thermal energies by a considerable amount. Both actions are to be expected, the reduction of forces doubtless being more gradual in its change of K. It is not strange that from the sharp breaks in the curves of the Bristol group, the inference should have been drawn that the binding forces to the smaller ions are greater and should permit breakup only at higher energies. However, a similar agreement applies to the increase in mean free paths with increasing energy.

In 1938, A. V. Hershey (22) in the author's laboratory, used the

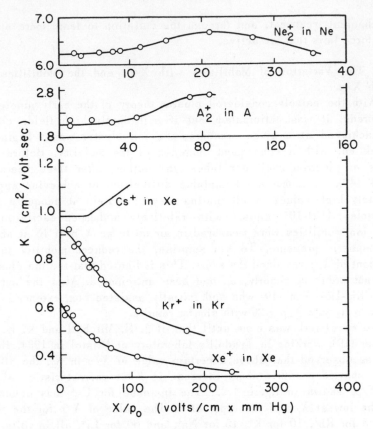

Fig. 1.31. Munson and Tyndall's mobilities of certain ions
at high X/p in various gases.

Townsend magnetic-deflection method for K[+] ions in the gases H_2,
N_2, He and A, for values of X/p, from values where the mobilities
were normal and in good agreement with those of the Bristol group
up to values of X/p that ranged from a low of 30 for He to 150 for
N_2. While the data showed some pressure dependence at lower pressure (~ 1 mm) which was of instrumental origin, the data at higher
pressures were quite satisfactory. Hershey observed the rise noted
in N_2 by the Bristol group for various ions in all gases. In N_2, his
rise for K[+] was not so sharp, and occurred at 40% higher X/p than
did the rise of Mitchell and Ridler. The rise was least in He and
prominent in H_2, but sharpest in A. In all Hershey's studies the
rise reached a peak and then the mobility declined, as seen in figures
1.15 to 1.18 (*supra*, part one).

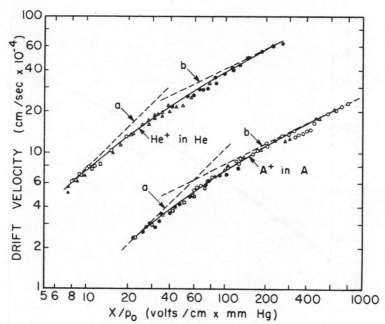

Fig. 1.32. Hornbeck's drift velocities of ions in He and A
as a function of X/p on a log-log scale.

Subsequent to Hershey's studies, R. J. Munson and A. M. Tyndall
(35) in 1941 obtained data for ions assumed to be Ne$^+$ ions in Ne,
A$^+$ ions in A, Kr$^+$ ions in Kr, Xe$^+$ ions in Xe, and Cs$^+$ ions in Xe,
which are shown in figure 1.31. Today it is clear that the ions were
Ne$_2^+$ and A$_2^+$ ions in Ne and A, but Kr$^+$ in Kr, Xe$^+$ in Xe, and Cs$^+$
in Xe. The ions Ne$_2^+$, A$_2^+$, and Cs$^+$ in Xe showed the initial rise and
subsequent decline, while those for the monatomic ions Kr$^+$ and
Xe$^+$, in their own gases, did not show any rise, but began to decline
at once.

With the advent of pulsed techniques, the studies of J. A. Hornbeck
(32), R. N. Varney (79), and of L. M. Chanin and M. A. Biondi (81),
have given much data on values of k for the inert gas ions, atomic
and molecular, in their own and other gases. The data of Hornbeck
and Varney do not go all the way down to low X/p, since they must
have ionization by collision to make their method operative. Chanin
and Biondi, however, carry their curves nearer to low X/p values.
From their curves it is clear that despite much scatter, the initial
rise and subsequent decline of k as a function of X/p apply generally to the molecular or alkali ions in gases where forces are

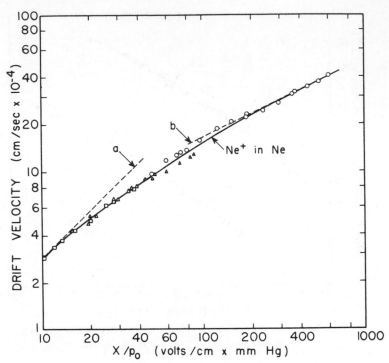

Fig. 1.33. Hornbeck's drift velocities in Ne as a function
of X/p on a log-log scale.

largely polarization forces. For the ions like He⁺ in He to Xe⁺ in
Xe, where exchange forces and change of charge predominate, it
appears that the initial rise is absent and beyond a certain X/p the
curves show a monotonic decline.

The data of Hornbeck on He, Ne, and A over a range of values
of X/p, and of Varney on Kr and Xe, are shown in figures 1.32, 1.33,
and 1.34, where drift velocities are plotted as a function of X/p.
Figures 1.35 and 1.36 show the data of Hornbeck and Varney plotted
as the reduced mobility to 0° C. and 760 mm as a function of X/p
(for limited ranges of values in Hornbeck's case). The data of Chanin
and Biondi for He, Ne, and A are shown in figures 1.37, 1.38, and
1.39, plotted as reduced mobility against X/p nearer the origin. In
the last two figures the solid line represents Holstein's theory, the
long dashes represent the measurements of the Bristol group, and the
short dashes bracket the spread of Hornbeck's values.

It must now be noted that the mobilities of the molecular ions
cannot be studied at high X/p; in fact, not beyond $X/p = 75$. This

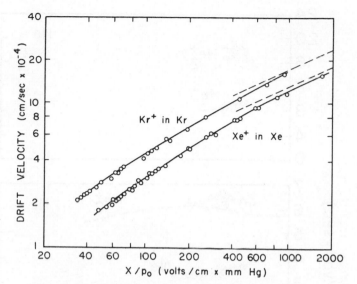

Fig. 1.34. Varney's drift velocities in Kr and Xe
as a function of X/p on a log-log scale.

comes from the difficulty of forming appreciable numbers of the
molecular ions at the low pressures needed to make measurements
at high fields. Thus, the studies of all the ions at truly high X/p
occur for the atomic ions, with exchange forces and charge exchange
dominating. Except for K^+ in N_2, most of Hershey's data did not
extend beyond $X/p = 100$, while most of the significant data to be
discussed in gases appear above X/p of the order of 300.

At lower X/p, the drift velocity is strictly proportional to the
value of X/p, and the reduced mobility is constant. At higher X/p,
the drift velocities increase more rapidly than X/p, reach constant
value, and then increase more slowly than X/p, tending to vary as
$\sqrt{X/p}$. The reduced mobilities are thus constant for low X/p; and
for polarization force, ion-gas combinations increase, reach a maximum, and decrease as X/p increases, while exchange-force ion-gas
combinations begin to show decreased mobilities beyond a certain
X/p. At extremely high X/p, both ion-gas combinations have drift
velocity proportional to $\sqrt{X/p}$, and the reduced mobility proportional
to $1/\sqrt{X/p}$. For large ranges of X/p, it is customary to plot drift
velocity against X/p on a log-log plot and note the slopes of the
asymptotes in the curves.

The curves shown and plotted as indicated give enough data to
enable further theoretical discussion. The first attempt at a theory

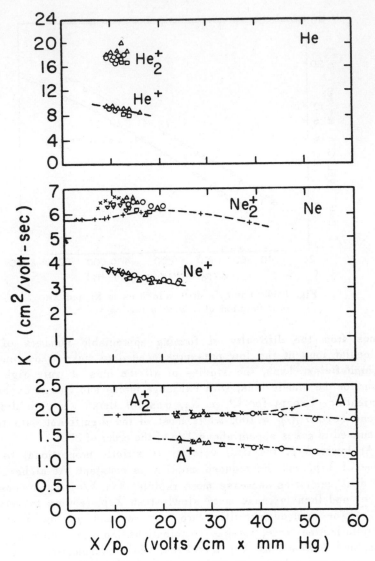

Fig. 1.35. Hornbeck's mobilities in He, Ne, and A, reduced to
0° C. 760 mm as a function of X/p.

for ionic mobilities at high X/p was that of K. T. Compton, given
in its later form in Compton and Langmuir's (36) article in *Reviews
of Modern Physics* in 1930. The equation was derived assuming a
Maxwellian distribution of velocities and solid elastic impacts with
collision cross sections independent of velocity, ignoring any attractive forces. It came from an adaptation of Compton's early theory

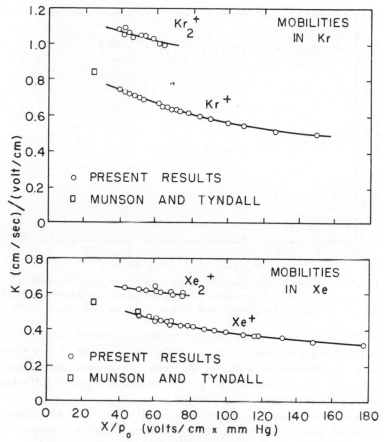

Fig. 1.36. Varney's mobilities in Kr and Xe, reduced to
0° C. 760 mm as a function of X/p.

for electron mobilities as a function of X/p, which, in its general form, and except for certain constants, still holds below excitation energies, despite non-Maxwellian distributions of energy. This theory yields an equation which reads

$$(1.10) \quad k = \frac{0.815\lambda_0 e}{(2em)^{1/2}} \left[\frac{1 + \left(\frac{m}{M}\right) \dfrac{1}{\dfrac{1}{2} + \left\{\dfrac{1}{4} + \dfrac{\lambda_0^2 X^2 (M+m)^2}{6.02 \, \Omega^2 Mm}\right\}^{1/2}}}{\left[\dfrac{\Omega}{2} + \left\{\dfrac{\Omega^2}{4} + \dfrac{\lambda_0^2 X^2 (M+m)^2}{6.02 \; Mm}\right\}^{1/2}\right]^{1/2}}\right]^{1/2}.$$

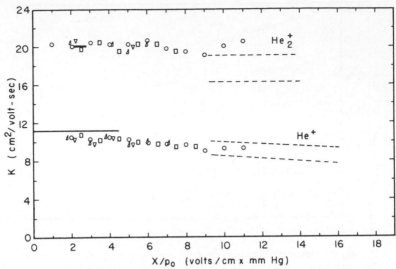

Fig. 1.37. Chanin and Biondi's mobilities for ions in He, reduced to 0°
C. 760 mm, compared with Hornbeck's data (short dashes), Massey's calculated
value for He$^+$ (long black line), and Bristol data for He$_2^+$ (short black line).

Here the Ω is the average thermal energy, λ_0 is the mean free path,
and M and m are masses of ion and molecule. The use of this equation
relative to Hershey's work for K$^+$ ions in various gases leads to
the dashed curve labeled "I" in the curves of figures 1.15 through
1.18 (*supra*, part one).

Subsequent to his experimental work, Hershey applied Langevin's
and Hassé and Cook's point center of force theory to these calculations. The heavy curves labeled "II" result from the use of Langevin's
equations with solid elastic spheres and dielectric polarization
forces, listed in tables 1.5 and 1.6. The curves labeled "III" come
from the Hassé and Cook center of force theory, using inverse fifth-
power polarization force, inverse seventh-power van der Waals attraction, and an inverse ninth-power repulsive force. Actually, Hershey
adjusted the resulting potential diagrams slightly to yield the Bristol
values indicated by the arrows at the intercepts of the solid curves
with the ordinate axis. It will be noted at once that both computed
curves show the hump manifested by the experimental curves with
points on them. It will also be noted that these bracket the observations, the solid elastic theory of Langevin showing less variation
and a lower peak compared to the soft-repulsive force theory. This
difference is in line with the difference shown by the theories when
applied to the temperature variation, the center of force theory show-

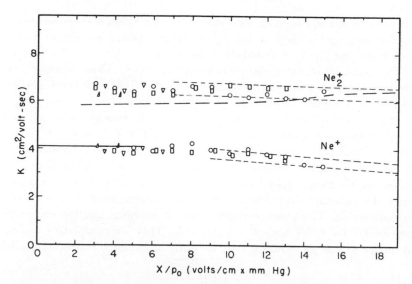

Fig. 1.38. Chanin and Biondi's mobilities for ions in Ne, reduced to $0°$ C. 760 mm, compared with Hornbeck's data (short dashes), Bristol data for Ne_2^+ (long dashes), and Holstein's theory for Ne^+ (solid line).

ing much more change with temperature than experiment or the Langevin theory. Probably an inverse eleventh power would have yielded better agreement, though the Langevin equation is not too bad.

Hershey's approach to the solution of the problem for ion mobilities at high X/p is discussed in detail in §11, *infra*, by G. H. Wannier, who treats the generalized problem of mobilities. It appears that while Hershey's assumptions concerning energy distribution are faulty in principle, the treatment he used with an inverse fifth-power law is still capable of yielding fairly good values of the drift velocity, since it is possible to evaluate velocity averages on inverse fifth-power attraction ignoring the distribution function. Thus, the degree of agreement achieved by Hershey is not accidental, though it is desirable eventually to produce a relation based on sounder general principles.

Before proceeding further, it is essential to indicate yet another theory for mobilities of ions in a gas, which was derived by G. D. Yarnold (37). Yarnold recognized that in principle the distribution of energies is not Maxwellian. He had previously attempted to deduce an electron-drift velocity equation on certain basic assumptions, such as elastic impacts, constant free paths, etc., by a step-by-step process of analysis of the angular and momentum dispersion of electrons in a field, solving his statistics by withdrawing numbered angular sequences from a hat for a large number of times. These procedures led him to a distribution law.

The same procedure was carried out for ions. This assumed low ion densities; that the energy gained from the field was much greater than thermal energy (high X/p); that free paths had a constant length L; that no attractive forces were active at this energy; and assumed elastic impacts between spherical ions of mass M in a gas of molecules of identical mass. This led at once to an average distribution of momenta, making an angle of 55° with the field rather than 90°, as for an isotropic distribution. The gain in energy between paths made the average direction before impact even more nearly in the field direction. The average distribution of energies had the empirical form of $f(E) = \epsilon^{-E/\bar{E}}$ with $\bar{E} = 1.06\ XeL$. This oversimplified calculation for $m = M$ gave him a drift velocity v in the field direction, of

$$(1.11) \qquad\qquad v = 1.1\sqrt{\frac{XeL}{M}}\ .$$

This law is to be compared with the limiting value from Compton's equation, when $XeL \gg e\Omega$, which reads

$$v = 0.7\sqrt{\frac{XeL}{M}}\ .$$

Actually, the law deduced by Yarnold on certain very special assumptions is limited in scope, and recourse should be had to a more generalized theory, such as that of Wannier.

However, it is of interest to note that Wannier, as a result of his generalized theory, has been able to show that for ions like He$^+$, Ne$^+$, etc., in their own gases, where exchange of charge is active, the force fields are such as to lead to *isotropic scattering* with *constant cross sections* as long as X/p is high. Under these conditions the drift velocity is given by

$$(1.11a) \qquad\qquad v = 1.147\left(\frac{XeL}{M}\right)^{\frac{1}{2}}.$$

It is seen that quite generally, independent of detailed differences, the drift velocity at high X/p will tend toward a limiting form in which v is proportional to $(XeL/M)^{\frac{1}{2}}$. Since L is proportional to $760/p$, then v varies as $(X/p)^{\frac{1}{2}}$, and since the reduced mobility K is given by

$$K = \frac{v}{X'}\left(\frac{p}{760}\right) \text{ at constant temperature,}$$

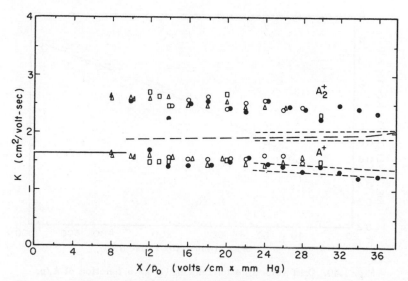

Fig. 1.39. Chanin and Biondi's mobilities for ions in A, reduced to 0° C. 760 mm, compared with Hornbeck's data (short dashes), Bristol data (long dashes), and Holstein's theory for A^+ (solid line).

K at high fields will vary as $\sqrt{1/X/p}$. A. M. Tyndall and R. J. Munson (7) had found that for Kr^+ in Kr and Xe^+ in Xe, the variation of K with X/p indeed followed the law indicated. This was shown even more strikingly in the curves of Hornbeck and Varney, indicated in figures 1.32 to 1.36.

Here, except for lack of detail, the log-log plot of drift velocity against X/p shows the regions where v is proportional to X/p at low X/p, and to the $\sqrt{X/p}$ at high X/p with a transition region between. Most of Hershey's curves lay in the low X/p and in the transition region.

The use of this equation for yielding solid elastic cross sections in connection with experiment, which yield proper mobilities when substituted into solid elastic equation 1.1a, has been indicated before, and is illustrated in tables 1.11 and 1.15, *supra*. It is believed that enough has already been said to account for the curves of drift velocity against X/p, observed at high X/p, to account for observation in general. There are, however, two matters directly related to high X/p measurements which should be discussed. One of these is the immediately following study of Varney on ions in O_2, N_2, and H_2 over a range of X/p. The other is the generalized theory of G. H. Wannier, which appears in § 11, *infra*.

Probably no better conclusion to the high X/p study can be given than

$8

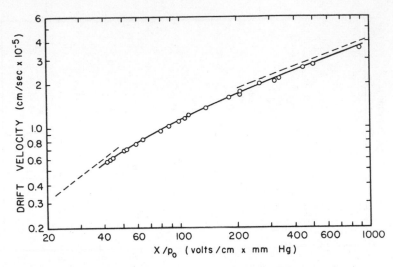

Fig. 1.40. Drift velocities for ions in O_2 as a function of X/p,
observed by Varney on a log-log plot.

to report the recent work of R. N. Varney (79), who extended Hornbeck's
studies. He has extended Hornbeck's analysis of the theory to give
complete quantitative curves. This leads to more accurate evaluations
of ion-drift velocities, and accurate evaluations of the secondary
coefficient for positive ion bombardment γ. Details of these calculations are too lengthy to include here.

In pure O_2 he observed a unique *mobility* at high X/p that changed
from proportional to $\sqrt{p/X}$ (drift velocity $\propto \sqrt{X/p}$), to a constant mobility (drift velocity $\propto X/p$) at low X/p, shown in figures 1.40 and
1.41. The extrapolated value of K at zero X/p is 2.25 ± 0.1 cm2/volt
sec. The ion is doubtless O_2, which has a reduced mobility because
of charge exchange, and was the only likely ion observed near the
operating conditions by Luhr with a mass spectrograph, since little
O^+ is created. These ions correspond to crossing times of the order
of 10^{-4} sec or less. At the pressure and in this time, possibly O_4^+
cannot form.

In pure N_2 the ion at high X/p was one with drift velocity proportional to $\sqrt{X/p}$ and of low value, indicating a charge-exchange
retardation. At intermediate X/p it underwent a transition to a faster
ion. This transition, unlike those observed by the Bristol group at
low temperatures, or with Li^+ in H_2O and inert gases, had only a
single value that increased with X/p. As low X/p values were approached, it reached values that dovetailed smoothly into those of
Mitchell and Ridler at Bristol, with mobility constant and drift veloc-

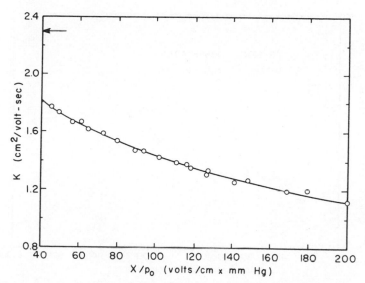

Fig. 1.41. Reduced mobilities for ions in O_2 as a function of X/p, at $0°$ C. 760 mm, observed by Varney.

ity proportional to X/p. This is clearly seen in figures 1.42 and 1.43. In N_2, Luhr had observed ions of N^+, with N_2^+, N_3^+, and N_4^+ predominating. Thus, the ion at high X/p is doubtless N_2^+, which undergoes a transition to N_4^+ at intermediate X/p according to the relations:

(1) $N_2^+ + N_2 \rightarrow N_4^{+V}$—vibrationally excited of long life, τ_v.

$N_4^{+V} + N_2 \rightarrow N_4^+ + N_2$—stable, of heat of formation ~ 0.2 volts.

(2) $N_4^+ + N_2 \rightarrow N_2^+ + 2N_2$ — when available energy from field in impact exceeds 0.2 volts.

It may be assumed that the collision frequency of N_2^+ with N_2 is z_1, that of N_4^{+V} with N_2 is z_2, and that presumably the collision frequency of N_4^+ with N_2 is not very different from z_2. Then if $\tau_v \gg 1/z_2$, creation of N_4^+ by reaction (1) is assured and will not be influenced by pressure changes, even though z_2 may decrease somewhat. Such stability of N_4^{+V} is reasonable from the molecular structure and the low energy of 0.2 e.v.

The lifetime of N_2^+, τ_1, is determined by $1/z_1$ and by the probability that collision in a field of given X/p occurs at such low energy, e.g., below 0.2 volts, that N_4^+ can form. The lifetime of N_4^+, τ_2, is determined by $1/z_2$, and the chance that as a result of the field X/p, the collision between N_4 and N_2 will give an energy in excess of 0.2 volts.

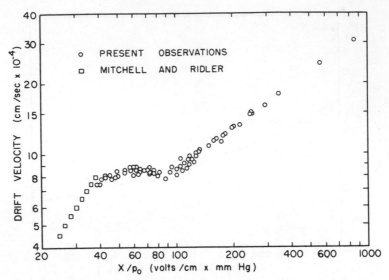

Fig. 1.42. Drift velocities in N_2 as a function of X/p,
observed by Varney on a log-log plot.

Note that r_1 and r_2 depend on z_1 and z_2, and thus decrease as
the N_2 pressure increases; that is, they are pressure-dependent in
absolute value. However, Varney measures the drift velocity in a
transition region of X/p, and of possibly changing p where reactions
(1) and (2) are occurring. The drift velocity observed will be $\bar{v}$, an
average given by $\bar{v} = v_1 (r_1)/(r_1 + r_2) + v_2 (r_2)/(r_1 + r_2)$, with v_1 and v_2 as
the drift velocities of N_2^+ and N_4^+ in the narrow transition range of X/p.
It is seen, then, that while $r_1/(r_1 + r_2)$ and $r_2/(r_1 + r_2)$ vary with X/p,
they will be independent of p, since z_1 and z_2 are both proportional to
p. Such average values of $\bar{v}$ will be observed in the region of X/p
at which $r_1 > r_2$ and $r_2 > r_1$; that is, above some limiting lower X/p
and below some limiting higher value of X/p. At very high X/p, v_1
will be the unique velocity above transition; at low X/p, v_2 will be
the unique velocity below transition. This is just as observed.

There is, however, one more condition imposed for clean-cut results:
the times r_1 and r_2 must be much less than the ion-transit time T
defined by $\bar{v}T = d$, where d is the gap length. Perhaps better stated,
the condition is that $(r_1 + r_2) n = T$ must be fulfilled, with n a large
number. At low values of p, where z_1 and z_2 are large, the condition
may fail; but at such pressures it is doubtful if drift velocities representing equilibrium values of electron energy exist, and measurements are futile.

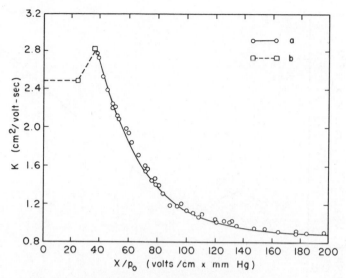

Fig. 1.43. Reduced mobilities of ions in N_2 as a function of X/p, at $0°$ C. 760 mm, observed by Varney.

Strangest of all is the study in CO. Here the mobilities at high X/p show a behavior similar to that in the other gases, indicating the ion to be CO^+, with decreased mobility caused by charge exchange of 1.60 cm^2/volt sec extrapolated to zero field. As it reaches intermediate values of X/p, a transformation not unlike that in N_2 appears; the ion gradually changes its mobility to a higher value of 2.25 cm^2/volt sec extrapolated to zero field. However, in the transition region a *second ion* appears, of uniformly higher mobility than the transition ion. This also changes its value continuously with X/p. At the point where the lower-velocity new ion has essentially reached its proper mobility, the high-mobility ion's values rapidly drop to follow closely the values of its companion ion. These changes are clearly seen in figures 1.44 and 1.45.

Though several interpretations are possible, the one proposed is interesting and has some corroboration. At high X/p the ion is uniquely CO^+. As the value of X/p, and in consequence, the energy of CO^+ ions goes down, a new ion can form which is quasi stable. This ion is $(CO)_2^+$, which is the slower of the two transition ions noted. Its mobility increases as X/p decreases, since it spends more time as $(CO)_2^+$ and less as CO^+ in transit. However, $(CO)_2^+$ is not very stable. As X/p decreases and the ions $(CO)_2^+$ exist for longer times, the $(CO)_2^+$ undergoes an internal chemical rearrange-

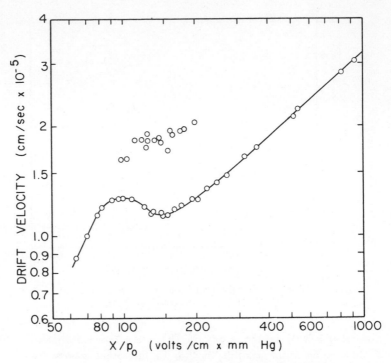

Fig. 1.44. Drift velocities in CO as a function of X/p,
observed by Varney on a log-log plot.

ment leading to a C^+ ion and a CO_2 molecule. The C^+ ion corresponds
to the higher of the transition curves with decreasing X/p. Its ultimate decline and the appearance of one ion of higher mobility result
from the universal formation of C^+ from $(CO)_2^+$ and attachment to CO
with decreasing X/p. The initial increase of the observed drift
velocity of the C^+ transition ion is caused by its earlier formation,
as the $(CO)_2^+$ ion exists for longer times at early phases crossing
the gap. The reactions occurring are then:

$$CO^+ + CO \rightarrow (CO)_2^+$$
$$(CO)_2^+ \rightarrow C^+ + CO_2, \; C^+ + CO \rightarrow C_2O^+.$$

Eventually, at lower X/p, the $(CO)_2^+$ forms early, increasing in amount;
but dissociates entirely, giving only a C^+ ion in the low X/p region.
At low X/p no CO^+ or $(CO)_2^+$ ions are observed, but a complex appears
liberating C^+ on the cathode.

This seemingly complicated explanation is strongly indicated by
the appearance of CO_2 in the liquid-air traps once X/p sinks to the

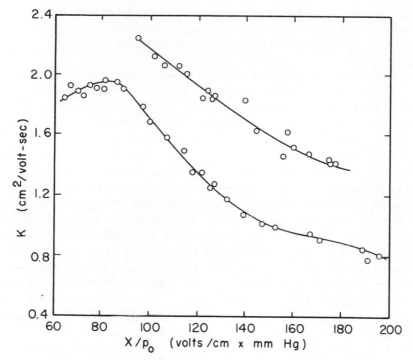

Fig. 1.45. Reduced mobilities of ions in CO as a function of X/p, at $0°$ C. 760 mm, observed by Varney.

value where two mobilities appear. In addition, the presence of C leads to deposits of carbon on the cathode leading to quite low values of γ and showing as a black C dust on the cathode. It is clear that the conditions for creating this change require energies so low (limiting X/p) that attractive forces permit CO^+ to give a $(CO)_2^+$ ion for sufficient time for it to transform to C^+ and CO_2. From the work of the Bristol group, and ultimate decline to an ion of mobility of 2.25 cm2/volt sec, it is probable that C^+ quickly attaches a CO molecule and gives a C_2O^+ complex which accounts for the low mobility of the C^+ ion.

This is a beautiful illustration of complex ion formation by internal molecular rearrangement, in this case creating a smaller initial ion. Above all, these new reactions make it very clear that it is highly improper to assign given structures to ions in gases on the basis of the simple dielectric laws, or in analogy to other gas ion behavior. Thus, the inert gases show ionic complexes of a very different nature from N_2, or from Li^+ in H_2O, or inert gases, or from those in O_2 and

CO. It thus behooves workers to be very careful in identifying ions until the studies are made more extensive than usual, and mass spectrograph should be invoked wherever possible.

§9. Difference in Mobilities of Positive and Negative Ions, and Aging.

Having the theoretical background established, it is now essential to consider further evidence yielded by experiment, which is not amenable to direct interpretation by theory. The evidence involves, among other factors, the difference in mobilities of positive and negative ions. This difference is *not* indicated by the dielectric constant D in the force equation 1.2, for D is not charge-sensitive. The difference in mobilities is in turn closely associated with certain results indicating changes of mobility with time, referred to as "aging effects." The same difference is also closely related to the effect of gaseous impurities and the question of mobilities in mixtures of gases. Accordingly, one phase cannot adequately be considered apart from the others. All of these phenomena lie in common beyond theory, in that they largely involve selective actions of charge which bring in forces beyond the scope of any present theory. The discussion is complicated by the fact that only a few of these phenomena have been studied in very pure gases and with known ions, as in the work at Bristol. In consequence, the material is complicated and controversial.

While the differences between the mobilities of positive and negative ions of the order of 10% to 30%, usually observed over measuring time intervals of 10^{-2} second, were initially ascribed to the differences in the size of negative and positive ion complexes or clusters, no substantiating data were at hand. Probably the first indication of the validity of this assumption came in 1921, when H. A. Erikson (4), by air-blast methods using room air, observed that the initial positive ions in air had the same elevated mobility of 1.8 cm²/volt sec as the negative ions. However, if the positive ions were *aged* for some hundredths of a second, they changed sharply in mobility to the lower value of 1.4 cm²/volt sec normally observed on the apparatus as calibrated by Erikson on the Zeleny mobility scale (38). The change was unique and sharp over the time interval observed. The high resolving power of the method *showed only two peaks*, and as the time lengthened, the amplitude of the high-mobility peak declined and the other one rose in proportion. There was no indication of mobilities of intermediate value. It appeared that the change took place in a single act of addition within far less than 10^{-2} sec.

Since Erikson's work, many other observers have obtained similar results under better control of purity, notably Tyndall and Grindley (6), Bradbury (5), Loeb (40), and Tyndall, Munson, and Hoselitz (7). More in detail, J. J. Mahoney (41) succeeded in showing that the aging which had been observed by Erikson to occur in *room air* in 10^{-2} sec actually occurred in less than 0.0014 sec in the absence of H_2O vapor, i.e., in really dry air. Addition of water vapor, and even more effectively of NH_3 gas, delayed the aging down to the time interval reported by Erikson or even longer, depending on the amount of water vapor.

Aging may go through several steps. The author observed, in a metal chamber with Na^+ ions from a Kunsman catalyst in H_2, two successive changes in mobilities, from 17 to 13 and from 13 to 8.6 (40). The time intervals ranged from 10^{-5} to 10^{-4} sec and to 10^{-2} sec for the stable existence of each of the ions.

In a composite gas, such as air, where X-ray or ionization processes can alter the chemical composition, it would be expected that after some 10^{-2} sec or more, there would be a large number of ions with different masses and a spread of values of mobility. Most methods of mobility measurement used in the past do not detect such a spread, as they have low resolving powers. However, the growth of a "mobility spectrum" with time can be nicely seen in figure 1.46, taken by Bradbury for positive ions in air (5). Aging experiments in *pure* N_2 shown in figure 1.6 show no temporal change in mobility, while Bradbury's results in H_2 show the disappearance of the fast ion of mobility 13.1 in H_2 in figure 1.7 (part one, *supra*).

Mahoney's aging curves for positive ions in moist air are shown in figure 1.47, where circles represent the unchanged negative ion peak and crosses represent the positive peaks. The broad-mobility peaks observed in air after some 10^{-1} sec have been called a "mobility spectrum," and have been observed by Zeleny, Hamshere, Bradbury (5), Fontell, Varney, and others (42). Luhr (43) made a study of the positive ions present in ionized air by mass spectrograph some 10^{-5} of a second after formation. As anticipated, mass numbers ranging from N^+ at 14 to Hg^+ at 200 were observed. Hg^+ ions have also been observed created by exchange of charge in the experiments of Mitchell and Ridler (19) at greater ages. In the oldest gas, Luhr found the ions N^+, O^+, N_2^+, O_2^+, and mass numbers 42, 48, 56, 60, 64, 76, 82, 96, 108, and 160, which remained unidentified.

The amounts of impurity which can change mobilities in time intervals of less than 10^{-2} sec are small indeed. They depend only on the collision frequency of the ions and the chance that attach-

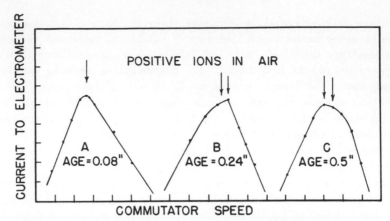

Fig. 1.46. Bradbury's curves for growth of a spread of mobilities with age of ions in the composite gas air.

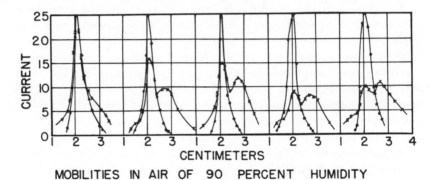

MOBILITIES IN AIR OF 90 PERCENT HUMIDITY

Fig. 1.47. Mahoney's curves for aging of positive ions in moist air at various ages, 1×10^{-3} sec to 10^{-1} sec. The high peak is the faster ion. Ion currents are plotted against downstream distance of the ion. These curves are typical of all aging experiments.

ment or charge exchange will occur at an encounter. It is seen that unless extraordinary precautions are taken in measuring a mobility in outgassed and pure systems, on ions which cannot exchange charge and over relatively short time intervals, one cannot be sure of the *nature of the carrier* the mobility of which is being observed. For example, on O_2 ions 10^{-3} sec or less old, Bradbury (5), who prepared the O_2 in the standard fashion used in atomic weight determinations by heating $KClO_3$, found mobilities obviously affected, presumably by traces of oxides of Cl, or by Cl itself. Only by using pure, fractionated tank oxygen or by heating $KMnO_4$ could he get the values of mobilities characteristic of O_2 in an outgassed chamber in these time intervals. Even then it is known from Varney's studies that these ions could not be O_2^+ ions with $k = 2.25$, and it is believed that they may have been Hg^+ ions.

One must realize that mobilities measured under the older standard conditions of 10^{-1} to 10^{-3} sec of age in any gas have significance in value only *relative* to that gas, the method of production, the cleanliness of the chamber, and the age of the ions. Therefore, the earlier published tables of determinations of ion mobilities are of *no value*, except perhaps as orienting magnitudes. Results of theoretical significance can only be expected in connection with known ions under controlled conditions. It follows that there is no room in this chapter to list data from the countless mobility measurements of the past. The only significant and valid data on recognized ions are in the tables of results from the Bristol group, and those from the recent pulsed measurements of Hornbeck, Varney, and of Chanin and Biondi.

To yield orienting magnitudes in relatively pure common gases at atmospheric pressure and 20° C., under conditions usually encountered with ages between 4×10^{-2} and 0.5 sec, the results of Bradbury are presented in table 1.16. Bradbury used an X-ray ionization method of high resolving power in an all-glass, baked-out chamber, using gases prepared with the best techniques. There may have been 10^{-3} mm of Hg vapor present from the gauges in all gases. The values in parentheses in the table are those which are as near the commonly reported aged values as Bradbury's conditions of purity permit.

It should be noted that the positive ion mobility in pure O_2 at this age is far less that Varney's value of 2.25. Bradbury's value in pure He is 17, compared to the 20 of Tyndall and Powell. The value in N_2 is in agreement with Huber's, with Varney's, and the Bristol group values reduced to 22° K. The value for the ion in H_2 is probably in agreement with those to be found in modern work.

The values of Bradbury, even where they disagree, are *good* experimental values; they are *not wrong*. Their significance is at present obscure. This statement requires that a word of caution be issued, in view of very recent happenings. The data of the Bristol group in the inert gases were taken in really pure gases and by a *good* method. Yet, when they obtained a value of an assumed He^+ ion in He of 21.4 in the face of the wave-mechanical calculation of 12 for He^+ ions, and of certain microwave data, it was at once implied that their gas was impure or their results were inaccurate. However, their data were *valid* and *accurate*, and the wave-mechanical theory was also correct. The difficulty was resolved when the predominating

TABLE 1.16*

Mobilities of Common Ions in Relatively Pure Gases at Over 10^{-2} sec Age

Gas	Source	Purity	K^+	Age	K^-
Air	Filtered Room	p.	(1.59)	—	(2.21)
O_2	$KClO_3$	(?)	1.71	—	2.65
O_2	$KMnO_4$	p.	(1.58)	—	(2.18)
O_2	Tank	p.	(1.58)	—	(2.18)
N_2	NaN_3	i.	1.60	—	Electron
N_2	Tank	p.	(2.09)	—	Electron
			2.37	—	—
			2.34 †	—	—
N_2	Tank	i.	1.81	—	2.21
H_2	Tank	p.	(8.20)	—	Electron
			13.10	—	—
			13.40 ‡	—	—
Na^+ in H_2	Tank	i. (Loeb)	8.40	10^{-2} sec	—
			13.50	10^{-4} sec	—
			17.50	10^{-5} sec	—
H_2	Tank	i.	6.70	—	9.60
He	Tank	i.	7.10	—	Electron
			14.00	—	—
He	Tank	p.	(17.00)	—	Electron

*The table given by Bradbury in his paper is confusing, because he failed to indicate in it the sign of the ion. Thus, the data for air, O_2, and N_2 have the negative ion in column 4 and the positive ion in column 6, while the order is reversed for H_2 and He. The present table gives consistent tabulation.

† Huber's value.
‡ Lauer's value.

ion at their pressures and ages was found to be He_2^+, and the Bristol data have been confirmed. In fact, their values are probably the most accurate values extant for the ions.

Thus, it must be recognized that in general, the experimental values of mobilities observed for ions in a given gas by a good method depend critically and sometimes unpredictably on the method and conditions of measurement, the age of the ions, the character of the purification of the gas, and opportunities for contamination. It is, therefore, not essential that the values observed by any investigator, especially one using an indirect or new method, conform to the best or the most reliable results indicated in that gas. That is, the respective results of any two studies may be completely valid in their setting, and need not agree unless the work of one of the observers be duplicated. However, owing to differences in conditions, some obvious and some perhaps subtly hidden, the values may not be the same. On the other hand, when the nature of the carriers is known; when the gases are sufficiently pure to retain the identity of the carriers; when measurements are made where charge exchange, etc., cannot alter the carrier; and if the data for a theoretical computation are adequate—then, and only then, can the theory be invoked to call into question an experimental observation from a completely developed method by a competent observer. Theory is at present good perhaps to 10%, and experiment such as that of the Bristol group is good to 2%. Where differences occur, further work should be undertaken to clarify the discrepancy; but the results should not be condemned until the facts are in.

It may also be added that if mobility data are needed on other than the standard gases so far listed, the measurements had best be made anew with techniques adequate to modern standards. While the data acquired earlier in the century, before the development of methods of short time resolution, and the employment of clean gases of high resolving power in outgassed systems, were valid in their setting, they have little significance today. Thus, the data in tables of critical constants on ion mobilities in various gases may be inaccurate in absolute value by at least 20%, as shown by the author in 1923 (90). It is furthermore likely that owing to aging and unknown impurities, even the relative values of mobilities for positive and negative ions may be reversed in relative magnitude. Irrespective of these difficulties, the values have little utility except as orienting magnitudes in modern studies, unless these are being conducted under the conditions of the older work.

Until just preceding World War II, little information was at hand of the kind needed for a further analysis of these problems. Perhaps the author and his students (44) were the first to study mobilities in mixtures of polar molecules with high D, mixed with relatively nonpolar molecules such as H_2, air, etc. They observed that the addition of the *smallest amounts* of the polar impurities often changed the mobility of ions of one sign, or the other, or both. These changes were sometimes an *increase* of the mobility, as with positive ions on addition of NH_3 to H_2 or to air. Sometimes the mobilities decreased, as with positive ions where ethyl ether or propylamine were added to air or to H_2. In rare cases, while attachment was likely, no change in mobility resulted such as with positive ions in methyl amine. Similar results in other systems were observed by A. M. Tyndall and L. R. Phillips, and by H. F. Mayer (45). The author interpreted the effect of these gases as being caused by the formation of *charge-*

specific complex ions akin to ions such as the NH_4^+, $CuNH_3^+$, or $Cu(NC)_2^-$ in solutions.

In gases where the attached molecule, like the NH_3 molecule, made a smaller positive ion than the normally attached impurity, the mobility was increased. With CH_3NH_2, the molecule made an ion of the same size as the normal impurity molecule. In this instance, the mobility was unchanged. With $CH_3CH_2CH_2NH_2$, the molecule was large, and the mobility of the positive ion was decreased. This was demonstrated by K. Dyk (44). Tyndall and Phillips observed similar results for a series of alcohols ROH of increasing R with the negative ions (45). By 1928, this information, coupled with the aging experiments, led the author to the conclusion that *clusters*, or better, *complex ion formation*, were possible, but *usually of a charge-specific nature*; and that these clusters included only *one or two added molecules*. In fact, he preferred the term *complex ion formation* because of the specific chemical nature of the reaction. At the time there was no indication of larger aggregates and little if any evidence of *labile* ions. The so-called "Debye effect," which was a form of deviation of mobilities from Blanc's law for mobilities in mixtures observed by the author, was erroneously attributed by him to a *statistical cluster* formation, as will be seen later.

At this state of knowledge, the last papers of the Bristol group came in 1940-41 to clarify the situation. These studies began with the first of a series of three papers by R. J. Munson, A. M. Tyndall, and K. Hoselitz (39), in which small amounts of water vapor were introduced into the various inert gases in which were studied alkali ions from a properly cooled Kunsman source. The customary four-gauze shutter technique was used. The alkali ions, however, first entered a drift space, where with a field X_1 they traversed a distance in which they could collide with molecules and attach. They then entered the measuring space, where a field X_2 drove them from the entering to the exit shutter. Usually, X_1 was set as 0.66 X_2, and X_1 and X_2 were raised simultaneously in proportion to reduce the age of the ions. With the length of X_1 appropriately larger (three times) than that of X_2, it was unusual for any more than 8% of the clustering process to occur in X_2. However, X_1 and X_2 could be varied independently, and were so varied on controls.

The concentration of water vapor was varied from 0.008 to 2.8%, though control was difficult at the lower concentration because of water absorption by the glass tubing. Lower pressures could be obtained by cooling the water to CO_2 slush temperatures, giving 0.0004 mm. The results observed for Li^+ ions in argon gas with dif-

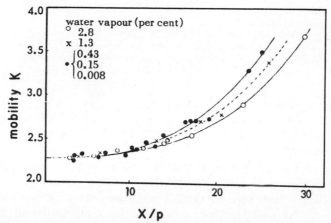

Fig. 1.48. Represents the results obtained by the Bristol group on mobilities of Li^+ ions in A as a function of X/p for various percentages of water vapor. The low X/p value represents the clustered ion. As X/p increases the cluster loses and adds molecules more readily, the lower the percentage of water vapor.

TABLE 1.17

Mobilities of Clustered and Unclustered Alkali Ions of Inert Gases at 20° C. 760 mm, According to the Bristol Group

Ion	He		Ne		A		Kr		Xe	
	Uncl.	Cl.	Uncl.	Cl.	Uncl.	Cl.	Uncl.	Cl.	Uncl.	Cl.
Li^+	25.60	11.70	11.80	5.28	4.99	2.26	3.97	1.46	3.04	0.98
Na^+	24.20	11.15	8.70	5.25	3.23	2.26	2.34	1.43	1.80	0.94
K^+	22.90	11.85	8.00	5.26	2.81	2.19	1.98	—	1.44	0.92
Rb^+	21.40	12.80	7.18	5.38	2.40	2.10	1.57	1.37	1.10	0.87
Cs^+	19.60	13.40	6.50	5.48	2.23	2.18	1.42	—	0.97	0.83

ferent percentages of H_2O are shown in figure 1.48 as a function of X/p. The mobility is seen to approach a limiting low value at low X/p. The values of k increase with X/p, but at higher rates, the lower the pressure of H_2O vapor. Corrections were included for the effect of varying amounts of H_2O by Blanc's law. The interpretation of these curves is that at low X/p the ion is clustered, and that as the cluster grows, the binding energy for additional molecules goes down. A dynamical equilibrium between loss by impact and gain is thus approached, the size fluctuating about a mean value. The size limit is here set by steric hindrance and similar effects.

TABLE 1.18

Estimated Number of Ions in Cluster for Various
Alkali Ions in Inert Gases, by Bristol Group

Gas	Li^+	Na^+	K^+.	Rb^+	Cs^+
A	6.4	5.7	6.2	6.5?	2.5?
Kr	5.9	5.8	—	4.6?	—
Xe	6.4	6.6	6.4	6.3?	6.7?

The values of mobilities for clustered and unclustered ions, corrected to no water vapor, are given in table 1.17.

To estimate the size of the cluster, the Bristol group estimated the *mass* of the clustered ion, assuming the applicability of the dispersion law of figure 1.21 and equation 1.7, *supra*. This procedure was incorrect, as has been indicated earlier, since the physical radius of the ion would also be altered. This weakness was recognized by the Bristol group. It is to be recalled, however, that the effect of the physical radius is apparently small in A, Kr, and Xe. On this basis, these workers estimated the *maximum* number of molecules in the clusters in these gases, as shown in table 1.18.

The table is not too significant, as the authors themselves recognize. It is likely that as the size of the alkali atom increases, it is less capable of holding molecules through steric effects. Attempts to use the full Langevin theory (equation 1.8) led to an estimate of 4 molecules instead of 6 for the Li^+ ion. Cs^+ might not have been expected to cluster, but the mobility was observed to be reduced.

By reducing the value of X/p, it might have been expected that the discrete ions, with 1, 2, 3, etc., water molecules, would appear successively in the mobility curves as aging progressed. Strangely, *this does not occur*, though of course the *average mobility of the clustered ion varies with* X/p. At high fields only the unclustered ions appear, and at low fields only the "fully clustered" ions appear. In between, *two, and only two, groups of ions are observed, the clustered ions of* k *varying with* X/p *and unclustered ions of fixed* k, *whose relative abundance can be estimated from the amplitudes of the curves*. The resolving power of the method could not *clearly* have separated out the low-amplitude mobility peaks with a height of 10% of the main peaks, or less. However, such ion peaks could have been detected unless the mobilities were very close together.

Leaving aside the contingency of the presence of small groups of intermediate ions, the evidence, *in conformity with all other aging*

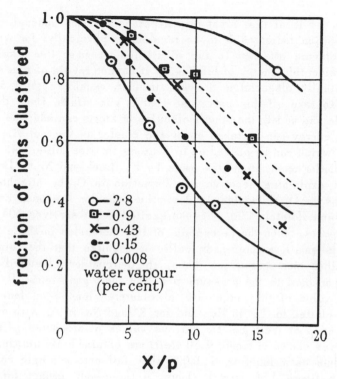

Fig. 1.49. The fraction of ions clustered as a function of X/p at varying percentages of water vapor for Li^+ ions in A, according to the Bristol group.

experiments, points to the existence of either *clustered* or *unclustered* ions. As X/p is raised, the *fraction of the clustered ions decreases,* that fraction varying with the density of the water vapor present. This result is illustrated in figure 1.49, for Li^+ ions in argon, for various percentages of water vapor. As X/p increases, the mobility of the single *clustered* group of ions rises. This cannot be ascribed to *attachment* in the measuring field, because of the relative values of the lengths and fields in the drift space and measuring space. It must be connected with the *breakup of a cluster* and the *reduction of attractive forces,* as X/p *is relatively high where this occurs.*

To explain the anomaly of the appearance of only *two* mobilities and yet the *variation* of the *mobility* with X/p, the following hypothesis was made by Munson, Tyndall, and Hoselitz (39): A cluster cannot form readily. It is assumed that until the *first molecule is attached, there can be no attachment.* Once the first molecule attaches, the attachment of the other molecules follows in *quick* suc-

cession. While at first sight this hypothesis seems unusual, careful
consideration indicates it to be reasonable physically; for when the
first molecule attaches to the alkali ion, it must free itself from
the considerable energy of binding. If it cannot get rid of this energy,
it eventually dissociates. It may, in fact, require *a third body at
impact* to take off this energy so that it can attach. Once the first
molecule has added, the other molecules or atoms can add; the excess
binding energy can be taken up by the cluster as internal vibrational
energy, which can be passed on to A atoms in later collisions.

A similar assumption was made by F. Bloch and N. E. Bradbury
(46) in explaining negative ion formation in O_2 by attachment of
electrons to O_2 molecules; and similar behavior has been noted by
Biondi and Holstein (75), because excited He_2^{+*V} survives 10^5 molecular impacts. Since the percentage of H_2O molecules in these experiments is small, a three-body collision requires that the third body
be another inert gas atom. Thus, the percentage clustered should
be proportional to the pressure p of the inert gas atoms. If the observed value of the percentage of clustered ions as a function of
X/p is plotted for Li^+ in He, and for K^+ and Na^+ in A, with different
pressures p of inert gas for various values of pressures p' of H_2O,
the curves shown in figure 1.50 (*left*) are obtained. By plotting these
same data as a function of X/p^2, they fall onto a single curve, as
seen in figure 1.50 (*right*). Thus, a three-body impact for initial
attachment seems plausible.

From the initial addition of the first H_2O molecules in a three-
body impact with an inert gas atom, the other H_2O molecules in the
cluster can add as rapidly as encountered up to the equilibrium number. This might be 1, 2, or 3 more beyond the first one. The average
number of these molecules in the *labile* cluster resulting will vary
as the energy of the ion varies. Below the highest X/p possibly
only the original molecule will remain with one labile-attached molecule. These will be attached or detached part of the time, giving
a *continuously* varying mean mobility of the clustered ions for each
X/p value. Thus, the increase in mobility of the clustered ion with
an X/p which increases to values above those of the thermal energy
of agitation, can be explained by the decrease in the average size
of the labile cluster for molecules when $\beta PE/KE \sim 1$. With increasing
X/p, it must also be recalled that a *small* ion will *increase* its mobility owing to *reduction of attractive forces* with energy. This factor
is also active with clustered ions. At an X/p of 20, the Li^+ ion has
an energy of 0.032 e.v., which is that of thermal agitation and corresponds to a temperature increase of the gas to about $546°$ K. This

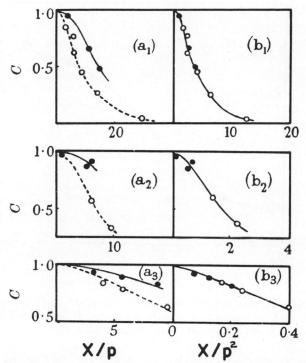

Fig. 1.50. *Left*: The percentage of clustered ions as a function of X/p for Li^+ ions in He, and for K^+ and Na^+ ions in A, with different pressures p of inert gas at various pressures of H_2O vapor. *Right*: Here appear the same data, plotted as a function of X/p^2, falling onto a single curve. These data come from the Bristol group.

effectively decreases the clustering and momentum exchange by attraction of the H_2O molecules and A atoms, and the mobility increases in proportion.

It is not inconceivable that the energy of the ion can become great enough to decluster the ion completely. Thus, it is to be expected that the values of k will increase to the unclustered-ion value as X/p is increased. The less tightly bound ions will do this at a lower X/p. A case where declustering is unmistakably active is shown in the curve for Cs^+ in Xe with 0.6% H_2O vapor, illustrated in figure 1.51. It is seen that up to an $X/p = 20$, unclustered Cs^+ ions in Xe suffer no increase in mobility, while the water-vapor cluster changes mobility from that of 0.83 to 0.97 as X/p increases from about 5 to 20. As indicated earlier, the reason for intermediate mobilities as the cluster breaks up, is that labile clusters will add on and lose

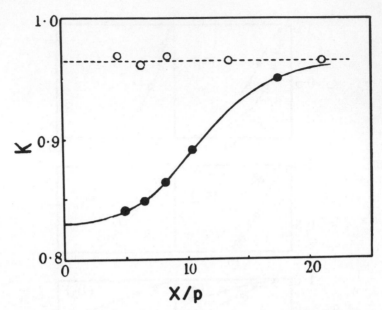

Fig. 1.51. Mobility of clustered Cs^+ ions in Xe with 0.6% H_2O vapor as a function of X/p, reported by the Bristol group. Note the initial clustered ion at low X/p and the declustered Cs^+ ion at high X/p.

molecules as they move through the gas if $\beta PE/KE \sim 1$, as it always is for a clustered labile ion to the limit set by steric hindrance at low ion energy. The mean mobility will depend on the relative times the ion spends as clustered or unclustered.

By making the field X_1 low, so that all ions were clustered, and by increasing X_2 so that ions could break up in the field, it was observed that the ions quickly reached equilibrium in the analyses. The number of clustered ions was not reduced until X_2/p exceeded the value of breakup. Then only unclustered ions were observed.

These conclusions appeared to run into serious difficulty when a quantitative survey of the process was made. If the effect of attractive forces between ion and molecules is neglected, the collision frequency at the pressures and fields used is too low to give the needed three-body impacts to permit attachment of the first molecule. Thus, with 0.003% H_2O in Xe at 2.27 mm, the chance of an Li^+ ion making a three-body collision is of the order of 10^{-4}. The chance rises to 2×10^{-2} only for 1% H_2O. Attractive forces would help at higher concentrations of H_2O through statistical changes in density, but not adequately. This would require that the *radius for the three-body impact* for carrying away the energy of ion formation *must be materially increased above the kinetic-theory values for* σ *assumed by*

Munson and Hoselitz, within the time set for such a three-body impact. There is thus involved a space and time factor, $\sigma\tau$, surrounding one H_2O molecule, the alkali ion Li^+, and the inert gas atom for the transfer of the energy of association of Li^+ and H_2O to the system-ion complex and inert atom, about which nothing is known. Here σ represents a cross section for energy transfer, and τ the duration of an excited molecular state. Thus, the discrepancy 10^4 in time and space, based on solid elastic collisions and a transit time used in calculation, is not too disturbing. For instance, the energy of association could well be taken up for an appreciable time, 10^{-5} sec, in the H_2O molecules as vibrations. Similar difficulties are encountered in electron attachment to O_2. Recently, M. A. Biondi and T. Holstein (75) have shown that low-energy vibrational states of the $He_2^{+*}V$ molecule can survive 10^6 impacts with He and last $\sim 10^{-5}$ sec.

From these data, it is clear that with high values of the dielectric constant, or attractive force, ions of known type can add molecules of the dielectric. This action should occur equally well for positive and negative ions *if the forces are purely dielectric*, which they probably are not. This is indicated by the preference of negative ions for molecules of the type ROH and positive ions for those of the type RNH_2. If the first molecule added forms a new compound, the heat of formation is great, thus accounting for the reluctance to attach the first molecule. The molecules will attach more readily, the smaller the ionic radius. They can do so only under appropriate circumstances, i.e., through a three-body impact to remove the energy of ion formation. Accordingly, they will remain unclustered until the conditions of pressure, time of observation, and energy permit ion formation by addition of the first molecule. At this time many of the ions form completed labile clusters by adding on as many other molecules as the forces permit. Thus, there are either *unclustered ions* or *equilibrium labile-clustered ions*, the proportion present depending on the time of observation relative to the mean time for achievement of the triple impact.

The mobility of the clustered ion is not constant, but shows a variation with X/p, increasing as X/p increases. This indicates that X/p exerts some influence on the mobility, either by affecting the attractive forces or by changing the average size of the labile cluster formed. The size of the labile cluster probably varies with ion species, polar molecules, temperature, X/p, etc. It is definitely not larger than 6 molecules, and is probably less than 4. Most observed results could be ascribed to not more than 2 or 3, and general indications are that there are not very many.

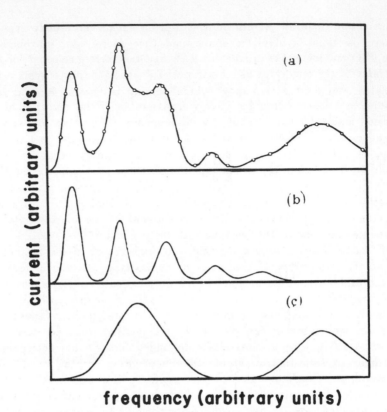

frequency (arbitrary units)

Fig. 1.52. Current-frequency relations observed with two ion species as observed in the four-gauze shutter method of the Bristol group. Curve (a) shows the observed record; curves (b) and (c) show the two ion components, unclustered and clustered ions for Li$^+$ ions in Xe at 300° K. Discrimination is such as to detect down to 10% of one ion species.

This finding raises the question as to whether other than the strongly polar molecules can cluster. Light was thrown on this point by the work of R. J. Munson and K. Hoselitz (28). They used the four-gauze method to study the mobilities of alkali ions at low fields in various nonpolar gases, to test for the presence of ions of lowered mobility. The presence of clustering *was observed* at *low temperatures* in *some gases*, and even *at room temperatures* with *Li$^+$ ions in Xe gas*. Figure 1.52 shows at (a) the response curve of the four-gauze mobility device when electrometer current was plotted against frequency in the case of Li$^+$ ions in Xe at room temperatures; (b) and (c) show the breakdown of the curves into two components; (b) for the unclustered, faster ions, and (c) for the slower, clustered ions.

TABLE 1.19

Effect of Temperature on Ion Clustering, Computed by Bristol Group

Ion	Gas	Temp. °K.	$\dfrac{k \text{ ion}}{k \text{ cluster}}$	$C/(1-C)$	n	r	Computed Dissociation Energies in e.v. $1/r \sum_1^r D_r$
Li$^+$	He	20	1.10	> 3	1.8	1	> 0.016
Li$^+$	He	77	1.10	< 1	1.8	1	·=.0.017
Li$^+$	He	90	1.10	—	1.8	1	< 0.080
Li$^+$	Ne	90	1.98	> 1	?	3?	> 0.130
Li$^+$	Ne	195	1.10	< 1/10	?	1?	< 0.160
Li$^+$	A	195	2.38	> 10	2.7	2	> 0.250
Li$^+$	A	290	2.38	< 1/3	2.7	1	< 0.290
Li$^+$	Kr	290	3.09	> 10	2.6	2	> 0.310
Li$^+$	Kr	360	3.09	< 2	2.6	1	< 0.350
Li$^+$	Xe	290	3.84	> 20	2.6	1	> 0.420
K$^+$	A	70	1.00	< 1/10	1.0	1	< 0.060

It is noted that *only two curves appear superposed at one time.* The distance between the successive order peaks for the ions gives the mobility. The relative amplitudes of the curves give the relative amounts of clustered and unclustered ions.

By analyzing the ion stream over a range of values of X/p within which clusters appear, and extrapolating to $X/p = 0$, the fraction C of ions clustered and the mobility of the cluster are obtained. The results are given in table 1.19, in terms of the ion, the gas, and the temperature. In addition are given the ratio of the mobilities of the clustered and unclustered ions; the ratio of fraction of clustered to unclustered ions, $C/(1-C)$; n, the maximum possible number of ions in the cluster from the dispersion curve at the temperature given; r, the probable assumed size of the cluster and the dissociation energy computed for the assumed r from the data. If $C/(1-C) < 0.1$, no clusters were detected, as this was the limit of resolution of the method.

It is noted that the Li$^+$ cluster is more stable at higher temperatures, the larger the molecule and the higher the D. K$^+$ in A showed no clustering at all. Thus, it takes a small, compact ion to hold a clustered nonpolar molecule by dipole attraction. It is suspected that the clustered ions are smaller than those estimated, so that perhaps 2 is the maximum of clustered molecules in these cases. In Ne and He, the size of the ion is important in evaluating k, and thus n probably equals unity. For clustering in He, the resolution of the apparatus was not adequate. However, with Li⁺ in He, the mobility as a function of X/p at 20° K. rose from a value of 1.3 at $X/p = 0$ to 1.4 at $X/p = 20$, and remained there until $X/p = 30$, when it began to increase linearly. This is the effect of the energy of the ion on the free paths, as influenced by forces. The first rise in mobility with X/p is thus ascribed to a clustering. At 290° K. there was no initial rise.

With the number of molecules present in these experiments, the role of the triple impacts in causing the initial clustering already mentioned can be quantitatively tested. Call p the total pressure of mixed gases, p' the partial pressure of Xe, and T the time spent by the lithium ion in reaching the analyzer. It can then be shown that C, the fraction of clustered ions on arrival, is given by $C = 1 - \epsilon^{-\beta T p'}$, where β is a function of a number of quantities, depending on the mechanism of attachment. If a third body is needed and no atom but Xe can be effective, then β is proportional to p'. If any atom can serve, it is proportional to p. As a test, p was varied from 15 to 3 mm and p' from 0.4 to 2.5 mm in He mixtures, in argon mixtures, and in Xe. C, plotted as a function of $pp'T$, puts all points on a single smooth curve within the limits of error, the value being $C = 1 - \epsilon^{-6 \times 10^3 pp'T}$.

Other possible expressions for β were tried, none of which succeeded. Thus, the triple-collision mechanism is indicated with He, A, and Xe equally, probably as third bodies. The value of 6×10^3 and the mean free path of the ion give an opportunity of calculating the radius if the probability of attachment within such a radius is unity. If the charge on the ion is of no effect, which is not strictly true, the radius is 7.5×10^{-8} cm, a reasonable value. It should be noted that the critical radius of triple impact for clustering with inert gases must be of *atomic* dimensions, since unlike the case of clustering with H_2O, there are no vibrational states to absorb the energy temporarily.

Making certain simplified assumptions, Munson and Hoselitz showed that it is possible to calculate the dissociation of the cluster from the ratio of the total clustered ions of 1, 2, 3 atoms to the unclustered ions C_r and C_0, expressed in the form of the relation

$$(1.11b) \quad \frac{C_r}{C_0} = \epsilon^{\sum_1^r \frac{D_r}{kT}} \left[\left(\frac{h^2}{2\pi m k T} \right)^{3/2} N \right]^r \left(\frac{M + rm}{M} \right)^{3/2} \left(\frac{2\pi^3 l_r kT}{h^2} \right).$$

Here D_r is the energy to remove the outermost molecule, and r is the number of ions in the cluster when r is not greater than 3. The masses of ion and gas atom are M and m, with I_r the moment of inertia of the r atom cluster and T the absolute temperature. N is the number of gas atoms to be clustered per cm^3. The Planck constant is designated as h, and k is the Boltzmann constant. From the experimental data were estimated the upper and lower limits for the dissociation energies of the clusters in He, Ne, A, and Kr; while for Xe, with data for one temperature point only, the lower limit was calculated. The calculated values in electron volts have been given in table 1.19. An independent check on these values comes from some data of Lennard-Jones and of Hassé and Cook, regarding the interatomic and ionic forces. For Li^+-He, the value calculated is 0.057 e.v.; and for the K^+-A molecule, 0.058 e.v. These are in satisfactory agreement with the table.

In a third paper belonging to this set, R. J. Munson (39) discussed the change of mobility of the cluster of H_2O molecules about ions from Li^+ to Cs^+ as a function of X/p up to values as high as 120. Certain trends of behavior are indicated, but no new information is added.

§ 10. Mobilities in Mixtures.

With the clarification introduced by the newer data presented, it is now possible to discuss the variations of the mobility in gaseous mixtures. Historically, the first studies were initiated in 1908 by A. Blanc, who measured mobilities of relatively stable ions in mixtures of H_2, air, and CO_2 as a function of the composition of the binary mixtures (47). His measurements led to the simple law called by his name. The law can be derived very simply, as follows.

By experiment and definition, $v = k_A X$ for ions under normal circumstances. Since the mobility k_A is inversely proportional to the gas density, it is possible to express $1/k_A$ by equating it to N_A, the density of gas molecules of type A, and a constant of the ions in gas A, Q_A, such that

$$(1.11c) \qquad \frac{1}{k_A} = Q_A N_A.$$

The impulse per unit time of the field X on the ion of charge e is the force on the ion Xe, which can be written $eX = e\, v/k_A = evQ_A N_A$. The ion is in a steady state of drift motion with a velocity v. Accordingly, $ev\, Q_A N_A$ is the rate of transfer of momentum by the ions to the gas molecules. Thus, an ion of a given drift velocity v transfers a quantity of momentum $ev\, Q_A$ per molecule per unit time to the gas. This transfer takes place only during collisions, which are quite independent because of the large mean free paths and low ion densities. Assume a binary mixture of two gases A and B with concentrations N_A and N_B of their respective molecules, such that $N_A + N_B = N$. The reciprocal of mobilities of the ions of one kind in the individual gases will be $1/k_A = Q_A N_A$ and $1/k_B = Q_B N_B$. If, in the *mixture*, the ions move with a drift velocity $v = k_{AB} X$, then it is possible to write $eX = ev\, Q_A N_A + ev\, Q_B N_B$ as the transfer of momentum to the gas. Thus, the mobility in the mixture k_{AB} is given by

$$\frac{1}{k_{AB}} = \frac{X}{v} = Q_A N_A + Q_B N_B.$$

In consequence, it follows that $1/k_{AB} = (1/k_A + 1/k_B)$. However, by definition of the mobility constants, or reduced mobilities, K_A and K_B, $k_A = K_A(L/N_A)$, $k_B = K_B(L/N_B)$, and $k_{AB} = K_{AB}(L/N)$, where N is the total number of molecules/cm³ in the binary gas mixture and L is the Loschmidt number. Thus,

$$\frac{1}{K_{AB}} \frac{N}{L} = \frac{1}{K_A} \frac{N_A}{L} + \frac{1}{K_B} \frac{N_B}{L} \; ;$$

or better,

$$\frac{1}{K_{AB}} = \frac{f_A}{K_A} + \frac{f_B}{K_B} ,$$

where N_A/N and N_B/N can be set equal to the mole fractions f_A and f_B by dividing through by L. Again, for a binary mixture, $f_B = 1 - f_A$. Blanc's law in its elementary form, therefore, becomes

$$(1.11d) \qquad \frac{1}{K_{AB}} = \frac{f_A}{K_A} + \frac{1-f_A}{K_B} = \frac{f_A K_B + (1-f_A) K_A}{K_A K_B} ,$$

and

$$(1.11e) \qquad K_{AB} = \frac{K_A K_B}{f_A K_B + (1-f_A) K_A} .$$

From this derivation, it is clear that the assumptions underlying the law are:

1. Conservation of momentum.

2. $v = kX$ where k is a constant, the law thus holding for low X/p, where k is constant independent of X/p.

3. Gases of relatively low density, and ions of low density, so that only binary collisions play a role and no ionic interactions occur. This is true if $1/k = QN$.

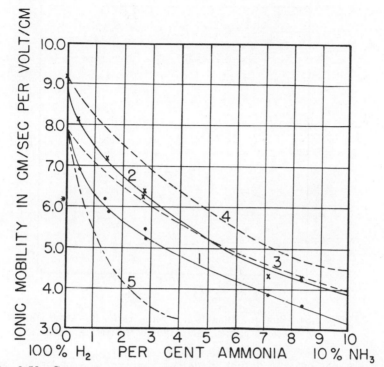

Fig. 1.53. Curves for ionic mobilities K_{AB} of ions in H_2-NH_3 mixtures, as observed by the author. Curve 2 is observed for the negative ions, apparently unaltered by mixing. Blanc's law, computed starting with observed values for K in NH_3 and in H_2, is shown in curve 4. It is seen that mixing causes a deviation from Blanc's law here. The star at 100% H_2 and $K = 6$ is the mobility K^+ of the positive ion in pure H_2. Addition of a trace of NH_3, less than 10^{-2}%, increases K^+ to 7.8. From there on the observed K^+ curve follows curve 1, while Blanc's law, starting at 7.8, would lead to curve 3. Here again a deviation from Blanc's law, indicating more rapid decline in K^+ with percentage of NH_3, occurs as for the negative ion. This deviation was called the "Debye effect" when discovered.

4. The ion retains its identity on mixing; i.e., the ion is the same ion in the mixture that it is in the gases A and B. Thus, for low X/p, the only factor that can cause a deviation from Blanc's law is a change in the nature of the ion with concentration; i.e., deviations occur only if the ion is a labile cluster.

The relation 1.11e for the reduced mobility K_{AB} in the mixture as a function of the concentration of gas B in a mixture, is hyperbolic in form, and if $K_A > K_B$ it will fall from K_A at $f_B = 0$ to K_B at $f_A = 0$. While such a curve is characteristic, small departures from Blanc's

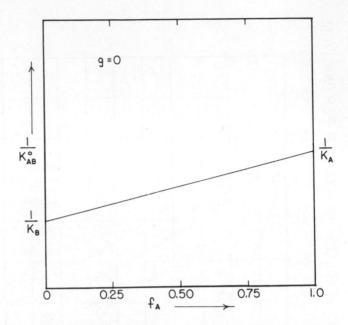

Fig. 1.54. Plot of a Blanc's law curve as for H_2-air mixtures
when $1/K$ is plotted against mole fraction f_A of air.

law are not easy to detect visually. The law was observed experimentally and deduced by Blanc in 1908, and was expected to hold
generally so long as the ions in gases A and B were not changed
in the mixing. By chance, Blanc (47) used mixtures of gases where
this situation obtained. In the early 1920's, when the author (40)
started studies of more heterogeneous mixtures such as of polar and
nonpolar gases, the simple conditions were not met and deviations
from Blanc's law were observed. In order to observe deviations more
clearly, the value of the *reciprocals* of the mobilities may be plotted
against f_B, as shown in equation 1.11d, with

$$R_{AB} = \frac{1}{K_{AB}} = \frac{f_B K_A + (1 - f_B) K_B}{K_A K_B}.$$

This relation is linear in f_B. If $K_A > K_B$, then the curve of $1/K_{AB}$ rises
linearly from $1/K_A$, the lower value at $f_B = 0$ to $1/K_B$, the higher value
at $f_B = 1$ and $f_A = 0$. Any departure from Blanc's law will stand out
very sharply in this form of plot.

Figure 1.53 shows the curves for positive and negative ions in
NH_3-H_2 mixtures, plotted in terms of K_{AB} against f_B, the concentration of NH_3. Note that the negative ion follows the full curve 2,

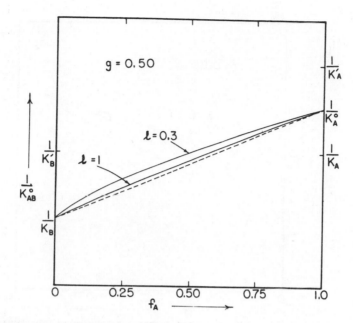

Fig. 1.55. Curves for $1/K_{AB}$ against mole fraction f_A in a mixture of gases A and B. Dashed curve is for Blanc's law. Parameters l and g, as well as the values $1/K_B'$, $1/K_A'$, and $1/K_A^0$ are derived from a theory of Overhauser. Here $g = 0.50$ and $l = 0.3$ and 1.

while Blanc's law predicts the dashed curve 4. The positive ion in pure H_2 has a mobility of about 6, indicated by the star. The addition of traces of NH_3 gives a *new* mobility around 7.8, indicating the formation of an NH_3^+ complex ion or cluster. This ion *appears stable* thereafter and follows the full curve 1, while Blanc's law would follow the dashed curve 3, even starting with an ion of increased mobility 7.8. The influence of the impurity on the whole curve plotted as $1/K_{AB}$ is illustrated for Blanc's law in the generalized plot of figure 1.54, which is linear.

The type of curve to be expected by plotting the observed curves of figure 1.55 for NH_3 in this way, is shown by the curves for $l = 0.3$, $g = 0.50$; and $l = 1$ and 0.3 for $g = 0.80$, in figures 1.56 and 1.57. When the author observed such curves, he discussed them with P. Debye, who at the time was working on his theory of solutions. Debye suggested that this effect could be caused by some sort of *statistical* clustering produced by an increased density of molecules about the ion in virtue of the force field $(D-1)e^2/2\pi N r^5$ on such polar mole-

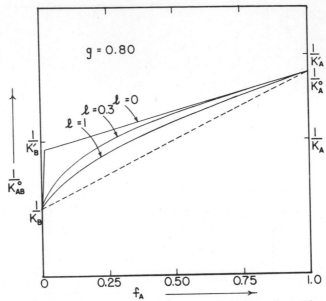

Fig. 1.56. Overhauser's computed curves for deviations from Blanc's law with $g = 0.80$, and $l = 0$, 0.3, and 1. The $l = 0$ curve is offset at the origin to indicate its change with traces of gas B.

cules. Such a *statistical* cluster *differs* from the labile one in that, unlike a labile cluster, the molecules are not bound semipermanently to the ion, but appear as a clouds of increased density whose molecules change continually as the ion moves in the gas. E. U. Condon put the expression for this increased density produced by the force field into equation form, using the Boltzmann law for change of concentration in a force field.

The author attempted to develop this into a relation, giving a chance for quantitative test with observation, but was only partially successful. More recently, A. W. Overhauser showed that such a statistical clustering properly applied could give curves analogous to those observed. He also showed that (unfortunately) the values of the mobilities used in deriving Blanc's law (*supra*) already include the retarding influence of the statistical cluster, so that this factor may not be invoked again, as in the author's or Overhauser's initial treatment. In a recent paper, Overhauser (48) has formally proved that statistical clustering cannot be invoked to account for the Debye effect, and in place of this has substituted a proper theory of the effect.

In the last set of papers from the Bristol group, H. G. David and

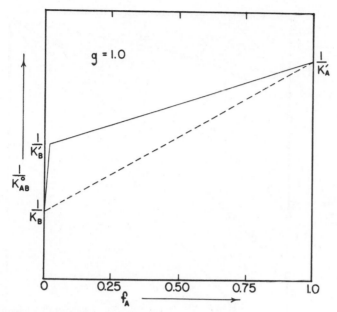

Fig. 1.57. Overhauser's computed curves for deviation from Blanc's law for $g = 1.0$. The full curve is offset at the origin to indicate change with traces of gas B.

R. J. Munson (39) present the results of their measurements of the mobilities of the alkali ions Li^+, K^+, and Cs^+ in He, A, Kr, and Xe with polar water vapor mixtures as a function of the concentration of water vapor. They substantiated the author's findings, regarding both the formation of complex ions and the curvilinear departure from Blanc's law. Typical results for Li^+ ions in the series of inert gases listed, are shown in figure 1.58, plotted as $1/K_{AB}$ against the percentage of water vapor. The value of $1/K_{AB}$ at very small percentages of H_2O vapor represents the already clustered, or better, the complex ion. In He, Blanc's law is followed, but deviations increase progressively in the heavier gases, reaching a maximum in Xe. In this paper, the authors came to the conclusion (later reached independently by Overhauser (48), and formally deduced in his paper) that the Debye effect, or bowing of the curves, cannot be due to a statistical clustering, since this effect is already included in the mobility theory of Langevin. They proposed, however, that the bowing in plots of $1/K_{AB}$ for mixtures must be accounted for by the change in the average size of the labile clusters, previously inferred by them, as the concentration of water vapor increases. While their

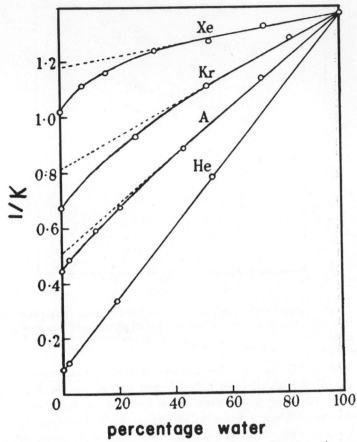

Fig. 1.58. Bristol results of a study of $1/K$ as a function of percentage of H_2O vapor for Li^+ in He, A, Kr, and Xe, showing deviations from Blanc's law.

observations were qualitatively discussed on this basis, no quantitative theory was proposed. Later, Overhauser arrived at the same conclusion quite independently, and worked out the quantitative theory on simple assumptions which in part are given here.

Assume, in agreement with the previous deductions, that since the mobility of ions is inversely proportional to the density of gas molecules N, $1/k$ can be set equal to QN, i.e., $1/k = QN$, and that the reduced mobility or mobility constant may be defined by the relation $1/K = QL$, where L is the Loschmidt number. If a gas is composed of N_A molecules per cm³ of constant Q_A, and N_B molecules per cm^3 of constant Q_B, then, if the nature of the ions does not change on mixing, the mobility in the mixture will be given by

$$\frac{1}{k_{AB}} = Q_A N_A + Q_B N_B .$$

The mole fractions f_A and f_B are given by $f_B = N_B/(N_A + N_B)$, and $f_A = N_A/(N_A + N_B)$. The reduced mobility is thus given by

$$\frac{1}{K_{AB}} = \frac{f_A}{K_A} + \frac{f_B}{K_B} ,$$

which again is Blanc's law.

The effect of a labile-cluster formation in a pure, active gas A must now be considered. Assume that in drifting through the gas, an ion I can combine with 1 molecule of gas A, say NH_3 or H_2O, to form a new ion I', such that $I' = I + A$. Assume also that as I' drifts through the gas, it can be dissociated to I by molecular impacts. The ion, as it moves through the gas, is thus part of the time an ion I', and part of the time an ion I. This can occur if $\beta PE/KE \sim 1$. The mobilities of I and I' will be designated as k_A and k_A', and the reduced mobilities as K_A and K_A'. The observed mobility will not be either of these, but will have a value k_A^o such that $k_A' < k_A^o < k_A$. The value of k_A^o will depend on the relative distances that the ion drifts as I or I'. Call x the average distance the ion drifts as I, and x' the average distance it drifts as I'. The observed reduced mobility will be

(1.12)
$$\frac{1}{K_A^o} = \frac{x}{(x + x') K_A} + \frac{x'}{(x + x') K_A'} .$$

It is possible to define a new quantity, the *clustering coefficient* of ion I in gas A, as

(1.13)
$$g = \frac{1}{1 + x/x'} .$$

Equation 1.12 then becomes

(1.14)
$$\frac{1}{K_A^o} = \frac{(1-g)}{K_A} + \frac{g}{K_A'} .$$

The clustering coefficient may now be evaluated in terms of the clustering process. Call μ_A the probability per collision that the ion I will change to I' in collision with gas A. Let ν_A be the probability per collision that ion I' will dissociate to form I as a result of impacts with the gas. The quantities μ_A and ν_A will depend upon temperature and upon the nature of the materials involved. It will be assumed that they are independent of the pressure of the gas.

This is justified, inasmuch as David and Munson refer $1/K$ to the already clustered gas; i.e., they assume that the first molecule of H_2O has already added. This apparently requires a triple collision, and is temperature- and pressure-dependent, while the second H_2O molecule can add on impact. Call $\bar{x}$ the mean distance that the ion I drifts in the field direction before it associates to form I', and $\bar{x}'$ the mean distance I drifts before it dissociates to I.

The collision frequency of I with A molecules is $Z_A = \bar{c}_A \sigma_A N_A$, where $\bar{c}_A$ is the mean relative velocity and σ_A is the collision cross section. The time spent in traversing 1 cm in the field direction is $t_A = 1/k_A X = Q_A N_A/X$. Thus,

$$\bar{x} = \frac{1}{Z_A t_A \mu_A} = \frac{X}{\bar{c}_A \sigma_A Q_A N_A^2 \mu_A};$$

and similarly,

$$\bar{x}' = \frac{X}{\bar{c}_A' \sigma_A' Q_A' N_A^2 \nu_A}.$$

Thus,

(1.15)
$$p = \frac{\bar{x}}{\bar{x}'} = \frac{x}{x'} = \frac{\bar{c}_A' \sigma_A' Q_A' \nu_A}{\bar{c}_A \sigma_A Q_A \mu_A},$$

and

(1.16)
$$g = \frac{1}{(1 + p)}.$$

Since p is independent of N_A, so is g. Thus, $1/K_A^0$ is proportional to N_A in active gases as well as in inactive gases, which follows from the assumption that μ_A and ν_A are independent of N_A. It would be expected that ν_A is independent of N_A from the nature of the process. Were the question of cluster formation one involving the first molecule of A, the previous work of Tyndall and associates indicates that a triple impact would occur. Thus, μ_A would be given by $\mu_A = a N_A$. However, the present evidence is that with a complex ion, the energy of association of a further molecule can be accommodated in the system until the next impact, so that this assumption is not warranted here. Thus, μ_A would be assumed constant.

It is now possible to consider what occurs if the active gas A is mixed with an inactive gas B; e.g., H_2O (an active gas) and Ne (an inactive one). The ions I and I' do not cluster with B molecules, so that $\mu_B = 0$. On the other hand, collisions of $I' = I + A$ with B molecules can dissociate I' to I with a dissociation probability ν_B, which will differ from ν_A because of differences in mass, etc. In the mixed gas, l and l' will have different mobilities, given by

$$\frac{1}{k_{AB}} = Q_A N_A + Q_B N_B;$$

$$\frac{1}{k'_{AB}} = Q'_A N_A + Q'_B N_B.$$

Calling y the average total distance that the ion drifts as l in this mixture, and the quantity y' the corresponding quantity for l', the mobility k_{AB}° observed will be

$$\frac{1}{k_{AB}^{\circ}} = \frac{y}{(y+y') k_{AB}} + \frac{y'}{(y+y') k'_{AB}}.$$

For l', the time to drift 1 cm in the field direction is

$$t = \frac{1}{k_{AB} X} = (Q_A N_A + Q_B N_B)/X.$$

The collision frequency of l with A molecules is $Z_A = \bar{c}_A \sigma_A N_A$. These expressions lead to a value of $\bar{y}$ (the mean distance that l drifts before attaching) given by $\bar{y} = X/(Q_A N_A + Q_B N_B) \bar{c}_A \sigma_A N_A \mu_A$. For l', t' is correspondingly given by $t' = 1/k'_{AB} X = (Q'_A N_A + Q'_B N_B)/X$, and for collision with molecules A and B, $Z'_A = \bar{c}'_A \sigma'_A N_A$ and $Z'_B = \bar{c}'_B \sigma'_B N_B$, respectively. The quantities $\bar{c}'_A$ and $\bar{c}'_B$ are different, being mean relative velocities. These quantities lead to the values

$$\bar{y}' = 1/(Z'_A \nu_A + Z'_B \nu_B) t'$$

and

$$\frac{y}{y'} = \frac{\bar{y}}{\bar{y}'} = \frac{(Q'_A N_A + Q'_B N_B)(\bar{c}'_A \sigma'_A N_A \nu_A + \bar{c}'_B \sigma'_B N_B \nu_B)}{(Q_A N_A + Q_B N_B) \bar{c}_A \sigma_A N_A \mu_A}.$$

From the latter expression and the relation for k_{AB}°, the equation for K_{AB}°, the reduced mobility in the binary mixture, with $N_A + N_B = L$, is given as

$$(1.17) \quad \frac{1}{K_{AB}^{\circ}} = \frac{\left(\dfrac{f_A}{K_A} + \dfrac{f_B}{K_B}\right)\left(\dfrac{f_A}{K'_A} + \dfrac{f_B}{K'_B}\right)\left[f_A + (f_A + l f_B) \dfrac{K'_A}{K_A} \dfrac{1-g}{g}\right]}{\left(\dfrac{f_A}{K_A} + \dfrac{f_B}{K_B}\right) f_A + \left(\dfrac{f_A}{K'_A} + \dfrac{f_B}{K'_B}\right)(f_A + l f_B) \dfrac{K'_A}{K_A} \dfrac{1-g}{g}}.$$

This expression is a function of the mole fractions, the reduced mobilities of l and l' in gases A and B, and two characteristic constants g and l. The quantity g is the *clustering coefficient* of I in pure gas A. It is given by

(1.18)
$$g = 1 \Big/ \left(1 + \frac{\bar{c}'_A \, \sigma'_A \, Q'_A \, \nu_A}{\bar{c}_A \, \sigma_A \, Q_A \, \mu_A} \right).$$

It can have values ranging from $g = 0$ to $g = 1$, where stable clusters form. The quantity l is a *dissociation parameter*, and is a measure of the relative efficiencies of A and B molecules in causing dissociation on impact. Its value is

(1.19)
$$l = \frac{\bar{c}'_B \, \sigma'_B}{\bar{c}'_A \, \sigma'_A \, \nu_A},$$

which can have any positive value. Unless the gases have very disparate masses, l will be close to unity.

The solutions of the equation for suitably chosen values of K_A, K'_A, K_B, and K'_B for several values of g and l, are shown in figures 1.54, 1.55, 1.56, and 1.57. In figure 1.54, with $g = 0$, the conventional Blanc's law appears as $K_A = K'_A$, $K_B = K'_B$, and $g = 0$. When $g = 0.50$, as in figure 1.55, a slight curvature is apparent which increases as l decreases. When $g = 0.80$, as in figure 1.56, the bowing is marked and the *limiting curve* for no declustering, $l = 0$, is composed of two linear elements, one of which is displaced from the vertical to indicate its presence. Figure 1.57 shows the linear relation for $g = 1.0$, immediate clustering, from ion I' of mobility K'_B, in pure gas B, to I' in pure gas A, with mobility K'_A. Again the vertical rise is displaced from the vertical to indicate what occurs.

Reference to the literature recording experiments on the subject will indicate that this theory is capable of describing all the types of curves observed. The equation assuming *only one molecule attached*, at least *in form*, can account for observed phenomena. With six arbitrary constants, K_A, K_B, K'_A, K'_B, g, and l, one could fit almost any observed curve. In practice, however, these constants are not all arbitrary. With data such as are possible in the experiments with the four-gauze method and the use of known ions, it is possible to estimate or know some or all of the mobilities involved. Direct measurement of the mobilities of the ions in gas A as a function of X/p should yield values of K_A and K'_A, as indicated by Munson and Tyndall (39). K_B could be directly measured by choosing ideal conditions, but with difficulty. In any event, from the values of K_A and K'_A by use of Langevin's equation, assuming relatively few ions in the cluster, some predictions can be made as to K_B and K'_B. If $l \ll 1$, then K_B' can be obtained. With K_A and K_A' known, a measurement of K_A^o will evaluate g as

$$g = \frac{(1/K_A^o - 1/K_A)}{(1/K_A' - 1/K_A)}$$

Then, with estimates of K_B and K_B', the quantity l may be evaluated.

It will be seen that a simplified theory such as Overhauser's will serve to clarify the question of ion mobilities in general, even including those in mixtures. While it is doubtful whether some of the ions considered in these studies consist of merely the positive alkali ion nucleus plus one H_2O or polar molecule for the first complex, and that the ion $l = Li^+ + H_2O$, while $l' = Li^+ + 2H_2O$, as pictured above, it is seen that such an hypothesis can serve to assist in the analysis. More complete studies of the values of the mobilities in different gas combinations and at varying X/p, and perhaps over extended temperature ranges, should furnish enough independent relations for a more exact and complete analysis of cluster size, heat of association, collision cross sections and probabilities and mechanisms of ion formation and behavior. In principle, the problems have been fairly delineated and present no major difficulty.

§ 11. Generalized Theory of Motion of Ions through Gases.

During the preparation of the later chapters of this book, an able mathematical physicist of the modern school, Dr. G. H. Wannier of the Bell Telephone Laboratories staff, became interested in the problem of the motion of ions in gases at higher values of X/p, in connection with the experiments of his colleagues J. A. Hornbeck and J. P. Molnar. His very excellent *general* analysis of the mobilities and diffusion coefficients in gases so impressed the author that he invited Wannier to contribute a section of his material to this book. After the section was released, the time elapsed in the completion of later chapters permitted Wannier to extend the study far beyond the stage at which his study was submitted. Some conclusions of Wannier's (32), (79), (87) have already appeared in print under his own name and in connection with papers of Hornbeck, Hornbeck and Wannier, and of R. N. Varney, the latter three having been discussed earlier in this chapter.

The complete analysis to date has appeared in an 85-page article published in the *Bell System Technical Journal* for January, 1953 (87). This general analysis of the problem throws so much light on the nature and meaning of the several theories that it must be given. Since there is hardly room for such an extended treatment in this book, and as the earlier section of Wannier's is out of date, there will be given only the introductory qualitative remarks in the later article in Wannier's own words, followed by an outline of the essential content of the subsequent study. The latter paraphrases Wannier's excellent comments without recourse to the mathematical details. For the mathematical procedures in detail, the interested reader must consult the original monograph.

♦ ♦ ♦ ♦ ♦

Quoting from Wannier:

Part I — General Theory of Strong Field Motion

I*a. Qualitative Discussion.*

It is well known that if we consider a mixture of gases under no external forces, the steady velocity distribution which establishes itself in the mixture does not depend on the interactions between the gas molecules; we have always a Maxwellian distribution for each species, with a temperature common to all. This result arises from statistical mechanics; the derivation of it is simple and requires few assumptions, yet it enjoys a wide degree of generality. As soon, however, as a nonequilibrium feature is imposed upon the system this simplicity vanishes, and the subject acquires ramifications. Results must now be derived by kinetic theory. The amount of labor required increases, while, at the same time, the result achieved becomes less general.

A mixture of charged particles (ions or electrons; in the following often simply referred to as ions) and gas molecules can in principle never be in equilibrium, since the presence of the former in itself represents an instability. However, one might expect that equilibrium exists in a restricted sense, for instance, as regards motion. Even this is rarely the case under actual conditions of observation. The nonequilibrium features of greatest importance for analyzing ion motion are a constant force (electric field) acting upon one species but not the other (mobility theory), and a concentration gradient for one particular species (diffusion theory). It is the purpose of this paper to apply kinetic theory to these problems, and to compute with its help most important properties which such a gas of charged particles possesses. The work will be distinguished from similar ones in that the electric field will not be supposed weak; velocity distributions which have no resemblance to the Maxwellian distribution will thus make their appearance. Furthermore, the mass of the charged particles will not be assumed small, which means the possibility of getting results for gaseous ions as well as electrons.

Magnetic fields, plasma, and a.c. phenomena will, however, be excluded. The quantities of interest under those conditions are the drift velocity of the ions, their energy, energy partition, and diffusion constants. These quantities will be calculated by assuming plausible mechanical models. The work just outlined has been published in part in abbreviated form in the *Physical Review* (87); the exposition to follow will, however, proceed independently from these articles.

Much of the work which concerns itself with transport processes in gases makes use of perturbation theory. This method permits us to predict the behavior of a gaseous assembly under an electric field or a concentration gradient in the limit when the field or the gradient is vanishingly small. The result of so perturbing a Maxwellian distribution can be expressed through certain constants, such as the mobility or the diffusion coefficient, which involve the Maxwellian distribution *and* the internal interactions, but not the perturbation itself.

The limits of such a procedure can easily be estimated. In the case of an electric field, perturbation techniques apply if the kinetic energy acquired by the ion from the field is small compared to thermal energy. This means at least that the energy acquired in one mean free path be small, i.e.,

$$eX\lambda \ll kT,$$

where e is the electronic charge, X the electric field, k Boltzmann's constant, T the absolute temperature, and λ the mean free path. Actually, the situation is not even that favorable. If the mass of the ions and the molecules is very different, the energy transferred upon collision is small, and hence the ions possess the ability to store the acquired energy through many collisions; for this reason, the inequality reads more properly

$$\left(\frac{M}{m} + \frac{m}{M}\right)eX\lambda \ll kT,$$

where m is the mass of the ions and M the mass of the gas molecules. After some substitutions this estimate becomes

$$(1.20) \qquad \left(\frac{M}{m} + \frac{m}{M}\right)eX \ll p\sigma,$$

where p is the true gas pressure and σ the collision cross section.

Taking as an example an ion traveling in the parent gas, we find

$$\frac{X}{p} \ll 2\frac{\sigma}{e} \sim 2 \cdot \frac{4\pi \cdot 10^{-16}}{5 \cdot 10^{-10}} = 5 \cdot 10^{-6} \text{ e.s.u.,}$$

or, in commonly employed units,

$$\frac{X}{p} \ll 2 \text{ volt/cm (mm Hg).}$$

It is clear that this limit is often surpassed in experimental situations.

The cases in which the limit 1.20 is applicable are of no further interest here because they are well covered in the literature (50). A field will be called "low" when it satisfies the criterion 1.20 and "high" when the inequality is reversed. It is important to notice that a fixed field at a fixed gas density may shift from "low" to "high" through a drop in temperature.

All calculations to follow will contain the assumption of "low ion concentration" which is often made in studies of this sort. It means that all effects which ions exert upon each other are neglected. The equation for the distribution function of ionic velocities is then linear instead of quadratic. It is clear that this simplification presents great advantages from the point of view of calculation.

In deriving a criterion for the validity of this assumption, we must distinguish two types of effects of the ions upon each other. The first is the space-charge effect. In this effect the ions at large distances make the major contribution. Its magnitude depends on apparatus dimensions. The criterion for no space-charge distortion of the field X is

$$(1.21) \qquad\qquad n \ll \frac{X}{4\pi e \Lambda} ,$$

where n is the number density of the ions and Λ a suitable length chosen from apparatus dimensions. Inequality 1.21 is quite stringent, because it predicts field distortions at values of n of the order of 10^8 cm^{-3}. This is the value at which it will become impossible, or at least difficult, to make significant experimental measurements. But from the point of view of theory this criterion is not relevant. Space charge does not change the character of the velocity distribution of the ions, because the type of ion-ion interaction producing the space-charge field is long-range and creates only a smooth modification of the electric field, which we may presume to have been included in the original field. What we are concerned with here are ion-ion interactions which have a random character, and thus are apt to upset a velocity distribution derived from the "low-concentra-tion" theory. From this point of view, neighboring ions are most effective because their relative location fluctuates rapidly, and hence, the Coulomb force between them will induce mutual scattering. The magnitude of this force is of the order $e^2 n^{2/3}$ where n is the number density of the ions. It is known from theory (51), (52), that the effect of a Coulomb force is preferably not represented by discrete "colli-sions," but by a continuous bending of the entire path. Thus, we come to the conclusion that random ion-ion forces have no effect if the force given above cannot produce a significant deflection in one mean free path. This means

(1.22) $$e^2 n^{2/3} \lambda \ll \text{mean ion energy.}$$

According to whether we are in the high or low field region, we get different criteria from this. At low field the thermal energy predomi-nates, and we get

(1.23a) $$e^2 n^{2/3} \ll p\sigma.$$

At high field the "field" energy predominates, and we get

(1.23b) $$e^2 n^{2/3} \ll eX \left(\frac{M}{m} + \frac{m}{M} \right).$$

A rough evaluation of inequality (1.23a) for one mm Hg pressure gives

$$n^{2/3} \ll \frac{10^3 \cdot 4\pi \cdot 10^{-16}}{25 \cdot 10^{-20}} = \frac{1}{2} \cdot 10^7 \text{ cm}^{-2};$$

$$n \ll 10^{10} \text{ particles/cm}^3.$$

This corresponds to a current of about 10^{15} particles/cm^2 sec or $200 \, \mu$ amps/cm^2. At lower pressure the criterion becomes more strin-gent. Equation 1.23b gives similar results.

It is appropriate to survey at this point the past theoretical work treating the "low-concentration" theory of ionic motion for arbitrary fields. A rather complete body of work exists for electrons where the following three assumptions seem appropriate: (a) that the mass of an "ion" is very small compared to the mass of a molecule; (b) that the total kinetic energy is conserved in each encounter; and (c) that the angular distribution is isotropic in the center of mass system.

These three assumptions lead to a distribution law given by

Chapman and Cowling (53). The law has considerable flexibility, because it permits the substitution of an arbitrary relationship connecting mean free path and speed of encounter. In addition, it contains no assumption as to whether we have low or high field. A more specialized and explicit distribution law is obtained if we assume in addition: (d) that the collision cross section is independent of the speed of encounter (hard sphere approximation); and (e) that we deal with the high field case only. The special law resulting in this case is the distribution law of Druyvesteyn.

If an improvement over the Chapman-Cowling distribution for electrons is desired, account should be taken of inelastic collisions; that is, assumption (b) should be discarded. Work in that direction has been carried out by Smit (54), Allen (55), and others.

The assumption to be discarded first in theory of ionic motion is, of course, assumption (a). In order to understand what this implies, we must understand what advantages assumption (a) has in a calculation. In the limit when the ionic mass is very small, the encounters with gas molecules become such that momentum is lost quickly, but energy is accumulated in the form of random motion. As a result of this, we end up with a distribution function which is very nearly spherically symmetrical in velocity space. Such a situation permits obvious procedures through which the entire calculation is simplified. These procedures will not longer be available when assumption (a) is dropped.

Knowledge concerning the structure of the velocity-distribution function for gaseous ions is practically nonexistent at this time. Hershey, who deals with the motion of ions in the high-field case, simply substitutes for it a Maxwellian distribution with an unknown offset of the origin and unknown temperature parameter (9). He then computes these two parameters by applying the laws of conservation of momentum and kinetic energy. It is to be expected that this procedure should give reasonable values for the mobility and the mean energy of the ion; indeed, if we consider the polarization force only, we get *exactly* the right values; the reason for this is that one may evaluate velocity averages for inverse fifth-power forces, ignoring the distribution function (87), and that he did this in effect for the drift velocity and the total energy. In order to test whether an offset Maxwellian distribution is a satisfactory approximation, we have to go one step farther and examine the partition of the energy among the three degrees of freedom. There we find Hershey's distribution in error, for he assumes equipartition for the random motion, while in reality, the random energy parallel to the field is much higher than at right angles (87), giving the distribution a decided "ridge" structure. This discrepancy could be taken into account by the use of an elliptically distorted Maxwellian distribution, and this may prove to be convenient in some applications.

For a detailed knowledge of the distribution function, it is necessary to specify the interaction between an ion and a molecule. This interaction can be, broadly speaking, summarized under three headings: (a) the polarization force; (b) the short-distance repulsion; and (c) symmetry effects. The polarization force arises because an ion, when passing close to a molecule, induces on it a dipole moment; this moment is then attracted by the charge of the ion. The attractive force F resulting from this is

$$(1.24) \qquad F = \frac{2e^2 P}{r^5} = \frac{e^2(D-1)}{2\pi N r^5},$$

where $P = (D-1)/4\pi N$ is the polarizability of a gas molecule and e the charge of the ion. The force varies inversely as the fifth power of the distance r; for such a force the cross section σ varies inversely as the speed of encounter u. Whenever the cross section shows this type of variation, it is advantageous to define a mean free time τ rather than a mean free path λ. The formula is

$$(1.25) \qquad \tau = \frac{1}{N\sigma u}.$$

There is a standard difficulty which arises when one tries to make use of a formula of the type 1.25. For most force laws, a total cross section σ cannot be defined; a differential cross section per unit solid angle always exists, but it becomes infinite in the forward direction because of small deflections suffered by particles passing by each other at a large distance. Thus, equation 1.25 is, strictly speaking, meaningless. This is actually never a difficulty in the computation of a physical quantity. However, equation 1.25 is convenient for order-of-magnitude thinking, and the question arises how it can be reasonably interpreted. The general method of salvaging 1.25—excluding a small forward cone from consideration—is of little value for this purpose. An analysis of the inverse fourth-power attractive potential shows a better way out. The potential gives rise to two kinds of orbits: orbits of large angular momentum, which look somewhat like hyperbolas, shown in figure 1.59 at "a"; and orbits of small angular momentum for which the particles are "sucked" toward each other in a spiraling movement until a repulsive force

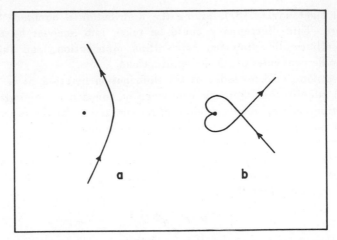

Fig. 1.59. Characteristic orbit types for atoms interacting with polarization forces. At "a" is shown the open, hyperbola-like orbit when relative velocity is great. At "b" appear the spiraling orbits with high polarization forces at low energies.

reverses the trend, as shown in figure 1.59 at "b."[20] A calculation of Hassé (15) shows that the latter type of motion is much more efficient in scattering than the former, and one gets therefor a picture which is semiquantitatively correct if one substitutes into equation 1.25 the cross section for spiraling collisions and assumes isotropic scattering (87). This cross section equals

$$(1.26) \qquad \sigma = 2\pi \sqrt{\frac{1}{m} + \frac{1}{M}} \; \frac{\sqrt{P}\,e}{u}$$

A numerical estimate of the cross section 1.26 automatically leads one to compare it with the short-distance repulsion familiar from the kinetic theory of gases. The two are of the same order, but for the usual gaseous speeds (which enter into 1.26 through u) and small molecules, the cross section 1.26 is bigger. This situation is accentuated in an actual scattering calculation, which shows an attractive force to be generally more efficient than a repulsive force of equal range.

A detailed numerical discussion of these questions is found in Massey and Mohr (56) for the case of He^+ ions moving through He gas. Their interest is in the low-field mobility. They show that for this problem the repulsive force makes so little difference that it could be neglected entirely without much affecting the results. It does finally come out that the polarization force gives a mobility

---

[20]There are quantum-mechanical analogues to these classical ideas; they should lead to practically identical answers unless the angular-momentum quantum number is small.

which is too big by a factor of 2. But the additional scattering is due to an effect which we listed above under (c): namely, a resonance attraction between the He atom and the He^+ ion for which the cross section is abnormally large. It should be possible to eliminate this effect by increasing the cross section 1.26 until it masks even this special effect. Lowering the field is not sufficient to achieve this because of the temperature motion; it would be necessary in addition to reduce the absolute temperature by a sizable factor and so to decrease the value of u in 1.26. Thus, we are led to the prediction that if the temperature of He is reduced, the mobility of He^+ ions in He should gradually rise from its "anomalous" value of 12 $cm^2/volt$ sec to the "normal" value of 22 $cm^2/volt$ sec, which one gets by taking account of polarization forces only.

(End of excerpt from Wannier's paper.)

♦   ♦   ♦   ♦   ♦

After a suitable glossary of notations which is part I*b*, Wannier proceeds to give a formal survey of the theory in part I*c*. He indicates that the motion of the carriers in the gas may be described by their density in phase space. The change in time of this function is described by a Boltzmann equation. The various terms in this equation are discussed, especially the second and third terms on the left-hand side, which arise from an electric field and a density variation. Assuming the density variation to be sufficiently small, the third term can be treated by perturbation theory, while the field term is so large that the equilibrium distribution no longer represents a first approximation to the solution. The equation is solved in two stages. (1) Only the second term on the left is retained, and the resulting equation is treated rigorously. (2) The field equation is used, but the new terms are taken as perturbations.

If field and density are assumed uniform and time-independent, the dependence on the position vector and time drop out. This enables a distribution function dependent on the electrical field causing acceleration to be obtained, hereafter referred to as equation A. It differs from the Maxwellian distribution in that it is not symmetric about the origin. The vectorial mean of the velocity is therefore not zero: $\langle \vec{c} \rangle = f(\vec{c})\, \vec{c}\, d\vec{c} \neq 0$. This is the drift velocity of the ion in the field, which is reached as a compromise between acceleration $\vec{a} = \vec{X}e/m$ and frictional losses caused by carrier-atom collisions. The structure of equation A indicates that the velocity depends on the gas density and the field, only through $Xe/mN = a/N$. Here a is the acceleration and N is the number density of *molecules*. Thus, the velocity depends on the well-known factor X/p_0 of experiment.

This also applies to the mean energy and other averages of the energy-distribution function.

It is further noted that a more important formal prediction can be made about the second stage of the contemplated computation. It will be shown that the diffusion concept is still applicable in a strong electric field. It is true that if there is a variable density in space, the primary motion observed is not diffusive, but a displacement of the entire density pattern with the drift velocity v_x. However, once this dominant component is subtracted out, then a supplementary current proportional to the density gradient is identified. The constant of proportionality is anisotropic; i.e., there is a diffusion tensor rather than a diffusion coefficient. The tensor is axially symmetric about the field direction, yielding a longitudinal and a transverse diffusion coefficient. This is then demonstrated mathematically, assuming a special type of variation of ion density in space, and leads to the second or diffusion equation hereafter designated as equation B.

Part Id is devoted to a dimensional analysis in a qualitative discussion of the two equations A and B set up for solution; equation A involving the motion in the field, and equation B involving the diffusive motion. The results derived in such a study are of value in solving the equations at a later point. To do this, the two limiting cases of high and low field must be borne in mind. Some assumptions must further be made about $\sigma(u)$, the *collision cross section* that is a function of the *speed of encounter* u, and $\Pi(\chi)$, the probability of scattering, which is unity for isotropic scattering—both of which terms occur under the integral sign in equation A. It is convenient to make $\Pi(\chi)$ independent of u. This happens to be true for two models treated in detail; the polarization force model and the hard sphere model. Actually, $\Pi(\chi)$ can be taken as approximately independent of u in a wider sense. The forces which produce scattering are either repulsive or short-range attractive; i.e., long-range attractive forces are absent. When this is the case, the scattering is roughly isotropic and hence can change little with u.

To dispose of $\sigma(u)$, it is assumed that $\sigma(u)u^{\alpha} = \Gamma$ where α and Γ are constants. This assumption has two important special cases which arise, taking $\alpha = 0$ and $\alpha = 1$. The case $\alpha = 0$ is that of a constant mean free path as exemplified by a hard sphere model. The case $\alpha = 1$ is that of a constant mean free time. It is applicable to the polarization force. When the restriction imposed on $\sigma(u)$ is introduced into equation A, the quantities $Xe/m = $ a, N, and Γ enter only in the combination $Xe/mN\Gamma = $ a$/N\Gamma$. The quantity $(a/N\Gamma)^{1/(2-\alpha)}$ has the dimensions of a velocity. A second such quantity is $(kT/M)^{1/2}$, which arises from the Maxwellian functions (pertaining to the molecules) under the integral sign. In the high-field case, the latter quantity does not enter. That is, the velocity-distribution functions for the molecules could be replaced by δ functions at the origin. Thus, the first combination controls all velocity averages, so that it is possible to write for the mean drift velocity,

$$\langle v_x \rangle = \text{const} \left(\frac{a}{N\Gamma} \right)^{\frac{1}{2-\alpha}}.$$

This gives the variation of the drift velocity with the field X. For the two special values of α, the explicit expressions follow.

For constant free path, $\alpha = 0$.

$$\langle v_x \rangle = \text{const } a^{\frac{1}{2}} \lambda^{\frac{1}{2}} = \text{const} \left(\frac{Xe}{m} \lambda \right)^{\frac{1}{2}},$$

where drift velocity varies as $\sqrt{X}$, $k \propto 1/\sqrt{X}$; and for constant free time, $\alpha = 1$.

$$\langle v_x \rangle = \text{const } a\tau = \text{const} \frac{Xe}{m} \tau,$$

where the drift velocity is proportional to X (k is constant).

In the low-field case, one of the two velocity parameters $(kT/M)^{\frac{1}{2}}$ cannot be disregarded. Then equation A is to be solved by perturbation theory only. It then yields a drift velocity varying as $a/N\Gamma = Xe/mN\Gamma$, i.e., with the first power of X/p.

Dimensional analysis also yields the variation of mobility with temperature, for which case

$$\langle v_x \rangle = \text{const} \frac{Xe}{mN\Gamma} \left(\frac{kT}{M} \right)^{\frac{\alpha-1}{2}},$$

with the special cases

$$\langle v_x \rangle = \text{const } a\lambda \left(\frac{kT}{M} \right)^{-\frac{1}{2}} = \text{const} \frac{Xe}{M} \lambda \left(\frac{kT}{M} \right)^{-\frac{1}{2}}$$

for constant free path $\alpha = 0$; and

$$\langle v_x \rangle = \text{const } a\tau = \text{const} \frac{Xe}{m} \tau$$

for constant mean free time $\alpha = 1$.

It will be noted that for both cases of $\alpha = 0$ in high and low fields, the expression for $<v_x>$ is the same. This is later shown to follow from the more complete solution in Wannier's part IIIa.

The diffusion problem requires the addition of the quantity $nk/N\Gamma$ to the list of previous parameters, where n now represents the *number density of ions*. The current is always linear in this quantity, which means that the diffusion coefficients contain the factor $1/N\Gamma$, and beyond this depend on the same variables as before. This yields for the high-field case

$$D = \text{const} \frac{1}{N\Gamma} \left(\frac{a}{N\Gamma} \right)^{\frac{1+a}{2-a}},$$

with special cases

$$D = \text{const } a^{\frac{1}{2}} \lambda^{3/2} = \text{const} \left(\frac{Xe}{m} \right)^{\frac{1}{2}} \lambda^{3/2}$$

and

$$D = \text{const } a^2 \tau^3 = \text{const} \left(\frac{Xe}{m} \right)^2 \tau^3 .$$

For the low-field case, diffusion is independent of the field with

$$D = \text{const} \frac{1}{N\Gamma} \left(\frac{kT}{M} \right)^{\frac{1+a}{2}},$$

and with the special cases

$$D = \text{const } \lambda \left(\frac{kT}{M} \right)^{\frac{1}{2}}$$

and

$$D = \text{const } \tau \left(\frac{kT}{M} \right).$$

The information in the diffusion relations is new, but is dependent on the low-field velocity relations through a universal relation first discovered by W. Nernst, and derived independently for gases by J. J. Thomson. It is widely known as the "Einstein relation." This states that the diffusion coefficient D is given by

$$D = \frac{\partial <v_x>}{\partial a} \frac{kT}{m}.$$

A more specialized form of this relation, for constant mobility, is the relation 2.4; viz., $k/D = Ne/P$, discussed in chapter II.

The above dimensional results may be correlated with the experimental results of Hornbeck and Varney for the inert gas ions He^+ to Xe^+ in their own gases. The high-field relation is quite informative taken in conjunction with experiment, and allows of an evaluation of a mean free path λ. The slope of unity on the low-field log-log plots of the experimental data is not equally informative, as such a slope is common to all low-field cases. To discriminate between the possible situations, the temperature variation of the mobility is required. There is a certain likelihood that the parameter Γ of the equation fixing $\sigma(u)$ permits a to drift from 0 to unity as the speed of the ions is reduced. This has been indicated earlier for He^+ ions in He.

Part II of Wannier's paper takes up the more exact solution of the high-field case, which begins in part IIa with the formulations of the Boltzmann equation. In the introduction to the detailed analysis, Wannier points out that from the dimensional analysis, it appears that there is an intrinsic simplicity to the high-field case which is comparable to the low-field case, while the intermediate case is more difficult. Since, with the exception of that by Hershey, little study has been made of the high-field case, it is essential that this be done. Since the field term of equation A cannot be treated as a perturbation term, it is necessary to attempt a solution using the basically simple features of the problem indicated by the preceding dimensional analysis. To do this, Wannier substitutes δ functions for the Maxwellian velocity distributions in his basic field equation A. These permit of a reduction of the number of integrations from five to two.

The involved study leads to equations ultimately obtained by Legendre decomposition, which are still in general mixed integral differential equations in one dependent variable, hereafter designated as equation C. Further simplification is possible only in special cases, some of which are discussed later. It appears that in general, an even more simple form of the Boltzmann equation can be achieved if the idea of determining the velocity distribution is abandoned, and its moments are studied instead. That is, the Boltzmann equation can be looked upon as a system of relations between velocity averages, and as such it becomes a linear algebraic system. Utilizing this approach, the equation referred to above is integrated and yields equation D, which contains all possible derivable relations between averages as special cases, three of the more important of which are given as E1, E2, and E3. It is to be noted that while all the averages entering into the solution are not always the desired ones, all solution methods evolved in the treatment that follows use this equation system as a starting point, rather than other forms.

Part IIb deals with the mean free-time model at high field. If the angular distribution in the center of mass system is independent of speed, and the collision cross section varies inversely as the speed, then the above developments permit a solution of the Boltzmann equation. This is a solution in the sense that all significant velocity averages can be obtained directly, without knowledge of the velocity-distribution function.

The derivation followed is in a sense artificial. It was shown by Maxwell for related problems, that if the mean free time between collisions was assumed constant, very simple techniques could be employed to get constants of experimental importance. These techniques are used in what follows. They consist essentially of multiplying equation A by a suitable multiplier, followed by integration over $\vec{c}$. Used are the high-field averages obtainable from equation D. The analysis results in three equations, F1, F2, and F3, yielding the drift velocity, the total energy, and the energy partition of the traveling ion. The drift-velocity equation yields a constant mobility, and can be derived from low-field theory. It also indicates that for problems involving a constant mean free time, high- and low-field mobilities are numerically identical. It might be suspected that the intermediate-field value would also fall into line, as is shown in part III. The total-energy relation also yields an interesting relation; that the

$$\frac{\text{random energy}}{\text{visible energy}} = \frac{\text{molecular mass}}{\text{ion mass}}.$$

Here the *visible* energy is the energy of drift motion, and the *invisible* energy is the random part of the mean energy. This exhibits in a quantitative fashion the capacity of storing energy in the form of random motion possessed by light ions in a heavy gas.

For ions traveling in the parent gas, the ordered and random part of the energy are just equal; and for heavy ions in a light gas, the disordered fraction becomes negligible. The expression is derived for the mean energy in a direction at right angles to the field. This relation shows the equipartition property for small m/M, and the overwhelming preponderance of the motion in the field direction for large m/M. It appears also that for large m/M, the component of random energy in the field direction does not grow indefinitely as does the total energy, but stops instead at a value which is about four times one of the values along the other axes.

Part IIc treats the case of large mass ratios, e.g., that of electrons or of heavy ions. While the electron case has been investigated by others, the calculation is carried out by Wannier for the high-field case for the sake of completeness. Here all features of the law of scattering are left open, except that conservation of kinetic energy is assumed. The development in spherical harmonics carried out in part IIa is suitable to small m/M, since distribution is almost spherically symmetrical, and the expansion in spherical harmonics is also an expansion in powers of m/M. Solution leads to an expression already found in the work of Sydney Chapman and T. G. Cowling (53), except for the dependence on the angular-scattering law. Its most important special cases are obtained for constant time τ as a pseudo-Maxwellian distribution, and for $\tau = const/c$, which leads to a Druyvesteyn distribution. The derivation requires a further proof that the second expansion term of the velocity in Legendre polynomials is small compared to the first.

Next investigated is the case for large m/M, which has not been previously considered. From the three relations F1, F2, and F3 it can be inferred that the total ionic velocity increases indefinitely with m/M, but that the relative deviation from the mean decreases, so that the distribution function approaches a δ function. This again simplifies calculation, starting with an earlier stage in the development of equation C, and results in an expression that is a Maxwellian distribution with elliptic distortion along the field axis and a shifted origin, as indicated at the end of part Ia. The resulting expression indicates the main features for heavy ions, but may be faulty in details because of neglect of derivatives higher than the second.

Part IId deals with the case where m/M approaches unity, applicable to ions in the parent gas. It is just in this region that the simplifications are not possible; and while a theory *may* be possible, it has so far eluded search. Resort was thus had to a numerical determination of the distribution, in collaboration with R. W. Hamming, by the so-called Monte Carlo method. This is the same sort of procedure as used for ions by G. D. Yarnold (37), who had far inferior facilities. It is one in which statistical information is gained about a system by following an individual member through a large number of random processes. This gives the knowledge about one member of the assembly for a long period of time. Various time averages can be obtained from such data, and these averages are then set equal to instantaneous averages over the assembly, in accordance with ergodic theory. Hamming followed an ion through 10^4 collisions. On the average, the collisions were isotropic in the center of mass system $\Pi(\chi) = 1$, and obeyed a mean free-time condition $\tau = const.$ Actually, free-time and scattering angles varied from collision to collision, the angles varied in a random fashion over a unit sphere, and τ was random within an exponential distribution.

The calculation consisted of three parts. (1) Random numbers having the required distributions were obtained and recorded. In this problem there were three random numbers for each collision; namely, a time and two angles. They were placed on 10^4 I.B.M. cards with suitable identification. (2) The calculating machine simulated successive collisions, and kept a record of the initial and final velocities for each one. (3) The numerical material accumulated in the second part was analyzed statistically. For the first part of the calculation, values had to be chosen for the acceleration $a = Xe/m$, and mean free time τ. The values were $a = Xe/m = 1$ and $\tau = \log 10e = 0.43429$. From dimensional analysis, these constants would enter only through their product $a\tau = Xe\tau/m$, which scales all velocities. Thus, the results were analyzed as a dimensionless variable of the form $\vec{w} = \vec{c}/a\tau$.

The data previously gathered for the mean free-time problems in part IIb permitted use of the statistical data from the Monte Carlo method in two ways: (a) to check the numerical computation itself; or (b) to gain new information not otherwise available. The three averages for the random-velocity component along the field, the square of the transverse component, and the square of the component along the field from the equations earlier deduced, were compared for a sampling covering 9,492 out of the 10^4 collisions, and gave reasonable agreement. Fluctuations were large in any event, and some of the deviations noted were no doubt due to systematic errors introduced by the operator in rejecting certain runs. Some of the errors lay in an underestimate of τ by the Monte Carlo method. The reliability of the scattering data was not tested, and this may have operated to introduce some of the errors noted.

The velocity-distribution function obtained by the Monte Carlo method, as in item (b) above, is plotted, and in general shows the asymmetry along the field direction, as well as the offset from the zero point predicted in part Ia. Here, again, it is probable that the results, while correct in principle, are not accurate in detail. For example, it is shown that the distribution function is infinite along the entire positive-velocity component parallel to the field axis c_x. In fact, a defect of all three attempted approaches to the value of the distribution is that they give no information concerning the nature of the infinity for $c_x > 0$. From the Monte Carlo figure, one is tempted to infer that the infinity cannot be very strong, and something like a singularity is discernible at the origin. The inevitable conclusion is that the singularity for large c_x becomes a weak, narrow ridge rising more or less abruptly in an otherwise well-behaved function.

Part IIe attempts, by a new procedure, to solve the drift velocities and average energies for the case of equal masses. In view of the complexities in the structure of the velocity-distribution function, it is desirable to find a method whereby such quantities as the drift velocity, or average energy, can be derived directly from the Boltzmann equation without full knowledge of the entire distribution.

Maxwell's original work shows how to achieve this for molecules obeying the mean free-time condition of part IIb. A general method is next described which will permit determination of such averages for an arbitrary law of force between ions and gas molecules. The study is limited to the case of mass ratio 1. Analysis again starts from equation $\dot{C}$. The proposed method is tested on the successfully treated theoretical and Monte Carlo calculations for constant mean free time. By successive approximations, this method is shown to agree well with previous data.

The method, as applied to the hard sphere model of ion-atom collision, offers no new feature of principle. The working out of results is more complicated, mainly because the correction diagram for the incursion system is more involved. The drift velocity $<w \cos \theta>$, energy, and energy partition are calculated. These yield the fraction of the total energy in ordered motion, and the fraction of the energy in motion along the field direction, to be

$$\frac{<w \cos \theta>^2}{<w^2>} = 0.559,$$

and

$$\frac{<w^2 \cos^2\theta>}{<w^2>} = 0.751,$$

respectively.

The first ratio actually equals 0.500 for all free-time models, and the second ratio is 0.778 for free-time models with isotropic scattering. Thus, deviations from the earlier results are not drastic. In certain derived relations, differences are more drastic. Thus, a good measure of the anisotropy of the diffusion process is furnished by the ratio of the random energy along the field to the energy at right angles. By the method above, this number is

$$\frac{<w^2 \cos^2 \theta> - <w \cos \theta>^2}{\frac{1}{2}(<w^2> - <w^2 \cos^2\theta>)} = 1.54.$$

For the mean free-time case, this number equals 2.50. Hershey assumed it to be 1.

A comprehensive list of velocity averages is given in tabular form.

The calculations on the hard sphere model are immediately applicable to the data of Hornbeck and Varney. The data, where the drift velocity varies as $a/N = Xe/mN$, indicate a model with constant mean free path and with nearly isotropic scattering between ion and atom. They characterize the hard sphere model. The relation applicable here is

$$< c_x > = 1.147 \sqrt{\frac{a}{N\sigma}} = 1.147 \sqrt{\frac{Xe}{mN\sigma}}.$$

In the log-log plot of $< c_x >$ against Xe/mN, the intercept of the line of slope $1/2$ which fits these data thus equals log $1.147/\sqrt{\sigma}$, leading to the evaluation of the cross sections shown in table 1.10 (§ 6, supra). The ratio of about 3 for the atom-ion σ compared to atom-atom value (applicable to gases from He to Xe) has been noted before.

In connection with the calculations by this procedure, Wannier indicates that the method developed is potentially of very wide application. For instance, a question arises as to whether a careful kinetic calculation is necessarily restricted to certain models, or whether ion-atom cross sections known numerically might be used to derive therefrom kinetic properties. Wannier believes this procedure to be possible. Thus, for example, Wannier likes to assume that if $\sigma(c)$ is available as a function of c for the collision of He$^+$ ions and He atoms, and that this cross section satisfies the isotropy condition $\Pi(\chi) = 1$ to a good approximation, it will then be possible to derive for this eventuality, conditions on the first term of the high-field distribution function $h_0(c)$ which are more general than the previously derived special case expressions. He proceeds to do this for one of the earlier equations, achieving a more general relation than the directly derived relations, which are special cases.

Part III of Wannier's paper deals with the motion of uniform ion streams in intermediate fields. The important high-field and low-field solutions of equation A have been considered previously. The region of intermediate values of the variables can be handled qualitatively, both in concept and practice, by some sort of interpolation between high and low field, so that this area of study does not assume the importance of the previous solutions. Furthermore, precise measurements can always be pushed to either of the two extremes. Therefore, the analyses to be pursued in this section are only carried as far as they will go without resort to numerical methods.

Part IIIa gives a complete solution of the intermediate-field problem for the mean free-time model of part IIa. A convolution theorem is proved which reduces the velocity distribution for arbitrary field and temperature to two components, one containing field but not temperature, the other temperature but not field. The variable parameter scales out in each of these components. Thus, the general distribution reduces to two basic components; one being the Maxwellian, while the other is partially worked out in the calculations of part IIc and part IId.

The special case of heavy ion mass has been published independently by T..Kihara (94) without any apparent knowledge of the convolution theorem, which was available in the literature without complete proof. The general distribution function cannot be written down explicitly, because this goal was never achieved for $h(\vec{c})$. However, a result is found which is almost a substitute for this; namely, that all averages of products of integer powers of Cartesian velocity components which were shown capable of computation in the high-field case, can be computed for intermediate- and low-field range as well. The solution is given, but adds nothing new in interpretation beyond that given in the high-field case.

Part IIIb details the results for the polarization force and the isotropic Maxwellian model. The polarization force between ions and molecules, which predominates over other forces at sufficiently low temperatures, satisfies the mean free-time requirement of the preceding section. Hence, the complete theory given for those conditions applies to this force. The magnitude of the force is that given by equation 1.3, viz.: $PE = (D-1)e^2/8\pi Nr^4 = e^2P/2r^4$. Classical instead of quantum theory can usually be applied to the scattering by the potential, because angular-momentum quantum numbers run as high as 30 to 50 in normal situations, as indicated earlier by H. Margenau and S. Bloom, and also by T. Holstein in a private communication to Wannier. This classical type of theory, first developed by Langevin, calculates the angle of deflection χ due to a potential of the type of equation 1.3. The result is

$$\chi = \pi - 2 \int_0^{\zeta_1} \frac{d\zeta}{\left\{ \frac{1}{b^2} - \zeta^2 + \frac{e^2P}{b^2 u^2} \frac{M+m}{Mm} \zeta^4 \right\}^{\frac{1}{2}}} ,$$

where b is the impact parameter and ζ_1 is the lower of the two positive roots of the polynomial in the denominator. If the polynomial has no roots, integration goes from 0 to ∞. The question as to whether or not the orbit has a root is related to the nature of the orbit. If b is sufficiently large, a root exists, and the orbit looks like an hyperbola. For small b, no root exists, and the particles are sucked toward each other in a spiraling orbit, as shown (*supra*) in figure 1.59, at "b." The two regimes are separated by a limiting orbit in which the two particles spiral asymptotically into a circular orbit. The limiting orbit is found by setting the discriminant of the square root in the above expression equal to 0. Then

$$b^4_{\lim} = \frac{4e^2P}{u^2}\left(\frac{M+m}{Mm}\right).$$

From this value of $b_{\lim}$, can be derived a cross section and a mean free time τ_s for spiraling. This leads to

$$(G1) \qquad \tau_s = \frac{1}{2\pi e N}\left\{\frac{Mm}{(M+m)P}\right\}^{\frac{1}{2}}.$$

This is indeed a constant mean free time as stated, the speed of encounter u having dropped out. $1/\tau$ is the dimensional quantity entering into the averages $<\phi(\chi)/\tau>$, which occur in parts IIb and IIIa. Hassé worked these out in detail, but had to take account of hyperbolic collisions also. In so doing, two further conditions are derived, so that equation G1, and the new equations G2 and G3, completely define the nature of the averages appearing in previous sections. The integral of equation G3 was computed numerically. It happens that in the course of the evaluation the integral naturally decomposes into two parts. The one for which $b/b_{\lim}$ varies from 0 to 1, deals with spiraling collisions and exists for any $\phi(\chi)$. For $b/b_{\lim}$ between 1 and ∞, the contribution of the hyperbolic collisions to the average appears. This part is finite only if $\phi(\chi)$ vanishes for small-angle deflections. Combining the averages due to spiraling and to hyperbolic collisions with the basic expression for the drift velocity derived in part IIIb, the drift velocity becomes

$$(1.7) \quad <v_x> = \frac{0.9048}{2\pi}\frac{X}{N}\sqrt{\frac{4\pi N}{(D-1)}}\sqrt{\frac{M+m}{Mm}} = 0.51 \times \sqrt{\frac{1}{(D-1)P}}\sqrt{\frac{M+m}{m}},$$

which is the center of force Langevin equation without solid elastic impacts found to apply so very well when polarization forces are large. The interesting new fact that comes from this derivation is that the equation is exact at high as well as low electric fields.

The expression for the total energy needs no discussion for a special model, since in the form used at the end of part IIIa it does not involve the angular distribution. Thus, for an ion traveling in the parent gas, its total energy is obtained by doubling its apparent energy observable in drift and adding to this the thermal energy $(3/2)kT$.

Further inferences may be drawn by applying the general relations to the case of constant mean free time coupled with isotropic scattering, a case which, strictly speaking, is physically impossible of realization, since no mechanical forces are known that yield such a combination. Using the relations deduced in part IIIa, the drift velocity, the energy, and the partition relation (which counts random energy only) are obtained on the unreal model. Comparison of these quantities with those for the polarization theory terms shows that the difference between the two cases is remarkably small from the kinetic standpoint.

As a notable example, the comparison of the polarization results with an isotropic case in which the mean free time is given by $\tau = 0.9048\ \tau_s$, shows that the two drift velocities and energy relations are identical. Thus, it appears very nearly correct to state that scattering is isotropic for the polarization force. This comes chiefly from the predominant effect of the spiraling collisions. In fact, the relation $\tau = 0.9048\ \tau_s$ shows that a modification of only 10% in τ_s takes into account the main influence of the hyperbolic collisions.

Thus, this relation has a wide field of application when ion-drift measurements are extended to low temperature. The results also apply at room temperature whenever small ions are dealt with, and when the special scattering mechanisms having large cross sections, such as change of charge, do not occur. A particular case relates to the *molecular* inert gas ions in the parent gas, the drift velocity of which was measured by Hornbeck and Varney at relatively lower X/p.

As seen in tables 1.11 and 1.15 ($6, *supra*), the agreement is excellent between observation for $k = v/X$ and the values calculated by equation 1.7. There is also little observed variation with the field, as predicted by theory. Wannier believes that the discrepancies existing can be used to determine the hard-collision cross section superposed on the polarization force in the so-called full Langevin theory, equation 1.8.

In part IIIc of the paper, Wannier, for the sake of completeness, mentions the intermediate-field distribution function originally derived by Davydov for electrons. The derivation does not deviate in principle from the one in part IIc for electrons in the high-field case. Carrying through the calculations, the Davydov distribution is obtained.

Part IV is devoted to the diffusive motion of ions, which does not properly belong in this chapter. In part IVa is treated the diffusion for the mean free-time models; and in part IVb, the longitudinal diffusion for the hard sphere model.

It is important to note that this very illuminating mathematical

physical analysis brings out certain points that are often overlooked
by the experimental physicist, who is preoccupied with his data and
with the models derived therefrom. Thus, aside from complications
like clustering and other events which abruptly alter the nature of
carriers, the assumption of certain force laws, etc., leading to a
specific model (which may be right or wrong) are inherently associated
with certain more general mathematical physical concepts which
predetermine the behavior and lead to a certain law. For instance,
in considering some sort of force law or physical model, e.g., the
polarization centers of force, or the change-of-charge mechanism, it
is not at all clear that these mechanisms assume constant mean free
time or constant mean free path, and because of some peculiar detail
of mechanism, both lead to isotropic scattering. Further, it is not
suspected that it is these relatively hidden aspects resulting from
model behavior that cause the model to yield data in agreement with
experiment, when in fact the model is often a crude and defective
one, through omission of some factor or through oversimplification.

The contribution of Wannier in this regard is of greatest significance to the experimentalist, in that it gives him perspective in
understanding the success and weaknesses of this model. Above all,
it should keep him from trying to extrapolate a model, successful
for hidden mathematical physical reasons in a limited regime, as
yielding the *only* successful solution to a general problem. A similar
clarification will follow from the general analysis of recombination
through the work of Jaffé in chapter VI. With this clearly in mind,
it is proper to consider the summary of forces active in ionic behavior
and their consequences.

§12. Summary of Conclusions on the Nature of Gaseous Ions, and Their Behavior.

A. *Types of Forces.*

The forces between charged atoms and atoms or molecules (some
types of forces, in essence, merge into each other) may be listed
as follows.

1. Forces of dielectric attraction of the inverse fifth-power type,
expressed as $+ (D-1)e^2/2\pi Nr^5$, with D the dielectric constant of the
gas in bulk. These forces are *not charge-specific,* and probably hold
up to 10 Å and even closer to the ion center. Minor corrections with
possible reductions occur in the neighborhood of 2 Å.

2. Repulsive forces of the classical type, expressed as $- \gamma/r^n$,
with n taking on values ranging from 9 to 14.6. A commonly used
repulsive law is the one leading to a *solid elastic radius* σ_0. Assuming

spherical symmetry, this implies that the repulsive-force law is zero up to within σ_0 between ionic and molecular centers, and then is γ/r^n, with $n = \infty$. It could be approximated by making n large in the force law and adjusting the constant γ so as to give an approximate collision radius σ_0 in relation to the attractive force at 300° K., as indicated by R. H. Fowler (82). In the past, most thinking hinged upon the nature of σ_0 and its change by accretion of a permanent group or cluster of molecules about the original charge. While such actions are believed to take place, they will be limited in scope, as indicated later.

3. Chemical forces that are associated with impacts or with the inverse fifth-power law of attraction (which brings molecules and ions together), lead to the *rearrangement of charges on the molecules, forming very stable, complex molecular ions.* These are sharply saturated forces, and the binding energies are very high (possibly of the order of a tenth to several electron volts) compared to the inverse fifth-power type. These forces lead to *stoichiometrical chemical complexes* which are well known to chemists for ions in solution, such as NH_4^+, $Cu(NH_3)_2^+$, $Cu(CN)_2^-$ ions, with gaseous analogues such as $Na(NH_3)^+$ or $Na(NH_3)_2^+$, as well as to simple molecular ions such as He_2^+, Ne_2^+, N_4^+, etc. In such cases, the ionic charge will not necessarily reside on the original atom. These complex ion formations are charge-specific in their nature; for example, alcohols go to negative ions, while amines go to positive ions; He_2^+ or N_4^+ can form, while He_2^- or N_4^-, etc., do not form. They apparently form readily with the presence of very small concentrations of the active gases, but may require removal of the heat of association by triple impact. They are more or less permanently stable. They may cause mobilities to increase or decrease relative to the initially ionized structure, depending on whether the complex ion has a smaller or larger effective σ_0 than that of the former ion, or whether change of charge is prevented. Thus, He_2^+ has a higher mobility than He^+ in He. These complexes account for the differences in positive and negative ion mobilities, and for some of the aging effects observed.

4. Van der Waals and quadrupole *attractive* forces between ion and molecule. These forces are both of the inverse seventh-power type, with inverse sixth-power potential. The quadrupole forces result from the divergent field of the ion at the molecule. The van der Waals type forces come from polarization of the ion by the rapidly rotating dipole fields of the molecule. The coefficients B_1 of the quadrupole forces add directly to the coefficient B_2 of the van der Waals forces. For Cs^+ ions in He, the van der Waals forces far exceed the quad-

rupole forces by a factor of 11; and for Li^+ in Xe, the quadrupole forces exceed van der Waals forces by a factor of 5. The forces combined are greatest for Cs^+ in Xe. If a solid elastic radius of suitable value be chosen, comparable to the closest approach of ion and molecule in collision, the energy for the polarization force and the quadrupole and van der Waals forces may be compared. For Cs^+ ions in He, the polarization force is only slightly more than the inverse seventh-power forces. For Cs^+ in Xe, it is twice as great; and for Li^+ in Xe, it is six times as great. Thus, at the minimum distance, the inverse seventh-power forces must be included.

5. Exchange forces are wave-mechanically defined forces replacing the classical repulsive forces of paragraph 2, and take a form ϵ^{-ar} rather than r^{-n}. Exchange forces may be associated with change-of-charge (electron-transfer) effects, in which event they are attractive. Their use alone allows of proper correction for the change-of-charge effects where change of charge is frequent, as with He^+ in He. They have recently been proved successful in accounting for the observed mobilities.

The exchange-of-charge phenomenon exerts considerable influence on mobilities in various ways. If an ionized atom or molecule A^+ has an ionization potential greater than some other constituent B of the gas, whether B is the gas or a contaminant, such as Hg vapor, then the ion A^+ on impact has a chance of taking an electron from B, neutralizing itself, and leaving an ion B^+ behind. If the ionization potentials are fairly close together, the probability of charge transfer is very high. It is not known to what extent an electron transfers from the *negative* ion to another. It is likely, from the energy of ion formation, that an O_2^- ion might cede its electron to a Cl_2 molecule, or an O^- ion to a Cl atom, to give Cl^-. No observations exist on this point. The phenomena have been observed entirely on positive ions. The energy difference is given out as increased kinetic energy of the new ion and neutral molecule. This exchange reaction is the most frequent cause of decrease of mobility in time in all ionized gases. In rare cases it could cause an increase. With 10^8 or more impacts with molecules per second, the chance of the initially ionized atom or molecule losing its charge to an impurity molecule in 10^{-2} sec is very high. The change of charged carrier changes both mass and σ_0 of the ion, and thus its mobility. It is responsible for aging in a considerable measure. To avoid it, the alkali ions from Li^+ to Cs^+ are the only ones to use, as their ionization potentials are normally lower than those of other molecules or atoms. One of the commonest impurities involved in this action is Hg from gauges and pumps. The reaction also removes *multiply* charged ions in gases. Its primary action, in connection with the mobilities here considered, lies in its alteration of carriers in time.

The same process further manifests itself in interactions between ionized atoms or molecules in gases of their own species. Such action affects mobilities in another fashion, since it increases attractive forces and lowers mobilities. Thus, A^+ ions in A will exchange charges, altering the mobility in the order of perhaps 50%. Under such conditions, since the momentum gained by the charged carrier from the field is practically wiped out in many of these charge exchanges, the effect is to increase momentum exchange and lower the mobilities appreciably; i.e., it acts in the same way as strong attractive forces. The influence of such forces on the mobility is best calculated wave-mechanically. The effects have been widely observed in mobility studies made to date. If the drift velocity can be measured at high X/p, when $v \propto \sqrt{X/p}$, when exchange forces are active as for He^+ in He, it is possible to derive an equivalent solid elastic cross section for collision from the data. This cross section can then be conveniently used to calculate mobilities in the low X/p region by means of a solid elastic mobility equation, as indicated by Wannier. Experiment, wave-mechanical theory, and Wannier theory are now in good agreement as to magnitude.

B. *The Effect of Forces.*

1. The repulsive and attractive wave-mechanical exchange forces are largely responsible for the delineation of an effective collision cross section between ions and molecules. To these forces can roughly be ascribed the role of establishing an effective collision radius σ_0 of the spherically symmetrical solid elastic type. Actually, the value of σ_0, using center of force relations, will also depend on the attractive forces and the temperature, quite independently of the condensed phase. Thus, in figuring the effective σ_0, both repulsive and attractive forces should be considered. Primarily, the value of σ_0 will depend on the nature of the ion or condensed phase of the system and the gas molecule in collision; i.e., whether the ion is an H^+, He^+, He_2^+, Hg^+, N_2^+, or a large configuration like $Li^+(H_2O)_2$, or $Na(NH_3)_2^+$.

2. The various attractive forces that are singly or simultaneously active can cause a wide range of interaction between ions and molecules. These range all the way from the formation of stable, charge-specific, chemical ion complexes, or of new molecular ions of binding energies of the order of volts, through clusters of a labile sort with progressively less tightly bound molecules, to merely an increased

density of molecules in the neighborhood of the ions; or, what is equivalent to this, an enhanced energy and momentum exchange with gas molecules, either by collision or at a distance, leading to decreased free paths and mobilities. The effect of change of charge in systems like He^+ in He is to increase momentum loss acquired in the field direction. It effectively acts as an attractive force, reducing the force path and increasing collision cross section. Also, insofar as it is independent of ion velocity, it can be evaluated as an effective solid elastic collision cross section at high X/p where polarization forces are negligible.

C. *The Types of Ions Observed and Their Occurrence.*

1. Monomolecular or monatomic positive ions are observed in many pure gases over short time intervals, say less than 10^{-3} sec, and at pressures below 1 mm, and have been extensively studied. Notable are the ions of the inert gases in their own gases, as well as N_2^+ and O_2^+ at low, intermediate, and high X/p. The most surely studied monatomic ions are the alkali ions from Li^+ to Cs^+ at 300° K. and above, and in all but very polarizable or polar gases. Thus, Li^+ may add a Xe atom at room temperature and Ne atoms at 70° K. So far, all ions that have been observed are singly charged. Multiply charged ions lose their charges by stealing electrons from the ambient gas atoms or molecules with a very few collisions. While multiply charged ions are observed in mass spectrographs and at low pressures, no certain evidence of multiply charged ions above 1 mm or after 10^{-4} sec in gases is at hand. In oil-drop studies, Millikan found evidence that 10% of the He ions created by a particles were doubly charged. Actually, capture by his oil drops could not have distinguished between *existing* doubly charged ions and *initially created, doubly charged* ions that had become two ions by charge exchange within 10^{-4} or less second of capture.

2. Monomolecular, or perhaps monatomic, *negative* ions are *usually* found only in electron-attaching gases, such as O_2, SO_2, Cl_2, etc. Atomic, and some molecular, negative ions can be formed in small quantities from heated filaments with oxide or molten salts or on bombardment of metal surfaces by energetic positive ions. Many negative ions are formed by sending high-energy positive ions through thin metal foils. Monatomic and molecular negative ions are created in special cases as a result of ionization by electron impact. The most notable case is that of the creation of H^- ions by ionization of a gas contaminated with water vapor. It is found at the edge of striations in an H_2O-contaminated glow discharge. In most pure, non-

electron-attaching gases, the negative carriers are electrons. If negative ions form in such gases, then impurities are present. Most negative ion forming gases, by attachment of thermal electrons (other than the halogens, which yield negative ions by dissociative attachment at thermal energies), are molecular, and form molecular ions. All other negative ion formation, except for the few molecular types indicated, occurs by dissociative attachment, acquiring a threshold value of the electron energy. No data are at hand as to whether these remain monatomic or monomolecular. It is probable that they quickly attach a molecule of omnipresent water vapor to give a complex ion.

3. *Complex ions*, positive or negative, are stable aggregates of relatively few molecules, or of atoms and molecules of definitely stoichiometrical character. With relatively high binding energies and saturated forces, these complex ion formers are charge-specific. They form readily, but require removal of heat of formation frequently in three-body impacts. They are stable, and have analogues among chemical ions in solution or in gases, such as He_2^+ or N_4^+. They account for some aging and for all differences in positive or negative ion mobilities. They have been observed in studies of mobilities in mixtures, and in the case of the $Na(NH_3)^+$ complexes. Their mass has been estimated by the Bristol group.

4. *Labile-cluster ions* have been the center of controversy for many years. When the question was initially raised as to whether the inverse fifth-power dielectric attractive forces, with added van der Waals and quadrupole attractions, could cause one to several molecules to attach permanently or semipermanently to a charged atom or molecule to give a *cluster ion*, an answer was sought on the basis of a stability criterion. This classically conceived criterion was fixed by stating that if the potential energy of the cluster ion PE was equal to or greater than the kinetic energy KE of the ambient gas molecules, then the cluster would form. Applied in the form of the inverse fifth-power law, expressed as a ratio of potential to kinetic energy as $(D-1)e^2/12\pi p r^4 > 1$, the indications were that most gases at n.t.p. should form stable clusters. Naively considered, these clusters could consist of up to 12 or more hard spherical molecules. It has been shown that this naive concept was overoptimistic as to the number of molecules attached. It was also shown that such clusters will be what are termed *labile* clusters, since the binding forces are long-range and do not saturate. These are clusters that build up to the largest size possible with the condition $PE/KE > 1$. The outer, more loosely bound molecules must then be knocked off and added on again continually. The resulting mobilities should

not be too sharply defined, and should vary *continuously* with X/p and T, decreasing as these increase. Early in the century, it was experimentally established that most ions studied *showed no such behavior* with X/p up to values where the ion energies were very high (49).

The failure to observe the common occurrence of such mobility behavior is now ascribed to the fact that as a rule, in most common gases at room temperatures, *labile clustering does not occur*. Theoretical physicists agree that the reason for the failure to form clusters when the early criterion, $PE/KE > 1$, indicated they *should* form, lies in an error in that criterion. In setting $PE/KE = 1$ as the basis for cluster stability, the earlier physicists failed to recognize the fact that the entropy of a cluster is lower than that of the dispersed state of ion and separated molecules. Thus, the statistical weights should be included in the criterion. The introduction of the statistical weights of the clustered and unclustered states reduces the value of the criterion $PE/KE > 1$ to $\beta PE/KE > 1$, with β a fraction which can be very small. The statistical weights of the states are unfortunately not calculable in the form to yield the naively considered coefficient β. The classical criterion used thus falls by the wayside, and the cluster ions under dielectric attractions will be far less stable than formerly suspected.

The clustering criterion, under certain assumptions as to the spacing of energy levels, can be computed and has been worked out for a particular case, neglecting solid elastic radii and steric hindrance. In agreement with more recent, controlled experiment, it establishes the existence of *labile* clusters under certain circumstances. If a very small ion such as Li^+ is allowed to interact with a polarizable gas such as Xe, even at room temperature, a labile cluster *can* form.[21] The studies with Li^+ in inert gases alone show both the *complex ion* formation and a *labile cluster*. The labile-clustered and unclustered (and sometimes complex) ions exist side by side under some conditions, the clusters having a mobility which varies with X/p. In mixtures of H_2O and inert gas, the clustered ions show mobilities following the Debye deviations from Blanc's law.

The curves showing these effects are closely parallel to the

---

[21] The same is true for Li^+ in He, but only at very low temperatures, since the gas He is not very polarizable. K^+ will not form clusters with any inert gases. It is also observed that clustering takes place where ions Li^+ to Cs^+ encounter H_2O vapor, which is strongly polar in gaseous mixtures of inert gases from He through to Xe at room temperature.

theoretical curves deduced by Overhauser (48), on the basis of a labile cluster. The ion shows some reluctance to cluster formation, as indicated by the coexistence of labile and unclustered ions. The reluctance probably arises from the loss of the energy of association in a three-body impact in order to add the first cluster molecule, or to form the initial complex ion. Once the first molecule adds on, the other molecule or molecules of the labile cluster follow at once. As X/p increases, the added molecules spend less and less time in the attached phase, and the mobility increases. At high enough X/p, declustering by impact is complete. It is possible that at sufficiently low temperatures, most ions are in some measure labile clusters. The number of molecules in a labile cluster is small. In most cases observed it is probably less than four. In order to account for the Debye effect in mixtures, only one added labile molecule would suffice. To account for the results of the Bristol group, it requires a minimum of one molecule added to facilitate cluster addition, either to a complex ion or a one-molecule addition product, and at least one more to give the labile effects. In any case, there is no evidence of large labile ion clusters. Clustering is also limited by repulsive forces of the molecules of the cluster among themselves. This has never been included in calculations. It is called "steric hindrance" by the chemists.

5. "Statistical clusters" is a term that was coined by the author to describe the increased density of molecules in the neighborhood of a charged carrier because of the dielectric potential field $(D-1)e/8\pi Nr^4$ about itself. The molecules are never *attached* to the ion, even in a temporary sense. They undergo momentum exchange with the ion as it moves in their neighborhood. To this extent, the molecules temporarily "accompany" the ion on its way. This rather picturesque "Flying Dutchman" cloud of molecules that surround the ion is actually an alternate way of describing the shortened mean free paths and increased collision frequency, which in turn increase momentum transfer and decrease the ionic mobility. The term is unfortunate, is now obsolete, and should *not* be used.

6. Irrespective of the existence of clusters or complex ions, *all* ions are subjected to the increased drag on their motion in the field produced by momentum and energy exchanges with molecules and atoms, owing to the sum total of the dielectric, van der Waals quadrupole and exchange forces with the surrounding molecules. Normally, were no forces acting, the exchange in momentum would depend on the solid elastic collision cross sections $\pi\sigma_0^2$, caused by repulsive forces. The added attractive forces produce a reduction in mobility,

either by increasing the effective molecular density (kinetic-theory approach of Reiganum); or, regarded another way, by so curving the mean free paths as to increase the effective collision cross section beyond $\pi\sigma_0^2$ (approach of Sutherland). In fact, a theory that is physically incorrect through the neglect of solid elastic impacts at an effective σ_0, based on the attractive-force terms $(D-1)e^2/2\pi Nr^5$, accounts very successfully for the absolute and relative observed mobilities of many ions. Thus, it must be assumed that such forces play a predominant role in determining mobilities, except where change of charge intervenes.

The predominance of this type of action results from longer-range attractive forces, which cannot produce clustering because of entropy factors and steric hindrance at normal temperatures and values of X/p. However, for accuracy in detail, the repulsive-force fields and so-called effective solid elastic radii *do* play a role, and must be included in any correct theory. The behavior of normal, stable gaseous ions, some of them doubtless complex, is thus governed largely by the force laws indicated. The temperature variation of mobilities and the independence of mobility on X/p until critically high values are reached, are explained successfully by these long-range forces.

The studies of Hershey (22) at high X/p for known alkali ions in He, A, H_2, and N_2, as well as those of Hornbeck (32) and of Chanin and Biondi (81), where there is an initial increase in k with values of X/p above the critical value, followed by an ultimate decline eventually as $\sqrt{p/X}$, are accounted for by the long-range forces alone, clustering occurring in only special cases. As X/p passes a critical value, ionic mobilities begin to increase, owing to the reduction in effective momentum transfer through the weak $(D-1)e^2/2\pi Nr^5$ forces as the time integral of the force on a molecule at higher velocities decreases. As X/p increases still more, the average energy of the ions increases above that given by $\frac{1}{2}MC_i^2 = (3/2)kT$ for the gas molecules. The increase in C_i^2 as indicated in equation 1.1b will lead to a decrease in the mobility k as observed. Where the change-of-charge effects predominate there is no rise as X/p increases, the mobilities declining beyond a certain X/p, eventually following the $\sqrt{p/X}$ rule, applicable to all types of action at high X/p.

It must be added that with this general picture, and the considerations as to the kinetic-theory behavior of charged carriers in fields given by Wannier, the subject has been covered quite satisfactorily by theory, though there is much more to be learned in detail.

§ 13. Mobilities of Large Ions.

Thus far, the discussion of ions and their mobilities has dealt primarily with the ions commonly observed when a gas breaks down electrically or various ionizing agents are acting on it, the gases used being relatively clean and carriers being studied over time intervals of a second or less. These are the so-called "normal ions." As noted, they are of molecular dimensions and not much larger. Nothing in nature, however, prohibits the presence in gases of suspended foreign bodies, solid particles, dust, fumes, smokes, globules of sprayed or condensed liquids, and nuclei of various sorts. With saturated vapors present, the particles may grow by condensation. Such suspensions are termed *aerosols*. If present, these particles can acquire charges by picking up the ions formed by natural ionization processes that surround the earth's surface.

It is well known that cosmic rays, the earth's gamma radiation, and radioactive contamination of the air and chamber walls normally produce on the order of 20 ions/cm^3 of enclosed volume per second. If recombination between normal positive and negative ions takes place, these "natural" ions in air and other gases will always be present in an equilibrium concentration to the extent of some 1,000 or so ions of both signs per cm^3. If the normal ions are rapidly picked up by foreign particles, recombination is much reduced, and the charged carriers can accumulate up to nearly 10^5 ions per cm^3. Gases may also be ionized by many other methods; e.g., by corona discharges or flames, thus charging up any foreign particles present. Finally, many such foreign particles are charged in production by frictional processes, spraying, flame ions, etc. Thus, carriers different from "normal" ions exist in "natural" air, or in gases which have not been filtered, and particularly in *moist*, clean gases, or gases purposefully filled with dusts that have been ionized by corona discharge for the purpose of electrically precipitating the dust.

Most of the visible dusts and fumes that have been charged have not been called *ions*, presumably because they are clearly defined and not mysterious. Being large, their mobilities are low, and they are not effective carriers. They have, however, considerable technical importance in industry. Irrespective of these matters, they are *carriers of electricity in gases*, and should probably be classed as ions, together with the other carriers. In addition to these *obvious* carriers, some more mysterious *unseen* carriers of both signs and of *low mobilities* have been observed in natural air and other gases, mostly in the presence of moisture or saturated vapors. The carriers are relatively few in number, being thus hard to study or control.

They appear to fall into two groups; *large* or *Langevin* ions, with mobilities of the order of 10^{-3} cm²/volt sec, and *intermediate* ions, of mobility of the order of 7×10^{-2} cm²/volt sec (58). Some of these carriers are definitely not associated with obvious, solid particles (59).

In view of the existence of such carriers, the analysis, study and application of which are of some interest, possibly a word should be said about mobility theory over an extended range of particle sizes. As indicated in the author's *Fundamental Processes of Electrical Discharge in Gases*, the mobility equations derived are consistent, and are connected by transition forms of semiempirical character where direct derivation is difficult. Thus, the theories cover the whole range of possible values of mobility, from those of charged visible small spheres down to point center of force ions interacting with similar molecules. As R. A. Millikan (60) has shown, for particles extending from larger sizes to dimensions where the radius a of the particle becomes comparable with the mean free path of the gas molecules at the existing pressure, one can use the well-known Stokes law. This says that $Xe = F = 6\pi\eta av$, where v is the velocity, η the coefficient of viscosity of the gas, and Xe the driving force of the field on the ion. Thus, the mobility is given by

$$(1.27) \qquad k = \frac{v}{X} = \frac{e}{6\pi\eta a}.$$

If the shape differs from spherical, a small correction can be made for the shape factor. In the region where a is of the order of L, the mean free path, the semiempirical Cunningham correction to the Stokes law can be applied, which makes

$$(1.28) \qquad k = \frac{\left(e(1 + \frac{L}{a}) \right)}{6\pi\eta a}.$$

Where the latter fails, and down to radii a, where the target area for impact πa^2 is of the order of the quantity $\pi\sigma^2$, with σ^2 the target area for collision between ion and molecule in consequence of attractive forces, the classical Langevin equation 1.1a suffices:

$$k = 0.815 \frac{e}{M} \frac{L}{C} \sqrt{\frac{m + M}{m}}.$$

Below ions of this size, the conventional small-ion theories or the more complete equations must be used. Perhaps the region of size most inaccurately covered by theory would be that falling between the Cunningham correction term equation and the Langevin theory. Probably, either of the limiting forms of relations 1.28 or 1.1a could be adjusted to straddle the intermediate region by a suitable empirical change in constants.

Thus, except for minor deviations, the Stokes law type of equation can be used to predict the mobilities of the larger ions within 10 to 20% for particles of stated size. Conversely, the law can be used to evaluate the particle size from measured mobilities in this range. There is, however, some caution to be exercised in the latter analysis. With larger particles, the mobility is strictly proportional to the ionic charge. Thus, if the charge is known, the size can be inferred from the mobility. If the charge is *not known*, the size is *in doubt*. Large, multiply charged particles cannot discharge themselves by the Kallmann-Rosen effect with neutral molecules, since their surface fields are too low. Therefore, unless the charged particles pick up *ions* of the same or opposite sign, they retain their initial charge. Spray-electrified liquids and frictionally charged dusts are initially charged with from 1 to 1,000 or more electrons of charge (61). The larger they are, the larger their charge. Even particles of 10^{-5} cm radius will often be found with up to 10 electrons. Suspended in the air with natural ionization, highly charged particles will in general reduce their initial charges by picking up ions of the opposite sign (62).

On the other hand, neutral dust particles in natural air, and even more in the dense ionization of negative point corona discharge, will pick up a number of charges to reach a highly charged equilibrium value. This value will be fixed by the condition that the electrostatic potential of the ion at the surface of the carrier just equals the energy of agitation of the electrons or ions. For ions with a radius of the order of $a = 3 \times 10^{-6}$ cm, an equilibrium value of several electronic charges would not be surprising under ordinary conditions. In fact, W. B. Kunkel, on NH_4 particles with $a = 0.5$ microns and up, has observed equilibrium values up to 10 electrons (62). Thus, large visible carriers of known radii present no problem except as to the uncertainty of the charge carried. All these data, if desired, can be found from the mobility and the Stokes law velocity of fall under gravity, or by use of the Hopper-Laby modification of Millikan's oil-drop method (63).

Concerning the nature of the so-called *invisible* larger ions; the *Langevin* and the *intermediate* ions found in natural, unfiltered gases, there has been a degree of uncertainty until the last few years. Some doubt still remains regarding the intermediate ions. The Langevin ions of mobility of 5×10^{-3} cm^2/volt sec, if singly charged, can be estimated to have a radius of some 3×10^{-6} cm and to be composed of 3×10^6 water molecules. They can be multiply charged, as noted above. These particles would be microscopically invisible, but are just visible as diffraction patterns in the ultramicroscope. The intermediate ions have a mobility of about 6×10^{-2} cm^2/volt sec, and will have a radius of 3.3×10^{-7} cm, containing some 4,000 H_2O molecules if singly charged (the most probable condition). Both of these types of ions were initially discovered by Langevin, and were studied by him (58). He ascribed them to charges picked up by pre-existing nuclei.

The ions were later studied by J. A. Pollock, who associated them definitely with the presence of moisture in the gas (59). If carefully filtered air was used, under certain conditions he found that despite adequate moisture and ionization, no large ions were discernible. This was probably correct, as will be seen; but for various reasons that differ from those stated by Pollock. This fact, and a study of their mobility as a function of humidity, led Pollock to the belief that the large and the intermediate ions were condensed liquid and gaseous aqueous envelopes, respectively, about some *solid* nuclei. He found that the normal ions disappeared in the gas at the same rate as the number of large ions increased. He concluded that the growth of large ions was not a condensation of water vapor about normal ions, but that some sort of solid nuclei with water-vapor mantels captured the normal ions to make Langevin ions. G. R. Wait (64) observed that Langevin ions do *not* change their mobility with relative humidity, which vitiates Pollock's conclusions. Subsequently, other careful studies have ruled out Pollock's assumption of *common solid particles* as the basis for nuclei (64), (65). The disappearance of normal ions to give intermediate or large ions, and of intermediate ions to give large ions, was further established thereafter (64), (66).

O. W. Torreson, *et al.*, have shown that the large ions are related to *nuclei of cloudy condensation* in the atmosphere (67). These nuclei are known to be produced by chemical action, e.g., combustion and industrial pollution. It is thus fairly established that there exist in the atmosphere two types of nuclei, definitely related to the content and degree of saturation of water vapor present in the atmosphere, that pick up existing charges and thus become intermediate or large ions. The intermediate ion appears to be a transient, short-lived form. The large ions form nuclei that are stable and develop into drops that are visible on adequate supersaturation.

Much knowledge has been derived about such nuclei from two fields of study; i.e., the C. T. R. Wilson cloud-chamber studies, and spray electrification. As indicated by J. J. Thomson, a small particle of water will evaporate owing to surface-tension forces unless the atmosphere is quite supersaturated with water vapor (68). This supersaturation can be achieved by adiabatic expansion. Most volatile liquids, including water, show these properties. If supersaturation is high enough, a cloud will condense on nuclei despite surface tension. For H_2O at 20° C., this occurs at 8-fold supersaturation. If an electrical charge is picked up by the drop, the effect of this charge is to make the drop grow to visible size at a lower supersaturation in virtue of the electrostatic forces counteracting the surface-tension forces, as Thomson showed. For water, the condensation occurs at 6-fold supersaturation for nuclei with positive charges, and at 4-fold supersaturation for nuclei with negative charges. In ethyl alcohol, on the other hand, the positive charge is more active than the negative in facilitating condensation.

Other substances act differently. Nonpolar substances show no sign preference, but are stabilized by ions; and some polar substances, such as $C_6H_5NO_3$, show no sign preference, but condense more readily on all ions (69). Thus, clean, apparently unnucleated, ionized gas saturated with a vapor (e.g., H_2O), as a rule will show no condensation until the vapor is supersaturated to an adequate degree (e.g., 4- or 6-fold for negative and positive ions in H_2O). The condensation sets in on the ions, showing molecular structural sign preferences of an unusual sort in some cases. Once the condensation has taken place through adiabatic expansion, the visible cloud of droplets on the charged particles re-evaporates. The charge, however, has stabilized the droplets on re-evaporation so that they evaporate to a radius where the surface-tension forces decrease with the decreasing drop size, because with small radius the surface forces can no longer saturate. Such droplets appear to be about 3×10^{-6} cm in radius, and have been observed as Langevin or large ions. Note that *it took a supersaturation on some particles stabilized by ions* to give these nuclei. These ions, once formed, always reappear as a cloud of droplets on re-expansion and supersaturation. There is *no sign preference* on such *recondensation* once the Langevin ions are formed. In the C. T. R. Wilson cloud-chamber studies, however, appear other persistent nuclei that are *stable* and *uncharged*. They usually come from unfiltered room air. In fact, they are such a persistent background nuisance in cloud-chamber studies that only gas aged in tanks is used in this work (69). These particles have been identified as nuclei of atmospheric pollution. They presumably represent the condensation of considerable aggregates of water about hygroscopic molecules, such as CO_3, HCl, HNO_3, etc.

W. F. Hillebrand believed that he had shown that Pacific Ocean fog droplets have at least one molecule of salt per droplet (70). Similar conclusions were reached by E. J. Workman and S. E. Reynolds in their study of nuclei in New Mexico. These droplets are condensed by supersaturation in air filled with evaporated sea spray. The same conclusions were arrived at by Dessens regarding NH_4Cl and NaCl in gases (70). Obviously, such pollution nuclei can also pick up ions; and, in combination with 'lowered vapor pressure because of dissolved salts and hygroscopic substances, can grow to the size of the Langevin ions even in moderately saturated atmospheres (62). On this score, the nature of the probable nuclei of the large or Langevin ion is pretty well clarified.

The extensive and careful researches of A. F. Kip and A. W. Einarsson in the author's laboratory (69) revealed that the sign preference in cloudy condensation (which, among other agencies, leads to Langevin ions) cannot be explained on J. J. Thomson's theory, which accounts only for the Langevin type of nuclei that are not sensitive to sign of charge. Sign preference can only be interpreted through the existence in partially saturated (or saturated) vapor of *smaller nuclei of pseudocrystalline form*. These nuclei would have radii of the order of 3×10^{-7} cm with some 4,000 molecules, and would thus be too small to have surface tension active. Thus, they would tend to form arranged groupings of molecules, as in small crystals. If the added positive or negative charge were such as to favor linkage with the surface structure by orienting the incoming dipolar molecules in the vapor in the right sense, that charge would favor condensation relative to the other sign. All evidence on sign preference fits into such a concept as interpreted by the physical chemist. There is evidence on hand to indicate the existence in saturated and supersaturated vapor of nuclei whose mobility would be 7×10^{-2} cm/sec per volt/cm if they were singly charged. In the unsaturated or near-saturated air, such nuclei can form, but would re-evaporate unless stabilized by picking up a charge. When the vapor is supersaturated, these pseudo crystals condense to visible droplets if charged, and then re-evaporate to Langevin ions.

Evidence for the existence of such ions and of another method of creating them is found in the spraying or bubbling of liquids. When pure H_2O, or H_2O with small amounts of acids, bases, and salts dissolved, was atomized or bubbled, so that very small droplets of radii 10^{-7} or less were created, Seville Chapman observed quite an array of mobilities in *moderately dry* and *saturated* air (71). The ions ranged from the normal negative and positive ions in air to ions of mobility 0.06 cm/sec per volt/cm. Most of these ions showed peaks of clearly defined mobilities in his apparatus. Thus, negative ions of mobilities 1.8, 0.8, 0.5, 0.3, and 0.18 cm/sec per volt/cm were observed. The positive ions with somewhat broader peaks had mobilities of 0.8, 0.3, and 0.48 cm/sec per volt/cm.

In Lenard's theory of spray electrification, it is assumed that in consequence of surface-tension forces, about 1 in 10^4 of the outer layer of water molecules carries an extra electron or OH^- ion. Deeper in the liquid, at 5×10^{-8} cm, there is a corresponding excess of H^+, or else of Na^+, etc., ions if Na salts are dissolved. The groups of ions observed by Chapman were assumed to represent hydrated groups about the H^+, OH^-, Na^+, Cl^-, etc., nuclei. Some of these ions may have borne multiple charges. In addition, a group of larger ions of some spread was observed, having mobilities of the order of 0.125 to 0.06 cm/sec per volt/cm and somewhat lower. In fact, if much sugar or salt is added to the water, the small ions disappear and only the larger groups remain. These ions have considerable dissolved material, and may be relatively stable. Thus, spraying and similar processes also lead to the formation of intermediate ions. In any case, the nature of these ions is accounted for. They are relatively unimportant, even in the atmosphere, as they gradually disappear in one fashion or another to give the more stable Langevin ions.

Recently, G. Vassails (65) has made an exhaustive study of the production of one type of large ions in air and other gases. Above all, he has been able to *produce* the nuclei, and has *seen* them in the ultramicroscope. Vassails's technique of mobility measurement was primitive, and the resolving power was poor. Thus, some of his data are probably interpreted well beyond their validity; a matter which can only be determined on careful statistical analysis of the original data. The method of observation yields the charge collected by an electrode over various time intervals from the concentric cylindrical measuring chamber in which the ions are generated. The plots of charge against voltage gave curves with elbows, in what in theory should otherwise be linear elements for a single mobility of carrier. Unless very many points are measured, the passing of straight lines through a succession of points to determine elbows is dangerously misleading (72). On the basis of such elbows and the analysis of many curves, Vassails reported the presence of *distinct mobility groups of large ions.* He reported, with some confidence, mobilities in the following classes: 4.3-5.5, 1.2-1.7, 1.1-1.3, 0.9-1.03, 0.75-0.85, and 0.60-0.65, all times 10^{-3} cm/sec per volt/cm. Vassails has kindly sent the author one of his data sheets. From these it would appear that in some cases enough points were observed to justify accepting the breaks. Vassails admits that some of his observed breaks may be spurious. However, enough data are at hand to indicate the existence of several mobilities.

The difference in mobilities need not be ascribed to grouping of the droplets in size. Later analysis has revealed that the nuclei may all be of about the same size. Vassails ascribed the difference in observed mobilities to multiple charges. Recent measurements by W. B. Kunkel (62) in NH_4Cl, for particles of about 0.5 to 2 microns in size, confirm that small particles may pick up multiple-equilibrium charges over some time in air.

While some of Vassails's data may be open to question, what is not open to question is *that he created the ions by creating the nuclei.* He did this primarily by subjecting his gases to ultraviolet light of varying wave lengths, or to X-rays. The gases used were not pure. They were filtered to remove gross particles, and comprised such gases as CO_2, H_2, and air, all of them containing probably an equilibrium amount of moisture. The active ultraviolet light was transmitted from powerful sources through windows of quartz, thin plastic, or other material. The shorter were the wave lengths, the more active was the ultraviolet. The nuclei grew in number and size with the duration of illumination.

These nuclei probably were the same as those that Pollock *had filtered out* of his air, but *did not regenerate,* because he used no ultraviolet light. Thus, Pollock observed no large ions in filtered air. The large ions were produced by the acquisition of charges by the nuclei through picking up the normal ions produced by natural ionization. If moderate external ionization was used, the nuclei acquired their charges more rapidly. There were not more nuclei produced by ionizing agencies unless the external X-radiation was intense.

Vassails estimated the charge variation responsible for mobility groups observed as lying between 1 and 10 electrons, which is not unreasonable in view of Kunkel's observations of equilibrium charges on NH_4Cl particles. If these charges were appropriately chosen, Vassails calculated that in general the nuclei had the same radius (about 8.8×10^{-6} cm), as computed from the Stokes-Cunningham law. These ions had mobilities lying between 1.2 and 0.52×10^{-3} cm/sec per volt/cm. Since the size calculated indicated that they could be seen in an ultramicroscope, he observed the chamber with such a device during the nucleus formation by ultraviolet irradiation. Filtered air showed no particles. On illumination through a thin quartz window with light from a mercury arc, small particles appeared, of scattering intensity and of size smaller than those of tobacco smoke. The number increased with time or irradiation up to 10 minutes, when 20 were visible in the field at once. Change of air removed them. When CS_2 was placed in the chamber, the ultraviolet light produced innumerable bright nuclei. On illumination, this same substance also led to the copious production of Langevin ions when studied electrically. The radius of the nuclei was estimated as $5\text{-}8 \times 10^{-6}$ cm. The density of the nuclei produced in air when 20 ions were in the field of view at once, was estimated as 25,000 per cm^3. Under similar conditions, the density of Langevin ions electrically measured, assuming each to carry unit charge, was 10^5. If the ions had had multiple charges, the number of nuclei *seen* visually was not very different from that of the nuclei and ions measured electrically.

It is thus clear that the nuclei leading to Langevin ion formation are the products of chemical reaction that produce droplets in moderately humidified air. Vassails studied different systems of substances as producers of nuclei, and indicated the following three classes of substances affecting the creation of nuclei under ultraviolet irradiation. (1) Activating vapors that facilitate or increase nucleation in air on illumination. These are SO_2, CS_2, H_2S, CCl_4, C_2HCl_2, and NO_2. All of these, by dissociation and oxidation, can give either hygroscopic substances like SO_3, HNO_3, HCl, etc.; and/or (according to Vassails) solid substances, e.g., colloidal sulphur with H_2S. (2) Neutral substances, such as NH_3, CH_3NH_2, C_2H_2, and CH_3OH. All of these substances react with ultraviolet light to give gaseous products which do not condense water vapor or give solid nuclei. (3) Inhibiting vapors, namely, C_2H_5OH, CH_3COH, CH_3COOH, and CH_3I. These substances have strong absorption bands in the ultraviolet region used, i.e., from 1,250 Å on up. They therefore inhibit by removing the activating wave length.

While Vassails agrees to the existence of aqueous condensation about hygroscopic nuclei where water vapor is present, he inclines to the belief that the *centers of nucleation*, in some cases like CS_2, are small, solid aggregates of substances, such as S, etc. In the case of CS_2, the photodissociation products are S and CS; and with CCl_4, the product is C_2Cl_6. S, CS_2, and C_2Cl_6 are solid, and S is not hygroscopic. Possibly, S dissolves in the CS_2 vapor and makes a droplet; CS and C_2Cl_6 do not. Thus, the aggregates of 10^6 atoms in the large ion might conceivably be solid particles. The amount of photodissociation gives enough particles, but it is hard to visualize the growth of solid particles of this size in the time of observation. On the other hand, in the artificial creation of NH_4Cl from NH_3 and HCl, Kunkel observed the growth of particles of 2 micron radius with time in the presence of enough NH_3 and HCl. In Kunkel's work, the electron microscope revealed that the NH_4Cl particles of 0.5 to 2 micron diameter were spherical, which pointed to small globules of water dissolving the NH_4Cl. In any case, the general nature of the intermediate and Langevin ions is now pretty well understood.

BIBLIOGRAPHY TO CHAPTER I

(1) J. Zeleny, Phil. Trans. Roy. Soc. *A195*, 193, 1900.
(2) L. B. Loeb, *Fundamental Processes of Electrical Discharge in Gases*, John Wiley & Sons, New York, 1939, pp. 12 ff.; L. B. Loeb, Jour. Franklin Inst. *196*, 771, 1923.
(3) L. B. Loeb, *Fundamental Processes of Electrical Discharge in Gases*, John Wiley & Sons, New York, 1939, p. 30, gives a more extensive list of methods and a critique in chap. I, part A.
(4) H. A. Erikson, Phys. Rev. *17*, 400, 1921; *18*, 100, 1921; *19*, 275, 1922; *23*, 110, 1924; *24*, 502, 1924; J. J. Mahoney, Phys. Rev. *33*, 217, 1929; Seville Chapman, Phys. Rev. *52*, 184, 1937.
(5) N. E. Bradbury, Phys. Rev. *40*, 508, 524, 1932.
(6) A. M. Tyndall and G. C. Grindley, Proc. Roy. Soc. *A110*, 341, 1926.
(7) A. M. Tyndall, L. H. Starr, and C. F. Powell, Proc. Roy. Soc. *A121*, 172, 1928; A. M. Tyndall, Proc. Roy. Soc. *A129*, 162, 1930; *A134*, 125, 1931; L. Brata, Proc. Roy. Soc. *A141*, 454, 1933; R. J. Munson, A. M. Tyndall, and K. Hoselitz, Proc. Roy. Soc. *A172*, 28, 1939; R. J. Munson and A. M. Tyndall, Proc. Roy. Soc. *A177*, 187, 1941; H. G. David and R. J. Munson, as well as K. Hoselitz, Proc. Roy. Soc. *A177*, 192, 1941.
(8) N. E. Bradbury and R. A. Nielsen, Phys. Rev. *49*, 388, 1936; R. A. Nielsen, Phys. Rev. *50*, 950, 1936; R. A. Nielsen and N. E. Bradbury, Phys. Rev. *51*, 69, 1937.
(9) J. S. Townsend and H. T. Tizard, Proc. Roy. Soc. *A88*, 336, 1913; A. V. Hershey, Phys. Rev. *54*, 237, 1938; *56*, 909, 1939 (for positive ions); W. P. Allis and H. W. Allen, Phys. Rev. *52*, 703, 1937. L. G. H. Huxley and A. A. Zaazou, Proc. Roy. Soc. *A196*, 402, 1949, give the latest corrections to electron application. An extensive discussion, including Bailey's method, is given by R. H. Healey and J. W. Reed in their book, *The Behaviour of Slow Electrons in Gases*, Amalgamated Wireless Press (Australasia), Ltd., Sydney, 1941.
(10) H. F. Lusk, Master's thesis, Univ. Calif., May, 1927; A. M. Cravath, Phys. Rev. *34*, 605, 1929; N. E. Bradbury, Phys. Rev. *44*, 883, 1933; L. B. Loeb, Phys. Rev. *48*, 684, 1935.

(11) P. Langevin, Ann. Chim. Phys. *28*, 317, 495, 1903; *5*, 245, 1905.

(12) K. T. Compton, Rev. Mod. Phys. *2*, 218, 1930.

(13) G. B. M. Sutherland, Phil. Mag. *18*, 341, 1909; E. M. Wellisch, Phil. Trans. Roy. Soc. *A209*, 249, 1909.

(14) P. Langevin, Ann. Chim. Phys. *5*, 245, 1905.

(15) H. R. Hassé, Phil. Mag. *1*, 139, 1926.

(16) J. J. Thomson, Phil. Mag. *47*, 337, 1924.

(17) L. B. Loeb, Phil. Mag. *48*, 446, 1924; *49*, 517, 1925.

(18) A. M. Tyndall and C. F. Powell, Proc. Roy. Soc. *A129*, 162, 1930; *A134*, 125, 1930; *A136*, 145, 1932; C. F. Powell and L. Brata, Proc. Roy. Soc. *A138*, 117, 1932; L. Brata, Proc. Roy. Soc. *A141*, 454, 1933.

(19) J. H. Mitchell and K. E. W. Ridler, Proc. Roy. Soc. *A146*, 911, 1934.

(20) A. M. Tyndall and A. F. Pearce, Proc. Roy. Soc. *A149*, 434, 1935; A. F. Pearce, Proc. Roy. Soc. *A155*, 490, 1936.

(21) K. Hoselitz, Proc. Roy. Soc. *A177*, 200, 1941.

(22) A. V. Hershey, Phys. Rev. *56*, 916, 1939.

(23) H. Margenau, Philosophy of Science *8*, 603, 1941.

(24) V. M. Goldschmidt, Trans. Faraday Soc. *25*, 253, 1929.

(25) H. R. Hassé and W. R. Cook, Phil. Mag. *12*, 554, 1931.

(26) H. S. W. Massey and C. B. Mohr, Proc. Roy. Soc. *A144*, 188, 1931.

(27) R. Meyerott, Phys. Rev. *66*, 242, 1944.

(28) R. J. Munson and K. Hoselitz, Proc. Roy. Soc. *A172*, 43, 1939.

(29) M. A. Biondi and S. C. Brown, Phys. Rev. *75*, 1700, 1949; *76*, 1697, 1949; M. A. Biondi, Phys. Rev. *79*, 733, 1950; *83*, 1078, 1951.

(30) D. R. Bates, Phys. Rev. *77*, 718, 1950; *78*, 492, 1950.

(31) R. A. Johnson, B. T. McClure, and R. B. Holt, Phys. Rev. *80*, 376, 1950; P. Dandurand and R. B. Holt, Phys. Rev. *82*, 278, 818, 1951; A. Redfield and R. B. Holt, Phys. Rev. *82*, 874, 1951; R. B. Holt, J. M. Richardson, B. Howland, and B. T. McClure, Phys. Rev. *77*, 239, 1950.

(32) J. A. Hornbeck, Phys. Rev. *80*, 297, 1950; *83*, 374, 1951; G. H. Wannier, Phys. Rev. *82*, 458, 1951; J. A. Hornbeck, Phys. Rev. *84*, 615; J. P. Molnar, Phys. Rev. *84*, 621, 1951; J. A. Hornbeck, Phys. Rev. *84*, 1072, 1951.

(33) R. L. F. Boyd, Proc. Phys. Soc. Lon. *A63*, 543, 1950.

(34) T. Holstein, Phys. Rev. *82*, 567, 1951.

(35) R. J. Munson and A. M. Tyndall, Proc. Roy. Soc. *A177*, 187, 1941.

(36) K. T. Compton, Rev. Mod. Phys. *2*, 210, 1930.

(37) G. D. Yarnold, Phil. Mag. *38*, 186, 1947.

(38) L. B. Loeb, *Fundamental Processes of Electrical Discharge in Gases*, John Wiley & Sons, New York, 1939, p. 34; L. B. Loeb, Jour. Franklin Inst. *196*, 4, 537, 1923.

(39) R. J. Munson, A. M. Tyndall, and K. Hoselitz, Proc. Roy. Soc. *A172*, 28-54, 1939.

(40) L. B. Loeb, Phys. Rev. *38*, 549, 1931.

(41) J. J. Mahoney, Phys. Rev. *33*, 217, 1929.

(42) J. Zeleny, Phys. Rev. *34*, 310, 1929; *36*, 35, 1930; *35*, 1441, 1930; *38*, 2239, 1931; R. N. Varney, Phys. Rev. *42*, 547, 1932; J. L. Hamshere, Proc. Roy. Soc. *A127*, 298, 1930; N. Fontell, Soc. Sci. Fenn. Comm. Phys. Math. *6*, 6, 17, 1932; M. LaPorte, Ann. Phys. *8*, 466, 1927.

(43) O. Luhr, Phys. Rev. *38*, 1730, 1931; *44*, 459, 1933.

(44) L. B. Loeb and M. F. Asheley, Proc. Nat. Acad. Sci. *10*, 351, 1924; L. B. Loeb, Proc. Nat. Acad. Sci. *12*, 35, 42, 677, 1926; L. B. Loeb and K. Dyk, Proc. Nat. Acad. Sci. *15*, 146, 1929; L. B. Loeb, Phys. Rev. *32*, 81, 1928.

(45) A. M. Tyndall and L. R. Phillips, Proc. Roy. Soc. *A111*, 477, 1926; H. F. Mayer, Phys. Zeits. *27*, 513, 1926; *28*, 637, 1926.

(46) F. Bloch and N. E. Bradbury, Phys. Rev. *48*, 689, 1935.

(47) A. Blanc, Jour. Phys. 7, 825, 1908.

(48) A. W. Overhauser, Phys. Rev. *76*, 250, 1949.

(49) L. B. Loeb, Phys. Rev. *8*, 633, 1916; Kia-Lok Yen, Phys. Rev. *11*, 337, 1918.

(50) A. M. Tyndall, *The Mobility of Positive Ions in Gases*, Cambridge University Press, 1938, chap. IV.

(51) H. Mott and H. S. W. Massey, *The Theory of Atomic Collisions*, Oxford University Press, 1933, chap. III.

(52) W. R. Haseltine, Jour. Math. Phys. *18*, 174, 1939; J. H. Cahn, Phys. Rev. *75*, 293, 838, 1949; W. P. Allis, Phys. Rev. *76*, 146, 1949; L. Landau, Phys. Rev. 77, 467, 1950.

(53) Sydney Chapman and T. G. Cowling, *The Mathematical Theory of Nonuniform Gases*, Cambridge University Press, 1939, sections 18.7-18.74. Other references are there indicated.

(54) J. A. Smit, Physica *3*, 543, 1937.

(55) H. W. Allen, Phys. Rev. *50*, 707, 1937.

(56) H. S. W. Massey and C. B. Mohr, Proc. Roy. Soc. *A144*, 544, 1931.

(57) F. B. Pidduck, Proc. Lon. Math. Soc. *15*, 89, 1915.

(58) P. Langevin, Compt. Rend. *61*, 232, 1905; Le Radium *4*, 218, 1907; J. A. McClelland and D. Kennedy, Proc. Roy. Irish Acad. Sci. *30*, 71, 1912; J. A. Pollock, Proc. Roy. Soc. N. S. Wales *43*, 198, 1909.

(59) J. A. Pollock, Phil. Mag. *29*, 514, 617, 1915.

(60) R. A. Millikan, *The Electron*, University of Chicago Press, 1917-1925, chap. III ff.

(61) Seville Chapman, Physics *5*, 150, 1934; W. B. Kunkel, Jour. App. Phys. *21*, 820, 1950.

(62) W. B. Kunkel, Jour. App. Phys. *21*, 833, 1950.

(63) W. B. Kunkel and J. W. Hansen, Rev. Sci. Inst. *21*, 304, 1950.

(64) G. R. Wait, Phys. Rev. *48*, 383, 1935. Also communicated in a letter from G. R. Wait, December 27, 1934.

(65) Gerard Vassails, *Large Gaseous Ions* (thesis), Faculty of Sciences, University of Paris series H2117, May 1, 1948.

(66) G. R. Wait and O. W. Torreson, Terrest. Mag. and Ats. Elect. *39*, 111, 1934; G. R. Wait, Phys. Rev. *48*, 383, 1935.

(67) O. W. Torreson, Terrest. Mag. and Ats. Elect. *39*, 65, 1934; J. J. Nolan, R. K. Boylan, and G. P. DeSachy, Proc. Roy. Irish. Acad. Sci. 37, 1, 1925.

(68) J. J. Thomson, *Conduction of Electricity through Gases*, Cambridge University Press, 1931, 3d ed., vol. 1, pp. 320-333.

(69) L. B. Loeb, A. F. Kip, and A. W. Einarsson, Jour. Chem. Phys. *6*, 264, 1938.

(70) E. J. Workman and S. E. Reynolds, report at conference on thunderstorm electricity under U. S. Air Force, Air Material Command, Geophysical Research Directorate, and the University of Chicago, Chicago, April 10-14, 1950 (University of Chicago Department of Meteorology, sec. IV, p. 38, October, 1950).

(71) Seville Chapman, Phys. Rev. *52*, 184, 1937; *54*, 520, 528, 1938.

(72) W. B. Haines, Phil. Mag. *30*, 503, 1915; *31*, 339, 1916; J. J. Nolan, Proc. Roy. Irish. Acad. Sci. *36*, 31, 1922; Phys. Rev. *24*, 16, 1924; H. B. Wahlin, Phys. Rev. *25*, 630, 1925; J. J. Nolan and T. E. Nevin, Proc. Roy. Soc. *A127*, 155, 1930. In refutation, see O. Blackwood, Phys. Rev. *19*, 281, 1922; *20*, 999, 1922; L. B. Loeb, Phys. Rev. *25*, 101, 1925; K. Przibram, *Handbuch der Physik*, vol. 22, chap. IV, part 1, pp. 363-365.

(73) M. A. Biondi, Phys. Rev. *79*, 733, 1950.

(74) M. A. Biondi, Phys. Rev. *83*, 1078, 1951.

(75) M. A. Biondi and T. Holstein, Phys. Rev. *87*, 962, 1951; A. V. Phelps and S. C. Brown, Phys. Rev. *86*, 102, 1952.

(76) D. Alpert, Jour. App. Phys. *24*, 810, 1953; *25*, 202, 1954; Rev. Sci. Inst. *22*, 536, 1951; *21*, 571, 1950.

(77) A. Doehring, Zeits. f. Naturforschung *7a*, 253, 1952.

(78) K. B. Persson, Sixth Conference on Gaseous Electronics, Washington, D. C., October 23, 1953. (Special paper.)

(79) R. N. Varney, Phys. Rev. *88*, 362, 1952; *89*, 708, 1953; Bell Telephone Laboratories technical report (Mem. 52-110-53), August 23, 1952.

(80) E. J. Lauer, Jour. App. Phys. *23*, 300, 1952; E. Gatti, L. Colli, and U. Facchini, Phys. Rev. *80*, 92, 1950.

(81) L. M. Chanin and M. A. Biondi, Phys. Rev. *94*, 910, 1954.

(82) R. H. Fowler, *Statistical Mechanics*, Cambridge University Press, 1929, pp. 211 ff., and pp. 227, 229.

(83) P. Herreng, Compt. Rend. *217*, 75, 1943.

(84) E. D. Klema and J. S. Allen, Phys. Rev. 7, 661, 1950; E. J. M. Kirschner and D. S. Toffolo, Jour. App. Phys. *23*, 594, 1952.

(85) H. Raether, Zeits. f. Phys. *108*, 91, 1937.

(86) S. Bloom and H. Margenau, Phys. Rev. *85*, 670, 1952.

(87) G. H. Wannier, Phys. Rev. *83*, 281, 1951; *87*, 795, 1952; Bell System Tech. Jour. *32*, 170, 1953.

(88) S. Geltman, Phys. Rev. *90*, 808, 1953.

(89) O. Tuxen, Zeits. f. Phys. *103*, 418, 1936.

(90) L. B. Loeb, Jour. Franklin Inst. *196*, 537, 771, 1923.

(91) R. Schade, Zeits. f. Phys. *105*, 595, 1937; *108*, 353, 1938; R. Buttner, Zeits. f. Phys. *111*, 750, 1939; M. J. Druyvesteyn and F. M. Penning, Rev. Mod. Phys. *12*, 87, 1940.

(92) A. D. MacDonald and S. C. Brown, Phys. Rev. *75*, 413, 1949.

(93) M. A. Biondi, to be published, Phys. Rev., 1954.

(94) T. Kihara, Rev. Mod. Phys. *24*, 45, 1952.

Chapter II

THE DIFFUSION OF CARRIERS IN GASES

---

§ 1. Introduction.

Since carriers in gases are in constant contact with the ambient gas molecules, they partake of the random chaotic heat motions of the molecules. In consequence of the character of such motions, any accumulation or concentration of carriers of one type in a gas will in time (for purely geometrical reasons) move in such a fashion as to spread in space, decreasing the initial concentration. This process is termed *diffusion,* and diffusive motion is ever present and superposed on all more directed motions. Historically, the early study (in 1899) of diffusion of ions in gases yielded important data concerning the electronic and ionic charges (1). In 1913, J. S. Townsend and H. T. Tizard (2) made studies of electron diffusion in gases in uniform electrical fields in order to evaluate electron energies as a function of the ratio X/p. Other than that, the study of diffusion was relatively neglected in the intervening years until in 1925, V. A. Bailey (3), (4), in Townsend's laboratory, applied it in an evaluation of the attachment coefficient of electrons in gases. At the same time, G. Hertz (5), in a theoretical analysis of the energies of electrons in electrical fields in gases, called attention to the importance of diffusion. Since then, as time has gone on, the importance of diffusive motions in numerous aspects of electrical discharge and conduction in gases has been increasingly recognized.

In the motions of carriers in gases in fields of relatively low X/p, the diffusion of the otherwise sharply defined geometrical boundaries of carrier concentrations in time and space is very marked, thus complicating all measurements. Under the same conditions, the loss of electrons to the cathode by back diffusion is so extensive as to lower the secondary emission of electrons by factors of 10 to 100, again seriously affecting breakdown thresholds. In all discharges confined by containing walls at relatively low pressures, and especially at high electron energies, the radial ambipolar diffusion of electrons and ions to the walls causes a serious loss of carriers, thus affecting the discharge economy. In microwave breakdown studies the principal loss of carriers at pressures under 1 mm consists of ambipolar diffusion to the walls. Such losses thus determine the breakdown thresholds in the gases. The very important role played by diffusion at plasma surfaces, leading to sheath formation and governing the use of probes, must also be mentioned. Finally, by utilizing the ambipolar-diffusion loss of carriers from a plasma, the mean diffusion coefficient of the prevalent positive ions can be determined; and where there is a unique ion, the ion may be identified by the mobility derived from the diffusion coefficient. Thus, the fundamental principles and characteristics of this important phenomenon must be understood early in the study of gaseous behavior.

§ 2. Definition of Diffusion Coefficient and Statement of Basic Relations.

It should be noted that in general, the second-order partial differential equations characteristic of diffusive motion in space and time present lengthy and awkward mathematical tasks in their solution. The situation is rendered more difficult, since the solutions are closely tied in with the diverse and very numerically specific boundary conditions, the solution for each case of which presents a separate problem. Thus, in what follows, the differential equations only will be presented, and the solutions needed will be indicated for specific values of variables used. It may be added that these same complications have caused the diffusive actions to be ignored in the solution of many discharge or other calculations in which they should have been included.

In what follows there will be given a discussion of the nature of diffusion and a statement of the theoretical approaches to the methods of study. There will then follow sections on the early measurements of diffusion, the relation between the coefficient of diffusion and mobility, and an effective experimental method of establishing this important ratio. Next will be given the statistical considerations of diffusive motion and relations needed in making rough corrections for average effects. There will then follow a short section on the principles of ambipolar diffusion. The more detailed application of diffusion studies to the solution of special problems must, however, be taken up under the section appropriate to that study.

One of the advantages in the study of diffusion of ions or electrons in gases in contrast to the study of similar problems for neutral gas molecules, lies in the fact that one deals with relatively small concentrations of tagged, easily measured carriers, diffusing in a gaseous medium of a much greater concentration of its own neutral particles. Hence, with ions, unlike the problem of diffusion in gases, where the *interdiffusion* of two gases must be studied, the much simpler process of *self-diffusion* is largely encountered.

Consider, for instance, a mass of identical ions or electrons localized at an instant in a given concentration at a point in a gas. Such concentrations may be generated photoelectrically, thermionically, and by corona discharge of either sign for either electrons or negative and positive ions. In general, densities of ionization in gases achieved by such means are not high, perhaps ranging at the outside to 10^9 ions per cm^3. In contrast to this, there are about 3×10^{19} molecules per cm^3 in a gas at n.t.p. In an aqueous molar *solution* of ions, with 6×10^{23} ions in 1,000 cm^3, the ionization is even more dense. The average distance between ions in a molar solution is $1/\sqrt[3]{6 \times 10^{20}} = 1.15 \times 10^{-7}$ cm, while in the case of a thoroughly ionized gas it is of the order of 10^{-4} cm.

The forces between ions at 10^{-7} cm are such that the potential energy is of the order of 1.5 e.v., which is far greater than the energy of thermal agitation at 0° C. In molar solutions, then, electrostatic forces are predominant and diffusion of individual particles is complicated by forces between individual ions. With 10^{12} ions per cm^3, the average kinetic energy at 0° C. is twenty times the potential energy between ions. Thus, under most conditions where carrier diffusion in gases is considered, the electrostatic forces between individual carriers can be neglected.[1] The carriers may be regarded as merely tagged, charged bodies whose Brownian motions in space and time are independent. They are the direct result of thermal motions of the surrounding molecules, or of their own proper thermal energies where these are not in equilibrium with the gas molecules among which they move. The latter contingency exists when electrical fields act on them.

In consequence of this thermal motion, consider an infinite plane slab dx cm thick separating two ionized regions. In one of these regions, N_1 carriers per cm^3 of mass m and thermal velocity u are

---

[1] If ion concentrations exceed 10^8 ions/cm^3, another situation can arise. This comes from the electrostatic space-charge fields stemming from segregated groups of ions of one sign. Since electrons frequently have higher energies than the ions, and since, because of their small inertia, they move much more rapidly than the more massive ions, they will diffuse out of the plasma of equal numbers of ions and electrons. If they reach a surface, they will charge this negatively. Then the positive ion excess and the negative wall create a field drawing positive ions to the surface. This produces a special type of diffusion called "ambipolar diffusion." Such conditions do not permit of free individual carrier diffusion, and this state might be taken as defining the beginning of plasma formation.

moving at random. In the other, there are N_2 carriers per cm³ in equilibrium with the gas and having the same mass and velocity as those on the other side. The carriers of concentration N_1 will exert a partial pressure p_1, given by $p_1 = (1/3) N_1 mu^2$, while those of concentration N_2 will exert a partial pressure p_2, given by $p_2 = (1/3) N_2 mu^2$ in the gas. If the plane partition is removed, the random-heat motions, for purely geometrical reasons, will carry more carriers from N_1 to N_2 per second than in the reverse sense. Hence, there will be a *net flow of carriers* from the N_1 side to the N_2 side. The flow will effectively be produced by the difference between N_1 and N_2. This follows from simple kinetic theory, which gives the number of molecules striking unit surface per second as $N\bar{c}/4$, with the average velocity $\bar{c}$ constant.[2] If $(N_1 - N_2)$ is multiplied by $(1/3) mu^2$, it is possible to write that $(1/3) mu^2 (N_1 - N_2) = (p_1 - p_2) = dp$. Thus, it is possible to ascribe the flow or diffusion to the action of the partial pressure difference dp, acting across the slab dx cm thick. It is clear that the flow will be faster the greater dp, the smaller dx; and that the flow will be proportional to the area A of the plane involved. If the masses of the carriers differ from those of the gas molecules, there will also be an effective *mass* transfer, and a mass velocity of flow. At present, however, only the number of carriers and their densities need be regarded.

From what has gone before, it is not surprising that simple, controlled experiments with gases have shown that dn, the net number of charged carriers or molecules flowing by diffusion along the x axis across an area A in a time dt for the case of the two infinite planes dx apart, with a pressure difference dp across them, is given by $dn = -B(dp/dx) A\, dt$. Since dp is proportional to the difference $(N_1 - N_2) = dN$ of the carrier concentrations; i.e., $dp = (\frac{1}{2}) mu^2 dN$, it is possible to write

$$(2.1) \qquad \frac{dn}{dt} = -DA \frac{dN}{dx}.$$

Here dn is the *net number* of carriers crossing in dt, and N is the *concentration* of carriers, while constants B and D are related by the difference between p and N. The constant of proportionality D is called the "coefficient of diffusion." This has the dimensions $L^2 T^{-1}$, and its reciprocal is characteristic of the resistance offered by the gas to the flow of the carriers. The coefficient D is thus a constant of the properties of the gas and carriers as regards the

---

[2] The velocity $\bar{c}$ is a special average velocity, differing from, but proportional to, the velocity u used above.

"transparency" of the gas for the carriers. It should therefore not be surprising to find that D is fundamentally related to the mobility k of the carriers in an electrical field. The negative sign in the equation indicates that the flow is always determined relative to the distance x in such a fashion that it goes from high to low values of N; i.e., dN/dx has a negative slope.

While the equation given is the defining equation for the coefficient of self-diffusion derived for the simple case of steady-state flow along one dimension, it is not of direct value in the solution of many problems. The common problems encountered require the prediction from the concentrations at one time and in one region, given the variation of concentration in that region with time, of what the concentrations will be at any other time and in other regions. The general differential equation expressing the changes of concentration in time and in the three Cartesian co-ordinates x, y, and z, derived from the defining equation above, is given by

$$(2.2) \qquad \frac{dN}{dt} = D \left(\frac{\partial^2 N}{\partial x^2} + \frac{\partial^2 N}{\partial y^2} + \frac{\partial^2 N}{\partial z^2} \right) = D \nabla^2 N.$$

The derivation of this equation from the simple relation defining D is analogous to that for the Fourier heat-conduction equation

$$\frac{d\theta}{dt} = h^2 \left(\frac{\partial^2 \theta}{\partial x^2} + \frac{\partial^2 \theta}{\partial y^2} + \frac{\partial^2 \theta}{\partial z^2} \right) = h^2 \nabla^2 \theta.$$

This is derived from the basic equation defining the coefficient of heat conduction K, namely, $MC d\theta/dt = -(KA) \, d\theta/dx$. Here M is the mass, C is the specific heat, and θ is the temperature. In this case, $h^2 = K/\rho C$, with ρ the density of the material and h^2 the "temperature diffusivity."

The solution of the equation for the distributions of ion density or heat in three dimensions as a function of time comes from the solution of this linear partial differential equation of the second order. The form of the solution depends on conditions imposed by a given problem, such as how N varies with t at some point, and the values of N as a function of x, y, and z at some given time t. Such information furnishes the so-called boundary conditions imposed by the problem. Solution of the equation of this type for N as a $f(x, y, z, t)$ is simplified if the variation of N with t can be expressed as the sum of a series of sine and cosine terms developed by Fourier for just this purpose. The equations have been set up and solved in many thermal problems. The solution of the equations in the thermal analogue may in some cases aid in the solution of the problem for the case of diffusion. It is clear from this that, in general, the inclusion of diffusion with the differential equations of current flow in a discharge can very much complicate solution of the problem. Thus, in many cases, the diffusion terms for the sake of simplicity are omitted in the general solutions for currents in gases when they should be included.

§ 3. The Experimental Determination of D for Gaseous Ions.

For many years the only study of ionic diffusion was that done by J. S. Townsend in the late nineteenth century (1). At that time the study had important theoretical significance. The first measurements of the coefficient of diffusion of ions were made, using an air-blast method. In a chamber C of figure 2.1, ions of both signs were generated by X-rays in the volume. They were sorted out by fields between wire gauzes perpendicular to the gas stream at C and T when desired. The air blast transverse to the direction of the rays in C carried the ions into a battery of tubes T T. The tubes in this battery had a small radius a, so that diffusion to the walls far outweighed the volume recombination when ions of both signs were used. Usually, the ions were sorted out by the fields between gauzes. Otherwise, the apparatus was designed so that negative ions produced by shining ultraviolet light onto a negative electrode in C could be drawn by a field across the chamber C. There were several batteries of equal numbers of metal tubes having different lengths, x_1, x_2, etc.,

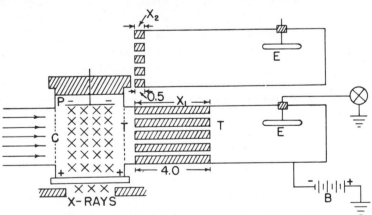

Fig. 2.1. Townsend's air-blast apparatus for measuring the coefficient of diffusion of ions in gases. The tube nests of length x_1 and x_2 were mounted on an axis, so that like the chambers of a revolver, one or the other length of tube could be swung into place.

and constant radius a. The battery of tubes was built into a solid wall, open at both ends. The batteries, with an adjacent downstream section of large diameter enveloping metal tubing, could be slipped into each other's place relative to the collecting chamber E, somewhat analogous to the chambers in a revolver. At a convenient downstream position beyond the tube battery was placed a collecting electrode E connected to an electrometer which measured the ions escaping diffusion beyond the tubes T T. The field drawing the ions out to E was given by a battery B. The ionization was started, as was the constant-velocity nonturbulent gas stream, and allowed to steady down with one set of tubes x_1 in place. When a steady state was reached, the current i_1 was read at E. Then the tubes x_2 were rotated into place, and at a steady state the current i_2 was recorded. It was then possible theoretically to evaluate the ratios $i_1/i_2 = n_1/n_2$ of current to E under diffusion through x_1 and x_2.

Townsend used sets of tubes with ratios $x_1/x_2 = 4$ and $x_1/x_2 = 8$. The differential equations pertaining to this arrangement were set up for the diffusion of carriers to the walls of a cylinder of radius a in a uniformly ionized column of gas passing downstream a distance x with a velocity v. Solutions of the equations with the boundary conditions actually used gave the value of the ratios

$$(2.3) \qquad \frac{i_1}{i_2} = \frac{n_1 e}{n_2 e} = \frac{0.195 \epsilon^{\frac{-7.313\, Dx_1}{2a^2 V}} + 0.0243 \epsilon^{\frac{-44.5\, Dx_1}{2a^2 V}}}{0.195 \epsilon^{\frac{-7.313\, Dx_2}{2a^2 V}} + 0.0243 \epsilon^{\frac{-44.5\, Dx_2}{2a^2 V}}}.$$

Here V is the velocity of the gas stream and D is the coefficient of diffusion. Using plausible values of a quantity $z = 7.31\, Dx_1/2a^2 V$ appropriate to the apparatus, it was possible to compute a set of

TABLE 2.1

Early Values of Townsend for Coefficient of Diffusion D for Positive and Negative Ions in Some Gases, Including Interdiffusion Coefficients of Similar Gases for Comparison

Gas	D_+ Ions cm2/sec	D_- Ions cm2/sec	D for Molecules Gas into Gas cm2/sec	
Air	0.028	0.043	O_2 into N_2	0.171
CO_2	0.023	0.026	CO_2 into N_2O	1.5-1.0
H_2	0.123	0.190	H_2 into N_2	0.739

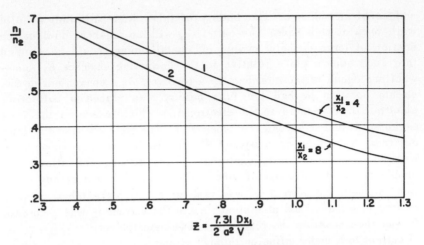

Fig. 2.2. Computed curve for the ratio of currents n_1/n_2 plotted against a parameter $z = (7.31\ Dx_1)/(2a^2V)$ for values of the ratios of tube lengths $x_1/x_2 = 4$ and $x_1/x_2 = 8$. From values of the ratio of currents picked up when tubes x_1 and x_2 were in place, the corresponding abscissae of the curve give z, and from the values of x_1, V, and a, D can be determined.

curves for n_1/n_2 for each ratio, $x_1/x_2 = 4$ and $x_1/x_2 = 8$, used in the measurement as a function of z. Then, from the curves shown in figure 2.2, evaluation of i_1/i_2 for a given ratio x_1/x_2 at once fixes a point on the appropriate curve, and this yields a value of z. Since all quantities except D in the relation for z are known constants of the measurement, D is evaluated.

Using this method, Townsend in 1899 found the values of D for gaseous ions in the several gases to be those noted in table 2.1.[3] For comparison are given the interdiffusion coefficients of some gaseous systems similar to the ions used.

From the table it is to be noted that, in general, diffusion coefficients of uncharged molecules are from three to five times as great as those for ions. A similar ratio was early noted between ion mobilities and those computed neglecting the electrostatic forces.

As will be seen later, theory predicts that the ratio of mobility to diffusion coefficient $k/D = Ne/p$. By taking the ratio between the mobility k from Zeleny's work and his own diffusion coefficients, Townsend in 1899 was able to evaluate Ne from $pk/D = Ne$. The value

[3]It is to be noted that these experimental values are orienting magnitudes only as they suffer from all the ills of gas-blast methods. In Townsend's early work the values were fortunately comparable in accuracy and character to similar air-blast mobility values such as those obtained by J. Zeleny (1). This led to a successful confirmation of theory much needed at this time.

observed was that corresponding to the Faraday constant applying to the Loschmidt number of univalent ions. At that time the charge on the electron had not been evaluated, and the large ratio of e/m for electrons had thrown some doubt on the assumption that the electronic charge was equal to that of the H^+ ion in electrolysis. The evaluation of Ne by Townsend for photoelectrons and for ions produced by X-rays indicated that electrons carried the same value of the charge as univalent ions in solution, and thus that the electron was a new entity of mass $1/1,837$ that of the H atom.

§ 4. The Ratio between Diffusion Coefficient and Mobility.

The ratio between mobility and diffusion coefficient for ions indicated above must now be derived, for it plays a very important role in many discharge phenomena. In a gas an electrical field X acting with a force Xe on an ion gives it a uniform *drift* velocity $v = kX$. Gas ions urged by their partial pressure will diffuse with velocity v, which is related to the coefficient of diffusion D. Since the resistance of the medium to the motion of the ion with a given velocity v is assumed independent of the type of force acting to move it, it is justifiable to equate the diffusion force for the same velocity to the electrical field force, and thus get the ratio of k/D.

Consider a *unit* area normal to the direction of diffusion along the x axis. The *number* n of ions diffusing through unit area per second is $n = (D)dN/dx$, disregarding the sign and calling N the concentration of the ions. The velocity of diffusion v across unit area is defined by writing $n = vN$. Accordingly, the velocity v is given by $v = (D/N)(dN/dx)$. The partial pressure p is proportional to concentration N, i.e., $p = bN$ with $b = 1/3\ mu^2$. Consequently, $dp = bdN$ and $dN/N = dp/p$. It thus follows that $v = (D/p)(dp/dx)$, or that $dp/dx = pv/D$. For 1 cm^3 of gas, the force acting on unit area across $dx = 1$ cm is dp/dx (1 cm^2) (1 cm) $= dp/dx$. This is the force on N ions. For one ion the force of the partial pressure is $(1/N)\ dp/dx$. From the relation $dp/dx = pv/D$ above, the diffusive force at velocity v on one ion is therefore $f_D = pv/ND$. The force of the field on an ion is $f_x = Xe$. Again, $v = kX$, whence it follows that $f_x = ve/k$, when it produces a velocity v. It is then possible to equate the force producing the same velocity v, such that $f_D = f_x = pv/DN = ve/k$. It at once follows that

$$(2.4) \qquad \frac{k}{D} = \frac{Ne}{p} .$$

If p is taken at 0° C. 760 mm, then N is the Loschmidt number, which is the number of molecules in 1 cm^3 at 0° C. 760 mm, for N was chosen as the number of ions per cm^3. Thus, Ne is the charge on 2.687×10^{19} ions in the cm^3, and p is the pressure in dynes per cm^2 at n.t.p.

The same law follows directly from kinetic theory if the kinetic-theory expressions for the mobility k and the coefficient of self-diffusion D following from the *same derivation procedure* are chosen. Thus, equation 1.1b for mobility reads

$$k = 0.815 \frac{e\,L}{m\,C_i} \sqrt{\frac{M+m}{M}}.$$

The corresponding expression for the diffusion coefficient is

(2.5) $$D = 0.815 \frac{C_i L}{3} \sqrt{\frac{m+M}{M}}.$$

It then follows at once that

(2.6) $$\frac{k}{D} = \frac{0.815 \sqrt{\dfrac{m+M}{M}}}{0.815 \sqrt{\dfrac{m+M}{M}}} \frac{3\,Le}{LmC_i^2} = \frac{e}{(1/3)mC_i^2} = \frac{Ne}{(1/3)NmC_i^2} = \frac{Ne}{p_t}.$$

The value of the ratio $k/D = Ne/p_t$ may be computed for monovalent ions as follows: Let e be the charge on monovalent ions in electrolysis, and k equal to the mobility in cm/sec per volt/cm. Furthermore, $22,414\ Ne = N_A e$, which is the Faraday equal to 9,650 absolute e.m.u. per gram atom equivalent. The pressure of one atmosphere $p = 1.013 \times 10^6$ dynes/cm^2, and the volt is 10^8 e.m.u. Thus, k/D becomes 12,810 as expressed in e.s.u. Since 1 e.s.u. = 300 volts, the value of k/D as usually measured and expressed in terms of cm^2/volt sec over cm^2 per sec is given by $k/D = 42.7$ volt^{-1}, or $D = 0.0235\ k$, with k in cm^2/sec. This exact relationship makes it unnecessary in practice to measure D, which is sometimes difficult, for the value of D is accurately given if k is measured. The *accurate* measurement of k is more readily achieved than that of D in the majority of cases.[4]

As earlier stated, Townsend in 1900 evaluated k/D for ions from his and Zeleny's (1) measurements, and found values of Ne of 1.25 to 1.03×10^{10} e.s.u./cm^3. For monovalent ions in solution, the value of Ne is 1.3×10^{10} e.s.u./cm^3. For negative ions, the values observed ranged from 1.25 to 1.31; while for positive ions, they ranged from

---

[4] In certain more recent studies involving microwave breakdown, k cannot be measured directly. Thus, the reverse procedure of inferring k from measured values of D is applied (6).

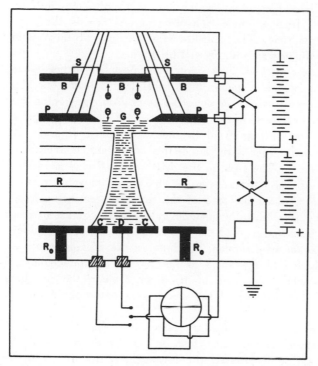

Fig. 2.3. Townsend's device for measuring the ratio of mobility k to diffusion coefficient D directly by observing the lateral spread of a beam of carriers moving in a vertical field X.

1.45 to 1.63 in O_2 and H_2. This agreement between theory and observation is *fortuitously good*, a fact that was unknown to Townsend. Fortunately for theoretical advance at that time, the agreement was as good as indicated. However, Townsend placed too much confidence in the accuracy of his experimental values, and ascribed the higher values observed for the positive ions to a possibility of the presence of doubly charged positive ions, while negative ions derived from the electrons carried the unit charge. In fact, from independent mobility data, James Franck concluded that perhaps 10% of the positive ions were doubly charged (7). This conclusion was based on an assumption that the doubling of the charge doubled the mobility. This is now recognized as a doubtful assumption with normal ions. Because of these conclusions, Townsend, alive to the difficulties of measuring k and D on different ions under different conditions in two independent measurements of k and D, devised a most original and ingenious method by which the *ratio* of k/D could directly be ascertained from a single measurement on ions in the same gas and at the same time. The ultimate implications of this method proved to be far-reaching indeed, as will be seen.

In the new method, ions were generated by X-rays coming through windows S of the chamber B P in figure 2.3. Fields appropriately directed drove positive or negative ions from the region B P through a circular aperture G in the lower plate P.[5] Between P and a grounded plate R_0, the uniform field in the drift space R some 10 cm long drove the ions from G to the central disc and concentric ring electrodes D and C. The field in the drift space R was maintained uniform by means of equipotential vanes. The whole chamber was in cylindrical symmetry about the axis of the ion beam emerging from G. In the drift space, the initially uniform cylindrical column or beam of ions emerging from G traversed the gas-filled space with a velocity $v = kX$. In the absence of diffusion, the ions in the column would all impinge on D, which had the same radius as G. In consequence of lateral diffusion during the time of traverse $t = d/v$ the ion beam spread laterally. Thus, some of the beam was intercepted on the annular disc C.

It is clear from elementary principles that the spreading of the beam must depend in some fashion on the ratio of k/D, the spread of the beam being greater, the larger is D relative to k. Thus, if u, v, and w are the velocities of the ions along the x, y, and z axes, x being the field axis, the numbers N_x, N_y, and N_z of ions moving across 1 cm² of area normal to the x, y, and z axes respectively, are

$$(2.7) \qquad N_x = uN = -D\frac{dN}{dx} + XkN,$$

$$(2.8) \qquad N_y = vN = -D\frac{dN}{dy},$$

and

$$(2.9) \qquad N_z = wN = -D\frac{dN}{dz}.$$

---

[5]In later work, in order to measure k/D and k for electrons in the same chamber, Townsend and his students used a rectangular entrance slit and a single disc electrode cut parallel to the slit axis at two points equidistant from the center. The equations were set up and solved for that geometry. Later, L. G. H. Huxley (4) conceived of a mobility device based on the more accurate coaxial cylindrical geometry.

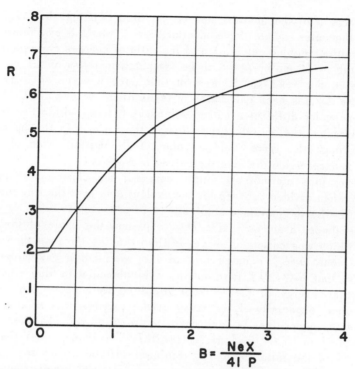

Fig. 2.4. Townsend's computed calibration curve relating $B = NeX/4lp$ as abscissae to the ratio R of currents caught by sector D to that caught by $D + C$.

The equation of continuity states that

(2.10)
$$\frac{\partial(Nu)}{\partial x} + \frac{\partial(Nv)}{\partial y} + \frac{\partial(Nw)}{\partial z} = 0.$$

Thus, calling N the concentration of ions, the equation of continuity becomes

(2.11)
$$-D\frac{\partial^2 N}{\partial x^2} + Xk\frac{\partial N}{\partial x} -D\frac{\partial^2 N}{\partial y^2} -D\frac{\partial^2 N}{\partial z^2} = 0,$$

whence

(2.12)
$$\nabla^2 N = \frac{\partial^2 N}{\partial x^2} + \frac{\partial^2 N}{\partial y^2} + \frac{\partial^2 N}{\partial z^2} = \frac{kX}{D}\frac{dN}{dx} = \frac{NeX}{P}\frac{dN}{dx}.$$

The equation may then be thrown into cylindrical coordinates and solved, putting in the boundary conditions imposed by the experiment. The length along x was chosen by Townsend as about 7 cm, with the radius a of the aperture and of the disc D being about 7.5 mm, while the outer radius of the annular disc C was 2.5 cm. Solution of the equation enabled calculation of the ratio of charges $R = n_1/(n_1 + n_2)$ collected by D and by $D + C$ to be computed in terms of the variable parameter $B = NeX/41p$. It is seen that once a curve such as that of figure 2.4 has been calculated in terms of the values of the dimensions used for different assumed values of B lying within the experimental range, the actual *observation* of the ratio R in the apparatus will through the curve yield a value of B. Multiplication of B by $41/X$ at once yields the existing values of $Ne/p = k/D$.

If the ions are not all singly charged, the observed values of $41B/X$ when divided by Ne/p for monovalent ions give the true *average* value of e for the ion-cloud studies.

The theory assumes that $k/D = Ne/p$, and the value of the ratio Ne/p which was computed above, implied that for the ions the energy of the ions $\frac{1}{2}mC_i^2$ equaled that of the surrounding gas molecules; namely, $\frac{1}{2}mC^2 = (3/2)kT$. It is not inconceivable that in high electrical fields the energy of the carriers could be well above that of the molecules, especially if the mass of the carriers was smaller than that of the molecules. In such case, the ratio of k/D observed would correspond to $\frac{1}{2}mC_i^2$, and not to $(3/2)kT$. This means that the p to be used in the ratio Ne/p as calculated will be higher by a factor of, say $\eta = \frac{1}{2}mC_i^2/(3/2)kT$. This occurs, since by kinetic theory for ions of velocity C_i, $p = (1/3)NmC_i^2$. If $\frac{1}{2}mC_i^2$ is actually greater than $\frac{1}{2}MC^2 = (3/2)kT$ for molecules of the gas, then it is permissible to write that

$$(2.13) \qquad p = (1/3)NmC_i^2 = \eta(1/3)NMC^2 = \eta(3/2)NkT = \eta p_{\text{mols}}.$$

Under such conditions, the quantity $41B/X$ observed when divided by the expected ratio of Ne/p_{mols} will be smaller than unity by a factor $1/\eta$. In this way it is possible to observe ionic, or carrier, energies above those belonging to the ambient molecules, and to determine the factor η by which their energies exceed $(3/2)kT$. It is therefore seen that this method is capable of useful application to problems well beyond that of detecting the multiple charge on ions.

Townsend and Haselfoot (8), however, first applied the method to the study of normal ions in air under standard conditions. For clean, dry gases the value of Ne for positive and negative ions *was the same*, and equal to the value calculated above from electrolysis within the limits of experimental uncertainty. By soiling the chamber with vaseline, high values were observed for Ne with positive ions.

These were at the time ascribed to multiply charged ions. The cause for this result is obscure. Because it came as a result of sloppy conditions purposefully introduced, it cannot be assumed to be very significant, for it is unlikely that multiply charged positive ions could have been observed in these gases over the times involved.

It must be noted here that while k may be independent of e because the free path L is inversely proportional to e, a proper evaluation of D introduces e into D through L, so that at all times $k/D = Ne/P$. The reason for the inability to detect multiply charged ions should be clear from the preceding chapter on ionic mobilities. There it was shown that though doubly charged ions are generated, they lose their double charge by Kallmann-Rosen effect in very short time intervals compared to those needed to measure diffusion, so that for most of these ions the charge will be unity.

The significant factors in Townsend's studies were the values of Ne/P observed for negative carriers at low pressures. These were observed to be surprisingly low, and obviously suggested that the energy of the carriers under these conditions was greater than that of the surrounding gas molecules.

§ 5. The Distribution of Particles in Space and Time under Diffusion; Average Velocities of Diffusion.

In 1905, A. Einstein considered the distribution in space and time of a group of particles moving independently of each other with chaotic heat motions. To simplify matters, consider an origin at $x = 0$ and consider the component of displacement along the x axis only as time goes on. At $x = 0$ there are N_0 particles at $t = 0$. According to the analysis, the number N_x out of the N_0 particles originally located at $x = 0$ at $t = 0$ that can be found to have components of displacement between x and $(x + dx)$ at time t is

(2.14)
$$N_x = \frac{N_0}{\sqrt{4\pi D t}} \epsilon^{-x^2/4Dt} \, dx.$$

Here D is the coefficient of diffusion. The form of the function of x as a function of time is the well-known Gaussian error curve. As time goes on the form remains inviolate, but its scale factor $4Dt$ increases. Since the number of particles is constant, the curve decreases in height (i.e., N_x/N_0 decreases) and flattens, extending farther and farther along the x axis. Such an evolution is depicted in figure 2.5 for negative ions in air at n.t.p. after 0.1, 1, and 10 seconds.

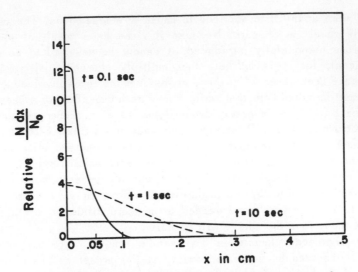

Fig. 2.5. Curves showing Gaussian distribution of ions along
the x direction after 0.1, 1, and 10 seconds of diffusion.

The expression also yields the relation that if N_0 is the ion *density*
in an elementary volume at $t = 0$, the density N at a distance r from
this volume at a time t produced by the diffusion of particles will
be given by

$$(2.15) \qquad N = \frac{N_0}{(4\pi Dt)^{3/2}} \epsilon^{-r^2/4Dt} .$$

From expression 2.14 it can be shown that the square root of the
average squared displacement along one axis is

$$(2.16) \qquad \sqrt{\overline{x^2}} = \sqrt{2Dt} .$$

For diffusion in two and three dimensions, the values are

$$(2.17) \qquad \sqrt{\overline{r^2}} = \sqrt{x^2 + y^2} = \sqrt{4Dt}$$

and

$$(2.18) \qquad \sqrt{\overline{r^2}} = \sqrt{x^2 + y^2 + z^2} = \sqrt{6Dt} ,$$

respectively.

The average displacement $\bar{x}$ is not the same as $\sqrt{\overline{x^2}}$, but is related to it by the expression

$$(2.19) \qquad \bar{x} = \sqrt{2/\pi} \, \sqrt{\overline{x^2}} = \sqrt{\frac{4Dt}{\pi}} .$$

If a finite number of such random displacements are observed, the probable value of $\bar{x}$ is given by $\bar{x} \pm (\sqrt{n}/n)\, \bar{x}$. In three dimensions, the value of

$$(2.20) \qquad\qquad \bar{r} = \sqrt{12Dt/\pi}\,.$$

These relations are useful in estimating the average dispersion of particles in time, or the average distance that a particle diffuses in a time t. Such data are handy in theoretical treatments and rough calculations.

Since D is readily obtained from $D = kp/Ne = 0.0235k$ cm²/sec in many cases, or since theory gives $D = \frac{1}{3}\bar{c}L$, the expressions can be solved for any given case and used where needed. For negative ions in air the value of k is 2.2 cm²/volt sec, yielding $D = 0.0518$ cm²/sec. For a free electron in air under the same conditions, k is of the order of 5×10^3 times that for the ion yielding $D_e = 259$ cm²/sec for electrons.

In t seconds, the value of $\bar{x}$ for ions is $\bar{x} = \sqrt{0.066\ t} = 0.257\sqrt{t}$ cm for ions, and $\bar{x} = 18.2\sqrt{t}$ cm for electrons. Thus, in the time of ordinary ion-mobility measurements, the ion displacement of 0.0257 cm in 10^{-2} sec is negligible compared to distances involved in measurement. The value of the average diffusion displacement for electrons is 1.82 cm. The latter may well be a considerable fraction of the drift space used.

The coefficient of diffusion D is obviously a function of gas density, pressure, temperature, and mass. Since, in the kinetic-theory derivation cogent to this text, the coefficient of diffusion (2.5) is set as

$$D = 0.815\ \frac{C_i L}{3}\sqrt{\frac{m+M}{M}}\,,$$

it is clear that since C_i is independent of density, while L is inversely proportional to density ρ, D will vary as $D = (D_0)\rho_0/\rho$. Here D_0 is the diffusion coefficient at n.t.p., ρ_0 is the corresponding density, and D is the value of the coefficient of diffusion at density ρ. If temperature is constant, the density ρ is proportional to gas pressure p. Thus, at constant temperature and at a pressure p, $D = (D_0)\,760/p$, where D_0 is the diffusion coefficient at 760 mm pressure.

As C_i is proportional to the $\sqrt{T}$ when $\frac{1}{2}mC_i^2 = (3/2)kT$, then at constant density with temperature variable, it is clear that D will vary as the $\sqrt{T}$, provided L is constant. Actually, the ionic free path L may vary with temperature. If it follows the Sutherland law, L varies as $1/(1+b/T)$, so that the variation of D will be more like

$\sqrt{T}/(1 + b/T)$. From equation 1.1b, $k = 0.815\,(e/m)(L/C_i)\sqrt{(M+m)/M}$. On the small-ion theory, and from some observations, k is nearly independent of T, which means that L, as shown in equation 1.1b, varies nearly as C_i or as $\sqrt{T}$. Under these conditions $(D)_\rho$ would be expected to vary more nearly in proportion to T. This is clear at once from the relation

$$(2.21) \qquad (D)_\rho = \frac{kp}{Ne} = \frac{k(1/3)mC_i^2}{e},$$

if k is independent of T for ρ constant. Thus, for ions it may be expected that $(D)\rho$ will increase somewhat more rapidly than proportional to the $\sqrt{T}$ for most small ions.

From simple kinetic theory, where the coefficient of self-diffusion is given as $D = (1/3)cL$, if L is independent of the mass m of the diffusing agency, then D would be proportional to $1/\sqrt{m}$, as is *conventionally* stated, since c is proportional to $1/\sqrt{m}$. From the Langevin type of mobility relation 1.1b for solid elastic impacts, the persistence of velocity factor entering into L, which takes the form $\sqrt{(M+m)/M}$, should be included. Thus, from the relation

$$(2.22) \qquad D = \frac{0.815}{3}\,LC_i\sqrt{\frac{M+m}{M}},$$

it would appear that D is proportional to $\sqrt{(M+m)/Mm}$ as C_i is proportional to $1/\sqrt{m}$. When $M = m$, then this term becomes proportional to $1/\sqrt{m}$, as simple theory indicates. Since the ionic free path L is altered by the size of the ion in complex ion formation, or clustering, then not only m is changed, but L will be decreased by increase in ionic radius. Thus, as in kinetic theory in general, while D should vary as $1/\sqrt{m}$ for the carrier, it will not accurately be observed to vary so; for any change in mass m is accompanied by a corresponding change in L through change in collision cross section with ionic mass.

For example, using the $1/\sqrt{m}$ rule, the He_2^+ ion should diffuse $1/\sqrt{2}$ times as fast as the He^+ ion in He gas. Actually, the persistence of velocity factor in equation 2.22 favors He^+ in the ratio $\sqrt{4/3} = 1.15$ only. Actually, $k_{He_2^+}/k_{He^+} = D_{He_2^+}/D_{He^+} = 2$ by observation, meaning obviously that the exchange-of-charge reaction makes $L_{He_2^+}/L_{He^+} = 2.3$.

A very good illustration of the effect of diffusion in ionic studies lies in the discussion of the following experiment. Figure 2.6a shows a plane parallel condenser $E\,L$ with a group of ions liberated at plate L as a sharply limited small slab $A\,B$ with its central plane at F

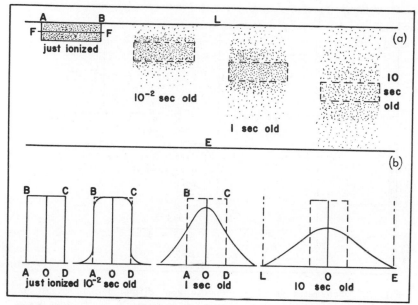

Fig. 2.6 (a and b). Schematic diagrams showing how the ionization diffuses beyond the boundaries of an initially ionized slab of rectangular cross section as time progresses from 0 to 10 secs, the ion slab meanwhile slowly drifting as a whole from plate L to E in a weak electrical field. At (b) are shown the density distributions about the center for each of the times indicated for (a). After 1 second the rectangular distribution has become essentially Gaussian.

at a time $t = 0$. Decreasing fields across $D\,E$ (figure 2.6b) drive the ions from L to E, so that the ionized masses are depicted at various points representing progress across the plates after 10^{-2}, 1, and 10 seconds time. The outline of the initial ionization is indicated by the dashed rectangles. The distribution of ions is seen dispersed along the direction of the field X relative to the rectangles and as a numerical distribution in figure 2.6b. It is noted from figure 2.6a that for 1 and 10 seconds, some of the ions have been altogether lost through return to plate L by back diffusion. Thus, where the field is weak and/or D is great, considerable *loss* of carriers will result in longer time intervals.

The importance of this diffusive action was initially pointed out in 1925 by G. Hertz (5), for electrons colliding elastically with molecules in a field. This was experimentally illustrated in the study of photoelectric currents in gases by N. E. Bradbury and the author, and later by J. K. Theobald (9). Diffusive action in thermionic-emitting cathodes in gas-filled tubes near the filaments is of considerable

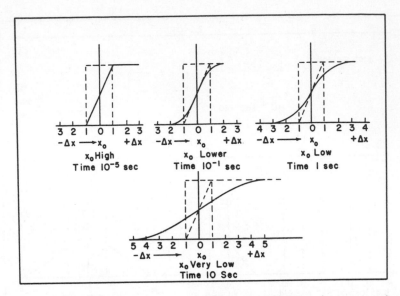

Fig. 2.7. Schematic drawing showing how diffusion changes an ionic current from the ionized slab of figure 2.6 as it would be recorded were it received by plane E of that figure with different applied field strengths X_0 after crossing a distance x_0. X_0 is applied for the constant time T_0 for crossing of the center of the slab indicated for each curve, the ions having a unique mobility.

importance. It is responsible for the negative potential trough with hot filament emitters. Back diffusion is nicely illustrated in the curves of Penning and Kruithoff for evaluating Townsend's α, shown in chapter VIII. Diffusion is responsible for the intense ionization in the anode glow, and also accounts for the increase in electron multiplication near positive wires or points at high X/p, as P. L. Morton and G. W. Johnson have recently shown (10). In many of these examples the coefficient D is so large that it ranks in importance with the drift velocities. This is largely because the average random velocity of electrons in the field, together with the small electron mass, makes D exceptionally high.

Having digressed to relate the pictorial events of figure 2.6 to actual occurrences, it is fruitful to inquire what sort of effects such dispersion produces on the current received at an electrode like E as a function of time. Let X_0 be the field needed to cause the center $F F$ of the group of ions of figure 2.6 to cross to E in times T_0 of 10^{-5}, 10^{-2}, 1, and 10 seconds. In a measurement designed to evaluate these times of crossing by pulsed fields of different strength X, the value of X will be changed in increments $\pm\Delta X$ about the value of X_0, corresponding to the exact arrival of the center of the group $F F$ at E. The influence of this change in X is effectively to advance $F F$ different distances x from its position at $t = 0$ on either side of the plate distance x_0 by spatial increments of $\pm\Delta x$ along x. Thus, $\pm\Delta x = (XkT_0 - x_0) = \pm\Delta\, XkT_0$, with k the ionic mobility. From figure 2.7 it is clear that this will lead to a gradual rise in current as X increases from below X_0 to above that value, in varying degrees of steepness, depending on T_0 and the amount of diffusion that has occurred in transit. The discussion which has preceded showed that the number N_x of particles of coefficient of diffusion D which reach a distance x in a time T, is given by equation 2.14:

$$N_x = \frac{N_0}{\sqrt{4\pi Dt}}\, \epsilon^{-x^2/4Dt} \qquad dx.$$

In a time of 10^{-5} second, the amount of diffusion is negligible, and the rectangular slab of ionization of figure 2.6b will reach E, with but negligible alteration. Its contour of ion distribution in space is shown in figure 2.6b as the area $ABCD$ about the line $F F$ represented as 0. The section in this figure that takes 10^{-2} sec to cross will have its outer boundaries $A B$ and $C D$ altered in the amount indicated by the Gaussian type of equation above, so that it has the contour shown. The alteration in the cases with $T_0 = 1$ and 10 seconds is indicated in the same figure. Thus, the increase of charge as a function of $X = X_0 \mp \Delta X$, beginning at large values of $-\Delta X$ and increasing X, will be that shown in figure 2.7 for the various values of T_0. These curves are the integral of the curves of figure 2.6b. It is seen that the rise in current in X is only sharp at $T_0 \sim 10^{-5}$ sec. Otherwise, it rises with an asymptotic foot, and more and more gradually as T_0 increases.

Thus, with diffusion, a problem arises as to what point on the curve to choose for the value of X_0 responsible for the crossing in T_0. If the origin of $F F$ and the distance x_0 of $F F$ to E are known, this value would correspond to the field X_0, at which the line $F F$ reached E at a time T_0, and to the time of arrival of the point 0 at E in each case. If the diffusion had been uniform everywhere, it would be logical to choose the point of inflection of the curve. This can best be roughly found by graphical differentiation of the observed curve which has its peak at that point.

In most ion studies where such a decision was required, this procedure was *not* used. This was largely because instrumental effects, such as ill-defined ionization edges, introduced similar asymptotic rises and blurring of their own which might not have been Gaussian. Since the worker was not sure as to what extent the feet were caused by diffusion, he hesitated to make a correction. What was usually done, *assuming the feet to be of instrumental origin*, if T was not too great, was to draw a tangent to the steep part of the curve near the foot and to take the intercept of this with the axis of abscissae as the value of X corresponding to the point A of figure 2.6b, or the abscissa −1 of figure 2.7. With much diffusion, this procedure is incorrect; as seen where the time was 10 sec, for giving a large $-\Delta x$, it underestimates the real value of X needed by a considerable figure. More careful workers have chosen this intercept near the foot and deducted the value $\overline{\Delta x} = \sqrt{4Dt/\pi} = \overline{\Delta X k T_0}$ from that intercept to correct X for diffusion and to get the value of X_0 for the edge A B. Such correction is better than none, and is only palliative at best. Neglect of correction for diffusion will always yield estimated values of X too low, even with the correction for Δx subtracted. In mobility measurement this would give values that are too high. Some of these errors can be obviated by choosing corresponding points Δx on curves for each T_0, and computing k from these data. This is especially useful if x_0 is varied for T_0 constant, and distortion is not caused by other factors.

§ 6. Ambipolar Diffusion.

At the beginning of this chapter it was indicated that the interionic forces were to be and could be neglected in many studies of diffusion. This, however, is not always true. Thus, it can happen, even with lower ion densities in the absence of individual inter-ionic interaction, when carriers of both signs are present, that the more rapid diffusion of one sign of carrier will produce local *net space-charge fields* of considerable magnitudes. In contrast to the forces between individual ions, such fields at moderate densities can alter the diffusion of both signs of carriers. Under certain conditions these space charges play a very important role in the economy of discharge phenomena, and thus merit study.

Before proceeding further it must be remarked that the exact solution of the general problem of diffusion, or individually of the Brownian movement of particles in electrical fields, introduces almost insoluble difficulties except in certain limiting cases. For instance, it is not possible to solve accurately for the motions of positive and negative ions which attract each other inversely as the square of the distance in a gas as they drift from infinity through the region $r_0 = e^2/(3/2)kT$, where kinetic and potential energies are equal. Thus, in general, the diffusion of carriers at higher densities is not studied.

However, where differences in rates of diffusion of carriers of opposite sign create *gross space-charge fields*, it is again possible to study the problem. As an example, consider a gas in an ionized condition in which q positive ions and electrons are created per cm^3 per second. These carriers may be moving through the gas in consequence of fields, as in a glow discharge; or the carriers may be at rest, as in ultrahigh-frequency breakdown in the absence of steady fields. It will be assumed that in consequence of these conditions, the concentrations of the carriers of both signs in the body of the gas are sensibly equal; viz., that

$$(2.23) \qquad N_+ = N_- = N .$$

Near the boundaries of the ionized space, the electrons, with their high value of the coefficient of diffusion D_e, will move away from the mass more rapidly than the slower positive ions with coefficient of diffusion D_i. The diffusion of the negative electronic charges away from the neutral plasma, if the value of N is high, will quickly build up a negative space charge outward and leave a positive ion space charge in the inner volume. The over-all densities N_+ and N_- will not be disturbed seriously, for as soon as the space charges form, the net fields will be built up so as to retard electron diffusion and accelerate the positive ion diffusion if N is adequate to give the space charge needed. Hence, the changes in the relatively large values of N are small. Thus, it is safe to set expression 2.23, $N_+ = N_- = N$, in what follows.

The effect of the space-charge field on the positive ions is, as indicated, to speed them up and to retard the diffusion of the negative electrons so that equilibrium will be reached, leaving the gas as a whole essentially neutral except for the small fields X at the edges, produced by the separation. It is thus possible to write, as a second condition, that $\bar{v}_+$, the average positive ion velocity, equals $\bar{v}_-$, the average negative ion velocity in the region. Hence, it may be written that

$$(2.24) \qquad \bar{v}_+ = \bar{v}_- = \bar{v} .$$

The flow of positive and negative ions under the combined action of diffusion and mobility in X is then represented by

$$(2.25) \qquad (N_+ \bar{v}_+) = D_+ \frac{dN_+}{dx} + N_+ k_+ X$$

and

$$(2.26) \qquad (N_-\bar{v}_- = -D_- \frac{dN_-}{dx} - N_-k_-X.$$

Setting $N_+ = N_- = N$, $\bar{v}_+ = \bar{v}_- = \bar{v}$, and eliminating X from the equations, it follows that

$$(2.27) \qquad \bar{v} = \frac{D_+k_- + D_-k_+}{k_+ + k_-} \frac{1}{N} \frac{dN}{dx}$$

per unit area. Now this equation may be compared directly with the flow of carriers under a *fictitious average coefficient of diffusion* D_a, called the *coefficient of ambipolar diffusion*. This states that $N\bar{v} = D_a (dN/dx)$ for unit area, whence

$$(2.28) \qquad D_a = \frac{D_+k_- + D_-k_+}{k_+ + k_-} .$$

Since

$$(2.29) \qquad \frac{k_+}{D_+} = \frac{k_-}{D_-} = \frac{Ne}{p} = \frac{e}{kT} ,$$

with k the Boltzmann constant, and since $\frac{1}{2}m_e C_e^2 = (3/2)kT_e$, and $\frac{1}{2}MC_i^2 = (3/2)kT_i$, with T_e many times greater than T_i, it is possible to set

$$(2.30) \qquad D_a = D_+ T_e/T_+ = D_- k_+/k_- .$$

If $T_e = T_+$, as in Biondi and Brown's microwave studies (6), D_+ is sensibly equal to D_a. There accordingly results a diffusion of the ionized plasma of gas as a whole in such fashion that it can be mathematically treated as a single diffusing mass with an ambipolar coefficient D_a. The consequence is that any neutral surface in contact with an ionized gas having positive and negative carriers, one sign of which moves more rapidly (i.e., has a higher D) than the other, will be charged to a potential whose sign relative to the gas adjacent is that of the faster carrier. While the phenomenon is universal, in view of the great disparity of diffusion coefficients of electrons and ions, the effects are striking where electrons are present, the surfaces being distinctly negative. It is clear that since for electrons, T_e in many discharges is of the order of 10,000° to 2,000° K., while T_+ is of the order of 500° K. or less, D_a will be several times (in these cases 4 to 20 times) that of the ions. The potentials taken on by the walls adjoining such discharge plasmas are known as the *wall potentials*, and are negative relative to the potential of the corresponding ion-bearing space.

For ordinary discharges, the values of the wall potentials are of the order of 0.1 to perhaps 3 volts negative. The resulting current density to the walls $j = eN\bar{v}$ is called the *wall current*. It removes charges from the gas and carries them to the walls. There in two-dimensional surface space, electrons readily recombine with the positive ions, the heat going to heat the walls of the container. If the gas contains electrons, negative ions, and positive ions, it is possible to determine a value of the ambipolar-diffusion coefficient D_a. If it be assumed that there are x electrons and $1-x$ negative ions, D_a becomes

$$(2.31) \qquad D_a = \frac{x(k_+ D_e^- + D^+ k_e^-) + (1-x)(k_+ D_i^- + k_i^- D^+)}{k_+ + \{k_e^- x + k_i^-(1-x)\}} .$$

The symbols used are self-evident. In addition to tests of the theory by the use of probes and in glow discharges and arcs, recent studies of M. A. Biondi and S. C. Brown (6) with microwave breakdown of gases give beautiful and complete verification of the theory. They also lead to an evaluation of the ion mobility k from the value of D_a observed, as D_a is largely that of the ions when $T_e = T_i$. It should be indicated that unless electron energies are high and ion densities are sufficient,

$$(2.32) \qquad j = eN\bar{v} = eD_a \frac{dN}{dx} = eD_+ \frac{Te}{T_+} \frac{dN}{dx} ,$$

so that $(T_e/T_+)(dN/dx)$ is large, j will be small. At 1 mm pressure in N_2 gas with $T_e = 2,000°$ K., $N = 10^8$ ions/cm^3 and $dN/dx = 10^{10}$ (a reasonable figure), the value of $j \sim 6 \times 10^{-7}$ amp/cm^2, which is quite small. The corresponding value of V_w will be about 0.5 volt. Thus, this action ceases to be important at ion densities much below this value.

BIBLIOGRAPHY TO CHAPTER II

(1) J. S. Townsend, *Electricity in Gases*, Oxford University Press, 1914, chap. V. See also Phil. Trans. Roy. Soc. *A193*, 129, 1899. J. S. Townsend, *Electrons in Gases*, Hutchinson's, London, 1947; J. Zeleny, Phil. Trans. Roy. Soc. *A195*, 193, 1900.

(2) J. S. Townsend and H. T. Tizard, Proc. Roy. Soc. *A57*, 357, 1912; *A88*, 336, 1913.

(3) V. A. Bailey, Phil. Mag. *22*, 825, 1925.

(4) L. G. H. Huxley and A. A. Zaazou, Proc. Roy. Soc. *A196*, 402, 1949.
     See also R. H. Healey and J. W. Reed, *The Behaviour of Slow Electrons
     in Gases*, Amalgamated Wireless Press (Australasia), Ltd., Sydney, 1941.
(5) G. Hertz, Zeits. f. Phys. *32*, 298, 1925.
(6) M. A. Biondi and S. C. Brown, Phys. Rev. 75, 1700, 1949.
(7) J. Franck and W. H. Westphal, Verh. d. Deutsch. Phys. Gesell. 7, 146,
     276, 1909.
(8) J. S. Townsend, Proc. Roy. Soc. *A80*, 207, 1908; *A81*, 464, 1908; *A85*,
     25, 1911; C. E. Haselfoot, Proc. Roy. Soc. *A82*, 18, 1909; *A87*, 350,
     1912.
(9) N. E. Bradbury, Phys. Rev. *40*, 980, 1932; J. K. Theobald, Jour. App.
     Phys. *24*, 123, 1953.
(10) P. L. Morton, Phys. Rev. *70*, 358, 1946; G. W. Johnson, Phys. Rev. *73*,
     284, 1948.

Chapter III

THE VELOCITIES OF ELECTRONS IN GASES

---

§ 1. Introduction.

The electrons possess masses so small compared to the molecules in the gases in which they find themselves, that in elastic collision with the heavier molecules they will rebound and retain a large fraction of their momentum. It is thus obvious that even where low fields are present, the electrons will retain energy gained from the field and thus possess energies different from those of the surrounding gas molecules. Such energies will affect the random velocities and hence influence the electron mobilities. In this respect they might be expected to behave differently from the more massive ions.

Since the energies of electrons in fields in gases strongly affect their drift velocities, these should be studied together. In fact, the more esoteric generalized studies of the energy distribution of electrons in fields in gases at the same time yield relations which give the energy distribution and the corresponding electron velocities. However, to gain a clear physical understanding of what is involved, the analysis here given will follow essentially the simple classical kinetic-theory approach to the study of the electron velocities in gases. Once this is established, the reader will be in a better position to understand the more involved approach in terms of energy distributions.

The velocities of electrons were initially measured for *low pressures* by J. S. Townsend and his students beginning in 1912, using his magnetic-deflection method (1). In 1920-1921, the author extended the measurements to electrons in gases at atmospheric pressure, using the best means of purification then possible (2). His Rutherford sinusoidal alternating-potential method left much to be desired, but gave the only approach for studies in this pressure range at that time. In 1930, R. A. Nielsen and N. E. Bradbury (3) adapted the author's electron filter as an electrical shutter and made what the author believes the best direct measurement to date of these velocities in very pure standard gases over a large range of pressures and fields. Today these still represent some of the most reliable values below $X/p = 20$. The recent summary of the work of V. A. Bailey (4)

211

and his students, as given by R. H. Healey and J. W. Reed in their book, *The Behaviour of Slow Electrons in Gases*, indicates that some of the later refinements of Bailey's (1) methods and techniques may yield results of accuracy better than the earlier ones in the high- and low-energy regions (1). This includes also the recent study of L. G. H. Huxley and A. A. Zaazou (1). While the accuracy still leaves something to be desired, the application of pulsed fields for observing the movement of electrons in the region of ionization by collision, using the cloud-chamber techniques as developed by H. Raether (5), or the oscillographic methods of J. A. Hornbeck (6), give direct, graphically recorded data leading to values of electron velocities and diffusion in the high-energy range. Variants of pulsed methods have yielded data of accuracy comparable to Bradbury and Nielsen's values (26), (31), (32), and (33).

§ 2. The Simple Theory of Electron Velocities and Their Evaluation in Terms of Experiment.

It will be recalled that the simple kinetic theory for ionic mobilities had two alternate forms, the form of equation 1.1b being adapted to carriers of mass m lighter than the molecules of mass M.[1] This equation is then the one to apply to the movement of electrons. The equation, using the *average* electron velocity $\bar{c_1}$, reads

$$(1.1b) \qquad k = 0.75 \, \frac{e}{m} \, \frac{L}{\bar{c_1}} \, \sqrt{\frac{m+M}{M}}.$$

It should be noted that the average speed $\bar{c_1} = 0.922 \, C_1$, where C_1 is the root-mean-square speed on the assumed Maxwellian energy distribution. Since with electrons $M >> m$, the term under the radical is unity within the accuracy of measurement. *If the electrons are in equilibrium with the gas*, then it would be expected that

$$(1/2)\, mC_1^2 = (1/2)\, MC^2 = (3/2)\, kT,$$

so that $\bar{c_1}$ can be evaluated. Again, by kinetic theory the value of the electron free path λ differs from L (that for molecular ions), for the molecules are assumed to act like solid elastic spheres in collision with point electrons. Impacts between ion and molecule will occur at a distance σ between centers, while with an electron

------

[1]Equation 1.1b, cited here for the sake of uniformity, comes from Langevin's expression for ions of atomic dimensions moving among molecules. Stricter accuracy is claimed for a more appropriate expression with a modified constant by some observers. This will be introduced at a more opportune time. Actually, later and more complete studies (34) indicate that Langevin's expression is probably as good as any.

of radius $\sim 10^{-13}$ cm, the distance between electron and molecule center at impact is $\sigma/2$. Furthermore, because for an electron the value of C_1 is very much greater than C (the value for a molecule), the Maxwellian correction term for relative velocity, $\sqrt{2}$, drops out. Thus, while for an ion,

$$L = \frac{1}{\sqrt{2}\pi\sigma^2 N},$$

the value for an electron is

$$\lambda = \frac{1}{\pi(\sigma/2)^2 N}.$$

It thus follows that in principle $\lambda = 4\sqrt{2}\,L$. Inserting these changes in equation 1.1b, it follows that for electrons the mobility should be

(3.1) $$k_e = 0.75\,\frac{e}{m}\,\frac{\lambda}{\bar{c}_1}.$$

It should accordingly be easy to verify this theory of electron mobilities, for e/m is a well-known constant, and all the other quantities are known.

J. S. Townsend and H. T. Tizard in 1912 applied their magnetic-deflection method to electrons. They were surprised to discover that the mobility as given by the deflection method did not follow the simple expression 3.1. According to equation 3.1, the value $k_e = (1/\bar{H})\,(a/2e)$, as derived from evaluation of $\bar{H}$, should be independent of field strength X and should vary as $1/p$. They observed that k_e varied with X, and that $K_e = k_e\,p/760$ was not constant, but varied with X/p. This discovery that K_e was not a constant indicated that the elementary theory was in error. It also implied that it is hardly proper to speak of a mobility, or a reduced mobility, for electrons in gases. In fact, in recent years it has become the custom to refer to the *electron-drift velocity* only, and the mobility is not used. It will, however, be found that on occasion it is convenient to include the mobility k_e of equation 3.1, realizing that this is not constant with X/p.

The reason for the deviation from the simple theory of equation 3.1 was quite clear to Townsend, for it meant that in the gas the ratio λ/c_1 was not properly evaluated by the simple kinetic theory. He suspected, in view of the relative masses of electrons and molecules, that the electrons had an energy greater than $\frac{1}{2}MC^2 = (3/2)kT$.

If this were so, the observed k_e would be less than the value predicted by equation 3.1, since $C_1 > \sqrt{3kT/2M}$, and should depend on X and p. For as X and p change, the electron's rate of gain of energy changes, and thus changes the average value of C_1. On the basis of his observations, Townsend assumed that the energy of the electrons was $\frac{1}{2}mC_1^2 = \eta\frac{1}{2}MC^2 = \eta(3/2)kT$ for the molecules, where η is a factor greater than unity. In consequence, he modified equation 3.1 to read

$$(3.2) \qquad k_e = 0.75 \, \frac{e}{m} \, \frac{\lambda}{\bar{c}_1 \sqrt{\eta}}.$$

He then set about evaluating η by direct experiment. For, as shown in chapter II, the lateral spreading of an electron stream in a field in a gas makes it possible to evaluate $k/D = ne/P$. Thus, if for electrons $\frac{1}{2}mC_1^2 = \eta\frac{1}{2}MC^2$, then measurement of k/D by the spreading of a stream should evaluate

$$(3.3) \qquad k/D = \frac{Ne}{\eta p}.$$

Thus, by dividing the observed ratio of k/D by Ne/p, it was possible for Townsend[2] to obtain a value of η. This was done for a number of gases in the earlier days, and has been carried out for somewhat purer gases in more recent years by Townsend's pupils, notably L. G. H. Huxley and particularly V. A. Bailey (1) and his pupils. A characteristic set of data taken by Townsend for O_2 is shown in table 3.1.

To be observed in this table is the variation of k_e with X/p; notably, that it decreases. The high values of η should be noted as well. An unexpected development in this study was the *seeming variation* of the *mean free path* λ with X/p; that is, with electron energy. With the relative crudeness of the earlier work, some of this variation could have been ascribed to instrumental difficulties. However, as indicated by later, more direct studies (notably by Ramsauer and others), electron-collision free paths vary in most complicated fashions with electron energies. This is especially true for impacting electrons having energies of the order of magnitude of the potential energies of electrons in the outer atomic and molecular valence

---

[2]It should here be stated that this method of evaluating η is correct so long as X/p is so low that the electrons do not ionize by impact. In fact, theoretical study by Harriet W. Allen and W. P. Allis (7) justifies these measurements in general in this region. More complete analysis as applied to recent practice may be found in a paper by L. G. H. Huxley and in Healey and Reed's book (1). It should be noted that Townsend and his group carried out measurements to values of X/p higher than this. Such data must be regarded with caution.

TABLE 3.1

Townsend's Data on Drift Velocities, Coefficient η, Random Velocity and Electron Free Path in O_2 as a Function of X/p

X/p in volts/cm (mm)	0.4	0.6	1	2	5	10	15	20	30	40	50
p in mm of Hg	1	1	1	1	1	1	1	1	1	1	1
$v = Xk_e$ in cm/sec $\times 10^{-6}$		1.6	2.2	3.0	4.3	6.0	7.8	9.8	13.6	17.2	20.5
k_e cm/sec per volt/cm $\times 10^{-6}$	2.5	2.67	2.2	1.5	0.86	0.60	0.52	0.49	0.45	0.43	0.41
η	6	8.4	13	24	47	64	77	90	113	133	150
$\sqrt{\eta}\,\bar{c}_1$ in cm/sec $\times 10^{-6}$	28.2	33.4	41.3	56.3	78.8	92.0	101	109	123	133	141
$\lambda = (m/0.75e)\sqrt{\eta}\,\bar{c}_1 \times 10^{-6}$	4.93	6.22	6.39	5.91	4.89	3.86	3.67	3.74	3.87	3.99	4.05

shells. Under these conditions peculiar resonance effects cause abnormal momentum exchanges. Thus, the work of Townsend *first* revealed a very important factor in electronic behavior in gases which was clearly recognized and accurately studied a decade later.

Using electron beams of unique velocity sorted by a magnetic-velocity selector, C. Ramsauer (8) succeeded in getting the energy variation of the *collision free path*, or collision cross section, for electrons in many gases over a large spread of energy ranges. The work was carried farther by others in later years, including E. Brüche, R. B. Brode, and C. E. Normand. [3] The mean free paths observed by Ramsauer and others, while lying in the order of magnitude of the classical kinetic-theory values, vary by factors of 10 and more about the kinetic-theory value in the energy range from 1 to 100 electron volts. No accurate data exist below 1 volt. [4] The shapes of the curves are characteristic of the electronic structure of the atoms, being similar for isoelectronic configurations but varying much in magnitude in such sequences. They are to be ascribed to resonant wave-mechanical interactions of the electron and the outer atomic shell. Although the absorbing cross sections, or their reciprocal, the mean free paths, may be above or below the classical kinetic-theory value in the range of great variation, all of them eventually tend gradually to lengthen the paths beyond the classical values in a systematic fashion with energy increase as the energy gets much above 100 volts.

The free paths observed by Ramsauer were precise and sharp, as electron energies were confined to sharp, narrow bands. The variations of the mean free paths yielded by the Townsend measurements are in rough agreement with the Ramsauer free paths and follow the same general trend. However, as will later be seen, the energy of an electron swarm in a field in the gas is delineated by a distribution law of a wide range of values within the distribution. Since the broad distribution in values has forms which vary with X/p and thus are usually not known, the average value cannot be clearly defined relative to the spread of energies. Until the later work of Huxley and of Bailey, as shown by Healey and Reed, the Druyvesteyn distribution was not used in the Townsend studies. Even this law does not apply under most circumstances, as the work of Bradbury and Nielsen shows (3). Thus, the values of λ observed by Townsend's method are some

---

[3] Recent applications indicate that Ramsauer's values are more nearly correct for use in calculations that those of Normand (9).

[4] Very recently the study of ultrahigh-frequency breakdown plasmas has made it possible to develop microwave techniques for the analysis of the plasma which give the free paths near thermal electron energies.

sort of smoothed average values corresponding to an ill-defined average energy for an inadequately known distribution law. It should be added that the earlier data also suffered considerably through the inadequate purity of the gases, which can materially affect the drift velocity. Later data as given by Healey and Reed are more accurate (1). It is hardly to be expected that such values should agree with the more direct data obtained by Ramsauer. Probably, for carefully theoretical studies, the Ramsauer data should be used, as assembled and reported by Brode (8). For thermal electrons, microwave data should be used (10). In a study of the behavior of electron swarms in gases, it should be proper to use the values given by Healey and Reed in the comparable energy range.

As regards electron-velocity measurements, the data of Bradbury and Nielsen are preferable to those using the methods of Townsend, as these gases were all adequately purified. They have recently been confirmed repeatedly by several observers (26), (30), (31), (32), and (33). This is not true of the *earlier work* of the Townsend school, especially with inert gases, where impurities are particularly troublesome. Huxley's latest values in air agree with those of Bradbury and Nielsen if the proper distribution law is used. The data reported by Healey and Reed should be scrutinized in the original papers with reference to purity control before being used in preference to those of Bradbury and Nielsen.

On the other hand, the only data on the energy of the electrons in which ηkT is expressed as a function of the experimental parameter X/p, come from the work of the Townsend group. Thus, this very important datum in all gaseous studies, *the energy of the electron swarm in a field in a gas* as a function of X/p, can at present be obtained *only by the method of Townsend*, and resort must be had to that work where this information is required. Since there will always be some uncertainty as to the meaning of the average value given by η as a function of X/p, so long as the form of the distribution laws is unknown, these data will not be too satisfactory; but they are better than nothing. As will later be seen, the best present-day approach to the accurate knowledge of what η means at a given X/p will come from theoretical studies yielding the energy-distribution laws directly from experimental data, such as drift velocities and particularly the Ramsauer free paths. It will be shown in chapter IV that the variation of the mean free path with velocity is the primary cause of the deviation of electron-energy distributions from the standard Druyvesteyn form to be expected at lower X/p. Thus, probably more than any other factor, the Ramsauer free paths influence the energies and hence the velocities of electrons.

As stated, Townsend's results covered electron mobilities or velocities for values of X/p from about 0.5 on up to very high values of about 50 or even more. No data were at hand for electrons in gases at n.t.p. and thus for very low X/p. The deficiency was remedied in some measure by the author and H. B. Wahlin (2) in the period from 1921 to 1924, using the Rutherford a.c. method with sinusoidal wave form, which is not suited for these measurements. However, the gases used were relatively pure. This work for a long time yielded the only data on electron velocities or mobilities for values of X/p as low as 0.01 and up, and for atmospheric pressure in some standard gases. Later, Bradbury and Nielsen obtained data covering some of this region with their more flexible method. The author's values did not differ too seriously from those of Townsend and of Bradbury and Nielsen, where they overlapped.

In order to correct the data for the fact that k_e varied with the field strength in the a.c. cycle, the author attempted to find the theoretical form for the variation of k_e with X/p. In other words, he attempted to evaluate $(3/2)\eta kT$ theoretically at higher pressures in order to insert $\sqrt{(3/2)\eta kT}$ for the denominator of equation 1.1b for k_e. An evaluation of the energy of an electron in a field had been attempted in 1913 by F. B. Pidduck (11). Pidduck proceeded by using a method which H. A. Lorentz had applied to the movement of free electrons in metals. At the time the variable Ramsauer free paths were not known, nor was the *small fractional loss of electron energy in impact with molecules* recognized as important. Pidduck thus lacked an energy-balance relation coming from the momentum loss on impact, needed to complete his study. He thus had to assume a Maxwellian energy distribution for use in his evaluation of the average energy. Pidduck's theory yielded a relation of Maxwellian form which gave energies for electrons in the field in agreement with a theory deduced in 1918 by K. T. Compton by use of the more fallible classical kinetic-theory methods, in which he applied the same basic assumptions. Thus, in 1922 the author had at hand and attempted to use Compton's earlier theory giving $(3/2)\eta kT$ in terms of fields and mean free path. His attempt to average energies by using Compton's early equation was not rigorous. It yielded enough information to enable the author to correct his observational data to yield mobilities. These developments led Compton to derive a more nearly correct theory of electron energies and thus of electron mobilities, including the fractional electron-energy loss on impact (12). This paper was published simultaneously with Wahlin's paper on mobilities in N_2 (2). It yielded a check on the theory, as the peculiar form of the variation of the predicted mobility with X/p at low X/p was that observed by Wahlin.

The chief defect of Compton's theory lay in the fact that it assumed a Maxwellian distribution of energy among the electrons. Unfortunately, such a distribution is rare indeed when electrons in gases are not densely associated, or encounter conditions where their energy lies around and below the excitation or ionization potential of the gas. In such gases, if Ramsauer free paths do not vary much with energy, the energy distribution is actually that deduced in 1930 by M. J. Druyvesteyn for energies below excitation. This law does not differ very seriously from Maxwell's law. It does, however, alter the value of mobilities derived from magnetic-deflection methods, as shown by Huxley and by Healey and Reed (1). Thus, for some gases where all the cogent data were known, the Compton theory of 1923, as modified by Bradbury and Nielsen, gave fairly satisfactory agreement (3). Since Compton's theory clearly indicates how the various factors affect the mobility, and since its elements are useful for rough approximations in considering the behavior of electrons in gases, it will be developed at this place and compared with the results of Bradbury and Nielsen. It should be noted that analogous and some less correctly derived expressions have been used under the limiting conditions by different workers at various times. All relations have the same form, but differ in the constants used. An example is seen in von Engel and Steenbeck's excellent book (13). The different expressions are indicated in chapter IV.

§ 3. The Compton Theory of Electron Mobilities.

The procedure followed by Compton (12), (13), was in essence to write the expression for energy gain and loss by the electron from the field as a result of molecular impacts, and to set this expression equal to zero at the point of equilibrium. To do this it was necessary to assume an elementary electron-mobility relation, such as equation 1.1b.

As indicated earlier, equation 1.1b was derived from the original Langevin relation for atomic ions moving in atomic gases under conditions where $\frac{1}{2}mC_1^2 = \frac{1}{2}MC^2 = (3/2)kT$ with a Maxwellian energy distribution. This gave

(1.1a)
$$k = 0.815 \frac{e}{M} \frac{\lambda}{C} \sqrt{\frac{M+m}{m}}.$$

It is asserted that it is not proper to use this equation if $\frac{1}{2}mC_1^2 = E_1$

differs from $E_2 = \frac{1}{2}MC^2 = (3/2)kT$.[5] Thus, one must resort to a more accurate averaging process applicable to electrons moving in a molecular gas with energies greater than $(3/2)kT$ for the gas. What may give a more properly averaged expression was derived independently by K. T. Compton and by J. S. Townsend (15). Irrespective of its validity as a correction it must be presented, as it lays the foundation for later extensions of studies using Townsend's method of analysis.[6] Compton took the rather accurately determined expressions of J. H. Jeans for the coefficient of interdiffusion of two gases, D, and the mean free path λ of one carrier in some other gas, and placed these in equation 2.4, $k = (Ne/p) D$. This equation was taken as defining the mobility k in terms of D with proper averaging. From these relations, Compton (14) arrived at an expression for the mobility of a carrier subscript 1 in a gas of molecules of subscript 2 which reads:

$$k_{12} = \frac{2e}{(3\pi)^{\frac{1}{2}} \pi N \sigma_{12}^2 \, \overline{E}_1} \left(\frac{\overline{E}_1}{m_1} + \frac{\overline{E}_2}{m_2} \right)^{\frac{1}{2}} = \frac{0.921 \, e}{\pi N \sigma_{12}^2 \, m_1 C_1} \left(1 + \frac{\overline{E}_2 \, m_1}{\overline{E}_1 \, m_2} \right)^{\frac{1}{2}}.$$

This relation is assumed to be equally applicable to ions and electrons in a gas with a Maxwellian energy distribution. For electrons, the mean free path $\lambda = 1/\pi \sigma_{12}^2 N$. Inserting the value $1/\lambda$ for $\pi \sigma_{12}^2 N$, setting $\overline{E}_1 > \overline{E}_2$, and replacing m_2 by M and m_1 by m, with $M >> m$, the expression may be written as

(3.4)
$$k_e = \frac{0.921 \, e\lambda}{mC_1} = \frac{0.85 \, e\lambda}{m\overline{c}_1},$$

instead of Langevin's equation 3.1 used earlier, which read,

(3.1)
$$k_e = \frac{0.815 \, e\lambda}{mC_1} = \frac{0.75 \, e\lambda}{m\overline{c}_1}.$$

Accepting the relation 3.4 as sufficiently accurate, and leaving the value c_1 as unspecified at present with λ a constant, the analysis

---

[5]The author is not greatly impressed by the fine hairsplitting in the calculation of the "correct averages," using classical kinetic-theory procedures, when dealing with processes which belong to the field of nonequilibrium gas theory. Thus, it is probably trivial and immaterial to the theory whether a constant 0.921 or 0.815 is used. Real errors are probably greater than the 10% here involved.

[6]The matter is still more doubtful, as Druyvesteyn and Penning (15), two real authorities in 1940, derive for a Maxwellian distribution an equation with a constant of 0.927 but state that a *still more rigorous derivation* yields the original Langevin factor of 0.815. G. H. Wannier (34) arrives at the same relation with 0.815.

follows. The ratio $\bar{c_1}/\lambda$ is z, the *collision frequency*, and $\lambda/\bar{c_1}$ is $T = 1/z$, the *time* between impacts. In this time T, on the average the electron drifts a distance $s = k_e XT = 0.85\ \lambda^2 eX/(mc_1^2)$ in the field direction. As the electron is moving in an electrical field, its energy gain in falling through a potential difference is best expressed in terms of electron volts. Thus, it is convenient to express $\bar{c_1}$ in terms of equivalent electron volts. That is, the electron energy is eu, where e is the electron and u is the potential difference in volts. Accordingly, $eu = \frac{1}{2}mC_1^2$, making $u = 1.18\ m\bar{c_1^2}/2e$. This gives the electron advance in the field direction between impacts as $s = 0.502\ \lambda^2 X/u$.

Studies by Compton and later by A. M. Cravath (16) have shown that the electron of mass m in impact with neutral spherical molecules of mass M moving with a Maxwellian energy distribution of average energy in electron volts of $e\Omega = (3/2)kT$ loses on the average a fraction of its energy f at each impact. The value of f is

$$(3.5) \qquad f = (8/3)\frac{Mm}{(m+M)^2}\left[1 - \frac{\Omega}{u}\right].$$

This applies so long as the electron energy is low enough not to cause any inelastic impacts due to excitation of the molecule or atom. If the value of X/p is high, i.e., greater than 0.1, the value of $u \gg \Omega$ and Ω may be neglected, while below this energy the term must be retained. Again, within the accuracy of the experiment, $mM/(m+M)^2$ is essentially m/M. Thus, for most purposes, it is possible to set

$$(3.6) \qquad f = 2.66\ m/M.$$

Neglecting the diffusive motions of the electrons in the gas, the change of energy of the electron edu as it moves in the field may be expressed by the simple relation

$$(3.7) \qquad edu = eXdx - feu\frac{dx}{s};$$

for in advancing dx in the field direction, the electron gains $eXdx$ from the field and loses $feu\,(dx/s)$ in the dx/s impacts it makes in advancing dx. Inserting the values for f and s, the relation becomes

$$(3.8) \qquad \frac{du}{dx} = X - 5.32\frac{mu}{M}\left(\frac{u-\Omega}{\lambda^2 X}\right).$$

This equation[7] gives the rate of energy gain of the electron in the field X. It indicates that the electron starting from an energy $e\Omega$ gains energy as its displacement x along the field direction increases to a point where u is so large that its loss per collision equals its gain in the field. At this point $du/dx = 0$. When this occurs it is possible to write

(3.9)
$$X = 5.32 \, \frac{mu_T}{M} \left(\frac{u_T - \Omega}{\lambda^2 X} \right).$$

Thus, in a field in a gas, an electron increases its energy as x increases, asymptotically approaching a terminal energy $u_T e$ given by equation 3.9. This value of eu_T is the energy which is being sought, for it gives the value of C_1 through the relations $\frac{1}{2}mC_1^2 = eu_T = \frac{1}{2}MC^2\eta$ to be inserted in equation 3.4. Equation 3.9 may be solved for u_T as

(3.10)
$$u_T = \frac{1}{2}\Omega + \sqrt{\frac{\lambda^2 M X^2}{5.32 \, m} + \frac{\Omega^2}{4}}.$$

If $u_T >> \Omega$, then u_T may safely be written as

(3.11)
$$u_T = \frac{\lambda X}{2.31} \sqrt{\frac{M}{m}}.$$

Before proceeding to place the value for u_T in the mobility equation, it is of interest to study the relation for du/dx in order to see at what rate u approaches u_T. This is essential in many experimental studies, for it enables one to estimate the distance of travel to reach u_T, a quantity needed in designing the apparatus. Integration of the expression for du gives the distance x which an electron requires to acquire a certain fraction (0.9, 0.99, etc.) of its terminal energy u_T.

In this connection, the reader's attention is directed to the discussion immediately following.

♦   ♦   ♦   ♦   ♦

Dr. C. W. Rice has kindly pointed out an inaccuracy in the integra-

---

[7]The constants here given differ from those used by Compton in earlier publications in that they include the Cravath factor 2.66 instead of the 2.0 of Compton's earlier work.

tion of equation 3.8. In what follows, $5.32\,(m/M)\,(1/\lambda^2)$ will be designated as a^2. The expression set up for integration is

$$\int \frac{du}{\dfrac{X^2}{a^2} + a\Omega - u^2} = \int \frac{a^2}{X}\,dx.$$

Setting $u = u_0$ at $x = 0$, integration and insertion of the limit, with the expression $\sqrt{(\Omega^2 + 4X^2)/a^2} = \sqrt{B}$ yields

$$(3.12) \quad 2u - \Omega = \sqrt{B}\ \frac{[2u_0 - \Omega + \sqrt{B}]\,\epsilon^{\frac{a^2x\sqrt{B}}{X}} + [2u_0 - \Omega - \sqrt{B}]}{[2u_0 - \Omega + \sqrt{B}]\,\epsilon^{\frac{a^2x\sqrt{B}}{X}} - [2u_0 - \Omega - \sqrt{B}]}.$$

If $u_0 = 0$ when $x = 0$, then

$$(3.13) \quad u_x = \frac{\Omega}{2} + \frac{1}{2}\sqrt{B}\ \frac{[\sqrt{B} - \Omega]\,\epsilon^{\frac{a^2x\sqrt{B}}{X}} - [\sqrt{B} + \Omega]}{[\sqrt{B} - \Omega]\,\epsilon^{\frac{a^2x\sqrt{B}}{X}} + [\sqrt{B} + \Omega]}.$$

In the limits $x = v,\, u_x = 0$, as set,

$$(3.14) \quad x = \infty,\quad u_\infty = \frac{\Omega}{2} + \tfrac{1}{2}\sqrt{\Omega^2 + \frac{4X^2}{a^2}},$$

which agrees with Compton's value. When $\Omega = 0$,

$$(3.15) \quad u_x = \frac{X}{a}\ \frac{\epsilon^{2ax} - 1}{\epsilon^{2ax} + 1},$$

which is again in agreement with Compton.

If $X = 0$ the equation is indeterminate, but equation 3.12 indicates that then $u = 0$ or $u = \Omega$. Rice suggests that it is best to assume that $u_0 = \Omega$ at $x = 0$, which appears logical. In this case equation 3.12 yields

$$(3.16) \quad u_x = \frac{\Omega}{2} + \frac{\tfrac{1}{2}\sqrt{B}\,[\Omega + \sqrt{B}]\,\epsilon^{\frac{a^2x}{X}} - [-\Omega + \sqrt{B}]}{[\Omega + \sqrt{B}]\,\epsilon^{\frac{a^2x}{X}} + [-\Omega + \sqrt{B}]}.$$

Under these conditions, when

$$x = 0,\ u_0 = \Omega,\ \text{assumed}$$

$$x = \infty,\ u = \frac{\Omega}{2} + \tfrac{1}{2}\sqrt{B},\ \text{as before;}$$

$$\Omega = 0, \quad u_x = \frac{X}{a} \frac{\epsilon^{2ax} - 1}{\epsilon^{2ax} + 1}, \quad \text{as before;}$$

$$X = 0, \quad u_x = \Omega.$$

(*End of discussion concerning Dr. Rice's comment.*)

◆   ◆   ◆   ◆   ◆

Calling $5.32\,(m/M)\,(1/\lambda^2) = a^2$, integration from $n = 0$ at $x = 0$ to $u = u$ at $x = x$ yields

$$(3.17) \qquad u = \frac{1}{2}\Omega + X \sqrt{\frac{1}{a^2} + \frac{\Omega^2}{4X}\; \frac{\epsilon^{2a^2\sqrt{\frac{1}{a^2} + \frac{\Omega^2 x}{4X^2}}} - 1}{\epsilon^{2a^2\sqrt{\frac{1}{a^2} + \frac{\Omega^2 x}{4X^2}}} + 1}} \qquad ,$$

if at $x = 0$, $u = \Omega$. If X is very large, so that Ω may be neglected, the value of

$$(3.18) \qquad u = \frac{X}{a} \frac{\epsilon^{2ax} - 1}{\epsilon^{2ax} + 1} .$$

As $x \cdot = \infty$, $u \cdot = u_T = X/a$. This makes

$$(3.11) \qquad u_T = \sqrt{\frac{\lambda^2 M X^2}{5.32\,m}} = \frac{\lambda X}{2.31}\sqrt{\frac{M}{m}},$$

as above. This value applies to most electron mobility measurements.

The average number of collisions in going x cm from the cathode is given by

$$(3.19) \qquad \overline{n} = \int_0^x \frac{dx}{s} = \int_0^x \frac{u}{0.502\,\lambda^2 X}\, dx .$$

On inserting the value u when $u \gg \Omega$ and integrating,

$$(3.20) \qquad \overline{n} = \frac{M}{4m}\left[\log_e (2 + \epsilon^{2ax} + \epsilon^{-2ax}) - \log_e 4\right]$$

$$= \frac{M}{2m}\log_e \cosh ax .$$

As $x \doteq 0$, $\bar{n} \doteq 0$, and if x is large, $\bar{n}$ approaches x/S_T with

(3.21) $$S_T = 0.502 \, \lambda^2 \, X/u_T.$$

The average number of impacts per cm is then

(3.22) $$1/S_T = (0.85/\lambda) \sqrt{M/m}.$$

If the value of u is set as some fractional value of u_T, such that $u/u_T = \phi$, where ϕ takes values such as 0.1, 0.90, or 0.99, it is possible to calculate the distance $x = x_\phi$ needed to reach this value. The calculation is simple for the case where $u \gg \Omega$, and yields

(3.23) $$x_\phi = \frac{1}{2a} \log \frac{1 + \phi}{1 - \phi}.$$

The average number of collisions made in reaching ϕ is

(3.24) $$\bar{N}_\phi = \frac{M}{4m} \log \frac{1}{1 - \phi^2} \text{ under these conditions.}$$

It is interesting to note that x_ϕ and $\bar{N}_\phi$ depend critically on $f = 2.66$ m/M and λ, but not on the field X. It should be noted that while in some cases, such as for the monatomic gases and with a Maxwellian energy distribution, f can be evaluated as given by Cravath's equation 3.6 in terms of m and M, practically all other gases have inelastic impacts at such low values of X/p that the observed experimental values of f must be used in place of the Cravath relation. It will be noted that in place of a constant λ the experimental variable Ramsauer free paths must also be included. Since the latter vary with electron energy, such calculations can be very difficult. Thus, the relations above must be used with due caution as orienting magnitudes only.

It is now possible to insert the expressions for u_T into the basic electron-mobility equation in place of C_1. This is accomplished through the relations $\frac{1}{2}mC_1^2 = eu_T$, $e\Omega = (3/2)kT = aT$. These give

(3.25) $$C_1 = \sqrt{\frac{2eu_T}{m}} = \left[\frac{2e}{m} \left\{ \frac{\Omega}{2} + \frac{\Omega^2}{4} + \frac{X^2\lambda^2 M}{5.32 \, m} \right\} \right]^{\frac{1}{2}};$$

and when $u_T \gg \Omega$,

(3.26) $$C_1 = \left[\frac{2e}{m} \frac{\lambda X}{2.31} \sqrt{\frac{M}{m}} \right]^{\frac{1}{4}}.$$

These expressions can at once be inserted for C_1 in equation 3.4 yielding the electron mobility.

As will be seen later, the comparison of theory with experiment, except for the case of the inert gases, requires that the ideal classical value of f deduced by Cravath be replaced by the fractional loss of energy on impact derived from experiment, which may vary with electron energy. In order to include this, it is best to rewrite equation 3.11 as

$$(3.27) \qquad u_T = \frac{\lambda X}{2.31} \sqrt{\frac{M}{m}}.$$

This gives

$$(3.28) \qquad u_T = \frac{0.707 \; X\lambda}{\sqrt{f}},$$

so that

$$(3.29) \qquad C_1 = \left(\frac{1.416 \; eX\lambda}{m\sqrt{f}}\right)^{\frac{1}{2}},$$

and

$$(3.30) \qquad k_e = \frac{0.921 \; e\lambda}{mC_1} = 0.775 \sqrt{\frac{e\lambda\sqrt{f}}{mX}}.$$

It is seen that a knowledge of λ, e/m, X, and f will allow the calculation of the r.m.s. value of the average terminal energy u_T expressed in electron volts, and of the electron mobility assuming a Maxwellian energy distribution. For many purposes the *average* quantities so computed are not seriously in error even if the distribution is *not* Maxwellian. It is only in studies such as that for Townsend's first coefficient, where the *form* of the distribution law is paramount, that deviations from this law become really serious. Thus, the relations 3.28, 3.29, and 3.30 are useful.

Unfortunately, while λ is known as a function of electron energy as a result of the Ramsauer free-path techniques in many pure gases, f, or its equivalent, is not known for any molecular gases, nor is it known where excitation and ionization are occurring. On the other hand, there have been methods since 1938 which allow accurate direct measurements of $v = k_e X$, the drift velocity of electrons in fields, even where ionization occurs. Thus, both Raether (5) with cloud-track techniques and Hornbeck (6) with pulsed discharges have directly measured v under discharge conditions. It is therefore desirable to eliminate f from equations 3.28 and 3.30 and develop an expression for the potential u_T in volts, or E, the average r.m.s. electron energy expressed in electron volts. Since equation 3.30 makes

(3.31)
$$v = 0.775 \sqrt{\frac{Xe\lambda}{m}} \sqrt{f},$$

then

(3.32)
$$\sqrt{f} = \frac{v^2 m}{0.601 \, Xe\lambda},$$

such that placing this expression in that for u_T gives

(3.33)
$$u_T = \frac{E}{e} = 0.424 \frac{X^2\lambda^2 e}{v^2 me} = 0.424 \frac{X^2\lambda^2}{v^2 m}.$$

Use of the Langevin equation 1.1b makes

$$u_T = 0.33 \frac{\lambda^2 X^2}{v^2 m}.$$

Variants of this relation appear, owing to the use of different constants in the elementary equation for mobility. Thus, von Engel and Steenbeck (13), and after them Raether (5), set

(3.34)
$$v = \frac{Xe\lambda}{m\bar{c}_1} = 1.085 \frac{Xe\lambda}{mC_1}.$$

Omitting the factor 0.921, they derive the ratio between C_1 and $\bar{c}_1$, and setting $f = 2(m/M)$,

(3.35)
$$u_T = \frac{X\lambda}{\sqrt{2f}},$$

thus making

(3.36)
$$u_T = \frac{\lambda^2 X^2}{2v^2 m} = 0.5 \frac{\lambda^2 X^2}{v^2 m},$$

with 0.5 in the numerator instead of 0.424 for Compton's and 0.33 for Langevin's. Langevin's expression is theoretically more accurate, as the later and really more accurate theoretical approximations to equations give the same values.

It should be added that the data derived from this method should be good to 20% if the Ramsauer free paths λ are known. To get a good solution, u_T must be guessed at to choose λ. Then solution will give a better value of u_T, so that λ can be found more accurately. With the third approximation, the values of u_T deduced should be as trustworthy as Maxwell's law permits.

In attempting to apply the equation to the computation of their observed mobilities, Bradbury and Nielsen rearranged the equation in terms of the collision cross section $\pi\sigma_1^2$ for the electrons as given by Ramsauer free paths, the observed f, X, p, and temperature T. Their equation (with a misprint eradicated) reads as follows:

$$(3.37) \qquad k_e = \frac{1.115 \times 10^{-10}\,(1/p)\,(1/\sigma^2)\,T^{\frac{1}{2}}}{[1+\{1+1.265 \times 10^{-31}\,(X/p)^2(1/\sigma_1 4f)\}^{\frac{1}{2}}]^{\frac{1}{2}}} \quad ,$$

giving k_e in cm/sec per volt/cm, with X in volts/cm, and p in mm Hg. At high values of X/p, it is possible to use

$$(3.38) \qquad k_e = 6.02 \times 10^{-3}\,\frac{1}{p}\,\sqrt{\frac{T\sqrt{f}}{\sigma_1^2\,(X/p)}}$$

in cm/sec per volt/cm.

§ 4. The Comparison of Theory and Experiment.

The measurements of the author at lower X/p allowed of direct comparison between the early Compton theory and experiment. It was found that in He and H_2, fair agreement between theory and experiment could be had over a limited range if the mean free paths were adjusted to give agreement. Wahlin's careful data in N_2, extending to still lower values of X/p, while yielding a proper *form* to the curve given by the Compton theory, *could not be fitted by adjusting the mean free paths alone.* It was clear from these results that both f and λ needed adjustment in order to make theory and experiment agree. The failure to achieve agreement with Wahlin's data for molecular gases by adjustment to a suitable mean free path alone was actually to be expected. James Franck and G. Hertz, in their early studies of excitation and ionization potentials, had discovered that in molecular gases electrons did *not* make elastic collisions as with the inert gases at energies below electronic excitation levels. Thus, the factor $f = 2.66\ m/M$ for the fractional loss of energy of electron impact against assumedly spherical *molecules* is only applicable to the atoms of the inert gases below their excitation potentials.

In molecular gases, impacts of electrons are inelastic at much lower energies. This was demonstrated by H. Baerwald, W. Harries, and H. Ramien (17) in a clear fashion at a much later date. Ramien's work showed that in H_2 the electrons collide elastically until they get enough energy to excite one of the vibrational states of the H_2 molecule. Then, through the mechanism of the Franck-Condon principle, the electron has a certain probability P_e of losing its energy to excitation. Thus, in a swarm of electrons moving through a gas, as the electrons gain the energy eu from the field, occasional inelastic impacts at appropriate *relatively low* energies reduce their energy

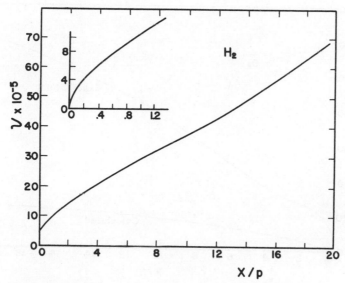

Fig. 3.1. Bradbury and Nielsen's values for the electron-drift velocity v in cm/sec in pure H_2 as a function of X/p.

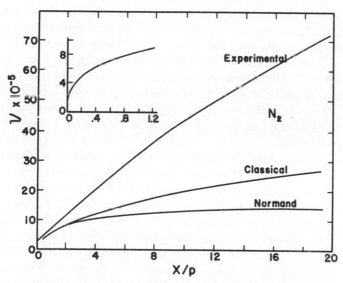

Fig. 3.2. Bradbury and Nielsen's values for the electron-drift velocity v in cm/sec in pure N_2 as a function of X/p.

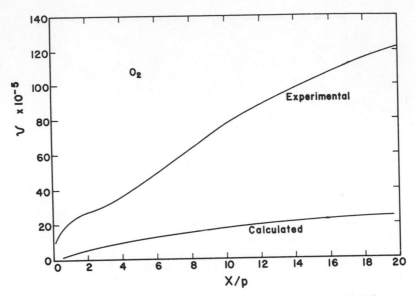

Fig. 3.3. Bradbury and Nielsen's values for the electron-drift
velocity v in cm/sec in pure O_2 as a function of X/p.

to zero, and the gain again begins. In consequence, the average
energy of the electron swarm is less than eu_T, as calculated by using
equation 3.28, so that f appears to be greater than that given by
classical kinetic theory. The loss is not insignificant, and for N_2
and H_2, f is of the order of per cent compared with 10^{-4} for the inert
gases. Only in one molecular gas has the loss been estimated as
a function of electron energy, and this was in the work of Ramien
for H_2. The calculation of f, its significance and variation, is presented in detail toward the end of section 3, chapter V, in a discussion of Bailey's f.

With adequate data on electron velocities covering a large range
of X/p in pure gases, Bradbury and Nielsen proceeded to put the
Compton theory to test. The results of their measurements are shown
in figures 3.1 to 3.4, inclusive. Using the value of f from kinetic
theory, together with Normand's (18) values of the electron free
paths,[8] they obtained the agreement between the observed and theoretical mobility curves in He, Ne, and A shown in figures 3.5, 3.6,
and 3.7. In order to estimate the proper values of the Normand free
paths to use, the values of $(3/2)\eta kT$ corresponding to their experi-

---

[8]Recent studies indicate that Normand's data are *not* as good as those of
Ramsauer, and that better agreement would have resulted if Ramsauer's data
had been used.

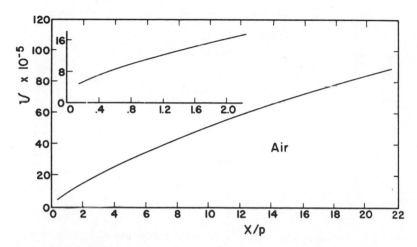

Fig. 3.4. Bradbury and Nielsen's values for the electron-drift
velocity v in cm/sec in pure air as a function of X/p.

mental values of X/p had to be taken from the data of the Townsend
group. This threw some uncertainty into the calculation, since the
gases used for η were not of comparable purity with those used by
Bradbury and Nielsen, and since the meaning of the average η in
relation to energy distributions is not clear, as will be indicated
elsewhere. It is seen, however, that the Normand values of the free
paths in general give fair agreement with the experimental values
below values of $X/p = 2.25$, 0.4, and 1.75 in He, Ne, and A respectively. Beyond this the observed mobilities increase in greater or
less measure above the theoretical values.

This increase is directly attributable to the fact that above these
values of X/p, *inelastic impacts to excitation* set in for the inert
gases. Such impacts increase f and lower C_1, so that mobilities must
increase. The proof that inelastic impacts actually set in at these
values of X/p must await discussion at a later point. Before proceeding further the final comparison of the theory with experiment can
be made through the results in H_2. In this case, extrapolation of
Ramien's data on f in H_2, together with the proper Ramsauer cross
sections, leads to the agreement shown in figure 3.8. Here the range
of X/p values, before the occurrence of even more inelastic impacts
to excitation beyond those noted by Ramien, is so high that there
is little room for doubt that the Compton theory is applicable in
principle if the data are known. However, it is likely that the neglect
of diffusion as well as the simple kinetic-theory approach used in
the derivation of the equation will not lead to a completely successful

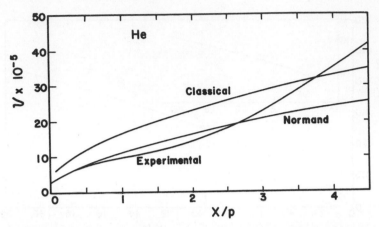

Fig. 3.5. Bradbury and Nielsen's observed values for electron-drift velocities v in cm/sec in He as a function of X/p, on the curve marked "experimental."
The computed curve from equation 3.37 with classical values of λ and Normand's
values of λ are shown for comparison.

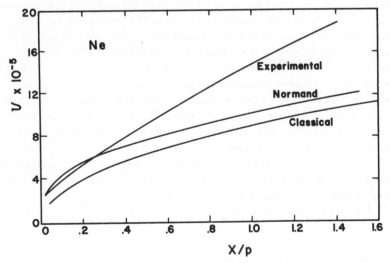

Fig. 3.6. Bradbury and Nielsen's observed values for electron-drift velocities v in cm/sec in Ne as a function of X/p, on the curve marked "experimental."
The computed curve from equation 3.37 with classical values of λ and Normand's
values of λ are shown for comparison.

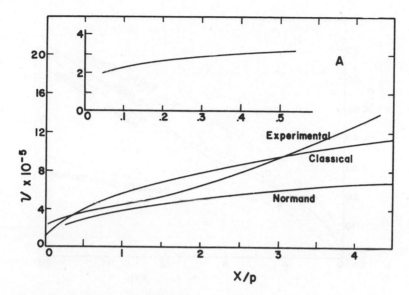

Fig. 3.7. Bradbury and Nielsen's observed values for electron-drift velocities v in cm/sec in A as a function of X/p, on the curve marked "experimental."
The computed curve from equation 3.37 with classical values of λ and Normand's
values of λ are shown for comparison.

agreement, since Compton's theory assumes a Maxwellian distribution
of energies.

It is essential here to point out to investigators that at the present
time, neither any theory, nor the data needed to place in it to get
electron-drift velocities, is equal or superior to good experimental
measurements. Further, it is not to be assumed that anyone's own
observed data taken under a given set of conditions must conform
to data (no matter how good) taken by any other particular group.
Differences in techniques and slight, unforeseen differences in purity
or preparation may cause appreciable differences in values. The
author currently believes that the Bradbury and Nielsen data represent
the most consistent, comprehensive set of values developed to date.[9]
Some of the values of the Townsend school taken in late years may
be of comparable value, as will be shown. This *does not warrant
a given worker using a new, untried method in judging as the best
data, those which conform to his results.* The results of work such

[9]Their data in H_2 (32) and A (26), (30), (31), (32) have been duplicated so
often to within 1% by careful investigators that there is no room for doubt.
Where observers have recently differed, they have subsequently been found
to be in error.

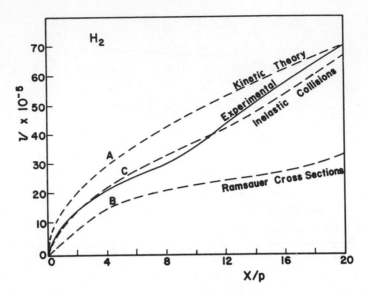

Fig. 3.8. Bradbury and Nielsen's data in H_2, shown by the full curve. Curve A gives the computed value using Compton's theory with classical mean free paths. Curve B is the theory using Ramsauer cross sections. Curve C is the same as curve B, but uses Ramien's extrapolated values of f, leading to fair agreement.

TABLE 3.2

Bradbury and Nielsen's Data on the Departure of Drift-Velocity Curves in He, Ne, and A, from Theory in Terms of X/p, Average Energy, and Critical Potentials

Gas	Deviation Observed at X/p	Energy in Volts of r.m.s. Maxwellian Equivalent Velocity	Energy in Volts at most Probable Velocity	Maxwellian Energy Exceeded by Fastest 5% of Electrons	First Excitation Potential E_i
He	2.25	4.25	2.83	16-17	19.77
Ne	0.40	4.30	2.86	16-17	16.58
A	1.75	11.10	2.33	41	11.57

as that of Bradbury and Nielsen have been yielded by several years' development and improvement of techniques of direct measurement, as have the data of L. G. H. Huxley and of V. A. Bailey and his pupils.

It is essentially at the point of deviation of the observed curves at higher X/p that the studies of Bradbury and Nielsen serve a most useful purpose (3). In table 3.2, in the second column, there are presented data as to the value of X/p at which the observed curves for k_e begin to deviate notably from the Compton theory. These values of X/p should correspond to the energies at which electrons begin to suffer inelastic impacts and thus increase f. From the values of η as a function of X/p taken by the Townsend school, these values of X/p in He, Ne, and A may be related to *root-mean-square* electron energies expressed in volts, as given in the third column. Bradbury and Nielsen estimated that if the most energetic 5% of the electrons in the Maxwellian distributions corresponding to these r.m.s. values collided inelastically, the observed beginning of the upward trend of the curves would be accounted for. From the Maxwellian curves they therefore estimated the energy which was exceeded by the fastest 5% of the electrons in the distribution, as indicated in the fifth column. Comparing these energies with the first excitation potentials of the corresponding gases, as shown in the sixth column, certain surprising features appear.

In neon, the agreement with the supposition that the fastest 5% are encountering inelastic impacts to excitation is reasonably well established. In helium, the *electrons should not produce excitation and begin to depart if the electron-energy distribution is Maxwellian*. In fact, the electrons do not have enough energy to awaken the 5% inelastic impacts needed. In argon, on the contrary, the deviations from the Compton equation should have occurred at a *much lower* X/p than 1.75. The conclusion drawn by Bradbury and Nielsen was that the *energy distribution of the electrons in helium and argon was not Maxwellian*, while it was nearly so in neon. It should be noted that here the thresholds correspond to the tails of the distribution law, which are drastically changed as the law changes, even if average energies active in drift velocities differ little.

As will be seen later, it was already known to Bradbury and Nielsen that even below excitation potentials, the electrons did not accurately have a Maxwellian energy distribution. The theoretical studies of M. J. Druyvesteyn, A. M. Cravath, B. Davydov, P. M. Morse, W. P. Allis, E. S. Lamar (19), (20), and others had shown that when diffusion as well as elastic impacts and constant free paths were considered, a new energy-distribution law applied; that of Druyvesteyn. The Druyvesteyn law, however, was not sufficiently different from Maxwell's to account for the differences noted above.

After ascertaining by another approach the validity of his interpretation of the discrepancies as being due to differences in the energy-distribution law, Nielsen proceeded to look for the cause

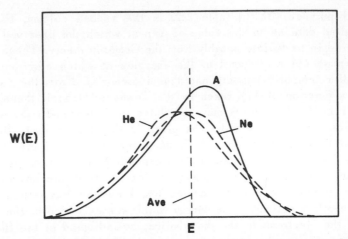

Fig. 3.9a. The effect of increase or decrease of free paths on the electron-energy distribution in He, Ne, and A. In Ne, the free path is sensibly constant and the law is essentially that of Druyvesteyn, which, when plotted about the same average energy, is not materially different in appearance from that of Maxwell as seen in figure 3.9b. In He, where free paths increase as energy increases, the curve is spread out. In A, where free path rapidly decreases with electron energy, there are few electrons of high energy. These curves were computed by Harriet W. Allen (21).

of such deviation. The deviation is not hard to explain, for it stems directly from the consideration of the *variation of free paths with electron energy*. If the free path increases as electron energy increases, as in·He gas, the more energetic electrons will have larger free paths and thus further augment their energy, while those with shorter paths will have less energy. The distribution curve for He will then rise more steeply on the low-energy side and will decline more gradually on the high-energy side than the corresponding Maxwellian distribution, as indicated for He in figure 3.9a. Thus, relative to the average energy as derived by assuming a Maxwellian or Druvesteyn distribution, there will be more high-energy electrons, and excitation energy will appear to occur at lower values of X/p than expected.

In the contrary case of argon, where the mean free path decreases sharply as energy increases, the result will be that the more energetic electrons will gain less energy and the higher-energy electrons will be sharply reduced in numbers. This loss, because of curtailed free paths, will augment the intermediate-energy electrons. The electrons of lower energy will on the other hand have longer free paths, and will gain more energy, reducing the number of very low-energy electrons and augmenting the central group. Such action will result in

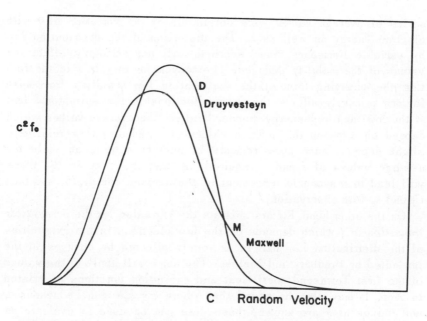

Fig. 3.9b. Maxwell's and Druyvesteyn's electron-velocity distributions
compared, as given by Morse, Allis, and Lamar.

a distribution curve with a more gradual rise on the low-energy side,
a concentration of electrons in the intermediate-energy range, and a
sharp decline on the high-energy side. All electrons will tend to
have their energies sharply limited on the high-energy side. Thus,
the average energy deduced from the centroid of such a curve would,
on a Maxwellian distribution, lead one to expect many more electrons
of high energy than are observed. This situation for argon is seen
in the curves of figure 3.9a. The reasoning has subsequently been
substantiated through the theoretical studies of Harriet W. Allen (21),
using the more esoteric methods of analysis for energy distribution
and mobilities, including the variable Ramsauer free paths. In fact,
the curves shown were taken from those computed by Allen. The
difference between the Maxwellian and Druyvesteyn distributions
plotted with velocity as the ordinate, as given by Morse, Allis, and
Lamar, is shown in figure 3.9b.

It was noted that where proper values of the Ramsauer free paths
and fractional loss of energy at an electron impact can be had as a
function of X/p, or the electron energy, agreement of the Compton
theory with the observed velocities is quite satisfactory. When inelastic impacts of a higher order set in, such as to excitation to light
emission or ionization, the theory would still be valid if a satisfactory

series of average values were obtainable of the variation of f with electron energy as well as λ. The distortion of the distribution law by variable Ramsauer cross sections will not seriously affect the values of the mobility deduced. The reason for this lies in the fact that the changing form of the distribution law resulting from such factors primarily affects the fewer electrons in the asymptotic feet at the low- and high-energy ranges. It alters the average values which depend on X/p and the average values of λ and of f to a relatively slight degree. Since measurements of another nature can yield the *average* values of f and λ required, as was the case in H_2, these will lead to reasonable agreement of the average energy, η, and thus C_1 and k_e with observation.

On the other hand, factors such as the X/p value for the *perceptible transition* in f which depends on the few electrons in the extremities of the distribution law will be seriously affected by changes in the law noted by Bradbury and Nielsen. The same will apply to the values of the first Townsend coefficient and excitation functions as related to X/p. It may also be added that where $v = k_e X$ can be measured, and values of λ are known, these data can be used to evaluate an equivalent value of f and the value of $u_T e = \overline{E}$, the average electron energy as a function of X/p, by the use of the Compton equations 3.35 and 3.36. The average values so inferred in terms of an equivalent Maxwellian law will not be very much in error. It is probably safe to assume *average energies so computed to be good within 20%, and possibly 10%*. If, however, the average values so inferred were to be used in estimating the number of electrons at relatively high or low energies on the basis of a Maxwellian distribution, the predictions could be orders of magnitude in error.

The distribution of energies of electrons in a field in a gas had been the subject of study beginning with the excellent pioneer work of F. B. Pidduck (11) in 1913, and of G. Hertz in 1925 (22). More intensive study in terms of the generalized methods of kinetic-theory analysis using diffusion, elastic impact, and constant free paths began with the work of M. J. Druyvesteyn in 1932 (19). However, the more complete general derivation of the mobility equation on the basis of such methods was not properly carried through until the work of W. P. Allis and his student Harriet W. Allen in 1937 (21). Their analysis made use of an extension of the method of H. A. Lorentz for determination of the energy distribution by P. M. Morse, W. P. Allis, and E. S. Lamar, applied to electrons in a field in a gas which used constant free paths, elastic impacts, and included diffusion. As will be seen in chapter IV, this general method of analysis yields two expressions, one of which leads to the energy distribution and the other to the drift velocity of the electrons. In their 1935 derivation these authors solved the expressions for constant-collision cross sections or mean free paths, but indicated the procedure in case it varied. The relation for the electron mobility there given expressed in the terminology of this text is

$$(3.39) \quad v = \frac{\pi^{\frac{1}{2}}}{3\Gamma(\frac{3}{4})} \left(\frac{3m}{M}\right)^{\frac{1}{4}} \left(\frac{2eX}{mNQ}\right)^{\frac{1}{2}} = 0.6345 \left(\frac{m}{M}\right)^{\frac{1}{4}} \sqrt{\frac{2Xe\lambda}{m}}.$$

In this relation the mean free path for momentum transfer is written as $1/NQ = \lambda$. Equation 3.39 does not differ seriously from the expression derived by Compton, when $u_T >> \Omega$, which in the same notation reads

$$(3.31) \quad v = k_e X = 0.775 \sqrt{\frac{e\lambda X \sqrt{f}}{m}} = 0.688 \left(\frac{m}{M}\right)^{\frac{1}{4}} \sqrt{\frac{2e\lambda X}{m}}.$$

It is to be noted that the accurate deduction of Morse, Allis, and Lamar, which involves the Druyvesteyn energy distribution, yields a lower value of the constant than that of Compton (13), (14), (15), and one that is not seriously different from the 0.618 to be expected from Langevin's 0.815 relative to Compton's 0.912 of equation 3.1.

Following Nielsen's demonstration of the importance of the variable free paths, Allis and Allen carried out two investigations. The first involved a study of the Townsend methods for evaluating η, or the electron temperature (7),

$$(3.40) \quad\quad\quad\quad\quad T_e = \frac{eXD}{kv},$$

and the other of the method for measuring the electron velocities by the magnetic-deflection method; for since the energy distributions are not Maxwellian, the analyses of Townsend could be in error. In this study they used the functions already derived by Morse, Allis, and Lamar. Constant cross sections and free paths were used. The results of the analysis do not throw much light on the significance of the measurement of T_e. It was shown, however, that the magnetic field reduced the number of high-velocity electrons, that the drift down the field of electrons of a given energy was not altered by the magnetic field, and that the lateral drift increased with the random velocity. It was finally shown that the ratio of the velocities in electric and magnetic fields leading to the deflection of the beam was given by 1.06 Hv/X, while Townsend's derivation yielded Hv/X.[10]

---

[10]See later studies in Healey and Reed and L. G. H. Huxley (1).

Thus, mobility data from Townsend's magnetic-deflection method are theoretically correct so long as λ is constant, even with the Druyvesteyn distribution.

Allen later proceeded to apply variable Ramsauer cross sections to the analysis of the mobilities of electrons in He, Ne, and A, as well as to derive the energy-distribution functions in these gases (21). Then, making somewhat arbitrary assumptions about the form of the distribution functions when *inelastic impacts set in*, an attempt was made to calculate the electron velocities above this region. The result of her analysis showed that the form of the distribution functions in the three gases below excitation was just as predicted by Bradbury and Nielsen. The Ramsauer collision cross sections used are shown in figure 3.10, with the resultant energy distributions adjusted in abscissae to give the same mean energy shown in figure 3.9a. With constant-collision cross sections the Druyvesteyn law is compared to that of Maxwell in figure 3.9b. In order to compute the velocities above the point where inelastic impacts set in, Allen noted that at this point the electron temperatures tend to approach a constant value, with a corresponding increase in the drift velocities or mobilities. Above the first excitation potential, inelastic collisions will reduce the number of electrons in the high-energy range. At the same time the electrons that have been removed from the high-velocity region by inelastic impacts revert to the low-velocity region and begin to regain energy. Thus, there will be a redistribution in the low-energy region where an excess of electrons will appear.

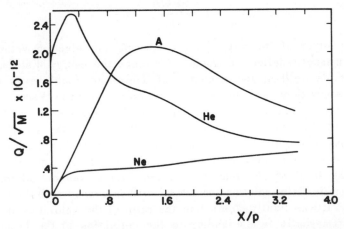

Fig. 3.10. Variable Ramsauer free paths used by Allen to derive the electron-drift velocities and the energy-distribution curves shown in figure 3.9a.

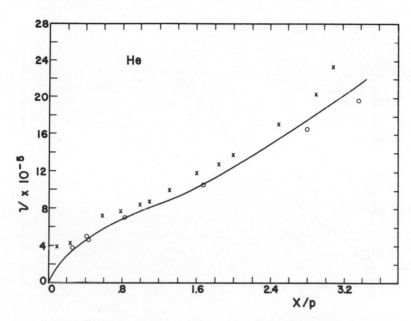

Fig. 3.11. Full curve gives Allen's computed drift velocity in He as a function of X/p compared to experimental values of Bradbury and Nielsen and of Townsend's group. Townsend's observed points are circles and Bradbury and Nielsen's values are crosses. Allen used an arbitrary cutoff value for the law between ionization and excitation potentials to give a fit with Townsend.

On the basis of the previous theory, a distribution was calculated that held up to the first excitation potential. This function was maintained to the point where it crossed the axis at an energy $u_T = u_{T1}$. Here u_{T1} was an adjustable parameter falling between the first excitation potential and the ionization potential.[11] By adjusting this cutoff and applying the distribution function above the point where excitation occurs, Allen was able to compute the values shown by the full curves of figures 3.11, 3.12, and 3.13 for He, Ne, and A. The experimental values of various observers are plotted on the curves as points. It is seen that the fit between Nielsen's results and the theory is really very satisfactory in the case of He, fair in Ne, and quite good in A. The agreement as noted is superior to that using Compton's equation.

[11] The justification for this arbitrary procedure was not given, except that the results showed the relations to be very insensitive to the value of cutoff chosen. The later analysis of D. Barbiere (9), following Holstein's method, clearly justifies this method, as shown in chapter IV.

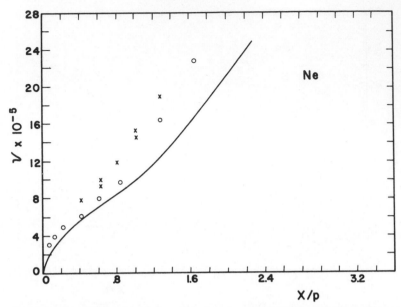

Fig. 3.12. Full curve gives Allen's computed drift velocity in Ne as a function of X/p compared to experimental values of Bradbury and Nielsen and of Townsend's group. Townsend's observed points are circles and Bradbury and Nielsen's values are crosses.

The data from observations based on Townsend's method are nearly as good as those of Bradbury and Nielsen as regards agreement with theory for He and Ne. Since the theory is at best only approximate above excitation, *no significance can be placed in the agreement* with either group of experiments. In the author's opinion, the difference of the data on argon by the Townsend method compared with that of Bradbury and Nielsen, is ascribable to the much purer argon available under the conditions of the work of Bradbury and Nielsen with outgassed, all-glass systems, relative to the metal chambers used in the early work of the Townsend group. This has been proved by later observers who confirm Nielsen's data (26), (31), (32). Argon should be particularly sensitive to impurities as regards *drift velocity* and *energy distribution*.

§ 5. **Later Developments of the Townsend Techniques.**

It is essential, in order to complete the discussion of electron velocities, to report on the later developments in this direction by the Townsend group. As indicated, the application of Townsend's magnetic-deflection method for the evaluation of electron velocities, to-

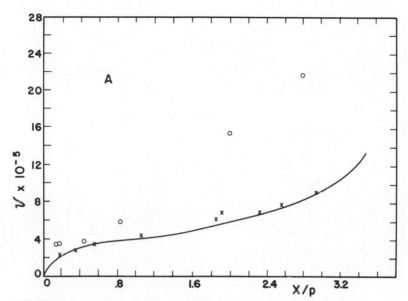

Fig. 3.13. Full curve gives Allen's computed drift velocity in A as a function of X/p compared to experimental values of Bradbury and Nielsen and of Townsend's group. Townsend's observed points are circles and Bradbury and Nielsen's values are crosses. The A of the Townsend group was known to have been impure. Allen's cutoff of distribution law was chosen to fit the Townsend curve.

gether with the diffusion study yielding data on energies and mean free paths, was initiated in 1913. Work with the method was continued on through the years by various investigators, with some improvements in technique and considerable improvement in the purity of the gases used. However, the agreement between the results of the different workers was not satisfactory, nor were the data in agreement with those of other workers, e.g., Bradbury and Nielsen.

This situation was recognized by L. G. H. Huxley in 1948 (1), (20). He set himself the goal of obtaining as a function of X/p, X and p at a temperature of 15° C., reliable measurements of the quantities, the electron-drift velocities $v = keX$, η the energy multiplier of Townsend, the electron free path L, and the mean fraction of electron energy f, lost at a collision with a gas molecule. He was able to accomplish this in consequence of his own and Townsend's (1) searching theoretical analyses of the action of magnetic fields on electronic motion in electrical fields in gases.[12] These analyses were carried out in the years

[12]Unlike the studies of Morse, Allis, and Lamar, Druyvesteyn, *et al.*, the kinetic theory of nonuniform gases of Chapman and Cowling was never used by these workers. The analyses are all based on the processes of averaging, using classical kinetic-theory procedures.

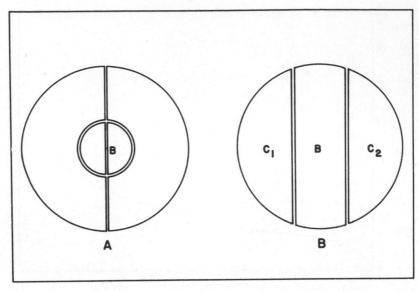

Fig. 3.14. Huxley's new form of electrode for the modified Townsend deflection method for electron-drift velocities is shown at "A," and Townsend's original method is shown at "B."

immediately preceding World War II. They led him to alter the design of the apparatus chiefly used by Townsend's pupils for the measurement of v and k/D in the later years to a form capable of mathematical solution in terms of the newer theoretical developments (1), (4). To this end, he returned to the initial coaxial geometry for the measurement of k/D and hence η by Townsend. This employed a central circular disc and an outer annular disc as collecting electrodes, with a cylindrical electron beam admitted into the drift field X by means of a circular aperture.

Since his work was to include measurements of the drift velocity v in the same apparatus with magnetic deflection, the apparatus used the same pair of concentric collecting electrodes. However, instead of a rectangular entrance slit forming the beam to the drift space parallel to the magnetic field H and a single circular collector having a single isolated strip parallel to the entrance slit of width a achieved by two vertical slots in the collector (as shown in figure 1.14), he used a different device. The admission orifice was a circular hole. The two concentric collector discs were sawed in half along a diameter parallel to the magnetic field H. These differences are shown illustrated in figure 3.14, at "A" and "B," for the Huxley and the Townsend systems respectively. This necessitated a different set of calibration curves for the ratio of currents R to the inner and the outer electrodes in terms of different values of the length of the drift field h, the radius a of the inner disc, and of a/h as a function of Xh/η_1, where η_1 is a special value of Townsend's η to be discussed. For the mobility measurements, the classical Townsend method with slits parallel to the field measured the value of the field $\overline{H}$ to cause the beam to be deflected a distance $a/2$. With this field, the elementary analyses of chapter I indicated v to be given by

(3.41)
$$v = \frac{X}{H}\left(\frac{a}{2h}\right).$$

This was shown to be inaccurate by Huxley and Townsend in 1937 (23). Toward this end the angle θ was defined as

(3.42)
$$\tan\theta = v_x/v_z,$$

where v_x is the drift velocity at *right angles* to the electrical field X and magnetic field H, and v_z is the component parallel to the electrical field X. In this case, Huxley found that

(3.43)
$$v_x = \frac{2}{3}\frac{X}{H}\left\{\overline{\frac{\omega^2 T^2}{1+\omega^2 T^2}\left[\frac{1}{2}+\frac{\omega^2 T^2}{1+\omega^2 T^2}\right]}\right\}$$

and

(3.44)
$$v_z = \frac{2}{3}\frac{X}{H}\left\{\overline{\frac{\omega T}{1+\omega^2 T^2}\left[1+\frac{\omega^2 T^2}{1+\omega^2 T^2}\right]}\right\},$$

with $\omega = He/m$ and $T = L/c$, the mean time spent between collisions. The lines over the braces indicate that the mean values averaged over all values of velocity c are to be used. In the diffusion experiments, pressures are such (1 to 6 mm Hg) that $\omega^2 T^2 \ll 1$. Thus,

(3.45)
$$\tan\theta = \frac{v_x}{v_z} = \frac{\omega \overline{T^2}}{2\overline{T}}.$$

Since, according to Huxley and Townsend's studies, the *correct* value of the drift velocity of the center of mass of a group of electrons moving in a gas in a constant electrical field is

(3.46)[13]
$$v = \frac{2}{3}\frac{Xe}{m}\frac{\lambda}{\overline{C}},$$

---

[13] The expression used by Huxley for the drift velocity of the electron is one derived by Townsend. Usually, as seen elsewhere, it has been assumed that

(1.1b)
$$v = k_e X = g\frac{e}{m}\frac{\lambda x}{C_1},$$

the equation above may be modified to

$$(3.47) \qquad \tan\theta = \frac{1}{2}\frac{H}{X}\frac{Xe}{m}\ \overline{T}\left(\frac{\overline{T^2}}{(\overline{T})^2}\right) = \frac{3}{4}\frac{Hv}{X}\frac{\overline{(C^{-2})}}{\overline{(C^{-1})^2}}\ .$$

Thus, it follows that the drift velocity

$$(3.48) \qquad v = \frac{4}{3}\frac{\overline{(C^{-1})^2}}{\overline{(C^{-2})}}\frac{X}{H}\tan\theta.$$

It is noted that in all this work the question of the proper averaging of velocities appears to play a most important role. In Huxley's paper there is given a complete summary of the values of the dimensionless products and ratios of the various velocity averages entering into these studies. These are evaluated for both the Maxwellian and Druyvesteyn distributions. Reference to this table and the relation for v therefore leads to correct evaluations of the electron velocity from the deflection studies in terms of the correct definition of the angle θ as

$$(3.50) \qquad v = 0.85\frac{X}{H}\tan\theta$$

for a Maxwellian distribution, and

$$(3.51) \qquad v = 0.943\frac{X}{H}\tan\theta$$

if a Druyvesteyn distribution is active.

In terms of the new definition of θ, Huxley calculated the ratio of currents $R_1 = i_2/i_1$ to the two semicircular halves of the electrodes

---

where g is a numerical factor resulting from averaging the free paths λ and velocities C_1. If the distribution is Maxwellian and the value of C_1 is the root-mean-square velocity C_1, then with λ fixed, g was set as 0.921 by Compton. Langevin's relations for molecules make it 0.815, while von Engel and Steenbeck set $g = 1$. Townsend and Huxley claim to have shown that owing to the action of the field on the time spent by the electron between collisions, the general expression v, the drift velocity, is

$$(3.49) \qquad v = \frac{2}{3}\frac{Xe}{m}\frac{\overline{\lambda}}{C_1}\ ,$$

where the expression $(\overline{\lambda/C_1})$ represents the results of an averaging process, and $g = 2/3$. If the mean free path is independent of velocity and in terms of the root-mean-square velocity C_1 is a Maxwellian distribution, the factor g becomes 0.92, or $kX = v = 0.92\ Xe\lambda/mC_1$. For the Druyvesteyn distribution, it takes on another value.

when a field H was applied. If there is no magnetic field, $i_1 = i_2$ for the properly adjusted apparatus. Thus, instead of splitting the beam for a given value of $a/2$ by properly choosing a field H, all that is done after centering the beam with $H = 0$ is to apply H and note the ratio $R_1 = i_2/i_1$ collected by the two halves of the electrode. By means of calculation, a series of curves for values of R_1 relative to $(XH/\eta_1)\,(v_x/v_z)$ ranging from 0.05 to 0.25 is obtained. Since from the diffusion experiments η_1 is evaluated in the same gas for the same X/p, X and p recourse to the values of XH/η_1 and R_1, fix v_x/v_z, and permit evaluation of the drift velocity v. The method thus yields η_1 from the ratio k/D using the diffusion study, and this in turn yields the drift velocity v by the succeeding measurement.

It must next be indicated that the value of η deduced has been shown by Huxley and Townsend not to be the direct multiplier, assuming a Maxwellian velocity distribution used in the earlier part of this chapter. Instead, it is a factor which depends on the averaging process, and will vary with the distribution law. Accordingly, the quantity η_1 appearing in the discussion above may be written

(3.52)
$$\eta_1 = A\eta$$

and

(3.53)
$$A = \frac{3}{2}\left[\frac{\bar{C}}{\overline{C^2}(\overline{C^{-1}})}\right].$$

For a Maxwellian distribution, $A = (3/2)\,(1/1.5) = 1$, and for a Druyvesteyn distribution it is $A = (3/2)\,(1/1.312) = 1.43$. From this, on the notation of Huxley, the ratio of k_e/D becomes

(3.54)
$$\frac{k_e}{D} = 40.3/\eta_1 = \frac{40.3}{A}\frac{1}{\eta}.$$

It has been seen that these studies on the theoretical side have made measurement more precise. They have rendered interpretation more flexible, since they define the various averages and permit of the averaging for the various distribution laws. This was the great difficulty with the system of Townsend during the earlier years.

In his paper on the behavior of slow ions in air, Huxley used the corrections indicated. With an all-glass system and other proper refinements, he evaluated η for electrons in air from $X/p = 0$ to $X/p = 25$. He then plotted the results as a function of X/p for both the Maxwellian and Druyvesteyn distributions. The electrons were created in a separate section of the apparatus by a point corona discharge. The values of C_1 are then $1.15\sqrt{\eta} \times 10^7$ on the Maxwellian, and $1.08\sqrt{\eta} \times 10^7$ on the Druyvesteyn laws.

The new method was applied to the evaluation of v, and a check indicated that the values of v were sensibly constant for variations in H from 35.8 to 71.5 oersteds. The data indicated that electron attachment at the fields of $X = 16$ volts/cm and $p = 4$ mm of Hg was negligible; i.e., $X/p = 4$.[14] The drift velocity was determined over a range of X/p from about 0.5 to 25, assuming both Maxwellian and Druyvesteyn distributions. The data *using the Druyvesteyn distribution* fall very closely on the observed results of Bradbury and Nielsen over most of the range. The studies also allow of a determination of the electron free paths at 1 mm pressure as a function of electron energy. The values decrease from about 4.8×10^{-2} cm to about 3.8×10^{-2} cm over the range studied in a monotonic decline. The classical kinetic-theory value of the mean free path is 2.76×10^{-2} cm. The data also allow of a quantity derived by V. A. Bailey for *convenience* in his studies to be computed. This is the average over-all electron energy lost per impact with a molecule. Let $Q = \frac{1}{2}m\overline{C}_1^2$ be the *mean* energy of agitation of an electron in the steady state. The average over-all loss of energy per collision is f determined by

$$(3.55) \qquad \left(\frac{\overline{C}_1}{\lambda}\right) f Q = X e v.$$

Reducing these data in terms of the various averages leads to

$$(3.56) \qquad f = \frac{3.41 \times 10^{-14} v^2}{[(\overline{C_1^2})\,(\overline{C_1^{-1}})^2]\eta_1}.$$

In terms of the Maxwell and Druyvesteyn distributions respectively, the values of f are $f = 1.79 \times 10^{-14}\, v^2/\eta_1$ and $1.68 \times 10^{-14}\, v^2/\eta_1$. The values for f in air are constant from near 0 to 1.5 electron volts of energy at $f = 1.3 \times 10^{-3}$. Above this the loss rises continuously as energy increases to about 5 electron volts, where it is close to 10^{-2}. This rise in energy loss per impact occurs in the same region of about 1.62 electron volts in O_2 where Bradbury observed energy loss to vibration and increased electron attachment. The values of η as a function of X/p, of v as a function of X/p, of λ as a function of random electron velocity, and of f as a function of electron energy, as observed by Huxley for clean, dry air, are given in table 4.4a.

It might be added that Bailey, in order to discuss the reaction of the ionosphere with radio waves, has derived a quantity G defined by $f = G\,(1 - 1/\eta)$ which makes f vanish, as it should do when $X = 0$

---

[14]Actually, it is just beyond this (at $X/p = 6$) that dissociative electron attachment in air with large cross section begins, as shown by R. Geballe and M. A. Harrison (25).

and electrons are in thermal equilibrium with the gas; i.e., when $\eta = 1$. Thus, as long as $1/\eta$ is less than the experimental error, $f = G$, with $G = 1.3 \times 10^{-3}$ in air, assuming Druyvesteyn's distribution. The exact significance of f is considered in chapter V near the end of section 3. Its use is of little value except as an indication of changes of energy on impact. The energy loss on impact f is a quantity that is reflected in the drift velocity and η as well.

It is seen that by means of the more rigorous analysis, Huxley has corrected and reinterpreted the significance of the various averages. He has, furthermore, improved techniques of the magnetic-deflection method as regards purity control and accuracy to a point where the electron velocities, electron energies, and other parameters can be obtained as reliable *averages* within two significant figures. Finally, he has reconciled his values with those of Bradbury and Nielsen, and so far as gross average values are concerned, he has indicated that the energy distribution is of the Druyvesteyn rather than the Maxwellian form. It must, however, be pointed out that since λ decreases with electron energy, the *accurate distribution law* will, as Harriet Allen has shown, deviate from the Druyvesteyn law in the direction of having more high-energy electrons in the tail of the distribution, and less low-energy electrons. This shift *will not seriously affect the average values used*, which are not very sensitive to changes in form of the law. On the other hand, these deviations play an important role at the point where curves alter, owing to onset of inelastic impacts and where excitation and ionization become of interest.

On the basis of the theoretical discussions, it was possible, in terms of X/p, the mean free path λ, and f, for Huxley to derive an expression for electron-drift velocity. In form, the resulting expression does not differ materially from that of the Compton equation 3.37, with 2.66 m/M replaced by $G = f/(1 - 1/\eta)$. It reads:

$$(3.57) \quad v = \frac{\lambda(X/p)}{7.85 \times 10^{-9}} \frac{1}{(\eta)^{\frac{1}{2}}} = \frac{1.127 \times 10^8 \, \lambda(X/p)}{\left\{ \dfrac{1 + [1 + 960 \, \lambda^2 (X/p)^2/G]^{\frac{1}{2}}}{2} \right\}^{\frac{1}{2}}} \, ,$$

with the Druyvesteyn distribution assumed. If data are confined to the fixed values of $\lambda = 4 \times 10^{-2}$ and $f = 1.3 \times 10^{-3}$, which occur in air below $X/p = 2.5$, the expressions for η and v are

$$(3.58) \qquad\qquad \eta = 1 + \{1 + 1180 \, (X/p)^2\}^{\frac{1}{2}}/2$$

and

(3.59)
$$v = \frac{5 \times 10^7 (X/p)}{\left\{ \dfrac{1 + [1 + 1180\,(X/p)^2]^{1/2}}{2} \right\}^{1/2}}.$$

In addition to this development as regards electron velocities, attention must be called to a more indirect approach to the problem by V. A. Bailey and his students. The approach requires the development of a considerable body of theory, which will appear more properly in chapter V, concerning electron attachment and negative ion formation. The method enables measurement of electron velocities where ion formation is taking place. It is treated *in extenso* in a book by R. H. Healey and J. W. Reed (1).

In principle, the method hinges on letting a mass of electrons in a field in a gas flow through a series of circular apertures in diaphragms lying in equipotential planes normal to a uniform electrical field X along the common axis of the apertures. The entrance orifice is in a diaphragm labeled 5. At a known distance c there is another diaphragm 3, and at another distance c there is a third diaphragm 1. Below these there is a collecting plate 0. In later modifications of the apparatus, the distances c between 5 and 3, and 3 and 1 could be varied. Actually measured are the currents to 3 and 1 and 0, and of importance are the ratios ξ and ζ of the currents 1/3 and 0/1. With distances c fixed, these ratios are measured for two values of pressure p and for the same ratio of X/p. These enable the intricate equations for the diffusion of ions and electrons to the collector diaphragms to yield values of Townsend's η and of a quantity $a = hc/\lambda v$. In a the quantity h is the probability of electron attachment, c the random velocity of the electron, λ its free path, and v the drift velocity of the electron. With this information it is possible, with knowledge of c, λ, and v, to determine h. Actually, a measurement of v and the evaluation of η give c and λ.

Bailey (1) next studied the effect of a magnetic field H applied along the axis of the apertures and parallel to the electrical field X; i.e., a longitudinal magnetic field. It appears that the distribution ratio $R(X/\eta c)$ observed when the magnetic field H is 0 is changed to one that is $R(X\phi/\eta c)$ on application of H where $\phi = 1 + (Hv/X)^2$. The actual method of measurement may be differently applied. In one procedure, η and a are determined with $H = 0$. Then H is put on and adjusted until the spread of the beam of electrons and ions is reduced by H to that of a beam of *ions*. This particular value of H is denoted by H_{01}, and the value of ϕ corresponding to it is ϕ_0. Then $R(X\phi_0/\eta c) = R(X/c)$, whence

(3.60) $\eta = \phi_0 = 1 + (H_0 v/X)^2$.

From this, v can be obtained. Other more accurate procedures are possible. In any case, it is possible by this means to evaluate v, and other properties in gases like HCl and the halogens, where electrons attach readily to form ions. The analysis was carried over to mixtures diluting the attaching gases, so that enough electrons were present for measurement.

In general, according to Healey and Reed, the values of the quantities deduced by this method are in satisfactory agreement with those obtained by Townsend's method. Certainly, in H_2 gas the values of v obtained by Bailey from $X/p = 0.625$ to $X/p = 20$ are within a few per cent of those obtained by the deflection method. However, it is clear in all these studies that the accuracy cannot be much better than some 5%, which is perhaps as good as can be expected in any case, considering the uncertain effects of small amounts of unavoidable impurities.

§ 6. Electron-Velocity Measurements at Ionizing and Sparking Fields.

It is not proper to close this chapter without reference to some of the latest measuring techniques, applicable where the more conventional measurements fail. These are, first, the very pretty, direct observations of the velocity of travel of the head of the cloud of ionizing electrons made by the C. T. R. Wilson cloud tracks (5), and secondly, the measurement of the time of passage of these avalanches across a measured gap, using pulsed discharges and an oscilloscope (6).

A. The Cloud-Chamber Method.

While the method cannot yield any great accuracy, it is a direct method capable of application in a limited region of pressures on gases fouled with saturated water and alcohol vapors. However, it extends the measurements of velocity right into the very important region where electrical breakdown occurs. The method was evolved by H. Raether about 1935, and definite results were achieved and published in his excellent paper of 1937 (5). The work is summarized in an article in *Ergebnisse der Exakten Naturwissenschaften* (5). As far back as 1887, Helmholtz and Regner had used adiabatic expansion of saturated gases to study the vapor trails resulting from impulse ionization. No real progress was made until 1934-1935, when Raether began to apply the very highly developed techniques of the nuclear physicist to the study of impulse-controlled ionization proc-

§6

esses in uniform and nonuniform electrical fields, with the C. T. R. Wilson cloud chamber.

The following method was used: Light from a spark was passed through a small quartz window in the upper plate anode of a plane parallel electrode system. The upper plate was separated from the lower plate by an appropriate cylindrical glass ring some 3.6 cm high and 10 cm in diameter. This could be illuminated from the side to reveal the tracks. The tracks were photographed by camera in a direction at right angles to the illuminating beam. The lower plate cathode consisted of a fine meshed gauze of the diameter of the cylinder, with a small disc of metal at its center from which the ultraviolet light liberated photoelectrons. Just below the gauze cathode and sealed off by a rubber diaphragm was a piston of limited travel. This could, by opening a valve below it, or by mechanically operated plunger, be made to descend rapidly a measured distance below the gauze. This produced an adiabatic expansion of volume ratio in the order of 1.2 to 1.4 of the air or gas between the electrodes. Such adiabatic expansion served to condense cloud droplets on the ions created by the avalanche. The gases used in the cylindrical glass Wilson cloud chamber were air, O_2, H_2, N_2, CO_2, and argon, saturated with a mixture of one part ethyl alcohol to three parts water, as is conventional in cloud chambers where condensation on both types of ions is desired.

The measurements were conducted in the following fashion: An auxiliary spark gap had its light focused by a quartz lens through the window onto the disc on the cathode. Enough intensity was used to obtain several photoelectrons liberated per 10^{-8} sec from the disc. The spark was triggered to initiate the electrons at a given instant. An impulse from this spark started a wave of potential, with sharp rise and decline, on its way to the electrodes over a suitable delay line so as to start when electron emission from the disc had set in. The potentials were such as to give fields of the order of 8 to 15 kv/cm across the electrodes with the lower gauze negative. The duration of the pulse could be varied so that the electron avalanches starting from the cathode were exposed to a field for a given known time.

Shortly after the decline of the square pulse of potential, the trip on the exhaust value of the cloud chamber was operated and an adiabatic expansion followed, condensing a cloud on the tracks left by the ionization. Gas pressures varied from 200 mm to atmospheric, with chamber temperatures of the order of 20° C. The duration of the pulses ranged from a few times 10^{-8} sec to 10^{-6} sec, or in that region.

By varying the duration of the potential pulses, the electron avalanches produced by single photoelectrons from the cathode could
be photographed after various times of travel in the field, and at
various imposed field strengths and pressures.

Now a single electron leaving the cathode in a field X at a pressure p will proceed (above a critical value of X/p characteristic of
the gas used) from cathode to anode, producing n new electrons.
These electrons are created along the path length x. According to
the law,

$$n = \epsilon^{ax} - 1.$$

Here a is the first Townsend coefficient, which is a *known* function
of X/p for each gas *if it is pure*. In these studies X/p was varied
so that values of n ranging from about 20 to 10^7 could be observed
in distances x of the order of 1 to 3 cm from the cathode. As the
initial electron and its progeny cross the gap they advance their
position with drift velocities v of the order of 10^7 cm/sec, and leave
behind the positive ions, which are practically immobile on time
scales of 10^{-6} sec.

In addition to these ion and electron clouds, there are created
in the gas a considerable number of nuclei of a hygroscopic character
as a result of dissociation and chemical action produced in the dirty
mixed gases N_2, O_2, H_2O, and C_2H_5OH. The intense ultraviolet light
accompanying the avalanches of electrons will also produce many
nuclei, not only along the tracks but in zones surrounding the avalanches. Such nuclei have been noted by Raether, as well as by
W. S. Gorrill (24) with similar techniques in the author's laboratory.
Now with appropriate expansion ratios the C_2H_5OH and H_2O will
condense on positive and negative ions and on the nuclei present.
In fact, condensation on nuclei is more likely in many cases than
on ions. That is, such nuclei will condense drops at lower expansion
ratios than will the ions. This circumstance requires some study of
the expansion ratios relative to tracks obtained, so that the significance of the observed tracks is understood. However, with appropriate
expansion ratios, the clouds will clearly delineate the tracks of
single electron avalanches and permit them to be photographed.

Characteristic cloud tracks of such avalanches, taken from Raether
and Riemann's papers, are shown in N_2 at 280 mm (figure 3.15a)
and in N_2 and CO_2 at 150 mm (figure 3.15b). The four avalanches
in N_2 of figure 3.15a were liberated within a few 10^{-9} sec of each
other, which accounts for the slight differences in length of tracks.
The accelerating field was applied for the order of some 5×10^{-7}

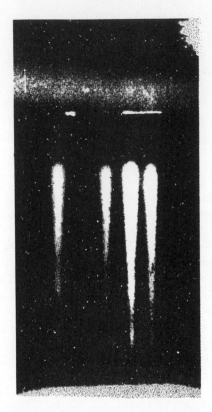

Fig. 3.15a. Electron avalanches in N_2, photographed by the
cloud-chamber techniques of H. Raether; cathode at bottom.

sec. In these photographs the tracks are quite dense and the fields
were high, making $\epsilon^{\alpha x}$ in excess of 10^4 or even more. Figure 3.16a
shows tracks taken after 1.07×10^{-7} sec at "a" and 1.74×10^{-7}
sec at "b," at 525 mm and 11 kv/cm in H_2; while the tracks at "c"
were after 2.6×10^{-7} sec at 275 mm and 7 kv/cm in H_2.

It is clear that by varying the impulse time t at a given X/p, X,
and p, and by measuring the distance x traversed across the chamber,
electron-avalanche velocities may directly be determined. In order
that accurate data can be had, the track lengths must be capable
of measurement and reduction from the photographs, which does not
present much of a problem. The actual length of an avalanche as
seen is hard to delineate because of diffusion and photoionization.
If corresponding points on two avalanches at different times are
used, accuracy is better. More difficult is an accurate evaluation

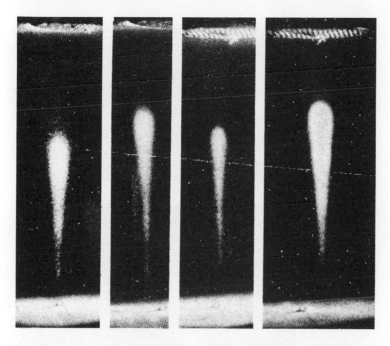

Fig. 3.15b. Electron avalanches in N_2 and CO_2 at 150 mm, taken by Raether with cloud-chamber techniques; cathode at bottom.

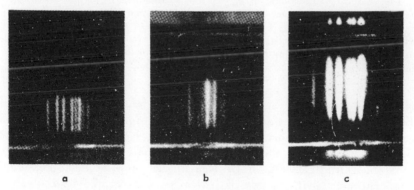

a   b   c

Fig. 3.16a. Electron avalanches photographed by Raether in H_2 with cloud-chamber techniques, pressure 525 mm at "a" and "b." Time of pulse at field of 11 kv/cm was 1.07×10^{-7} sec at "a" and 1.74×10^{-7} sec at "b." Tracks at "c" were taken at 275 mm with 7 kv/cm and 2.6×10^{-7} sec duration. In all these, the cathode is at the bottom.

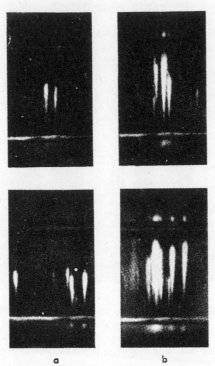

Fig. 3.16b. Another sample of electron avalanches in pulsed techniques with Wilson cloud chamber, by Raether. The "a" and "b" figures are separated by 10^{-7} sec in time; cathode at the bottom. Differences in distances of advance in any one picture are due to differences in time of electron liberation during the spark flash. The few initial ions near the cathode do not show. Some droplets evaporate owing to heat from the cathode.

of the potential, and hence field, applied by the square pulses of 1937. Not only were rise time and decline not very sharp, but the potential was presumably not constant. Thus, the value of the applied field X inferred from the circuit was no doubt inaccurate owing to possible multiplication by reflection of the pulse at the electrodes. Last but not least, the statistical time lags of the photoelectric electron liberation following the triggering spark caused a definite "jitter," and thus an uncertainty as to how long electrons traveled relative to the pulse. This jitter was reduced by initiating the triggering spark with a high approach voltage and using high overvoltages. However, adjustments and timing had to be very carefully made to avoid considerable error.

Raether himself was skeptical of the values of the applied field. As a check on this in order of magnitude, he initiated the following

TABLE 3.3

Values of X/p and Electron Multiplication Calculated for Avalanche Tips
at the Limit of Visibility to Test Potential Pulse (by Raether)

Gas	X/p	a Gas	a H_2O	$N = \epsilon^{ax}$
O_2	31.0	0.30	0.26 ⎫	
Air	32.7	0.73	0.36 ⎬	10-20
N_2	32.4	0.60	0.32	–
H_2	20.7	–	–	–

study. It has been estimated by a study of tracks under different
conditions that the cloud became perceptible if there were some
10 to 20 droplets formed in 1 mm^2 of field of view of cloud track.
Thus, 10 drops per mm^2 of area as viewed by the camera would in
Raether's opinion delineate the edge of the cloud track, or would
just be perceived as a cloud. Adjusting the expansion ratio so that
he was sure that *cloud droplets would condense on all ions*, positive
and negative. Raether lowered X/p in O_2, air, N_2, and H_2 so that
after some 2 cm of path he could just perceive the cloud at the *end*
of the avalanche, which assumedly consisted of 10-20 ions per mm^2
in his pictures. The values of X/p, as computed from his circuit
constants for the square wave pulse under these conditions, are
given in column two of table 3.3.

With these values of X/p, the approximate values of Townsend's
coefficient a for the gas and H_2O mixture were computed. Then, from
the length of track x, ax and ϵ^{ax} could be computed. The numbers so
obtained lay in the region of 10-20 ions in agreement with the just-
perceptible clouds. This constituted a check on the consistency of
the data; e.g., the accuracy of the computed field and the adequacy
of the expansion ratio to condense on all ions and omit most nuclei.
The agreement gave him confidence in the accuracy of the assumed
applied potential to better than order of magnitude.

However, it must be considered that the accuracy in determination
of ϵ^{ax} is not convincingly high, nor are the values of a computed or
estimated for gas-H_2O mixtures at all certain. That is, a could be
50% or more in error. It is not known whether 10 or 20 drops are first
perceived as a cloud, etc. Consistency of data does not constitute
a verification. If the expansion ratios were *not adequate* to insure
condensation on all ions, then, when the cloud was perceived, more
than 10-20 ions were really present. Thus, actually the fields might
not have been as indicated by X/p, but were possibly higher. In other
words, quantitative conclusions based on cloud condensation demand

TABLE 3.4

Riemann's Data on Electron-Drift Velocities in cm/sec and "Wedge Angles"
for Electron Avalanches, from Cloud-Chamber Studies

Gas	Pressure in mm at $0°$ C.	X/p in volts/cm	v in cm/sec	Angular Aperture of the Avalanche "Wedge Angle"
CO_2	285	36	1.72×10^7	9.1×10^{-2}
O_2	290	34	1.63×10^7	10.4×10^{-2}
Air	285	37	1.47×10^7	6.7×10^{-2}
N_2	280	38	1.20×10^7	6.8×10^{-2}
N_2	143	39	1.24×10^7	8.5×10^{-2}
N_2	93	42	1.29×10^7	11.8×10^{-2}
H_2	467	22	0.68×10^7	6.3×10^{-2}
H_2	305	20	0.80×10^7	6.5×10^{-2}
H_2	121	31	0.92×10^7	11.2×10^{-2}
A	528	12	0.43×10^7	12.3×10^{-2}
A	290	16	0.53×10^7	13.0×10^{-2}

special extensive study with expansion ratios to insure *any* validity.
This could be achieved, as in cosmic-ray studies, by observing β
or γ ray tracks in a field separating the ion pairs and where ions
per mm path are known. Raether and Riemann made no such studies.

Today, probably improved pulse techniques and the use of properly
matched circuit constants could yield more satisfactory values. More
extensive studies of expansion ratios must also be made. The data
taken by Riemann are shown in table 3.4.

As a partial check, it may be noted that Bradbury and Nielsen, in
pure, clean, dry H_2, measured v at an $X/p = 20$ as 0.69×10^7 cm/sec.
Raether's study in the alcohol-water mixture in H_2 at an $X/p = 22$
yielded a velocity of 0.68×10^7 cm/sec. This gave Raether some
confidence that the work at least was yielding correct order of magnitude for the data. It could hardly do more until v in H_2 with 15% H_2O
and C_2H_5OH was known.

In column five of table 3.4 there are presented certain data that
are of interest. These are the "wedge angles" $2y/x$ of the cloud
tracks photographed. Here x is track length and y is track radius.
They were obtained by adjusting the expansion ratios until the profiles of the cloud tracks gave nice, straight-line edges delineating
a cone of aperture $2y/x$. The width of the avalanche at its head $2y$
was then divided by the length of the track from the cathode and
recorded as the "wedge angle." This procedure was carried out according to the following reasoning: As the electron cloud advances

with a velocity v in the field direction in consequence of the field, the electron-avalanche cloud, owing to the high energy of the electrons, is superposing its diffusive motion on the drift motion. Thus, as it advances, the cloud swells in the field direction as well as laterally. In the study of sparking it is of great value to know the *real radius* of the avalanche cloud resulting from this diffusive motion.

Roughly speaking, it was seen that in a time of advance t the average lateral diffusive expansion of such diffusing electrons is given by

(2.17) $$\bar{r} = \sqrt{4Dt},$$

where D is the coefficient of diffusion. This depends on electron energy

$$\frac{1}{2}mC_1^2 = \frac{3}{2}\eta kT.$$

However,

(3.3) $$D = \frac{k_e \eta p}{Ne},$$

as seen in chapter II, and $v = kX$. In consequence, equation 3.36 of this chapter makes it possible from Ramsauer free paths λ and v to estimate the terminal electron energy

$$\frac{3}{2}\eta kT = \frac{1}{2}mC_1^2 = eu_T,$$

and to fix η and D. Thus, through equation 2.17 above, it is possible to fix $\bar{r}$ to be used in such computations.

In regarding the cloud tracks, Raether hoped to be able to justify such calculation by the observed width of tracks. Now the radius r is one which will contain a fraction $1 - 1/e$ of the ions or electrons created, but it will *not* necessarily delineate the cloud profile of an electron avalanche. It will also follow that the calculation leads to a contour for $\bar{r}$ in which $\bar{r} = A\sqrt{x}$, where x is the track length. This sort of wedge angle (if one may speak of such a thing), is

$$\theta = \frac{2\bar{r}}{x} = 2A/\sqrt{x},$$

and the profile is parabolic. If θ and x can be measured from such a track, A is evaluated, and this will lead to the evaluation of eu_T and η if v is known. There is *no way* in which such a constant can be evaluated, since $\bar{r}$ does not delineate any cloud-track profile.

On the other hand, use of the Einstein diffusion law given by equation 2.14 permits of the application of the *visibility* criterion to the delineation of the cloud-track profile. If it is assumed that 10 ions per mm² mark the limit of visible condensation, then combining this condition with equation 3.3 leads to the relation that the width of the head of the avalanche $2y$ is related to the track length x by an equation $y = A'x$. Here A' through D in equation 3.3 is related to the electron energy

$$eu_T = \frac{1}{2} mC_1^2 = \frac{3}{2}\eta kT.$$

Thus, by properly observing the wedge angle, it should be possible to check on electron energies as well as velocities in these studies.

While in earlier studies of v, the condensation ratios used were not considered of importance so long as condensation was adequate, this was not the case in Riemann's study. If figures 3.16a and 3.16b are studied, it is seen that the avalanche profiles have various shapes, some of them being *reasonably parabolic.* By the time Riemann's study was made it had been decided that the contour of the avalanches should be *rectilinear,* such that $y = A'x$, following the reasoning cited but not otherwise. Thus, expansion ratios were *adjusted* and doubtless reduced to give the linear profile. When this was done, the values of the wedge angles so observed were used to calculate the electron energies eu_T. The values of electron energies obtained were of the order of 0.5 to 1.5 e.v. in all the gases, and at high X/p values where considerable ionization by collision was occurring. These very low values *are not consistent* with ionization by collision. The observed values further vary from gas type to gas type in an utterly senseless manner, and are *not* in agreement with the values calculated by means of equation 3.36, using v and λ. These data on v and λ and the theory of equation 3.36 are certainly good to 10% or 20%. They could not be 300% too high. Raether, however, believed that the wedge-angle values of eu_T represented the correct average energy values, and later applied them to sparking studies, leading to further inconsistencies.

Since the theory lies within the scope of this chapter, it is the appropriate place to discuss the discrepancy. The error is easily discerned. Raether's theory of the cloud-track profile and his 10 droplets per mm² are perhaps logical criteria and are properly applied to the track to give a linear profile $y = Ax$. If, however, to obtain *clean-cut linear track profiles* in the face of the action of disturbing agencies, foreign nuclei, etc., the *expansion ratios are reduced* so that every ion does not produce a droplet, then there will be adequate droplets to give the track edge only at smaller distances y. The wedge angles so observed will be too small. This will yield values of D that are also too small. Since the inferred values of eu_T as a function of $2y/x$ vary as the square of the ratios of the values of $2y/x$ observed, it is clear that it does not take *much reduction* in $2y/x$ to give much too low values of eu_T.

Those who have had to work with cloud tracks know full well that it takes very careful studies and adjustment of conditions to insure that all ions make droplets and that the other nucleation does not add false counts to quantitative ion studies. There is no indication that Riemann ever made such a study of expansion ratios, using β tracks of known densities of ionization and separating fields to insure that the expansion caused droplets on all ions. Until such study is made, cloud-track profiles and drop counts may *not* be used for quantitative evaluations. On the other hand, reduced condensation will not noticeably shorten the avalanche length used in velocity measurement. The parts of the tracks at low x near the cathode will disappear with reduced expansion, as well as in consequence of heat radiation and conduction from the cathode; but the velocity evaluations will stand within the limits imposed by spark lag and pulse uncertainties.

Enough has been reported to indicate the possibilities of the new method of measurement of electron velocities under high-field conditions, and to suggest further improvement and other studies in this direction.

B. *Electron-Mobility Measurements with Pulsed d.c. Fields.*

This method was developed by J. A. Hornbeck as the by-product of a time study of the development of an electrical spark in a uniform field. The study of Hornbeck was made using a Townsend gap with a suitable potential, and by flashing a triggering source of radiation onto the cathode for some 10^{-7} sec duration (6). The pulse of electrons produces an avalanche, the arrival of which at the cathode is indicated by a suitable oscillographic recording. The theory of the method, as well as the results, which represent one of the first attempts at using modern pulse techniques in such studies, will be given in chapter IX, section 16, for economy of space. Suffice it to state that the values of Hornbeck in inert gases are in good agreement with the results of Townsend and Bailey, and with the calculations of Harriet Allen, where they overlap. This is remarkable, since the accuracy claimed is only 10%. With proper modifications the uncertainty could be reduced to 5%.

Actually preceding the work of Hornbeck, P. Herreng (26), in Langevin's laboratory, pulsed a narrow beam of X-rays between plane

parallel plates at a distance from the cathode that could be altered
by moving the chamber a known amount relative to the X-ray beam.
The flash of X-rays and the sweep of the oscilloscope were triggered
by the same pulse. A uniform field of constant value and a fixed
plate separation at a given pressure of gas were employed. The
current between the electrodes caused by the movement of charges
could be observed on an oscilloscope screen, using the iR drop
across a resistor in series with the plates. The arrival of electrons
at the anode caused a sharp drop in the current recorded. This drop
suffered as usual from the ill-defined edges of the X-ray beam and
by diffusion. By *moving the X-ray beam known distances from the
anode* and *using corresponding points on the decline curve*, it was
possible to get the distance traveled by two similar sections of the
pulse. With this technique, using metal electrodes in a clean glass
cylinder in argon, the electron velocities observed were in remarkably
good agreement with those of Nielsen.

Using various theoretical approaches, Herreng was able to approximate the mobility for low X/p. Fairly close agreement at $X/p\sim0.1$
was given by a modification of Langevin's mobility theory for ions
as altered by Herreng. Otherwise, as with Nielsen's measurements,
Harriet Allen's theory was satisfactory over a longer range. The
study, while it did not use the best available techniques, was done
by a capable worker in the laboratory of one of the great leaders in
the gaseous electronic field, and represents a thoroughly workmanlike
achievement. While X-ray pulses are much more diffuse than desired,
and better pulses could be used (e.g., photoelectrons from the cathode),
the messy consequences of X-rays and diffusion are avoided by use
of *corresponding points* on a curve with *variation in a distance* capable
of exact measurement. This is thoroughly sound technique—which
is more than can be said for some of the later work.

It is unfortunate that some physicists (including some really good
ones), in their zeal to make gadgets suitable for research studies
of the "higher type," undertake to carry on gaseous electronic measurements and make theory. They do this without even taking the
trouble to read and understand what has been done, and to learn
how such work may still be done, even when that of others has been
reduced to a recording in books. What is worse, having undertaken
such a study in the ignorance of common pitfalls—when they have
achieved results of some sort, they have the temerity to publish them
and *to impugn classical work of real value.* Such publications clutter
up the literature with contradictory and false information, and often
require later researches to rectify the errors. Apparently stimulated

by the excellent and well-executed study of Herreng, several "gadget-minded" groups have undertaken to apply the pulse techniques to studies of electron mobility in gases used in ionization chambers for the express purpose of facilitating ion collection.

It seems that initially Hudson (27) derived the equation for a current produced by pulsed discharges, using X-rays that filled the whole distance between two parallel plate uniform field electrodes. He applied this method to study electron mobilities in A. The theory of the method as derived did not agree with the observed curves. The data observed in A disagreed seriously with Nielsen's values. In order to clarify the situation, Klema and Allen (28) carried out a redetermination of the mobilities with the method, using an α-particle polonium source giving 3,000 particles per minute plated directly on the cathode. The α particles had a range of about 3.4 cm at 760 mm, and the plate separation was 2.6 cm. Argon, N_2, and A contaminated with N_2 and O_2, were used up to 3 atmospheres. The chamber was all-brass, sealed with a Koroseal gasket.[15] Ionization across the gap was not even uniform. The metal chamber and gasket technique harks back to the "gay nineties," when purity was unheard of. The gas was passed continually over a Ca-filled "purifier" held at 300° C., and was circulated in the chamber. This was supposed to overcome all contamination. Voltage pulses triggered the sweep circuit, and after passing a delay line were imposed on the plate system for 50 microseconds. The amplified output pulses were observed in the oscilloscope, and the *time was measured from the beginning of the sweep to the maximum height of the pulses.* Corrections of various sorts were required to reduce to zero sweep time and to allow for other errors of this crude type of measurement. The peaks were broad, and resolution was poor at best.

The results in "pure" argon gave fantastic curves which in some regions were as much as three times as high as Nielsen's curves. In N_2 the curve observed lay fairly close to Nielsen's curve. Curves were obtained for mixtures of A and O_2 and A and N_2. However, the data were "better" than Hudson's in A. The authors again had the temerity to suggest that Herreng and Nielsen's A was not pure. The fact that N_2 agreed roughly with Nielsen's data should have clearly indicated that their sensitive A had some small active impurity present. The authors then tried to apply the naive theory of Allen and Rossi (29), derived initially by Stout and Rossi (29), to calculate

[15]It is doubtful if any worse technique could have been conceived than that of using the columnar α-particle ionization, a metal chamber, etc., for mobility studies in A gas.

the electron mobility in mixtures of A and N_2. The calculated curves, needless to say, were from 100% to 30% high.

In consequence of these researches, the problem was again tackled by E. J. M. Kirschner and D. S. Toffolo (30). The method was that of Hudson, using an X-ray flash filling the whole chamber between the plates. Great care was used in purifying the gas in a properly baked-out glass system. Hudson's theory was corrected for an obviously neglected factor. It then gave results *more* in accord with the observations. Details of measurement and calculation were not given. The method cannot give really good resolution or accuracy. It is not understood why such poor methods were used, when the same circuitry applied to already proven methods would have yielded at worst 2% accuracy. However, crude as were the results, both the results and the conclusions drawn were significant. Agreement for really pure A was achieved with the curve of Nielsen to *within 10%*, which is all that this method permits. Had they used Herreng's technique, the agreement would have been closer to 2%; but not having heeded the lessons of the past on mobility measurement, no better results could have been expected. It is gratifying that they were able to duplicate the curves of Klema and Allen and/or Hudson, if they *contaminated* their A by 1% and 2% of N_2 gas respectively, as could have been inferred from Klema and Allen's work.

It is merely necessary to add that progress and useful data are not achieved in such a fashion in the present era of potentially excellent and accurate techniques, if they are but noted and followed. Even more recently, L. Colli and U. Facchini (31), using plane parallel geometry and single-particle ionization along a line parallel to the cathode in regions of X/p 0.8 volt/cm per mm in pure A, and A plus N_2, evaluated electron-drift velocities in an effort to clarify Klema and Allen's work. Drift velocities in pure A checked Nielsen's values to 1%. The curves of Klema and Allen corresponded to A gas with between 0.1% and 1% N_2. The resolving power of the single α-particle track method is very high if track collimation is good. It is noted that the poor work of one man required three subsequent investigations to rectify it, and then the original data of Nielsen were established as best.

On the other side of the ledger was an investigation of E. J. Lauer (32) designed for another purpose. To study in detail the mechanisms active in a coaxial cylindrical condenser discharge with central wire positive and an Ni outer cylinder, a well-collimated α-particle source was set up which fired the particles out of a fine capillary closely parallel to the tube axis, near the outer Ni cylinder. Single *a* particles came at the rate of a few per minute. The particles give rise to from 10^4 to 1×10^5 electrons along a straight track in 3×10^{-8} sec. The electrons are created within 10^{-2} cm of the beam axis. If accurately collimated, this gives a very narrow flash of electrons which cross to the anode wire and arrive simultaneously, except for the diffusion, in 10^{-6} sec. They are amplified by the field near the anode. These electrons, on arriving at the anode and being absorbed by it, suddenly unmask a positive space charge out in the gap, which alters the image force on the Ni cylindrical cathode. This draws a current from ground to the cathode through resistor across which an oscilloscope is placed. As the positive ions cross to the cathode, the current decays hyperbolically and drops to zero sharply but with asymptotic tail as the ions enter the cathode. The width of the sharp decline of the pulse as the ions enter the cathode is determined by the positive ion distribution in the gap and by diffusion. By measuring the elapsed time between the rise and fall of the pulse, the *ion* transit time can be determined. Despite the variable field in the gap, the carriers spend most of their time in the lower X/p regions near the cathode.

From a knowledge of this field, correcting even for space-charge distortion of the gap field by the ions, mobilities in H_2 and A for positive ions were measured to within at least 3%, and *agreed with standard values of Hornbeck and of Tyndall and Powell* in the pure gases A and H_2, permitting the identification of the ions in A as A_2^+. In this same measurement in H_2, at the time of maximum ionization, within two ionizing free paths of the anode wire, the electron avalanches released a flood of photons. These photons, within probably 3×10^{-8} sec, trigger a burst of photoelectrons from the cathode. If the field is high enough, these new electrons create avalanches which in turn create a new set of photolectrons. Thus, Lauer observed successive peaks of ionization on the oscilloscope on a 10 microsecond sweep scale. The separate peaks were about 1 microsecond apart. Varying X/p, he was able to measure the transit times at various values of X/p quite accurately. Then, taking Nielsen's values for electron mobilities in H_2 as a function of X/p and integrating them across the variable field from cathode to anode, he could compute the transit times corresponding to his observed electron-transit times. *The results agreed with Nielsen's values to well within 2%.*

It might be added that Lauer's H_2 was in an all-glass and baked-out chamber with ion-bombarded metal electrodes. The gas purity *had to be very high,* since the corona discharges studied were supersensitive to impurities. Thus, it is not surprising that his agreement with Nielsen's values was good. It must be indicated here that Nielsen learned his techniques for gaseous purity from his teacher, N. E. Bradbury, who had been among the first to develop such techniques in the author's laboratory. Bradbury was not only purity-conscious to a high degree, but he had developed modern, unimpeachable techniques for the achievement of and control of gaseous purity. Thus, when an investigator cannot duplicate Nielsen's values in the region of X/p, where these were made, he should first *look to his own experimental techniques* before he condemns the work of Nielsen or of Bradbury and Nielsen. It must be added that the photoelectric photonpulse technique is good only if the photons are not delayed in transit to the cathode by resonance or other processes. The photon-avalanche peaks are smeared when this occurs.

In view of this work, it is proper to close the chapter with the following conclusions. Satisfactory experimental values of electron velocities have been obtained for standard gases. Improvements in accuracy and in the cleanliness of gases, as well as the extension of the range of measurements to higher X/p values, are desirable in some cases. With techniques available since World War II, these improvements are possible. Both elementary theory and the more complete theories are in agreement with experimental findings in the measure that the required basic data are available. Tables and curves giving the data are found in this chapter for the work of Bradbury and Nielsen, while data yielded by the Townsend method are given in connection with other data yielded by those studies in chapter V.

At the present time, the data and analyses from the magneticdeflection method and the evaluations of k/D yielding η have progressed to a point where they are in sensible agreement with direct methods in cases where the gases are of sufficient purity. Modern developments in techniques now permit improved accuracy of the direct methods if needed. The data yielded by the Townsend studies on η permit fairly good estimates to be made of electron energies in gases as a function of X/p. Equally good data on electron energies can be obtained through the observation of Ramsauer free paths and measured values of the drift velocities, together with elementary theory. Needless to say, these energies are in relatively good agreement with the Townsend data in some clean gases. In all these studies the relations used cannot yield accurate results, being based on classical kinetic theory and either Maxwell or Druyvesteyn distribution law. Owing to the insensitivity of average values to variations in the distribution laws, the values of η or of electron energies, deduced by measurement and this theory, are certainly better than 20%, and in most cases accurate to better than 10%.

Great care must be used in accepting data from other experiments which are greatly at variance with electron energies derived from the studies outlined. On the other hand, where properties of the electron swarms depend on the few electrons in the high-energy tails of the distribution law curves, the *form of the law* is critical, and errors of several orders of magnitude may result in the use of an average energy and an assumed form of law. Such errors would affect the appearance of increased mobilities dependent on the threshold for inelastic impacts.

BIBLIOGRAPHY TO CHAPTER III

(1) J. S. Townsend and H. T. Tizard, Proc. Roy. Soc. *A87*, 357, 1912; *A88*, 336, 1913. See also, J. S. Townsend, *Electricity in Gases*, Oxford University Press, 1914, pp. 122 ff.; R. H. Healey and J. W. Reed, *The Behaviour of Slow Electrons in Gases*, Amalgamated Wireless Press (Australasia), Ltd., Sydney, 1941; and lately, L. G. H. Huxley and A. A. Zaazou, Proc. Roy. Soc. *A196*, 402, 1949; J. S. Townsend, *Electrons in Gases*, Hutchinson's, London, 1947.

(2) L. B. Loeb, Phys. Rev. *19*, 24, 1922; *20*, 397, 1922; Proc. Nat. Acad. Sci. *9*, 335, 1923; Phys. Rev. *23*, 157, 1924; H. B. Wahlin, Phys. Rev. *21*, 517, 1923; *23*, 169, 1924.

(3) R. A. Nielsen and N. E. Bradbury, Phys. Rev. *49*, 338, 1936; *51*, 69, 1937; R. A. Nielsen, Phys. Rev. *50*, 950, 1936.

(4) J. S. Townsend and V. A. Bailey, Phil. Mag. *42*, 873, 1921; *43*, 594, 1922; *44*, 1033, 1922; *46*, 657, 1923; *47*, 379, 1924. For later papers of V. A. Bailey, see complete bibliography in Healey and Reed (1).

(5) H. Raether, Zeits. f. Phys. *107*, 91, 1937; W. Riemann, Zeits. f. Phys. *120*, 16, 1942; *122*, 216, 1944; Erg. d. Exakt. Naturwiss., Julius Springer, Berlin, 1949.

(6) J. A. Hornbeck, Phys. Rev. *80*, 297, 1950.

(7) W. P. Allis and Harriet W. Allen, Phys. Rev. *52*, 703, 1937.

(8) C. Ramsauer, Ann. d. Physik *64*, 513, 1921. See summary by R. B. Brode, Rev. Mod. Phys. *5*, 256, 1933; C. E. Normand, Phys. Rev. *35*, 1217, 1930.

(9) D. Barbiere, Phys. Rev. *84*, 653, 1951; also reported by C. Kenty, M. A. Easley, and B. T. Barnes, Jour. App. Phys. *22*, 1006, 1951.

(10) O. T. Fundingsland, Phys. Rev. *84*, 559, 1951.

(11) F. B. Pidduck, Proc. Roy. Soc. *A88*, 296, 1913.

(12) K. T. Compton, Phys. Rev. *22*, 333, 432, 1923.

(13) A. von Engel and M. Steenbeck, *Elektrische Gasentladungen*, Julius Springer, Berlin, vol. I, pp. 180 ff.

(14) K. T. Compton and I. Langmuir, Rev. Mod. Phys. *2*, 219, 1930.

(15) J. S. Townsend, Phil. Mag. *22*, 153, 1936; bottom and footnote. See *contra*, M. J. Druyvesteyn and F. M. Penning, Rev. Mod. Phys. *12*, 896, 1940.

(16) A. M. Cravath, Phys. Rev. *36*, 248, 1930.

(17) H. Baerwald, Ann. d. Physik *76*, 829, 1925; W. Harries, Zeits. f. Phys. *42*, 26, 1927; H. Ramien, Zeits. f. Phys. *70*, 351, 1931.

(18) C. E. Normand, Phys. Rev. *35*, 1217, 1930.

(19) M. J. Druyvesteyn, Physica *10*, 69, 1930; A. M. Cravath, Phys. Rev. *46*, 332, 1934; B. Davydov, Phys. Zeits. d. Sowjetunion *8*, 59, 1935; J. A. Smit, Physica *3*, 593, 1937; T. Holstein, Phys. Rev. *70*, 367, 1946.

(20) L. G. H. Huxley and A. A. Zaazou, Proc. Roy. Soc. *A196*, 402, 1949.

(21) Harriet W. Allen, Phys. Rev. *52*, 707, 1937.

(22) G. Hertz, Zeits. f. Phys. *32*, 298, 1925.

(23) L. G. H. Huxley and J. S. Townsend, Phil. Mag. *23*, 2, 1937.

(24) W. S. Gorrill, Ph.D. thesis, University of California, 1939.

(25) R. Geballe and M. A. Harrison, Phys. Rev. *85*, 372, 1952; *91*, 1, 1953.

(26) P. Herreng, Compt. Rend. *215*, 79, 1942; *217*, 75, 1943.

(27) D. E. Hudson, MDDC *524*.

(28) E. D. Klema and J. S. Allen, Phys. Rev. *77*, 661, 1950.

(29) H. H. Stout and Bruno Rossi, Nat. Nuclear En. Series, Los Alamos Project, McGraw-Hill, New York, 1949, vol. II; also, J. S. Allen and Bruno Rossi, MDDC *448*, p. 1.

(30) E. J. M. Kirschner and D. S. Toffolo, Jour. App. Phys. *23*, 594, 1952.

(31) L. Colli and U. Facchini, Rev. Sci. Inst. *23*, 39, 1952.

(32) E. J. Lauer, Jour. App. Phys. *23*, 300, 1952.

(33) A. Doehring, Zeits. f. Naturforschung *7a*, 253, 1952.

(34) G. H. Wannier, Bell System Tech. Jour. *32*, 170, 1953.

Chapter IV

THE DISTRIBUTION OF ENERGY OF ELECTRONS
IN A FIELD IN A GAS

PART ONE—THEORY AND GENERAL CONSIDERATIONS

§1. Introduction.

The knowledge of the distribution of energy among the electrons in an electrical field in a gas is a very important item in the analysis of any gaseous discharge. From its data can be derived the excitation and ionization functions of the atoms or molecules present, as well as the mobility and the diffusion of the electrons. Experimentally, the various phenomena occurring in gaseous breakdown are observed in terms of the electrical field strengths X and pressure p of the gas. To interpret the phenomena, the corresponding average electron energy and the distribution in energies must be known.

Unfortunately, because of the time scale of electronic events which alter the distribution, *there are no adequate experimental techniques for directly evaluating these quantities except in the limited regime where probes can be used.* Where the use of probes is precluded, the only recourse is to resort to theoretical computation of an elaborate sort. The problem of the evaluation of the distributions is complicated through the existence of regions where the mean free path of the electrons in the gas changes the character of its variation with electron energy. Where this occurs, not only does the average electron energy change, but the *form of the distribution law* is changed as well. This is especially true in the inert gas group, with the exception of the gas Ne. This increases the number of curves to be computed as X/p changes.

A theoretical analysis of the energy distributions of electrons in fields in gases requires consideration of the following factors. Electrons gain energy from the field as a result of diffusive displacement and drift velocity in the field direction. They alter their directions and lose energy to atoms and molecules by elastic impacts. If electron densities are high, they interact with each other through their Coulomb force fields. When electrons collide with the relatively heavy atoms, the fractional loss ΔE on impact is very small in some cases, but cannot be neglected. The probability of elastic impacts is related to the collision cross section and, in the range from 1 to 100 volts electron energy, these are functions of the electron energy. These probabilities have now been experimentally established by the researches of Ramsauer, Brode, Normand, and others (III.8).[1] In addition to such energy losses, the electrons above energies which can excite vibrational levels in molecules or raise atoms and molecules to higher electronic states, or even ionize them, will lose energy to excitation and ionization. The cross sections for those transfers are also a function of electron energy. Their cross sections are much less than those for elastic collisions. In consequence, the problem of the mathematical evaluation of energy-distribution functions presents considerable complexity.

Finally, it must be realized that such information is required over a large range of electrical fields, including nonuniform, alternating, and steady fields, and a large range of densities, as well as gaseous pressure and vessel size. Is it thus not strange that with the wide diversity of gaseous types (though a considerable literature has arisen in the field), there are still serious gaps in knowledge. In a text of this scope it will obviously be impossible to cover even a small section of the intricate mathematical development that has taken place. It is therefore intended to report the various significant contributions to the field in approximately chronological order, indicating the important items so that the interested reader may go to the correct source for solution of his problems.

§2. Chronological Summary of the Work on Electron-Energy Distribution.

Historically, the study of this problem was initiated by F. B. Pidduck (III. 11), (7) in 1913, when the electron-mobility studies of Townsend had indicated that the average energy of electrons in a field in a gas was greater than that of the surrounding gas molecules. To attempt to derive the mobility, he used the general approach to the problem initially used by H. A. Lorentz in the study of the electron velocities in metals, assuming perfectly elastic impacts with no energy loss by electrons on impact. Despite the early date of this study and the handicaps inherent in the lack of later knowledge,

---

[1]Hereafter, where references are cited in an earlier chapter (unless fundamental to the discussion), they will be indicated by the chapter number in roman numerals followed by the reference number, in order to reduce the bibliography to reasonable compass.

the analysis of Pidduck appears to have been far beyond its time in general character. The method, in amplified and somewhat more specialized form, was later successfully used by P. M. Morse, W. P. Allis, and E. S. Lamar (1).[2]

The method as *initially* used by Lorentz lacked an additional equation securing a detailed balance of energy in each velocity range. Thus, in 1913, a Maxwellian form of energy distribution had to be assumed and applied in some form to the evaluation of the electron-drift velocity. It is, therefore, not surprising that at a much later date, Morse, Allis, and Lamar, with the well-developed atomic theory, were able to show that the early results of Pidduck were not of the correct form. In 1916 and 1918, K. T. Compton, stimulated by the Franck and Hertz experiments on the elasticity of electron impact, attempted to use these concepts of electron-energy gain and loss to calculate the distribution of energy of electrons in a field in a gas, and from these to derive the values of the first Townsend coefficient for ionization by collision in a gas (2). The first attempt, using perfectly elastic impacts of electrons against the molecules with a classical kinetic-theory approach, again yielded a Maxwellian distribution. In the later treatment, the fractional energy loss of electrons in collisions with molecules was included, but the form of the law was not altered in consequence of the type of analysis.

In 1925, G. Hertz deduced a rigorous expression for the diffusion of electrons in a gas between parallel plates, with an electrical field between the plates (II.5). He assumed perfectly elastic electron impacts on atoms, with no fractional loss of energy due to momentum exchange. The deduction not only initiated a new approach to the study of such problems, but served to show the importance of diffusion in conduction problems. It led to an expression for the drift velocity of the electrons, and was used in estimating the collision frequency and the number of exciting impacts of electrons in mercury vapor in some work done by H. Sponer (3). This analysis was further extended by W. Harries and G. Hertz to the case where electrons were emitted with an initial velocity (4). The effect of Ramsauer free paths was also considered. The actual results of this work were

---

[2]It should be added that this type of approach had already been developed by Maxwell and Boltzmann in the kinetic theory of gases. In fact, the Boltzmann transport equation gives the basis of over 70% of the later work on electron-energy distribution. In 1916-1917, S. Chapman and Enskog independently applied this approach to the study of nonuniform gases. This method, now refined and formalized, was published by Chapman and Cowling in their treatise, *The Mathematical Theory of Nonuniform Gases*, in 1939. This method seems to constitute the basis for all later studies.

not significant in themselves. The questions considered, however, stimulated later very important work.

In 1930, using the general approach to the problem initiated by Hertz, M. J. Druyvesteyn (5) made the first successful attempt to derive a distribution law assuming that (1) low electron densities were present, (2) the electrons lost the fraction f of energy at each impact with atoms required by the law of conservation of momentum, (3) no inelastic impacts occurred, and (4) the mean free paths were independent of velocity or energy. The effect of diffusion, as indicated by Hertz, was included in the analysis. For the case where electrons reach their terminal velocity in the gas, i.e., for electrons in a steady state of energy with uniform drift velocity, Druyvesteyn deduced his now famous distribution law. This differs from that of Maxwell chiefly in having the argument E/E_A in the exponential term squared, i.e., $(E/E_A)^2$, in contrast to the first-power ratio in Maxwell's law. This solution is the correct one if the values of X/p are appropriate to insure that the electrons in the gases are below excitation and ionization energies, and that they have constant free paths. Under the same limitations, the law has been derived by *all other treatments of the problem*. Where different forms of this distribution have been obtained by investigators under the conditions assumed above, the derivations have been shown to be in error (6). Owing to inadequate data, a later attempt by Druyvesteyn to calculate the distribution in Ne where inelastic impacts were occurring, was not very successful.

In 1930-1935, A. P. Didlaukis (6) derived a distribution law, using statistical considerations of time fluctuations of energy. The law deduced was so at variance with Druyvesteyn's law under similar conditions that A. M. Cravath undertook a deduction, using the same approach as that of Didlaukis. In a brief abstract to a paper given at the American Physical Society meetings in 1934, Cravath (6) presented a rather complete derivation of the distribution law, using Didlaukis' approach. His results furnished the most complete study of the problem up to that time, but appear in print only in summary form. He deduced the Druyvesteyn law as a special case of his more general relations, and pointed out the reason for the failure of Didlaukis. He stated, "Didlaukis' term $D + E$ should have contained the mean square of the component of velocity in the direction of the field instead of the square of the mean component."

In 1930, and again in 1936, J. S. Townsend, in a very involved analysis, making certain approximations concerning the distribution of energies about a mean value E in place of kT, arrived at a rather peculiar distribution law *resembling* the Druyvesteyn law, except that there was a constant term A subtracted from the ratio $(E/E_A)^2$ in the exponent (6). In other words he found exp $(E/E_A - A)^2$ where Druyvesteyn found $(E/E_A)^2$. He replaced kT of the Maxwellian form by the experimental value $E_A = \eta kT$ derived from his diffusion experiments. The appearance of the constant term involves the appearance of a few high-energy electrons experimentally observed by him and by Llewellyn Jones. From the nature of its derivation, as well as its peculiar form, it is clear that this was not a completely successful derivation.

In 1935, P. M. Morse, W. P. Allis, and E. S. Lamar (1), using the amplified method of H. A. Lorentz, deduced both the distribution law and expressions for the velocity of the electrons for the conditions outlined above; viz., constant free paths, fractional loss of energy on electron impact as indicated by conservation of momentum, and no inelastic impacts. They again found the Druyvesteyn law, as might be expected. In 1936, F. B. Pidduck (7) pointed out that the Druyvesteyn law is a special case of the more general result that he had obtained in 1913. The method of Morse, Allis, and Lamar was extended later by W. P. Allis and Harriet W. Allen (III.7), (III.21) to include an analysis of the Townsend method of measuring electron diffusion and mobility and the study of electron mobilities and distribution in rare gases with variable Ramsauer free paths. It was also extended approximately by Allen to the cases where inelastic impacts due to excitation and ionization were occurring (III.21). The mobilities calculated by Allen were in satisfactory agreement with the results of Bradbury and Nielsen. The basic method appears to be a useful one, and because it is a prototype to the approach for many studies and is relatively simpler, it is the only analysis to be presented in this book.

Probably one of the most careful, accurate, and complete derivations of the distribution law is that due to B. Davydov in 1935 (8). His method was rigorous, and his study was notable for the fact that it included the distribution of energies and the drift velocities for the case where the ratio of X/p is low and the energies of the molecules cannot be neglected in comparison to those of the electrons. This analysis also yielded the Druyvesteyn distribution under conditions where it should appear.

In 1936, Druyvesteyn attempted a derivation for the distribution of energies when inelastic impacts occur. The problem was studied for one gas only (Ne), and applied to the case of Ne with small amounts of A (9).

Finally, in 1937, J. A. Smit (10) developed a step-by-step method of analysis for the distribution laws and the drift velocities which was the most complete and flexible of all methods up to that time. It was based on the initial approach of Hertz and of Druyvesteyn. It enabled the complete study of the distribution of energies to be made, not only where elastic impacts occur, but in the region of inelastic impacts due to excitation and ionization, including variable free paths and the probabilities of excitation and ionization. With it he calculated a number of distribution curves for He for four values of X/p. The deduction again yields the Druyvesteyn distribution where it occurs. In later years, S. H. Dunlop (11), under K. G. Eméléus, extended the calculations for He to higher values of X/p in order to permit the evaluation of the first Townsend coefficient in He from the theory of Eméléus, Lunt, and Meek.

Shortly after World War II, G. D. Yarnold (12) attempted a most unique method for calculating the distribution law. Yarnold discussed the problem in detail and proceeded to set up the various elements needed in a calculation. After setting up the equations for energy gain and loss of electrons in encounters with molecules at various angles, it was necessary either to assume probable variations and to derive averaged values, or to follow the careers of individual electrons through a series of successive impacts and so arrive at a distribution. Yarnold accomplished this by choosing the appropriate collision parameters and placing these in terms of the proper numerical values and probabilities into a container on appropriately distributed cards. Then at random, some one of the parameters was drawn out of the container and appropriate calculations were made on this step of the electron's career. Then a new number was chosen for the next successive collision. By increasing the numerical value of the fractional loss of energy per impact, the number of operations for each electron to equilibrium was reduced. The statistical distribution of the electron energies could then be estimated by choosing enough steps and adequate electrons.

In this work 1,000 particles were followed through and studied. The result led to a distribution in agreement with the distribution law of Townsend (6), so far as the Townsend law goes. It differed markedly from the Druyvesteyn law in having far too many electrons of high energy. As will be seen, since *all* derivations except the faulty one of Didlaukis and that of Yarnold (6), both of which come under the conditions leading to the Druyvesteyn law, give the Druyvesteyn law, one must regard Yarnold's derivation with caution. The matter was studied by R. J. Wijsman (13), who discovered a very subtle error in the setting up of Yarnold's equations. In Yarnold's equation 8 for the gain of energy in the field in the gas, he calculated the energy gain Xes in terms of s, the distance of advance of the electron in the field under its drift velocity u and the field. In doing so, Yarnold set

$$Xes = Xeut \cos \theta + X^2e^2t^2/2m,$$

where θ is the angle of the *initial free path* of length l with the field direction. He then made the approximation that the time t between impacts is $t = l/u$, giving

$$Xes = Xel \cos \theta + X^2e^2l^2/2mu^2.$$

In doing this, it is clear that when $\cos \theta = 1$, s exceeds l. By definition, l is the free path terminated by collision, and s cannot logically exceed it. The correct equation for the energy gain under these conditions should have been

$$Xes = Xel \cos \theta + (X^2e^2l^2/2mu^2) \sin^2\theta.$$

Therefore, the energy gain calculated by equation 8 is too large, especially for electrons having $\theta = 0$. This accounts for the deviation from the Druyvesteyn law obtained by Yarnold. It is unfortunate that such an error crept into an otherwise rather pretty and original method of solution. The same technique used for electrons was later applied by Yarnold to a study of the energy distribution of positive ions in an electrical field in a gas. In this study the subtle error made with electrons did not occur, and the results of the distribution law are of interest.[3]

In the chapter on electron mobilities it was noted that relatively recent analyses of Townsend, Huxley, and of V. A. Bailey (III.1) and his students had done much to clarify the nature of the various velocity averages involved in their methods of estimating electron-drift velocities and the average electronic energies. This clarification made possible corrections in the data obtained on the two quantities mentioned, such that multiplication by appropriate factors for a given

[3]At a much later date, G. H. Wannier (61), in a generalized study of carrier motion in all types of fields, independently applied the Monte Carlo method, using an electronic computer covering 10^4 successive steps. This is indicated in the outline in chapter I, part two.

distribution law yielded true absolute values of electron-drift velocities and energies. It was also noted that very recently L. G. H. Huxley
and A. A. Zaazou had measured electron-drift velocities in air (III.20).
When their values were multiplied by an appropriate correction factor,
assuming a Druyvesteyn distribution of energies, they fell very near
the values observed directly by Bradbury and Nielsen. When Maxwell's
law was assumed, their values fell below those of Bradbury and
Nielsen. The method of Bradbury and Nielsen involves no assumption
as to the distribution law in the calculation of its data. It yields
merely the velocity observed for the bulk of the electrons. The drift
velocities as evaluated by the magnetic-deflection method, and more
generally the velocities and energies as measured by the Bailey
methods, involve numerical factors representing the ratios of various
averages that differ with the form of the law.

What Bradbury and Nielsen measure in terms of a characteristic
curve for the shutter action of the grid fields, is the time for a group
of electrons of the swarm to cross a measured distance between
shutters. Each electron in the swarm at each instant has a velocity
appropriate to the distribution. After each electronic free path those
particular electrons change velocity. Thus, if they make enough
impacts in going the measured distance, they all have on the average
the same velocity of drift v. This average value depends on a term
in the equation denoting the average $(\overline{\lambda/c})$, where λ and c are instantaneous free path and velocities. If fixed values of λ independent
of c are used, the value of $(\overline{\lambda/c})$ is essentially $\lambda/\bar{c}$, with $\bar{c}$ the average
velocity for a Druyvesteyn distribution, and is comparable with
Huxley's treatment. But if λ is a function of c, then the method does
not give the same value as Huxley's, and it is meaningless to draw
conclusions from his law by making a fit. Thus, Huxley and Zaazou
assume precisely that in fitting their results to those of Bradbury
and Nielsen with the Druyvesteyn constant, they establish a proof
that air has a Druyvesteyn distribution over the range of X/p studied.

R. H. Healey and J. W. Reed (III.1), in their monograph, *The
Behaviour of Slow Electrons in Gases*, published in 1941, go even
farther in drawing some *general conclusions* on the energy distribution
in gases. It was discovered by the various workers in this group that
the original, simple formulae used to calculate the electron-energy
factor η, the electron random velocity c, the electron-drift velocity v,
the electron free path λ, the mean electron-energy loss at a collision
f, and the probability of electron attachment to molecules h, from
the complex measurements involving diffusion as well as electrical
and magnetic fields, could be appreciably in error. It was shown

by Healey that the value for η, the Townsend multiplier by both Townsend's and Bailey's methods of measurement, was related to the true η by a factor $(3/2)$ A, where A is a dimensionless ratio of various velocity averages. This ratio varied with the distribution law that was active. The correction yielded certain expressions for the calculation of v, λ, f, and h from experimental data differing from those given. The formulae actually used were presented by Healey and Reed in the form of a table. These authors then calculated the ratios of the various constant factors used by Townsend and by Bailey in these evaluations to the corresponding factors in terms of Healey's corrections. The calculations for the corrections were carried through in terms of four assumed distribution laws.

1. All electrons have the same velocity.
2. The distribution reads $A \exp(-Bc^4)c^4dc$.
3. The distribution reads $A \exp(-Bc^4)c^2dc$, the Druyvesteyn law.
4. The distribution reads $A \exp(-Bc^2)c^2dc$, the Maxwellian law.

The variation of some of these ratios with the law can be plotted in a nomogram by means of lines drawn through the points corresponding to each ratio under a given law. The ratios initiating the lines spread from 0.3 to 1.5 for the law of equal velocities, and those terminating the lines spread from 0.9 to 1.5 for Maxwell's law. They appear to *intersect the Druyvesteyn law* near a ratio of 1 for all quantities, the spread being from 1 to 1.2. According to the authors, in all gases so far experimentally investigated by Townsend's and by Bailey's methods independently, there is a remarkably close agreement between corresponding sets of results. This can only occur if the prevailing distribution is such that V_T/V_{cor} for Townsend's method is nearly equal to V_B/V_{cor} for Bailey's method with V_{cor} from the Druyvesteyn law. Thus, they conclude that the *Druyvesteyn law* is the prevalent distribution for most of the gases studied between values of η of 5 and 100.

This conclusion must be analyzed briefly. It is correct that the Druyvesteyn law is *generally derived under the simplifying assumptions of constant free paths and elastic impacts.* This is, however, an *ideal situation.* As was noted in chapter III, and will be noted later, if λ varies with energy, the form will *not* be Maxwellian *or* Druyvesteyn, but may be much distorted. Since in general, the free paths vary with energy, and since in some cases this variation is very great in the range from 1 to 10 or more electron volts, it is clear that generalizations such as those made above are inaccurate. The deviations from the Druyvesteyn or Maxwellian law can be of critical importance in the study of excitation and ionization functions. Thus, *care must be used in accepting the form of the law based on the evidence above.*

What really emerges from this analysis is the following: The extreme variation of the ratios mentioned lies between a uniform velocity distribution and Maxwell's distribution. This produces at most changes by factors of the order of 1.5 to 1 in the more directly measurable quantities, *omitting the ionizing functions.* Between the Maxwellian and Druyvesteyn laws the ratios and correction factors differ in the extremes *by no more than 10%.* For example, the multipliers of $X/H \tan \theta$ to give v are 0.85 and 0.943 respectively for Maxwell's and for Druyvesteyn's laws. The approximations which go into the theory of some of the experiments concerned, as well as the nature of the measurements and accuracy of the ratios observed, produce uncertainties of the order of 2 to 5%.[4] Small differences introduced by the distribution laws can hardly be taken as indicative of more than a general trend toward a certain type of distribution law.

What this statement signifies physically is that the *ratio of the averages,* such as the root-mean-square average and the average velocity, *are not too significantly shifted* relative to each other as the shape of the law changes. It is possible that quite dissimilar laws, especially as regards both extremes of values in the distribution, may not differ very greatly in the *relative displacements* of the different averages. This follows because both in some measurements and as affecting averages of curves, the energies of the bulk of the carriers weigh most heavily, and these are usually not seriously displaced by the changes in energy distribution observed. On the basis of such insensitive tests as these averages yield, one cannot agree with the conclusion of Healey and Reed that the *distribution is invariant* and of the *Druyvesteyn form* for such wide ranges of gases, extending from the halogens to inert gases and over large ranges in energy. In fact, the work of Bradbury and Nielsen, Harriet W. Allen, and Smit indicates quite the contrary.

From the assumed uniformity of the law inferred over such ranges, Healey and Reed conclude that the law is independent of the elasticity or otherwise of the impacts. They thus conclude that the formulae deduced are capable of wider application to gases where collisions

---

[4]In this connection it should be noted that neither the evaluation of η nor that of v by the methods used can be of much significance if X/p is such that much ionization by electron impact occurs in the measuring fields. Since extending measurements above an X/p varying from 5 volts/cm per mm in pure, inert gases to 40 volts/cm per mm in air introduces such ionization, the meaning of averages and values may well be questioned within these limits.

are not so elastic. The assumed failure of the distribution to vary over a wide range of energies is presumed to substantiate an early conclusion of Pidduck that for inelastic collisions the distribution is that corresponding to the value of η, which would be acquired in the same electric field with perfect restitution.[5]

Considering what has gone before, it is hardly necessary to indicate that such generalizations are not justified when based on the data given. The complete solution to the energy-distribution problems has been indicated in the excellent analyses of J. A. Smit (10) and of T. R. Holstein (14). Pidduck's generalization can thus readily be put to test by making the rigorous solutions for some gas, including the different assumptions indicated. The full curves so obtained will indicate the validity of these assertions.

Later work on the energy distributions of electrons in electrical fields embraces the postwar studies that were developed largely with a view of application in analyses of the microwave breakdown in gases, which became important in the development of radar. Probably the most comprehensive, complete, and polished analysis of the energy-distribution functions, using generalized methods, is that of T. R. Holstein (14). The study had as its initial purpose the development of methods of calculating the energy distributions for electrons in gases of low ion density under the influence of high-frequency a.c. fields. The analysis includes methods of treating the d.c. case as well; and, like those of Druyvesteyn and Smit, it attempts to cover not only the distribution with elastic collisions at low and high fields, but also with inelastic collisions to excitation and ionization. As indicated, both Druyvesteyn and Smit in general used the approach initiated by C. Hertz.

Holstein uses the more standard approach afforded by the Boltzmann transport equation, first used successfully by Morse, Allis, and Lamar. The method is used to obtain an equation for the high-frequency distribution function, and to rederive the d.c. equation of Druyvesteyn and Smit. The treatment is limited to cases where electron densities are low compared with those of molecules. The electron energies are such that elastic-collision cross sections are large compared to inelastic cross sections. Linear dimensions of the discharge region are assumed large compared to the elastic-collision free paths, and the frequencies impressed are larger than lower limits set by the

[5]Actually, as Wannier (61) indicates, and as noted in the summary of his analysis in chapter I, the governing parameters are questions of the constancy of mean free paths or mean free times and isotropy of scattering implied by the several models treated.

pressure, gas type, and dimensions of the discharge region. Simplified examples illustrating the methods of solution of the intricate relation are given for the a.c. case and for the d.c. case. The d.c. solution agrees with those of Druyvesteyn and other authors. Comparison of the high-frequency distribution and the d.c. distribution equations suggests useful correlations between the two cases.

Similar analogies, such as microwave analogues for the first Townsend coefficient a, were independently discovered by W. P. Allis (15) and the microwave breakdown group at Massachusetts Institute of Technology. These assisted the group in the formulations and analyses of their results. Incidentally, the analysis of Holstein not only makes possible the calculation of electron-drift velocities and the distribution laws, but also yields calculations of the first Townsend coefficient for the d.c. field case.

Nearly contemporaneously but quite independently, beginning in 1946, H. Margenau (16) initiated a series of theoretical investigations of the distribution of energies of electrons in fields of high frequency. The initial study was carried farther in papers by Margenau, Margenau and L. M. Hartman, and by Hartman, published in 1948 (16), (17). Margenau's first study of the distribution law was undertaken while he was at the microwave laboratory at M.I.T. during World War II, in order to be able to calculate the current density and hence the (complex) conductivity of a gas as a function of electron densities, pressures, and frequency. That paper deals only with elastic collisions in a gas where n electrons/cm^3 exist, and no more are created. It starts from the Boltzmann transport equation, and the treatment is conventional. As usual for the d.c. case, the Druyvesteyn distribution is obtained. With a.c., a Maxwellian distribution is obtained with, however, an altered electron temperature. The conductivity is indicated for the approximate Maxwellian and the more exact cases, and the dielectric constant and index of refraction are computed.

The later articles attack the problem more generally. After showing the inadequacy of considering electrons as free in a.c. fields devoid of collisions, the problem of the distribution function is initiated again by recourse to the Boltzmann transport equation, first using elastic, and later inelastic impacts. The treatment utilized modifications of the methods of Smit and of Chapman and Cowling, chapter XVIII (1.53), in integral and differential representation. It includes ionizing and radiating impacts. The solution for a characteristic a.c. discharge with 10-cm waves in A at 6 mm Hg pressure is carried out for several values of the amplitude of the field strength. Including diffusion of electrons, the modifications owing to this circumstance are obtained.

Applying the newly derived data, an attempt was made to calculate the maintenance potential in high-frequency discharges. Using C. J. Brasefield's definition of the least maintenance potential for a high-frequency a.c. discharge with a curve type showing a minimum as a function of gas pressure, rough numerical agreement and a satisfactory solution were found by use of the theory. Later studies dealt with the development of the distribution function as a series of Legendre polynomials of the ratio of the drift velocity to the random velocity, and Fourier functions of ωt, where ω is the frequency, for the purpose of extending the calculations over larger ranges of variation. The study was limited to steady states and elastic collisions.

In still another paper, Hartman attempted to find a definition of the "breakdown" of a gas under microwave fields by studying the electron density as a function of field strength. The carriers in a relatively infinite volume were assumed to be removed by recombination only. The resulting equations showed a very sharp rise in electron density with field strength that could be used as a criterion for breakdown, and did not differ greatly from observed values for He and Ne at 3,000 megacycles. A final analysis of the theory developed by Margenau indicates that the well-known similarity principle common to the Townsend discharge as independent of space charges applies to this form of microwave breakdown. This does not imply that the principle holds for all breakdown, but it is applicable to this one region.

The studies of the Yale group initiated by Margenau were extended by J. H. Cahn in two further articles (18). In the first of these, the Boltzmann transport equation was solved for *high current densities* and low d.c. fields, where *electrostatic interactions between electrons may not be neglected.* For simplicity, the solution was checked for two cases. In one, in which the cross section for electron-molecule momentum transfer varies inversely with electron velocity, the distribution is Maxwellian at all densities. In the other, where the cross section is independent of electron energy, the solution varies from the Davydov distribution at low densities to the Maxwellian at high densities. Curves are given, showing the transition as the densities increase. The corresponding values are computed of the average energy drift velocity and average velocity for a typical but hypothetical gas. The importance of this study lies in the clarification which it gives to observed facts.

It had been noted that in many cases of discharges, the Maxwellian distribution was observed through the use of probes when the conditions in the gas would normally lead one to expect deviations. This was particularly true for low densities of electrons. Maxwellian distributions are expected when electron densities exceed 10^{12} or 10^{14} per cm³. An analysis of this problem had been undertaken in 1938, by W. R. Haseltine (I.52), under the direction of W. P. Allis. At the time Haseltine was unable to complete the analysis because of the formidable mathematical difficulties. Cahn's success was attributed by him to a paper by Landau (18) in 1936, in which Landau had developed an approximation to the Coulomb interaction term in the Boltzmann transport equation. Because of the long-range character of the Coulomb forces, the majority of collisions involve small momentum exchange, so that Landau had expanded them in powers of momentum exchange. Further assistance came from the justification and use of an assumption that Haseltine had found of value.

This leads to the neglect of electrostatic interactions so far as momentum conservation is concerned, but to their inclusion for energy conservation. Cahn's concluding paper then applies the relations deduced in a further extension of the work of Margenau and Hartman with high-frequency discharges, to a study of high current densities. The effect of electron density is determined and applied to the same two cases, one where collision cross section varies inversely with the velocity, and the other where it is constant. The variations in the distribution laws for three densities and constant cross sections using a model gas are computed and shown, together with a table of mean energies and velocities. With variable cross section, Maxwellian distributions are found, and the form is independent of density. With constant cross section, the Maxwellian distribution again holds at all densities; the lower densities, however, having higher electron temperatures than the gas. Certain differences in the conductivities and entropies with the d.c. case are indicated.

Probably the last significant contribution is one of I. B. Bernstein and T. Holstein (18a) on energy distributions in combined d.c. space-charge and a.c. fields. Usually, where conditions of this sort exist, the analyses assume as small the effects of d.c. space-charge fields, such as those produced by ambipolar diffusion. In this study such fields are considered large. Electrons thus move with a constant energy within the space-charge well in which the energy W equals the kinetic energy U, plus the *electrostatic potential energy*. The effects of collisions and the a.c. field are regarded as perturbations. It is assumed that on the average, the electron executes many oscillations in the well before suffering appreciable energy change due to collisions in the a.c. field. The new variable W introduced into the Boltzmann equation is quite useful in this case, instead of the usual kinetic-energy term.

The mathematical analysis leads to a difference-differential equation which can be solved under simplifying assumptions regarding cross sections. The distribution function and specific ionization rate thus derived can be compared with the corresponding terms for the case of no space-charge field. This relation, the opposite extreme to those previously treated, opens a new area of study; and together with the limits set by previous theory, enables predictions to be made as to what happens where d.c. space-charge fields and a.c. fields interact under conditions more usually encountered in practice. Probably of even more interest is the generalized treatment of energy distributions for all sorts of carriers by G. H. Wannier (61), presented in outline in chapter I.

It should also be stated that in 1950, D. Barbiere (21), working under Holstein, used Holstein's theory and derived certain valuable data which will be presented at a later point.

While the contributions described above constitute the developments which can be designated as specifically representing the advances made in research on energy distributions, the subject is not completely documented, in view of both experimental and theoretical advances of a more or less indirect nature made in the microwave research laboratory of the Massachusetts Institute of Technology by W. P. Allis and S. C. Brown and their succession of brilliant research students. On the return of Allis from duty in World War II, a course on "The Kinetic Theory of Electrons in Gases" was organized by him, which constituted the basis for the series of experimental investigations of the electrical behavior of gases under the skillful experimental direction of S. C. Brown. The lecture notes of the course by Allis were written up in dittoed form for distribution to the students at different intervals, beginning with 1946. They used the more general kinetic theory of nonuniform gases, and laid a systematic modern foundation for the study of the behavior of electrons in gases under varying conditions.

Since the microwave techniques and investigation in connection with radar were carried on at the laboratory at M.I.T. during the war, it is not surprising that the remaining workers should have applied these techniques to the study of electrons in gases. This is even more logical, since the use of microwave fields of appropriate strength, varying frequency, and varying pressure ranges, and in vessels of different shapes and sizes, permits of studies of the basic parameters controlling electrons in gases (such as energies), and of carrier motion, under ideal conditions. It permits a gas to be ionized by short-amplitude oscillations in the clear space of proper dimensions without the effect of currents and electrodes. Under proper conditions, the microwave technique causes a breakdown which depends only on the rate of electron production by the field, and loss by ambipolar diffusion with known or uniform carrier distribution. The gas can be left to itself with controlled or known diffusion loss, and its photon radiation or its electron density can be measured as a function of time by a nondisturbing microwave probing beam.

While the resulting studies involve the breakdown of the gas and diffusion and recombination processes, they also permit of evaluation of the energy distribution and the coefficient for ionization by collision, as well as the evaluation of Ramsauer free paths at energies from thermal upward. Studies can also be carried on in the presence of magnetic fields and in plasma-conditioned fields. Thus, while the question of energy distributions is dealt with specifically in only one or two of the papers of this group, it is omnipresent; and electron energies in the gas in these studies virtually underlie all theory and investigations. The theory involved in the studies is basically a logical extension of the foundations already indicated, that were laid by H. Margenau, J. C. Slater, and T. R. Holstein, but has been developed into a consistent whole by W. P. Allis.

It is obvious that this intricate theory can hardly be summarized in brief. Since it is further manifestly impossible to discuss in detail the achievements of this large and active group in regard to energy distributions and electron energies as a separate entity, divorced from the other material, there is given under reference (19) a rather complete chronological list of the major published contributions of the group, with titles and references, including the papers on experimental methodology, so that the interested reader can study them for himself. In later sections of this chapter and in later chapters of this book, the cogent contents of these papers will be discussed at appropriate places. A brief outline of experimental procedures and theory as applied to recombination studies is given in chapter VI. With this statement, it is possible to leave the summary of development of this field and proceed to more detailed discussion.

§ 3. General Approach to the Derivation of the Druyvesteyn Distribution Law.

As earlier stated, the material involved in the theoretical study of the energy distribution of electrons under various conditions could well fill a book. It would be futile to attempt to present, even in outline, the various analyses that have been successfully used to date.

From what has been said in the preceding section, it appears that while Druyvesteyn and Smit used modifications of Hertz's method, by and large the greater proportion of the investigators following Morse, Allis, and Lamar (1) have used various treatments of the Boltzmann transport theory for this purpose. In principle the method is outlined and discussed in general terms in Chapman and Cowling's book, *The Mathematical Theory of Nonuniform Gases* (I.53). It is also treated in *Kinetic Theory of Gases*, by Kennard (22). To present to interested readers a superficial glimpse of the procedures followed, the Druyvesteyn distribution law will be derived for elastic electron impacts with constant collision cross sections for a d.c. field, as initially presented by Morse, Allis, and Lamar (1). This treatment will serve sufficiently to indoctrinate the reader in the general line of reasoning used, and will not require as much space as the more complete and elaborate treatments. Following this, the various forms of the Druyvesteyn, Maxwell, and other laws will be given, together with the distribution derived in certain cases.

The probability that an electron of velocity c will collide elastically with an atom and be scattered at an angle θ with its initial direction is determined by the angular scattering function $\sigma(c, \theta)$, which may be described in terms of the elastic collision cross section, $q(c) = 2\pi \int_0^\pi \sigma(c, \theta) \sin \theta \, d\theta$. Here c is the random vector velocity of the electron. The loss of momentum in such collisions leads to the concept of the momentum-transfer cross section, which can be expressed as

(4.1)
$$Q(c) = 2\pi \int_0^\pi \sigma(c, \theta) (1-\cos \theta) \sin \theta \, d\theta.$$

The latter differs from the former expression only if there is excessive scattering in the forward or backward directions, which is uncommon. The fractional energy loss at collision, without considering the velocity distribution as elsewhere indicated, is

(4.2)
$$\Delta E/E = \frac{(2\Lambda c)}{c} = 2\frac{m}{M}(1-\cos \theta),$$

where m is the mass of the electron and M is that of the atom.[6]

It is now necessary to consider the loss and gain of energy of the electron in the field. The number of electrons in the volume element $d\tau = dx \, dy \, dz$, whose velocities fall in a range $d\gamma = du \, dv \, dw = c^2 \sin \omega \, dv \, d\omega \, d\phi$ will be $f(x,y,z: u,v,w) \, d\tau \, d\gamma$, where f defines the distribution function. To simplify calculations, the field and drift

[6]Averaged over a Maxwellian distribution, Cravath replaces 2 by 8/3.

motion, etc., will be confined to one axis, the x axis, so that distributions are homogeneous and isotropic in the yz plane. Thus, f is a function only of x, c, u, or x, c, and ω. The function now is to be determined by Lorentz's method and extended to include the possible variations of cross section with c and the energy loss at impact. Following Lorentz, it is assumed that f can be expanded in a series of Legendre functions of $\cos \omega = u/c$:

$$f(x, c, \omega) = f_0(x, c) + P_1 \cos f_1(x, c) + P_2 \cos \omega \, f_2(x, c)$$

(4.3)

$$= f_0(x, c) + (u/c) f_1(x, c) + \dots$$

The function f_0 represents the random distributions in velocity, and f_1 determines the electron drift. The higher terms in the series are nearly always small and do not correspond to any simple property in the distribution, but serve only to improve its form. Thus, in equation 4.3, all but the first two terms of the series will be neglected. The result will give *nearly* the correct values for the random and drift velocities in the normal range of values of the parameters to which solution is limited, as well as the correct form to the distribution. The basic condition yielding the form of f is obtained by setting up the detailed expression for balance between loss and gain of electrons in the volume element $d\tau \, dy$ in phase space. The number of electrons leaving this element due to the applied field X and diffusion is readily seen to be

(4.4)
$$g \, d\tau \, dy = \left(\frac{Xe}{m} \frac{df}{du} + u \frac{\partial f}{\partial x} \right) d\tau \, dy.$$

Here X is the field, e the electron, and m its mass. When the first two terms of the series in equation 4.3 for f are placed in this relation, two terms in u^2 appear. Since higher spherical harmonics than the first are being neglected, u^2 must be replaced by its average value $c^2/3$. Thus, approximately

$$g \, d\tau \, dy = \left[\frac{Xe}{m} \cos \omega \frac{\partial f_0}{\partial c} + \frac{Xe}{m} \frac{1}{3c^2} \frac{\partial (c^2 f_1)}{\partial c} \right.$$

(4.5)

$$\left. + c \cos \omega \frac{\partial f_0}{\partial x} + \frac{c}{3} \frac{\partial f_1}{\partial x} \right] d\tau \, dy.$$

The number of electrons leaving $d\tau \, dy$ through collisions is

(4.6) $a \, d\tau \, dy = Nc \int 2\pi f \sigma \, (c, \theta) \sin \theta \, d\theta \, d\tau \, dy = Nq(c) f \, d\tau \, dy,$

The Distribution of Energy of Electrons in a Field in a Gas

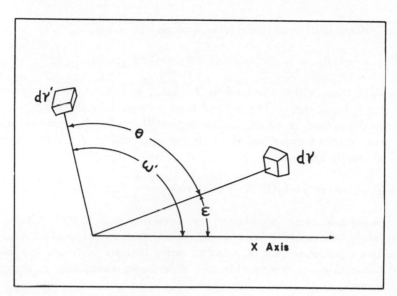

Fig. 4.1. Diagram showing the velocity elements $d\gamma$ and $d\gamma'$, with angles θ, ω, and ω' relative to the direction of the field X, in Morse, Allis, and Lamar's deduction.

where N is the number of gas atoms/cm³. This essentially forms the basis of the original Lorentz study. It is next essential to consider the number of electrons scattered into $d\tau\, d\gamma$, which were not considered by Lorentz. These are scattered in by collisions of other electrons. These electrons before collision had velocities in the element $d\gamma'$ shown in figure 4.1. Their initial velocity $c' = c + (mc/M)$ $(1 - \cos\theta)$ is larger than the final velocity in the ratio $\Delta E/E$ given by equation 4.2. It also follows from this relation that the size of $d\gamma'$ is given by $d\gamma' = (c'/c)^3\, d\gamma$.

Accordingly, the total number of electrons scattered into $d\tau\, d\gamma$ per second is

(4.7) $$b\, d\tau\, d\gamma = Nc \int_0^\pi 2\pi\, f(c', \omega')\, \sigma(c, '\theta\, \sin\theta\, d\theta\, (c'/c)^4\, d\tau\, d\gamma.$$

Thus, in consequence of collisions, the total number of electrons entering and leaving $d\tau\, d\gamma$ is

(4.8) $$(b-a)\, d\tau\, d\gamma = \left(2\pi \frac{N}{c^3}\right) \int_0^\pi [c'^4\, f(c', \omega')\, \sigma(c', \theta) - c^4\, f(c, \omega)\, \sigma(c, \theta)]$$

$$\sin\theta\, d\theta\, d\tau\, d\gamma.$$

As c' differs little from c, the integrand may be written as

(4.9) $c^4 [f(c, \omega') - f(c, \omega)] \sigma(c) + \Delta c \dfrac{\partial}{\partial c} [c^4 f(c, \omega')] \sigma(c, \theta).$

The first term is that obtained by Lorentz, and gives on integration, $-N Q c f_1 (c, \omega) \cos \omega$. The second term follows from the inclusion of energy loss, and is small, owing to (m/M) in Δc. In consequence, no great error is committed if in it f is replaced by f_0. Accordingly, $(b - a)$ finally becomes

(4.10) $(b-a) d\tau dy = [-Q(c)Ncf_1 \cos \omega + \dfrac{m}{M} \dfrac{N}{c^2} \dfrac{\partial}{\partial c} (c^4 Q(c) f_0) \, d\tau \, dy.$

The steady state is obtained by equating g to $(b - a)$. Equating separately, the terms in $\cos \omega$ and those that do not contain $\cos \omega$ give two equations. That is, relating terms that are isotropic in space and those that are not, yields two equations, containing f_0 and f_1. These are

(4.11) $Xe (\partial f_0/\partial c) + mc\partial f_0/\partial x = - NQ(c) \, mcf_1$

and

(4.12) $\dfrac{Xe}{2c} \dfrac{\partial(c^2 f_1)}{\partial c} + (\tfrac{1}{2}) \, mc^2 \dfrac{\partial f_1}{\partial x} = \dfrac{m^2}{M} \dfrac{3N}{2c} \left(c^4 Q(c) f_0 \right).$

The first of these equations (4.11) is the one obtained by Lorentz. It represents the gain of momentum due to diffusion drift down the field, and loss of momentum due to collisions. The second, which Lorentz did not have, represents the balance between gain of energy because of diffusion and drift down the field, and loss of energy by collisions. The quantity $1/NQ(c)$ is the electron mean free path for momentum transfer, i.e., is akin to the Ramsauer cross section.

The second energy-balance equation (4.12) secures a detailed energy balance in each velocity range, and enables solution for both f_0 and f_1. If f is independent of x, as in the case for a rough order approximation, equation 4.12 for energy balance integrates at once into

(4.13) $XeEf_1 = 6 \, (m/M) \, NQ(c) \, E^2 f_0 - B.$

Multiplying both sides by $(8\pi/3m^2) \, dE$, there results

(4.14) $\dfrac{8\pi Xe}{3m^2} Ef_1 \, dE - \dfrac{16\pi NQ(c)}{m^2} \dfrac{m}{M} E^2 f_0 \, dE = - jdE.$

Here B and j are constants of integration. The energy for the current carried by electrons with energies between E and $E + dE$, i.e., in the velocity element $dy = (4\pi/m)c\, dE$, is given as

(4.15) $$d\bar{j} + \overline{euf}\, dy = (ec/3)\, f_1\, dy.$$

This gives the energy taken from the field per cm^3 per sec by the current as

(4.16) $$Xd\bar{j} = \left(8\pi e\, \frac{X}{3m^2}\right) E f_1\, dE.$$

It is noted that this is the first term in the energy-balance equation (4.12). The second term is the energy lost by collisions. If these energies are to balance, B or j must be 0. But if not balanced, and say the energy lost is more than that gained, j is a measure of the loss. In this event, j is equal to the *number* of electrons per cm^3 losing energy and *passing through* the value E from higher to lower energies. The steady-state energy distribution and velocity represent the terminal state that is of interest in this discussion. For this condition, B or j is zero.

Since present interest lies in the distribution function f_0 instead of the drift velocity f_1, B in equation 4.13 is set equal to 0. The value of f_1 is then substituted in terms of f_0 for f_1 in the first of the two equations deduced, i.e., into equation 4.11. If $Q(c)$ is constant with c, it becomes merely Q. If f is independent of x, i.e., if interest focuses on the terminal, or steady-state energy, the solution for f_0 is obtained by integration in the form

(4.17) $$f_0 = A\, \epsilon^{-h^4 c^4} = A\, \epsilon^{-\left[\frac{3m}{M}\left(\frac{NQE}{Xe}\right)^2\right]}, \text{ with } h^4 = \left(\frac{3m}{M}\right)\left(\frac{NQm}{2Xe}\right)^2.$$

Normalization fixes the constant A as

(4.18) $$A = [nh^3/\pi\Gamma(\tfrac{3}{4})],$$

with n the density of electrons/cm^3.

Morse, Allis, and Lamar like to express their equations in terms of the energy $E_e = Xe/NQ$ and the random velocity $c_e = (2Xe/mNQ)^{\frac{1}{2}}$ gained by an electron in falling freely through $\lambda = 1/NQ$, or one mean free path in the field direction. Let the fractional loss of energy per impact $f = 2m/M$. It is then possible to write the average energy

E_A and drift velocity $\bar{v}$ as follows:

(4.19) $E_A = \dfrac{\Gamma(5/4)}{\Gamma(3/4)} \left(\dfrac{M}{3m}\right)^{1/2} E_e = 0.427 \left(\dfrac{M}{m}\right)^{1/2} E_e = 0.427\ Xe\lambda(M/m)^{1/2}$;

(4.20) $\bar{v} = \dfrac{\pi^{1/2}}{3\Gamma(3/4)} \left(\dfrac{3m}{M}\right)^{1/4} c_e = 0.6345 \left(\dfrac{m}{M}\right)^{1/4} c_e = 0.756 \left(\dfrac{e}{m} \lambda X\sqrt{f}\right)^{1/2}$

It is recalled that $\Gamma(5/4) = 0.9064$ and $\Gamma(3/4) = 1.2254$. In equations 4.19 and 4.20, for E_A and $\bar{v}$, the last expression is to be regarded closely. In chapter III, using simple kinetic theory and Maxwell's distribution, comparable results are obtained. From Compton's deduction[7] of E_A and $\bar{v}$ in a field where Maxwell's law holds, it appears that

(4.21) $E_{AM} = 0.435\ Xe\lambda \left(\dfrac{M}{m}\right)^{1/2}$ and $\bar{v}_M = 0.775 \left(\dfrac{e}{m} \lambda X\sqrt{f}\right)^{1/2}$.

It is seen that these two parameters for the Maxwellian and Druyvesteyn distributions differ only slightly in the constant term, and that both of them differ materially from the thermal energy kT, as Townsend observed. However, if these expressions for E_A are placed into the Druyvesteyn and the Maxwellian distribution laws, it will be seen that the two laws are distinctly different. The newly deduced Druyvesteyn law, as given by equation 4.17 above, becomes

$$N(E)dE = \dfrac{2N\Gamma(5/4)^{3/2}}{\Gamma(3/4)^{5/2}} \dfrac{E^{1/2}}{E_A^{3/2}} \epsilon^{-\frac{E^2}{E_A^2}\left(\frac{\Gamma(5/4)}{\Gamma(3/4)}\right)^2} dE$$

(4.22)
$$= 0.5196\ (2N) \dfrac{E^{1/2}}{E_A^{3/2}} \epsilon^{-0.548\frac{E^2}{E_A^2}} dE$$

$$= 0.5196\ (2N) \dfrac{E^{1/2}}{[0.427\,Xe\lambda\,(M/m)^{1/2}]^{3/2}} \epsilon^{-0.548\left[\frac{E}{0.427\,Xe\lambda\,(M/m)^{1/2}}\right]^2} dE .$$

The distribution in terms of velocity then is

$$N(c)dc = \dfrac{4N}{\Gamma(3/4)} \left[\dfrac{3m}{4M}\left(\dfrac{m}{Xe\lambda}\right)^2\right]^{3/4} c^2\,\epsilon^{-3/4\frac{m}{M}\left(\frac{m}{Xe\lambda}\right)^2 c^4} dc$$

(4.23)
$$= \dfrac{4N}{1.2254} \left[\dfrac{3}{4}\dfrac{m}{M}\left(\dfrac{m}{Xe\lambda}\right)^2\right]^{3/4} c^2\,\epsilon^{-3/4\frac{m}{M}\left(\frac{m}{Xe\lambda}\right)^2 c^4} dc .$$

---

[7]This uses Compton's constant 0.921 in equation 1.1a in place of Langevin's 0.815. It also uses the value of $f = 8/3\ m/M$ for a Maxwellian distribution.

With similar notation, the Maxwellian law in the energy form appears as

$$N(E)dE = 2\pi N \left(\frac{3}{2\pi E_A}\right)^{3/2} E^{1/2} \, \epsilon^{-3/2\left(\frac{E}{E_A}\right)} = 1.025 \, (2N) \frac{E^{1/2}}{E_A^{3/2}} \, \epsilon^{-3/2\left(\frac{E}{E_A}\right)}$$

(4.24)

$$= 1.025 \, (2N) \frac{E^{1/2}}{[0.433 \, Xe\lambda \, (M/m)^{1/2}]^{3/2}} \, \epsilon^{-3/2 \frac{E}{0.433 \, Xe\lambda(M/m)^{1/2}}} \, dE .$$

It is not profitable to express the Maxwell relation in the velocity form for comparison, since it will differ only in constant terms and in the fact that the exponential contains c^2/a^2 or $(c/c_A)^2$ instead of $(c/c_A)^4$, as in the Druyvesteyn form. Thus, it is seen that under simplifying assumptions, electrons in a gas in a field will have an average energy E_A, roughly equivalent to Townsend's ηkT, which is larger than kT for the ambient gas molecules. The average energies E_A at terminal velocity in the field differ very little from each other in the two cases. However, the Druyvesteyn law has an exponential term that varies much more rapidly with the ratio E/E_A than does the Maxwellian law. A comparison of the two laws in the velocity form, as given by Morse, Allis, and Lamar, is seen in figure 3.9b. The Druyvesteyn law is seen to fall off more steeply on the high-velocity side than does the Maxwellian law. Where it exists, it will therefore show *less* excitation and ionization than expected on the classical Maxwellian law in the extreme asymptotic foot, where there are too few collisions to disturb the distribution seriously.

In the event that $Q(c)$ or $Q(E)$ varies with the velocity c, or better, with energy E, then the distribution law ceases to be that of Druyvesteyn. It is given by

$$N(E) \, dE = A \, \epsilon^{-\left(\frac{N}{Xe}\right)^2 \left(\frac{6m}{M}\right) \int^{\bar{E}} E Q^2(E) dE} \, dE$$

and

(4.25)

$$f_1 = \frac{6m}{M} \frac{NQ}{Xe} \bar{E} f_0 .$$

This expression is not identical with equation 14 given in the original paper. Owing to a misprint, equation 14 is in error. The present form has been corrected by N. E. Bradbury. The normalizing constant A will now also be different, and will depend on the analytic form of $Q(E)$. Using this expression and the curves of Ramsauer and Kollath and of Normand shown in figure 3.10, Harriet W. Allen calculated the distribution laws to be expected for He, A, and Ne shown

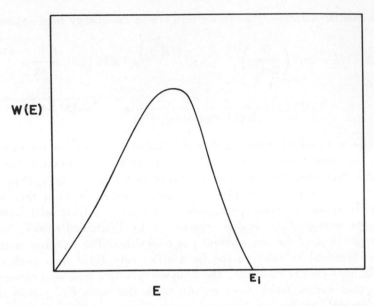

Fig. 4.2a. Distribution law assumed by Allen where inelastic impacts set in. The cutoff on the high-energy side is either at the excitation or ionization energy, and is arbitrarily chosen for best fit. As later seen, the curves are not very sensitive to the cutoff and to the degree of inelasticity assumed.

in figure 3.9a. In plotting these curves for E, f_0 was plotted as a function of $\sqrt{E}$, choosing abscissae having the same mean energy E_A. The sharp decline of the curve for A on the high-energy side should be noted, caused by an increase in $Q(E)$ with E. He, with a decline in $Q(E)$ with increasing E, shows a sharper initial rise with a longer gradual decline on the high-energy side. Ne gas with $Q(E)$ constant shows a Druyvesteyn distribution. These curves are in agreement with the appearance of inelastic impacts caused by excitation in the measurement of drift velocities $\bar{v}$ by Bradbury and Nielsen.

Harriet W. Allen then calculated the effect of inelastic impacts on the form of the energy-distribution curves. They will modify the form not only in the high-energy range, where inelastic impacts place a ceiling (so to speak) on further energy increase, but in the low-energy region as well. For, as electrons lose energy to inelastic impacts at high energy and are thus removed, they increase the population of the lower-energy states. This was first indicated by J. A. Smit. Allen used an approximate solution to the problem by applying the theory to the condition of inelastic impacts, but at the high-

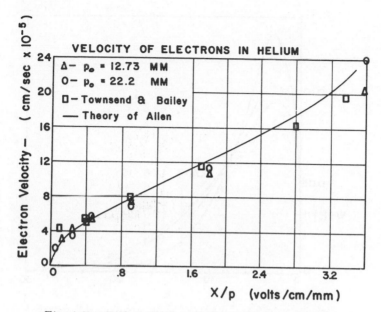

Fig. 4.2b. Drift velocities in He as given by Hornbeck,
compared to theory of Allen.

energy end, cutting off the distribution sharply at some point between
the first excitation potential and the ionization potential. Choice
as to the cutoff point was aided by study of the effects on the drift-
velocity curves in comparison with observation. Such an arbitrary
cutoff point was indicated by some measurements of H. C. Kelley
in He (23). It is useful only in getting values of the drift velocity.
The type of curve used by Allen in this energy range is shown in
figure 4.2a.[8] The accuracy of this method is illustrated by agreement
between theory and experiment, as shown in figure 4.2b. It obviously
cannot be used for computing the Townsend ionization coefficient
a, or in any critical studies of this nature.

More satisfactory and complete data were obtained by J. A. Smit
(10), using his theory for the case of He. The curves are shown in
figure 4.3 for the terminal distribution N_E plotted against energy E
expressed in terms of electron volts, as calculated for four steady
field-to-pressure ratios X/p, of 3, 4, 6, and 10. In these computations
it was possible to estimate the fraction of the energy gained by
electrons which was lost to elastic and inelastic collisions. This
is shown in table 4.1 as the number of such collisions divided by
$pN\sqrt{2/m}$, where N is the number of free electrons/cm³ and p is the

[8]The justification for this is seen in the work of D. Barbiere (21) to follow.

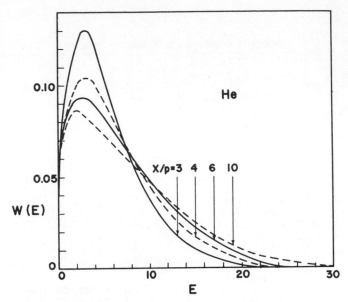

Fig. 4.3. Smit's calculated energy-distribution curves
for the energy distribution in He.

pressure in mm. The calculations of Smit have recently been extended
to higher values of E and X/p by S. H. Dunlop (11), working under
Eméleus, in order to enable him to calculate Townsend's first ionization coefficient α, using the theory of Eméleus, Lunt, and Meek. The
extended curves are shown in figure 4.4.

§ 4. Energy Distributions and Related Quantities Deduced from Holstein's Theory by D. Barbiere.

Since this chapter was initially written, the very elegant theory
of T. R. Holstein (14) has been applied to the problem of energy
distributions in He, A, and Ne under Holstein's direction. Using
certain approximations, the energy distributions for four low values
of X/p have been worked out in detail by Domenick Barbiere (21).
The data so compiled, as well as the basic procedure, seem so illustrative of the problem and of the relative importance of various factors
which are not indicated elsewhere, that the work is summarized
in extenso.

The generalized relations of Holstein (14), with simplifying assumptions based on symmetry considerations, are reduced to two differential
equations for the energy distribution $f(U)$ of electrons between plane
parallel electrodes with a constant uniform d.c. field X. These appear
on the next page, as equations 4.26 and 4.27.

TABLE 4.1

Here is shown the fraction of the energy gain by electrons in the field which is lost to elastic and inelastic impacts divided by $pN\sqrt{2/m}$, where N is the free-electron density and p is the gas pressure in mm. Note that as X/p exceeds 4 this fraction lost in inelastic impacts exceeds the elastic loss.

X/p	$\bar{E}$	E_{el}	E_{inel}	E_{total}
3	5.55	0.0735	0.0195	0.094
4	6.4	0.087	0.081	0.165
6	7.0	0.095	0.28	0.37
10	7.7	0.11	0.87	1.0

$$(4.26) \quad 0 = \frac{4a^2}{3} \frac{d}{dU}\left[U\lambda_D(U)\frac{df(U)}{dU}\right] + \frac{2m}{M}\frac{d}{dU}\left[\frac{U^2 f(U)}{\lambda_D(U)}\right] - \frac{Uf(U)}{\lambda_{ex}(U)} \text{ for } U > U_1$$

and

$$0 = \frac{4a^2}{3}\frac{d}{dU}\left[U\lambda_D(U)\frac{df(U)}{dU}\right] + \frac{2m}{M}\frac{d}{dU}\left[\frac{U^2 f(U)}{\lambda_D(U)}\right] + \sum_h (U + U_h)$$

(4.27)

$$\lambda_h^{-1}(U + U_h)f(U + U_h) \text{ for } U < U_1.$$

Here $a = eX/m$; $U = v^2$, the square of the electron velocity; M, the molecular or atomic mass; $\lambda_D(U)$, the *mean free path for momentum transfer*; $\lambda_h(U)$, the *mean free path between collisions which excite the gas to the excited level of value* h. The expression $(m/2)U_h$ is the energy of the level, $(m/2)U_1$ is the energy of the lowest excited level, and

$$\lambda_{ex}^{-1} = \sum_h \lambda_h^{-1}$$

is the mean free path between exciting collisions. Equation 4.26 applies to the electrons with velocities in the excitation region, and equation 4.27 applies to those with velocities less than U_1. The equations apply only to low values of X. The quantity $f(U)$ is the measure of electron density in the energy level between U and $U + dU$. The normalized probability of finding the electron in this interval is given by

$$(4.28) \quad f(U)\bigg/\int_0^\infty U^{\frac{1}{2}} f(U)\,dU.$$

The electron mobility is given by

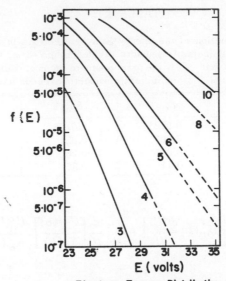

Electron-Energy Distribution.

Numbers on Curves are X/p Values

Fig. 4.4. Dunlop's extension of Smit's calculated curves
for the energy distribution in He.

$$(4.29) \qquad K_e = \frac{-2e}{3m} \int_0^\infty U\lambda_D(U) \, \frac{df(U)}{dU} \, dU \Big/ \int_0^\infty U^{1/2} f(U) dU \, .$$

The equivalent electron "temperature" T_e is given by

$$(4.30) \qquad T_e = \frac{-m}{2k} \int_0^\infty U\lambda_D(U) f(U) dU \Big/ \int_0^\infty U\lambda_D(U) \, \frac{df(U)}{dU} \, dU \, ,$$

with k the Boltzmann constant.

The quantity $\lambda_D(U)$, the mean free path for momentum transfer,
is a concept of importance in these equations.[9] No previously published curves exist for this quantity. They were calculated from
scattering data of Ramsauer and Kollath. If $\lambda_R(U)$ is the Ramsauer
free path, then

$$(4.31) \qquad \frac{1}{\lambda_R'(U)} = Q_R'(U) = n\{2\pi \int_0^\pi q(U, \theta) \sin \theta \, d\theta\},$$

[9]The concept is also used by Morse, Allis, and Lamar in their deduction,
but its importance is not indicated nor are any values given.

where $Q_R'(U)$ is the Ramsauer cross section for electrons of energy U expressed for 1 cm^3 of gas at 1 mm pressure at 0° C. The quantity n is the gas density in molecules per cm^3 at n.t.p. The quantity $q(U, \theta)$ is the differential cross section for scattering through angle θ by a molecule. Data on $q(U, \theta)$ for the inert gases were obtained by Ramsauer and Kollath up to U_1. They measured $Q_R'(U)$ directly. Their experimental results on $Q_R'(U)$ were checked by integration, and the agreement was excellent.

The diffusion cross section for momentum transfer is a most valuable concept, here evaluated for the first time. Expressed in terms of 1 cm^3 of gas at 1 mm pressure at 0° C., it is given by

$$(4.32) \qquad \frac{1}{\lambda_D'(U)} = Q_D'(U) = n\{2\pi \int_0^\pi q(U, \theta) \sin \theta (1-\cos \theta) \, d\theta$$

or

$$(4.33) \qquad \frac{Q_D'(U)}{Q_R'(U)} = 1 - \overline{\cos \theta},$$

where

$$(4.34) \qquad \overline{\cos \theta} = \frac{\int_0^\pi q(U_1\theta) \sin \theta \cos \theta \, d\theta}{\int_0^\pi q(U_1\theta) \sin \theta \, d\theta}.$$

Measurements of Q_R' but not of $q(U, \theta)$ were made by Normand. His values appear to be consistently 20% lower than Ramsauer and Kollath's results. $Q_D'(U)$ was also calculated from Normand's results. His data were multiplied by $\overline{\cos \theta}$ from angular scattering by Ramsauer and Kollath. The resulting drift velocity and electron temperatures calculated from these data do *not* agree very well with direct measurements. This indicates that care must be taken in the use of Normand's data, even though it is not proper to combine Ramsauer's $\overline{\cos \theta}$ with Normand's data and thereby to expect proper results. Equations 4.26 and 4.27 were solved for several limiting cases. These are:

1. Zero excitation cross section $1/\lambda_{ex}(U) = Q_{ex}(U) = 0$.
2. Infinite excitation cross section $Q_{ex} = \infty$.
3. Q_{ex} was chosen as some reasonable constant, such as 0.01 $Q_D'(U)$ for He and A as approximations to the curves of H. Maier-Leibnitz (24).

Under the first assumption, the two equations reduce to the old, familiar Druyvesteyn distribution. The resulting curves are shown, as detailed later. It appears that electron-drift velocity and temperature T_e are not very much influenced by the excitation cross section:

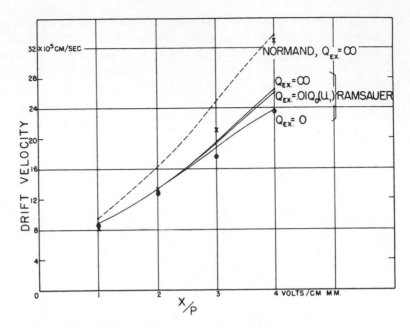

Fig. 4.5. Barbiere's calculated curves for drift velocities of electrons as a function of X/p in He. Lower curves use Ramsauer free paths with different excitation cross sections. Upper curve, Normand's elastic-impact cross sections with inelastic impacts to excitation.

the curves for $Q_{ex} = \infty$ and $Q_{ex} = $ const are almost coincident. Theoretical drift velocities agree well with data of Townsend and Bailey and of Nielsen. Nielsen's results in A are in good agreement with theory, while Townsend and Bailey's results are high, owing to impurity, as elsewhere stated. The value of T_e and Townsend's estimates of η in He are in good agreement, but the agreement is poor with Townsend's impure A. Normand's data do not yield good theoretical values of drift velocities, while the reverse is true of Ramsauer and Kollath (III. 8).[10] Separate sets of curves are also given, showing the dependence of electron-energy distribution on X/p, on diffusion cross section, and on excitation cross section. All curves have been normalized, i.e., the area from 0 to ∞ is equal to unity.

Perhaps most striking is the contrast in energy distribution for

[10]C. Kenty, M. A. Easley, and B. T. Barnes (III.9) recently reported similar difficulties with Normand's data vis-à-vis Ramsauer's. The same difficulty was also noted in the microwave study of A. V. Phelps, O. T. Fundingsland, and S. C. Brown (19).

TABLE 4.2

D. Barbiere's Tables of Values of Diffusion Cross Sections as a Function of Electron Energy for Electrons in He, Ne, and A, from 1 e.v. to the Ionization Potential

HELIUM				NEON				ARGON			
Electron Energy in e.v.	Ramsauer Cross Section	$1 - \cos\theta$	Diffusion Cross Section	Electron Energy in e.v.	Ramsauer Cross Section	$1 - \cos\theta$	Diffusion Cross Section	Electron Energy in e.v.	Ramsauer Cross Section	$1 - \cos\theta$	Diffusion Cross Section
1.8	20.8	1.102	22.9	0.99	5.06	1.023	5.18	1.1_5	5.92	.983	5.82
2.9	22.0	1.070	23.6	1.17	5.77	1.025	5.92	1.5	8.37	.855	7.15
4.2	20.8	1.081	22.5	1.35	6.01	1.016	6.11	2.0	12.2	.875	10.7
5.3_5	19.4	1.075	20.8	1.67	6.23	.972	6.05	2.3	14.0	.856	12.0
6.7_5	18.1	1.065	19.3	1.70	6.30	.973	6.13	2.4_5	15.1	.848	12.8
8.25	16.7	1.008	16.9	1.80	6.41	.938	6.02	2.8	17.5	.835	14.6
10.7_5	15.1	.992	15.0	2.2	6.94	.924	6.41	3.2_2	20.3	.835	16.9
13.8	14.2	.949	13.5	2.6	7.31	.883	6.46	3.3	20.7	.807	16.7
15.8	12.3	.928	11.4	2.8	7.42	.899	6.67	3.6	22.6	.842	19.0
19.2	11.3	.893	10.0	3.6	8.13	.825	6.70	4.0	24.2	.831	20.1
				4.9	8.91	.798	7.11	5.0	32.6	.857	27.9
				6.4	9.50	.767	7.29	5.4	34.5	.848	29.3
				7.9	10.1	.766	7.76	6.7	45.2	.879	39.8
				10.4	10.9	.768	8.36	8.0	53.5	.809	43.2
				13.1	11.5	.782	8.99	9.0	62.5	.833	52.1
				15.9	12.0	.790	9.47	10.3	71.6	.735	52.6
								12.5	78.6	.739	58.0

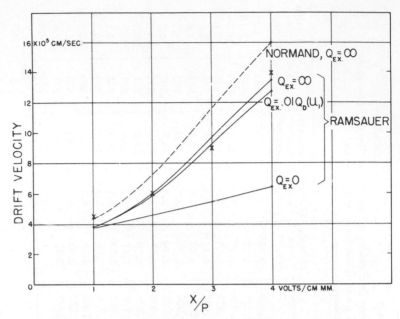

Fig. 4.6. Barbiere's calculated drift velocities in A. Conditions
are assumed to be analogous to those of figure 4.5 for He.

He and A in its relation to the type of variation of diffusion cross
section with energy, as first indicated by Bradbury and Nielsen. The
curves illustrating the dependence of energy distribution on excitation
cross section show that while this changes considerably from $Q_{ex} = 0$
to $Q_{ex} = \infty$, the curves for $Q_{ex} = $ const differ very little from those for
$Q_{ex} = \infty$. This is to be expected, because of the large energy loss
in collision. However, it is of importance to note that a value of
the cross-section excitation slightly above zero is enough (when the
steady state is reached) to force almost all electrons into the elastic-
collision region where they must remain. Some of Barbiere's conclusions are contained in table 4.2. They are included, not only for
their value as basic data, but for the more important reason that
they probably describe better than words the relations and depend-
encies of electron parameters in inert gases. The curves appear as
figures 4.5, 4.6, 4.7, 4.8, 4.9, 4.10, 4.11, 4.12, and 4.13.

§ 5. Electron Energies from Microwave Analysis.

A more recent development in the study of electron energies comes
from the techniques developed by W. P. Allis, S. C. Brown, and their
students (19), using microwave breakdown of gases. The use of the

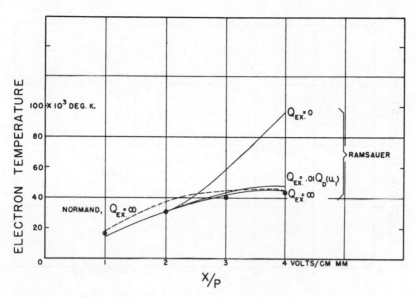

Fig. 4.7. Barbiere's computed electron temperatures in degrees K. in He as a function of X/p under various assumptions, as in figure 4.5.

microwave techniques leads to an evaluation of the ratio k/D, as in the earlier measurements by Townsend. The general principles of the method given by L. J. Varnerin, Jr., and S. C. Brown (20) merit presentation, despite the inaccuracy of the present data.

In outline, the microwave analysis starts from the general transport equation of Boltzmann, using the procedure of Morse, Allis, and Lamar that was presented earlier. This is

$$(4.35) \qquad C = \frac{\partial f}{\partial t} + \vec{v} \cdot \nabla f + \vec{a} \cdot \nabla_v f,$$

with C the net rate at which electrons appear in an element in phase space, $\vec{v}$ the velocity, $\vec{a}$ the acceleration, t the time, and ∇_v the gradient operator in velocity space. The distribution function may be expanded in spherical harmonics in velocity as

$$(4.36) \qquad f = f_0 + \frac{(\vec{v} \cdot \vec{f_1})}{v} + \dots$$

Thus, the distribution function f is expanded as before, with the spherically symmetrical term f_0 giving the energy distribution the dominant term. C arises from collisions, and can be expanded in spherical harmonics. The energy is expressed in a variable v, read in electron volts, defined by equation 4.37.

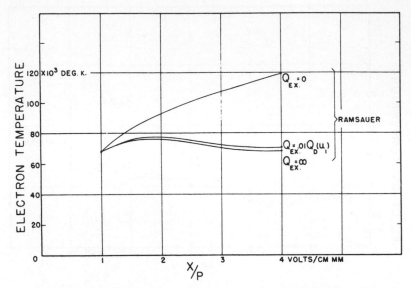

Fig. 4.8. Barbiere's computed electron temperatures in degrees K. in A
under same conditions shown for He in figure 4.7.

(4.37) $$ue = mv^2/2,$$

with v the *random* velocity and $\vec{X}$ the electrical field.[11] The general
production term of electron states through collisions is

(4.38) $$C_0 = \frac{\partial f_0}{\partial t} - \frac{v}{3u} \frac{\partial}{\partial u} (u\vec{X} \cdot \vec{f_1}) + \frac{v}{3} \nabla \cdot \vec{f_1}$$

and

(4.39) $$\vec{C_1} = \frac{\partial \vec{f_1}}{\partial t} + v\nabla f_0 - v\vec{X} \frac{\partial f_0}{\partial u},$$

the arrows indicating directed vector quantities.

For elastic collisions,

(4.40) $$C_{0,\,el} = \frac{2m}{M} \frac{v}{u} \frac{\partial}{\partial u} \left(\frac{u^2 f_0}{\lambda} \right)$$

and

---

[11]In *this section only*, to avoid confusion, the *random* velocity will be
represented by v instead of the symbol C otherwise used throughout in this
text. This v is *not* to be confused with the drift velocity kX, for which the
symbol v is used elsewhere.

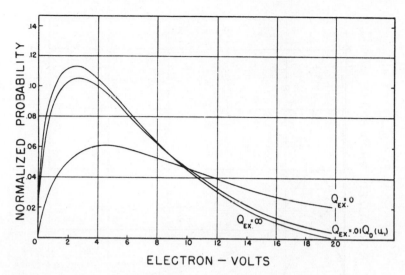

Fig. 4.9. Effect of cross sections on the energy distribution in He at $X/p = 4$, as computed by Barbiere. Note the effect on the shape of the curves of excitation cross sections setting in at about 19.5 volts. Note also that the value of the cross section between 0.01 of $Q_D(U_1)$ to infinity changes the distribution very little. This justifies the arbitrary cutoff of energies at excitation that was used by Allen.

(4.41)
$$\vec{C}_{1,el} = -\frac{v}{\lambda}\vec{f}_1 ,$$

as indicated in detail by the relations developed in section 3, using slightly different notations.

The quantity λ is the electron free path, m and M being electronic and atomic masses. The *inelastic* collisions add a term to C_0 given by $-(h_x + h_i)\nu_c f_0$, where h_x and h_i are the excitation and ionization efficiencies and $\nu_c = v/\lambda$ is the collision frequency. Putting in these terms, assuming that electrons suffering elastic impacts have no preferred direction and that there is no contribution to the $\vec{C}_1$ term, equations 4.40 and 4.41 become

(4.42) $$(h_x + h_i)\nu_c f_0 = \frac{\partial f_0}{\partial t} + \frac{v}{3}\left[\nabla\cdot\vec{f}_1 - \frac{1}{u}\frac{\partial}{\partial u}(u\vec{X}f_1) - \frac{6m}{M}\frac{1}{u}\frac{\partial}{\partial u}\left(\frac{u^2}{\lambda}f_0\right)\right]$$

and

(4.43) $$0 = \nu_c\vec{f}_1 + \frac{\partial\vec{f}_1}{\partial t} + v\left[\nabla f_0 - \vec{X}\frac{\partial f_0}{\partial u}\right].$$

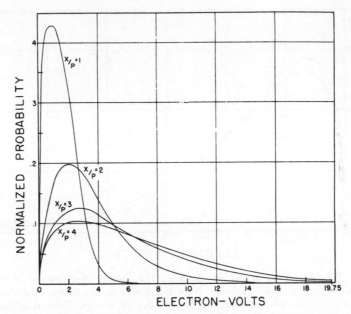

Fig. 4.10. Energy distributions in He with elastic impacts only,
at various values of X/p from 1 to 4, as computed by Barbiere.

For the pure d.c. study the electrical field is $\vec{X}_{DC}$, and for the pure
a.c. study it is given by $\vec{X}_{AC}\ \epsilon^{j\omega t}$, where ω is the radian frequency.
The d.c. study leads to an analysis such as given in section 3 in
simplified form. The a.c. field study has been developed in detail,
beginning with the work of Margenau (16) and continuing with that
of the M.I.T. group under Allis and Brown (19). In the present study
the experiments are carried out with both a.c. and *a small d.c. field
superposed*. Thus, the field used will be

(4.44) $$\vec{X} = \vec{X}_{DC} + \sqrt{2}\ \vec{X}_{AC}\ \epsilon^{j\omega t}.$$

Each term in the distribution function can be expanded in a Fourier
series in time:

(4.45) $$f_0 = f_0^0 + \sqrt{2} f_0' \epsilon^{j\omega t} + \ldots$$

and

(4.46) $$\vec{f}_1 = \vec{f}_1^0 + \sqrt{2}\ \vec{f}_1'\ \epsilon^{j\omega t} + \ldots$$

for the steady condition. The study is confined to conditions where
the mechanisms for density and energy decay are so slow that neither
density nor energy fluctuations occur during the high-frequency cycle.

The Distribution of Energy of Electrons in a Field in a Gas

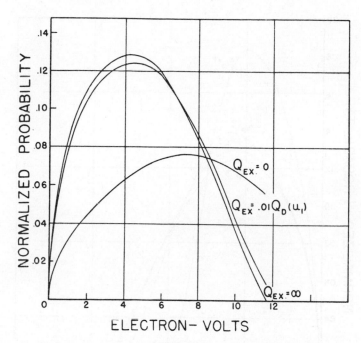

Fig. 4.11. Effect of cross sections for excitation on the energy distribution for A at $X/p = 4$, as computed by Barbiere. Compare the one with $Q_{ex} = \infty$ with the curve of figure 4.2a. Note the radical change in the A curve when even a small cross section for excitation sets in at 11.1 volts.

Thus, the f_0' term is not retained. If terms with the same frequency are grouped and second harmonic terms dropped, the product of $\vec{X}$ with f_0 and $\vec{f_1}$ gives

$$(4.47) \qquad \vec{X}f_0 = \vec{X}_{DC}f_0^0 + \sqrt{2}\,\vec{X}_{AC}f_0^0\, \epsilon^{j\omega t} + \ldots$$

and

$$(4.48) \qquad \vec{X}\vec{f_1} = \vec{X}_{DC}\vec{f_1^0} + \vec{X}_{AC}\vec{f_1'} + \sqrt{2}[\vec{X}_{DC}\cdot\vec{f_1'} + \vec{X}_{AC}\cdot\vec{f_1^0}]\,\epsilon^{j\omega t} + \ldots$$

The time-independent component of equation 4.42 is now given by

$$(4.49) \qquad -(h_x + h_i)\,\nu_c f_0^0 = \frac{v}{3}\left[\nabla\cdot\vec{f_1^0} - \frac{1}{u}\frac{\partial}{\partial u}\left(u\,\vec{X}_{DC}\cdot\vec{f_1^0}\right)\right.$$
$$\left. - \frac{1}{u}\frac{\partial}{\partial u}(u\,\vec{X}_{AC}\cdot\vec{f_1'}) - \frac{6m}{M}\frac{1}{u}\frac{\partial}{\partial u}\left(\frac{u^2 f_0^0}{\lambda}\right)\right].$$

The time-independent and first-frequency components of equation 4.43 give the next two equations.

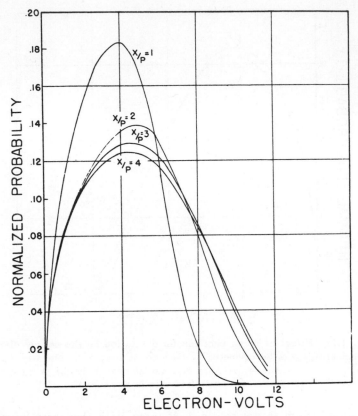

Fig. 4.12. Energy distribution in A with elastic impacts only, for
different values of X/p from 1 to 4, as computed by Barbiere.

$$(4.50) \qquad 0 = \nu_c \vec{f_1^0} + v \left(\nabla f_0^0 - \vec{X}_{DC} \frac{\partial f_0^0}{\partial u} \right)$$

$$(4.51) \qquad 0 = (\nu_c + j\omega) \vec{f_1'} - v \vec{X}_{AC} \frac{\partial f_0^0}{\partial u}.$$

Choosing co-ordinates so that X_{DC} is along the z axis, $\vec{f_1^0}$ and $\vec{f_1'}$
from equations 4.50 and 4.51 can be placed in equation 4.49. Then

$$-(h_x + h_i) \nu_c f = \frac{v}{3} \Big\{ -\lambda \nabla^2 f + \lambda X_{DC} \frac{\partial}{\partial u} \frac{\partial f}{\partial z} + \frac{X_{DC}}{u} \frac{\partial}{\partial u} \left(\lambda u \frac{\partial f}{\partial z} \right)$$

$$(4.52)$$

$$-\frac{1}{u} \frac{\partial}{\partial u} \lambda u \left[X_{DC}^2 + \frac{\nu_c^2}{\nu_c^2 + \omega^2} X_{AC}^2 \right] \frac{\partial f}{\partial u} - \frac{6m}{M} \frac{1}{u} \frac{\partial}{\partial u} \left(\frac{u^2 f}{\lambda} \right) \Big\}.$$

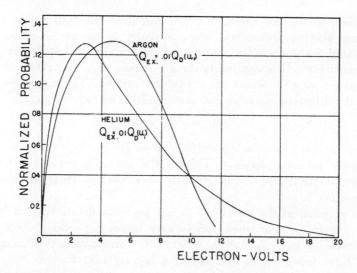

Fig. 4.13. Comparison of computed energy distributions in A with free path decreasing with energy, and in He with free path increasing with energy, as given by Barbiere.

Here f now represents f_0^0.

Solutions were made with the *collision frequency* ν_c *assumed constant.*[12] It was carried out for one gas (H_2), using Brode's value of $\nu_c = 5.93 \times 10^9 \, p \, \sec^{-1}$, with p in mm Hg. This enabled an *effective field* X_e to be introduced, which is defined by

$$(4.53) \qquad X_e^2 = X_{DC}^2 + \frac{\nu_c^2}{\nu_c^2 + \omega^2} X_{AC}^2 \ .$$

This is the field that is involved in most of these studies. A further simplification results in setting a quantity

$$(4.54) \qquad q = \frac{m}{e} \frac{3m}{M} \frac{\nu_c^2}{X_e^2},$$

which in this case for H_2 is

$$q_{H_2} = \frac{16.17}{(X_e/p)^2}.$$

The equations for the pure a.c. and d.c. cases are then considered separately in order to compare the distribution functions for the

[12] This simplification essentially means a constant free path; not the variable Ramsauer path. This nearly applies for H_2. In the d.c. case *below* excitation, it leads to the Druyvesteyn law.

same field in the two cases. For convenience, the distribution functions are also separated into a space times an energy function. The two spatial functions differ through a function $\epsilon^{\alpha z}$, with α Townsend's first coefficient. This applies to the d.c. case, since ionization occurs along the z axis in which electrons are moving. The a.c. case, for which the diffusion equation had previously been solved, gave

$$(4.55) \qquad \nabla^2 f_{AC} = - f_{AC} / \Lambda^2 ,$$

where Λ is the *characteristic diffusion length of the container*. It is convenient to set $a/X_{DC} = \eta$. This is the first Townsend coefficient as used by the Philips group, and is discussed at length in chapter VIII, section 3.

The solution of the equations is not given in detail here. It leads to the conclusion that when $X_e \Lambda$ is very large, $f_{AC} = \phi_{DC}$, where ϕ_{DC} is defined by $f_{DC} = \phi_{DC} \ \epsilon^{(\eta u)}$. A large X_e corresponds to a range of small X_e/p. However, in this range, η is very low. Further reference to the detailed deduction (which is not given here) leads to the conclusion that $f_{DC} = f_{AC}$, and therefore the diffusion coefficient D, the mobility k, and the collision frequency, are essentially identical for the a.c. and d.c. cases. For larger effective field-to-pressure ratios, X_e/p, a comparison of f_{DC} and f_{AC} requires solution for the distribution functions. The solution for the a.c. case has been given in a previous paper (25). For the purpose of solution, the d.c. case is broken into two regimes, one of higher energies and the other of energies below 8.9 volts, at which $h_x + h_i = 0$. It is not important to give the solution for the d.c. case in detail.· By use of constants which can be adjusted, it is possible to join the lower- and higher-energy solutions together to give a smooth fit at a "patching-up" point, $u_p = 9.5$ volts.

From the study of the equations, it appears that the distribution function f_{DC} agrees with distribution function f_{AC} under excitation within 0.5% at $X_e/p = 70$, and within 1% at $X_e/p = 100$, for energies up to 20 e.v. This suffices for the discussion to follow. Actually, there are so few electrons at higher energies that they have little bearing on the distribution functions as regards average properties. This may not apply to the *accurate* evaluation of ionization coefficients.

It is next essential to determine the ionizing efficiencies ζ_e and $\eta = a/X_{DC}$ for the a.c. and d.c. cases from the distribution functions. The *effective* a.c. coefficient ζ_e is defined by

$$(4.56) \qquad \zeta_e = \frac{\nu_{AC}}{D_{AC} X_e^2} ,$$

where the subscript AC indicates that such quantities are to be calculated from f_{AC}. Now for breakdown in the a.c. case, it has been shown that

$$(4.57) \qquad \zeta_e = \frac{1}{\Lambda^2 X_e^2},$$

and ζ_e is determined from the values of X_e and Λ observed for breakdown.

The ionizing efficiency for the first Townsend coefficient for d.c. studies, viz., $\eta = a/X_{DC}$, is determined as follows: The number of ionizations per cm of electron drift a is ν_{DC}/kX_{DC}, since the drift velocity is kX_{DC}. Therefore,

$$(4.58) \qquad \eta = \nu_{DC}/k_{DC}\, X_{DC}^2 .$$

The subscripts DC mean that the quantities are to be calculated from f_{DC}.

Divide η by ζ_e for the same X_e (X_{DC} is the *effective field for d.c.* in both cases). Therefore,

$$(4.59) \qquad \frac{\eta}{\zeta_e} = \frac{\nu_{DC}}{\nu_{AC}} \frac{D_{AC}}{k_{DC}}.$$

The ionization rate $n\nu$ may be calculated, as shown, by means of MacDonald and Brown's (25) equation 16, by the relation

$$(4.60) \qquad n\nu = - 8\pi \left(\frac{e}{m}\right)^2 \int_{u_i}^{\infty} (u/v)\, v_c\, h_i\, f\, du ,$$

where u_i is the ionization potential. Since (as noted above), f_{AC} is nearly f_{DC} for the complete range of ionization, it follows that

$$(4.61) \qquad n_{AC}\, \nu_{AC} = n_{DC}\, \nu_{DC}$$

and

$$(4.62) \qquad k = - \frac{1}{n} \int_0^{\infty} \frac{\lambda v}{3}\, 4\pi\, v^2\, \frac{\partial f}{\partial u}\, dv .$$

This expression, on integration with ν_c constant, leads to the classical type expression

$$(4.63) \qquad k = (e/m)\, (1/\nu_c)$$

whether a.c. or d.c. is used, so that k without subscript applies to both cases.

When ζ_e and η are small for low X_e/p, $f_{AC} = f_{DC}$ and $\nu_{DC} = \nu_{AC}$, so that for *low X_e/p,*

(4.64) $$\eta/\zeta_e = D/k.$$

It is also shown that

(4.65) $$n = \int_0^\infty 4\pi v^2 f dv = 2\pi \left(\frac{2e}{m}\right)^{3/2} \int_0^\infty u^{1/2} f du.$$

Thus, the contribution to n in any interval is $u^{1/2}f$. That quantity (unnormalized) was calculated and plotted as a function of u at $X_e/p = 100$ for a.c. and d.c. functions.

Inspection of the figure (which is not given here) shows that there are 5% *fewer electrons* in the *low-energy range* (0 to 5 volts) for the d.c. than for the a.c. case in H_2. Thus, ν_{DC} is about 1.05 times as great as ν_{AC}. This comes from the circumstance that with d.c. the density varies as ϵ^{az}. The resulting large-density gradients send more fast electrons to diffuse back into the gas against the d.c. field, while those swept out by the field are drawn equally from all energy levels. The larger number of higher-energy electrons accounts for the increased ν. Similarly, D_{DC} varies by less than 5% from that calculated by f_{AC}. Since the present experimental accuracy is of the order of 10%, the small discrepancy may be taken as sufficiently accurate at $X_e/p = 100$ to write quite generally that

(4.64) $$\eta/\zeta_e = D/k.$$

Again, from the integrals for D and average energy u, it follows that

$$D = \frac{1}{n} \int_0^\infty \frac{\lambda v}{3} 4\pi v^2 f dv$$

and

(4.66) $$\bar{u} = \frac{1}{n} \int_0^\infty \frac{mv^2}{2e} 4\pi v^2 f dv.$$

This leads at once to the important relation

(4.67) $$D/k = 2/3 \,\bar{u}$$

when ν_c is constant. Therefore, D/k is a direct measure of the electron energy. Equation 4.67 holds reasonably well when ν_c is not constant; when the Druyvesteyn distribution applies, it becomes

(4.68) $$D/k = 0.736 \,\bar{u};$$

and for a Maxwellian distribution, $D/k = 2/3 \,\bar{u}$ as in equation 4.67, whatever the dependence of ν_c on energy.

Since the data obtained evaluating ζ_e and η come from breakdown studies, the a.c.–d.c. breakdown condition must be derived. The a.c. breakdown condition had been derived in previous papers. The gas in the cavity will break down (i.e., become conducting in a self-sustained fashion) when the losses of electrons to the walls of the cavity are replaced by new ions created in the body of the gas. With an a.c. field alone, electrons are primarily lost by diffusion, since recombination is usually low at the higher X/p ratios and lower pressures. When the small d.c. sweeping field is superposed on the a.c. field, electrons are lost both by diffusion and *conduction current*, depending on k. The flow of electrons $\vec{\Gamma}$ is given by

(4.69)
$$\vec{\Gamma} = -\eta k \vec{X}_{DC} - D \nabla n.$$

When electrons lost are replaced by new ones resulting from ionization, it is possible to write

(4.70)
$$\nabla \vec{\Gamma} = \nu n.$$

If X_{DC} is directed along the z axis, if follows that

(4.71)
$$\nabla^2 n + \frac{X_{DC}}{D/k} \frac{\partial n}{\partial z} + \frac{\nu n}{D} = 0.$$

This relation is solved for a cylinder of axial height L, axial co-ordinate z, radius R, and radial co-ordinate r. The rigorous conditions require concentration to be low at a *boundary* falling to zero within a mean free path beyond. With mean free path very small compared to cavity dimensions, the condition of zero concentration at the cavity walls may safely be set at the boundary condition. Separating variables

(4.72)
$$n = M(r) \, N(z),$$

two equations are obtained:

(4.73)
$$\nabla_r^2 M + k_1^2 \, M = 0$$

and

(4.74)
$$\frac{d^2 N}{dz^2} + \frac{X_{DC}}{D/k} \frac{dN}{dz} + \left(\frac{\nu}{D} - k_1^2 \right) N = 0.$$

The symbol k_1^2 is the separation constant and ∇_r^2 is the two-dimensional Laplacian in the plane perpendicular to z. The solutions are

(4.75)
$$M = \text{const } J_0 (k_1 r)$$

and

$$(4.76) \qquad N = \text{const} \sin(\pi/L) \, z \, \epsilon^{-\dfrac{k X_{DC} z}{2D}}$$

Here k_1 is given by

$$(4.77) \qquad k_1 = 2.404/R,$$

and J_0 is the zero-order Bessel function. The exponential represents the deformation of the normal sine caused by the sweeping of electrons. The solution is subject to the condition that

$$(4.78) \qquad \nu/D = 1/\Lambda_{DC}^2,$$

where Λ_{DC} represents a modified diffusion length caused by the d.c. compared to Λ for a.c. alone. The value of Λ_{DC} is determined by the relation

$$(4.79) \qquad \frac{1}{\Lambda_{DC}^2} = \frac{1}{\Lambda^2} + \left(\frac{X_{DC}}{2D/k}\right)^2.$$

With the cylinder of radius R and length L, the diffusion length for breakdown Λ for a.c. alone has been evaluated as

$$(4.80) \qquad \frac{1}{\Lambda^2} = \left(\frac{\pi}{L}\right)^2 + \left(\frac{2.404}{R}\right)^2.$$

The relations 4.78, 4.79, 4.80, 4.67, and 4.64 can now be used to evaluate D/k, and from $D/k = 2/3 \, \overline{u}$ (4.67) to evaluate $\overline{u}$, and from $\eta/\zeta_e = D/k$ (4.64) to evaluate η, if ζ_e can be determined.

Dividing equation 4.78, $\nu/D = 1/\Lambda_{DC}^2$, by X_e^2, there results

$$(4.81) \qquad \frac{\nu}{DX_e^2} = \frac{1}{\Lambda_{DC}^2 X_e^2}.$$

Now ζ_e was defined as

$$(4.56) \qquad \zeta_e = \frac{\nu_{AC}}{D_{AC} X_e^2}$$

when a.c. alone was applied. By making a series of breakdown measurements at different values of p, it is possible to get a series of values of ζ_e at fixed ν, and different X_e/p by evaluating X_e and plotting $1/\Lambda^2 X_e^2 = \zeta_e$ as a function of X_e/p.

If next the d.c. is superposed on the a.c., a breakdown will be observed at higher values of X_e/p owing to increased losses. However, since there was determined a functional curve of ζ_e against X_e/p for pure a.c. breakdown, it is possible to associate the effective ζ_e with the a.c.–d.c. value of X_e/p observed, and thus to get the *modified* value of ζ_e for a.c.—d.c. This value of ζ is given by $\zeta_e = 1/\Lambda_{DC}^2 X_e^2$, and thus yields a value of Λ_{DC}.

Since

(4.79)
$$\frac{1}{\Lambda_{DC}^2} = \frac{1}{\Lambda^2} + \left(\frac{X_{DC}}{2D/k}\right)^2 ,$$

then by insertion of Λ_{DC}^2, Λ as calculated from L and R, and X_{DC} into this relation, the value of D/k is obtained. From this ratio both the average energy $\bar{u}$ and η can be calculated.

Experimentally the procedure is relatively simple once the radar techniques are understood. A continuous-wave tunable magnetron in the range of 10 cm wave lengths supplies power to a coaxial line. A power divider provides continuous variable control over the fraction of power incident on the measuring cavity. Unused power is dissipated by an unmatched load. A known fraction of the power incident on the cavity is coupled from the line by directional coupler to a power-measuring thermistor associated with a measuring bridge. A probe and slotted section in the coaxial line permit measurements of the standing wave pattern in the line immediately ahead of the cavity. Measurement of the standing wave ratio and voltage minimum as a function of frequency permits calculation of the cavity Q, as well as a fraction of the incident power that is actually absorbed by the cavity. For convenience, the power transmitted through the cavity is calibrated in terms of incident power. An oxygen-free Cu resonant cavity was used. This could be outgassed by baking to 290° C. The field within the cavity was determined by constructing an identical cavity structure provided with an axial small plug which could be inserted into the cavity. By observing changes in resonant frequency with plug insertion (following Slater), the relationship of stored energy in the cavity and the square of the electric field at the point of insertion could be determined. From the value of Q and power absorbed by the cavity, the field could be calculated. The field determinations were accurate to about 8%. The mean free path was in all cases much smaller than the cavity dimensions.

The results from spectroscopically pure H_2 are shown in figures 4.14 and 4.15a. Figure 4.14 shows the observed average energy $\bar{u}$ in e.v. as a function of X_e/p. The mean of the scattered points observed is indicated by the full curve. The 1921 data of Townsend and Bailey on less pure H_2 are shown by the dashed curve. The calculations for the energy from the distribution functions at four points are indicated by crosses. The agreement is here seen to be relatively satisfactory, with errors in X of the order of 8%.

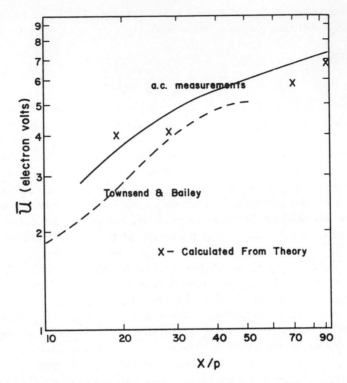

Fig. 4.14. Average electron energy as a function of X/p in H_2 gas as measured by microwave techniques, compared with Townsend and Bailey's magnetic-deflection studies on less pure H_2, and with theory.

Using values of D/k and ζ_e, $\eta = a/X$ was calculated and is plotted in average value to a log-log scale against X_e/p as the full, heavy curve of figure 4.15a. The data of Ayers (1923), in which purity is somewhat suspect, are shown in the dashed curve, while those of Hale are shown as the short, solid curve. Hale's H_2 was possibly purer than that from the microwave study, as he went to higher temperatures in his outgassing and avoided massive metal. Calculations from the theory, on the basis of which the a.c. data were obtained, yield the lower curve. These agree exceptionally well; but the same errors apply, owing to basic assumptions and approximations, indicating that the agreement should be good. It must be indicated that as a whole the agreement observed is relatively satisfactory. The quantity η or a is very sensitive to traces of impurity and to the *form* of the *distribution law*, especially in its high-energy end. The choice of ν_c will critically affect this region of the distribution,

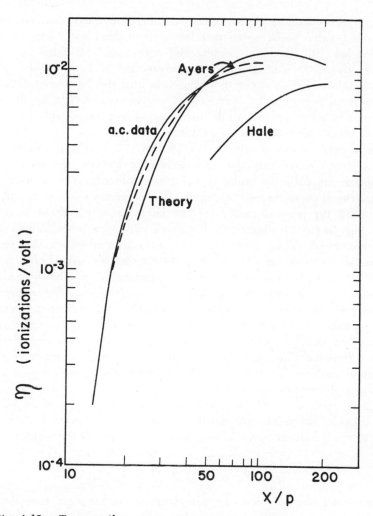

Fig. 4.15a. Townsend's ionization function $\eta = \alpha/X$ plotted against X/p by the microwave group under S. C. Brown. This is compared to direct d.c. evaluations of Ayers and Hale. Hale's H_2 was doubtless purer than that used here, which was exposed to metal without outgassing. Ayers' H_2 was definitely not pure.

and while changing α very much, will alter the average very little. The calculated α or η, as well as that inferred from measurements assuming constant ν_c, will probably tend to be high. Ayers' curve, with slightly Hg-contaminated H_2, should also be higher than is Hale's.

It is probable that if desired, more complete theory and improved

measuring techniques of the future will improve these data considerably. It is also to be noted that the method does not yield the *form*
of the law. It, like the magnetic-deflection and diffusion measurements, yields the average energy as a function of X/p. At the current
writing this is not so accurate as the data from the Townsend methods.
However, it furnishes an independent evaluation, confirming the data
of the Townsend group within its range of accuracy, and opens the
way to other approaches to the problem.

In a very recent article, A. V. Phelps, O. T. Fundingsland, and
S. C. Brown (19) show how the microwave method can be used to
determine the collision probability for momentum transfer of electrons
in gases at near-thermal energies. In Margenau's 1946 paper, he
developed the general theory for the behavior of electrons in a gas
with high-frequency electric fields when only elastic collisions need
be considered. This gave the complex conductivity of the gas in
terms of electron density N; frequency ω of the a.c. field; f_0, the
first term of the spherical harmonic expansion of the normalized
velocity distribution; and ν_c, the collision frequency for momentum
transfer of electrons of velocity v in the collision with neutral atoms.
The probability of such collision P_c is related to ν_c by $\nu_c = v/l = v p_0 P_c$,
where l is the free path and p_0 is the normalized pressure. Here P_c
differs from the Ramsauer type of collision probability, since it gives
the total collision probability, while Ramsauer's frequency is limited
in angle of scattering. The two quantities differ at most by a few
per cent only. If the electron-velocity distribution function is known,
the collision frequency can be determined from the ratio of σ_r/σ_i, the
real to the imaginary part of the conductivity, through the relation

$$\frac{\sigma_r}{\sigma_i} = -\int_0^\infty \frac{(\nu_c/\omega)\, v^3 df_0}{1 + (\nu_c/\omega)^2} \bigg/ \int_0^\infty \frac{v^3 df_0}{1 + (\nu_c/\omega)^2}.$$

Margenau showed that the steady-state distribution function for
electrons in an atomic gas in the absence of inelastic-collision loss
could be given as

$$\log f_0 = \int_0^u \left\{ \frac{kT_g}{e} + \frac{MeX^2}{3m^2\omega^2[1+(\nu_c/\omega)^2]} \right\}^{-1} du.$$

Here u is the electron energy in e.v., M is the mass of the atoms,
and X the r.m.s. value of the applied field. At low pressures, $\nu_c^2 << \omega^2$,
the distribution is nearly Maxwellian, with an energy:

$$<u> = \left(\frac{kT_g}{e} + \frac{MeX^2}{3m^2\omega^2} \right).$$

At low fields, $<u> = kT_g/e$. If the Maxwellian energy distribution is $f_0 = A \, \epsilon^{-u/<u>}$, the equation for σ_r/σ_i becomes

$$\frac{\sigma_r}{\sigma_i} = -\int_0^\infty \frac{(\nu_c/\omega)u^{1.5}\epsilon^{-u/<u>}}{(\nu_c/\omega)^2+1} du \bigg/ \int_0^\infty \frac{u^{1.5}\epsilon^{-u/<u>}}{(\nu_c/\omega)^2+1} du .$$

Phelps, Fundingsland, and Brown present the approximate solutions of this relation for ν_c. One is a low-field approximation for electrons in thermal equilibrium with the gas and assuming a simple velocity dependence of ν_c which is valid over the whole range of ν_c/ω. The other is a low-pressure approximation in which ν_c is restricted to values $(\nu_c/\omega)^2 \ll 1$. The low-field approximation assumes $\nu_c = a p_0 v^h$, with $P_c = a v^{h-1}$. Then, theoretical curves are calculated from the equation for σ_r/σ_i. These curves are compared with the observed ratios under known conditions of p, etc., leading to an evaluation of h and a. Experimentally, p_0 can be varied at constant ω and T_g to get a curve of $\sigma_r/p_0\sigma_i$ against σ_r/σ_i for values of σ_r/σ_i near unity. Then, the value of a quantity γ/p_0 dependent on a and h from theory is adjusted to give the best fit between experiment and theory for some value of h. Again, σ_r/σ_i can be measured as a function of p at two different values of T_g. The pressure and temperature which give the same value of σ_r/σ_i, and thus of γ, fix a value of h. The value of a then can be obtained from theoretical curves of σ_r/σ_i plotted against γ. The values of a and h so determined may *not* fit experimental data over a wide range of energies.

The low-pressure approximation comes from a measurement of σ_r/v_i at pressures so that $(\nu_c/\omega)^2 \ll 1$, which allows simplification of the equation for σ_r/σ_i. Then, σ_r/σ_i can be represented by a poly-nomial and by proper manipulation, and an inverse Laplacian trans-formation P_c comes out as a function of a summation of a series of terms in $a_j(u^{0.5})^j$. In this, the a_j's determined from experimental curves of $\sigma_r/\sigma_i p_0$ can be used to evaluate ν_c/p_0 and P_c as a function of u, the energy.

The change in resonant frequency and the change in conductance of a cavity at resonance can be used to evaluate σ_r and σ_i. Measure-ment of the change in cavity conductance rather than the width of the resonance curve avoids the problem of change in conductivity ratio occurring as the cavity impedance changes with frequency. The electrical field was determined in essentially the same manner as for the microwave breakdown studies. The coupling coefficient β was measured on the empty cavity.

An important problem in such studies, as well as others, is that

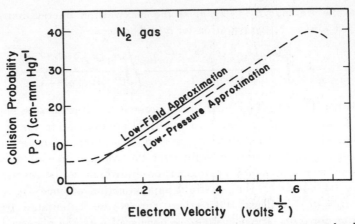

Fig. 4.15b. Phelps, Fundingsland, and Brown's determination of collision probabilities in N_2 as a function of electron velocity in √ volts for low energies. These are the first data at such energies.

of insuring that the electrons have cooled to T_g after breakdown. The rate of energy loss is equal to the product of the fractional energy loss per collision $2m/M$ for monatomic gases, the average excess energy $u - kT_g/e$, and the collision frequency. Thus,

$$du/dt = - \left(\frac{2m}{M}\right)\left(u - \frac{kT_g}{e}\right)\nu_c.$$

If ν_c is independent of v, the time constant for decay of energy is $M/2m\nu_c$. The time required to cool within 10% of thermal energies in He is about $90/p_0$ microsecond. In this work, times ranged from 200 microseconds in H_2 to 10^4 microseconds in He.

The results are illustrated in figure 4.15b, where P_o at 1 mm Hg pressure in units of cm^2/cm^3 as calculated from data in N_2, using the low-field approximation and the low-pressure approximation, is plotted as a function of the electron velocity in √volts, from 10^{-2} to 0.49 e.v. Values were roughly obtained for a number of gases at a mean thermal energy of 0.039 e.v. Expressed in the same units, these appear in table 4.3. The values for He, Ne, and A are in good agreement with those computed in 1931 by Allis and Morse (19a).

It is to be noted that the data, as extrapolated from trends of values from the Ramsauer-type measurement near 1 e.v., are in reasonable agreement with the new low-field values. Perhaps one more point can be made: In general, these studies indicate that the values of P_c given by Normand (III.8) in most cases, especially in H_2, are not so good as those of the workers preceding him.

TABLE 4.3

The Collision Probabilities P_c for Thermal-Energy Electrons in Various Gases, in per cent cm^2/cm^3 per mm Hg, as Evaluated by Microwave Techniques, Compared to the d.c. Data at About 1 e.v.

		He	Ne	A	Kr	Xe	H_2	N_2
Microwave	P_c	19	3.3	2.1	54	180	46	15
Observed near 1 e.v. (Ramsauer method)	P_c	20	2.0	2.6	20	45	40	25

Very recently, L. Gould (19) has extended the work of Phelps, Fundingsland, and Brown in measuring collision probability for momentum transfer to include measurements over average energies extending from 0.012 to 3 e.v., so as to dovetail into the Ramsauer measurements. Measurements of the real to the imaginary complex conductivity, using a new null method, were made in the afterglow of a pulsed discharge in helium by a new method of Gould and Brown in 1954 (19). The energy was varied by applying a microwave electric field in the afterglow, and under appropriate assumptions the average energy was determined from that field. Measurements from 0.012 to 0.052 e.v. were also obtained by varying the gas temperature from 77° K. to 700° K. The probability is 0.183 ± .02 from 0 to 0.75 e.v. It then increases slowly to peak at a value of 0.192 ± .02 at 2.2 e.v.

§6. Data Relating X/p, Electron Energies, and Associated Quantities, as Compiled from the Collected Studies by the Townsend and Bailey Methods.

In view of the urgent need for data concerning the energy distribution and energies of electrons in different gases under a considerable range of the ratio X/p, it is desirable to take advantage of the rather complete experimental data obtained over the years by Townsend, Bailey, and their students, relating X/p to average energies of electrons. Their investigations yield the only *extensive* data relating the average energy of electrons to the ratio X/p, assuming a Maxwellian distribution law, and thus furnish basic data needed by workers in gaseous discharge.

The complete data, together with a comprehensive treatment of these methods, will be found in Healey and Reed's treatise, *The Behaviour of Slow Electrons in Gases* (III.1). For the convenience of those using this book, there are assembled in the adjacent tables (together with the energies) a number of useful data for some of the more important gases. These tables are arranged as follows: In the first column is the ratio X/p, and in the second column is given the corresponding value of Townsend's η. This quantity represents the energy of the electrons as a number (η) multiplied into the root-mean-square *energy* of molecules in a gas at 15° C. in ergs. The third column contains C_1, the root-mean-square random velocity in multiples of 10^7 cm/sec. The fourth column gives the mean free path λ in multiples of 10^{-2} cm. The fifth column gives the drift velocity v in multiples of 10^5 cm/sec. Column six gives a rather questionable quantity, the average fractional energy loss f for electrons at impact in units of 10^{-4}. A discussion of the significance of this quantity is given in chapter V, end of section 3. The seventh and last column (when included) applies primarily to later measurements by the methods of Bailey and his students and gives the value of the electron-attachment probability h in multiples of 10^{-5}. In this case, the reader is again referred to chapter V for the meaning and value of the attachment process. Healey and Reed's treatise should be consulted for more complete data.

In these tables, the reference number in the heading following the name of the gas indicates the bibliographical reference to the original determination, and the date following the reference number indicates the *year when the work was done*. The reason for inclusion of the dates will become obvious later. It is of interest to note that the quantity η divided by 27 will closely give the *effective electron energy in electron volts*, and that the quantity C_1 is given by $C_1 = 1.15 \sqrt{\eta} \times 10^7$ cm/sec. Basically, the fundamental concepts and kinetic theory of the quantities and processes involved in the data here given are such as those used and derived by K. T. Compton in chapter III, section 3, or those given by von Engel and Steenbeck (III.13). They do not relate to the more esoteric modern analyses given.

In using these data, certain matters should be noted. The experimental values derived before 1936 should be regarded with caution, especially for the inert gases. The techniques of purity control were not adequately developed before this date. The inert gases are notoriously sensitive to impurities. Generally speaking, one should not place too much confidence in the accuracy or significance of the data. Since the distribution laws are in doubt, the dimensionless multipliers needed in converting the data are uncertain, possibly within the order of 10% in some cases. It is doubtful, in any case, since average values are determined with unknown distribution laws, whether greater accuracy than 5% is of significance in any studies of these quantities. At higher X/p the data are somewhat more unreliable, as measurements of some quantities involved were made with ionization by collision active. For the rough, rule-of-thumb analyses of gaseous ionic behavior needed by the physicist and engineer, these data, with their relating of energy and X/p, should prove invaluable. The painstaking workers who obtained the data merit the hearty thanks of all who use them.

In looking at the tables, the increase in f should be noted as one progresses from the inert gas group to more electronegative gases for the same range of energy. Again, the increase in f as electron energy increases is of considerable interest. It must be noted that the observed values for f in both He and A, as shown in tables 4.15 and 4.16, are *lower by a factor of about 3* than those to be expected from the classical theory for low X/p. In He they approach the expected values at about $X/p = 0.05$, and transcend these values at an X/p of 3, or at about 4 volts electron energy. It is probable that the low values of f are spurious, owing to the deviations of theory or to real changes in the distribution law relative to that assumed. An increase in f, originally pointed out by Bradbury and Nielsen as an increase in v ascribed to f, occurs at $X/p = 2.25$ in their He, which corresponds to 4.25 e.v. On a Maxwellian energy distribution this value is too low for He, since 5% of the electrons at 4.25 e.v. exceed only 16 or 17 volts, and they should exceed at least 19.5 volts. Thus, as concluded by Bradbury and Nielsen, the distribution law in He at about this energy is richer in high-energy electrons than either Maxwell's or Druyvesteyn's law requires, since here the Ramsauer free path increases with electron (see chapter III, section 4).

A similar situation applies to the low values of f in argon at low X/p. The appearance of marked inelasticity in A around $X/p = 1.0$ should be compared to the observed change in v by Bradbury and Nielsen at $X/p = 1.35$. The value at $X/p = 1$ corresponds to an energy of 8.4 e.v.; that of Bradbury and Nielsen corresponds to 11.1 e.v. This indicates the probability of some inelastic impurity in A (probably N_2 or Hg) in the work of Townsend and Bailey which was not present in Bradbury and Nielsen's work. However, even in that study, the value of X/p at which inelasticity sets in corresponds to an *average energy of 11.1 volts* (not that the detectable upper 5% has 11.1 volts). This energy is close to the excitation potential of 11.57 volts. Thus, inelasticity should have set in at a very much lower X/p in pure argon when about 5% had 11.1 volts. Assuming Bradbury and Nielsen's argon to be pure, then the distribution curve for A should fall off *very* much more steeply on the high-energy side than does that of Druyvesteyn. Since λ decreases rapidly with C_1 in this energy range, the A energy curve should be of the form as shown by Allen in figure 3.9a. Thus, care must be used in taking the data on A from the tables cited. There is no indication of distortion of data by ionization in He, but data in A could be distorted above $X/p = 10$. The values of λ are all given as reduced to λ_1 at 1 mm of Hg pressure.

The data for air in table 4.4a are not far off. The values of η_1 are the values of η, assuming that the distribution is that of Druyvesteyn. The values of f are about five times those expected for a monatomic gas of the atomic weight of air. This is to be expected. The variation of f below $X/p = 3.0$ is attributable to the distribution laws, as well as to the chance that, with increasing energy, more electrons in the swarm can lose energy to the O_2 molecule. The sharp increase in f at $X/p = 4$ is probably attributable to inelastic impacts with O_2 at 1.62 volts, as indicated by Bradbury. It is also likely that dissociative attachment to yield O^- ions begins near $X/p = 4$. To what the lower-energy losses below $X/p = 4$ are to be attributed, is not clear. Certainly, the losses in pure N_2, as shown in table 4.6, are such as to be expected from classical theory for an atom of mass 28.8 until an X/p of 2 and an energy of 1 volt cause an upward rise to values of f of the order of 1.65×10^{-3}. The increase at $X/p = 10$ at 1.5 volts in N_2 is again very marked. As this N_2 was probably not very pure, these values could be ascribed to collisions with O_2. The data in N_2 at X/p about 20 are doubtless due to the onset of ionization by electron impact, for this is observed to begin in that region.

The data in H_2 are again not too reliable. With an X/p of 20 in H_2, f is 11.7×10^{-3}, while Ramien by direct means found 8.4×10^{-3}, which is not seriously out of line. Ramien observed a linear increase of f with X/p, while table 4.7 gives a somewhat more rapid increase above $X/p = 20$ and a slightly slower decrease below. Appreciable ionization by collision begins in pure H_2 around an $X/p = 10$. Thus, the data beyond this in table 4.7 are suspect.

The data in O_2 should be more reliable. It is to be noted that the values of f *decrease* from $X/p = 0.25$ up to $X/p = 2$. This does not make sense unless there is a peculiar electron resonance at low X/p. Such resonance is not reflected in the value of λ_1 as energy increases. This quantity decreases monotonically with X/p. Ionization by electron impact sets in at about $X/p = 20$, and dissociative attachment occurs above an average energy of 1.6 e.v. Definite evidence of appreciable excitation and ionization appears at $X/p > 15$ in values

TABLE 4.4a—AIR (III.20) (1949)

Huxley and Zaazou's Data for Townsend Factors in Air

X/p $\dfrac{\text{volt}}{\text{cm}}$/mm	$\eta_1{}^*$	η	C_1 $\times 10^{-7}$ cm/sec	λ $\times 10^2$ cm at 1 mm	v $\times 10^{-5}$ cm/sec	f $\times 10^2$
0.5	11.0	9.65	3.58	4.65	9.43	.0124
1.0	20.5	18.0	4.88	4.45	13.2	.0128
2.0	37.5	32.9	6.62	4.20	18.8	.0137
3.0	52.5	45.5	7.78	4.00	23.5	.01560
4.0	62.0	54.5	8.5	3.90	27.4	.01830
6.0	75.0	65.7	9.35	3.80	35.8	.2670
8.0	87.0	76.3	10.1	3.75	43.8	.03480
10.0	98.0	86.0	10.7	3.70	51.4	.0428
15.0	124.0	108.5	12.0	3.70	68.5	.0636
20.0	146.0	128.0	13.0	3.70	84.0	.0838
25.0	166.0	145.5	13.9	3.70	98.0	.1010

$*\eta_1 = A\eta$ is Huxley's corrected value of the Maxwellian η of Townsend, where $A=1$ for Maxwell's distribution, and the values here use A for Druyvesteyn's distribution.

TABLE 4.4b—AIR (26) (1925)

Bailey's Data for Townsend Factors in Air

X/p $\dfrac{\text{volt}}{\text{cm}}$/mm	η	C_1 $\times 10^{-7}$ cm/sec	h $\times 10^5$
0.5	8.3	3.3	.33
1.0	15.2	4.5	.20
2.0	27.0	6.0	.07
2.5	32.5	6.6	.04

of f and h. The high-energy loss f per impact in Cl_2 is to be noted; yet it is not so large in Br_2 and I_2, although these attach electrons as readily as does Cl_2.

In the polyatomic gases CO_2 and H_2O, the high values of f should be noted. Not understandable is the decrease in f with electron energy in H_2O, and the increase and decrease in NH_3 and HCl. However, it is to be noted that for H_2O, Bradbury found two attachment processes at work. One of these was dissociative; the other was pressure-dependent. If such processes overlapped in the studies by the methods discussed, such mechanisms might lead to the results observed, owing to the indirect nature of the data. Again, the very low values of λ_1 at low energies in the strongly polar gases H_2O, NH_3, and HCl are of interest, and are perhaps to be expected.

TABLE 4.5—OXYGEN (27) (1939)

Healey and Kirkpatrick's Data for Townsend Factors in O_2

$\frac{X/p}{\text{volt}}{\text{cm}}/\text{mm}$	η	C_1 $\times 10^{-7}$ cm/sec	λ $\times 10^2$ cm at 1 mm	v $\times 10^{-5}$ cm/sec	f $\times 10^4$	h $\times 10^5$
0.25	5.5	2.7	10.0	13.3	60.0	10.4
0.5	9.5	3.55	7.9	16.1	51.0	7.25
1.0	19.0	5.01	5.66	16.3	26.0	2.2
2.0	32.0	6.5	3.80	16.9	15.5	—
5.0	43.0	7.54	2.86	27.3	32.4	5.2
10.0	52.0	8.29	2.86	49.5	88.0	16.7
15.0	57.5	8.71	2.71	67.0	145.0	17.2
20.0	62.0	9.05	2.57	81.5	199.0	7.0
30.0	71.0	9.7	2.23	99.5	260.0	0.0
50.0	95.0	11.2	2.47	159.0	494.0	0.0

TABLE 4.6—NITROGEN (28) (1921)

Townsend and Bailey's Data for Townsend Factors in N_2

$\frac{X/p}{\text{volt}}{\text{cm}}/\text{mm}$	η	C_1 $\times 10^{-7}$ cm/sec	λ $\times 10^2$ cm at 1 mm	v $\times 10^{-5}$ cm/sec	f $\times 10^4$
0.25	7.5	3.15	4.50	5.15	6.5
0.5	13.0	4.14	3.55	6.2	5.5
1.0	21.5	5.35	3.20	8.7	6.5
2.0	30.5	6.35	2.88	13.1	10.3
3.0	35.5	6.85	2.82	17.8	16.5
5.0	41.3	7.4	2.77	27.0	33.0
10.0	48.5	8.0	2.69	48.5	90.0
20.0	59.5	8.85	2.66	86.0	234.0
40.0	89.0	10.8	2.75	146.0	448.0
60.0	126.0	12.9	2.89	193.0	550.0

With these comments on the data and their interpretation, following the theory of chapter III, section 3, and part one of the present chapter, it is proper to leave the tables to those who are interested in the data which they offer.

TABLE 4.7—HYDROGEN (29) (1921)

Townsend and Bailey's Data for Townsend Factors in H_2

$\dfrac{X/p}{\text{volt}}$ /mm cm	η	C_1 $\times 10^{-7}$ cm/sec	λ $\times 10^2$ cm at 1 mm	v $\times 10^{-5}$ cm/sec	f $\times 10^4$
0.25	3.1	2.02	3.64	6.5	26.0
0.5	5.4	2.62	3.25	9.0	29.0
1.0	9.3	3.5	2.86	11.9	28.5
2.0	15.0	4.3	2.39	16.0	34.0
5.0	26.4	5.9	2.14	25.5	46.0
10.0	44.0	7.62	2.05	38.0	62.0
20.0	78.0	10.15	2.5	70.0	117.0
40.0	130.0	13.1	3.67	160.0	368.0
50.0	148.0	14.0	4.2	217.0	590.0

TABLE 4.8a—CARBON DIOXIDE (30) (1932)

Bailey and Rudd's Data for Townsend Factors in CO_2

$\dfrac{X/p}{\text{volt}}$ /mm cm	η	C_1 $\times 10^{-7}$ cm/sec	λ $\times 10^2$ cm at 1 mm	v $\times 10^{-5}$ cm/sec	f $\times 10^4$
2.0	1.9	1.6	0.7	13	160
3.5	3.0	2.0	1.0	26	400
4.5	5.9	2.8	1.8	44	590
6.0	12.0	4.0	3.1	66	655
7.5	24.0	5.6	4.5	87	583
9.0	35.0	6.8	5.3	102	555
11.0	48.0	0.0	5.8	119	535
14.0	59.0	8.8	5.9	130	530
16.0	70.0	9.6	5.8	139	510

TABLE 4.8b—CARBON DIOXIDE (30) (1922)

M. F. Skinker's Data for Townsend Factors in CO_2

$\dfrac{X/p}{\text{volt}}$ /mm cm	η	C_1 $\times 10^{-7}$ cm/sec	λ $\times 10^2$ cm at 1 mm	v $\times 10^{-5}$ cm/sec	f $\times 10^4$
0.25	1.2	1.2	0.42	1.2	2.34
0.5	1.3	1.3	0.45	2.5	8.95
1.0	1.5	1.4	0.54	5.5	37.4
2.0	1.8	1.5	0.63	11.8	144.0
5.0	9.0	3.5	2.39	50.0	516.0
10.0	47.0	7.9	5.91	108.0	460.0
20.0	75.0	9.9	4.76	138.0	472.0
50.0	139.0	13.6	3.67	195.0	506.0

§6

TABLE 4.9—WATER VAPOR (31) (1930)

Bailey and Duncanson's Data for Townsend Factors in H_2O

$\dfrac{X/p}{\text{volt}}{\text{cm}}/\text{mm}$	η	C_1 $\times 10^{-7}$ cm/sec	λ $\times 10^2$ cm at 1 mm	v $\times 10^{-5}$ cm/sec	f $\times 10^4$	h $\times 10^5$
12	3.78	2.21	0.37	30	423	0.6
14	5.67	2.72	0.48	35	418	1.9
16	8.64	3.37	0.63	42	400	13.0
20	18.9	4.98	1.07	62	369	30.0
24	37.0	7.00	1.65	81	328	45.0
32	48.9	8.04	1.69	96	352	50.0

TABLE 4.10—CHLORINE (32) (1935)

Bailey and Healey's Data for Townsend Factors in Cl_2

$\dfrac{X/p}{\text{volt}}{\text{cm}}/\text{mm}$	η	C_1 $\times 10^{-7}$ cm/sec	λ $\times 10^2$ cm at 1 mm	v $\times 10^{-5}$ cm/sec	f $\times 10^4$	h $\times 10^5$
10	41.0	7.4	3.80	76.0	260	140
15	57.6	8.7	3.40	91.6	270	105
20	65.0	9.3	2.70	90.8	230	74
25	69.7	9.6	2.30	91.0	220	56
30	73.0	9.8	2.15	91.6	218	46
50	80.8	10.3	1.60	101.5	230	24
80	92.0	11.0	1.30	137.0	370	0

TABLE 4.11—BROMINE (33) (1937)

Bailey, Makinson, and Somerville's Data for Townsend Factors in Br_2

$\dfrac{X/p}{\text{volt}}{\text{cm}}/\text{mm}$	η	C_1 $\times 10^{-7}$ cm/sec	λ $\times 10^2$ cm at 1 mm	v $\times 10^{-5}$ cm/sec	f $\times 10^4$	h $\times 10^5$
4	40.0	7.3	1.65	—	4	84
6	55.5	8.6	2.70	—	30	144
10	69.0	9.6	3.65	52.0	75	120
15	75.4	10.0	2.60	68.0	100	60
20	77.8	10.1	2.45	74.4	105	50
30	84.8	10.6	1.90	80.0	140	—
50	90.6	10.9	1.60	91.0	180	—
70	91.0	11.0	1.55	106.0	200	—

TABLE 4.12—IODINE (34) (1938)

Healey's Data for Townsend Factors in I_2

$\dfrac{X/p}{\text{volt}}$/mm $\dfrac{}{\text{cm}}$	η	C_1 $\times 10^{-7}$ cm/sec	λ $\times 10^2$ cm at 1 mm	v $\times 10^{-5}$ cm/sec	f $\times 10^4$	h $\times 10^5$
10	18.0	4.9	0.80	24.6	62	100
15	32.0	6.5	1.17	39.0	92	170
20	51.0	8.2	1.60	55.0	103	600
25	73.0	9.8	2.09	70.2	144	380
30	82.6	10.7	1.80	81.2	147	140
40	91.1	11.0	1.62	84.8	148	–
50	97.3	11.4	1.48	92.0	150	–

TABLE 4.13—AMMONIA (35) (1930)

Bailey and Duncanson's Data for Townsend Factors in NH_3

$\dfrac{X/p}{\text{volt}}$/mm $\dfrac{}{\text{cm}}$	η	C_1 $\times 10^{-7}$ cm/sec	λ $\times 10^2$ cm at 1 mm	v $\times 10^{-5}$ cm/sec	f $\times 10^4$	h $\times 10^5$
4	1.49	1.40	0.17	6.9	62	–
6	1.62	1.43	0.21	12.4	183	–
8	4.59	2.49	0.67	31.0	427	0.3
10	12.2	4.02	1.37	51.0	354	3.2
12	30.0	6.29	2.38	65.0	261	12.0
16	50.0	8.12	2.70	76.0	215	31.0
24	55.4	8.57	2.09	86.0	234	41.0
32	57.0	8.67	1.73	92.0	273	37.0

TABLE 4.14—HYDROGEN CHLORIDE (36) (1930)

Bailey and Duncanson's Data for Townsend Factors in HCl

$\dfrac{X/p}{\text{volt}}$/mm $\dfrac{}{\text{cm}}$	η	C_1 $\times 10^{-7}$ cm/sec	λ $\times 10^2$ cm at 1 mm	v $\times 10^{-5}$ cm/sec	f $\times 10^4$	h $\times 10^5$
10	3.78	2.24	0.41	26.0	330	4
15	5.40	2.64	0.51	42.0	600	17
20	7.02	3.04	0.49	46.5	560	41
30	12.2	4.02	0.49	52.0	420	47
40	22.4	5.46	0.56	58.0	280	44

TABLE 4.15—HELIUM (37) (1923)

Townsend and Bailey's Data for Townsend Factors in He

X/p $\dfrac{\text{volt}}{\text{cm}}$/mm	η	C_1 $\times 10^{-7}$ cm/sec	λ $\times 10^2$ cm at 1 mm	v $\times 10^{-5}$ cm/sec	f $\times 10^4$
0.013	1.77	1.53	9.14	1.11	1.30
0.02	2.12	1.68	7.8	1.33	1.56
0.05	3.68	2.12	6.6	2.14	2.3
0.1	6.2	2.87	5.95	2.96	2.6
0.2	11.3	3.87	5.3	3.93	2.5
0.5	27.0	5.96	4.8	5.74	2.3
1.0	53.0	8.4	4.85	8.25	2.4
2.0	105.0	11.8	5.25	12.7	2.85
3.0	137.0	13.5	5.5	17.5	4.5
4.0	152.0	14.2	5.85	23.5	6.75
5.0	172.0	15.1	6.4	30.2	9.8

TABLE 4.16—ARGON (38) (1922)

Townsend and Bailey's Data for Townsend Factors in A

X/p $\dfrac{\text{volt}}{\text{cm}}$/mm	η	C_1 $\times 10^{-7}$ cm/sec	λ $\times 10^2$ cm at 1 mm	v $\times 10^{-5}$ cm/sec	f $\times 10^4$
0.125	100	11.5	20.0	3.1	1.79
0.195	120	12.6	14.7	3.25	1.64
0.355	160	14.5	10.3	3.6	1.52
0.525	200	16.3	9.0	4.15	1.60
0.71	240	17.8	8.5	4.85	1.82
0.95	280	19.3	8.5	6.0	2.38
1.25	320	20.6	8.9	7.7	3.45
5.0	310	20.2	11.3	40.0	9.7
10.0	324	20.7	9.4	65.0	24.3
15.0	324	20.7	7.9	82.0	38.6

PART TWO—THE THEORY AND USE OF PROBES

§ 1. Introduction.

In part one of this chapter, the question of energy distributions of electrons in fields in gases, as well as their average energies, was discussed at some length. It was indicated that electrons in a field in a gas, depending on circumstances, will have quite diverse distribution functions, and that these change in form with field-to-pressure ratio for a given gas and with the nature of the gas, etc. It was further indicated that experimentally there was no general direct experimental method of evaluation of the distribution functions that would not disturb the distribution in the process of measurement. It was also stated that there was no method of evaluating even the average energy as a function of the experimental parameter X/p except the method of Townsend, or the newer microwave studies.

In the first method, the lateral diffusion of an electron stream in a gas is compared with its motion in the field. This method is strictly applicable only to values of X/p below ionization by electron impact in the gas. It yields an *average* electron energy in terms of X/p which has significance only so long as the distribution law is known. The other existing distributions and average energies can be evaluated only by very tedious calculation, if the Ramsauer free paths and various excitation functions, as well as other basic data are known, as seen earlier. How much more information the microwave techniques can yield is at present unpredictable.

However, while in many cases the Druyvesteyn and other complicated distribution laws hold, there are surprisingly many more circumstances in which the distribution is Maxwellian, despite action of the field (18). These circumstances occur in ionized gases, or *plasmas*, in which electron densities are high. Under such action, the long-range Coulomb forces between electrons yield a Maxwellian distribution. In some cases, densities as low as 10^8 electrons/cm^3 and generally densities above 10^{10}, independent of field action, show the Maxwellian form (18). This occurrence is indeed fortunate, because calculations of distribution functions in ionized gases are particularly difficult. It is also fortunate that when electron densities are high enough, it is possible to check the distribution function and obtain the average energy by the use of electrical probes.

While probes were used in gases by Crookes in the eighteen-nineties, and were discussed by J. S. Townsend as early as 1906, the proper method of employment and its value as a tool seem not to have been understood or appreciated much before 1923. The proper application of the probe to the study of ionized gases, which began in the early nineteen-twenties, owes much of its early analysis and perfection to I. Langmuir and H. M. Mott-Smith (39). Subsequently, much work has been done on probes by various workers (40), (41). Their use is limited in scope to fairly high densities, and there are many restrictions. Probe studies will yield information as to the average energy if the distribution is Maxwellian. Under some conditions, they yield the form of the distribution. They enable one to evaluate the so-called wall potential and the space potential, while rough estimates of ion and electron densities and positive ion energies in a plasma may sometimes be obtained by the use of probes.

The concept of the probe is basically familiar to students of elementary physics who have used probes in an electrolytic model trough to map the equipotential surfaces. In this technique, a probe having such high-resistance characteristics relative to the solution as not to distort the potential distribution by drawing current, yields points of equipotential relative to a fixed known section of the potential fall by a null indication on a suitable instrument. The gaseous discharge probe must, in general, fulfill the same function. In favor of the gaseous discharge probes, relative to those in solutions, there is a simplifying agency introduced by the *positive ion space-charge sheath* that separates the metal of the probe from the surrounding gas to be studied. This forms an effective plasma probe surface that does not excessively distort the discharge in its neighborhood by removal of carriers. Thus, the troublesome polarization effects at the electrode surface that necessitate the use of alternating potentials in the electrolytic model study are avoided in gases.

The literature up to 1930 is fairly well covered by K. K. Darrow in his book, *Electrical Phenomena in Gases* (40). A good presentation is also found in abbreviated form in von Engel and Steenbeck's book (41). An excellent summary of the theory is to be found in Langmuir and Compton's report on "Electrical Discharges" (42), with special emphasis on the correction factors for cylinders and spheres. While the probe is not specifically discussed, the data evaluated by probe studies are extensively considered by Druyvesteyn and Penning (43) in their summary of low-pressure discharges in 1940. Later studies usually deal with the development of probes for particular measurements. The limitations of probes are now more or less clearly recognized, and data yielded by probes must never be taken as conclusive.

In what follows, the theory and use of the simplest probe (the plane probe) will be given. The theory for the cylindrical and spherical probes is more complex, and will not be considered. Users of such probes are referred to the theory of Langmuir and to original sources cited. The weaknesses of probes and precautions in their use will be summarized briefly after the theory has been developed. The section will also include the two most recent contributions on the use of probes.

§ 2. Idealized General Assumptions, and Review of the Kinetic-Theory Concepts Involved.

The glowing mass of gas characterizing the luminous column of glow discharges, as typified by neon signs or the luminous column of glowing gas in an arc channel, was designated by Langmuir as *plasma*. In such discharges the electrons do not attach to molecules to make negative ions in significant numbers. Since these columns supposedly represent steady-state conditions, it is customary to consider that ion creation equals ion loss, and that as a whole the plasma is electrically neutral. It is thus assumed that in plasma there are N_- electrons and N_+ positive ions per cm³, with $N_+ = N_-$. These conditions may not hold near electrodes or walls. If negative *ions* form in appreciable numbers one must write $N_+ = N_- + N_i$, where N_i is the ion concentration. The theory to be given is then no longer applicable. In fact, errors in early studies may be attributed to this circumstance.

Furthermore, it is usually assumed that the energy distribution of electrons in the gas is Maxwellian, and that therefore for electrons,

$$(4.82) \qquad \tfrac{1}{2}m_- C_-^2 = \tfrac{1}{2}MC^2\eta = (3/2)\,\eta kT = (3/2)\,kT_- = eu_-,$$

where the symbols and relations indicated have earlier been discussed. It should, however, be noted that in writing $\tfrac{1}{2}m_-C_-^2 = (3/2)kT_-$, there are attributed to the electrons the *properties of black-body equilibrium* and an *equivalent temperature*, T_-. Since a Maxwellian energy distribution implies an equilibrium as well as steady-state condition, existing Maxwellian electron distributions, even in non-equilibrium conditions as regards the gas, permit the use of the expression "electron temperature," or better, "equivalent electron temperature," designated by the equation. The quantity k is the Boltzmann gas constant; η is the Townsend multiplier expressing the electron energy as a multiple of the molecular energy at the gas temperature T. The value of eu_- expresses the electron *energy* in equivalent electron volts, with e the electron and u_- a potential expressed in volts. A similar set of equivalent relations expresses the condition of the positive ions, namely,

$$(4.83) \qquad \tfrac{1}{2}M_+C_+^2 = \tfrac{1}{2}MC^2\eta' = (3/2)\eta'kT = (3/2)\,kT_+ = eu_+,$$

where the symbols are suggestively related to the corresponding electron case.

Again it must be recalled that in a gas with N molecules or particles per cm^3 undergoing their random heat motions with an average velocity $\bar{c}$, the number of these striking a cm^2 of surface per second from all directions is

$$(4.84) \qquad \nu = N\bar{c}/4 = NC/\sqrt{6\pi}.$$

The kinetic theory also expresses the Maxwellian distribution of velocities in terms of the number N_x of molecules out of N per cm^3 having a velocity component between x and $x + dx$ along the x direction, as

$$(4.85) \qquad N_x = N/\alpha\sqrt{\pi}\; \epsilon^{-c_x^2/\alpha^2}\, dc_x .$$

In this relation, α is the most probable velocity, expressed by $\alpha^2 = 2kT/M$, with α, $\bar{c}$, and C the probable, average and root-mean-square velocities, related by the ratios $1 : 2/\sqrt{\pi} : \sqrt{3/2}$ respectively. These relations apply equally to molecules, ions, and electrons, with appropriate changes in subscripts.

§ 3. The Probe Measurement.

Figure 4.16 schematically depicts a glow-discharge tube with cathode C and anode A, the cathode being grounded. It is served by a high, steady, potential source V_A, which maintains A at a potential of some hundreds to thousands of volts above C, depending on the nature of the gas and the pressure. The glow fills the whole tube to the surface of the glass walls of the tube. Adjacent to C there is a relatively short, dark space called the "Crookes dark space," followed by an intensely luminous plasma called the "negative glow," and by a second, fainter dark space called the "Faraday dark space." Beyond this is the luminous positive column which fills the tube to the walls and, extending to the anode, is separated from it by a faint dark space (the anode dark space), with a brighter glow on the surface of the anode called the "anode glow."

The justification for the use of probes lies largely in the application of the probe to the study of conditions in the luminous negative glow, and more particularly to the positive column plasmas. They

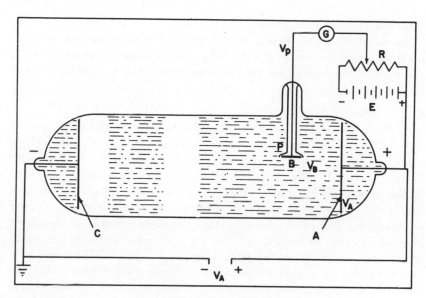

Fig. 4.16. Schematic drawing of arrangements for a plane probe
in a glow-discharge plasma.

are not so successfully applied nor so reliable in their interpretation
in the dark spaces, where space charges of one sign or another occur
and where ionization is sparse, with $N_+ \neq N_-$, etc.

At P in figure 4.16 there is placed a small plane probe with its
plane parallel to the discharge axis. It is shielded from plasma on
the back and sides by the glass shield. At B, the center of the probe,
the region of the gas transverse to the tube has a potential V_B, called
the "space potential." The anode potential is V_A. The probe is so
connected to the potentiometer R that by means of the battery E and
slide wire, the probe potential can be made very negative or positive
relative to V_B. The probe current is read by the galvanometer G.
The arrangement allows the probe to be made negative to the anode
by an amount $V_A - V_p$, so that the potential $V = V_p - V_B$ can be swung
from some tens of volts negative to the same amount positive relative
to V_B. What will be measured is the current i in G as a function of
V or V_p. In many cases it will be of interest to evaluate the current
density j. This will *not* always be i divided by the area of the probe
surface, since in certain cases the space-charge sheath represents
the active surface to which plasma carriers move, and its surface
replaces that of the metal. Care must be taken in being sure which
surface is used to calculate j, the current density.

§ 4. The Theory of the Probe.

In developing the theory, it will be found advantageous to start with the probe potential $V = V_p - V_B$, quite negative to begin with, and to let V gradually take on lower negative values, passing through V_B to positive values.

A. *The Strongly Negative Probe.*

If the value of V is strongly negative relative to the space potential V_B, $V_B > V_p$. Then electrons will be repelled by P, and only a positive, space-charge limited ion current i_+ flows to P. For, with V some tens of volts negative, even the most energetic electrons in the energy distribution in the plasma will not be able to diffuse into P in measurable quantity. That the positive current will be space-charge limited arises from the circumstance that at densities of positive ions in excess of 10^8 per cm³, space-charge limitation of currents begins at the existing values of V and d. The probe will be surrounded by a positive ion *space-charge sheath* from which the electrons are excluded to a distance d. There will thus be less ionization and excitation inside the region d cm from the probe, and the sheath of thickness d will appear relatively dark in that region. Thus, the value of d in cm can roughly be estimated visually. The value of d will depend on the ratio of V to the average density and energy of the electrons, i.e., on V and the probe current. The more energetic are the electrons, the closer they can approach to P before being turned back by the field, and the thinner is the sheath for a given V.

Since the normal discharge plasma is adjacent to the outer surface of the sheath and not to the electrode surface, then in calculating j_+, the current density from the measured current i, the outer surface area F of the space-charge sheath is used as the effective electrode area. As V is large and d is small, all positive ions impinging on F reach the probe. The probe current i_p will equal i_F, the current to F, if ionization by collision inside d is negligible, and if no electrons are liberated by other action within d. With these limitations, it is possible to write

$$(4.86) \qquad i_+ = + F \nu_+ e = F e N_+ \bar{c}_+ / 4,$$

with j_+ given by

$$(4.87) \qquad j_+ = i_+ / F = e N_+ \bar{c}_+ / 4.$$

The space-charge limitation of the current evaluates j_+ in terms of V and d, as shown in chapter VII. Thus,

$$(4.88) \qquad j_+ = \frac{1}{9\pi} \sqrt{\frac{2e}{M_+}} \frac{V^{3/2}}{d^2} = \frac{e N_+ \bar{c}_+}{4}.$$

With j_+ measured and M_+ known, the value of V used enables d to be computed. It also evaluates the ion density N_+ at which space-charge limitation occurs with a given set of conditions. The computed value compares favorably with the value of d observed visually. Since N_+ and $\overline{c_+}$ are unknown, it is impossible to extract further data from it. If $N_+ = 10^{12}$ ion/cm^3 with $\frac{1}{2}M_+C_+^2 = 0.1$ volt, or three times the thermal energy at room temperature (a reasonable value), the Hg$^+$ ion has the value of $\overline{c_+} = 3 \times 10^4$ cm/sec. Then, if $V = -81$ volts, d will equal 2.8 mm. This represents the order of magnitude of the width of the dark zone observed in the case in point.

B. *The Energy Distribution and Electron Temperature.*

Reducing the negative value of V_p makes V less negative, and the electrons in the high-energy tail of the energy distribution can reach the probe against V. When this occurs, the probe current i_p ceases to remain constant at i_+ as V_p is reduced and decreases. It takes on the value $i_p = i_+ - i_-$, where i_- is the electron current reaching P, which varies with V. It is assumed that the relatively few collisions which an electron coming from outside the sheath suffers within d will not alter the electron energy materially. If this is so, $i_+ - i_p = i_-$, so that the electron current reaching P against V is observed, as determined by the energy distribution.

In a Maxwellian energy distribution, the number of electrons striking an area A of electrode per second with an x component of velocity between c_x and $c_x + dc_x$, is given by

$$(4.89) \qquad \frac{A N_x c_x}{4} = \frac{A N_- c_x}{4a\sqrt{\pi}} \, \epsilon^{-c_x^2/a^2} \, dc_x .$$

Of these, all electrons with an x component of velocity C_v or greater can penetrate to P against V. C_v is thus defined as $\frac{1}{2}m_-C_v^2 > Ve$. The current i_- will then be given by

$$(4.90) \qquad i_- = \frac{A e N_-}{4\sqrt{\pi}} \int_{C_v}^{\infty} \frac{c_x}{a} \, \epsilon^{-c_x^2/a^2} \, dc_x = \frac{A}{2\sqrt{\pi}} \, e N_- a \, \epsilon^{-c_v^2/a^2} .$$

Since $a^2 = 2kT_-/m_-$, and $Ve = \frac{1}{2}m_-C_v^2$, the current of electrons i_- reaching P is

$$i_- = e A N_- \sqrt{\frac{kT_-}{2\pi m_-}} \, \epsilon^{-V/kT_-} ,$$

with

$$(4.91) \qquad j_- = \frac{i_-}{A} = e N_- \sqrt{\frac{kT_-}{2\pi m_-}} \, \epsilon^{-Ve/kT_-} .$$

If the distribution is not Maxwellian, the term $N_-/\alpha\sqrt{\pi}\ \epsilon^{-c_x^2/\alpha^2}\,dc_x$ will be replaced by $N_-f(c_x)\,dc_x$. Here $f(c_x)$ represents the form of the new energy-distribution function. Integration will then obviously lead to a new form for the current i_-.

Assuming the Maxwellian distribution, and that T_- and N_- are independent of V, the relations above can be written in the logarithmic form as

$$(4.92) \qquad \log_e j_- = \log_e\left(eN_-\sqrt{\frac{kT_-}{2\pi m_-}}\right) - \frac{Ve}{kT_-} = B - \frac{Ve}{kT_-}.$$

Plotted logarithmically against V, log i_-/A or log j_- yields a straight line, with its slope giving the value of Ve/kT_-, and its intercept with the j_- axis evaluating B. Thus, it is possible to write

$$(4.93) \qquad \frac{d\log_e j_-}{dV} = \frac{d\log_e j_-}{dV_p} = -\frac{e}{kT_-}.$$

Since the constants e and k are known, the slope at once yields the value of T_-, the electron "temperature," in the form:

$$\frac{d\log_e j_-}{dV_p} = -\frac{1.17\times 10^4}{kT_-},$$

with V in volts and j_- in amps/cm^2. To avoid measuring the slope, it is possible to designate the quantity ΔV_p as the difference of potential for two values of V_p, V_{p1} and V_{p2}, at which j_{-1} and j_{-2} are in the ratio 1:2.718. Then it follows that $T_- = 1.17\times 10^4\Delta V_p$.

C. *The Wall Potential.*

As V still further decreases in negative value, a point will be reached when $i_p = i_+ - i_- = 0$. Designate this value of $V = V_p - V_B$ as V_w, and name it the *wall potential*, for reasons which will shortly become clear. When $i_- = i_+$, the electron current due to diffusion just equals the positive space-charge limited current drawn in by the potential V_w. The potential V_p is, however, still negative to V_B, and is thus not the same as the space potential V_B, but lies at V_w volts negative. The electrons having an energy above that of the molecules,[13] and in virtue of their small mass having high random speeds, will reach P even against a negative potential V_w, and will reach it in greater numbers than the slow positive ions. They will thus cause V to have a negative value V_w. This is just enough to

---

[13] The circumstance that $T_- \gg T_+$ arises because the fractional energy loss f of electrons on molecular or atomic impact is less than 10^{-2}, while that for ions is 0.3, as seen in chapter III.

draw in the positive space-charge limited current to the point where $i_- = i_+$, so that no net current flows. The potential V_w is thus the potential which an isolated probe or bit of isolated wall drawing no *net* current would have.

Carriers of both signs, electrons and positive ions, reach the probe or wall in equal numbers. At the surface of the probe or wall the electrons and ions moving over the surface in two dimensions readily recombine, giving their heat of combination to the wall. The walls of such a discharge tube are therefore warmer than the gas inside. This diffusion to the walls then causes a loss of carriers from the plasma to the wall; in fact, in the positive column of most glow discharges at lower pressures, it accounts for the majority of the carriers lost from the column. As the mechanism is basically one of diffusion involving both carriers, it is called *ambipolar diffusion*. This particular form of diffusion has already been defined and more properly discussed in chapter II, in the section dealing with ionic diffusion. Since under normal conditions the electrons reach the surface of a probe or wall relatively of the order of a thousand or more times faster than the positive ions, it is not surprising that V_w builds up to a negative value of the order of one or two volts.

The process of ambipolar diffusion described above has been studied in detail primarily in plasmas where conditions are relatively simple, and usually only one ion type and the electron are considered without interaction of the electrode material. It thus is natural to overlook the fact that such processes are quite universal, and are not confined to plasmas alone. They appear with solid surfaces in contact with liquids, on contact of liquids with other liquids, and with solids and solids. The effects are more pronounced for electrons in gases where $\bar{c}_- \gg \bar{c}_+$, but occur wherever the carriers of different sign have different mobilities. In many cases other than gases, ambipolar-diffusion processes are complicated by action of the surfaces themselves.

The value of V_w can at once be taken as $V_w = V_p - V_B$ from the point where $i_- + i_+$ and i_p equal zero. Theoretically, it then follows that when $V = V_w$,

$$(4.94) \qquad i_+ = \frac{eN_+\bar{c}_+}{4} = \frac{eN_-\bar{c}_-}{4} \epsilon^{-eV_w/kT_-} = i_- .$$

If $N_+ = N_-$, then the relations simplify to

$$(4.95) \qquad V_w = \frac{kT_-}{e} \log \frac{\bar{c}_-}{\bar{c}_+} = \frac{kT_-}{2e} \log_e \frac{T_- M_+}{T_+ M_-} .$$

Even if $T_- = T_+$, since $M_+/m_- = 1,836\ A^+$, where A^+ is the atomic weight of M_+, the logarithmic term is positive. Thus, since the electronic charge e is negative, V_w will be negative. In an Hg discharge plasma where $T_- = 2,000°$ K. ~ 0.2 e.v., $T_+ = 400°$ K., $M_+/m_- = 1,836 \times 200$. This gives $V_w = -2.46$ volts.

The value of V_w allows additional information to be gained. From the value of i_+, since T_- and thus $\bar{c}_-$ have been evaluated for the strongly negative probe, given V_w, all quantities in equation 4.94 are known except N_-. Thus, N_- can be inferred from T_- and V_w. Since for plasmas where these relations apply, $N_+ = N_-$, this enables $\bar{c}_+$ to be evaluated, or using equation 4.95, T_+ can be evaluated. However, it is to be noted that the values of N_- so obtained are not very reliable. V_w cannot be evaluated very accurately, and since V_w appears in an exponent, small errors in V_w give large changes in N_-. The method is useful in giving orders of magnitude, and may be reliable within a factor of 5. This does not apply to the evaluation of T_+, which for very involved reasons often comes out orders of magnitude high, as shown in section 6, *infra*.

D. *The Space or Plasma Potential, V_B.*

Further reduction of V in negative values carries the potential V down from V_w to 0. At this point, $V = V_p - V_B = 0$, and $V_p = V_B$. This means that the center of the probe is at the potential of the surrounding plasma. There is no repulsion of either electrons or positive ions. The positive ions and electrons reach the probe in proportion to their normal rates of diffusion. The space-charge sheath is gone; i.e., $d = 0$. The electrons will diffuse to the electrode more rapidly than the positive ions. The current i_- is greater than i_+, and i_p has a net negative value below V_w. These negative values begin just below V_w, and increase as the negative value of V decreases to zero. In theory, at least, at $V = 0$ all electrons *can* diffuse to the probe, for ϵ^{-Ve/kT_-} is unity, and i_- becomes

$$ i_{-V_B} = eN_-\sqrt{\frac{kT_-}{2m_-}}. $$

Positive ions are also diffusing to the probe, and

$$ i_{+V_B} = eN_+\sqrt{\frac{kT_+}{2\pi M_+}}. $$

These two relations represent the relations for the diffusion currents resulting from $N_-\bar{c}_-/4$ and $N_+\bar{c}_+/4$ expressed in terms of temperature. The net current i or current density

$$ j = j_{+V_B} - j_{-V_B}. $$

Just beyond V_B, or $V = 0$, at a positive probe potential, the *positive ions are repelled* and electrons are attracted by positive values of V. As T_+ for positive ions is usually low, perhaps a few tenths of a volt, V need be very little positive to *repel all positive ions* and give a negative space-charge sheath. The absence of positive ion contribution to the current, with electrons being drawn to the probe by the positive value of V, should cause an increase in negative current to the probe. However, the rate of increase will be slower than the previous rate, even with small negative values of V, as the electron current is now space-charge limited and changes as $V^{3/2}/d^2$ instead of exponentially. With the decreasing negative values of V the negative current was increasing exponentially, while with positive values it should increase only proportionally to the three-halves power of V, as the electrons are being brought in by the field with space-charge limitation of current which is modified by high *diffusive energies*. Thus, in principle with high electron densities, the electron current for positive values of V will be space-charge limited, so that below $V = 0$ and $V_p = V_B$,

$$(4.96) \qquad i_- = \frac{eFN_- \bar{c}_-}{4} = eFN_- \sqrt{\frac{kT_-}{2\pi m_-}} = (2/9)\, F \sqrt{\frac{2e}{m_-}}\, \frac{V^{3/2}}{d^2},$$

with the current density $j_- = i_-/F$. Thus, it is seen that the log j_--V curve will in theory undergo an abrupt change in slope at $V = 0$ and $V_p = V_B$. Such changes in slope actually do occur under these conditions, but the *change observed is not ideally sharp at V_B*, as theory might suggest. This condition is caused by many disturbing factors, such as liberation of electrons by positive ions on impact with the probe surface, which will decrease in number as V decreases. The gas near the probe may have been ionized by electron impact, and this will vary with sheath thickness and V. Electrons may be reflected from the probe. All of these factors vary with V. Finally, beyond $V = 0$, log j_- is no longer a linear function of V as it is at more negative values. Thus, the transition in slope of the log j_--V curves near $V = 0$ is gradual from a steeper slope to a less steep one. The situation in this region is further discussed in section 6.

A fair approximation to the transition point, and thus evaluation of $V = 0$, can be had by drawing two straight lines through the two more nearly linear segments of the curve and choosing the intersection. In this fashion it has been customary to locate the plasma potential V_B from V_p where $V = 0$. As indicated above, this leads to the relations that follow.

$$(4.97) \qquad j_{-V_B} = eN_- \sqrt{\frac{kT_-}{2\pi m_-}} \, .$$

Since $\bar{c}_+ = \sqrt{8kT_+/\pi M_+}$, j_{+V_B} at this point is

$$(4.98) \qquad j_{+V_B} = \frac{eN_+\bar{c}_+}{4} = eN_+ \sqrt{\frac{kT_+}{2\pi M_+}} \, .$$

The location of V_B at once gives the value of

$$i_{V_B}/A = j_{V_B} = j_{-V_B} + j_{+V_B} = eN_- \sqrt{\frac{kT_-}{2\pi m_-}} + eN_+ \sqrt{\frac{kT_+}{2\pi M_+}}$$

$$(4.99)$$

$$= i_{-V_B}/A - i_{+V_B}/A \, .$$

As i_+ has been evaluated for the negative probe and j_{V_B} is observed, j_{-V_B} is evaluated. Since

$$j_{-V_B} = eN_- \sqrt{\frac{kT_-}{2\pi m_-}} \, ,$$

and since T_- has been evaluated from the data for the slope of the log j_{-}-V curves for the very negative probe, it is probably possible to evaluate N_- more accurately than it can be evaluated from V_w, for reasons previously stated. If $N_+ = N_-$, as assumed, the relation

$$j_{+V_B} = eN_+ \sqrt{\frac{kT_+}{2\pi M_+}}$$

should in theory give a reasonable value of T_+, which it does not in view of peculiar alterations in the sheath, as seen in section 6.

Such evaluations have been used. Owing to many disturbing factors, one cannot place too much confidence in such values. This is especially true, despite the insensitivity of variation of j_{V_B} in this region to variation with V, because the influence of the electrode surface in contact with the plasma may alter the current values in an unpredictable fashion. Thus, while ideally the location of V_w and V_B should yield values of N_-, N_+, and T_+, these values may well be falsified in actual measurements. They do, however, aid in assigning an order of magnitude to some of these quantities.

E. *The Positive Probe.*

Increasing V in positive values, i.e., making V_p greater than V_B, introduces a negative or electron space-charge limited current in place of the negative and positive diffusion currents. For values of V, only a few tenths of a volt positive reduces diffusion current i_+ to zero,

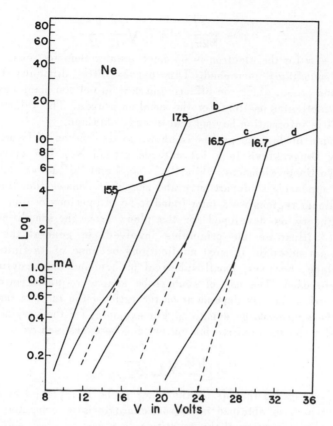

Fig. 4.17. Characteristic plots for i_p relative to $\log V_p$ for electrons in a hot cathode Ne arc, as given by Druyvesteyn. Curve "a" has a Maxwellian energy. Curves "b," "c," and "d" are falsified, yielding a non-Maxwellian distribution at higher energies. This now is believed to have been caused by changes in contact potential between probe and anode by evaporation of something from the oxide-coated cathode that gradually changed V with time during measurement. In curve "a" the temperature $T+$ computed from the break point was about five times too large.

as indicated above. The situation resembles that of the very negative probe with signs reversed. There is an electron or negative space-charge sheath with a value d_-, which is vastly different from that for the positive sheath. The relations as indicated read:

$$(4.100) \qquad i_- = \frac{eFN_-\bar{c}_-}{4} = eFN_- \sqrt{\frac{kT_-}{2\pi m_-}} = (2/9) F \sqrt{\frac{2e}{m_-}} \frac{V^{3/2}}{d_-^2},$$

with

§5

(4.101) $$j_- = eN_- \sqrt{\frac{kT_-}{2\pi m_-}} = (2/9) \sqrt{\frac{2e}{m_-}} \frac{V^{3/2}}{d_-^2} .$$

Since e/m for the electron is so much greater than for ions, d_- will be correspondingly increased. This causes little difficulty for the large plane probe, since the effective area A is not too much changed, but it complicates matters for the smaller probes. The relation furnishes little information beyond that already obtained.

A sample of data for probes is shown in the curves of figure 4.17, taken by Druyvesteyn in a hot cathode arc in Ne. The curve "a" shows two linear elements, while "b," "c," and "d" show electronic regions, appearing to depart more and more from Maxwellian linearity. The nonlinear regions were later found to be of spurious origin.

The theory as developed for the plane probe is simplified, and serves to illustrate the principles involved. In general the plane probe is not practical in most applications because of its finite size. In its place, however, small spherical probes and small cylindrical probes are used. The use of such probe shapes requires corrections for geometrical factors dependent on the ratio of the radii of the probe r_s, and the space-charge sheath r_0. For example, for the very negative spherical probe the positive ion current can be expressed as

(4.102) $$i_+ = (4/9) \sqrt{\frac{2e}{M_+}} \frac{V^{3/2}}{\phi_k} .$$

Here it is observed that d^2 for the plane probe is replaced by a function ϕ_k, which is obtained only from characteristic computed curves expressed as a function of the quantity $r_0/r_s - 1$.

For the proper relations to be used, the reader is referred to von Engel and Steenbeck (41), Langmuir and Compton (42), or to the original literature. It should be added that in plasma where electron densities change with time; for example, in decaying plasma following excitation by a discharge, the readings of the single probe may not be significant, since all conditions are altering, including wall potential. Under such circumstances, E. O. Johnson and L. Malter (44) have shown that the situation may be studied by two probes fairly close together. This technique had previously been used by R. C. Mason (45), and was recently used by W. G. Dow (46) in atmospheric studies. The work of Malter indicates that the procedure requires careful consideration, and the methods are given for getting the energy distribution by its use. Details of these methods are given later.

§ 5. The Determination of the Distribution Law by Probe Studies.

As indicated, the log j_--V relation is linear if the energy distribution is Maxwellian. Then the slope of the line

$$\frac{d(\log_e j_-)}{dV} = e/kT_- ,$$

and T_- is evaluated. If the energy distribution is of the Druyvesteyn form, which is characterized principally by having the exponential multiplier of the form $\epsilon^{-E^2/(kT_-)^2}$, the integration would give the current-potential relation as

(4.103)
$$\log j_- = B^1 - \left(\frac{eV}{kT_-}\right)^2.$$

Under these conditions, the relation between $\log j_-$ and V is not linear but parabolic. Thus, it is seen that the observed $\log j_- \text{-} V$ relation is very sensitive to the form of the distribution law. It is also clear that from the form of the observed $\log j_- \text{-} V$ relation, it might be possible to derive the form of the existing distribution law. This was apparently first systematically investigated by M. J. Druyvesteyn (47). It may be assumed that the distribution law has some form given by $f(c)dc$ for the chance of a vector velocity between c and $c + dc$. Then, in accordance with the treatment in section 4B, the electron current i_- can be obtained by the integration of the expression

(4.104)
$$i_- = \tfrac{1}{2}\, eF \int_{\sqrt{\frac{2eV}{m_-}}}^{\infty} f(c)dc \int_0^{\theta} c \cos \psi \sin \psi\, d\psi.$$

In this case, since c is the vector velocity and not the x component as before, that component is replaced by $\int c \cos \psi \sin \psi\, d\psi$, where ψ is an angle normal to the surface. The integration must then be carried out over the limits 0 to an angle θ, defined by $\tfrac{1}{2}mc^2 \cos^2 \theta = eV$. The current i_- is in consequence given by

(4.105)
$$i_- = \frac{eF}{4} \int_{\sqrt{\frac{2eV}{m_-}}}^{\infty} cf(c)dc \left(1 - \frac{1}{c^2}\frac{2eV}{m_-}\right).$$

If this expression for i_- is differentiated twice with respect to V, then

(4.106)
$$\frac{d^2 i_-}{dV^2} = \frac{e^2 F}{4m_-}\frac{1}{V} f\left(\sqrt{\frac{2eV}{m_-}}\right).$$

Thus, if the observed curve of i_- plotted against V is twice differentiated with respect to V and multiplied by $4m_- V/Fe^2$, the quantity $f(\sqrt{2eV/m_-})$ is obtained. This gives the form of the distribution law.

In differentiating the observed relation, it is not necessary to differentiate the actual potential V, since V differs from the applied variable probe potential V_p by the constant term $-V_B$ only. The relation obtained is the same in form, irrespective of whether the plane, the cylindrical, or the small spherical probes are used for gathering data. In his original paper, Druyvesteyn applied this method to the study of distribution of energy in an arc operating from a Ba or Sr oxide-coated filament. As reported in that paper, the data shown in figure 4.17 yield a distribution which departs radically from the Maxwellian form in having far too few electrons between 4 and 9 volts of energy. The actual distribution is not shown here.

Later study by von Engel discloses that the student carrying out the analysis of this curve for Druyvesteyn made some blunder, and that the curve should have shown a second peak with entirely too many electrons in the 4 to 9 volt region instead of the dip reported in the paper. Later studies by van Gorcum reveal several other instances of apparent departures from a Maxwellian distribution having two peaks instead of the one, with the second peak on the high-energy side, as noted here by von Engel. In these arcs, if conditions are normal, the *carrier densities should be such as to give the Maxwellian distribution.* It now appears that van Gorcum found that if the probe was *far from the oxide-coated cathode*, the distribution was normal, with no second peak. As the probe approached the oxide-coated cathode, the double maxima appeared. This suggests, as Wehner and Medicus (54a) have recently indicated, that the probe was being contaminated by the Ba or Sr from the cathode, having its contact potential altered during measurement through transfer of the cathode coating to it. In fact, probe surfaces are so sensitive to this action that Wehner and Medicus used probes to study sputtering. In any event, the situation is one that again indicates caution in the interpretation of peculiar second-derivative data from probe characteristics in terms of changes in the energy distribution only.

The principal difficulty in this type of analysis lies, as might be expected, in the *inaccuracies attendant on two successive graphic differentiations* on data which, by their very nature, cannot be too precise. In fact, in the light of present-day knowledge of the conditions existing in many of the so-called stationary d.c. discharges of the past, it is remarkable that the earlier probe data are so reliable and consistent.

To overcome the difficulties of graphic differentiation, K. G. Emeléus proposed a most ingenious experimental method, that was developed by R. H. Sloane and E. I. R. MacGregor (48). It was later utilized by A. H. van Gorcum, who discusses the procedure in detail (49).

A current-potential curve, with no discontinuities such as would follow from probe measurements when $V > 0$, may be expressed by an equation of the form

$$(4.107) \qquad i = a + \beta V + \gamma V^2 + \delta V^3 + \eta V^4 + \ldots .$$

If, with such an expansion, a *small* alternating potential of form $E = A \sin pt$ is superposed at any value of V, it has been shown by Landale, on expansion of the expression $i = f(V + E)$ by Taylor's theorem, that the current is given by

$$i = f(V) + A^2 f''(V) + A^4 f''''(V) + [Af'(V) + (A^3/8) f'''(V)$$

$$+ \ldots .] \sin pt - [(A^2/4) f''(V) + (A^4/48) f''''(V)$$

$$(4.108)$$

$$+ \ldots .] \cos pt - [(A^3/24) f'''(V)$$

$$+ \ldots .] \sin 3 pt + [(A^4/192) f''''(V) + \ldots .] \cos 4 pt.$$

In this expression, f', f'', and f''' are first, second, and third derivatives of i with respect to V. The superposition of the alternating potential thus has led to two new direct-current terms besides $f(V)$. These come from the second and fourth derivatives. If the alternating amplitude A is small, the increase in steady current due to the fourth derivative is negligible. Hence, the increase in the d.c. component produced by the small a.c. is directly proportional to the second derivative. Thus, at a series of values of V, the initial d.c. current is observed; then, on superposition of the a.c. component, there is an increase in the d.c. current Δi, given sensibly by

$$(4.109) \qquad \Delta i = \frac{A^2}{4} f''(V),$$

which can be measured. A plot of $(4/A^2)\Delta i$ as a function of V will then give the form of the distribution law. Also of academic interest is the fact that if the *alternating current* is measured for small A, its value is in a great measure determined by the term $\Delta i_{AC} = Af'(V)$ $\sin pt$ in the expansion above. Thus, by evaluating Δi_{AC} with the Maxwellian distribution, the value of V_B can be determined accurately. In non-Maxwellian distributions, V_B may not be located accurately because the linear elements of the log j--V curves are missing. Sloane and MacGregor discuss the evaluation of V_B in this event, and suggest taking the value of V_B as that of V_p when the second derivative of current Δi vanishes.

The extensive investigations of van Gorcum (49), Emeléus and Ballantine, Grieves and Johnston (50), and the group at Belfast under Emeléus probably comprise the most extensive, comparatively recent studies of probe behavior prior to World War II. They certainly indicate not only techniques but the weaknesses and sources of error inherent in probe studies. In particular, despite the ingenuity of the method of Sloane and MacGregor for experimentally establishing the form of the distribution law, Emeléus, in discussion with the author in 1947, stated that the method was of doubtful value. The cause for this lies primarily in the fact that in applying the small alternating potential needed, the plasma responds to such potentials in a variety of unexpected ways. This results from the resonant properties of ionized plasma associated with plasma oscillations, yielding fictive negative inductances and capacities. In view of these unforeseen interactions, Emeléus believed that not too much confidence should be placed in the distribution derived by this technique. Similarly, the double graphic differentiation necessary with the Druyvesteyn procedure has its weaknesses. Accordingly, the author reluctantly concludes that hope must be abandoned for any certain and accurate determination of energy-distribution laws for electrons in·plasma by means of probe techniques. On the more optimistic side, from recent theoretical studies (18) it is probable that under most conditions where probes can be used, the distributions are sensibly Maxwellian.

§ 6. The Boyd Analysis of Sheath Disturbance and Ion Temperatures.

Very recently, an interesting contribution has been made to probe theory by R. L. F. Boyd (51), working in collaboration with H. S. W. Massey. In the conventional Langmuir probe theory the probe is assumed to be covered by a protecting positive ion sheath, so that ions and electrons diffuse into it from unaltered plasma. It appears that in practice, on assuming that the positive ions in the sheath have a Maxwellian energy distribution, their temperature T_+, as computed from the conventional theory and experimental Langmuir curves, frequently yields impossibly high values. In fact, the values deduced from fairly sharp breaks are often comparable with T_e, the electron temperatures. This deviation is too serious to be ascribed to conventional inaccuracies. The very fundamental character of the cause of this deviation had been indicated in principle by Langmuir as early as 1929, on the basis of the double sheath observed at the cathode of a discharge. The significance of this indication was not recognized until the present work of Boyd.

At the probe surface, the *velocity* distribution of the positive ions is geometrically one-sided, which places unexpected restrictions on theory. Disturbed by the situation, Langmuir had suggested that taking the ratio of j_{-V_B} to j_{+V_B} from equations 4.97 and 4.98, the conventional value

(4.110)
$$\left(\frac{i_-}{i_+}\right)_{V_B} = \left(\frac{T_-}{T_+}\right)^{\frac{1}{2}}\left(\frac{M_+}{m_-}\right)^{\frac{1}{2}}$$

should read

$$\left(\frac{i_-}{i_+}\right)_{V_B} = \frac{1}{2}\left(\frac{T_-}{T_+}\right)^{\frac{1}{2}}\left(\frac{M_+}{m_-}\right)^{\frac{1}{2}},$$

the $\frac{1}{2}$ coming from the asymmetrical condition. However, this was not sufficient to alleviate the difficulty, which proves to be more fundamental.

It is presented by Boyd as follows: If the ideal plane probe is at a potential negative to the space, the potential V at a distance x from the probe is

(4.111)
$$\frac{d^2V}{dx^2} = -4\pi e\,(n_+ - n_-).$$

At the sheath edge, the space charge is almost neutralized, so that $n_- = \phi n_+$, where ϕ is a constant near unity. The sheath edge is then defined by Boyd as the region where the condition $n_- = \phi n_+$ is fulfilled. At a point δx inside the sheath edge, let V be δV less than at the edge. Then it follows from equation 4.111, on substitution for n_+ and n_-, that

(4.112)
$$\frac{d^2V}{dx^2} = -4\pi e\,n_{+s}\left\{\frac{\int_0^\infty f(E)\,E^{\frac{1}{2}}\,dE}{\int_0^\infty f(E)\,(E + \delta V)^{\frac{1}{2}}\,dE} - \phi\;\epsilon^{-\frac{\delta V}{V_e}}\right\}.$$

Here $f(E)$ is the distribution of energy associated with the x component of positive ion velocities at the sheath edge, $V_e = kT_-$, and subscripts 0, s, and x will refer to the undisturbed plasma, the sheath edge, and x, respectively. The quantity $f(E)$ can appear in the numerator and denominator of equation 4.112 only if collisions within δx can be neglected. When a sheath forms, V must increase rapidly, which implies that

(4.113)
$$\int_0^\infty (f(E)\,E^{\frac{1}{2}}\,dE) \Big/ \left(\int_0^\infty f(E)\,(E + \delta V)^{\frac{1}{2}}\,dE\right) > \epsilon^{-\frac{\delta V}{V_e}}.$$

For small values of δV, the inequality approximates to a *sheath criterion* in the form of

$$(4.114) \qquad \int_0^\infty (f(E) E^{\frac{1}{2}} dE) \bigg/ \left(\int_0^\infty f(E) E^{-\frac{1}{2}} dE \right) > \frac{1}{2} V_e \,.$$

This very important condition for sheath formation sets certain restrictions on the form of the positive ion distribution at the sheath edge. The condition, among other things, *cannot be satisfied by the one-sided Maxwellian distribution normally assumed*. Unless the criterion is satisfied, *the probe field penetrates the plasma*, so that it is no longer undisturbed. This penetration of the field then must alter the plasma so as to cause it to comply. In the extra sheath region into which this sheath field penetrates, since $\phi \simeq 1$, the positive ion sheath density is given by

$$(4.115) \qquad n_{+_x} = n_{+_0} \epsilon^{-V/V_e} \,.$$

The subscript 0 indicates a point of zero potential. The consequence is that the potential distribution must adjust itself to comply with equation 4.115, and at the same time the energy distribution at the sheath edge must comply with condition 4.114.

It appears impossible to satisfy the distribution condition 4.115 if the ions fall freely in the extra sheath field, unless ionization in that region is taken into account or the probe is sufficiently small for the field to be distorted by geometry. There are, therefore, three regions under which relation 4.115 may be satisfied:

1. The high-pressure region (around 1 mm Hg) where ion flow is diffusive.
2. The low-pressure region where the extra sheath field penetration continues until ion production by normal discharge processes becomes sufficient to satisfy equations 4.114 and 4.115.
3. For very small cylindrical and spherical probes. The theory for the small cylindrical probe at low pressure has already been developed fully and correctly by Langmuir.

It is expedient at this point to define the *extra sheath* region of disturbance of the plasma by the penetrating field. It is taken as the region beyond that where $\phi = 1$, and the conditions are satisfied in a surface where the mean normal component of velocities of positive ions is equal to that which they would have acquired in penetrating the field if they were assumed to have started from rest. This surface may be approximated, in the case of a probe parallel to the plasma field at high pressures, by the surface at which the penetrating field becomes equal to the plasma field which existed in the absence of the probe.

Boyd[14] applied the analysis to inert gases at higher pressures. In doing so, it was assumed that the cross section for charge exchange for ions was larger than the cross section for gas-kinetic collisions. Then each ion starts from rest at the position of its production in a charge-exchange process. This assumption forms the basis of a mobility mechanism described by Sena (52) in 1946, which leads to a particularly simple relation and permits analysis of the problem. Let λ_+ be the free path for charge exchange, and let a number of ions drift in a field X. Then the probability of a particle having an energy E is

$$(4.116) \qquad \frac{1}{\lambda_+ X} \epsilon^{-E/\lambda_+ X} \, dE = f(E) \, dE .$$

The criterion for sheath formation then becomes

$$(4.117) \qquad \lambda_+ X > V_e ,$$

assuming the field constant over a mean free path.

Let v_{+0} be the mean normal velocity with which ions enter the disturbed region. Let the potential at the boundary of entry be zero, and at a point x inside let it be V_x with a drift velocity v_{+x}. Then combining Sena's mobility equation, which reads:

$$v_{+_x} = k \left(\left| \frac{dV}{dx} \right| \Big/ p \right)^{\frac{1}{2}} ,$$

where k is Sena's mobility constant and p is the pressure, and noting that $n_{+x} v_{+x} = n_{+0} v_{+0}$, integration yields

$$(4.118) \qquad V_x = -\left(V_e/2 \right) \log_e \left\{ 1 - \frac{2}{V_e} \left(\frac{v_{+0}}{k} \right)^2 p x \right\} .$$

Introducing condition 4.117 into 4.118, an expression is obtained for the potential of the sheath edge in the form of

$$(4.119) \qquad p\lambda \left(\frac{v_{+0}}{k} \right)^2 \epsilon^{2 \frac{\Delta V}{V_e}} = V_e .$$

If $\lambda p = \beta$, then

$$(4.120) \qquad \Lambda V = \tfrac{1}{2} V_e \log_e \left\{ \frac{V_e}{\beta} \left(\frac{k}{v_{+0}} \right)^2 \right\} .$$

[14]Boyd's original article contains some obvious typographical and numerical blunders. The argument is unaffected by these. The present version has been corrected through the kindness of E. E. Dodd.

The quantity ΔV is the important quantity in this discussion. It is the potential difference between the *space potential* (at which electron-current saturation occurs) and the *potential at which a positive ion sheath forms*, resulting in positive ion current saturation. *Over the range of voltage below the space potential, the probe is not covered by a sheath.* The fact that saturation does not occur in practice until the sheath forms, shows that the current entering the disturbed region is not independent of its extent. Thus, the probe must be ΔV negative to the space potential before a sheath forms and the positive ion current saturates.

Equations 4.118 for V_x and 4.120 for ΔV can be combined to give the extent d of the disturbed extra-sheath region as

$$(4.121) \qquad d/\lambda = (V_e/2\beta)\,(k/v_{+0})^2 - \tfrac{1}{2}.$$

In this region, λ is small; therefore, d is small, so that ionization in the disturbed region will not contribute to the probe current, and the positive ion saturation current will equal that entering the disturbed region, namely $-en_{+0}v_{+0}$.

It is reasonable to assume that $v_{+0} = k(X_L/p)^{\frac{1}{2}}$ where X_L is the axial field down the discharge tube. The ratio of electron and ion saturation currents is then

$$(4.122) \qquad \left(\frac{i_-}{i_+}\right)_{\text{sat}} = \frac{n_{-0}\,(e/m_-)\,(V_e/2\pi)^{\frac{1}{2}}}{n_{+0}\,k\,(X_L/p)^{\frac{1}{2}}} = \frac{5.22 \times 10^3}{k}\left(\frac{V_e}{X_L/p}\right)^{\frac{1}{2}}.$$

The units are practical, and p is in mm of Hg. For $X_L/p < 0.75$ the ion energies are roughly thermal, and $v_{+0} = (2\pi)kT^{-\frac{1}{2}}$, where T is the gas temperature. At 290° K., the relation becomes

$$(4.123) \qquad \left(\frac{i_-}{i_+}\right)_{\text{sat}} = \left(\frac{M_+}{m_-}\right)^{\frac{1}{2}} 40\, V_e^{\,\frac{1}{2}}$$

and

$$(4.124) \qquad \Delta V = \tfrac{1}{2}\, V_e \log_e\{1.58 \times 10^2\ M_+\ V_e\,(k^2/\beta)\}.$$

The quantity $(i_-)_{\text{sat}}$ cannot be measured by a plane probe at high pressures, because the drain of electrons to the region is too great to be replenished by diffusive flow. It can be inferred from electron temperature and ion densities found by other means.

The low-pressure case when the ionization rate is constant was solved by Langmuir. The potential distribution obtained was analogous to that given by equation 4.118, except that the fall near the cathode

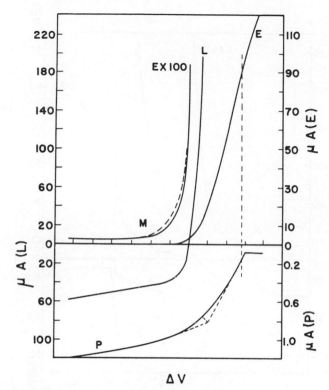

Fig. 4.18. Boyd's screened grid characteristics for A gas at 0.026 mm pressure. L is a Langmuir curve; E is the electron component; P is the positive ion component; M is for a Maxwellian curve compared to E, multiplied by 100-fold. One division of abscissae is 5 volts; currents are in microamperes.

is not so sharp as that at higher pressures. This relation of Langmuir yields

$$(4.125) \qquad\qquad V = 0.7\ V_e$$

and

$$n_{+_s} = n_{-_0}\ \epsilon^{-0.7},$$

with

$$(4.126) \qquad \left(\frac{i_-}{i_+}\right)_{\text{sat}} = n_{-_0}\left(\frac{V_e}{2\pi m_-}\right)^{\frac{1}{2}} \Big/ n_{+_s}\ 0.77\left(\frac{V_e}{M_+}\right)^{\frac{1}{2}} = 1.04\left(\frac{M_+}{m_-}\right)^{\frac{1}{2}}.$$

The theory was put to experimental test in a discharge tube 3 inches in diameter and 18 inches in length, using an Ni disc anode 2.5 inches in diameter with a W hot wire spiral cathode carrying 17

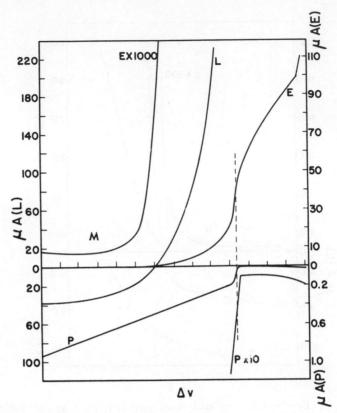

Fig. 4.19. Boyd's screened grid characteristics for A gas at 0.004 mm pressure. L is a Langmuir curve; E is the electron component; P is the positive ion component; M is for a Maxwellian curve compared to E, multiplied by 100-fold. One division of abscissae is 5 volts; currents are in microamperes.

amps. A feature of the study was the separation of various current components using a screened grid plane probe. An attempt to use screened grid probes was previously made on several occasions.

Until the time of Boyd's study, methods had not been developed of constructing the very fine grids which make it possible to operate at voltages positive to the discharge. With such a grid over the probe surface, the Langmuir characteristic could be separated into its two components, as seen in figures 4.18 and 4.19. Since positive ions reached the grid through a retarding field, there was no disturbance of the energy distribution by a field from the grid. Details of Boyd's measurements are omitted here. The value of ΔV essential for sheath formation was confirmed as lying between 1 to 4 volts in A gas. The effect of the penetrating field on the saturation positive ion current as predicted by the conventional theory is given by equation 4.122, but quantitative agreement was not possible, owing to limitations produced by edge effects on the small probe used. At pressures of 1 mm and above, the saturation current to a negative probe is, as indicated, approximately equal to the random current of positive ions in the gas. At pressures below 0.1 mm Hg it is considerably greater, being nearly equal ιο that which the conventional theory would give if the positive ions had a temperature equal to that of the electrons. The retardation of the positive ion current enabled the determination of a "temperature" corresponding to the transverse component of ion velocities to be measured. At 4×10^{-3} mm pressure it was 0.3 of the electron temperatures, and at 9×10^{-4} mm it was about 0.04.

Observations were made on the anisotropy of ion- and electron-energy distributions, and the screened grid probe appeared to be especially useful in studying departures of the electron-velocity distribution from the true Maxwellian form at high energies, using the Druyvesteyn theory. The effect of secondary emission by photons and metastable atoms from the Pt collector in A gas amounted to about 10% of the positive ion saturation current. It caused no difficulties in measurement or in interpretation.

A further published contribution by Boyd (51a) refers to small probes. Subsequent to these disclosures, Boyd has found that the initial optimistic estimate of this probe is not fulfilled, and at present no explanation is forthcoming. The author has been told by workers in this country that the Boyd probes did not work out as expected. Despite failure of the probe, it is believed that the theory is valid in principle.

§ 7. The Double-Probe Technique.

It has long been recognized that disturbance of the plasma by the probe can seriously complicate measurement, as indicated in section 6. This is particularly true in a weakly ionized or decaying plasma after cutoff of the field, where the carriers removed by probe currents cannot be replaced. Under such conditions the measurement seriously alters the plasma. It has recently been shown by E. O. Johnson and L. Malter (44) that the various quantities can be determined by the use of the double floating probe with considerably greater assurance than by the single-probe method.

It may be recalled that the electron temperature is measured by the single probe with Maxwellian distribution by determining the slope of the negative current density $j-$ as a function of probe potential, using relation 4.92 on the following page.

$$(4.92) \qquad \log_e j_- = \log_e \left(eN_- \sqrt{\frac{kT_-}{2\pi m_-}} \right) - \frac{Ve}{kT_-} .$$

The current density j_- is the negative part of the probe current divided by the area A of the plasma sheath, and T_- is the electron temperature. The probe current is given by $i_p = i_+ - i_-$. Here i_+ is the space-charge limited positive ion current equal to the diffusion current into the sheath, and i_p is the actual probe current measured. The electron current is i_-, and is given by $i_+ - i_p$. Thus, by measuring i_+ and i_p as a function of V, the value of i_- is achieved. This permits relation 4.92 to be written in Malter's terminology as

$$(4.127) \qquad \log_e i_- = - \frac{e}{kT_-} V + \log_e A j_0 ,$$

where

$$j_0 = eN_- \sqrt{\frac{kT_-}{2\pi m_-}} ,$$

and V is the plasma potential relative to the probe for the relatively negative probe.

If V_s is the cathode-plasma potential and V_p is the cathode-probe potential, V is essentially $V_s - V_p$, so that the expression becomes

$$(4.128) \qquad \log_e i_- = \frac{eV}{kT_-} + \log_e A j_0 - \frac{eV_s}{kT_-} .$$

This expression is equivalent to expression 4.92, with potentials referred to the cathode instead of the anode. Now expression 4.128 is only significant if V_s, T_-, A, and j_0 do not change with V_p. Actually, the changes produced by V_p may be such as even to alter the visual appearance of the discharge. This occurs if i_- is an appreciable fraction of the discharge current. In an arc discharge, with high values of N_- and a regeneration of carriers to supply losses to the walls, i_- may be kept low relative to the arc current. In a decaying plasma, currents such as i_- can well alter the whole plasma near the probe.

In an attempt to reduce the disturbance, the double-probe method is employed, with the two probes floating. It is thus essential to consider the potentials of such probes in the decaying plasma. Such a plasma is one in which a discharge is interrupted and the plasma decays by ambipolar diffusion. Thus, since electrons diffuse to the walls and make them negative, the plasma is slightly positive to the wall. In decaying plasma this will be a few tenths of a volt. Assume that some section of the envelope of such a plasma is in-

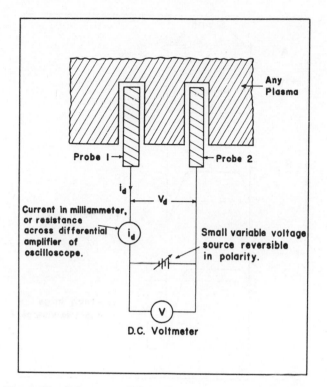

Fig. 4.20. Johnson and Malter's double-probe connections.

creased in potential with respect to the remainder. Excess electrons
flow to this section and cause the positive plasma potential to rise
until balance between loss and gain is again achieved. This leads
to the conclusion that the plasma then assumes a potential that is
slightly positive to the most positive electrode with which it makes
contact. This property can be demonstrated directly with an oscilloscope.

The floating potential E_f of a probe was measured at various times.
It followed the anode supply potential E_p very closely. The plasma
potential E_s was always slightly positive to the floating potential.
Thus, the space potential followed the potential of the most positive
electrode very closely. The equilibrium conditions were reached
in a fraction of a microsecond, which was the limit of resolution of
the oscilloscope and was probably of the order of 10^{-8} sec.

The double probes used are each like a single probe. They are
interconnected, as shown in figure 4.20.

V_d is the differential voltage and i_d is the circuit current. Studies

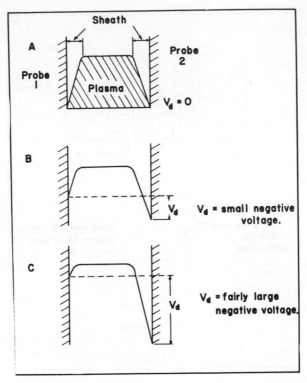

Fig. 4.21. Schematic representation of the effects of
potential differences on the double probe.

are made of the variation of i_d with V_d. It is assumed that the energy
distribution is Maxwellian and that the electron current is governed
by the Boltzmann exponential law. Kirchhoff's law requires that the
total net current of positive ions and electrons flowing from the
plasma through the circuit must be zero. Assume that both probes
have equal area, and that no contact-potential differences, or differences in plasma potential from point to point, exist. Assume
further that V_d has no effect upon the ion current to the system,
which is closely true in practice. At $V_d = 0$, the conditions are shown
in figure 4.21, at "A." Each probe collects 0 net current from the
plasma, and each probe will ride at the same floating potential.

The current $i_d = 0$. This gives point 0 on the curve of figure 4.22.
Now let V_d be a small negative voltage, as in figure 4.21, at "B."
Probe potentials, with respect to the plasma, must adjust so that
the basic current conditions are still satisfied. These can only be
achieved (as in figure 4.21, at "B'") where probe number 1 moves

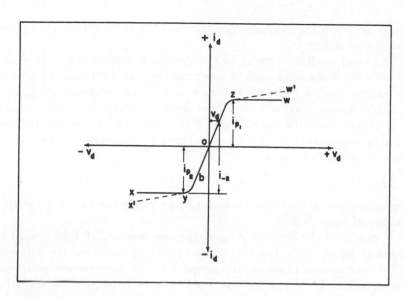

Fig. 4.22. Ideal current-potential characteristics of the double probe.

down closer to the plasma potential, while probe number 2 moves farther away from the plasma potential. Being more negative, it collects fewer electrons. The extra electrons flowing to probe number 1 pass through the circuit to make up the deficiency at probe number 2. All conditions are again satisfied, and the system is located at some point b in figure 4.22. If V_d is somewhat more negative, the situation depicted in figure 4.21, at "C," is reached. Probe number 1 moves still closer to the space potential and collects the entire current to the system, since probe number 2 is so highly negative with respect to the plasma that no electrons can reach it. Half the electrons that reach probe number 1 pass through the external circuit to probe number 2. All conditions are satisfied, and the system locates at some point y in figure 4.22.

Further increase in negative value V_d can cause no further change in current distributions, because probe number 1 already collects a sufficient electron current to balance the entire positive ion current flowing to the system. Probe number 1 remains fixed with respect to the plasma, and probe number 2 goes negative along with V_d. That probe is saturated with regard to positive ions as the system moves along the flat portion yx of figure 4.22. In practice this flat portion has a slight slope, as shown by the dotted portion yx' This is caused by an expansion of sheath thickness as the probe goes more negative with respect to the plasma. Reversing polarity owing to symmetry merely reverses the previous results when V_d is positive, giving the portion $0zw$ or $0zw'$.

The total positive current to the system is simply the sum of the positive ion current to both probes, and so can be found by adding the magnitudes of the currents at y and z, as indicated at i_{p1} and i_{p2}. The electron current which flows from the plasma to probe number 2 is simply the difference between the total space current and the positive ion current of this probe. Thus, the electron current i_{-2} to probe number 2 is given by

$$| i_{-2} | = | i_d | - | i_{p2} | .$$

The derivation of (i_{-2}) from these relations was made on the simplified diagram of figure 4.20.

A generalized potential diagram for the system of figure 4.20 is shown in figure 4.23. The potentials V_1 and V_2 represent the voltages of the surrounding plasmas with respect to the corresponding probes. The potential V_c represents any small difference in plasma potential which may exist between the regions surrounding probes, plus the total contact potentials acting on the system.

The equality of currents sets

(4.129) $$i_{p1} + i_{p2} = \Sigma i_p = i_{-1} + i_{-2} .$$

The values of i_{-1} and i_{-2} can be given by the Boltzmann relations to yield

(4.130) $$\Sigma i_p = A_1 j_{01} \epsilon^{-\phi V_1} + A_2 j_{02} \epsilon^{-\phi V_2} ,$$

with

$$\phi = \frac{e}{kT_-} = 11,600/T_- \text{ in volts} .$$

The diagram of potentials leads to setting

$$V_1 + V_c = V_2 + V_d$$

or

(4.131) $$V_1 = V_2 + V_d - V_c .$$

If 4.131 is placed in 4.130, rearrangement leads to

(4.132) $$\log_e [(\Sigma i_p / i_{-2}) - 1] = -\phi V_d + \log_e \sigma = \log_e \Gamma .$$

Here Γ and σ are given by

(4.133) $$\Gamma = [(\Sigma i_p / i_{-2}) - 1]$$

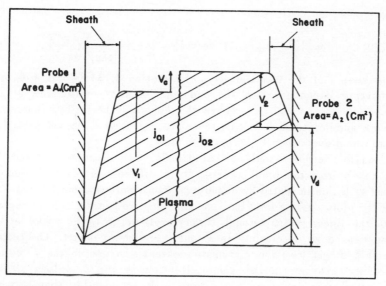

Fig. 4.23. Generalized schematic diagram for the use of the double probe.

and

(4.134) $$\sigma = (A_1 \, j_{01} / A_2 j_{02}) \, \epsilon^{\phi V_c}.$$

It is seen that a plot of $\log_e \Gamma$ against V_d should yield a straight line, the slope of which yields ϕ and is a measure of T_-. This relation bears a similarity to the single-probe relation, except that with the double probe Γ is used instead of the electron current i_-. It is to be noted that the slope of equation 4.132 is essentially unaffected by any factors included in σ; that is, probe areas, random electron current densities, differences in plasma potentials between probes, and contact potentials are not affected by V_d. This is not true of the single-probe method. In the latter, the value of the probe potential relative to the space is altered, and for other than plane probes, corrections enter, involving changes in A. With the double probes, V_d merely alters the current flow through the probes, but does not affect the floating potentials. For an unambiguous determination of T_-, the random current densities j_0 should not change with probe current. This is much more likely to be true with the double-probe method than with the single-probe method, since the current drain can be hundreds of times smaller with the double probe. Comparing equations for single and double probes,

(4.128) $$\log_e i_- = \frac{eV}{kT_-} + \log_e A j_0 - \frac{eV_s}{kT_-}$$

and

$$(4.132) \qquad \log_e \left[(\Sigma i_p / i_{-2}) - 1 \right] = - \phi V_d + \log_e \left(\frac{A_1 j_{01}}{A_2 j_{02}} \right) \epsilon^{\phi V_c} ,$$

it is seen that the constant term of equation 4.134 is free from any restricting dependence on the plasma potential, while the single probe depends on V_s. This makes the double-probe method inherently a more general method. It can, therefore, be used during or after discharge, and even when V_s varies with time.

Possible errors should be mentioned. The currents i_{p1} and i_{p2} are taken from the break points. It is difficult properly to choose y and z. If this is tested by choosing various values about the regions, the log plots deviate from the linearity observed in the central region. With the linear region through 0 very well defined, the errors at the ends caused by uncertainty in x and y are of no import. The reason for this stems from the circumstance that changes in the i_p values introduce changes in the same direction in the i_- values. Thus, $[(\Sigma i_p / i_{-2})-1]$ is inappreciably affected. It is possible that between y and z the ion currents of each of the probes vary, owing to small changes in sheath thickness. Again, it turns out that such changes do not seriously alter the ratio.

The material presented here is sufficient to show some advantages of the double-probe method and how it can be used to measure T_-. The method indicated involves cumbersome computation. The properties of the equations permit of a more rapid determination called the "equivalent resistance method," and a second rapid method called the "intercept method" in examples where the former method is not accurate. The article then describes the character of the methods in applications to discharges with decaying plasmas. Thus, a tube plasma in A at 1 mm was studied 400 μ sec after a discharge lasting 8 μ sec. The range in values of V_d was from -0.8 to $+0.8$ volts in contrast to the tens of volts used in the single-probe method. The currents i_{p1} and i_{p2} were of the order of microamperes. One concern involved in this method is that with small ranges in V_d only a relatively small section of the electron-energy distribution is used; e.g., of the order of the top 1% in one case. It is not sufficient to detect curvatures in the $\log_e$ $j_- - Ve/kT_-$ plots indicative of failure of the distribution to be Maxwellian. A larger range of values may be studied by increasing the ratio of the probe areas.

The method may be used to estimate the electron and ion densities and the wall potential. It is possible to do so if the positive ion temperature T_+ is known. In a decaying plasma this is very close to the gas temperature because of the rapid energy loss of ions in impact. The method is not very accurate, and so will not be given. For details of the use of this method, as well as its advantages, the reader is referred to the original paper. Enough has been given to indicate the value of this new technique and its underlying theory.

§ 8. Sources of Error in Probe Technique.

Despite the extensive use of probes and their seeming success, the experience derived from years of study indicates definite limitations to their use, and numerous possible sources of error in the data which they yield, or in their interpretation. It is therefore essential to summarize the most important of these deficiencies.

1. It is assumed that the presence of the probe does not alter the potential or charge distribution in the space or in the plasma, and that the energy distribution of electrons reaching the probe is the same as that in the undisturbed plasma.

a) This implies that the probe must be small relative to significant changes in potential over the space it occupies. Extensive plane probes at a uniform potential will disturb the fields even in the absence of space charges. Thus, under most circumstances, the simple and convenient plane probe cannot be used. This requires the use of small cylindrical or spherical probes. It also precludes the use of probes at higher pressures where field gradients are steep, i.e., near corona points. It makes the use of probes of doubtful value in the dark spaces of discharges, such as the Crookes dark space of the glow, with rapidly changing potentials even at lower pressures. The corrections resulting from the use of such small probes set further limitations on the measurements, which are inherent in applying proper geometrical and other corrections for the effective areas, etc.

b) The probe should not draw enough current to disturb the plasma. The presence of space-charge sheaths prevents serious drains where they are not disturbed, as seen in section 6.[15] The currents drawn are space-charge limited. In fact, for even the very negative probe, the maximum current density entering the plasma sheath is limited to $j_+ = eN_+c_+/4$, as indicated elsewhere. If N_+ is 10^8 ions/cm^3 and a small probe of area 10^{-3} cm^2 is used, the magnitude of current to be expected for ions of intermediate mass and temperature is of the order of 5×10^{-10} amp. Such a current is at the limit of convenient measurements with galvanometers. Thus, probe measurements have

---

[15]Even here there is some question as to whether or not the probe alters the plasma, according to W. M. Webster and L. Malter; however, the seriousness of the effect is the first consideration.

generally been confined to discharges where N is of the order of 10^{10} ions/cm^3 or greater.

c) In principle it is assumed that the space-charge sheath representing the active surface in probe measurements prevents disturbance of the plasma by the action of the metal surface (see section 6). It is also assumed that the sheath surface is little disturbed by the probe and by the electrical forces of the probe field. Such assumptions are not accurate, strictly speaking. The disturbance is least at lower negative probe potentials, where most of the electrons penetrate fairly close to the probe and the sheath thickness d is small.

In general, for the strongly negative probes, the following factors are active to make the results inaccurate: (1) The majority of the electrons entering the sheath are repelled by the probe. Thus, the center zone of the sheath has electron densities enhanced by incoming and repelled electrons, while the densities are diminished near the probe surface and positive ion densities are high by convergence. Thus, the charge distribution at the sheath surface is not exactly that of undisturbed plasma. (2) Under such conditions, if pressures are not too low, the electrons will collide with molecules after entering the sheath. They will then lose energy by elastic and inelastic exciting and ionizing impacts. Consequently, in thick sheaths the energy distribution reaching the probe may not be that existing in the undisturbed plasma. This effect is the one that precludes the use of probes in evaluating energy distributions in plasmas at lower X/p and higher p. (3) The new ions and electrons created in the sheath by electron impact will change the carrier densities relative to the undisturbed probes, as well as the energy distribution. These disturbances and the extension of the field beyond the sheath are indicated by the fact that a second probe placed near an initial one, even if their sheaths are separated by plasma, will influence the reading of the initial probe, indicating a disturbance of the plasma.

d) It is assumed that all carriers striking the sheath surface will reach the probe and register as current, and that only such carriers as represent the original plasma outside the sheath will reach the probe and yield the probe current. This condition is not fulfilled and the failure is greater, the more negative the probe and the thicker the sheath. The contributing factors are here enumerated: (1) Collisions of electrons *with molecules in the sheath* which direct some electrons from the probe. Where this effect is small, Druyvesteyn has derived a correction factor. (2) Reflection of electrons and ions from the probe surface, i.e., low accommodation coefficient. This effect is probably small for these carriers at the probe metal surfaces.

(3) The current of electrons and ions which were not initially present in the plasma and are created in the sheath by electron impact, metastable atoms, and high-energy photons. This factor can be important in some cases. It would be most important in mixtures of gases like He or Ne with A, Hg, or impurities of low ionization potential. In conjunction with actions under the next factor, the disturbances are particularly bad. (4) The emission of electrons by the probe surface due to photons from the sheath, and secondary electrons liberated from the metal surface by positive ions and metastable atom impact. With strongly negative probes, the secondary electrons can also multiply in the sheath. The electronic carriers, when emitted, give the probe a positive charge and falsify the values of j_+.

It is clear that very hot probes emitting electrons thermionically will likewise cause serious difficulties of the sort indicated. Thus, in arcs and other hot discharges, swinging probes that pass through have been used. In flames, the temperatures of the gas near the probes change the plasma densities, so that probe studies in flames are valueless. Similarly, electrons which fail to reach the probe reduce i_-. Electrons released from the probe or created in the sheath lead to the presence of more low-energy electrons than are present in the original distribution. Such currents all vary with V and pressure, the secondary emission from the probe being less at higher pressures. These effects, as expected, complicate and confuse the interpretation of measurements.

These factors, as well as those acting to produce electrons in the gas, can be very important. Metastable atoms in some gases and in mixtures can produce considerable effect. How serious these can be, and the relative importance of various agencies, are still controversial matters. Doubtless, the relative importance of the different agencies varies widely with conditions. The surface effects can be reduced by using probes of insensitive metal surfaces such as Mg. They are further improved by thoroughly outgassing, preferably by ion bombardment and heat. The gases that cause the most trouble are those like helium and neon, that have high-energy ions, metastables, and photons. The earlier probe studies were particularly subject to error resulting from these agencies, both at the probe surface and in the sheath.

2. The indication given by the potentiometer used to read V_p may not represent the *true potential* difference between the reference electrode and the probe. Unless probe surface metals and reference electrode (in the illustrative arrangement used, this electrode is

the anode) are of the same metal and have undergone closely similar history as regards exposure to gases, bombardment by ions, and heating, it is *certain* that they have an intrinsic contact-potential difference. This adds to or subtracts from the potential applied. These potentials derive from differences in the work functions of the two surfaces. The contact-potential differences arising from this can be evaluated by one of several classical methods, but require special auxiliary arrangements in the tube which are often inconvenient to install. Even the employment of initially similar electrodes does not insure equality of work functions, though it lessens ultimate differences. In the course of running the discharge or the probe measurements, the difference in work functions may change by notable amounts, owing to differences in ion bombardment.

Recent studies of Oatley and of Weissler (53) have shown that bombardment of Pt, Ag, or W by O^+ ions raises the work functions possibly as much as 1.6 to 2 volts relative to bombardment by H^+ ions. If different metals are used, the contact-potential difference may falsify values of V_w or V_B, as read on the potentiometer, by as much as 0.5 to 3 volts. If these quantities are required with any accuracy, it is clear that contact-potential measurements must be made before and after the probe study. Since V_B and V_p are *both* measured relative to the reference electrode, the values of $V = V_B - V_p$ will not be affected. Thus, contact-potential differences will not disturb energy-distribution measurements *unless the contact-potential difference changes during the run*. Electron-energy distributions are often falsified by this factor. On the other hand, the values of V_w, V_B, and the wall currents and ion densities may be completely falsified.

In a relatively recent paper, T. A. Anderson (54) has shown how to obtain the potentials if the contact potential of one electrode changes rapidly with time under bombardment. For this he uses an alternating-current method. Usually such rapid changes are rare, but slower changes are to be expected. Thus, quite generally significant data of broad scope can only be obtained under conditions where the existing contact-potential difference is measured and corrected for preceding and following the run.

G. Wehner and G. Medicus (54a) presented studies in 1952 of the falsification of data resulting from changes in work function of the probe. These can be of the same order as the electron velocities or plasma potentials to be measured. They observed changes in the work function produced by oxidation, contamination with Ba compounds (used as getters), or from oxide-coated cathodes; by sputtering, and by evaporation from the probe. These effects were sorted out by using different cathodes and automatic recording of the data, which took only some seconds for a curve. In oxide or Ba cathode tubes, the work function of a W probe near the cathode decreases so fast that reliable results can be obtained only if the measurement lasts some seconds after cleaning. In the anode region, oxygen released from the oxide cathode predominates, as the Ba is largely ionized and returns to the cathode. With proper probe-cleaning procedure, no deviation from the Maxwellian velocity distribution over a range of four powers of ten could be found, even with oxide cathodes at pressures of 150 microns with a probe only 10 mm from the cathode.

This particular aspect of probe behavior appears to be more and more important in the light of other studies. M. A. Easley (54b) reported probe characteristics for discharges in Hg vapor in the presence of A or Kr gas. In many cases nonlinear probe plots were due to changes in the contact potential during measurement by condensation of Hg on W probes. These led to changes in slope and various peculiar effects, which were interpreted as being due to non-Maxwellian distribution, when, in fact, distributions *were* Maxwellian. Proper results could have been achieved by heating or bombarding the probe *before each reading*. On the other hand, oscillations, such as evidenced by traveling striations, caused real non-linear plots with two electron groups of temperatures differing by a factor of 2. Tubes containing less than 0.5 microns of CO or CO_2 gave false data by change of contact potential, even when the probe was bombarded before each measurement, since contamination was so rapid. Such wrong data might occur as a result of stopcock grease vapors unless there was a trap between the stopcock and the system.

3. The theory given assumed the negative carriers to be electrons and the positive carriers to be atomic or molecular ions. It assumed an essentially neutral plasma, with $N_+ = N_-$. In gases where appreciable numbers of electrons attach to form negative ions, it is clear that N_- will be composed of carriers of mostly different mobilities, ions and electrons. The simple theories that are given no longer apply under such conditions. Probably, electron-energy distributions can still be roughly determined. A theory could doubtless be evolved, but results would be unreliable and difficult to interpret. Thus, in general, probe studies used to determine anything more than the space and wall potentials should be used only in gases where electrons remain free.

4. It is naturally assumed that information such as that derived from probe studies would apply only to discharges of a steady or

direct-current type. Even here, only average conditions can be determined (i.e., approximate equivalent temperatures) which exist at a
localized region. It was also indicated that a small alternating
potential superposed on the steady probe potential could be used to
determine the form of the distribution law where this was required.
This condition also assumes steady discharges. If now the discharge
itself has its potentials fluctuating or varying with time, the situation
can become complex indeed.

At various times, the values of the local wall and space potentials
have different values, and if the time rate of variation of the applied
potential is relatively low (less than 10^6 cycles per sec), certain
electron and ion temperatures, as well as N_+ and N_-, will vary with
time. If the potentiometer sweep could be made in cycles of such
frequency as to determine the currents at which the energy in the
a.c. cycle underwent little change, the oscillations of the quantities
could be recorded on an oscilloscope screen, giving a fairly complete
delineation of what took place. The results would still be complex,
for while ionization and energy distributions would follow the field,
the rate of recombination would be low compared to many alternating
frequencies. Thus, ion concentrations could change cumulatively up
to a high level, different from those in individual cycles. Owing to
smearing of data, interpretation would then be difficult in the extreme.

However, if the a.c. is rapidly executed relative to the potentiometer sweep frequency, or even (with slow oscillations) if the sweep
is executed manually, the measurements will record average values
of V_B and V_w and a composite of the electron-energy distributions
existing at the various phases of the a.c. The concentrations of
carriers N_+ and N_- will represent some cumulative equilibrium value
related to rate of ionization and loss by recombination and diffusion,
and will not represent the individual cycles.

If by chance a relatively low-voltage d.c. discharge is studied
with probes in the conventional fashion; and if, unsuspected, there
is superposed on this steady gradient a high-frequency oscillation
of large amplitude, e.g., if 40 volt 10^5 cycle oscillations are superposed on a 10 volt d.c. Hg arc, the electron-energy distribution
observed will certainly not be Maxwellian, nor will it correspond
to the 10 volt potential difference applied. Many low-energy electrons
characteristic of the d.c. field will be observed, owing to the zero-
potential phase, for electrons lose the energy of the higher fields
rapidly with the high collision rates. On the other hand, appreciable
numbers of 40 volt electrons will be observed. This was precisely
the observed distribution noted by Langmuir in 1925 for certain Hg

arcs with oxide-coated filament cathodes at high current densities and low pressures.

F. M. Penning (55) confirmed the observations, and first associated the high-energy electrons with suspected and observed oscillations in 1926. A. F. Dittmer (56) in 1926 confirmed Langmuir's observations, and indicated that oscillations might be involved; an explanation that Langmuir had considered as less probable. Final confirmation with theoretical interpretation was due to L. Tonks and to Langmuir and Tonks in 1928-1929 (57). Accordingly, at that period it was generally accepted that plasma, when disturbed, could undergo electrical oscillations. It was shown by Tonks that the oscillations could be either electronic or ionic, and that the frequencies depended on the mass of the carrier and the ion or electron density N_+ or N_-.

The positive ion frequencies lie in the general range of 10^5 cycles per second, while electron-plasma oscillations lie in the order of about 3×10^9 cycles per second. During the war, physicists of various nations tried to develop the electronic plasma oscillations as sources of microwaves for military purposes. Electron plasma oscillations have mostly been observed at lower pressures with the higher current densities. Disturbances in the plasma near the cathode start oscillations which velocity-modulate the cathode ray beams from the hot cathode source present. These velocity-modulated electron beams, under proper conditions, interact with the circuit regeneratively (probably through wall potentials) to build up a sustained system of oscillations. Various tube arrangements can be made to enhance these, but it is doubtful if they will ever yield powerful sources of ultrahigh frequency.

A very comprehensive review of plasma properties was written preceding World War II by R. Rompe and M. Steenbeck (58). It contains a complete bibliography to 1939. A more complete general mathematical treatment of the theory of plasma oscillations has been developed recently (59).

How some electron and all-ion plasma oscillations are sustained is not clear at present, for in addition to the ability of a plasma to oscillate, properly timed periodic input of energy is needed to sustain them. It is suspected that these input conditions, as well as those responsible for other lower-frequency oscillations, may arise from inherent cathode instabilities in various types of discharges. Unstable cathodes become overvolted and start a chain reaction of cumulative ionization. Such complete breakdown with much electron emission is periodically interrupted by potential changes caused by the plasma oscillations which it initiates. Probably, all discharges tending toward negative voltage characteristics may start such discharges. Once started, periodic feedback by proper circuitry can also sustain such oscillations.

At this point, the origin and nature of such oscillations is not of import. What must be recognized is that oscillations of considerable amplitude and in at least two different frequency ranges occur in certain types of discharges at high current densities. These may not be readily detected, but will produce anomalies in the probe readings, necessitating extreme caution in drawing conclusions from the data. It must now be noted that probes operate in plasma, and that they are thus susceptible to oscillations of their own, and to their own frequencies. Furthermore, a.c. superposed on probes for delineating distribution laws can interact with inherent plasma oscillations at certain frequencies. Thus, it is not strange that with a.c. on probes, plasma exhibits remarkable electrical properties under some conditions. These are so bad that Eméleus warns against the inferences drawn about energy distribution from probes by the method of Sloane and MacGregor.

Unfortunately, the existence of the occasional high-frequency plasma oscillations indicated above is not the only possible complicating feature of this nature in glow and other supposedly steady-state discharges. Very recently, G. H. Dieke and T. M. Donahue (60) turned photomultiplying cells on various portions of normal, steady-appearing, uniform, glow-discharge plasmas. The cells showed that the columns of these discharges in many instances were traversed by waves of ionization, which they called "striations." In these waves, the light intensity fluctuated periodically at a given point; in some cases, from zero to the maximum value. These striations moved from negative glow to anode, or from anode to negative glow, at velocities which differed (the former being faster), and which varied with current, pressure, tube diameter, etc. Oscillographs placed across the electrodes showed potential fluctuations of some 10% synchronized with the luminous oscillations. Some oscillations were synchronized and regular; others were highly irregular. Definite, stable modes of oscillation could be observed under varying conditions. Frequencies ranged from 1,000 cycles up to the ion-plasma frequencies.

It is clear that such processes, while not representing plasma oscillations of the conventional type, will do much to confuse the probe investigations. Unfortunately, up to the present, oscillographic analysis of probe findings in such discharge columns has not been made and correlated with the oscillations. Doubtless, the study of the probe in this way, at different d.c. potentials, might help to clarify the interpretation of the observations.

In any case, these findings indicate caution in the interpretation of probe readings, especially if the energy distributions are at all irregular. Probably, routine tests of the discharge for the presence of any oscillations should be made in all cases where a serious attempt at probe study is undertaken.

5. As indicated in the text, the use of small cylindrical or spherical probes requires that correction factors should be applied in order properly to interpret the current densities from current readings. The correction factors as given are highly idealized, and are not accurate (42). The existence of these correction factors imposes conditions on the measured current-voltage characteristics of the probes which are not included in the developed theory. This difficulty can be overcome only by a tedious series of graphical correction approximations which are hardly worth the effort. This is especially true, since the corrections achieved by this means are small compared to the inherent uncertainties caused by secondary electron liberation, oscillations, etc.

6. The final difficulties and their interpretation in probe studies lie in the possibility of the existence of non-Maxwellian energy distributions. Fortunately, it is probable that in the many discharges amenable to probe studies, electron densities are such that Maxwellian distributions can be expected. This has only been recognized somewhat recently as a result of theoretical studies (18). The region where serious deviations from the Maxwellian distribution are likely is usually at low electron densities, and under field conditions where exciting and ionizing impacts are rare, and mean free paths vary rapidly with energy. However, if the observed log j_--V curves are not linear, then an analysis of the Druyvesteyn type might be called for. However, before too much reliance is placed in the distribution law so observed, the question of oscillations and change of work function must be ruled out as well. Even then, interpretation of the observation requires considerable caution.

From the foregoing it would appear that probe studies are of very doubtful value. Actually, within the limiting conditions to which such studies are applicable, it can be said that the data yielded by probe studies have been invaluable. They serve to delineate, with significant accuracy, the space and wall potentials and their course in certain regions. They yield energy distributions, and in many cases fairly reliable electron temperatures, certainly in order of magnitude. They indicate by their form where such temperature estimates may be illusory or in error. They lead to an estimate of the wall current and the loss of carriers by ambipolar diffusion. Finally, under some conditions, they indicate the local densities of electrons and ions, perhaps within about half an order of magnitude.

BIBLIOGRAPHY TO CHAPTER IV

(1) P. M. Morse, W. P. Allis, and E. S. Lamar, Phys. Rev. *48*, 412, 1935.

(2) K. T. Compton, Phys. Rev. 7, 489, 501, 509, 1916; *9*, 234, 1918.

(3) H. Sponer, Zeits. f. Phys. 7, 185, 1921.

(4) W. Harries and G. Hertz, Zeits. f. Phys. *46*, 177, 1928.

(5) M. J. Druyvesteyn, Physica *10*, 69, 1930.

(6) A. P. Didlaukis, Ann. d. Physik *5*, 211, 1930; Zeits. f. Phys. *82*, 709, 1933, A. M. Cravath, Phys. Rev. *46*, 332, 1934; J. S. Townsend, Phil. Mag. *9*, 1138, 1930; *22*, 153, 1936; also, Townsend, *Electrons in Gases*, Hutchinson's, London, 1947, chap. IV, p. 82.

(7) F. B. Pidduck, Quart. Jour. of Math. 7, 199, 1926; Proc. Lond. Math. Soc. *15*, 89, 1915.

(8) B. Davydov, Phys. Zeits. d. Sowjetunion *8*, 59, 1935.

(9) M. J. Druyvesteyn, Physica *3*, 65, 1936.

(10) J. A. Smit, Physica *3*, 543, 1937.

(11) S. H. Dunlop, Nature *164*, 452, 1949; S. H. Dunlop and K. G. Emeléus, Brit. Jour. App. Phys. 2, 183, 1951.

(12) G. D. Yarnold, Phil. Mag. *36*, 185, 1945; *38*, 186, 1947.

(13) R. J. Wijsman (in the author's laboratory) reported this error. It was submitted to Phil. Mag. and Phys. Rev. just after the war. Owing to lack of space and the polemic character of the article, it was withdrawn. The obvious source of error is pointed out here for the benefit of any interested neutral party who may wish to verify it.

(14) T. R. Holstein, Phys. Rev. *70*, 367, 1946.

(15) L. J. Varnerin, Jr., and S. C. Brown, Phys. Rev. *79*, 948, 1950.

(16) H. Margenau, Phys. Rev. *69*, 508, 1946; *73*, 297, 1948.

(17) L. M. Hartman. Phys. Rev. *73*, 316, 1948.

(18) J. H. Cahn, Phys. Rev. *75*, 293, 838, 1949; L. Landau, Jour. Phys. U.S.S.R. *10*, 25, 154, 1946; reply by W. P. Allis, Phys. Rev. *76*, 146, 1949; L. Landau, Phys. Rev. *77*, 567, 1950.

(18a) I. B. Bernstein and T. R. Holstein, Phys. Rev. *84*, 1074, 1951.

(19) A rather complete *Kinetic Theory of Electrons in Gases* appears in the form of lecture notes of Prof. W. P. Allis in course 8.232 at Massachusetts Institute of Technology, beginning in 1946 and extending on for several years. This has appeared in dittoed form, and copies may be available for loan. It should some day appear as a book, and would represent perhaps the most comprehensive and valuable treatise developed to date.

"Breakdown of a Gas at Microwave Frequencies," M. A. Herlin and S. C. Brown, Phys. Rev. *74*, 291, 1948; "Electrical Breakdown for a

Gas between Coaxial Cylinders at Microwave Frequencies," M. A. Herlin and S. C. Brown, Phys. Rev. *74*, 910, 1948; "Microwave Breakdown for a Gas in a Cylindrical Cavity of Arbitrary Length," M. A. Herlin and S. C. Brown, Phys. Rev. *74*, 1650, 1948; "High-Frequency Gas Discharge in Helium," Phys. Rev. *75*, 411, 1949; "Limits for Diffusion Theory of High-Frequency Gas Discharge Breakdown," S. C. Brown and A. D. MacDonald, Phys. Rev. *76*, 1629, 1949; "Admittance of High-Frequency Gas Discharges," E. Everhart and S. C. Brown, Phys. Rev. *76*, 839, 1949; "High-Frequency Gas Discharge Breakdown in Hydrogen," A. D. MacDonald and S. C. Brown, Phys. Rev. *76*, 1634, 1949; "Electron Diffusion in a Spherical Cavity," A. D. MacDonald and S. C. Brown, Can. Jour. Res. *A28*, 168, 1950; "Microwave Determination of Average Electron Energies and First Townsend Coefficient in Hydrogen," L. J. Varnerin, Jr., and S. C. Brown, Phys. Rev. *79*, 946, 1950; "Effect of a Magnetic Field on the Breakdown of Gases at Microwave Frequencies," B. Lax, W. P. Allis, and S. C. Brown, Jour. App. Phys. *21*, 1297, 1950; "Electron-Density Distribution in a High-Frequency Discharge in the Presence of Plasma Resonance," W. P. Allis, S. C. Brown, and E. Everhart, Phys. Rev. *84*, 519, 1951; "Electron Recombination and Collision Cross Section Measurements in Hydrogen," L. J. Varnerin, Jr., Phys. Rev. *84*, 563, 1951; "Microwave Determination of the Probability of Collision of Slow Electrons in Gases," A. V. Phelps, O. T. Fundingsland, and S. C. Brown, Phys. Rev. *84*, 559, 1951; "High-Frequency Electrical Breakdown in Gases," W. P. Allis and S. C. Brown, Phys. Rev. *87*, 419, 1952; "Techniques of High-Frequency Measurements in Gaseous Discharges," D. J. Rose and S. C. Brown, Jour. App. Phys. *23*, 711, 719, 1028, 1952; L. Gould and S. C. Brown, Jour. App. Phys. *24*, 1053, 1953; L. Gould and S. C. Brown, Phys. Rev. *95*, 897, 1954.

(19a) W. P. Allis and P. M. Morse, Zeits. f. Phys. *70*, 567, 1931.

(20) L. J. Varnerin, Jr., and S. C. Brown, Phys. Rev. *79*, 946, 1950.

(21) D. Barbiere, Phys. Rev. *84*, 653, 1951.

(22) E. H. Kennard, *Kinetic Theory of Gases*, McGraw-Hill, New York, 1938.

(23) H. C. Kelley, Ph.D. thesis, Mass. Inst. Tech., June, 1936.

(24) H. Maier-Leibnitz, Zeits. f. Phys. *95*, 499, 1935.

(25) A. D. MacDonald and S. C. Brown, Phys. Rev. *76*, 1634, 1949.

(26) V. A. Bailey, Phil. Mag. *50*, 825, 1925.

(27) R. H. Healey and C. B. Kirkpatrick, in Sydney. See Healey and Reed (III.1), p. 94.

(28) J. S. Townsend and V. A. Bailey, Phil. Mag. *42*, 873, 1921.

(29) J. S. Townsend and V. A. Bailey, Phil. Mag. *42*, 873, 1921.

(30) V. A. Bailey and J. B. Rudd, Phil. Mag. *14*, 1033, 1932; also, M. F. Skinker, Phil. Mag. *44*, 994, 1922.

(31) V. A. Bailey and W. E. Duncanson, Phil. Mag. *10*, 145, 1930.

(32) V. A. Bailey and R. H. Healey, Phil. Mag. *19*, 725, 1935.

(33) V. A. Bailey, R. E. B. Makinson, and J. M. Somerville, Phil. Mag. *24*, 177, 1937.

(34) R. H. Healey, Phil. Mag. *26*, 940, 1938.

(35) V. A. Bailey and W. E. Duncanson, Phil. Mag. *10*, 145, 1930.

(36) V. A. Bailey and W. E. Duncanson, Phil. Mag. *10*, 145, 1930.

(37) J. S. Townsend and V. A. Bailey, Phil. Mag. *46*, 657, 1923.

(38) J. S. Townsend and V. A. Bailey, Phil. Mag. *44*, 1033, 1922.

(39) I. Langmuir and H. M. Mott-Smith, Gen. Elec. Rev. *26*, 731, 1923; *27*, 449, 583, 616, 726, 810, 1924; Jour. Franklin Inst. *196*, 751, 1923; Phys. Rev. *28*, 727, 1928; I. Langmuir, Phys. Rev. *31*, 357, 1928; *33*, 954, 1929; *33*, 195, 990, 1929; L. Tonks, or L. Tonks and I. Langmuir, Phys. Rev. *33*, 239, 1939; *34*, 876, 1929; *37*, 1458, 1931; T. J. Killian, Phys. Rev. *35*, 1238, 1925. Summary of earlier work in I. Langmuir and K. T. Compton, Rev. Mod. Phys. *3*, 191-257, 1931.

(40) K. K. Darrow, *Electrical Phenomena in Gases*, William Wilkins, Baltimore, 1932. Pages 344 ff. give a good summary.

(41) A. von Engel and M. Steenbeck, *Elektrische Gasentladungen*, Julius Springer, Berlin, 1934, vol. II, secs. 14-16.

(42) I. Langmuir and K. T. Compton, "Electrical Discharges," part II, Rev. Mod. Phys. *3*, chap. III, pp. 214 ff., 1931.

(43) M. J. Druyvesteyn and F. M. Penning, Rev. Mod. Phys. *12*, 87, 1940.

(44) E. O. Johnson and L. Malter, Phys. Rev. *80*, 58, 1950.

(45) R. C. Mason, Research Report R-94290-D, Westinghouse Res. Lab.

(46) W. G. Dow and A. Reitman, Phys. Rev. *76*, 988, 1949.

(47) M. J. Druyvesteyn, Zeits. f. Phys. *64*, 790, 1930.

(48) R. H. Sloane and E. I. R. MacGregor, Phil. Mag. *18*, 193, 1934.

(49) A. H. van Gorcum, Physica *3*, 207, 1936.

(50) K. G. Emeléus and R. J. Ballantine, Phys. Rev. *50*, 672, 1936; F. D. Grieves and J. E. McF. Johnston, Phil. Mag. *21*, 659, 1936; R. H. Sloane and K. G. Emeléus, Phys. Rev. *44*, 333, 1933; K. G. Emeléus, F. D. Grieves, and E. Montgomery, Proc. Roy. Irish Acad. *A43*, 35, 1936; K. G. Emeléus and W. L. Brown, Phil. Mag. *22*, 398, 1936.

(51) R. L. F. Boyd, Proc. Roy. Soc. *A201*, 22, 1950.

(51a) R. L. F. Boyd, Proc. Phys. Soc. Lon. *B64*, 795, 1951.

(52) L. Sena, Jour. Phys. U.S.S.R. *10*, 179, 1946.

(53) C. W. Oatley, Proc. Phys. Soc. Lon. *A51*, 318, 1939; G. L. Weissler and G. Kotter, Phys. Rev. *73*, 538, 1948; G. L. Weissler and T. N. Wilson, Phys. Rev. *76*, 591, 1949; Jour. App. Phys. *24*, 472, 1953.

(54) T. A. Anderson, Phil. Mag. *38*, 179, 1947.

(54a) G. Wehner and G. Medicus, Jour. App. Phys. *23*, 1035, 1952; Phys. Rev. *93*, 647(A), 1954; G. Wehner, Jour. App. Phys. *25*, 270, 1954.

(54b) M. A. Easley, Jour. App. Phys. *22*, 590, 1951.

(55) F. M. Penning, Physica *6*, 241, 1926.

(56) A. F. Dittmer, Phys. Rev. *28*, 507, 1926.

(57) I. Langmuir and Jones, Phys. Rev. *31*, 357, 1928; I. Langmuir and L. Tonks, Phys. Rev. *33*, 195, 990, 1929; *34*, 876, 1929; C. T. Chow, Phys. Rev. *37*, 524, 1931; G. W. Fox, Phys. Rev. *37*, 815, 1931; Brown and Coman, Phys. Rev. *38*, 376, 1931; J. H. Merrill and H. W. Webb, Phys. Rev. *55*, 1191, 1939; M. J. Druyvesteyn and N. Warmholtz, Physica *4*, 51, 1937.

(58) R. Rompe and M. Steenbeck, *Ergebnisse der Exakten Naturwissenschaften*, Julius Springer, Berlin, 1939, vol. 18. Contains a complete bibliography to 1939.

(59) W. O. Schumann, Naturforsch. u. Med. in Deutsch. *15*, part 1, p. 222, 1946; Zeits. f. Phys. *121*, 7, 629, 1943; Sitzber d. Bayerisch Akad.

d. Wiss., pp. 281, 256, 1948; Zeits. f. Naturforschung *4a*, 486, 1949; Zeits. f. Angewandte Phys. *2*, 393, 1950. Also, E. B. Armstrong and K. G. Emeléus, Proc. Inst. Elec. Eng. *96*, 391, 1949; T. R. Niell and K. G. Emeléus, Proc. Roy. Irish Acad. *A53*, 197, 1951; F. Borgnis, Helv. Phys. Acta *20*, 207, 1947; P. R. Pierce, Jour. App. Phys. *19*, 231, 1948; Phys. Rev. *76*, 565, 1949; D. Bohm and E. P. Gross, Phys. Rev. *75*, 1851, 1864, 1949.

(60) G. H. Dieke and T. M. Donahue, Phys. Rev. *81*, 248, 1951.

(61) G. H. Wannier, Bell System Tech. Jour. *32*, 170, 1953.

Chapter V

THE FORMATION OF NEGATIVE IONS

---

§ 1. Introduction.

Relatively early in the study of ionic behavior in gases it was noted that at pressures somewhat below atmospheric in air and other gases, the mobility of the negative carriers seemed to be far higher than the value $k_- = K_- (p_0/p)$ indicated. What is more, with the methods then in use the increase in the abnormal value of k_- above that to be expected as pressure decreased was a gradual one. At the lower pressures, Townsend early had recognized the negative carriers to be free electrons. At nearly the same time, with the improvements in achieving gaseous purity, James Franck discovered that in N_2 and He the mobilities of the negative carriers were rather high (200-1,000 cm^2/volt sec) (1). This was observed even at atmospheric pressure. The positive ion mobilities observed in the same gas had, however, the normal values to be expected in these gases. Franck correctly identified the negative carriers as free electrons. On this basis he classified molecular gases as belonging either to a type which he termed "electronegative" with electron affinity, or to a type in which electrons remained free. In using the term electronegative, he was referring to the ability of the *molecules* to pick up electrons and form negative ions in analogy to similar tendencies in certain well-known electronegative *atomic* species, e.g., Cl, O, etc. Thus he classified O_2, SO_2, HCl, and Cl_2 as electronegative molecules readily attaching electrons to give negative molecular ions, while He, Ne, A, N_2, and H_2, if sufficiently pure, left electrons free.

The gradual abnormal increase of negative ion mobility in air with falling pressure to values that were clearly of electronic magnitudes was generally interpreted as being caused by the *gradual breakup of the supposed negative ion cluster* and ultimate electron detachment, owing to the increase in the ratio of X/p. No analogous change, or even more limited change, in the mobility of the positive ions with decreasing pressures in the same range was definitely established (2). This circumstance appeared paradoxical, since there was no reason for believing that the stability of the positive ion cluster was much greater than that for negative ions. A correct inter-

pretation of the cause of the increase of the negative ion mobility
as pressure went down was complicated by the confusing results
of two different methods of observation. A. F. Kovarick (3), using
the Rutherford square-wave a.c. method of mobility measurement
with photoelectrically generated ions from the source plate in air,
observed curves that began showing pronounced asymptotic feet at
pressures of 100 mm or under, but otherwise were smooth-looking
curves typical of the method. The intercept of the steep slope with
the potential axis V^1, however, gave values of mobility that increased
progressively below 100 mm. The author later showed that either
increase in frequency or in electric field would bring the changes
at higher pressures (5). At about 40 mm in air with a frequency of
700 c.p.s., the mobilities observed had reached approximately electronic magnitudes.

About 1915, E. M. Wellisch (4) had measured mobilities, using
the Franck modification of the Rutherford a.c. method, in which the
ions were generated below a gauze by radioactive agencies. The ions
were driven into the square-wave a.c. measuring field by an auxiliary
d.c. field below the gauze. As pressure was reduced, Wellisch, at
all but the lowest pressures, found mobility curves with breaks in
them. The lower-current portion of the curves had asymptotic feet,
and the curves were typical of the curves observed by Kovarick.
These, as stated, gave a rapidly increasing negative mobility as
pressure went down. Farther up on the current curve (the higher,
the lower the pressure for all but the lowest pressures), there were
sharp increases in current. These appeared at voltages where one
would expect to find normal negative ions. Thus, Wellisch found
both pseudoelectronic and electronic carriers and *normal negative
ions* simultaneously at all but the lowest pressures. On this basis,
Wellisch concluded that negative ions *did not "break up"* in the
measuring field. He assumed that the electron attached to a molecule
to make a negative ion immediately after generation, or that it failed
to do so and remained free. This implied that attachment could occur
only if the electron had sufficient energy. He assumed that as pressures decreased, the fraction of electrons failing to attach and give
negative ions increased. Thus, fewer and fewer negative ions were
observed as pressure decreased. He developed a theory to account
for this effect, but did not explain the apparent increase in mobility
of his *electronic* carriers as pressures decreased.

At about the same time (1915), J. J. Thomson (6) had suggested
a theory to account for the observations of Kovarick. This was that
some molecular types could attach electrons to form negative ions,

while others could not. He assumed, however, that the negative ion forming molecules did not attach such electrons on the first impact. Instead, he assumed that there was a certain chance (h) of an electron attaching to a given molecular species to make a negative ion. This value of h was supposed to be dependent on the chemical nature of the molecule and, perhaps, on the aspect of the molecule encountered by the electron at the impact. It is to be presumed that for the sake of simplicity he did not consider the probability h to be a function of the electron energy. While the theory of Thomson accounted for the results of Kovarick in a qualitative fashion, the experimental data were not adequate for making a quantitative test. Since the theory was published early in World War I, little more work was done at the time.

In 1916, the author had shown that neither normal negative nor positive ions appeared to shed their clusters in air, even though the values of X/p used well exceeded the values at which the negative ion cluster appeared to begin to show abnormal mobilities as pressure was reduced in Kovarick's work (2). On resuming work after World War I in 1919, the author set himself the task of clarifying the conflicting data and explanations extant in 1915. He did this by repeating the experiments of both Kovarick and of Wellisch, with full cognizance of J. J. Thomson's theory. He discovered that by increasing the auxiliary fields in Wellisch's method, the proportion of electronic carriers could be increased, and that under very high auxiliary fields the Wellisch curves went over to the curves observed by Kovarick. The data obtained by the author and later by his student and collaborator, H. B. Wahlin (7), enabled them once and for all to reject the Wellisch theory and to conclude that the qualitative phenomena could all be accounted for on the basis of J. J. Thomson's theory. The interpretation of the apparent increase in mobility of the negative ions as pressure, or time in traversing the air gap decreased, was simple. It had to do with the formation of negative ions by attachment of electrons to molecules *in the measuring field*. There was no evidence of any breakup of negative ion clusters.

Values of mobilities intermediate between electrons and normal negative ions are a direct consequence of the finite value of the probability of attachment. With the resultant attachment of the average electrons in the measuring field, carriers were observed that had crossed the first part of the gap as fast electrons, and the last part of the gap as slow ions. The average time taken to cross the gap was, therefore, essentially the time of traversing that portion of the gap from the point of average ion attachment, since the mobility of the electron is of the order of 10^3 times that of the ion. With this orienting picture, it is possible to take up the theory of J. J. Thomson and to indicate how it was established.

§ 2. The Electron-Attachment Theory of J. J. Thomson (6).

Let h be the chance that an electron will attach to a given molecular species on a single impact. The value of h is assumed to be a function of the species only, and is independent of the electron energy. The average random velocity of the electron is $\bar{c}_1$ and its average free path is λ. The collision frequency is $z = c_1/\lambda$. In a field of strength X, an electron moves with a drift velocity $v = k_e X$ cm/sec, with k_e the electron mobility. An electron advances a distance of 1 cm in $1/k_e X$ sec, making $(\bar{c}_1/\lambda)(1/k_e X)$ impacts en route. In advancing dx cm in the field direction, an electron will make $dx\ \bar{c}_1/\lambda k_e X$ impacts. If n electrons leave a plane photoelectric source plate $x = 0$ at a certain instant, the number dn which attach in advancing dx cm in the field will be

$$(5.1) \qquad dn = - hn\ \frac{\bar{c}_1}{\lambda k_e X}\ dx.$$

This follows, since h is a pure chance, and thus dn depends on $nzh\ dx$. If $n = n_0$ at $x = 0$, and $n = n$ at $x = x$, integration at once gives

$$(5.2) \qquad \log_e \frac{n}{n_0} = \frac{h\bar{c}_1}{\lambda k_e X}\ x,$$

or

$$(5.3) \qquad n = n_0\ \epsilon^{\frac{h\bar{c}_1 x}{\lambda k_e X}}.$$

This gives the survival law, that out of n_0 electrons that start at $x = 0$, the number n surviving attachment after traversing x cm in the gas will be given by expression 5.3. The fraction attaching between x and $x + dx$ is

$$(5.4) \qquad \frac{dn}{n_0} = - \frac{h\bar{c}_1}{\lambda k_e X}\ \epsilon^{- \frac{h\bar{c}_1}{\lambda k_e X}\ x}\ dx.$$

The average distance $\bar{x}$ that the electrons must go in order to attach is found at once to be

$$(5.5) \qquad \bar{x} = \frac{\int_0^{n_0} x\ dn}{\int_0^{n_0} dn} = \frac{\lambda k_e x}{h\bar{c}_1},$$

and the average number of impacts required to attach will be

(5.6)
$$\bar{n} = \frac{\bar{x}\,\bar{c_1}}{\lambda k_e X} = \frac{1}{h}.$$

Since the quantities $\bar{c_1}/\lambda$ are not easy to evaluate directly except by Townsend's methods, it is possible, as the author showed, from equation 3.1 to write

$$k_e = 0.815\,\frac{e}{m}\,\frac{\lambda}{\bar{C_1}} = 0.75\,\frac{e}{m}\,\frac{\lambda}{\bar{c_1}},$$

and thus that

(5.7)
$$\frac{\lambda}{\bar{c_1}} = \frac{mk_e}{0.75e}.$$

Accordingly, relations 5.3, 5.4, and 5.5 become

(5.8)
$$n = n_0\,\epsilon^{-\dfrac{0.75\,ehx}{mk_e^2 X}} = n_0\,\epsilon^{-\dfrac{1.35 \times 10^{15}\,hx}{k_e^2 X}},$$

(5.9)
$$\frac{dn}{n_0} = -\frac{0.75\,eh}{mk_e^2\lambda}\,\epsilon^{-\dfrac{0.75\,ehx}{mk_e^2 X}}\,dx,$$

and

(5.10)
$$\bar{x} = \frac{k_e^2 mX}{0.75\,eh} = \frac{k_e^2 X}{1.35 \times 10^{15}\,hx},$$

with X the field strength in volts/cm.

Since the days of J. J. Thomson, and much more since 1937, it has become customary to describe various electronic and other events in terms of equivalent cross sections. Thus, it is now customary to consider events such as elastic impacts, excitation, ionizing, and photon absorption in terms of equivalent atomic cross sections for purposes of comparison. In such considerations it is assumed that experiments will yield the number of electrons or photons n out of n_0 surviving without elastic impact, or excitation, electron attachment, etc., after x cm random path in the gas. If this is so, then it is permitted to write

(5.11)
$$n = n_0\,\epsilon^{-\pi\sigma^2 N_1 px}$$

for collisional, or encounter, events where $\pi\sigma^2$ is the "atomic cross section" for the event, collision, excitation, etc.; N_1 is the number of atoms or molecules of gas per cm^3 at 1 mm Hg of pressure; p is the pressure in mm; and x is the distance traversed in which the events could occur. For photon absorption, Beer's law also permits of writing

$$(5.12) \qquad I = I_0\,\epsilon^{-\mu x} = I_0\,\epsilon^{-\pi\sigma^2 N_1\,px}.$$

Often the total cross section for 1 cm at 1 mm pressure is used; $\pi\sigma^2 N_1 = Q$.

This treatment lends itself to applications for electron attachment in ion formation. The quantity h is defined as the probability of attachment relative to elastic collisions with atoms. The Ramsauer free path is

$$(5.13) \qquad \lambda = \frac{1}{\pi\sigma_R^2\,N} = \frac{1}{\pi\sigma_R^2\,N_1 p} \quad \text{with } \lambda_1 = \frac{1}{\pi\sigma_R^2\,N_1}.$$

Therefore,

$$(5.14) \qquad \pi\sigma_R^2 = q_R = \frac{1}{\lambda_1 N_1}.$$

If the cross section for attachment is $q_a = \pi\sigma_a^2$, then by definition

$$(5.15) \qquad h = q_a/q_R = \frac{\pi\sigma_a^2}{\pi\sigma_R^2}.$$

To convert h into values of q_a, all that need be done is to write

$$(5.16) \qquad q_a = h\,q_R = h\,\pi\sigma_R^2 = \frac{h}{\lambda_1 N_1}.$$

Note that the equation 5.3 used for evaluating h from loss of electrons to attachment when moving in the field direction

$$n = n_0\,\epsilon^{-\frac{\bar{c}_1\,hpx}{\lambda_1 pv}}$$

is *not* to be set parallel to the equation

$$(5.12) \qquad n = n_0\,\epsilon^{-\pi\sigma_a^2 N_1\,px},$$

as the x used in equation 5.3 is a directed motion in the field X, and not a random distance in the gas; which, together with Ramsauer free paths, defines q_a.

To give an idea of the order of magnitude of q_a, Bradbury gives $h = 3 \times 10^{-4}$ for O_2 at $X/p \sim 0.6$. The value of $N_1 = 3.53 \times 10^{16}$ per cm³, and at $X/p = 0.6$, table 3.1 of Townsend gives λ_1 for O_2 as 6.21×10. Thus, $q_a = 1.36 \times 10^{-19}$, which is less than one-tenth of the excitation and ionization cross sections.

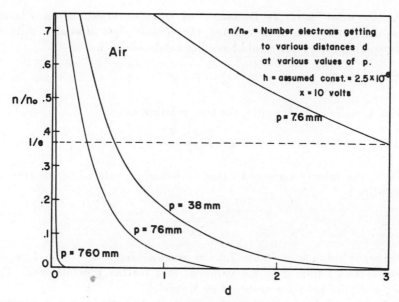

Fig. 5.1. Rough values of n/n_0, showing loss of electrons in air by attach-ment at several pressures as a function of distance x in the field direction.

The significance of these relations is seen by reference to figure 5.1, which shows rough values of n/n_0 plotted against x for h constant in air at several pressures. The value of $\bar{x}$ is the value of x at which $n/n_0 = 1/e$. It is seen to increase rapidly as p decreases from 760 mm to $p = 7.6$ in air. Roughly, it is the value of $\bar{x}$ that effectively determines the mobility observed for the attaching electrons as they cross from the photoelectric plate or origin to the collecting electrode in Kovarick's method. Assume the plate distance to be d cm and the applied square-wave potential to be a variable V. The extrapolated intercept V^1 of the current-potential curve on the potential axis corresponds roughly to the potential needed to carry the electrons from the photoelectric plate to the collecting electrode. These elec-trons went $\bar{x}$ cm from the plate as electrons in sensibly 0 time, attached to make ions at $\bar{x}$, and thereafter crossed the remaining $d - x$ cm as ions with a mobility k_i. The field with potential V^1 was $X^1 = V^1/d$, and with the method for the ions crossing in a half cycle T, the relation

(5.17) $$k_i \frac{V^1}{d} T = (d - \bar{x})$$

represents the true conditions leading to the current arising at V^1.

On the other hand, in ignorance of what occurred, using V^1, and assuming that the *ions* crossed the *whole* plate distance d in T, the mobility computed would have been determined by

(5.18) $$k_c \frac{V^1}{d} T = d,$$

with $k_c = d^2 / V^1 T$. Actually, the true relation is

(5.19) $$k_i = \frac{d(d - \bar{x})}{V^1 T}.$$

Thus, the falsely computed value k_c would be related to the true ion mobility by

$$\frac{k_c}{k_i} = \frac{d}{(d - \bar{x})}.$$

Hence, in going from 760 to 7.6 mm pressure for a 3-cm gap, k_c would appear to go from k_i to the value of that for the free electron. This is the sort of behavior observed by Kovarick.

It was on the basis of such crude considerations that the author, in 1920, guessing at the value[1] of the electron mobility in air at the attaching pressures, arrived at the first rough estimate for h in air from the values of $\bar{x}$. It was quite clear at this time that values of h could be determined only if values of k_e were known. Consequently, when circumstances brought H. B. Wahlin to the author's laboratory at Chicago, the author turned over to him the rough method he had evolved for using $\bar{x}$ to evaluate h from mobility measurements of the hybrid carriers in Kovarick's method. The author then devoted his time to evaluating electron mobilities in the pressure ranges covered by Wahlin in ion-attachment studies. However, Wahlin's measurements of h extended over such a range of different gases that it was not possible to gather the needed data on k_e. Thus, Wahlin's values of h, as published, indicated only the roughest orders of r..agnitude (7). These established the existence of a wide range of values of h, and associated these with molecular species. Such data were badly needed at that time in order to test Thomson's concept. These studies showed that electrons appeared not to attach in N_2, H_2, CO, and NH_3 in appreciable numbers at the low X/p used by *Wahlin*. The gases C_2H_4, C_2H_2, and C_2H_6 gave doubtful values, and their purity was not assured. The gases N_2O, C_2H_5Cl, air, O_2, and Cl_2 showed increasingly rapid attachment in the order named; i.e., the values

---

[1] It must be noted that the values of k_e for electrons from the deflection methods of Townsend did not then extend to the pressures and X/p values at which $\bar{x}$ had suitable values for extimating h.

of h observed increased in value in the order of gases named, which seemed reasonable.

By 1923 the author had carried his electron-mobility measurements to the point where he obtained fairly good values for electron mobilities in air over a range of X/p and p values covered by attachment measurements (8). At the same time, Melvin Mooney had worked out the complete theory of the current-voltage curve for attachment in a gas like air, using the Rutherford a.c. method as developed by the author and Wahlin for this work. Thus, it was possible accurately to evaluate h from one measurement, and to apply this to the computation of the curves for current i against potential V given by the method, which could then be compared with direct observation (9). Choosing a single fixed value of h from an intermediate pressure range, the author computed the complete family of curves for ion current to the collector as a function of frequency, potential, plate distance, etc., for a whole series of pressures. Compared with the observed curves, the fit of the curves for the pressure at which h was chosen was fairly good, as were, to a less extent, the curves for two adjacent pressures. For greater ranges of pressure to both sides of the fitted value, while the calculated evolution of the curve shapes was in general agreement with the observed curves, the observed evolution progressed much more rapidly than the computed evolution as pressure changed.

The sort of agreement obtained could be compared to that observed with a van der Waals equation and its observed curves at different temperatures derived from one pair of values, the constants a and b. The type of fit there implied that the constants a and b were varying with one of the other parameters in the van der Waals curves, e.g., with T. In the case of the mobility data, fits could have been obtained by varying the value of h with X/p. The author felt at that time that this was not warranted by data on k_e, and the involved character of the equations that were used. It was thus concluded that while the theory of Thomson more than qualitatively explained the phenomenon, it did not do so quantitatively. The author, therefore, temporarily abandoned studies of h until a better instrumental method should present itself. This method came in 1926 with the author's invention of the electron filter, which was destined to make the evaluation of h a direct and accurate one.

In the meanwhile, the cause of the author's failure in 1923 to achieve a quantitative proof of the Thomson theory, using the alternating-current method of study, was discovered by V. A. Bailey (10). This came with the experimental evaluation of h at three values of X/p by Bailey, using a new method. That study showed that h *varied with electron energy*, or X/p, and that h decreased as X/p increased. This progressive change in h might have been observed by the author with the a.c. method had he solved for h over a large range of X/p, thus forcing a fit to observation by adjusting h. However, he had used the most sensitive values of X and p applicable in order to make a good evaluation of h, and had not realized that the variation in h might be real.

§ 3. The Method of Bailey (10), (11).

It is now essential to present the method of Bailey. For simplicity, assume an electron mean free path λ which does not vary appreciably with velocity, and an average velocity of thermal agitation $\bar{c_1}$. The collision frequency of the electrons is $z = c_1/\lambda$. If the drift velocity is v, then the time to move x cm in the field direction is x/v. Thus, n electrons make $n\bar{c_1} x/v\lambda$ collisions in advancing x cm in the field direction. With an attachment probability h, the number of collisions resulting in attachment is $h(n\bar{c_1}x/\lambda v)$. Bailey defined a quantity a which represents the number of electrons attaching per cm advance in the field direction. Thus, according to the definition of a, $nax = hn\bar{c_1}x/\lambda v$, so that

$(5.20)^2$
$$a = \frac{h\bar{c_1}}{\lambda v} .$$

This relation is inexact to the extent that λ is a function of $\bar{c_1}$, and that $\bar{c_1}$ represents the average random velocity of all electrons. Corrections for the various average values used in experiment and theory, as indicated by Bailey, are small. Even for a Maxwellian distribution law they are represented only by a factor 0.92. In other energy distributions the corrections for averages differ from unity by even less.

The development of the method depends on measurements of the relative lateral diffusion losses to a series of perforated plates from an appropriately shaped beam of electrons moving in an imposed electrical field along the axis.

The diffusion device first used by Bailey consists of a plate A, from which electrons originate through illumination by ultraviolet light, as shown in figure 5.2. Below this are four parallel plates numbered 5, 3, 1, and 0. Of these, 5, 3, and 1 are perforated with slits of equal width parallel to the y axis and accurately aligned. 0 is a collection electrode, and together with plates 5, 3, and 1, it can be applied to a device for measuring currents which they receive. Plates 4 and 2 are guard rings so placed that the system of plates 5, 4, 3, 2, 1, 0 represents a uniform electrical field driving electrons

---

[2]Note: $a \equiv 1/\bar{x}$, equation 5.5.

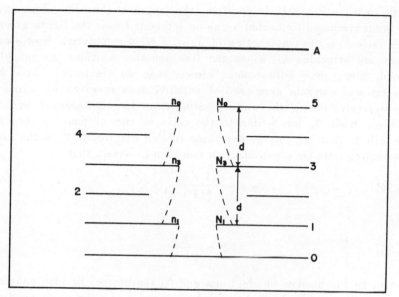

Fig. 5.2. Schematic drawing of V. A. Bailey's
diffusion method for measuring h.

from A to 0 at constant speed along the x axis. The distance between
plates 5 and 3 and between 3 and 1 is equal, and is designated by d.
The ratio R of currents collected as a result of diffusion along the
x axis at either of the plates 1 or 3 relative to that at 0 can be
measured for the initial current passing through the slit at 5. The
normal distribution curve for electrons, as shown earlier in this book,
is given by the diffusion equation

$$(5.21) \qquad \nabla^2 n = \frac{NeX}{\eta P} \frac{\partial n}{\partial x},$$

where X is the field along x, N is the Loschmidt number, P is the
gas pressure at n.t.p., and η is the Townsend energy factor. In this
case the solution is given in the form

$$q(y, x) = A x^{\frac{1}{2}} \epsilon^{-(40.5\, xy^2/4\eta X)},$$

with

$$(5.22) \qquad q(y, x) = \int_{-\infty}^{+\infty} n\, dy.$$

The ratio R of currents collected is then given by

$$(5.23) \qquad R = \frac{\int_0^a q(z, d)\, dz}{\int_0^\infty q(z, d)\, dz},$$

with $2a$ the slit width. In practice, the length of the slits along y is so great compared to $2a$ that y can be integrated over the limits given. The ratio R is thus a function of $X/\eta d$, i.e., $R = R(X/\eta d)$. Now electrons are attaching all along the line and the relations are complicated, since ions diffuse more slowly than do electrons. Let ξ be the ratio of currents composed of negative ions received by 1 and 3 respectively, and χ the corresponding ratio for electrodes 0 and 1. For electrode 3, let S_3 denote the ratio of current passing through the slit to that arriving at the plane of that electrode. S_1 is the corresponding ratio for electrode 1. It can then be shown that

$$(5.24) \qquad\qquad S_3 = \frac{\xi(1 + \chi)}{1 + \xi(1 + \chi)}$$

and

$$(5.25) \qquad\qquad S_1 = \frac{\chi}{1 + \chi}.$$

Let n_0 be the number of electrons and N_0 the number of ions passing per second through slit 5. Let n_3, N_3, n_1, and N_1 be the corresponding values for electrodes 3 and 1 respectively. Of the n_0 electrons passing through 5, a number $n_0 \, \epsilon^{-ad}$ arrive at plane 3. These electrons have a distribution ratio $R(X/\eta d)$, where R is a known function. For negative ions, $\eta = 1$, so that it is the function $R(X/d)$ that must be used. For electrons which did not attach, $R(X/\eta d)$ would be equal to S_3 and to S_1. Then $n_3 = bn_0$, with

$$(5.26) \qquad\qquad b = R(X/\eta d) \, \epsilon^{-ad}.$$

In a like fashion, $n_1 = bn_3 = b^2 n_0$. In the space between 5 and 3, the remaining, or $n_0(1 - \epsilon^{-ad})$, electrons form ions which arrive at plane 3 with a distribution ratio r. It then follows that

$$(5.27) \qquad N_3 = N_0 \, R(X/d) + n_0 \, (1 - \epsilon^{-ad}) r = N_0 \, R + g n_0.$$

Similarly,

$$(5.28) \qquad\qquad N_1 = N_3 \, R + g n_3 = R^2 N_0 + (Rg + gb) \, n_0.$$

It is also seen that

$$(5.29) \qquad\qquad S_3 = (n_3 + N_3)/(n_0 + N_0),$$

and again,

$$(5.30) \qquad\qquad S_3 S_1 = (n_1 + N_1)/(n_0 + N_0).$$

These relations yield the equation

$$(5.31) \qquad\qquad b = S_3 \, (R - S_1)/(R - S_3).$$

In carrying out the measurement, a given set of values of X and p are chosen, and the ratios of currents ξ and χ are directly observed. From these values, S_1 and S_3 are computed from equations 5.24 and 5.25. Now the ratio X/d is known from the field X used and the construction of the apparatus, so that R for ions can be read directly from the normal distribution curve. This at once permits the value of b to be determined from equation 5.31.

The expression

$$(5.26) \qquad b = R(X/\eta d)\, \epsilon^{-ad}$$

contains two unknowns, η and a. This requires a second relation, which can be obtained from

$$(5.32) \qquad b_1 = R(qX/\eta d)\, \epsilon^{-qad}.$$

It happens that a/p is a function of X/p only, and that η is a function of X/p only. Thus, if a second measurement is made with X/p the same but X and p changed so that the field is qX and the pressure is qp, the different attachment between S_5 and S_3 and S_3 and S_1 will give a new value of b_1 following equation 5.31. The values of b_1 and b can then be used to evaluate both η and a.

This, in principle, was Bailey's original method. To get greater flexibility, the later work used a chamber in which the distances between 5 and 3 and 3 and 1 could be varied. This simplifies the calculation of η and a. Two values of b, namely b and b_1, are determined; the first corresponding to X, p, and d; the second corresponding to qX, qp, and qd. With X/p unchanged, it is possible to write

$$(5.26) \qquad b = R(X/\eta d)\, \epsilon^{-ad};$$

$$(5.33) \qquad b_1 = R(X/\eta d)\, \epsilon^{-q^2 ad}.$$

From these relations, it follows that

$$(5.34) \qquad (q^2 - 1)\, ad = \log_e (b/b_1);$$

$$(5.35) \qquad R(X/\eta d) = b^{\frac{q^2}{(q^2-1)}} \Big/ b_1^{\frac{1}{(q^2-1)}}.$$

Thus, from 5.34 a is evaluated, while from 5.35 η is evaluated.

It is hardly worth while to give here in detail the techniques developed by Bailey and his students for making measurements. These are described both in the original papers and in Healey and Reed. The apparatus was tested on H_2 in which $h = 0$ and for which values of η were known. For $R > 0.36$, the values of S_1 agreed closely with the values of R. Below the value indicated the difference between S_1 and R became greater. These effects were found to come from the ends of the slits. The values of S_3 were consistently 6% less than those of S_1. This difference was ascribed to lack of uniformity in the upper field and errors in the dimensions and locations of the slits. This necessitated the use of two distribution curves, one for each of the electrodes 3 and 1. For $R > 0.40$, the electrode-distribution ratio R'' was taken equal to the calculated values and equal to the experimental values of S_1 for smaller values of R. The ratio R' for electrode 3 was taken as 0.94 R''. This required a slight modification of the theory, which will not be given.

The method as modified was tried out on dry air. The values of η agreed with those previously given by Townsend and Tizard. As X/p varied from 0.422 to 0.750, values of a/p observed varied from 3.36×10^{-3} to 0.54×10^{-3}. Corresponding values of h were calculated, using results for v by Townsend and Tizard. These gave $h = 7 \times 10^{-16} \ av^2/X$, which comes from eliminating $\bar{c}/\lambda$ from the equation $a = h\bar{c}/\lambda v$ and $v = 0.815 \ (Xe\lambda/mc)$. These are the first observations of a variation of h with energy. These results, coming as they did in 1925 on the heels of the author's failure at quantitative agreement between Thomson's theory and the current-potential carriers in 1923, clarified the whole problem.

It is to be noted that Bailey's method evaluates only a/p and η. In order to evaluate h, it is necessary to know either v, λ, or f, the mean energy of an electron lost at an impact.[3] From the values of the quantities λ and η, or f, indicated in chapter III, it is possible to compute v, and by means of v, thus to determine h from X and a.

Bailey's measurements of h were later extended to NH_3 and HCl. Measured values of v, etc., did not exist for these gases, and would be hard to achieve on account of rapid attachment in HCl. It became clear that for the application of the method to gases effectively attaching electrons, there was required a further development of the method enabling v or some other of the three quantities above to be measured. The unsatisfactory values first obtained by Bailey in NH_3 led to a modification of the apparatus in which b was varied. Tests on H_2 again gave good agreement between calculated values of R, above $R > 0.50$, S_1 and S_3. Work was also extended to pentane,

---

[3]The quantity f is discussed in detail later in this section.

values of v being obtained in a separate determination with Townsend's magnetic-deflection method. In 1930, Bailey (10) extended the method for evaluating a and η by means of subsidiary measurements so that the data needed to evaluate a/p, η, v, λ, and f in a gas which attached electrons could be obtained with one and the same piece of apparatus. The principle of the extension depends on the effect of a magnetic field parallel to the movement of the carriers in the field along the x direction. Townsend had previously shown that in a magnetic field along the x axis, the diffusion coefficients

(5.36)
$$D_y = D_z = \frac{D}{1 + \omega^2 T^2},$$

and that $D_x = D$. In this equation $\omega = He/m$, T is the mean time between collisions, and D is the ordinary diffusion coefficient satisfying the relation

(3.3)
$$\frac{v}{D} = \frac{NeX}{\eta P}, \text{ or } \frac{k_e}{D} = \frac{Ne}{\eta P}.$$

For given values of X and p, the drift velocity v in the x direction is not affected by the presence of the magnetic field H. It also follows from the magnetic-deflection method of evaluating v that $\tan \theta = \omega T = Hv/X$, as shown in equation 3.47. The equations of motion then become

$$n u_y = - D_y \frac{\partial n}{\partial y}$$

(5.37)
$$n u_z = - D_z \frac{\partial n}{\partial z}$$

$$n u_x = - D_x \frac{\partial n}{\partial x} + nv .$$

Thus, from the equation of continuity, assuming a steady current, it may be written that

(5.38)
$$\frac{1}{\phi} \left(\frac{\partial^2 n}{\partial y^2} + \frac{\partial^2 n}{\partial z^2} \right) + \frac{\partial^2 n}{\partial x^2} = \frac{v}{D} \frac{\partial n}{\partial x}$$

where

(5.39)
$$\phi = 1 + \left(\frac{Hv}{X} \right)^2 .$$

In this relation, X is in e.m.u. and H is in oersteds. Equation 5.38 can be simplified by integrating each term with respect to y, i.e., parallel to the slit axis; since as n, and thus $\partial n/\partial y$, are nearly equal to zero at the side boundary, it follows that

$$(5.40) \qquad \frac{1}{\phi}\frac{\partial^2 q}{\partial z^2} + \frac{\partial^2 q}{\partial x^2} = \frac{v}{D}\frac{\partial q}{\partial x}, \text{ with } q = \int_{-\infty}^{\infty} n\, dy.$$

Then, since $v/D = 40.3\ X/\eta$, and replacing x by ξd, the relation becomes

$$(5.41) \qquad \frac{\partial^2 q}{\partial z^2} = 40.3\,\frac{X\phi}{\eta d}\frac{\partial q}{\partial \xi} - \frac{\phi}{d^2}\frac{\partial^2 q}{\partial \xi^2}.$$

If $X/\eta d$ is not too small, the second term on the right-hand side can be neglected relative to the first, so that it is possible to set

$$(5.42) \qquad \frac{\partial^2 q}{\partial z^2} = 40.3\,\frac{X\phi}{\eta d}\frac{\partial q}{\partial \xi}.$$

This makes the distribution ratio R a function of $\phi/\eta d$. With diminishing fields H, ϕ approaches unity and $X\phi/\eta d$ approaches $X/\eta d$. The new distribution ratio is obtained by replacing $X/\eta d$ by $X\phi/\eta d$.

From this theory it is seen that if a measurement is made with $H = 0$ and in the usual fashion, determining x and ξ by using values of X/p and Xq/pq, a/p and η are determined. The field H is then put on parallel to X and x. A new distribution ratio R will result that is determined by the effect of $X\phi/\eta d$ instead of $X/\eta d$. The evaluation of this ratio in the same fashion leads to the determination of

$$(5.39) \qquad \phi = 1 + \left(\frac{Hv}{X}\right)^2,$$

which yields the value of v. Several methods of evaluating v are possible, from measurements with H parallel to X. In one method, after the determination of a/p and η, the field H is applied until the divergence of the stream with H is just that for a stream of negative ions only. This is equivalent to saying that S_1 and S_3 are equal to $R(X/d)$. This observed field can be designated as H_0, and the value of ϕ corresponding to it will be called ϕ_0. Then $R(X\phi_0/\eta d) = R(X/d)$, with the result that

$$(5.43) \qquad \eta = \phi_0 = 1 + \left(\frac{H_0 v}{X}\right)^2.$$

Thus, evaluation of ϕ_0 yields the value of

(5.44)
$$v = \frac{X}{H_0}\sqrt{\eta - 1} \times 10^8,$$

with X in volts/cm.

As with all these preliminary basic analyses, the derivation of the relation is not accurate. It may be corrected by multiplying the v deduced by a factor which does not greatly deviate from unity. The results obtained by this method and those obtained by Townsend using magnetic fields differ surprisingly little. As stated before, once v and η are determined, h, λ, and f can be computed. The chief advantage of this method is that it can be used in the presence of considerable electron attachment. Healey and Reed (11) give other procedures for using the method to evaluate the various quantities. In order to study properties of some of the strongly electron-attaching gases, a method of mixing these gases with other more inert gases was developed. Using the relations already deduced and the known constants of the one gas, the method of Bailey permits the evaluation of $(a/p)m$ for the mixture and the solution for all the unknown quantities for heavily electron-attaching gases. Even more elaborate methods have been developed, using admixtures of the gas of unknown properties with two different known gases. This makes possible the determination of a/p, h, η, c, λ, f, and v for each gas of the mixtures, and the unknown gas from observations of H_0 in pairs of gaseous mixtures.

Despite the general agreement between the results of workers using the Townsend methods and those of Bailey, and the general rough agreement of these with the results of Bradbury and of Bradbury and Nielsen when the averaging processes are suitably adjusted, none of this work represents any high degree of precision. Thus, such quantities as *collision cross sections*, or *electron mean free paths*, are much more accurately determined in terms of narrow ranges of electron energies by the *direct measurements* of Ramsauer and other workers. It should also be indicated that the range of values of X/p is more limited, especially at the low end.

The meaning of the fractional energy loss f must now be analyzed. For an electron moving in an inert gas in a field where its average energy is far below the excitation of energy of any state, the electron, at each encounter with an atom in which it is deflected by an angle θ, loses the fraction

(4.2)
$$f_\theta = 2\frac{m}{M}(1 - \cos\theta)$$

of its energy E of agitation to the *elastic* encounter. While the angle

θ varies at each encounter.so that f_θ varies, the average value of θ with isotropic scattering is 90°, and $f = 2\ (m/M)$, as indicated earlier. Even when scattering is not isotropic, the value of $1 - \cos\theta$ is on the average not far from unity, as Maier-Leibnitz showed in his study of the scattering processes. From this it is clear that the behavior is characterized by relatively small losses of the order of $10^{-3}\ E = (\tfrac{1}{2}mC_1{}^2) \times 10^{-3}$ per impact; and that while the loss is not the same at each impact, it is very rarely zero, and averages up in relatively few impacts. Thus, as an electron goes through the gas at 1 mm pressure making 10^9 impacts per sec, it gains energy equal to $Xe\delta$ over a distance of advance δ in the field direction, and loses fE at each impact within δ. At equilibrium, the gain and loss are on the average equal. It is then possible to write that if an electron moves δ cm in the field direction with drift velocity v, the time taken is δ/v. If z is the collision frequency, then it makes $z\delta/v = c_1\delta/\lambda v$ impacts. The average loss by collision is $f(\tfrac{1}{2}mC_1{}^2)$, so that in δ cm the loss is $(\bar{c}_1/\lambda)\ (\delta/v)\ \tfrac{1}{2}fmC_1{}^2$, which at equilibrium just balances the gain $Xe\delta$ from the field. This balance then allows one to infer that

$$f = \frac{2Xe}{m}\ \frac{\lambda}{\bar{c}_1}\ \frac{v}{C_1^2}\,,$$

and with

(3.1)
$$v = Xk_e = \tfrac{3}{4}\ \frac{Xe\lambda}{\bar{c}_1}\,,$$

the quantity f becomes

(5.45)
$$f = \frac{8}{3}\ \frac{v^2}{C_1^2}\,.$$

The numerical coefficient 8/3 will vary with the averages used in equation 3.1, and Bailey uses 2. Thus, with the high value of z and the small collision loss, it is possible to speak of the fractional energy loss in an elastic impact, and to evaluate it directly by measuring v the drift velocity and evaluating C_1 from the value of η in a diffusion measurement.

If now the average electron energy gets high enough so that an appreciable number of the electrons achieve the energy of vibrational excitation of the molecules, or increasing still further reach electronic excitation or even ionization energies, new sources of loss appear. Such losses were first detected by Franck and Hertz in 1913, when they studied the reflection of electrons from molecular gases instead of the inert gases. The matter was further studied by Baerwald (III.17) in Lenard's laboratory, and almost simultaneously by W. Harries (III.17) in Franck's laboratory just about the time of the advent of wave mechanics in 1926. Harries studied N_2 and CO with 5.2 volt electrons. A much more exhaustive study was made by H. Ramien (III.17) in Franck's laboratory in 1931, on H_2.

The methods used involved studying the energy distribution of initially monoenergetic electrons (1 volt spread), using retarding potentials after some 20 to 100 collisions with molecules had been experienced. Comparison was made between the curves for He and for H_2. In He only energy losses to elastic impacts occurred. The comparison for curves in He and H_2 reduced the complications caused by the random directions of the electrons after many collisions, and yielded rather satisfactory results for H_2 from about 3.5 volts of energy up to about 12 e.v. The data that were obtained indicate clearly what is to be expected.

Other data that were obtained less directly by the methods of Bailey are complicated by many factors, and yield a somewhat peculiar f. The molecules of the more stable gases, such as H_2, N_2, CO, and O_2 are largely in their zero vibrational states at n.t.p. The lowest vibrational states set in at about 0.54 e.v. for H_2, 0.26 e.v. for N_2 and CO, and 0.2 e.v. for O_2. H_2 should dissociate at 4.16 e.v., while N_2 requires 9.6 e.v. and O_2 requires 5.1 e.v. The first excited electronic state of H_2 is around 12 e.v., and ionization sets in at around 15 e.v. For O_2, the first electronic state is one at 0.98 e.v., which requires quite a momentum charge from the ground state; while the next electronic state is at 1.62 e.v., and is one that is readily excited. Ionization sets in at 14 e.v. Rotational-energy levels are of course very much lower in energy.

It is clear, from experience with the inert gases, that the only loss of energy of electrons in elastic impacts is so small that it is not capable of materially influencing the translational motion of atoms and molecules, and is equally unlikely to excite rotations or vibrations directly. However, as Franck and Condon showed, an electron approaching a molecule perturbs the electronic states in transit. This transit time is usually *short* compared with the vibrational periods. It is the time for the electron at $5 \times 10^7 \sqrt{V}$ cm per second (V is the energy in volts) to go a distance σ. Thus, the electronic potential state of the molecule is temporarily altered adiabatically during transit.

If the distorted potential curve happens to have its temporary minima so displaced as to coincide with the end of the swing of the atoms of the molecule in the first excited vibrational state of the undistorted curve, the receding electron may leave the molecule excited to its first excited vibrational state as it reverts to its previous electronic potential state. It will thus leave with its energy reduced by just the amount E_v to awaken the vibrational state. It could likewise also leave the molecule in its second or third vibrational state. Since the chance of leaving it in its first state is small (of the order of 1 or 2%), the chances are much smaller for larger losses of energy.

If the electron has enough energy electronically to distort the potential diagram, thus causing the temporary excited curve to cross the undistorted curve at an appropriate point so that vibrational energy exceeds the energy of dissociation, the atoms may separate to infinity. So far as present observation goes, this does not occur for H_2 at 4.16 e.v. At 9 e.v., however, Ramien observed that some electrons suffered a large energy loss. This was interpreted as the transition from the $1^1\Sigma$ state of H_2 to the $1^3\Sigma$ state, which is unstable. The whole 9 e.v. of the electron is taken up, and the H_2 atoms separate with some 5 e.v. of kinetic energy.

It is thus clear that through the Franck-Condon principle, electrons of more than the energy to excite the first vibrational state E_v can in relatively rare impacts lose the energy E_v to vibrational energy. Since E_v is relatively small, the electron will not generally lose all its energy E, which in a field usually exceeds E_v, but only E_v retaining $E - E_v$. When it gets energies capable of causing dissociation, where this occurs, electronic excitation, or ionization, these energies being relatively large compared to those of the average electron, the loss is E_d, E_e, or E_i, and the electron usually is left with $E - E_e$ near zero. Thus, at higher average electron energies, electrons lose energy to elastic impacts fE at every encounter, vibrational energy E_v at one encounter in some hundred, and a great deal of energy E_d, E_e, or E_i on occasional encounters (about 1%), when it has E greater than these quantities.

Concerning the loss to vibration, it is possible that E_v can be lost as soon as the value of E for an electron exceeds this value. Since the process involves the electronic-transit time over the diameter of the molecule in a critical fashion, it is not certain that E_v will be lost as soon as E exceeds E_v. Experimentally, there has been no test of the lower limit, or of the probability of such excitation at the limit. At about seven to ten times the value of E_v in H_2 and N_2, measurements have been made; e.g., at about 3.5 and 5.2 e.v. In this region and above in H_2, the probability of excitation decreases linearly to about 7 e.v. This is in agreement with theory, which places the chance of excitation as being less, the shorter the transit time; and in fact $P_v(E)$ decreases as $T = (\sigma/C_1) \propto 1/\sqrt{E}$. In any event, the ratio of the cross section for vibrational excitation to that for elastic impacts, $\sigma_v/\sigma_R = P_v(E)$, is a function that above a certain limiting value of E, E_v, or greater, decreases as E increases. For excitation and ionization, and for the dissociation of H_2 at about 9 e.v., the process is definitely one for which $P_e(E) = \sigma_e/\sigma_R$ increases from E_d or E_e upward for a range in E perhaps as much as $E = 3E_e$, and then declines.

It is now possible to derive a more complete expression for the loss and gain of electron energy in a field, neglecting diffusive motion along the lines of equation 5.14. Again, assuming the elastic-collision frequency as $z = \bar{c}_1\delta/\lambda v$, introducing the chances of losses $P_v(E)$ above E_v and $P_e(E)$ above some higher critical energy E_e, with an energy distribution $f(E)dE$ with the mean energy $\bar{E} = \frac{1}{2}mC_1^2$, it is possible to write

(5.46)

$$\frac{\bar{c}_1}{\lambda}\frac{\delta}{v}\left\{f_e\,\frac{1}{2}mC_1^2 + E_v \int_{E_v}^{\infty} P_v(E)\,F(E)\,dE\right.$$

$$\left. + E_e \int_{E_e}^{\infty} P_e(E)\,F(E)\,dE = X e\delta\,.\right.$$

Setting $\frac{3}{4}\,Xe\lambda/m\bar{c}_1 = v$, dividing by $\frac{1}{2}mC_1^2$, and rearranging terms, the expression becomes

(5.47)

$$f = f_e + f_v + f_{ee} = f_e + \frac{E_v}{\frac{1}{2}mC_1^2}\int_{E_v}^{\infty} P_v(E)\,F(E)\,dE$$

$$+ \frac{\dot{E}_e}{\frac{1}{2}mC_1^2}\int_{E_e}^{\infty} P_e(E)\,F(E)\,dE = \frac{8}{3}\,\frac{v^2}{C_1^2}\,,$$

with

$$f_v = \frac{E_v}{\frac{1}{2}mC_1^2}\int_{E_v}^{\infty} P_v(E)\,F(E)\,dE$$

and

(5.48)

$$f_{ee} = \frac{E_e}{\frac{1}{2}mC_1^2}\int_{E_e}^{\infty} P_e(E)\,F(E)\,dE$$

and an observable

(5.49)
$$f = \frac{8}{3}\frac{v^2}{C_1^2} = f_e + f_v + f_{ee}.$$

It is seen that the quantity on the left-hand side is now the sum of three fractional quantities. The one f_e represents a true average small fractional loss of energy per impact, which is proportional to the energy of the electron E. The other terms are not properly proportional to the average electron energy $\bar{E}$, but set in above a threshold E_v, E_e, and E_i, and can be written as a fraction only when divided by $\bar{E} = \frac{1}{2}mC_1^2$. They do, however, depend on $\bar{E}$, since not only are they divided by it, but the argument in the exponent of $F(E)$ is represented by a ratio of $E/\bar{E}$.

It was further noted that the quantity $P_v(E)$ diminishes linearly with E, and that it has observed values in N_2, CO, and H_2 of the order of 0.01 to 0.03 in energy ranges frequently found in gases. Since, as $\bar{E}$ or $\frac{1}{2}mC_1^2$ increases at most at a ceiling of 1 e.v. or less, not only does the divisor in f_v of $\frac{1}{2}mC_1^2$ increase, but as $\bar{E}$ exceeds E_v the integral must decrease ultimately as $1/\sqrt{E}$. Thus, while f_v will set in as an important factor greater than f_e at about $\bar{E} \sim E_v$, e.g., certainly above 0.5 e.v. for most molecules, it may rise to a peak at some value and ultimately decline as $\bar{E}$ reaches values of some 4 e.v. for most gases. However, as $\bar{E}$ increases so that losses such as E_e or E_d can appear, there could be a sudden increase of f caused by f_{ee}.

Not enough is known about the character of such actions except in the case of H_2, where $P_e(E)$ is a quantity rapidly increasing above $\bar{E} = 9$ e.v. In O_2 the values of E_v become active at 0.2 e.v., and an appreciable loss sets in at 1.62 e.v., where E_e becomes active. However, while $P_v(E)$ and $P_e(E)$ may be known, the integral does not permit of much prediction as to f_{ee} or even of f_v, since the division by $\bar{E}$ is quite important. Therefore, it is not surprising, barring any errors and complications in observation, that the variations of f as computed by Bailey's methods vary in peculiar ways, increasing and decreasing as $\bar{E}$ increases.

At this point a further caution should be introduced relative to the validity of data, not only on f, but also on a, or h and η, or $\bar{E}$, in measurements of the Bailey type as well as those of Bradbury. As soon as $\bar{E}$ is such that an appreciable number of electronic states are excited, giving rise to photons in excess of 5 e.v., the Bailey method, using diffusion through metal diaphragms yielding a or h, and Townsend's measurement of η begin to be falsified, because photoelectrons from the diaphragms become numerous enough to yield spurious currents. These lead to underestimates of h, and possibly to overestimates of η. With Bradbury's fine wires the spurious currents are less important, but such actions were observed by the author, using larger grid members. At values of $\bar{E}$ where enough electrons exceed E_i to yield ionization in the gas, the techniques of Bradbury, Townsend, and Bailey are of no further value. The values of η are too large and the values of h become too small. The data of both Bradbury and Bailey in O_2 at X/p exceeding 16 are probably erroneous. This action was noted by the author to give very large spurious currents with the electron-filter technique. Then only the method of Geballe and Harrison is valid for evaluating h and α for ionization by collision.

Reference to the tables of chapter IV, yielding the data of the Townsend and Bailey group, indicates that this condition was also exceeded in numerous gases. It is only by comparing the values of X/p at which detectable ionization by collision begins, and perhaps choosing values of X/p somewhat below this, that it is safe to use the data of tables 4.4a to 4.16 for h and other data.

The following may be stated regarding the significance of Bailey's f in molecular gases: As a contribution to basic knowledge concerning processes active in gases, as seen from equation 5.45, it is hopeless. It has some value as a symbol in reduction of Bailey's data. Its abrupt change in value as a function of X/p indicates the appearance of a new mechanism of loss, i.e., new thresholds of inelasticity. This is indicated equally well by the appropriate changes derived from experiment in η and in v. Were one to calculate values of v by means of an equation of the Compton type, the f could be introduced for the quantity f in equation 3.31. However, since Bailey's f, except for elastic impacts, is determined from experimental values of v, it is better to use these values directly. Were it possible to evaluate f in a given region of X/p and not evaluate v, then f would be a useful concept. Actually, as tables show, these quantities are all determined simultaneously by the same experimental data. Perhaps the one area in which the value of f will be useful is in the calculation of the number of impacts and the distance of advance in the field direction required of an electron to achieve a given fraction ϕ of its terminal energy, as indicated in equation 3.23. Even here, owing to the character of the real energy loss depending on $P_v(E)$ with its low value, the estimate of ϕ could be misleading, especially at low pressures where it is of most interest.

Electron-drift velocities or mobilities are probably more accurately evaluated by direct means, such as the shutter methods of Bradbury and Nielsen and of Nielsen, or by the variants of these methods now possible, than by magnetic-deflection and diffusion measurements. There is a possibility that in measurements such as used by Bradbury and Nielsen, the interpretation of the average velocity inferred is partly determined by the operation of the shutters. This will not be the case for shutters actuated by pulsed square waves in place of sinusoidal a.c. Insofar as the shutter action does influence the value of v, it is possible that the Townsend method yields more significant results if *the form of the distribution is known.*

The value of the attachment coefficient h as obtained by Bailey is not too accurate in view of the very involved character of the theory (11). On the other hand, while the direct method of Bradbury (12) can give very accurate results, it can do so only if v, the drift velocity in the same gas and for the same X/p, *is accurately known.* In Bradbury's work he used his own determination of the drift velocities. The method was a photoelectric one derived from J. J. Thomson's theory of photoelectric electron currents in gases as a function of X/p, and plate distance d for plane parallel electrodes. As Healey and Reed correctly point out, the values of v so obtained are not too accurate, and the error is worse since v^2 enters into the calculation of h by this method. It is desirable that Bradbury's measurements on pure gases be repeated with a more reliable method of evaluating v. Under the *present circumstances*, the *author believes that there is not much choice between the data from the two methods,* as seen from the later accurate work of Doehring (18). Since they are not too radically different in values, either set of data is satisfactory. However, in combination with other data of the diffusion type of measurement, consistency indicates the use of the Bailey data, since these data were all interrelated in calculation and are *ipso facto* consistent.

The data obtained by the Townsend group are completely summarized in a set of tables in Healey and Reed's book (11). Since not only h but many other quantities, such as η, v, C_1, λ_1, and f, are derived as functions of X/p from the combined methods of the Townsend group and Bailey's group, it becomes difficult to know where to present such data in this text. Logically, tables of X/p, λ_1, and drift velocity v should go into chapter III. Chapter IV, part one, should contain data on X/p, η, C_1, and f, and the present chapter should here give tables of h as a function of X/p. Such duplication of tables is wasteful of space. Thus, all the data of the Townsend group on gases of probable interest to readers of this book are presented in tables 4.4a to 4.16 of chapter IV. At the seventh column of each table (where observed) are included data obtained on h by the Bailey methods. The data on the gases CO, NO_2, N_2O, C_5H_{10}, and C_2H_5, presented by Healey and Reed, are not presented in the tables, as they are not of sufficient importance to the reader. The data on h for the various gases there presented are in reasonably satisfactory agreement with the data of Bradbury (12). Since the data were not analyzed and discussed relative to atomic mechanisms by Healey and Reed in as much detail or with the controls achieved by Bradbury, no interpretation of the data will be made at this point. Further development and interpretation will follow in the results of Bradbury and others.

§ 4. The Direct Measurement of h.

As stated earlier, the author ceased attempts to measure h until more satisfactory means of measurement were at hand. In 1926, the author proposed to H. F. Lusk (14), as a master's thesis, that he study the use of a grid of parallel, electrically separated wires with a superposed high-frequency alternating potential difference, placed across alternate wires as an electron filter. Such a set of wires, with a suitable value of potential of this character imposed on the alternate wires, should filter out the mobile free electrons, leaving the more sluggish negative ions unhindered to pass through the grid in a field perpendicular to the plane of the grid. Lusk's preliminary studies showed that the device would work in the manner expected. Thereupon, the electron-filter grid was applied to the measurement of h by A. M. Cravath (15). Cravath designed the apparatus shown in figure 5.3, in which electrons from an oxide-coated filament in the plane of the plane electrode F left the filament and moved downward in a uniform field X at a pressure p. At some distance x from F was a grid G with the plane parallel to F and perpendicular to X. This grid consisted of plane parallel wires of diameter 0.008 cm which were 1 mm apart and insulated from each other by being mounted on a mica disc with a large hole in its center. At a distance d from G was the plane collecting electrode P, attached to an electrometer. Alternate grid wires were connected to a high-frequency oscillator with frequencies variable from 10^6 to 10^7 cycles, giving potentials ranging from 10 to approximately 200 volts. The whole system, with its plane parallel equipotential surfaces F, G, and P, was housed in a metal case and could be held at any convenient pressure.

Careful study of the currents received by G and P as frequency, grid potential, and X/p in the driving field varied, revealed that (under suitable conditions) the electrons that left F and traversed X without attaching were all picked up by G. The ions formed in the

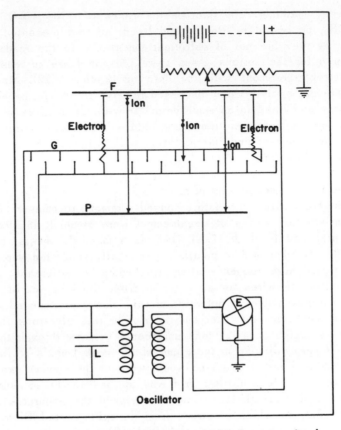

Fig. 5.3. Diagram of Cravath's device for measuring h,
using the Loeb electron filter.

distance x between F and G, except for those intercepted by the
geometrical cross-sectional area of the grids, passed through G and
reached P. Thus, by measuring the current i_0 to P with the alternating
potential $V_g = 0$, the whole current of electrons and ions that was
not intercepted by the cross-sectional area of the grid wires could
be measured at P. When the proper value of V_g and frequency ν were
applied to the wires of G, then only the current of electrons that
attached in the distance x to make ions reached P and registered
as i. Hence, i/i_0 yields the ratio of ions to initial electrons at a
distance x from F in a field X at a pressure p. Thus, $(1 - i/i_0)$ is
the fraction of electrons that escape capture in the distance x. Since
it has earlier been shown that

$$(5.8) \qquad (1 - i/i_0) = \frac{n}{n_0} = \epsilon^{-\frac{1.35 \times 10^{15} h x}{k_e^2 X}},$$

it is clear that since i, i_0, x, and X are known, then if k_e is known, h can be evaluated.

Obviously, a device of this character has its inaccuracies. It was observed that for a given X, p, and frequency ν, as V_g was increased, at first i/i_0 decreased exponentially to a somewhat constant value. The plateau of constant values could be observed over a range of tens to a hundred volts if the value of p was not too low and V_g was not too high. If ν was made too low, ions were captured and i decreased. If ν was too high, all electrons were not captured by G, and the value of i was high. If values of V_g were too high, at times i/i_0 reached a plateau, but rose again to a peak or hump. At higher pressures and very high values of V_g, the curves for i/i_0 usually decreased as V_g increased after passing a plateau. They then rose sharply, especially at low p and high X/p. The rise of the curve for i/i_0 with V_g after the plateau was reached was later shown by the author to be caused by the excitation of the gas by electron impact at high V_g and low p, and a secondary photoelectric emission from the grid wires. The decline of the curves at still higher V_g was caused by a *detachment* of electrons by the fields set up by V_g at low p, as originally suspected by Cravath. The author (16), (17) later showed that this occurred at an X/p of 90 in O_2. The subsequent large rise of all curves at still higher V_g was caused by ionization owing to collision by electrons between the grids.

All these facts were not clear to Cravath at that time, and he was particularly disturbed by the unexplained rise after the plateau was reached. By judicious choice of frequency, grid wire size and spacing, pressure range and V_g, all these effects can be reduced, and reasonably steady values of i/i_0 can be observed, as Bradbury later showed (12). Some estimate was possible of corrections to i for absorption of electrons by the cross-sectional area of the grids. Cravath's results in O_2 were fairly satisfactory, as later data indicated. The quantity h, observed by him in O_2, was independent of p. At first it declined, and then rose again as a function of X/p. In air the values of h as a function of X/p were *pressure-dependent*. They showed a decrease in h with X/p in all cases. Values of h in O_2 did not give results consistent with the values expected for air where O_2 was diluted with N_2 (a nonattaching gas). Probably most of Cravath's trouble stemmed from the use of a metal chamber and a *thermionic source of electrons*, which introduced unknown density gradients into his chamber and increased contamination.

The problem was later taken up by N. E. Bradbury (12) when he went as Research Fellow to Massachusetts Institute of Technology. He used an all-glass system with Zn electrodes, which could be outgassed by heating, as shown in figure 5.4 (a and b). The electrons were created photoelectrically by light from a quartz mercury arc focused through a window onto the plate F. In place of one grid, Bradbury used two retractable grids, G_1 and G_2, at distances x_1 and x_2 cm from the plate F. The collecting electrode P was provided with a guard ring and equipotential vanes at various distances between F and P. While Cravath had to use the values of v from Townsend's magnetic-deflection methods to evaluate k_e and thus h, Bradbury used another method (13). As will be shown elsewhere, the photoelectric current between two plane parallel electrodes in a uniform electrical field X at a pressure p is given by

$$(7.1) \qquad \frac{i}{i_0} = \frac{\sqrt{6\pi k_e X}}{C_0 + \sqrt{6\pi k_e X}}$$

In this equation, i is the current at the field X and pressure p, i_0 is the saturation photo current at zero pressure, k_e is the electron mobility, while C_0 is the average velocity of electron emission at the cathode.

The value of C_0 can be determined by liberating photoelectrons from a zinc electrode Z surrounded by a similar zinc surface (figure 5.4b), and running a retarding potential curve. This was done by Bradbury (13). The values of k_e established in this fashion were accurate within about 10 to 20%. At that time there were no suitable means of evaluating k_e applicable to the same apparatus and gas, especially at higher pressures. The use of Townsend's values for this quantity did not seem warranted, in the light of Cravath's difficulties. Today, the use of the grids could lead to both values of i/i_0 as well as to k_e, and thus to h, all accurate to 2%. Bradbury later showed that the grids could be used as electrical shutters for measuring electron velocities v. The *accurate* determination of h still awaits simultaneous application of these techniques.

Bradbury used the two grids to eliminate absorption and other grid conditions. The grids were so fixed that G_1 and G_2 could, by means of an iron lug and an external electromagnet, be slipped into the measuring field through which ions and electrons passed in going from F to P. Then, adjusting the values of frequency ν, potential V_g, pressure p, and field X to give optimum filtering conditions,

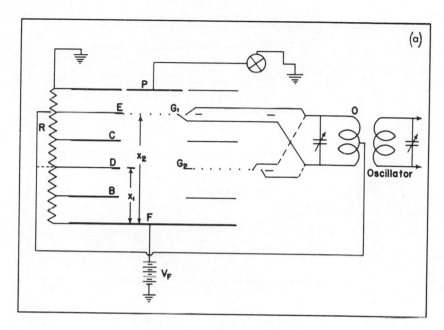

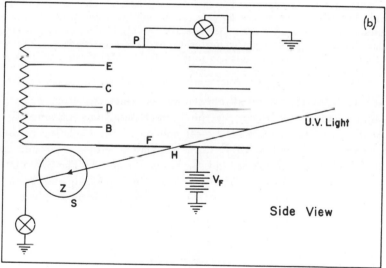

Fig. 5.4 (a and b). Diagrams of Bradbury's two-electrode filter device for measuring h.

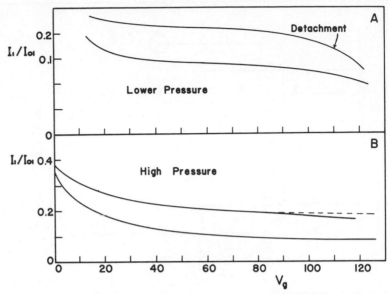

Fig. 5.5 (A and B). Bradbury's curves for the ratio of currents i_1/i_{01} to plot with grid G_1 in place and high-frequency a.c. on and off between grid wires. The sample curves are for low (5.5A) and high pressures (5.5B). Note constancy of curves above 60 volts in 5.5B. The slight decline in 5.5B is due to increased capture of ions by the grids, according to Bradbury. The sharp decline in 5.5A above 100 volts is due to electron *detachment* by collisions of negative ions at high X/p.

Bradbury used the survival equations for electrons from F to grids G_1 and G_2 at x_1 and x_2 to get the correct data. The currents i_{01} and i_1 to P were measured, with V_g off and on at G_1, G_2 being retracted. The currents i_{02} and i_2 to P were measured, with V_g off and on at grid G_2, G_2 being in place and G_1 being retracted. The ion currents i_{s1} and i_{s2} surviving capture at G_1 and G_2 are $i_{s1} = i_{01} - i_1$ and $i_{s2} = i_{02} - i_2$. Then, from the basic relation of equation 5.8, it is possible to write

(5.50)
$$\frac{i_{s2}}{i_{s1}} = \epsilon^{-\dfrac{1.35 \times 10^{15} h\ (x_2 - x_1)}{k_e^2 X}} \ .$$

In Bradbury's work, $x_2 - x_1$ was 2.40 cm. The plates F and P were 7 cm apart. The actual area of the grids was 10 cm². Mercury vapor and grease were carefully avoided by cold traps. The system was evacuated and baked out at 200° C. before filling. The value of C_0 was established as 0.7 volt at various times. The capture correction was largely eliminated by working the two grids under the same conditions.

Good ratios of i_{01} to i_1 and i_{02} to i_2 were obtained by careful choice of values of the control variables on the grids. Thus, except for the uncertainties inherent in the values of k_e, Bradbury was able to achieve reliable and reproducible directly determined values of h.

Typical curves of Bradbury for i_1/i_{01} for O_2 as a function of V between grid wires for the optimal frequency are shown in figure 5.5 (A and B) at low and high pressures respectively. It is seen that the current decreases slightly at higher values of V_g owing to increased capture of ions by the grids. At lower pressures (figure 5.5A), above a certain potential V_g there is a sharp decrease in the ratio which is caused by electron detachment, as shown later by the author.

Very recently, A. Doehring (18) has indicated a new method for measuring h, or better, the average number of attachments a per cm distance in the field direction x, defined by $n = n_0 \, \epsilon^{-ax}$, using a time-of-flight method. This is a modern modification of the author's initial study, using currents as determined by the Rutherford a.c. method with square wave form, as analyzed in detail by M. Mooney (9). It depends on the great difference of drift velocity of electrons and ions, and uses the time of flight of the ion formed in mid-field by attachment of electrons. In this case, however, the most modern techniques are used for a study of a in O_2 from $X/p = 0.6$ to about 9, and values of electron energies from 0.5 to 2.2 e.v.

Electrons from a hot filament are carried by a uniform field X through two pairs of grid shutters as used by Tyndall and Powell in the four-gauze shutter method of measuring drift velocities of ions (chapter I, part one, $6). The distance between the shutters is L, and the electrons entering the drift space attach at various distances x in an interval dx and proceed as ions in the uniform field X with drift velocity v_i. The grid pairs have a strong bias excluding negative carriers, except for small time intervals dt, when a short square-wave pulse of from 20 to 70 microseconds opens the entrance shutter, admitting the electron and ion carriers. At the end of various time intervals t a similar pulse is applied to the exit shutter. Its length can be varied independently of the entrance-shutter pulse. The current collected is amplified and registered on a cathode ray oscilloscope. If n electrons enter the first shutter, there will be

(5.51) $$n \, \epsilon^{-ax} dx$$

ions formed at a distance x, which will reach the exit shutter in $(L-x)/v_i$ seconds. The total time of transit is (as on the following page),

$$(5.52) \qquad t = \frac{x}{v_e} + \frac{L-x}{v_i} \equiv \frac{L-x}{v_i},$$

because $v_e \gg v_i$. The time interval in which the ions formed in dx reach the exit shutter is $dt = dx/v_i$. Thus, the number reaching the exit shutter at a time t is

$$(5.53) \qquad \nu(t)dt = nav_i \, \epsilon^{-a(L-v_it)} dt = A \, \epsilon^{av_it}.$$

Thus, the current of ions I_i is given by

$$(5.54) \qquad \begin{cases} I_i = B \, \epsilon^{av_it} \text{ for } 0 < t < L/v_i \\ I_i = 0 \ \text{ for } t < 0 \text{ and } t > L/v_i \end{cases}.$$

The idealized current as a function of time is shown in figure 5.6 as the dashed curve. Diffusion and the action of the shutters give the rounded curve. If the negative ions undergo attachment to molecules while in the measuring field X to produce slower negative ions, as could be inferred from Bradbury's earlier mobility measurements, then assuming drift velocities v_1 and v_2 for the ions of type X and Y, with attachment constant a_1 for electron to the molecule and a_2 for the ion X to make ion Y, with $v_1 > v_2$ the theory yields

$$(5.55) \ \nu_{1,2}(t)dt = Cdt \begin{cases} \epsilon^{a_1(v_2t-L)} - \epsilon^{-\left[(a_1-a_2)v_1t - a_1L\right]} & 0 < t < L/v_1 \\ \epsilon^{a_1(v_2t-L)} - \epsilon^{\frac{a_2v_1}{v_1-v_2}(v_2t-L)} & L/v_1 < t < L/v_2. \end{cases}$$

If $L = 1$, $a_1 = 1$, $a_2 = 1.5$, $v_1 = 3$, and $v_2 = 2$, then the ideal curves should have the form of figure 5.7. The method was carried out with a thorough background of the previous literature, and all precautions, such as those required by interpenetration effects in gauzes, etc., were carefully considered and put into practice. The work was done in a clean, modern, all-glass system. By using the gauzes as shutters at different pressures, the *ion-drift* velocities and *electron-drift* velocities could be evaluated, using the Tyndall-Powell method.

This was the first application of the four-gauze shutter method to negative ions. The square wave pulses used were a vast improvement over the sinusoidal a.c. of Tyndall and Powell, and had been advocated earlier by the author for this method. The square pulses could not be used for electron-drift velocities, as times were too short, so that the a.c. was used on the shutters. Because of the high peak values needed, the a.c., through interpenetration effects,

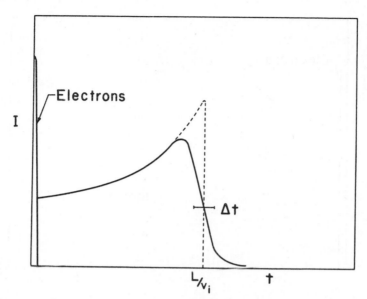

Fig. 5.6. Doehring's calculated current I for electrons attaching to ions, using the time-of-flight method. The dashed curve shows the ideal calculation; the full curve is to be expected as a consequence of diffusion and interpenetration effects of gauzes.

gave low values of the mobility. Had it been possible to vary L, the absolute values of drift velocities could have been determined and the apparatus calibrated in absolute measure to give true electron-drift velocities. This was understandably difficult to accomplish in the apparatus. Values of v_e were therefore low. The accuracy of values of v_i was set at 4%.

Observed curves for log i, plotted against t for three values of drift space field X at about 31 mm pressure of O_2, are shown in figure 5.8. The values of α at 1 mm pressure, defined as $\alpha = \Delta \log I_e / \Delta x$ at 1 mm, plotted against X/p at 0° C. and against electron energy in e.v., are shown in figure 5.9. There it is seen that good agreement between Doehring's values (curve C) and Bradbury's values (curve A) occurs at low energies, while Healey and Kirkpatrick's (11) values (curve B), using the diffusion method of V. A. Bailey, are not in accord. At higher X/p, however, Bradbury's values are high, while there is some agreement with Healey and Kirkpatrick. The data of Bradbury at high X/p suffer, according to Doehring, through capture of ions by the shutters, which yields high apparent values of α in Bradbury's work. This criticism of the author's electrical shutter method in this region may be valid, and it prompted Doehring to develop the new method.

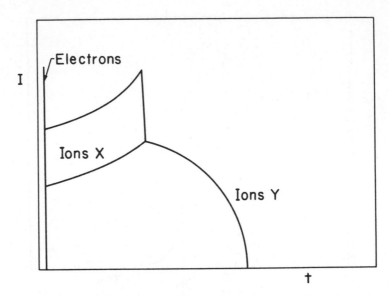

Fig. 5.7. Doehring's calculated curves for attachment of electrons to make ions in the measuring field, as for figure 5.6, in the event that ion X undergoes a decrease in mobility by attachment in the field to make ion Y.

The latter, however, is somewhat limited in range, being inapplicable to really low energies and X/p and to very high values.

The electron-drift velocities of Doehring are compared with those of Bradbury and Nielsen (1937), and of Healey and Kirkpatrick, in figure 5.10 (curves C, A, and B, respectively). Doehring believes Bradbury's data to be the most accurate, and explains his low values in terms of field interpenetration with the a.c. Healey and Kirkpatrick's values of v_e are notoriously bad, which accounts for the lack of agreement in a. Since the values of a, v_e, etc., in the Bailey methods are all interrelated in terms of measurements of three quantities, of which drift velocities are often an essential element, this indicates the degree of reliability of the data of these workers relative to modern direct techniques.

Neither the curves of figure 5.8, nor *any* of the experimental curves of Doehring, indicate the complexity of the curves of figure 5.7, and all resemble those of figure 5.6. This proves that Bradbury's assumption of attachment giving an ion of mobility 3.3 cm2/volt sec which changed in 10^{-2} sec to 2.65 cm2/volt sec, does not occur in Doehring's gas. The value of the reduced mobility for the ion observed by Doehring from v_i measurements is closely 2.68 cm2/volt sec. The mobility of the normal positive ion in O_2, recently determined

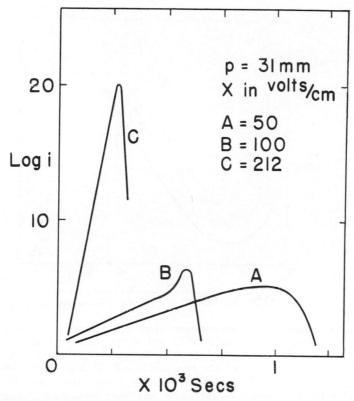

Fig. 5.8. Doehring's observed curves for log i, plotted against time for three values of field strength; 50 volts/cm (A), 100 volts/cm (B), and 212 volts/cm (C), at about 31 mm pressure in pure O_2.

by Varney and identified from Luhr's mass-spectrographic study as O_2^+, was 2.25 cm²/volt sec. Since O_2^+ ions undergo a charge exchange in O_2, the mobility would be expected to be lower than that of the O_2^- ion, which undergoes no such loss of momentum. The O_2 used by Doehring was presumably quite pure, being obtained from electrolytic O_2, dried and then frozen and fractionated. However, more work on the identification of ions is needed.

It will be noted that the methods hitherto discussed are applicable only at values of X/p below which there occurs appreciable ionization by electron impact, or photoelectric liberation by electronically excited states of the gas. Since measurable excitation and ionization by electron impact occur in O_2 at somewhat below $X/p = 20$, with an average electron energy of 3.17 e.v., it is seen that the range of study by conventional methods is definitely limited. The situation

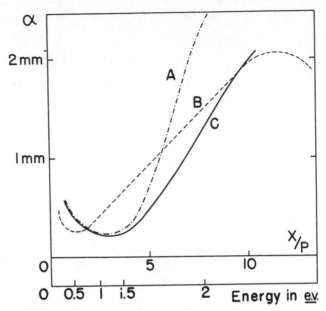

Fig. 5.9. Doehring's observed attachment per cm advance along field X, $\alpha = \Delta \log I_e / \Delta x$, plotted against X/p and approximate equivalent electron energy in electron volts (solid curve C), in O_2. Bradbury's data appear in curve A; Healey and Kirkpatrick's data, in curve B. Bradbury's curve deviates at higher energies as his electron filters capture ions. The causes for deviation of curve B are multiple, including inaccurate electron-drift velocities.

is aggravated by the fact that not all attachment processes are low-energy processes, as in O_2, SO_2, or Cl_2. In fact, the majority of the processes, and especially those having large cross sections which influence discharge, are dissociative attachment processes requiring in some cases electron volts of energy.

Fortunately, in the last two years a new method of study has been developed by R. Geballe and M. A. Harrison (28). Geballe and his associates were studying the nature of the action of spark-suppressant gases. Such gases as the halogens, CCl_4, freon, CCl_2F_2, CSF_8, and CF_3SF_5, are known to raise the breakdown potentials when mixed with other gases, or in themselves, above other gases by factors which may be three times as large as those for air. Even O_2 has higher breakdown potentials than many other simple gases. The increased breakdown strength was always associated with negative ion formation, though other factors enter in, such as dissociation of CSF_8 to CF_4 and SF_4, thus doubling the pressure. To gain further

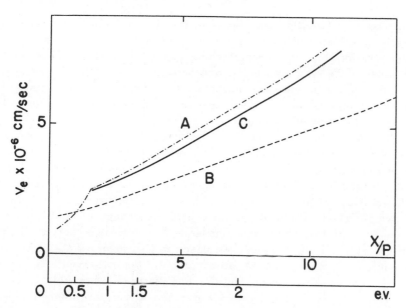

Fig. 5.10. Doehring's electron-drift velocities v_e in O_2, plotted against X/p and approximate equivalent electron energies (curve C). Bradbury and Nielsen's data appear at curve A; Healey and Kirkpatrick's indirectly derived values, at curve B. Doehring concedes greater accuracy to curve A, as his shutters give low values of v_e owing to interpenetration of fields.

information, Geballe and Harrison (1952-1953) studied the multiplication of photoelectrons liberated from a cathode by ultraviolet light as the distance between the plane parallel electrodes was increased at various values of X/p.

The increase in current in nonelectron-attaching gases with increase in gap length was shown by J. S. Townsend (1900) to follow a law $i = i_0\, \epsilon^{ad}$, as seen in chapter VIII, such that a log i/i_0 plot against plate distance d gives a straight line, the slope of which evaluates a, the number of new electrons created per cm advance of an electron in the field direction. This a is obviously a function of X/p, and is observed to rise asymptotically from zero along a curve of initially exponential form beyond a certain X/p which is characteristic of each gas. In theory, certainly, the rise from 0 should be asymptotic, since it is caused by the few electrons in the distribution at each X/p that have an energy in the field above E_i. The actual rise cannot be followed to very low values of a because of physical limitations on the sensitivity of detection against background fluctuation and the small range of variation in d. To the surprise of Geballe and Harrison the log i/i_0-d plots were not linear in the spark-suppressant gases, but dipped down rather sharply near the origin, while nonattaching gases gave nice linear plots. A study of O_2 was also made, and here at low X/p there was again a dip which was not so pronounced as in the more active gases. In air the effect is small indeed, and its observation requires just the right combination of variables.

The only study of a in O_2 at low enough X/p had been made by K. Masch, who had noted that his values of a/p as a function of X/p suddenly dipped sharply below their previous trend below $X/p =$ 40. He attributed this to attachment, but made no further analysis. Observation of the curvature of log i/i_0-d plots requires a large *range* of values of d. Thus, in air (where the change is small), neither Sanders, with his limited range at large d, or other workers, at limited ranges of small d (including even Masch in O_2), *observed the curvature*. Recognizing the action of attachment in the observed curvatures in the suppressant gases, Geballe and Harrison were able to carry out measurements in order to observe the effect, even in air. They also derived the expression for the log i/i_0-d curves when attachment occurs. These are derived more appropriately in chapter VIII. Assuming that η represents the number of electron attachments per cm advance in the field direction, in analogy to the quantity a for ionization, the equation for the current growth replacing $i/i_0 = \epsilon^{ad}$ becomes

$$(5.56) \qquad i/i_0 = \frac{a}{a - \eta} \epsilon^{(a-\eta)d} - \frac{\eta}{a - \eta}.$$

It is seen that the log i/i_0-d curve here is distinctly nonlinear. If a is much larger than η, the deviation is hard to observe with the natural scatter of points. The same occurs for large d, even if a is only slightly larger than η. In this event the additive terms are negligible, and the coefficient deduced will be $a - \eta$. For ranges of a few mm in d at small values of d, the deviation from linearity will again be slight. Here the slope of the straight line will have no simple interpretation. However, with a *sufficient length* of log i/i_0-d plot, the fitting of the theoretical equation to observed points yields both values of a and of η.

The apparatus used consisted of two polished Cu discs of 9 cm diameter, the anode disc having 400 small holes in a circle of 2 cm diameter about its center. This was rigidly mounted in a Pyrex vessel. The cathode could be moved quite parallel to its position between 0 and 4 cm by a fine nut and screw with 40 threads per inch through

TABLE 5.1

Geballe and Harrison's Values of α/p and η/p
as Functions of X/p for O_2 and Air

X/p	O_2			Air		
	α/p	η/p	$\alpha/p - \eta/p$	α/p	η/p	$\alpha/p - \eta/p$
25.0	0.0215	0.0945	−0.0730	0.00120	0.00495	−0.00375
27.5	0.0293	0.0900	−0.0607	0.00205	0.00473	−0.00268
30.0	0.0400	0.0851	−0.0451	0.00340	0.00460	−0.00120
32.5	0.0532	0.0795	−0.0263	0.00560	0.00460	+0.00100
35.0	0.0697	0.0735	−0.0038	0.00880	0.00475	+0.00405
37.5	0.0862	0.0685	+0.0177	0.0130	0.00497	+0.0080
40.0	0.107	0.0645	+0.043	0.0190	0.00530	+0.0137
42.5	0.128	0.0605	+0.068	0.0260	0.00575	+0.0203
45.0	0.152	0.0570	+0.095	0.0340	0.00635	+0.0277
47.5	0.179	0.0535	+0.126	0.0460	0.00700	+0.0390
50.0	0.206	0.052	+0.154	0.057	0.00780	+0.049
52.5	0.234	0.049	+0.185	0.070	0.00870	+0.061
55.0	0.263	0.047	+0.216	0.087	0.00967	+0.077
57.5	0.292	0.045	+0.247	0.102	0.0108	+0.091
60.0	0.323	0.043	+0.280	0.120	0.0119	+0.108
62.5	0.355	0.0415	+0.314	0.140	−	−
65.0	0.383	0.040	+0.343	0.170	−	−
70.0	0.450	−	−	−	−	−
72.5	0.482	−	−	−	−	−
75.0	0.518	−	−	−	−	−

the agency of an iron armature rotated by an external magnet. Ultra-violet light fell directly on the cathode through the small holes and through a quartz window below the anode. The light intensity was monitored by a photocell. The 5-liter flask container with minimum wall clearance of 4.5 cm from the electrode system was coated by aquadag on the inside. The potential of this coating could be controlled by potentiometer to keep the electron diffusion to the walls at less than 1%, even for 4 cm separation. The chamber was outgassed at above 400° C. The Cu electrodes could be reduced by H_2 if needed, and were cleaned mechanically whenever the photocurrent fell off seriously. The chamber maintained pressures of 10^{-5} mm for hours when the pumps were off. The H_2 was as pure as the conditions in the tube permitted, while the N_2 used could have been contaminated with NH_3 and hydrocarbons by generation from NaN_3. The air, O_2, and other gases were satisfactorily pure.

The data for α/p and η/p as a $f(X/p)$ are shown in tables 5.1, 5.2, and 5.3.

TABLE 5.2

Geballe and Harrison's Values of α/p and η/p for
CCl_4 and CF_3SF_5 as Functions of X/p

X/p	CCl_4			X/p	CF_3SF_5		
	α/p	η/p	$\alpha/p - \eta/p$		α/p	η/p	$\alpha/p - \eta/p$
255	2.70	3.73	−1.03	175	1.0	1.08	−0.08
260	2.34	3.29	−0.95	180	1.13	1.13	0.00
265	2.01	2.96	−0.95	185	1.27	1.20	+0.07
270	1.83	2.64	−0.81	190	1.41	1.27	+0.14
275	1.50	2.35	−0.85	195	1.58	1.36	+0.22
280	1.30	2.07	−0.77	200	1.76	1.45	+0.31
285	1.19	1.82	−0.63	205	1.98	1.55	+0.43
290	1.14	1.63	−0.49	210	2.21	1.66	+0.55
295	1.18	1.53	−0.35	215	2.46	1.77	+0.69
300	1.32	1.51	−0.19	220	2.75	1.90	+0.85
305	1.54	1.57	−0.03	225	3.10	2.03	+1.07
310	1.80	1.68	+0.12	—	—	—	—
315	2.15	1.84	+0.31	—	—	—	—
320	2.5	2.00	+0.50	—	—	—	—
325	2.93	2.18	+0.75	—	—	—	—
330	3.4	2.36	+1.04	—	—	—	—
335	3.9	2.53	+1.37	—	—	—	—

Geballe and Harrison's Values of α/p for Isopentane,
H_2, and N_2 as a Function of X/p

X/p	Isopentane	X/p	H_2	N_2
	α/p		α/p	α/p
70	0.033	25.0	0.026	0.0056
80	0.095	27.5	—	0.0095
90	0.175	30.0	0.064	0.016
100	0.31	35.0	0.118	—
110	0.46	40.0	—	0.053
120	0.66	—	—	—
130	0.85	—	—	—

Figure 5.11 shows the data for η/p in O_2 as a function of X/p for
Geballe and Harrison's work as compared to that of other workers,
while figure 5.12 shows the data for air. The data for freon and CF_3SF_5
are shown in figure 5.13. The data for O_2 and air are shown as attachment cross sections plotted against average energy in e.v. in figures
5.14 and 5.15.

To convert values of η into probability of attachment h or cross
section q_a for comparison with previous work (or vice versa), the
following should be noted. The drift velocity v advances the stream

TABLE 5.3

Geballe and Harrison's Values of α/p and η/p for
CCl_2F_2, SF_6, and $SiCl_4$ as Functions of X/p

X/p	CCl_2F_2			SF_6			$SiCl_4$		
	α/p	η/p	$\alpha/p-\eta/p$	α/p	η/p	$\alpha/p-\eta/p$	α/p	η/p	$\alpha/p-\eta/p$
80	0.2	0.87	−0.67	0.22	1.19	−0.97	—	—	—
85	—	—	—	0.33	1.17	−0.84	—	—	—
90	0.315	0.92	−0.60	0.44	1.15	−0.74	—	—	—
95	—	—	—	0.55	1.14	−0.59	—	—	—
100	0.45	0.95	−0.50	0.67	1.12	−0.45	0.050	0.043	+0.007
105	—	—	—	0.78	1.10	−0.32	0.070	0.053	+0.017
110	0.60	0.96	−0.36	0.90	1.08	−0.18	0.090	0.064	+0.026
115	—	—	—	1.01	1.06	−0.05	0.110	‣0.074	+0.036
120	0.78	0.94	−0.16	1.11	1.04	+0.07	0.152	0.084	+0.068
125	—	—	—	1.23	1.02	+0.21	0.200	0.094	+0.106
130	0.92	0.87	+0.05	1.34	1.00	+0.34	0.25	0.102	+0.148
135	—	—	—	1.47	0.97	+0.50	0.310	0.110	+0.200
140	1.15	0.77	+0.38	1.59	0.96	+0.63	0.375	0.117	+0.258
145	—	—	—	1.71	0.94	+0.77	0.44	0.123	+0.317
150	1.35	0.70	+0.65	1.84	0.91	+0.93	0.510	0.128	+0.382
155	—	—	—	1.97	0.88	+1.09	0.58	0.131	+0.449
160	1.56	0.63	+0.93	2.1	0.85	+1.25	0.65	0.133	+0.517
165	—	—	—	2.225	0.81	+1.44	—	0.134	—
170	1.75	0.56	+1.19	—	—	—	0.80	0.134	+0.666
175	—	—	—	—	—	—	—	0.132	—
180	1.95	0.50	+1.45	—	—	—	0.95	0.126	+0.824
185	—	—	—	—	—	—	—	—	—
190	2.15	0.45	+1.70	—	—	—	1.11	0.110	+1.00
195	—	—	—	—	—	—	—	—	—
200	2.32	0.39	+1.93	—	—	—	1.26	0.084	+1.18
205	—	—	—	—	—	—	—	—	—
210	2.50	0.34	+2.16	—	—	—	—	—	—

1 cm in $1/v$ sec. The elastic electron-collision frequency is $z = \bar{c}_1/\lambda$, such that in 1 cm there are $\bar{c}_1/\lambda v$ elastic impacts resulting in η attachments. Thus,

$$(5.57) \quad h = \frac{\eta \lambda v}{\bar{c}_1} = \frac{k_e X \lambda \eta}{\bar{c}_1} = \frac{m k_e^2 \eta}{0.75 e} X = \frac{k_e^2 X \eta}{1.35 \times 10^{15}} = 7.40 \times 10^{-16} \frac{v^2}{\lambda} \eta,$$

with v the drift velocity in cm/sec and X the field in volts/cm.[4] The attachment cross section is related to h through

$$(5.58) \qquad\qquad q_a = h q_R = h \pi \sigma_R^2 = h/\lambda N,$$

---

[4]Note the use of Langevin constants in equation 5.57, while Geballe and Harrison use Compton constants.

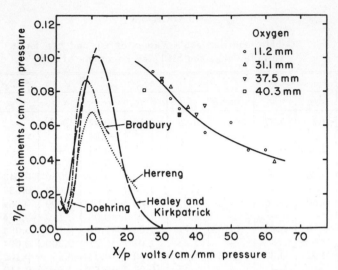

Fig. 5.11. Combined data for η/p as a function of X/p in O_2, as compiled by Geballe and Harrison.

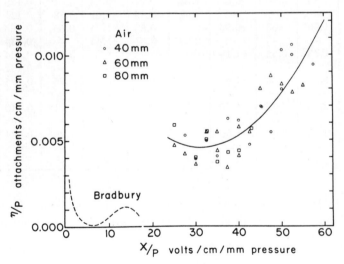

Fig. 5.12. Combined data for η/p as a function of X/p in air, as compiled by Geballe and Harrison.

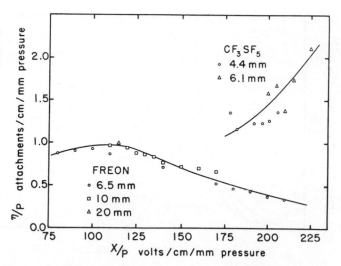

Fig. 5.13. Data on η/p for freon 12 and CF_3SF_5 as a function of X/p, according to Geballe and Harrison.

with q_R the Ramsauer cross section for elastic impacts, σ_R the Ramsauer collision radius, and λ the Ramsauer free path at a molecular density N per cm^3. Thus,

$$(5.59) \qquad q_a = \frac{h}{\lambda N} = \frac{\eta \lambda v}{\lambda N \bar{c}_1} = \eta \frac{v}{N \bar{c}_1} = \frac{\eta}{p} \frac{v}{\bar{c}_1 N_1},$$

with p in mm and $N = p N_1$. Discussion of the values and the data will come at a later point. It is seen, however, that the measurement of h or q_a can be made for gases at values of X/p at which ionization occurs, and above. The method is only good as long as h has finite values comparable with a. When a is very low or very high, this method ceases to be of use. Where η is small, the method is not too accurate and points show a scatter of some 20% or more about the mean.

A new direct method of measuring electron attachment follows in a recently published study of P. Herreng (29).[5] Herreng had measured electron-drift velocity, using a pulsed discharge in a uniform-field plane parallel electrode gap. A thin slab of X-ray ionization accurately parallel to the electrodes was flashed for a microsecond,

───────────────

[5]The work was actually done in Langevin's laboratory in 1943 during the occupation, and was submitted for publication in January, 1944. The work is technically far ahead of its time. It was published in 1952, the author presumably having disappeared during the occupation.

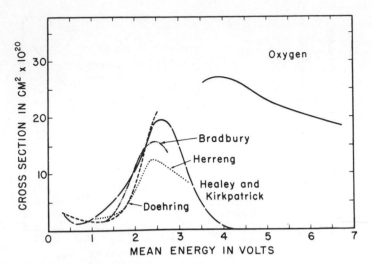

Fig. 5.14. Attachment cross sections in O_2 as a function of energy
by various observers, as compiled by Geballe and Harrison.

and the induced current to the electrodes resulting from carrier movement and separation in the gap was measured in time by the potential
delivered across the vertical plates of a cathode ray oscilloscope
from a suitable resistor in series with the gap. If attachment of
electrons occurs en route, the current will be modified, as will be
indicated. By displacing the chamber along the field axis so that
the X-ray beam flash enters through one of three windows at different
accurately known distances from the anode, the time elapsed between
the arrival of corresponding points of the current pulse at the anode
gives the time for the carriers to cross a known distance. Thus,
from the characteristics of the current-pulse form and the drift velocity
of the electrons, h can be evaluated. Herreng tried out his method
first on O_2-A mixtures in order to increase his intensity of ionization. He later increased the intensity of his X-ray flash to a point
where A was not needed. The theory of the method follows.

If c_1 is the random velocity of electrons, and λ is the free path,
the number of elastic impacts in dt is $c_1 dt/\lambda$. In the mixture the
fraction of these impacts,

$$(5.60) \qquad f = \frac{p_2/\lambda_2}{p_1/\lambda_1 + p_2/\lambda_2},$$

occurs against O_2 molecules, for which attachment probability is h.
Here p_2 and λ_2 correspond to the pressure, and Ramsauer's free path

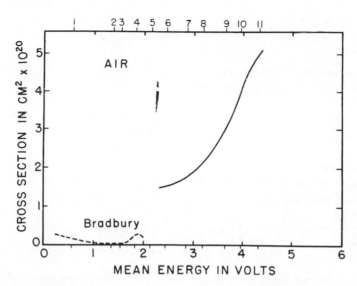

Fig. 5.15. Attachment cross sections in air as a function of energy, as compiled by Geballe and Harrison. The upper energy scale is that of Huxley and Zaazou, and the lower one is that of Townsend and Tizard.

of O_2 molecules and p_1 and λ_1 correspond to A atoms, to which there is no attachment. The attrition of electrons, or the rate of negative ion formation, is then given by

(5.61)
$$(dn/n) = (f\hbar\bar{c}_1/\lambda)\, dt.$$

At the end of a time t, the number is reduced to n from n_0, given by

(5.62)
$$n = n_0\, \epsilon^{-\frac{f\hbar\bar{c}_1 t}{\lambda}} = n_0\, \epsilon^{-Kt}.$$

If the decline of electrons can be measured, then the evaluation of K yields h through the relation $h = K\lambda/f\bar{c}_1$, and with the usual transformations to eliminate λ/c_1, using the drift velocity $h = (k/0.75)(m/e)(X/fv)$. If pure O_2 is used, $f = 1$. The current measured flowing in the external circuit $i(t)$ must now be calculated. Let $Q(t)$ be the instantaneous charge on the anode. Let the area of the electrodes be A. The instantaneous potential difference $V_0 - Ri$ is equal to the total integral of the electrical field across the gap of length d. To evaluate this, one must consider the total charge $+Q$ or $-Q$ carried by the electrodes, which yields a term $4\pi Qd/A = Q/C$; the positive ions in a thin slab j at x_j cm from the anode yield a term $2\pi q_j^+/A(d - 2x_j)$ as a result of the image force; and the negative ions, at a slab k at a distance y_k from the anode, lead to the term $2\pi q_k^-/A\,(2y_k - d)$. It is thus proper to write (as shown on the following page),

$$(5.63) \qquad V_0 - Ri = \frac{Q}{C} + \frac{2\pi}{A}\sum_{j=1}^{m} q_j^+ (d - 2x_j) + \frac{2\pi}{A}\sum_{k=1}^{n} q_{\bar{k}} (2y_k - d).$$

If the equation is differentiated with respect to t, since $dx_j/dt = v_j^+$ and $dy_k/dt = -v_{\bar{k}}$, the equation becomes

$$(5.64) \qquad R\frac{di}{dt} + \frac{i}{C} = \frac{4\pi}{A}\left[\sum_{j=1}^{m} q_j^+ v_j^+ + \sum_{k=1}^{n} q_k^- v_k^-\right].$$

The values of R and C were chosen in such a fashion that the time constant RC was negligible (10^{-7} sec) compared with the oscilloscopic time scale. The current, therefore, is practically given by

$$(5.65) \qquad i = \frac{1}{d}\left[\sum_{j=1}^{m} q_j^+ v_j^+ + \sum_{k=1}^{n} q_k^- v_k^-\right].$$

There are three sorts of carriers involved in this measurement: positive ions of velocity v^+, with quantity of charge q remaining constant; electrons of drift velocity v_1^-, with instantaneous quantity of charge at any time t of qe^{-Kt}, and negative ions of drift velocity v_2^-, which come from attached electrons with charge of $q(1 - \epsilon^{-Kt})$. Thus,

$$(5.66) \qquad i = \frac{q}{d}\left[v^+ + v_1^- \epsilon^{-Kt} + v_2^-\left(1 - \epsilon^{-Kt}\right)\right].$$

Since $v_1^- \sim 10^3 \, v^+$ or v_2^-, the current i as measured on the time sweep of the oscilloscope of several microseconds is primarily that corresponding to the electronic motion

$$(5.67) \qquad i = \frac{q}{d} v_1^- \epsilon^{-Kt}.$$

Measurement was made, using 1 microsecond X-ray flashes at 50 per second. The same weak triggering signal started the time sweep of the oscillograph and the X-ray flash. Oxygen pressures ranged from 10-15 mm Hg, fields going up to 400 volts/cm. The chamber was a Pyrex cylinder with plane parallel metallic electrodes. The whole was thoroughly outgassed, and gases were of highest purity. The value of d is not given in the later paper, but was 12 cm in the earlier work. The crossing time of electrons must have been of the order of 2 microseconds or more in the drift-velocity measurements. Electron drift-velocity measurements in O_2 coincided exactly with Bradbury and Nielsen's values, using the Loeb electron-filter shutters below $X/p = 5$, and may have been 10% low from $X/p = 5$ to $X/p = 20$.

The errors in velocity measurements may have been about 3%. The internal consistency of the measured values of K from exponential decline of the current was 5%, making K good to about 3% accuracy. Herreng sets 6% as his accuracy in h, since h involves both errors in v_1^- and K. The values obtained for h by Herreng closely agree with Bradbury's values to electron energies around 1.6 e.v. Beyond this they deviate, as seen in Herreng's curve as reported in Geballe's summary of the data (figures 5.11 and 5.14). Fairly good agreement is achieved over the region of decline of h with energy with a theory of Bradbury and Bloch at this pressure range, in which the constants were chosen to give a fit at one point.

Finally, the measurements made with microwave techniques must be presented. In these methods the gas is broken down in an outgassed quartz or glass container of appropriate size and shape. This container is placed in a suitable microwave cavity and pulsed discharges lasting from one to several microseconds are applied to the cavity. This causes the gas to break down. After some one to several microseconds of discharge time, the gas is left to itself and the electron random velocities are allowed to decline, He gas sometimes being added to speed the cooling process. Then the electron density is measured as a function of time by a weak probing signal yielding the Q of the cavity, the change in resonant frequency or perhaps the complex and real conductivity. The discussion of this technique and its underlying theory is given in detail in chapter VI, §5. There it is shown that electrons are lost by ambipolar diffusion according to

$$(5.68) \qquad n = n_0 \, \epsilon^{-t/\tau_1} \ \text{with} \ \tau_1 = \frac{\Lambda_1^2}{D_a},$$

where Λ is the diffusion length in the first mode characteristic of the dimensions and shape of the vessel, and D_a is the ambipolar-diffusion coefficient. Thus, a plot of $\log n/n_0$ against t leads to a line of slope $-1/\tau_1$, from which τ_1 is evaluated. It will be noted that as D_a varies as $1/\rho$ where ρ is the gas density, or at constant temperature as $1/p$, the value of τ_1 increases directly as the pressure. As pressure increases, τ_1 increases linearly with p. This means that the value of t needed for decline of n/n_0 to 0.37 will increase in direct proportion as p. Thus, for a given available *range* of time resolution there will be an *upper* pressure limit at which the decline of n/n_0 because of large τ_1 will be negligible within the resolving power of the measurement of n.

In the event of electron attachment, the loss of electrons with time is (as shown on the following page),

$$(5.69) \qquad n = n_0 \, \epsilon^{-\dfrac{h\bar{c}_1 t}{\lambda}} = n_0 \, \epsilon^{-t/\tau_2} \text{ with } \tau_2 = \dfrac{\lambda}{h\bar{c}_1} \, .$$

Now λ varies with $1/\rho$, or at constant T as $1/p$. Thus, in this case a log n/n_0-t plot will yield a slope of value $-1/\tau_2$. The τ_2 derived from this relation varies as $1/p$, so that the value t, at which n/n_0 falls to 0.37, will *decrease* hyperbolically as t increases. Thus, within a given time range of measurement and within limitations of the sensitivity of measurements of n/n_0, there will be a *lower* pressure limit below which attachment will be negligible, and the amount of attachment in a given time interval will increase as pressure increases.

Thus, despite the fact that a log n/n_0-t plot gives the characteristic linear decline yielding $-1/\tau_1$, and $-1/\tau_2$ in the case of diffusion and of attachment loss, the variation with pressure of τ_1 and τ_2 at once leads to a recognition of the mechanism active. The two processes can then be studied separately; τ_1 at low, and τ_2 at higher pressures.

Where recombination occurs, the decline n for electrons yields a linear $1/n$-t plot. Thus, if there is a large enough range of variation of t with sufficiently small experimental scatter of points, it should be easy to differentiate between a log n/n_0-t and a $1/n$-t behavior.

The recombination rate is given by $dn/dt = -an^2$, with n the electron = ion concentration if these are equal. Here unless *carrier* concentration n depends on pressure and a varies with pressure, there should be no choice of pressure in measurement. However, in general, the orders of magnitude of n do increase as pressures increase, the dependence on pressure probably being least with microwave breakdown. In principle, the quantity a should not increase with pressure for radiative or dissociative recombination, but under some conditions it will do so. Finally, in the microwave techniques especially, it appears that the n_e for electrons does not equal n for the positive ion species that recombine readily, so that usually $n_e > n$. Under such conditions, the $1/n$-t plots are no longer linear, but take the form

$$(5.70) \qquad \frac{1}{n_e} = \frac{1}{\Delta n_0}\left(1 - \frac{n_{+0}}{n_{e0}}\, \epsilon^{-a\Delta n_0 t}\right).$$

Here, Δn_0 is the initial difference between n_{e0} and n_{+0} at $t = 0$. Hence, a curved $1/n$-t plot *does not necessarily* indicate that there is attachment or diffusion. Since recombination studies in general are also favored by higher pressures, there is a good chance that recombination loss will compete with attachment loss if attachment can occur. If the two processes occur together, then since

$$\frac{\partial n}{\partial t} = - a n^2 - \frac{n}{\tau_2} ,$$

where τ_2 is the characteristic time for attachment or diffusion, and at higher pressures mainly attachment, then

(5.71)
$$\frac{n}{1 + a\tau_2 n} = \frac{\epsilon^{-t/\tau_2}}{(1 + a\tau_2 n_0)},$$

according to S. C. Brown; and if long enough range of t is available, both a and τ_2 may be evaluated.

It is quite clear in any event that if recombination *can* occur, the accurate evaluation of attachment by measurement of electron loss may not be possible.

M. A. Biondi used these techniques for the study of two processes. To date there are no detailed publications of these studies, and only the papers delivered at the Gaseous Electronic Conferences and their abstracts in the *Physical Review* are available. Using pure O_2 gas at a sufficiently high gas pressure and low electron densities, the data of Biondi (19) indicated attachment of electrons to be the dominant removal process. The electrons, having cooled down to about thermal energies, decreased in density at a rate leading to a value of h yielding $q_a = hq_R$ of 1.2×10^{-22} cm^2. The cross section at minimum energy observed in O_2 by Bradbury was of the order of 10^{-19} cm^2. The value of q_a observed by Biondi might be associated with a radiative capture of the electron. It is certainly not the same process observed in a somewhat higher-energy swarm of electrons (0.2-1 e.v.) in an absolutely cold gas consisting of O_2 molecules, now substantiated by many workers (13), (18), (40).

Biondi's O_2 was studied some milliseconds after having had 10^{11} electrons/cm^3 created together with much O, many O$^-$ ions by dissociative attachment, and doubtless O_3. Even after electron velocities had dropped to thermal values and the gas temperature was down, the gas could well have been emitting much infrared radiation because of imprisonment, of metastables, and slow equilibration of rotational and vibrational energy. It still had 10^9 electrons per cm^3 compared to the densities of less than 10^5 electrons/cm^3 in Bradbury's and Herreng's studies (13), (40). The different situations could well have produced an entirely different behavior in the two cases. For example, the radiation could have destroyed nearly all the O_2^- ions that were formed. The loss of electrons would then have been to the formation of some other ion. If the ion-forming agency had been O_3 instead of O_2, then, even with a large cross section, the value of h would have been multiplied by a factor

$$(5.72) \qquad f = \frac{p_2/\lambda_2}{p_1/\lambda_1 + p_1/\lambda_2},$$

where λ_2 and p_2 refer to the ozone and p_1 and λ_1 refer to the O_2. The independence of pressure indicates that the attachment process was perhaps a radiative capture or a triple collision with a large $\sigma\tau$ product for energy dissipation, which is also true of the attachment to O_2 in Biondi's pressure range. Correspondence with Biondi rules out any falsification by diffusion through pressure-variation studies. It also rules out the probing beam. There is one more possibility. The Bradbury-Bloch theory perdicts a decline of h or q_a at very low energies. The limitations on Bradbury's measurement preclude study below about 0.2 e.v. It is barely possible that Biondi, at 0.04 e.v., was actually observing q_a or some other attachment process beyond the peak when O_2^- cannot form.

The second study of Biondi (20) was that of the attachment of thermal electrons to I_2. To insure that in the heavy I_2 gas the electrons were cooled down to thermal energies during the measuring interval, He gas at 1 mm pressure was added to the I_2 vapor to act as a recoil gas. The He gas has excitation energies at such a high value that He did not enter into the discharge at all, except to cool electrons by elastic impacts. The cross section in I_2 gas was $q_a = 4 \times 10^{-16}$ cm^2 at 0.04 e.v. electron energy. Such a high value could only come from a dissociative attachment process. An earlier measurement by Buchdahl (21) found a peak value of q_a to be 4×10^{-17} at 0.4 e.v. Buchdahl had observed a decline toward low energies below the peak, which may have been instrumental. It is very likely that the cross section for such a process will decrease as electron energy increases, and thus electron velocity increases well above threshold, so that there may be no discrepancy between Buchdahl's value at 0.4 e.v. and Biondi's higher value at 0.04 e.v. It is of interest to compare Biondi's value at low energy in I_2 with data on the other halogens obtained by Bailey and by Healey. Their methods are not capable of going to very low X/p values in these gases. The data are assembled in table 5.4.

It is seen that the values of q_a from these measurements are low. Those for I_2 at about the same energy as found by Buchdahl are about

TABLE 5.4

Table of Data for Electron-Attachment Cross Sections in the Halogen Gases

Gas	X/p	Energy in e. v.	h	λ_1 at 1 mm in cm	q_R cm^2	q_a cm^2
Cl_2	10	1.4	1.4×10^{-3}	3.8×10^{-2}	7.4×10^{-16}	1×10^{-18}
Br_2	4	1.4	0.84×10^{-3}	1.65×10^{-2}	1.7×10^{-15}	1.4×10^{-18}
I_2	10	0.65	1.0×10^{-3}	0.8×10^{-2}	3.6×10^{-15}	3.6×10^{-18}
I_2	20	1.7	6×10^{-3}	1.6×10^{-2}	1.8×10^{-15}	1.1×10^{-17}
I_2	30	2.8	1.4×10^{-3}	1.8×10^{-2}	1.6×10^{-15}	2.2×10^{-18}

one-tenth as great and thus about 10^{-2} of the value at thermal energies found by Biondi. Note also the peculiar behavior of λ and q_a as X/p increases. It is not believed that the discrepancy between the values of the Bailey group and those of Biondi is very significant. One would perhaps be inclined to place more confidence in the direct measurement of Biondi than in the inferred values from the complex relationships and difficult measurements involved in the Bailey techniques. Comparable data for h in Cl_2 by Bradbury were obtained in Cl_2-A mixtures. There the value of h as a function of X/p varies from 5×10^{-4} at $X/p = 1$ to a peak of 2.5×10^{-3} at X/p about 7, and thereafter declines. No data are given as to the amount of A used. The value of h given is presumably reduced to collisions with Cl_2 molecules. Unknown, however, are the electron energies. Bradbury's value agrees sufficiently well with Bailey's value at $X/p = 10$. It must be concluded from this that the process of ion formation by electrons in the molecular halogens (which is an exothermal process) has a high cross section at low electron energies which rapidly decrease, perhaps by a factor of 10^2, as energies become 10 to 40 times thermal.

§ 5. Observed Attachment Coefficients.

The collected data for O_2 are shown in figure 5.11, with η/p plotted against X/p, as given by Geballe. It is seen that Doehring, Bradbury, and Herreng agree fairly well at low X/p, while Healey and Kirkpatrick's value agrees less well at low X/p. The latter data do fairly well around $X/p = 10$. Above this all of the curves decline at rather different rates. This general behavior of the Bailey type of data is consistent with the fact that their methods are most effective at higher X/p. It is seen that the data of Geballe above $X/p = 25$ differ materially from those of other methods, since they are not falsified by ionization by collision. However, it looks as if these extrapolated data would fit rather smoothly into those of Doehring, Healey, and Kirkpatrick at $X/p \sim 16$ before the sharp decline is observed. Figure 5.16 shows the variation of h with X/p in air as observed by Bradbury and earlier by Bailey. Figure 5.14 shows the collective data on the attachment cross section q_a in O_2 against *estimated average* electron energy in volts, as reported by Geballe and Harrison. Figure 5.16 gives the equivalent curve for h as a function of energy for O_2 and air, as given by Bradbury. The energy plots are of a great deal more significance from the viewpoint of interpretation than are the others.

The data for air in terms of η/p plotted against X/p are shown in figure 5.12, as given by Geballe and Harrison. Figure 5.15 gives Geballe and Harrison's calculation of cross sections q_a in air as a function of the mean electron energy in volts for Bradbury's data and for their own.

For the solution of different types of problems, it is convenient to have values of all three quantities; q_a, h, and η. Thus, the duplication of the same basic data in different forms is indicated, especially for air and O_2. While interconversion of h, q_a, and η/p as functions of X/p are relatively simple, because proper data (usually Ramsauer's) are at hand, the conversion of X/p to e.v. in different gases presents a problem. It should be noted that the translation of the observed X/p ratios to an energy scale in e.v. depends entirely on the measurements, using the Townsend techniques. Thus, owing to inherent differences in method, and possibly to incomparable degrees of purity of gases, some distortion will be present, and the data may not be reliable or consistent when reduced to average energies. Again, since the form of the distribution function is not known, and since it changes with changes in Ramsauer path and with changes in fractional energy loss f, the significance of average values can be misleading.

The interpretations given by Bradbury to the data in O_2 and air are as follows: The ion formed is presumably O_2^- by attachment of an electron to the O_2 molecule. In this process the energy of attachment (to be discussed later) must be dissipated. If the energy is small, it might be stored in the vibrational system of the $O_2^-{}^v$ configuration until a suitable impact with an O_2 molecule removes it. It is clear that the more kinetic energy the electron has, the more difficult it will be to hold the energy until the occurrence of a molecular impact; i.e., the shorter the life of the $O_2^-{}^v$ state, the less frequent is the successful capture. Thus, h and q_a will be expected to decrease rapidly as electron energy increases. This decrease is seen more effectively in the plots for h as functions of X/p and energy in e.v., as given by Bradbury, because of the scale of plotting. In fact, in air the value of h is near zero at an $X/p = 6$ with energy near 1 e.v. In O_2 the decrease does not appear to reach zero. The minimum value in this case is affected by an effective subsequent rise which sets in gradually. In the region of the decline, the ratio of values of h_{O_2} for O_2 and h_a for air are fairly well approximated by the relation

(5.73) $$h_{O2}/h_a = z_{O2}/z_a f_{O2},$$

where z_{O_2} and z_a are the electron-collision frequencies in air and O_2, and f_{O_2} is the mole fraction of O_2 present. This assumes following earlier studies of J. Franck (1) and of the author (2) that N_2 in air does not attach electrons, O_2 being the active molecules. Since

$$z_{O_2} = \frac{\bar{c}_1}{N_0 f_{O_2} \, q_{RO_2}}$$

and

$$z_a = \frac{\bar{c}_1}{N_0 f_{O_2} \, q_{RO_2} + N_0 f_{N_2} \, q_{RN_2}}$$

represent the collision frequencies, and since $f_{N_2} = 1 - f_{O_2}$,

(5.74) $$\frac{h_{O_2}}{h_a} = 1 + \frac{1 - f_{O_2}}{f_{O_2}} \, \frac{q_{RN_2}}{q_{RO_2}}.$$

The subsequent rise of the value of h as energy increases came as a surprise to Bradbury. It was clear to him from his studies in mixtures of O_2 with A, He, and N_2 that the minimum occurred at lower values of X/p for the gas having the highest electron energy at low X/p. The plots of the curves for h in O_2 and air as a function of estimated electron energy indicated the rise to occur at about the same electron energy, the sharp increase occurring at about 1.6 e.v. Now O_2 has an effective electronic excitation level from the ground $^1\Sigma$ state to the $^3\Sigma_g^-$ state, a metastable level at 1.62 volts. The excitation cross section for this is relatively high. Thus, perhaps in 3 out of 100 impacts at, or just above, 1.62 e.v., the electrons will give up most of their energy to excite the O_2 molecule. Such electrons have a very low energy, so that q_a or h is quite high. With the electron-energy distribution among the swarm in the gas, perhaps even at an average energy of 1 e.v., enough of the electrons suffer inelastic impacts in going 1 cm, so that the attachment cross section, which declined owing to the increase of average energy among the electron swarm from thermal values up with X/p, now attaches shortly after their inelastic impacts in O_2.

Obviously, when the average electron energy reaches 1.6 e.v., the inelastic impacts should be most frequent and the rate of attachment greatest. Obviously also, in air the electrons lose energy only 1/5 as readily in collision with O_2. Furthermore, as energy increases in the field, these low-energy electrons after impact rather rapidly gain energy before the electrons encounter the next O_2 molecules. This action again reduces the effectiveness of attachment in air by a factor of 5 or less. Hence, it is not surprising that as $q_{RO_2} \sim \frac{1}{2}\, q_{RN_2}$ to observe that at 1.8 e.v. $h_{O_2} \sim 5 \times 5 \times 2 = 50\, h_a$. Thus, the hypothesis of Bradbury to describe observations in O_2 and air as a function of electron energy seems to be satisfactory up to this point. It is obvious that ultimately X/p should become so high that the residual energy of the electron swarm after a 1.62 volt impact should considerably exceed thermal energies, and thus that h should again decrease, and this explanation by Bradbury also seemed plausible. In this case the decline appeared to come too sharply and too soon after the peak, as shown by Bailey's curves and by those of Healey and Kirkpatrick (11).

However, there appears to be one slight difficulty with Bradbury's explanation of the rise, which is that the increase in h is of such large magnitude. Unknown to Bradbury, a second mechanism for negative ion formation is possible in O_2 which could well begin to be perceptible in the region of 1.6 volts average electron energy. This is a reaction in which electrons with some 3.67 e.v. of energy cause dissociation of O_2 into O^- and O. The heat of formation of O^- is 1.45 e.v., and the heat of dissociation of O_2 is 5.12 e.v. Thus, electrons with 3.67 e.v. can attach to form negative O^- ions by a process known as "dissociative attachment," suggested to the author by J. Franck in 1928 in the case of the halogens and HCl. As Bradbury discovered in his extensive investigations in other gases, the large majority of the attachment mechanisms to molecules were of the dissociative attachment type. Thus, it is *energetically* possible for the dissociative attachment to occur for electrons of 3.1 e.v. of energy. Earlier, W. W. Lozier (22) observed the appearance potential for O^- ions in O_2 to occur at 6 e.v. and the peak to occur at 8 e.v. H. S. W. Massey (23) has indicated that the cross section for dissociative attachment at the peak value should be 8×10^{-19} cm^2.

Under these appearance-potential conditions, Bradbury was justified in not considering this process to appear in appreciable amount at 1.6 e.v. However, the experimental evidence obtained by Geballe and Harrison, as shown in figure 5.14, is that dissociative attachment is occurring at average electron energies of 3.5 e.v., with a peak of efficiency at 4.5 e.v., as indicated by the average electron energy calculated on the Townsend scale. The measured cross section for electrons of average energy of 4.5 e.v. is 3×10^{-19} cm². With the interval $dE/\bar{E} = 1$ in a Maxwellian energy distribution, about one-third of the particles have an energy of $\bar{E}$ and one-ninth of the particles have an energy $2\bar{E}$. It is clear that with the average energy at 3.5 e.v., about 10% of the electrons would have energies of about 7 e.v., and at 4.5 e.v., somewhat more would have an average energy around 8 e.v. It is thus not impossible that the average observed value of the cross section for the peak at 4.5 e.v. is 3×10^{-19} instead of Massey's computed 8×10^{-19}. Even so, the peak occurs at too low an average electron energy to agree with Lozier's appearance potentials.

The energy scale as derived from Townsend's η and a Maxwellian distribution of course can well be incorrect. The rather remarkable discrepancies between the energy scales of Huxley and Zaazou and of Townsend relative to X/p for air make this likely (figure 5.15). In this event, it is possible that the data of Lozier and Hagstrum are applicable (22). On the other hand, the question of the appearance potential as measured by techniques such as those of Lozier and Hagstrum may *not* represent the true threshold potential at which dissociative electron attachment initiates, since such observed thresholds are limited by instrumentation. Thus, if by chance the dissociative attachment begins not too far above the energetically indicated limit at a low value of the cross section, the observations of Geballe and Harrison would be in good agreement with the observations of Healey and Kirkpatrick and of Doehring, for it looks as if the extrapolation of those curves ignoring the decline would run smoothly into that of Geballe and Harrison.

In any event, there is no doubt about the presence of dissociative attachment, and that this begins during the rise of Bradbury's curve above a *supposed* 1.6 e.v. It must then be concluded that while there is little doubt but that Bradbury's explanation of the rise in O_2 and air is partially correct, the continued rise is in part owing to added attachment by the dissociative process. The relative proportions of these processes active at any value of energy cannot be estimated, but it might be suspected that below an average energy of 1 e.v., the process is largely Bradbury's attachment to form O_2^-, while at an average energy of 2 e.v., the process is perhaps 50% dissociative.

The decline in the values of h, η/p, and q_a above 2.5 e.v., noted for all the *direct studies*, is at once explained when it is realized that above this value an appreciable photoelectric emission from

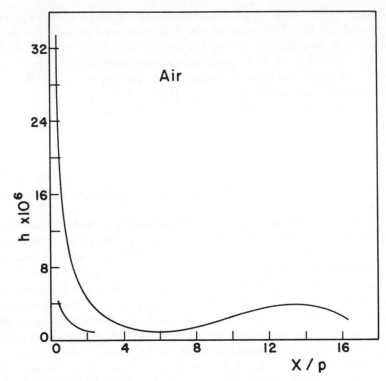

Fig. 5.16. Bradbury's curves for h as a function of X/p in air. Note the initial decline and later rise and decline, which is similar to O_2 but less pronounced. Bailey's three values for 1925 are shown as the short curve below. The values of Bradbury are probably more accurate, as Bailey's drift velocities are less accurate, as shown by Doehring in O_2.

the electrodes occurs, and when the average electron energy is 3 e.v., measurable ionization by electron impact occurs. The influence of such agencies on the author's electron-filter techniques is nicely illustrated by the curves in section 7, and the effect in the Bailey techniques would be analogous. Any electron-creating process in an attachment measurement of the type used will be falsified through the new creation of electrons by seeming to give a lowered attachment rate. Such a phenomenon does not affect measurements of the Geballe and Harrison type. The data given for q_a in air as a function of energy in figure 5.15 are plotted according to two energy scales, the one at the top being that of Huxley and Zaazou and the one below that of Townsend and Tizard. While Geballe and Harrison's data are poor in air because η/p is so small and there is a large experimental

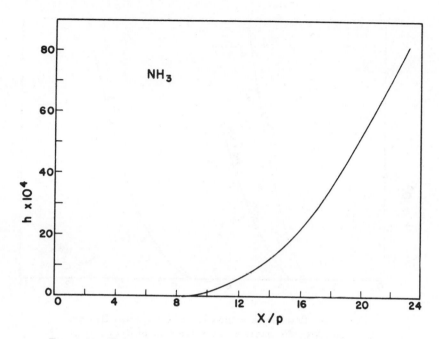

Fig. 5.17. Bradbury's values for h in NH_3 as a function of X/p.

scatter, it is seen that on either energy scale the rise noted by Bradbury will extrapolate smoothly into that of Geballe and Harrison if the decline due to electron creation is ignored. It is seen here that the value of q_a has not reached its peak at 4.5 e.v. using Townsend and Tizard's scale for air, or at 11 e.v. using an extrapolated Huxley and Zaazou energy scale. It is questionable whether with the very many inelastic impacts in O_2, the Druyvesteyn law assumed by Huxley and Zaazou to give their scale is proper. From trends one might guess at an energy peak at about 8 e.v. with a cross section q_a of 5×10^{-20} cm^2, if all impacts are counted in q_R.

In any event, ignoring the decline of the directly measured curves caused by ionization by collision, it is clear that the data of all workers are consistent and in accord with what is to be expected of attachment to O_2^- and dissociative attachment to form O^-. The only question involved appears to be the energy scale relating X/p to e.v. and the events to the energy. It is clear that in O_2 the energy scale used is probably too low, and yet a scale such as the extrapolated scale of Huxley and Zaazou in air unquestionably errs too far in the other direction.

In what follows will be given the results obtained for different

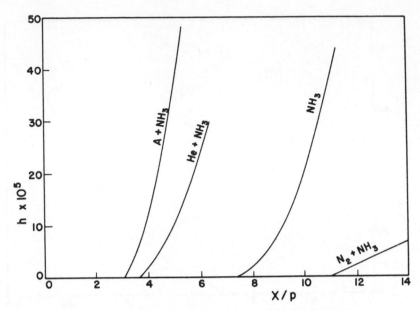

Fig. 5.18. Bradbury's values for h in NH_3-A, NH_3-He, and NH_3-N_2 mixtures as a function of X/p.

gases by various workers. The data for the Bailey techniques are given in tables 4.4a through 4.16. The curves will not be shown. Since Bradbury was primarily interested in the physics of the attachment processes as interpreted by modern atomic theory, his curves for h as a function of X/p and his experimental data will be discussed *in extenso*. Where cogent, the parallel data of the Bailey school will be presented. Bradbury's values of η (the attachment per cm) are made in probably purer gases by a direct method. Bradbury's values of h depend, however, on a method of measuring electron-drift velocity that is not too accurate. He performed control experiments to estimate electron energies and identify the processes.

Bradbury's curves for h as a function of X/p are given in figure 5.16 for air; in figure 5.17 for NH_3; in figure 5.18 for A-, He-, and N_2-NH_3 mixtures; in figure 5.19 for NO; in figure 5.20 for h as a $f(p)$ in NO at $X/p = 2$; in figure 5.21 for h as a function of X/p for Cl_2 in A; and in figure 5.22 for HCl in A. Curves are also given for h as a function of X/p for H_2S in figure 5.23; for N_2O in A and in N_2 in figure 5.24; for pure N_2O in figure 5.25; for SO_2 and SO_2 in A in figure 5.26; and finally, for H_2O in figure 5.27. Figure 5.28 gives the pressure of H_2 generated in a given time from NH_3 at different values of X/p above 10.

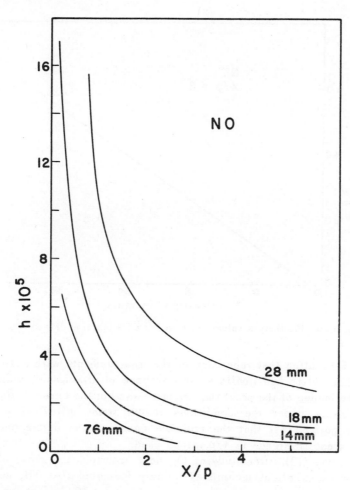

Fig. 5.19. Bradbury's values for h in NO as a function of X/p.

These results merit some discussion. In their original work on electron attachment in gases, the author and H. B. Wahlin (7), in the author's laboratory, had observed that at about 760 mm with X as high as 60 volts/cm, electrons remained quite free in *pure*, dry NH_3 gas, with $h < 10^{-9}$. V. A. Bailey studied NH_3, using his method under initially adverse conditions in Sydney (10). With NH_3 dried over P_2O_5, using no refrigerant or fractional distillation, there was observed a notable value for h. Failing to note that his work was at an X/p 160 times as high as that of the author and Wahlin, he severely criticized the author's work. The criticism was such as to call for a

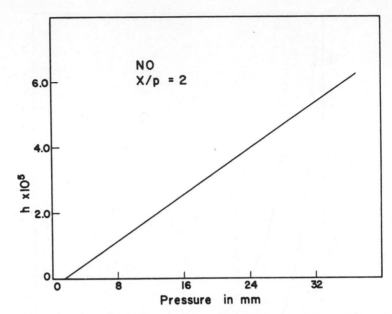

Fig. 5.20. Bradbury's values for h in NO as a function of p at X/p = 2.

reply (7) stating that repetition of the measurements with even purer NH_3 than before had confirmed the absence of attachment, indicating that the burden of the proof that impurity was not the cause of *Bailey's* attachments under the conditions rested with Bailey. The reply further pointed out that the probable cause of the discrepancy lay in the great difference in X/p values used.

Bradbury (13), after studying O_2, next undertook the study of NH_3. Bradbury's excellent techniques quickly indicated that NH_3 actually *does not attach electrons* below an X/p of about 10. In fact, as noted in figure 5.17, there is no sign of attachment until X/p reaches 10, after which h rises to 8×10^{-3} near X/p = 23. Bradbury also noted that above X/p = 10 the pressure in his chamber rose during the measurement. The residual gas after some time could be sparked with air, yielding H_2O, as Bailey had earlier observed. Bradbury measured the rate of generation of H_2 as a function of X/p for a given electron current run for a fixed time, and found that it increased as X/p increased, as seen in figure 5.28.

According to table 4.13, it appears that the electron energy in NH_3 at X/p = 10 is 0.42 e.v. The value of the average energy of 0.42 e.v. at an X/p = 10 in NH_3 from the Bailey techniques is indeed surprising. At an X/p of 12 the energy is 1.15 e.v., and at 16 it is

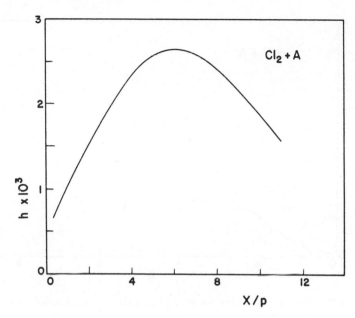

Fig. 5.21. Bradbury's values for h in Cl_2-A mixture as a function of X/p.

1.8 e.v. The fractional electron-energy loss in table 4.13 is at first relatively low, but jumps to an exceedingly high peak at an $X/p = 8$, which is seven times that at an $X/p = 4$. It then drops to four times its initial value. The only conclusion that can be drawn is that at lower X/p in NH_3 the energy distribution is far from Maxwellian, having many electrons at energies several times the average in a long, high-energy tail, and that when dissociation and attachment occur, the sudden, very heavy energy losses at inelastic impact completely alter the distribution. Thus, the average data are not relevant.

The rise in A observed by Bradbury indicates an electron energy of about 4 e.v. It is probable that the estimate of E from A is more reliable relative to known distributions than that in NH_3. Chemical studies on photodissociation indicate that with the heat of formation of NH^-, the energy needed for dissociative attachment of electrons to NH_3 follows that in the equation

$$NH_3 + e + 3 \text{ volts} - E_{NH^-} \rightarrow NH^- + H_2 .$$

That the ion formed is NH^- and not H_2^- follows from the fact that while H^- is stable, H_2^- is not, and H_2 is observed to be formed. While the other reaction,

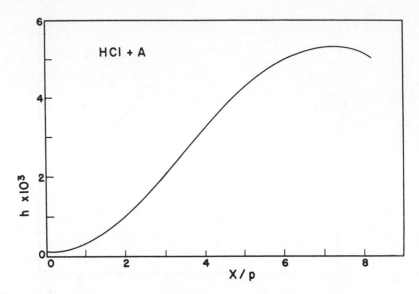

Fig. 5.22. Bradbury's values for h in HCl - A mixture as a function of X/p.

$$NH_3 + e + 4.52 \text{ volts} \rightarrow NH_2^- + H \text{ or } H^- + NH_2$$

is possible, the energy required is too high. Thus, from the photo-dissociation of NH_3 into NH and H_2, from the creation of H_2 in the reaction, and from the energy at which attachment occurs, it is safe to conclude that the negative ion formed is NH^- and not NH_2^- or H^-. However, the energies involved are not accurately estimated.

Bradbury investigated CO for X/p from 0.25 to 20, and found $h < 10^{-8}$, the limit of resolution of his apparatus. Since CO, like NH_3, has of itself no electron affinity, attachment would have to proceed by dissociation. To dissociate CO requires 9.1 volts, so that at least 6.9 e.v. are needed to dissociate CO and give O^-. Townsend's measurements indicate that the electron energy in CO at an $X/p = 20$ is of the order of 2 volts. Even if this average energy is too low, average energies would need be much higher in order to observe attachment.

As seen in figures 5.19 and 5.20, h in NO is at a maximum at low X/p, and is *pressure-dependent*. In fact, at a fixed X/p of 2, the increase of h with pressure is roughly linear. This means that attachment in NO is a process involving a multibody impact; that is, electrons need impacts with a third body to attach to NO. To test this further, Bradbury used equal parts of NO and N_2, and observed that h was one-third of that for the same pressure of NO. This can only

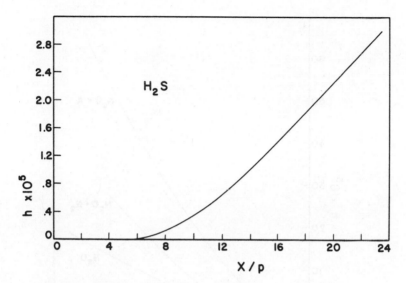

Fig. 5.23. Bradbury's values for h in H_2S as a function of X/p.

mean that N_2 acts as a diluent gas, impacts between NO, an electron, and an N_2 molecule being incapable of yielding NO^-. Thus, the reaction must be of the type

$$NO + NO + e \rightarrow NO^- + NO.$$

It is known that NO reacts with another NO molecule to form $(NO)_2$ with a heat of reaction of 0.05 e.v. The existence of any given concentration of $(NO)_2$ depends on the NO pressure, as the 0.035 e.v. energy of thermal agitation tends to dissociate $(NO)_2$. Thus, the process is

$$(NO)_2 + e \rightarrow NO^- + NO.$$

That is, NO has an electron affinity, but unlike O_2, cannot take up the energy of electron attachment in its vibrational system until an impact with some neutral molecule removes it. Thus, attachment needs low-energy electrons to find existent $(NO)_2$ complexes to which they attach dissociatively to form stable NO^- ions, the energy of attachment and excess kinetic energy from the field being taken up by the dissociating particles NO^- and NO. The probability is small, and rapidly decreases with electron energy. The dissociative attachment reaction

$$NO + e + 3.2 \text{ volts} \rightarrow N + O^-$$

probably does not occur until higher X/p values.

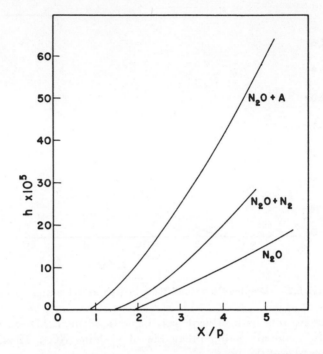

Fig. 5.24. Bradbury's values for h in N_2O-A and N_2O-N_2
mixtures as a function of X/p.

As indicated in the discussion of microwave techniques, James
Franck had told the author in 1928 that attachment to the halogens
should be a spontaneous dissociative attachment, occurring probably
even at thermal energies and of the form

$$Cl_2 + e \rightarrow Cl^- + Cl + KE.$$

The electron affinity of the halogens leads to a stable negative
halogen atom ion with heat of formation in excess of 3.2 and up to
3.78 e.v., while the heats of dissociation of the halogens are of the
order of 2.48 e.v. or less. It will be noted that in Cl_2 + A, as seen
in figure 5.21, Bradbury observed attachment even at his lowest X/p
values. His curve, however, rose to a peak at an X/p of about 5.
What energy this indicates is difficult to say, for while electron
energies in A are usually high at low X/p, this may not be so when
A is mixed with Cl_2, which has many low-lying excited states which
can absorb energy and lead to low values of energy for higher values
of X/p.

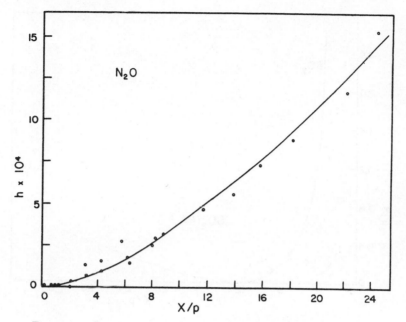

Fig. 5.25. Bradbury's values for h in N_2O as a function of X/p.

That the reaction proceeds as

$$Cl_2 + e \rightarrow Cl^- + Cl + (3.79 - 2.48) \text{ volts of } KE$$

is most likely.

However, it was in I_2 that Hogness and Lunn (24) detected only the formation of I^- and not I_2^- in the mass spectrograph. As indicated under Biondi's study (20), the cross section for the formation of I^- by dissociative detachment in I_2 is exceptionally large ($h \sim 1$) at thermal energies, and rapidly drops to yield $h \sim 10^{-2}$ or less at around 1 e.v. More work can and should be done in this field. However, there is little doubt that dissociative attachment at near-thermal energies applies to the three halogens Cl_2, Br_2, and I_2. The cross sections for this process are large, but exactly how they vary with electron energy has not been firmly established as yet. The failure in interpretation of what happens stems from the fact that all measurements of energies, as a function of X/p, come via Townsend's factor η. This quantity represents an average for distribution functions (some of unquestionably bizarre form), depending on how λ varies with c, and on those functions in which the form changes abruptly as soon as a characteristic inelastic-energy threshold is reached.

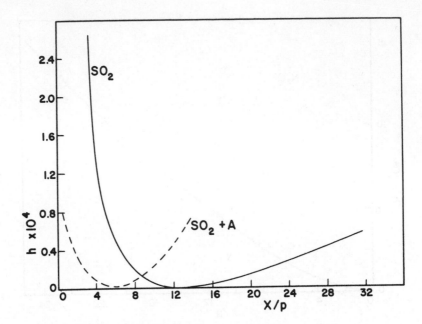

Fig. 5.26. Bradbury's values for h in SO_2 and SO_2-A
mixture as a function of X/p.

As indicated by J. Franck in 1928, HCl has a dissociation energy
of the order of 4.5 e.v., while the heat of negative ion formation with
Cl is 3.79 e.v. Thus, attachment in HCl should require an energy of
about 0.81 e.v. before the reaction

$$HCl + e + 0.81 \text{ volts} \rightarrow Cl^- + H.$$

This reaction was confirmed by Bradbury, who had to use HCl diluted
with A in order to measure the rapid reaction. The value of h rose
from very low values at an X/p above 1 to a peak with $h = 5 \times 10^{-3}$
at an $X/p = 7$, as seen in figure 5.22. Here again the average electron
energy is not known, so that the evaluation of the activation energy
is uncertain. In 1930, Bailey and Duncanson repeated Bailey's earlier
study of HCl. They found that $h = 0.4 \times 10^{-3}$ at an $X/p = 10$, with
an average energy of 0.14 e.v. and very inelastic impacts. The value
of h did not rise above 5×10^{-4}, even at an X/p of about 0.5 e.v.
Inelastic-impact loss was at a peak at $X/p = 15$. The discrepancy
between Bradbury's and Bailey's data may stem from the higher electron energies in A + HCl mixtures than those achieved in pure HCl,
where fractional energy loss f is indeed large. That Cl^- is formed,
and not HCl^-, was shown in mass-spectrographic studies of Barton
(38).

The Formation of Negative Ions

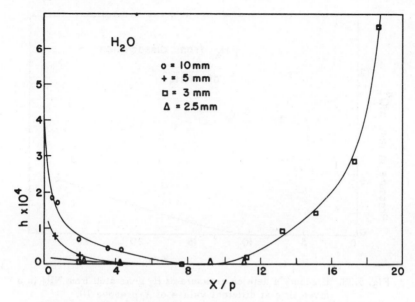

Fig. 5.27. Bradbury's values for h in H_2O as a function of X/p.

The study of N_2O ("laughing gas") by Bradbury is shown in figures 5.24 and 5.25. There it is seen that as in HCl and NH_3, the attachment occurs above an energy threshold, i.e., above $X/p = 2$ in pure N_2O, and above an $X/p = 1$ in $N_2O + A$. In pure N_2O the value of h rose to 1.25×10^{-3} at $X/p = 22$. Here again, trouble is encountered when comparison is made with the energy data of Bailey and Rudd (11) in 1932, replacing earlier data of Skinker and White of 1923. At $X/p = 2$ the average energy is indicated to be about 0.14 e.v., and their values of h do not begin until an $X/p = 3$ with $h = 0.16 \times 10^{-4}$, which is far less than Bradbury's value. Bradbury estimated that the rise occurred at about 1.7 e.v., from his study of N_2-N_2O mixtures. Two reactions could occur as a result of thermochemical studies. They are

$$N_2O + e + 3.84 \text{ volts} \rightarrow NO^- + N$$

and

$$N_2O + e + 1.8 \text{ volts} \rightarrow N_2 + O^-.$$

Since there is no pressure variation, the action is a dissociative attachment, forming O^- at the low energy. The comparison of Bradbury's data in HCl and N_2O with the Bailey data indicates the greater sensitivity of Bradbury's direct method, and a consistent underestimate of the electron energy from X/p values with Bailey's method. The

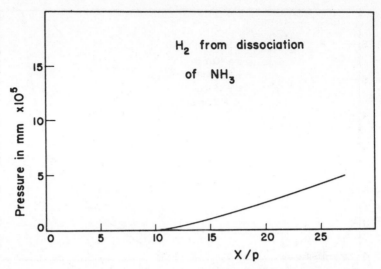

Fig. 5.28. Bradbury's data on pressure of H_2 generated from NH_3 in a given time at different values of X/p above 10.

cause of the latter difficulty is not clear. It may result from their universal acceptance of the Druyvesteyn law (11) and the reduction of their data in terms of the constants from the use of such a law.

Bradbury and Tatel investigated fractionated tank CO_2, and contrary to earlier findings by the author and Wahlin with HCl-generated CO_2, observed no attachment up to their highest X/p. J. B. Rudd (11), using the Bailey techniques, went up to $X/p = 16$ with electron energies up to 2.5 e.v., and found no attachment in CO_2. For a dissociation of CO_2 into $CO + O$, the energy required is 5.48 e.v., 1.45 e.v. of which could come from the formation of O^-. However, impacts in CO_2 are so inelastic that even at $X/p = 20$ the electrons do not receive the necessary energy of 3.5 e.v.

Figure 5.26 shows that the gas SO_2 is the only other gas besides O_2 that attaches electrons in a pressure-independent reaction without dissociation of some sort. As in O_2, h declines as X/p increases, and rises again at higher X/p. Use of A as a diluent (as in air) displaces the minimum to lower X/p values. This gas was not investigated by the Bailey methods. Bradbury estimates the minimum at $X/p = 12$ to correspond to between 4 and 6 e.v. The rises could be caused by a dissociative attachment, for at 5.7 and 5.71 volts three dissociative processes are possible, neglecting the unknown energy of ion formation:

$$SO_2 + e + 3.5 \text{ volts} \to SO + O^-;$$

$$SO_2 + e + 5.7 \text{ volts} \to SO^- + O ;$$

$$SO_2 + e + 5.7 \text{ volts} \to S + O_2^-.$$

While the third reaction may be energetically possible, the estimate depends on energy of formation of O_2^-, which is very small; certainly less than 0.5 e.v. It is thus much more likely that the more stable ion, O^- at 1.45 e.v., is the one created requiring only 3.5 e.v. That SO^- could form is also possible. Whether the first two reactions compete, or one or the other predominates, is not known. It may depend on which ion, SO^- or O^-, has the highest heat of formation. Bradbury considers that SO can form a negative ion.

In figure 5.23, Bradbury's data in H_2S are seen to resemble HCl and N_2O, with attachment beginning at about $X/p = 6$. The purification of H_2S was difficult, but the character of the results indicates that pure substance was dealt with. From photochemical data there are two possible reactions, according to Bradbury, again *neglecting heat of ion formation:*

$$H_2S + e + 3.2 \text{ volts} \to H_2 + S^-$$

and

$$H_2S + e + 3.82 \text{ volts} \to HS^- + H.$$

Use of A mixtures indicates that the formation of HS^- is more probable. H^- could form, but its heat of formation is small, so that the ion is probably HS^-. The cross section for this reaction is relatively small, with $h \sim 10^{-5}$.

As noted in figure 5.27, water presents a very complicated pattern. At low X/p a pressure-dependent process appears, of the same sort as noted in NO. However, above an X/p of about 10, a pressure-independent dissociative attachment occurs with a probability of the order of 4×10^{-4}. Argon mixtures showed that at $X/p \sim 8$ the electron energy was 5 e.v. For H_2O to dissociate to $H + OH$ takes 5.11 volts. Bailey and Duncanson detected attachment with $h = 6 \times 10^{-6}$ at an $X/p = 12$ in H_2O vapor. They fixed the average energy of the electrons as about 0.14 e.v. At an $X/p \sim 20$, $h = 3 \times 10^{-4}$, the average energy was 0.7 e.v. in their study.

Bradbury explained the reaction for dissociative attachment as

$$H_2O + e + 5.11 \text{ volts} \to HO^- + H.$$

If this reaction occurs, its threshold should be reduced by the heat of formation of OH^- ions, so that the threshold may well be considerably lower. Lozier (25) has reported some measurements with H_2O vapor at which electrons of 6.6 and 8.8 volts attach to H_2O^-, which breaks up, giving H^- and OH. The dissociation is accompanied by a recoil, the H^- having an energy of 1.5 or 3.2 e.v. for the two cases. The heat of formation of H^- is 0.74 e.v. A reaction

$$H_2O + e + \text{energy} \to H_2 + O^-$$

could occur. There is no indication that the ion formed in Bradbury's study was not O^-, and a mass-spectrographic study should be made. However, it is probable, from energetic grounds, that the first reaction is the one taking place. The second reaction, providing strong sources of H^- ions, has been observed from the heads of the positive column, and from striations in water-vapor discharges.

Bradbury explains the high-pressure attachment as caused by the appearance of nuclei of condensation that give negative ions at around 10 mm pressure of H_2O vapor. Dissolved gases O_2 (to which Bradbury adds CO_2) aid the effect. A and H_2 do not react to increase the effect. Bradbury accordingly likens the effect to that in NO, where $(NO)_2$ picked up an electron to give $(NO)_2^-$, which dissociated at once to give NO^- and NO, thus removing the heat of attachment. In H_2O he assumed that the reaction is

$$xH_2O + O_2 \to x(H_2O)O_2 + e \to x(H_2O)O_2^- \to x(H_2O) + O_2^-.$$

This is certainly a possible reaction. That CO_2 forms CO_2^- in this fashion is doubtful, since Bradbury asserts that CO_2 *does not* form a CO_2^- ion, even though Arnot reports CO_2^- ions in impact studies on metals. Arnot (44) also reported Hg^- ions, which have later been shown *not* to form. It is not precluded that

$$(H_2O)_2 + e \to e(H_2O)_2^- \to H_2O^- + H_2O,$$

as in NO, for there is no indication that H_2O^- cannot exist. In fact, it appears that molecules of a type ROH have a strong charge-specific affinity for negative ions.

Two gases were studied by the Bailey methods (11) that were not investigated by Bradbury. One was pentane, C_5H_{12}. For this gas, at low X/p of 1.25 and at near-thermal energies, h was a maximum at 1.3×10^{-3}. From there on it declined as X/p increased. This sort of behavior could have come from an impurity, the amount of which decreased as X/p increased and the value of p used decreased. It could, of course, have been a direct attachment with dissipation of

TABLE 5.5

Energies of Negative Atomic Ions in Electron Volts, after Bates (1947)

Extrapolation Down an Isoelectronic Series

Atom	State	Energy	Probable Value from Experiment or Exact Theory
H	$1S^2$	+0.74	0.747 e.v., calculated wave-mechanically. Observed in mass spectrograph.
He	$2S$	−0.53	
Li	$2S^2$	+0.47	0.54 e.v., calculated wave-mechanically. Observed in mass spectrograph.
Be	$2P$	−0.8	
B	$2P^2$	−0.1	
C	$2P^3$	+0.9	
N	$2P^4$	−0.6	
O	$2P^5$	+1.0	1.45. Experiment. Observed in mass spectrograph.
F	$2P^6$	+2.9	4.13. Calculated from cyclical process.
Na	$3S^2$	0.0	Observed in mass spectrograph (?).
Mg	$3P$	−0.9	
Al	$3P^2$	+0.2	
Si	$3P^3$	+1.7	
P	$3P^4$	+0.3	
S	$3P^5$	+1.5	
Cl	$3P^6$	+3.1	3.79. Calculated from cyclical process. (Probably more nearly 4.1)
Ne	−	−1.20	
A	−	−1.0	
Br	−	−	+ 3.82, 3.65, 3.54.
I	−	−	+ 3.14, 3.24, 3.15, 3.22.

energy by later impacts, but this is not likely. In the other gas (ethylene, C_2H_4) there was no attachment.

§ 6. **The Attachment Processes and Molecular Structure.**

It is strange in some ways that electrons should attach to molecules at all, as these are assumed to be fairly saturated structures. That atoms have an affinity for electrons follows from the character of the periodic table, and the tendency for atoms to gain electrons to achieve such external electron configurations as the electron pair of He and H_2, or the octettes of Ne or Cl⁻, etc. Thus, it is not surprising that electron-affinities of atoms exist in some cases, and that they may be high. It will also appear that there are certain molecular types (or better, states) that have a strong electron affinity. These characteristics, and the values of the binding energies of some of these species, are indicated in the two tables to follow. The first

TABLE 5.6

Bradbury Table of Molecular and Atomic States Forming Negative Ions
and Ion-Forming Mechanisms in Gases

Molecule or Atom	Ground State	Negative Ions form Directly	Electron Energy at which attachment Begins	Reaction Accompanying Attachment	Classification of Process
He, Ne, A, Kr, Xe.	$^1S_0$	No			
H_2, N_2, CO, CO_2.	$^1\Sigma$	No			
Cl_2, Br_2, I_2.	$^1\Sigma$	No	Large at thermal; decreases with energy.	$Cl_2 + e \rightarrow Cl^- + Cl + (3.79\text{-}2.48)$ volts.	Dissociative attachment. Very large cross section for $I_2, h \sim 1$.
HCl, HBr, HI.	$^1\Sigma$	No	In HCl > 0.7 e.v.	$HCl + e + (4.5\text{-}3.8)$ volts $\rightarrow$ $H + Cl^-$.	Dissociative attachment.
*NH_3	—	No	> 3 e.v.	$NH_3 + e + 3$ volts $\rightarrow NH^- + H_2$.	Dissociative attachment.
N_2O	$^1\Sigma$	No	> 1.8 e.v.	$N_2O + e + 1.8$ volts $\rightarrow O^- + N_2$. $N_2O + e + 3.84$ volts $\rightarrow NO^- + N$.	Dissociative attachment.
CO_2	$^1\Sigma$	No	> 3.5 e.v. X/p > 30.	$CO_2 + e + 3.5$ volts $\rightarrow CO + O^-$.	Dissociative. Has not been observed directly.
†H_2S	—	No	> 3.7 e.v.	$H_2S + e + 3.7$ volts $\rightarrow HS^- + H$.	Dissociative attachment.
‡H_2O	—	No	> 5.11 e.v.	$H_2O + e + 5.11$ volts $\rightarrow OH^- + H$.	Dissociative attachment.
H_2O	—	No	> 6.6 or 8.8 e.v.	$H_2O + e + 6.6$ volts $\rightarrow OH + H^-$.	

one is due to D. R. Bates (26), and applies to atoms. The calculated energy values come from extrapolation down an isoelectronic series, and are shown in table 5.5, with both computed and observed energies where they are known. It is to be noted that the inert gases, Be, B, N, and Mg, have negative energies, while Na has zero. Thus, negative ions are not to be expected with these atoms, and in fact have not been observed. In an earlier table by Bates and Massey, Hg was included with a positive energy. It is omitted in the later table; and after careful search, Hg^- has never been observed, despite earlier claims that it had been found.

The second table is due to Bradbury (12), and summarizes the result of his studies, especially for molecular ions, but also including some atomic ions. However, it does more than this, for it tells whether ions were observed, how they were formed, and identifies the spectroscopic states which add electrons. This information, as developed by the author beyond Bradbury's original data, is presented in table 5.6.

It will at once be noted that certain types of electronic ground states and the corresponding molecular states have no, or even negative electron affinity. Thus, the $^1S_0$ states, such as the ground states of the inert gases, show negative heats of formation, and thus do

*Reaction now identified as yielding H^- at 5.8 volts and NH_2^- at 6 volts.

†Reaction recently shown to give S^-.

‡Reaction yields H^- and no OH^-.

TABLE 5.6 — Continued

Molecule or Atom	Ground State	Negative Ions form Directly	Electron Energy at which Attachment Begins	Reaction Accompanying Attachment	Attachment Energy	Classification of Process
O_2	$^3\Sigma$	Yes	Thermal to 0.5 e.v. h decreases as energy increases, but may decrease from 0.1 e.v. down.	$O_2 + O_2 + e \rightarrow O_2^- + O_2$.	Between 0.2 and 0.5 e.v.	Direct attachment. Energy goes to vibration; lost in impact later.
O_2	$^3\Sigma$	No	> 2.9 e.v. May set in at higher energy.	$O_2 + e + 2.89$ e.v. $\rightarrow$ $O^- + O$.	2.2 e.v.	Dissociative attachment with large cross section.
*NH	$^3\Sigma$	Yes	In NH_3 > 3 e.v.	$NH_3 + e + 3$ volts $\rightarrow$ $NH^- + H_2$.	–	Dissociative attachment.
SO	$^3\Sigma$	May	In SO_2 > 5.7 volts.	$SO_2 + e + 5.7$ volts $\rightarrow$ $SO^- + O$.	–	Dissociative attachment. Not surely established.
SO_2	$^3\Sigma$	Yes	Thermal to ~ 1 e.v. h decreases as energy increases.	$2SO_2 + e \rightarrow SO_2^- + SO_2$.	–	Direct attachment. Energy goes to vibration; lost in impact later.
SO_2	$^3\Sigma$	No	> 3.5	$SO_2 + e + 3.5$ volts $\rightarrow$ $SO + O^-$.	–	Dissociative attachment, alternative to formation of SO^-, and may predominate.
CN	$^2\Pi$	Yes	–	–	–	No details known.
NO	$^2\Pi$	Yes	All energies.	$2NO \rightarrow (NO)_2$. $(NO)_2 + e \rightarrow NO^- + NO$.	–	Pressure-dependent. Depends on complex $(NO)_2$ formation to take off energy.
†OH	$^2\Pi$	Yes	In H_2O > 5.11 e.v.	$H_2O + e + 5.1$ volts $\rightarrow$ $OH^- + H$.	–	Dissociative attachment assumed by Bradbury.
H_2O	–	May	Low energies.	$(2H_2O) + e \rightarrow H_2O^- + H_2O$, or $(H_2O)_2 + O_2 + e \rightarrow O_2^- + (H_2O)_2$.	–	Pressure-dependent. Requires formation of complexes to take off heat of formation.
Cl	$^2P_{3/2}$	Yes	–	$Cl + e \rightarrow Cl^-$.	3.79 e.v.	Direct attachment if energy can be carried off by another atom.
O	$^2p\,^3p$	Yes	All energies.	$2O + e \rightarrow O^- + O$.	2.2 e.v.	Direct attachment if energy can be carried off by another atom.

not yield negative ions. On the other hand, H, Li, and perhaps Na in the $^2S_{1/2}$ ground states, do have an appreciable positive of heat of formation. Nitrogen in the ^4S state has no electron affinity, while O and S are in a $^2P\,^3P$ ground state and add electrons with a fairly

*It is now known that this reaction does not occur.
†It is now established that OH^- is unstable in gas phase.

high energy. The second group elements, like Be, are in the $^1S_0$ state, and do not form negative ions. B in a ^2P ground state does not attach electrons, while C in a ^3P ground state has a fairly high heat of formation. Al in a $3\,^2P_{1/2}$ state has an electron affinity. Cl in a $3\,^2P_{3/2}$ state also has a high electron affinity, which holds also for F, Br, and I. Thus, it is noted that atoms with closed shells, electron pairs, or octettes do not have an electron affinity, while most other atomic states do have such an affinity. Again, while an atom in the ground state may have no electron affinity, it could well have one in an excited state. However, such states do not last long enough to form negative ions by electron attachment, and then would decay on loss of energy of excitation. Thus, CO_2^+ by impact on a metal surface could create CO_2^{-*}, while CO_2 could not attach electrons.

It would thus be expected that molecules having the equivalent molecular ground states, e.g., Σ, would show analogous behavior. Thus, H_2, N_2, CO, CO_2, Cl_2, I_2, Br_2, HCl, HBr, HI, and N_2O, do not directly add electrons. At appropriate energies, those that can dissociate on electron impact will, at a threshold above the dissociation energy, less the heat of negative ion formation, lead to dissociative attachment with an ion formed of an appropriate atom or electron-attaching molecule. Molecules in the $^3\Sigma$, Σ, and $^2\Pi$ states do form negative ions. These are molecules O_2, SO_2, NO, and the configurations NH, SO, HS, OH, and CN. The negative configuration ions are formed on fragments from a dissociative attachment process, while the others form directly in the gaseous phase.

In all attachment processes the major question is the dissipation of the energy of attachment. In dissociative processes this poses no great difficulty, since the two dissociating fragments can remove the energy in a kinetic form. There are no data to insure that one of the dissociating configurations may not be in an excited state of lower value. Again, the threshold for actual dissociative attachment may not be just at the lower-energy limit, as some appearance-potential studies indicate. How the cross section for dissociative attachment varies with electron energy is not accurately known. At fairly near the appearance-threshold energy the cross section is large, and decreases rapidly as the electron energy increases. Obviously, if there is a threshold energy, the existence of the energy distribution among the electrons in a swarm in a gas in a field will make the measured cross section (using methods here outlined) appear to increase as electron energy increases. Ultimately, as the average energy of the electron swarm increases, perhaps somewhat above the threshold, the apparent cross section should decrease. Thus, as

X/p or average electron energy increases, the value of h or q_a will increase with X/p or energy, even though for electrons of unique energy the attachment cross section would be maximal at or shortly above energy threshold.

The mechanism varies for the energy dissipation in the few cases of direct attachment. For O_2 it appears very likely that the energy of attachment is taken up into the vibrational system for some period. If an impact does not remove this energy during the lifetime of the vibrational negative ion state, the electron will dissociate off again. Thus, ion formation in this case depends on a triple impact of a sort in which the newly formed ion must collide with a neutral molecule before dissociation takes place. This would make the attachment to O_2 pressure-dependent. No pressure dependence for O_2 was observed above about 3 mm. There is some question as to the validity of the low-pressure tests of attachment in O_2, because at low pressures the X/p might have been such as to lead to some dissociative attachment.

There need not be too great concern about the failure to show pressure dependence. All that theory yields is a product of a lifetime τ_v and a cross section σ_e for energy removal. If $\sigma_e \tau_v$ is large in order to conform to the observed independence ranges, this does not require that σ_e be too large, since τ_v may be quite large. The values of τ_v cannot always be calculated with precision. Some transfers of vibrational energy may be resonance phenomena where cross sections are larger than solid elastic collision cross sections. In such a process it is clear that the higher the electron energy, the less likely the process will be; i.e., undoubtedly h quickly goes down as energy increases. Thus, a characteristic of this process will be a rapid decline of h or q_a with increase in X/p or average energy much above thermal. Such a decrease is observed for O_2, SO_2, and NO. Theory for O_2 indicates a rise at very low energies, followed by a decline. The initial rise comes in principle through the condition that the electron velocity of transit near the molecule must be great enough so that the transition to the excited vibrational state is fast compared with the period of vibration. This should occur at extremely low energies. While the Bradbury-Bloch theory, to be given in the next section, indicates the peak to occur at 0.1 e.v., it could well be at less. In any case, such a decline has not been observed with any certainty to date.

In NO, and perhaps in H_2O, the situation is simplified by a polymer formation to which dissociative attachment takes place. Since the amount of polymer formation, e.g., of $(NO)_2$ or $(H_2O)_x$, is pressure-dependent, there will be a different curve for h as a function of energy, increasing in value of h as pressure increases. Here also there will be a decline of cross section as energy increases.

If a dissociative attachment can take place by forming a negative ion with one of the constituents of such a molecule at higher energy, this process will occur in addition to the other process; and if dissociation occurs at low energy, the two may overlap. If an inelastic impact can remove enough energy to render the electrons nearly thermal at some higher energy, the value of h or q_a will again appear to rise. In O_2 this occurs at nearly the same value of X/p as that at which dissociative attachment occurs, so that both processes overlap. In SO_2 the dissociative attachment apparently occurs before an inelastic electron impact can take place that wipes out most of its energy.

With these comments, one may leave the general question of attachment and its mechanisms until more data accumulate.

§ 7. Energy of Negative Ion Formation in O_2, and the Bradbury-Bloch Theory of Attachment to O_2.

The first attempt at evaluation of the energy of electron attachment in O_2 was that of the author (16), (17). The peculiar variations of the curves for current through the Loeb electron filters as the potential V_g applied to the alternate grid wires was increased (reported by Cravath and Bradbury), required investigation. In particular, a rather sharp decline of the electron capture at a certain value of V_g was interpreted by Bradbury as a possible detachment of electrons from the O_2 ions. To this end the author constructed the tube shown in figure 5.29. Electrons were created in O_2 by a high-frequency glow discharge between electrodes E in an all-glass chamber provided with a screened cup A toward which electrons and negative ions were drawn by making E negative to A. At S_1 an electron filter was set up to remove all electrons in the mixture of carriers coming from A. S_2, to which the carriers were urged by the field, consisted of a second electron filter of coarse grid wires of about 2 mm diameter spaced about 2 mm apart. By raising the potential V_g on the wires of this filter, which more properly should be termed the *smasher*, the filter, with its more uniform field between wires, acts on the ions, or any chance electron, to increase their energy until the ions get so much energy as to cause them to shed their electron. These electrons are withdrawn, and thus more and more ions are gradually captured, causing the plateau of curves to decline, as in figure 5.5 (*supra*). The currents to S_1, S_2, and to the collector plate P could be studied

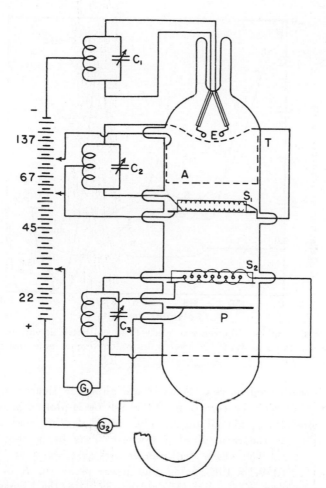

Fig. 5.29. Loeb's device for studying the electron detachment from negative O_2 ions by collision with O_2 molecules at high X/p. E, high-frequency
discharge. Electrons are extracted by field between E and A. S_1, electron
filter removing electrons and transmitting only ions. S_2, large grid wire electron filter to which a high potential could be applied to break up negative
ions. P, collecting plate. Currents to S_1, S_2, and P were recorded, those to
S_2 and P being read by galvanometers G_1 and G_2.

as pressure p, frequency ν on S_2, and V_g on S_2 were altered. The field
between the smasher grids varied from $1.318 \ V_g/d$ at the wire surface
to $0.879 \ V_g/d$ in the center. The pressure variation ranged from 2 to
60 mm, and frequencies varied over a range of 10, between 3×10^6
and 10^7 cycles.

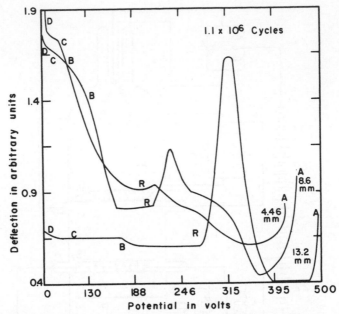

Fig. 5.30. Curves of currents to plate P as collected at various values of pressure indicated at 1.1×10^6 cycles as a function of potential applied to grids S_2.

The complicated curves observed are shown in figures 5.30, 5.31, and 5.32, in which the current to P through G_2 is plotted as a function of the potential V_g placed on S_2. The initial decline marked D is to be ascribed to the removal of a few electrons by S_2 that were not captured at S_1. The sharp declines B are only noted at lower frequencies ν. At 9.1×10^6 cycles and lower pressure, B is replaced by a rise or hump, H. Cravath (15) called the latter the "hump effect." This ultimately declines as beyond B at lower frequencies. The sharp peaks beyond this decline occur at all frequencies. These are the result of ionization by collision by electrons released from ions in the smashers, and breakdown between smasher wires. These increase the over-all current.

Of importance in this study is the beginning of the declines B, which various tests indicate to be the increased capture of electrons owing to the breakup of negative ions in the field, leading to capture of all the electrons if the frequency is not too high and the pressure is not too low. Thus, at or near B, the negative current to the plate given by G_2 should fall, and that at the S_2 read by G_1 should rise. In figure 5.32 it is seen that at 7 mm and low frequency, where there

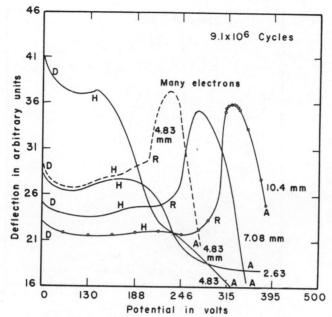

Fig. 5.31. Same as in figure 5.30, but at 9.1×10^6 cycles. The dashed curve at 4.83 mm is that through G_1, while that through G_2 corresponding is the full curve.

is only a plateau, G_1 rises and G_2 declines at the end of the plateau. At a higher frequency and the slightly lower pressure of 4.83 mm, it is seen that instead of a fall there is a sharp rise of negative carrier current through G_1 and a slower rise that does not decline to G_2 (figure 5.31).

In figure 5.31, at about 10^7 cycles, and more prominent at lower pressures, there is a rise near the point where the decline should occur, followed by a decline at lower pressures, and a rise followed by slight decline before breakdown. This is the "hump effect" that was first noted by Cravath, and caused him to lose confidence in the method. It is noted that in the one case where the current to G_1 is plotted, it rises parallel to that of G_2, the collector plate, but rises higher and then declines. Note that the *currents* are not to the same scale as read by G_1 and G_2; but the trends are significant.[6] The hump *begins* at an X/p not very different from that where the decline

---

[6] The reason that actual current values are not given is that in a tube such as this, the complicated nature of field interactions with motions of carriers to the walls using the a.c. breakdown source of electrons makes accurate data senseless, though the rough relations and trends are revealing.

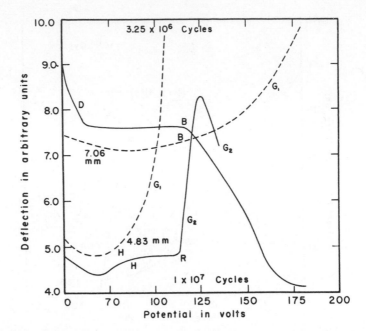

Fig. 5.32. Enlarged-scale plot of curves at 3.25×10^6 and 1×10^7 cycles, showing corresponding sections of currents through G_2 full and G_1 dotted.

corresponding to breakup occurs at lower frequencies. It is noted that the appearance of the hump corresponds to *increased* electron currents, both at smasher grids through G_1 and at the collector through G_2, while the decline in the absence of the hump or at its end, when measured at the plate, has an increased smasher current sometimes followed by a decline, as seen clearly in figure 5.32.

Interpretation is not too difficult. Where the smasher-grid current of electrons increases while that of negative ions at the plate declines, there is little doubt that negative carriers are being lost to the smasher grids and are not reaching the collector and G_2. Since frequencies are too high for *ion* collection, such change can only mean a detachment of electrons from ions and a capture of these by the smasher. With the hump both currents initially increase, so that one may suspect that *new carriers* are being generated at the smasher, some of which are collected by both plate and grid. The majority of electrons go to the grid, and the positive ions created move up to S_1 and the ion source.

The accumulated data on the values of V_g and p at which decline begins (which is also near the beginning of the hump) are shown in

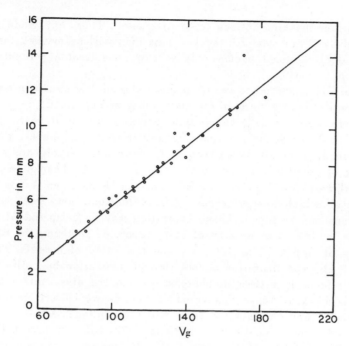

Fig. 5.33. The variation of the potential V_g on the smasher grid of S_2 at which electrons detach from ions as a function of pressure p of O_2 in mm of Hg.

figure 5.33. The linear character of the plot of V_g against p with fixed dimensions indicates that detachment, hump, and in fact all other rises and declines, are functions of X/p.

The value of interest here is that for the decline, or perhaps the beginning of the hump. The value of V_g for decline was 120 volts at $p = 7.6$ mm. The distance between grid-wire surfaces was 0.3 cm and their diameter was 0.2 cm. This gave an average field X_{ave} of 400 volts/cm. The field at 0.03 cm from the wire, which is perhaps the critical field for breakup and electron capture, is 1.2 X_{ave}. The important value of the alternating field is its peak value, though actually the time to accelerate the ion may be of longer duration than actual peak. The value of X_{max} was 680 volts/cm and $(X/p)_{max}$ was 89.5 volts/cm per mm Hg. This value then represents what could be considered the effective breakup X/p ratio.

The reason for assuming that the average energy of ions at this X/p would be the breakup energy, despite an energy distribution among the ions, stems from the relative sharpness of the break and the various masking actions to be discussed. Thus, any gradual loss caused by detachment for the few fast ions will be masked, and the sharp decline noted occurs only with a considerable percentage of breakup.

It is now essential to see what this value of X/p means in possible actions, so that the trend of the curves may be explained.

There were no data on *electron* energies and drift velocities in O_2 at an $X/p = 90$ at the time the author wrote his paper. He then used such makeshift data as could be assembled. There are still no values of electron energies in O_2 at an X/p of 90. Thanks to Healey and Kirkpatrick (11), there are now data in O_2 up to an $X/p = 50$ and below at which energy trends, drift velocities, and free paths of electrons can be found. These quantities may be compared with data for air, which go to an X/p of 100. According to them, the electron energy at $X/p = 50$ is 3.3 e.v., and the value of h is 0. That is, enough electron liberation occurs through ionization by collision and photo effects from their diaphragms so that the dissociative attachment is masked. Above this value of X/p, as we know from the work of Geballe and Harrison, much dissociative attachment is occurring to form O^- ions. Geballe and Harrison's (28) value of η/p in O_2 near $X/p = 70$ is 0.04. At this point the Townsend ionization function a/p is of the order of 0.4. Thus, at 7 mm pressure, there would be an a of 2.8 ions per cm, and the ionizing electron free path is ~ 3 mm.

While the average electron energy is not known in O_2 at $X/p = 90$, its value in air, which parallels O_2 fairly closely (within 10%), gives an average electron energy, according to Townsend, of 5.5 e.v. at $X/p = 100$. At $X/p \sim 90$, the average electron energy could well be around 5 e.v., and certainly not less than 4 e.v. Its value of a at 7 mm pressure would give an ionizing free path of not less than 1 mm. The electron free path in this region for both O_2 and air at 7 mm pressure is of the order of 4×10^{-3} cm with a drift velocity of the order of 1.5×10^8 cm/sec.

It is now possible to consider what happens in the gas at the smasher when an X/p of around 90 is reached. The time of a half cycle is 5×10^{-7} sec at the lowest frequency, and 5×10^{-8} sec at the highest. The high and effective portions of the field are of course on for only a fraction, say of the order of one-third of the times indicated. The breakup will be greatest near the wires where X/p is highest, but ionization by electron impact can occur along the whole mesh axis between grids. It is obvious that ionization by electron impact of any electrons *freed* in the gap *as a result of smashing*, will occur before much ion breakup. Likewise, any photoelectrons liberated from the negative smasher-grid wires by photoelectric action during negative phase can cause ionization by collision in the gas, also below the onset of much smashing. But *before* the ion *breakup* field is reached, there will be relatively few free electrons in the gap, if any.

At a low frequency, all electrons should be captured, since at 10^6 cycles the 1×10^{-7} sec of high field in the center of the gap with $X/p = 55$ should remove the electrons from 2 mm in $\sim 5 \times 10^{-9}$ sec. Accordingly, under conditions pictured when electrons are freed in the gap by ion breakup, the electrons will excite and ionize molecules on their way to the smasher wires. Thus, photoelectrons may be ejected from the negative wire when such energies are reached and ion breakup furnishes triggering electrons. These electrons can, as noted, produce perhaps 2 electrons and ions in the gap. If the field remains high enough for a sufficient period of time, the electron carriers created will all be absorbed by the smasher. The positive ions created will move upward from the plate in the field. In fact, the electron current to the smasher S_2 through G_1 will increase not only by electrons collected from broken-up negative ions, but also by excess electrons created in the gas by collisions. Thus, currents to G_1 should rise, and rise faster than the current to G_2 declines, if much ionization occurs.

However, ionization is not the only action, for the new electrons created and some of the detached electrons from O_2^- will certainly be picked up by dissociative attachment to give O^- ions. These ions will not be picked up by the field, but will proceed to the collector and G_2. Thus, O ions will be added to the current going through G_2 if they are formed far enough from the grids not to be captured. Since η/p is small compared to a/p above $X/p = 50$, it is unlikely that much dissociative attachment will occur, and increase in plate current due to this cause will be small. Still, it indicates that creation of new electrons not only will increase the current through G_1 considerably at low frequencies, but may also reduce the loss of ions to G_2 by substituting O^- ions for O_2^- ions.

Now as frequency goes up by a factor of 10, the active sweeping time for electrons is only about three times the fastest collection time along the mesh axis. However, not all electrons are created in the higher-field regions, and electron diffusion at the energies noted is high during the low-field periods. Thus, especially at lower pressures where diffusion is high, with constant X/p, it is clear that many electrons will escape that should have been captured. At least half of these electrons will be on the collector-plate side of the axis, and any electrons on the other side that yield O^- ions will also pass through the smasher.

Hence, at high frequencies, and at lower pressures where diffusion is increased, it is to be expected that when detachment yielding electrons at the smasher and photoelectric emission and ionization in the gas set in, with some dissociative attachment to give O^-, the collector-plate current through G_2 will at first rise by virtue of the negative ions created in the gas and lost from the smasher-current G_1 by diffusion. This ionization may in fact be sufficient to cause an increase of current, despite loss of ions by smashup. The smasher current through G_1 will increase at an even more rapid rate by virtue of electrons created in the gas that are swept up, while the positive ions migrate toward the filter grid in the longitudinal field.

However, as the X/p ratio increases above 90, so that no O_2^- ions can exist in the smasher field, and only few O^- ions form, the ionization by collision and creation of ions that can reach the collector and G_2 cannot make up for this loss, and the curves decline after passing a peak. The subsequent declines and rises of currents through G_1 and G_2 when ionization by collision occurs, ultimately leading to breakdown between the smasher grids, are of no interest. However, the foregoing discussion makes plausible the appearance of the decline, and/or at higher frequencies and lower pressures, the hump preceding the decline, and justifies the choice of the value of $X/p = 90$ at the decline as the detachment point for the average O_2^- ion.

It is next of interest, assuming that an $X/p = 90$ represents a sufficient number of detaching impacts, so that the average ion energy is significant, to calculate the average energy of the negative ions in the field. It had been relatively difficult to estimate this energy in the past, as so little was known about energies of ions in high electrical fields. Thanks to measurements of R. N. Varney (30) for O_2^+ ions in O_2 at values of X/p ranging from 40 to 1,000, it is possible to fix the drift velocity of the O_2^+ ions at 1×10^5 cm/sec at an $X/p = 90$. Extrapolated to low fields, the value is 2.3 $(760/p)$ X cm/sec. Now these ions suffer from charge-exchange energy loss, so that their drift velocity is low.

Studies of Hornbeck (31) and·of Varney (30) on inert gas ions in their own gases, show that in conformity with the generalized theoretical considerations of Wannier (32), there are correlations between mobilities of the molecular ions in these gases, which are retarded by polarization forces only, and the atomic ions in which charge exchange occurs with the enlarged solid elastic cross sections.

Now O_2^- ions presumably do not undergo charge-exchange encounters in O_2. The values of drift velocities at higher X/p for the ions He_2^+ and Ne_2^+, in which charge exchange does not occur and where the polarization forces predominate, are about twice those for He^+ and Ne^+ in their own gases, where exchange is very effective. But for polarization forces, the case where $m = 2M$ has an advantage of $\sqrt{3/2} : 1$, or 1.22 in drift velocity over that for an ion with a mass factor ratio with $m = M$. Thus, the factor of 2 set for the ratio of drift velocity for He_2^+ relative to He^+ should be reduced by 1.6-fold in the case of O_2^- relative to O_2^+ in O_2. This would make the drift velocity of O_2^- at low energy 3.7 $(760/p)$ X cm/sec, and at most 1.6×10^5 cm/sec at an $X/p = 90$. Observationally, the values of the drift velocities for O_2^+ and O_2^- extrapolated to low fields are 2.3 $(760/p)$ X cm/sec and 2.68 $(760/p)$ X cm/sec respectively. Thus, it is not impossible that the drift velocity of O_2^- at $X/p = 90$ is as low as 1×10^5 cm/sec at an X/p of 90. This is certainly an upper limit to the value at this X/p.

For such forces in such fields, Wannier has shown that the energy of the ions in the field is very nearly their "apparent" kinetic energy multiplied by 2 plus $(3/2)kT$ for the gas. The "apparent" kinetic energy referred to by Wannier is the energy of drift motion. This occurs because of the fact that in high fields ions of the same mass as the gas molecules have an offset asymmetrical energy distribution, with more energy along the field axis than transverse to it. Thus, it is possible to set the energy as $2(\frac{1}{2}mv_{90}^2) = 1.35 \times 10^{-12}$ erg, where v_{90} is the drift velocity at $X/p = 90$, for an O_2^- ion. In the O_2 gas at the thermal energy, $(3/2)kT$ is negligible compared to the drift energy, and so is not added. Thus, the kinetic energy of the O_2^- ions at $X/p = 90$ is of the order of 0.85 e.v. Since in impact, the energy available for electron detachment can only be one-half the total kinetic energy, the other half of the energy going to conserve momentum, it is clear that the energy of the detachment is of the order of 0.42 e.v.

This value of the energy is not seriously different from that calculated through a classical solid elastic relation of Compton, assuming a Maxwellian energy distribution, which reads:

$$(5.75) \qquad \bar{u} = \frac{L_0 X}{2.31} \frac{M + m}{\sqrt{mM}},$$

with $\bar{u}$ in e.v. if L_0 is the free path in cm at 1 mm and X is in volts/cm. Estimates of L_0 in O_2 place it at around 1×10^{-2} cm. Since $M = m$, the mass term is 2, and $X = 90$ at $p = 1$ mm. This makes $\bar{u} = 0.78$ e.v. and leaves 0.39 e.v. as the energy of detachment, which is in sensible agreement with the calculation based on Wannier's theory. That these radically different theories agree follows from some common general physical behavior consequent on using different models of this sort.

While it is probable that the value of average energy of the visible decline marked B might make the actual energy required for detachment greater than $X/p = 90$ because of the energy distribution, the value of X/p required is actually not much in excess of 90, and the energy increase is relatively slow with X/p in this region. The reason for this is that the concomitant ionization, occurring when breakup begins, masks the decline, so that a sharp decline takes place only when breakup is quite general.

The value of the energy given as not in excess of 0.5 e.v. and perhaps less, but probably not much below 0.3 e.v., is in general agreement with the difficulty of treating O_2^- in plasmas having much residual radiant energy, even though electrons are near thermal energies, as noted by Biondi. It would also make O_2^- ions difficult to detect in mass spectrographs unless such ions were created by grazing impact of O_2^+ ions on metals and experienced no collisions en route. There is certainly a marked difference in stability of O_2^- ions and O^- ions.

Further indications of this situation have come from some recent experiments of L. M. Branscomb and W. L. Fite (33), done at the Bureau of Standards. In this study H^- ions were obtained from the anode side of striations in an H_2O-contaminated glow discharge in H_2. They were accelerated to 200 volts in a beam, and after mass separation in a crossed field velocity selector, passed through a very high-intensity light beam of appropriate wave length in a high-vacuum space. The light source was chopped at 450 cycles per second. Using weak electric and magnetic fields transverse to the ion beam, an alternating current of some 10^{-13} ampere was measured. Using the measured intensity and the spectral distribution of the light, the measured velocity of the ions and the theoretical cross section, the theoretically expected ratio of photodetached electron current to ion current was calculated and compared with observation. The preliminary measurements confirmed the theoretical result of S. Chandrasekar and his colleagues, who reported a cross section with maximum value of 4.52×10^{-17} cm^2 at 8,275 Å, i.e., at 1.51 e.v., which is twice the heat of formation of H^- at 0.74 e.v. The use of yellow and red filters confirmed the approximate spectral distribution of theoretical cross section.

The photodetachment of negative ions in O_2 was next studied. Branscomb stated that they had expected the presence of O_2^- ions and thus photodetachment at low energy. Actually, photodetachment was observed for light of wave length only below 5,600 Å, indicating that the energy of the ion being photodissociated was of the order of 1.45 e.v. It is clear that only O^- ions were present in the beam, and that the estimate of the heat of negative O^- formation is correctly given by D. R. Bates (26) and H. D. Hagstrum (22) as 2.2 e.v.

Here again, as in Biondi's study with negative ions in a cooled-down plasma, the O_2^- ions are absent. Since in O_2 that is thoroughly cold at about 300° K., electrons are observed to attach to yield what is supposed to be O_2^-, it appears that the O_2^- ions are readily destroyed at relatively low energy. If the author's estimate of the heat of formation of O_2^- ions is correctly somewhere below 0.5 e.v., which represents a wave length of 24,700 Å, it could well be that in gases previously ionized to some 10^{12} electron-ion pairs/cm2, the residual radiation temperature in the gas, even after 5×10^{-3} sec, is such as to destroy O_2^-, even if electrons have reached nearly thermal energies and the gas temperature is only some 100° C.

§ 8. The Theory of the Negative Ion Formation in O_2.

The theory of the mechanism of capture of an electron by O_2, SO_2, or NO to form the molecular ion, as developed by F. Bloch and N. E. Bradbury (34), is in principle the following: It is assumed that the electron is captured into an orbit in the O_2 molecule, simultaneously increasing the vibrational energy by the binding energy A, plus the energy of motion of the electron E^* for which capture is permitted. Quantum-mechanical analysis yields for the capture cross section $(q_a)_{n'}$ into the vibrational level n' as

(5.76)
$$(q_a)_{n'} = a_{n'} \, \frac{m}{M} \, \frac{A^2 a^3}{v_0} \left(\frac{\delta}{a}\right)^{2(n'-1)} f(E^*),$$

with $n' = 1, 2, 3 \ldots$, the quantum number of the vibrational state. The average speed of the electron

$$v_0 = \int_0^\infty \left(\frac{2E}{m}\right)^{\frac{1}{2}} f(E) dE,$$

while $a_{n'}$ is a numerical coefficient of the order unity, m is the mass of the electron, and M is the arithmetic mean of the two atomic masses in the diatomic molecular model considered. The quantity a is related to A by the relation $\hbar^2/2ma^2 = A$. It will be of the order of magnitude of the orbital dimensions of the electron in its bound state, i.e., of the molecular dimensions. This follows from the fact that the binding energy A and average kinetic energy may be assumed as being of the same order of magnitude. The quantity δ^2 is the mean square of the elongation in the ground state of the nuclear oscillation. The relation only yields the right order of magnitude for q_a if n' is of the order of magnitude 1.

Since $E^* + A$ is the total energy lost by the electron on capture, and has to be equal to the increase of vibrational energy, $E^* = n'\hbar\omega - A$, with ω the circular frequency of the oscillation. This quantity must be positive, which means that

$$(5.77) \qquad A = n\hbar - E^* \lessgtr n\hbar\omega.$$

This gives an upper limit for A if n' can be determined.

Before applying quantitative data it must be indicated that if the vibrational energy is not removed by impact during the lifetime θ of the excited ion, then the electron will be re-emitted. Thus, vibrational energy transfer must occur in a time τ which is short compared to θ. This depends on the pressure and temperature of the gas. If $\bar{v}$ is the average velocity of molecules in the gas and s is the effective cross section for transfer of vibrational energy,

$$\tau = \frac{1}{N\bar{v}s} = \epsilon/p,$$

where ϵ depends only on temperature and p is the pressure.

The lifetime θ is pressure-independent, and is given following approximately the same treatment as for equation 5.76, by the relation

$$(5.78) \qquad \theta_{n'} = \frac{(2\pi)^2 \hbar^4}{(2m)^{3/2}(E^*)^{1/2} a_{n'}A^2a^3} \frac{M}{m} \left(\frac{a}{\delta}\right)^{2(n'-1)}.$$

Thus, equation 5.76 for q_a only applies if $\theta_{n'} >> \tau$. This condition is satisfied for different pressure ranges for different gases, but there always exists a lower pressure limit for each gas below which q_a becomes pressure-dependent. To get an approximate expression for the dependence, assume that the ion at $t = 0$ is in its excited state following electron transition. The chance of its still being there after t will be given by $\epsilon^{-t/\theta}$. On the other hand, the probability of a transfer collision after a time between t and $t + dt$ has elapsed is $\epsilon^{-t/\tau} dt/\tau$. The total probability that an excited atom will make a transfer collision is

$$(5.79) \qquad P = \int_0^\infty \epsilon^{-(t/\theta + t/\tau)} \frac{dt}{\tau} = \frac{\theta}{\theta + \tau},$$

and since τ is inversely proportional to p, $P = p/(p + p')$, where p' is the critical pressure for which $\theta = \tau$. Thus, multiplying the expansion for $(q_a)_{n'}$ by this factor, there results

(5.80)
$$(q_a)_{n'} = a_{n'} \frac{m}{M} \frac{A^2 a^3}{\hbar v_0} \left(\frac{\delta}{a}\right)^{2(n'-1)} f(E^*) \frac{p}{p + p'} \cdot$$

If $p >> p'$, q_a is independent of pressure. If $p << p'$, q_a is a linear function of pressure.

In order to compare theory with experiment, the value of h must be converted to q_a in terms of q_R. The value of q_R at low electron energies was not then known, but the microwave studies made later have shown that in general, Bradbury and Bloch's assumption that q_R approaches a constant value of the order of a^2 is not far wrong. This also agrees with the assumption that for low velocities inside the molecule, the wave function of the electron in its initial state will no longer depend on velocity. Thus, it is possible to write

(5.81)
$$h_{n'} = \frac{(q_a)_{n'}}{q_R} = \beta_{n'} \frac{m}{M} \frac{A^2 a}{v_0} \left(\frac{\delta}{a}\right)^{2(n'-1)} f(E^*) \frac{p}{p + p'} ,$$

where $\beta_{n'}$ is a new constant ~ 1. The value of h for O_2 in the pressure-independent regions is 10^{-4}, and it is possible to see which values of n' yield this value. For simplicity, A, E^*, and E_0 are assumed to be of the same order of magnitude. The quantity $f(E^*)$ will then become of the order of $1/E_0$, and $p/(p + p')$ will be of the order of unity. Thus,

(5.82)
$$h_{n'} \cong \left(\frac{m}{M}\right)\left(\frac{\delta}{a}\right)^{2(n'-1)} ,$$

with $m/M = 0.33 \times 10^{-4}$. Hence, if the equation is to be obeyed, $(\delta/a)^{2(n'-1)}$ will have to be about unity. Since $\delta/a \sim 1/10$, this requires that $n' = 1$. Now if $n' = 1$, then $A = \hbar\omega - E^*$, so that $A < \hbar\omega = 0.19$ e.v. Again, since $n' = 1$, h becomes

(5.83)
$$h = \beta \frac{m}{M} \frac{A^2 a}{v_0} f(E^*) \frac{p}{p + p'} ,$$

with $\beta \cong 1$.

Aside from order of magnitude, this relation gives the way in which h will vary with E_0, the average energy of the electrons, if $f(E)$ is known. The velocity distribution will be of the type $v^2 F(E/E_0)$, where F will approach a finite value for small arguments and drop off rapidly for large ones. The value chosen could be that of the Druyvesteyn type, with $b = 0.847$. Then,

$$F(E) = \text{const} \left(\frac{E^{1/2}}{E_0^{3/2}}\right) \epsilon^{-b(E/E_0)^2} ,$$

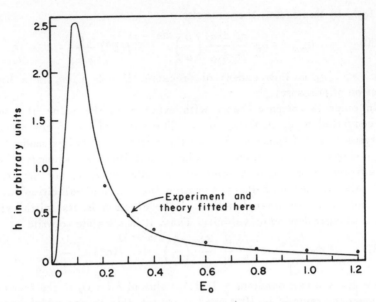

Fig. 5.34. Plot of h as a function of E_0 of the electron, as given by Bradbury and Bloch's theory. The theory was fitted at one point, and h is in arbitrary units. Note that at higher E_0 the agreement is good, but h is less at low values. Also note the peak and decline of theory at lower E_0.

the factor $E_0^{3/2}$ appearing because $f(E)dE = 1$. Thus,

$$h \propto \epsilon^{-b(E^*/E_0)^2} E_0^2.$$

The curve computed with $E_0 = 0.3$ volt, coinciding with the experimental value of h, is shown in figure 5.34. The circles are experimental points for O_2, the full line is the theoretical curve for $E^* = 0.08$ volt, corresponding to an A value of 0.11 volt.

As seen at low E_0, the theoretical curve rises rather too steeply. This may result from changes in varying values of q_a and q_R in this region that are not considered in this rough approach. The value of E^* used does not greatly alter the character of the curve for larger values of E. Since there is no experimental indication of h approaching the theoretical peak, even for the smallest values of E_0, this leads to the conclusion that E^* cannot be larger than 0.12. This then places a lower limit on A. Thus, it can be assumed that $.07 < A < 0.19$.

This conclusion is somewhat at variance with conclusions drawn from the observed value of X/p at which detachment occurs, which now appears to lie below 0.5 e.v., and might be as low as 0.3 e.v., but not much less. It is quite likely that studies of photodetachment of O_2^- ions that are now possible might clarify this matter. Exactly how critical to the theory is a value as low as 0.19 e.v. or less, derived from these data, it is very difficult to say. At best the theory is one based on orders of magnitude, and it is hoped that the stability could be slightly higher. In fact, one reason why Bates and Massey discard this conclusion is that they believe A should be about 1 e.v.; though how they can get around the author's detachment data is not clear. It is possible that Biondi's low value of h in O_2 at thermal energies could be a value to the left of the peak in figure 5.34.

The next question concerns the observed pressure independence of h above 3 mm of O_2. At very low pressure in O_2, there are (according to Bradbury) qualitative indications of a decrease in the value of h, as theory predicts. No pressure dependence is observed in air at several mm, though the concentration of O_2 molecules which can remove the energy in an assumed resonance collision is one-fifth of that in pure O_2. The actual measurement of h at pressures below 1 mm is exceedingly difficult because of other sources of loss of electrons (such as diffusion), and has not been accomplished.

The collision time r of O_2^- ions in O_2 at 3 mm pressure, using Doehring's value of $k = 2.68$, is close to 7×10^{-9} sec. The order of magnitude of θ, as estimated from equation 5.78 in the same manner as was done for h, is about 10^{-10}. This indicates that the cross sections for energy transfer by the excited atom are of the order of more than 10 and less than 100 times the cross section for *solid* elastic impact. The vibrational energy transfer from the excited O_2^- state to an O_2 molecule is supposed to be a resonance process, and Bradbury and Bloch believe that such cross sections for transfer are reasonable. The *radius* for transfer is thus between 3 and 10 times that for solid elastic impacts, so that the discrepancy does not seem unreasonable. However, Bates and Massey (35) disagree, and state that the ratio of cross sections is unreasonable. It is again difficult to arrive at anything more satisfactory on such an approximate theory, for which so many details are lacking.

It is believed that this theory of the phenomenon is correct in principle, but unless much more work is done, it must be accepted as tentative. One thing certain is that the process presents a characteristic variation of h or q_a with energy; and secondly, the process is one requiring such exacting conditions that it is not likely to be found occurring for many molecular species. Thus far, only one gas closely parallels O_2, and that is SO_2. NO does form NO^- ions by this process, but the conditions are such that the triple collision is achieved by the primary formation of $(NO)_2$ complexes, which then collide with an electron yielding NO^- and NO. Whether H_2O comes into this class is not clear as yet, though H_2O does show a pressure-dependent attachment, with h declining with energy.

§9. The Creation and Appearance of Negative Ions Other than Those Formed in Gas by Attachment Processes.

It has been indicated in table 5.5 that certain negative atomic ions are stable. In fact, it has been observed that negative Cl^- ions are readily formed in Cl_2 gas by an attachment process. Again, in table 5.6, it was shown that certain molecules or radicles that normally are chemically unstable or reactive in the free gaseous state, were observed to yield stable negative ions. Such, for instance, are NH^-, SO^-, and OH^-, in processes where attachment accompanying dissociation occurs. Thus, some atomic and many molecular negative ions are stable and can be observed. Some of these appear to come from reactions of electrons in the gas, as seen in table 5.6.

In addition, other negative atomic and molecular ions have been observed under conditions where attachment processes *in the gas* could not have taken place. In fact, many negative ions, including some of those also observed in gases, have been observed in vacuum and under various discharge conditions where direct attachment in the gas is impossible. It is essential to discuss these ions and the process of their formation, as they sometimes appear in electronic devices and cause difficulties.

With the development of his first mass spectrograph in 1912, J. J. Thomson observed parabolas indicating the presence of negative ions of O^-, Cl^-, H^-, and N^- when the corresponding molecular gases were present. At first he thought that the ionization of polar molecules by electron impact in the gas might be the source of these carriers. Further studies indicated that the ionization of polar molecules by electron impact *did not, generally*, split polar molecules into their polar constituents (36). Thus, the origin of these negative ions remained a mystery for some time. This was especially true, since no evidence of the presence of H^- and N^- was obtained in the study of pure ionized gases H_2 and N_2, although H and N atoms were known to be present.

In later years, spots of negative ions in mass-spectrographic studies have been noted repeatedly. Thus, O. H. Smith (37) reported negative ions of possibly H_2^- and O_2^- from a discharge tube akin to that of J. J. Thomson. O. W. Richardson, in his book, *Emission of Electricity from Hot Bodies*, early reported negative ions from hot salts, as did H. A. Barton (38). Later, D. W. Mueller and H. D. Smyth

(39) reported H$^-$ and OH$^-$ created by electron impact on H$_2$O vapor. In 1931, J. S. Thompson (40), working with A. J. Dempster on mass spectrographs, reported that when Li$^+$ ions from a heated spodumene source impinged on a target of Pt with 500 volts energy, negative ions of Cl$^-$ and OH$^-$ were observed. Two lighter ions, possibly H^{1-} and H^{2-}, were also noted. The OH$^-$ current was strong and steady for a Pt target that had not been outgassed. The Cl$^-$ ions were observed only with contaminated targets. Strong outgassing of the Pt caused the ions to disappear, although electrons were emitted by the Pt on bombardment by positive ions at all times.

Later in the same year, K. S. Woodcock, also from Dempster's laboratory (40), reported that when Li$^+$ ions struck targets at grazing incidence, negative ions were observed. These were F$^-$, Cl$^-$, O$^-$, and S$^-$ ions created by bombarding NaF, CaF$_2$, NaCl, CaO, PbS, and oxide-coated vacuum tube filaments. Clean metal targets of Pt, Au, Al, Ta, Ni, and W emitted electrons and negative ions of H^1, H^2, OH$^-$, Cl$^-$, and traces of what could have been N$^-$ and LiOH$^-$. Nearly all ions disappeared when the targets were flashed at bright-yellow heat for 5 minutes or more. Some few ions were observed at as low as 50 volts energy of positive ion impact.

In 1936, O. Tuxen (41) drew negative ions out of a glow-discharge tube and studied them with a mass spectrograph of the J. J. Thomson type. He had very complete coverage of the ions present. In H$_2$ he found H$^+$, H$_2^+$, and H$_3^+$, as well as H$^-$. He proved that H$^-$ came directly from the impact of H$_2$, H$_2^+$, or H$^+$ on metal, and not from OH or other bodies. In air he found N$^+$, O$^+$, N$_2^+$, NO$^+$, O$_2^+$, and O$^-$, OH$^-$ (impurity O$_2^-$, NO$_2^-$, NO$_3^-$). The last two were readily formed. In N$_2$, *no* negative N$^-$ ions were observed. This agrees with the prediction of Bates (26) in table 5.5. In He, Ne, and A, he observed not only He$^+$, Ne$^+$, and A$^+$, but molecular ions He$_2^+$, Ne$_2^+$, and A$_2^+$. No negative ions of inert gases were observed, as would be expected from the table.

In certain discharges in H$_2$O, or in H$_2$ contaminated with H$_2$O vapor, H$^-$ ions are created in considerable quantity, according to W. H. Bennett and P. F. Darby (42). They used an arc discharge with hollow cathode in H$_2$O vapor with 2,000 volts and 10-50 m.a. current. When the pressure was such that the discharge was of the abnormal type, and well-developed striations appeared, H$^-$ ions were generated. As the pressure fell, successive striations disappeared at the anode; and as each reached the anode, the H$^-$ beam, through a hole in it, increased to a maximum and fell to low value as the striation disappeared. The most intense beam came when the last striation had become the positive column. Here the pressure was

5×10^{-2} mm, the current was 10 m.a., and the potential 1,800, the H^- ion beam being 2×10^{-8} amp.

In general, the yield was greatest when there was a well-defined positive column above the anode without any striations. Use of an oxide-coated W filament conditioned in vacuum as cathode also gave an arc yielding ions. If too much water vapor was used, giving several striations, the filament was poisoned and had to be reconditioned in vacuum. At low pressure a dense discharge with 88 volts appeared, with positive column extending nearly to the cathode. The current was 50 m.a., and an even more intense beam was obtained than with the high-voltage arc. In the filament arc, when the dense discharge first appeared, a second ion spot as strong as the H^- spot was observed. Its carrier had a mass $\sim$ 16 to 18. This spot eventually disappeared, and reappeared only after the tube had stood for a long time. No spot of mass $\sim$ 2 was seen. Explanation of the process is not satisfactory as yet.

Lozier (25) reports studies where H_2O, at 6.6 or 8.8 volts, gains an electron yielding a transient H_2O^- ion that breaks up, giving OH and H^-, with 1.5 or 3.2 volts energy for the two attachment energies. Bennett states that the mechanism is borne out by appearance of H^- at the head of the positive column and striations where there are slowly moving electrons. Heavy negative ions (perhaps H_2O^- ions) appeared, sometimes with H^- ions. The rapidity of loss of H^- ions with low heat of formation, when not extracted at once from the source, indicates that they are formed in large quantities. It is suggested that the higher currents of H^- occur with a filament discharge, since destruction of H^- by collision with H^+ ions is the most effective removal process for H^- ions because of the Coulomb forces. The densities of the positive ions are perhaps less with the filament cathode than with the high-voltage breakdown.

Some theoretical discussion as to processes by which such negative ions can be formed was given in a paper by Massey and Smith (43) in 1936. Among these proposed processes was a suggestion ascribed to K. G. Emeléus that a slow atom of electron affinity A whose value is greater than the work function of the surface ϕe could rebound from the surface as a negative ion. The same applies for a fast atom of energy E, such that $A + E$ exceeds ϕe for the metal surface. If a positive ion of an atom having the positive electron affinity A strikes a metal surface with enough energy E, such that $E + A$ is greater than $2\phi e$, it may leave the surface as a negative ion. If a molecule is in a polar phase in its vibratory oscillations, and an electron impact imparting the dissociation energy arrives near the molecule in this phase, Massey showed that the molecule will dissociate into a positive and negative ion. Such a dissociation was observed in 1934 by Tate and Lozier (36), in the case of CO.

Studies of Arnot and Milligan (44), beginning in 1936, wherein they were observing the formation of Hg_2^+ ions from interaction of Hg metastables and neutral atoms forming a molecule Hg_2 and ionizing it, led them to the conclusion that they were also creating Hg^- ions by impact of Hg^+ ions at 200 e.v. on metal surfaces. This result seemed reasonable at the time, as according to Massey's forerunner of table 5.5, Hg^- had a value of A of +1.79 e.v. The studies of Arnot (44) and associates on Hg^- led them further to study the impact of positive ions of Hg^+, H_2^+, O_2^+, and CO_2^+ on Ni surfaces. They observed the ions indicated in table 5.7 for positive ions of 180 volts energy. Table 5.7 also gives data on the probability of liberation of such ions per positive ion impact. The probabilities are low, and of the order of 10^{-4} to 10^{-5} per positive ion. All these ions were created by direct impact of the positive ion on the metal surface. With H_2 and N_2 gases, only O_2^-, H^-, N^+, N_2^+, H^+, and H_2^+ were observed. *The negative nitrogen and molecular hydrogen ions were not observed.*

It is thus clear that J. J. Thomson must have observed in his early tubes, ions of CH_2^- or poorly resolved O^- ions, for the N^- ions have never been verified in many recent careful studies. This is in agreement with the value of $A = -0.6$ e.v. for N^- in table 5.5.

Woodcock (40) had observed rather energetic negative ions (tens of e.v.) in the beam which he obtained. Such ions were also discovered in the negative ions observed by Arnot (44), as shown in table 5.8. The energy of negative ions from 140-volt positive ions in this case reached as much as 55 volts in excess of the energy by which they were accelerated for study after emission. This energy came from the 140-volt positive ion impact. Some of the ions observed had energies below that to which they were accelerated for study, resulting from collisions with molecules en route to the collector.

In 1938, R. H. Sloane and R. Press (45), working in Eméleus' laboratory in Belfast, made a most careful study of these ions, using mass spectrographs. They even went so far as to use a double mass spectrograph; i.e., one to select out impacting positive ions of unique energy, and the other to ascertain the mass of the negative ions formed by impacting positive ions. They also made studies of the energy distribution of the emitted negative ions. The study was primarily undertaken to test the theory of Massey and Smith (43) and of Massey (46) on the formation of Hg^-. There had been some doubt about Arnot and Milligan's results with Hg^-, since H. Stille (47) had not observed Hg^- at all.

TABLE 5.7

Arnot and Milligan's Values of Probabilities of Negative Ion
Formation by Positive Ion Impact on Ni

Negative Ion	Positive Ion from Which Formed	Probability of Formation, Units of 10^{-4}
*Hg^-(?)	Hg^+	6.4
H^-	H_2^+	0.104
O^-	O_2^+	1.10
O_2^-	O_2^+	0.42
†CO_2^- (?)	CO_2^+	2.31
O_2^-	CO_2^+	2.51
CO^- ⎫		⎧ 10.8
O^- ⎬	77.4% CO_2^+ +22.6% CO^+	⎨ 3.37
C^- ⎭		⎩ (0.1)

*This ion does not exist, and this result is spurious.

†The existence of CO_2^- is doubtful, unless it is attachment to an electronically excited state.

TABLE 5.8

Arnot and Milligan's Data on Energy Relations Involved in Negative
Ion Formation by Positive Ion Impact on Ni

Negative Ion	Positive Ion from Which Formed	V_i Volts	V_j Volts	Excess Energy $V_i + V_j - 2$ Volts
*Hg^-(?)	Hg^+	10.39	1.79	2.12
H^-	H^+	13.5	0.76	4.20
H^-	H_2^+	15.5	0.76	·6.20
O^-	O^+	13.5	3.80	7.24
O^-	O_2^+	13.0	3.80	6.74
O^-	CO^+	14.1	3.80	7.84
O^-	CO_2^+	14.4	3.80	8.14
C^-	CO^+	14.1	1.37	5.41
C^-	CO_2^+	14.4	1.37	5.71

*Spurious, as Hg^- does not form.

The apparatus of Sloane and Press was capable of being well degassed, in contrast to Arnot and Milligan's arrangement. On first turning on their apparatus before degassing, Sloane and Press observed a complex negative ion beam with a "mass of the order of Hg^-." Once degassed, no trace of Hg^- was observed. When a hot cathode discharge was passed through Hg vapor, *light* atomic weight negative ions were produced from surfaces exposed to positive Hg ion bombardment. *No Hg⁻ ions were observed.* The energies of the light negative ions exceeded those obtained from the negative accelerating field of the mass spectrograph, as in Arnot's studies with O_2, CO_2, etc. A careful series of investigations by Sloane and Press showed that these excess energies did not come from electrical oscillations. They appeared to come as residual energy of emission in being "sputtered" from the occluded electronegative gas films on the metal under the action of positive ion bombardment. Thus, the "sputtered" negative ions may get some tens or more of volts energy from the incident positive ion beam that knocks them off.

The double mass spectrometer left no doubt as to the identity of the negative ions and the ions generating them, as well as to the process at work. Close proportionality between bombarding positive ion currents of Hg^+, CO^+, and Hg^{++}, and the negative ions of CO^- liberated, indicated the close relation between bombarding ions and liberated ions. They also yielded rough values of the probabilities of negative ion formation relative to positive ions of some 250 volts energy. The yields were of the order of 10^{-4}-10^{-5}, as noted by Arnot. The existence of an Hg^- ion definitely appears to be highly questionable in the light of this careful study, despite Massey's earlier prediction, now withdrawn (26). In a private communication to the author, dated June 7, 1947, Willard H. Bennett reported that he had made mass-spectrographic studies with a device far more sensitive than that of Arnot, and had failed to find any trace of Hg^- ions, thus confirming Sloane and Press.

Later studies of R. H. Sloane and H. M. Love (48) showed that bombarding an Ni surface with positive ions from an Li thermionic source gave negative peaks at mass numbers 6 and 7, indicating negative ions of the two Li isotopes. Other peaks with mass numbers 22 and 23 were interpreted as possibly being LiO^- for the two Li isotopes with O^{16}. The identification of the peak noted above at mass number 23 as LiO^-, at once also identified the weak peak obtained with an Na Kunsman source at mass number 23 as LiO^-. This peak had initially been attributed to Na^-, although its intensity variation even then was not consistent with such origin. Thus, it is clear that negative ions can be created when positive ions of a substance with an appreciable value of energy strike metals at grazing or normal incidence.

Such ions, and other positive ions striking gas-coated surfaces, will also set free negative ions of the surface gas for which the energy is great enough. The probability of the interaction is usually below 10^{-3}, and the ions liberated usually have some tens of volts of energy derived from the impact.

The study of the black spot that appears on cathode ray tubes after some time, at the point of zero deflection, had correctly been explained since 1935 by M. von Ardenne (49), and by I. Levy and D. W. West (49) as due to the impact of heavy *negative* ions on the phosphor. This led R. H. Sloane and C. S. Watt (50), as well as H. Schaefer and W. Walcher (51), to study the emission of negative ions from heated filaments. A mass-spectrographic study by Schaefer and Walcher with oxide-coated cathodes yielded the H^-, CH^-, OH^-, O_2^-, and Cl^- ions, along with eleven ions of lower intensity. The sharpness of the focused ions indicated that all ions except some of the OH^- came from the cathode surface. Some of the OH^- ions came from impact of H_2O molecules on the cathode. They studied the O_2^- emission as a function of the "forming" of the oxide cathode. Somewhat speculative conclusions were drawn as to mechanisms by which the ions are formed and emitted on the cathode surface. The O^-, OH^-, and Cl^- ions appear to be electrolyzed through the BaO layer, while CH^- and C_2^- ions must wander along the crystalline interfaces of the surface.

The investigations of Sloane and Watt, covering some years' study of oxide-coated cathodes in various types of mass spectrographs, yielded a wealth of information. Among other data, they yielded table 5.9, showing the various negative ions reported; ions which Sloane and Watt (50) have more or less certainly identified in association with oxide-coated filament emission. Using retarding potential measurements, the energy distributions, and hence the origin of the ions, could be ascertained. Some ions reported were definitely produced thermionically, and some came from bombardment of the cathode by positive ions. The thermionic emission was studied as a function of cathode temperature, time, accelerating field, and cathode surface condition. The results were compared with those of other workers.

It is clear from the foregoing summary of results that negative ions are formed by at least two other processes than those involving various types of attachment in the gaseous phase. It is also possible

TABLE 5.9

Summary of Negative Ions Identified from Oxide-Coated
Cathodes, after Sloane and Watt

Atomic Mass Number	Certain	In Doubt	Atomic Mass Number	Certain	In Doubt
1	H^-	—	27	Al^-	—
12	C^-	—	30	—	$\begin{cases} NO^- \\ HCHO^- \end{cases}$
13	CH^-	—	32	O_2^-	—
14	—	CH_2^-	35	Cl^-	—
16	O^-	—	37	Cl^-	—
17	—	OH^-	39	—	K^-
18	—	H_2O^-	40	—	Ca^-
19	F^-	—	42	CNO^-	—
23	—	Na^-	56	—	CaO^-
24	C_2^-	—	58	—	Ni^-
25	C_2H^-	—	79	Br^-	—
26	CN^-	$C_2H_2^-$	81	Br^-	—

that negative ions may in some cases be directly formed in ionizing acts by electron bombardment of vibrating polar molecules, in contrast to dissociative attachment, although this mechanism is not established as very common. The mechanisms involved in the investigations above are the thermionic emission or evaporation of negative ions from heated cathodes, and the "sputtering off" of negative ions from surface films, or else neutralization and negative charging of positive ions on impacts with surfaces. As yet, too little is known about the solid state to formulate clearly any mechanism by which negative ions can leave hot surfaces. It seems likely that negative ions can be electrolyzed through another salt and can then be evaporated, if the heat of adsorption of the negative ion on the surface is low enough. Probably the mechanism is more complex than this.

Some of the negative ions produced by positive ion bombardment of the surface are akin to the ions that are evaporated off. Thus, energetic and perhaps heavy positive ions should readily be able to sputter off electrically oriented and polarized constituents of the adsorbed layer of gaseous impurity, e.g., such as OH^-, H^-, etc.; and all evidence points to such action. How positive ions can neutralize themselves, add an extra electron, and come off as negative ions, is also not clear in detail. That this occurs is evidenced by the earliest mass-spectrographic studies. This action seems to be most probable at grazing incidence impact on the metal, probably because the ions have a greater chance of escape. In any case, whether at grazing or normal incidence, many of the ions formed in any impact appear to retain some of their initial energy as positive ions, indicating that they have not had too many impacts in the surface before re-emission.

The probabilities of such emission are low, being about 10^{-4} or 10^{-5} per positive ion striking. They are commensurate with data on the absorption of fast gas atoms in the cathode material on bombardment. In recent studies it seems that 10^{-4} of the ions striking strongly negative cathodes remain as occluded gas. This accounts for most of the gaseous cleanup in discharge tubes. The mechanism by which complex positive ions, such as CO_2^+, emerge from cathode surfaces as C^-, O_2^-, etc., ions is not clear. Possibly these gases are absorbed in the cathode and later sputter out. Probably much more will be understood of these processes once sputtering of cathode surfaces has been properly studied by direct means.

Aside from the question of mechanism, it is to be noted that the ions observed are all those of which formation seems possible by quantum-mechanical considerations, while none of the ions forbidden in table 5.5 seem to have been observed. With this information, it is fitting to close the discussion on the formation and occurrence of negative gaseous ions. Recent work of Waters presented in the Appendix I indicates that the charge transfer process of Arnot probably does not occur and the ions observed are probably sputtered off the dirty surface by the negative ions.

BIBLIOGRAPHY TO CHAPTER V

(1) J. Franck and W. Pohl, Verh. d. Deutsch. Phys. Gesell. *12*, 291, 613, 1910.
(2) L. B. Loeb, Phys. Rev. *8*, 633, 1916; Jour. Franklin Inst. *184*, 755, 1917. Also, Kia-Lok Yen, Phys. Rev. *11*, 337, 1918.
(3) A. F. Kovarick, Phys. Rev. *30*, 415, 1910.
(4) E. M. Wellisch, Am. Jour. Sci. *39*, 583, 1915; *44*, 1, 1917; Phil. Mag. *31*, 186, 1916; *34*, 33, 1917.
(5) L. B. Loeb, Phys. Rev. *17*, 84, 1921; Proc. Nat. Acad. Sci. 7, 5, 1921.
(6) J. J. Thomson, Phil. Mag. *30*, 321, 1916.
(7) H. B. Wahlin, Phys. Rev. *19*, 173, 1922; L. B. Loeb, Phil. Mag. *43*, 229, 1922.
(8) L. B. Loeb, Proc. Nat. Acad. Sci. *9*, 335, 1923.
(9) L. B. Loeb, Jour. Franklin Inst. *195*, 45, 1924.
(10) V. A. Bailey, Phil. Mag. *50*, 825, 1925; also, *9*, 560 and 625 (1930).

(11) For a complete discussion, with the more recent improvements of Bailey's method, see R. H. Healey and J. W. Reed, *The Behaviour of Slow Electrons in Gases*, Amalgamated Wireless Press (Australasia), Ltd., Sydney, 1941, pp. 24 ff.

(12) N. E. Bradbury, Phys. Rev. *44*, 885, 1933; Jour. Chem. Phys. *2*, 827, 840, 1934; N. E. Bradbury and H. E. Tatel, Jour. Chem. Phys. *2*, 835, 1934.

(13) N. E. Bradbury, Phys. Rev. *40*, 980, 1932.

(14) H. F. Lusk, M.S. thesis, University of California, May, 1927.

(15) A. M. Cravath, Phys. Rev. *34*, 605, 1929.

(16) L. B. Loeb, Phys. Rev. *48*, 684, 1935.

(17) L. B. Loeb, *Fundamental Processes of Electrical Discharge in Gases*, John Wiley & Sons, New York, 1939, pp. 283 ff.

(18) A. Doehring, Zeits. f. Naturforschung *7a*, 253, 1952.

(19) M. A. Biondi, Phys. Rev. *84*, 1072, 1951.

(20) M. A. Biondi, Phys. Rev. *87*, 337, 1953.

(21) R. Buchdahl, Jour. Phys. Chem. *9*, 146, 1941.

(22) W. W. Lozier, Phys. Rev. *46*, 268, 1934; H. D. Hagstrum, Rev. Mod. Phys. *23*, 185, 1951.

(23) H. S. W. Massey, *Negative Ions*, Cambridge University Press, 1950, second edition, p. 72.

(24) T. R. Hogness and E. G. Lunn, Phys. Rev. *30*, 26, 1927.

(25) W. W. Lozier, Phys. Rev. *36*, 1417, 1930.

(26) D. R. Bates, Proc. Roy. Irish Acad. *A51*, 153, 1947.

(27) L. B. Loeb, Phys. Rev. *48*, 684, 1935.

(28) R. Geballe and F. S. Linn, Jour. App. Phys. *21*, 592, 1950; R. Geballe and M. A. Harrison, Phys. Rev. *85*, 372, 1952; *91*, 1, 1953; R. Geballe and M. L. Reeves, Phys. Rev. *92*, 867, 1953.

(29) P. Herreng, Cahiers de Phys. *38*, 7, 1952.

(30) R. N. Varney, Phys. Rev. *89*, 708, 1953; *88*, 362, 1952.

(31) J. A. Hornbeck, Phys. Rev. *83*, 374, 1951; *84*, 615, 1951; and J. P. Molnar, Phys. Rev. *84*, 621, 1951; and G. H. Wannier, Phys. Rev. *82*, 458, 1951.

(32) G. H. Wannier, Bell System Tech. Jour. *32*, 170, 1953. See also chap. I, part two, sec. 11.

(33) L. M. Branscomb and W. L. Fite, Phys. Rev. *93*, 647(A), 1954.

(34) F. Bloch and N. E. Bradbury, Phys. Rev. *48*, 689, 1935.

(35) D. R. Bates and H. S. W. Massey, Phil. Trans. Roy. Soc. *A239*, 288, 1943.

(36) J. T. Tate and W. W. Lozier, Phys. Rev. *42*, 518, 1934.

(37) O. H. Smith, Phys. Rev. *7*, 625, 1916.

(38) H. A. Barton, Phys. Rev. *26*, 36, 1925; *30*, 614, 1927.

(39) D. W. Mueller and H. D. Smyth, Phys. Rev. *38*, 192, 1931.

(40) J. S. Thompson, Phys. Rev. *38*, 1389, 1931; K. S. Woodcock, Phys. Rev. *38*, 1696, 1931.

(41) O. Tuxen, Zeits. f. Phys. *103*, 463, 1936.

(42) W. H. Bennett and P. F. Darby, Phys. Rev. *49*, 97, 1936.

(43) H. S. W. Massey and R. A. Smith, Proc. Roy. Soc. *A155*, 472, 1936.

(44) F. L. Arnot and J. C. Milligan, Proc. Roy. Soc. *A156*, 359, 538, 1936; F. L. Arnot, Proc. Roy. Soc. *A158*, 137, 1937; F. L. Arnot and C. Beckett, Proc. Roy. Soc. *A168*, 103, 1938.

(45) R. H. Sloane and R. Press, Proc. Roy. Soc. *A168*, 284, 1938.
(46) H. S. W. Massey, "Negative Ions," *Cambridge Physical Tracts*, Cambridge University Press, 1938.
(47) H. Stille, Ann. d. Physik. *17*, 635, 1933.
(48) R. H. Sloane and H. M. Love, Nature *159*, March 1, 1947.
(49) M. von Ardenne, Arch. f. Elektrotech. *29*, 231, 1935; I. Levy and D. W. West, Jour. Inst. Elect. Eng. *79*, 11, 1936.
(50) R. H. Sloane and C. S. Watt, Proc. Phys. Soc. Lon. *A61*, 217, 1948.
(51) H. Schaefer and W. Walcher, Zeits. f. Phys. *121*, 679, 1943.

Chapter VI

THE RECOMBINATION OF IONS

§ 1. The Idealized Recombination Relations.

Whenever a gas has been ionized by creating positive and negative carriers from neutral molecules or atoms, the gas on standing loses its ions through diffusion of ions to the enclosing walls and through *recombination*. Recombination is a process by which ions of opposite sign neutralize each other's charges. The laws governing losses by diffusion and recombination with time differ, and in many cases one process or the other can be made to predominate by the proper choice of conditions. The loss by recombination was early investigated by J. J. Thomson's (1) research group at the Cavendish Laboratory, and has since then been extensively studied under various aspects.

The analysis of the process was initially guided by an elementary theory, based on very much simplified assumptions which for a long time were not recognized as being highly defective. It is logical to introduce the subject by using the classical considerations and later extending them in conformity with the true conditions existing.

Assume that there are present as positive carriers only carriers of a unique species A, and as negative carriers only molecular carriers of another unique species B. Let these be dispersed randomly in a volume—with, however, complete isotropy on the average, both on macro- and microscales (i.e., ions of opposite sign not being distributed preferentially in pairs or in initially confined regions). The average number density is given by n_+ and n_- for positive and negative carriers respectively, with n_+ being set equal to n_-, and written as n for simplicity. This last assumption is not unreasonable, since positive and negative carriers (created, for example, by X-rays in air) are present in equal numbers. It is now assumed that n varies in time only through "encounters" of positive and negative carriers in which neutralization by charge exchange occurs (i.e., by recombination), and that n is not altered by diffusion of carriers on a microscale or by diffusion to the walls. It is then permitted to write

$$(6.1) \qquad\qquad dn = -\,a\,n^2\,dt$$

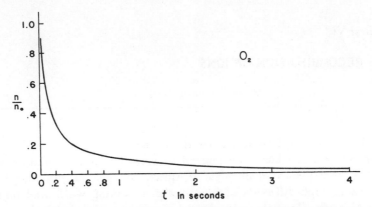

Fig. 6.1. Plot of number of ions per cm³ (n) surviving recombination out of n_0 per cm³ initially present in O_2 at n.t.p., as a function of time t.

as the differential equation for loss of ions by pure *ideal* recombination in time. It is to be noted that no detail of the process is indicated, such that a, the constant of the process (called the *coefficient of recombination*) is quite general, and may represent a number of different mechanisms.

If equation 6.1 is integrated, setting $n = n_0$ at $t = 0$ and $n = n$ at $t = t$, then

(6.2) $a = (1/t)(1/n - 1/n_0)$,

such that if n and n_0 are measured for known t, a is evaluated. Again,

(6.3a) $$n = \frac{n_0}{1 + n_0 \, a t}$$

and it is noted that n declines hyperbolically from a value n_0 at $t = 0$, as shown in figure 6.1, which is similar to the ideal case of positive and negative ions in O_2 at 760 mm.

From equation 6.2 it is clear that the dimensions of a are given by $a = 1/nt = V/(q/t) = L^3 T^{-1}/q$, which in the c.g.s. system is cm³/ion sec, where q represents the number of ions in V, with $n = q/V$. In measurements the charge qe is measured for a volume V, and q is derived by dividing the charge qe by the electron.[1]

If, owing to failure to achieve the microscopic isotropy and random distribution, microscale diffusion of ions alters n with time, a will *appear* time-dependent, and the quantity

(6.3b) $$a_t = \frac{1}{t_2 - t_1} \left(\frac{1}{n_2} - \frac{1}{n_1} \right)$$

_____

[1] This procedure is permissible, since multiply charged ions usually have very short lives.

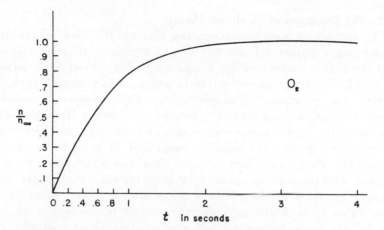

Fig. 6.2. Plot of growth of ions per cm^3 (n) relative to the equilibrium concentration $n\infty$ per cm^3 in O_2 at n.t.p., as it might be for a uniform rate of ionization Q per cm^3 of 5×10^5 per second.

must be used where t_2 and t_1 differ so little that a_t is representative of a at the mean age $(t_2 + t_1)/2$.

It is seen that equation 6.2 affords a method of evaluating a, which may be called the *method of loss*. If ions are produced at a constant rate Q per unit volume per second, and the only loss is by recombination, then

(6.4) $$dn = (Q - an^2) \, dt,$$

setting $Q/a = k^2$, integration with $n = 0$ at $t = 0$ and $n = n$ at $t = t$, yields

(6.5) $$n = k \frac{\epsilon^{2kat} - 1}{\epsilon^{2kat} + 1}.$$

This represents the rise of ions from $n = 0$ at $t = 0$ to an equilibrium number at infinite time, given by

(6.6) $$n\infty = \sqrt{Q/a}.$$

The relation for ions in O_2 at 760 mm, as given by a conveniently observed Q, is shown in figure 6.2.

It is seen that if Q and $n\infty$ can be measured, or if n is evaluated for two values of t, k and a, and thus Q and a, are evaluated. Relations 6.6 and 6.5 are known respectively as the methods of equilibrium and of growth for evaluating a.

§ 2. The Weakness of Idealized Theory.

In general, it must be recognized that all the ideal assumptions underlying equation 6.1 are not met in practice, although this was not thoroughly recognized for a long time. Thus, most early methods available for producing ionization in gases, α particles, β rays, and X-rays did not produce isotropic random distributions of carriers of opposite sign; e.g., α particles created very dense ionization along narrow tracks, and β and X-rays created a grossly random distribution of *pairs* of positive and negative ions, ions in pairs being in close proximity. Thus, diffusions of real localized concentrations n' to random distributions in space with time introduced elements which gave a variation of the observed a' with time, thus concealing the true value of a. While the *columnar type of recombination* in α-ray tracks was early recognized and studied, the initial type of recombination from X-ray ionization was not recognized and studied until refinements in technique revealed the variation of a' with time. The errors and difficulties were also enhanced, because in most measurements the values of n or n' were not directly determined, but instead the charge qe in a given volume V was measured, and n was set as $(qe/eV) = n$.

Two types of measurement of a to some extent avoided the anisotropy of ion production; these were methods which evaluated a in the case where negative and positive ions were moving past each other in fairly strong electrical fields. One of these was the current-measuring method of Thomson and Rutherford, later highly developed by Riecke and Mie (4), and the other was the ionization flash and field-removal method of Langevin (5). However, the former method did not yield accurate values, because of inability to measure the saturation current. Langevin's method was not used extensively for some reason, and in itself was subject to an unknown amount of falsification by anisotropies and by failure to achieve saturation currents.

Where ions are produced in discharge plasma, such as glows and arcs, the anisotropies on a microscale are avoided. However, owing to current flow, space-charge accumulations, and ambipolar diffusion, there are macroscopic anisotropies. Probably, only in the center of large-diameter and fairly long positive columns are conditions really proper for a recombination study after the discharge is cut off. Such discharge plasmas also suffer from another difficulty that is often encountered in plasmas from other ionizing sources. These are caused by the presence of carriers of one sign of two or more species with different values of a with the oppositely charged carrier.

These often change from one ion type to the other with time. Thus, in electron-attaching gases, negative carriers begin as electrons and change to negative ions with time. In inert gases electrons are free, but the atomic ions with a low a for electrons change to positive molecular ions in time, a being much higher in the second than in the first instance. These deviations from the ideal also cause a temporal variation in an observed a, but of a type different from that due to microscopic anisotropies. Finally, in some plasmas the initial ratio of actively recombining negative and positive carriers is not unity, so that in this respect the simple theory must be modified.

To date, measurements of n in discharge plasmas for study of a have been made only with probes or by the intensity of the light supposedly[2] emitted in the recombination process. Direct collection of ions by fields between electrodes in dense plasmas is inefficient, and saturation currents representative of n are impossible of achievement, the degree of saturation achieved varying with n. The value of probes in determining n, especially in a decaying plasma, has been called into question (10) except under particular circumstances; and identification of a given line system, or a continuum with recombinations, has recently been rendered doubtful.[2]

One set of plasmas of great density is created in the spark-breakdown channels or in condensed impulse discharges (6), (8). Here photomultiplier cell studies of carrier-density decay, in terms of individual spectral lines assumedly emitted in recombination, yield values of a. Absolute values of carrier densities are achieved by the use of Stark-effect broadening. Stark-effect density analyses have been used more or less successfully in decaying arc plasmas. At present, two difficulties appear to enter into such studies; the first being the unknown electron temperature, and the second consisting of doubts recently cast on the interpretation of ion densities from Stark-effect analysis.

With the advent of microwave techniques, considerable extension

---

[2]The suppositious nature of the light must be acknowledged today, for the reason that the atomic ion-electron recombination has probably been observed only in a hydrogen spark discharge (6). Here spectra could be anticipated. However, most recombination observed in such plasmas is dissociative molecular recombination, where emitted spectra often cannot be predicted (7). In some cases, continua interpreted as emanating from recombination have later been ascribed to a "bremsstrahlung" (8). Possibly this has also been observed in Ne and A discharges, but even here the spectra of atoms observed could have come from dissociative recombination of Ne_2^+ and A_2^+ (8). In He_2^+ the dissociative origin of the atomic He lines has been proved by Doppler broadening by M. A. Biondi (9).

of study of recombination over limited regimes of time and pressure is possible (11). The gas can be broken down by a high-energy microwave discharge in a quartz cell yielding relatively uniform, or else known, charge distributions; and the values of n are then directly determined within limits by observing changes in resonant frequency, or the changes in Q of the cavity at any time after the discharge has ceased. In such studies, the probing beam can only determine *electron* and not ion densities, and then only under rather limited ranges of density.

Results of these investigations have indicated the presence of multiple carriers of the same sign but of different a, with one carrier transforming to the other during measurement. They have revealed the inequality of the densities of recombining carriers, the great importance of impurities, and the effects of higher modes in ambipolar diffusion as complicating agencies. It may be added that some of these studies have revealed apparent pressure dependence of a where it should not have occurred. Again, inferences concerning recombination in the upper atmosphere have introduced a problem involving recombination when there is an ion of one sign recombining with two ions of different sign, the two ions having different values of a, and the being maintained in a constant ratio by a secondary reaction. For example, in the E layer of the ionosphere, positive ions of one sort (12) appear to recombine with electrons and negative ions, the electrons attaching to molecules to form ions, and being photodissociated by ultraviolet radiation so rapidly that the ratio of electrons to ions remains constant as recombination proceeds.

§ 3. The Extended Treatments of Recombination Processes.

In consequence of these conditions, some of which have been recognized only in the last four years, it is essential to extend the analyses of recombination to cases where initially n_{+0}/n_{-0} differs from unity, where ions A and B remain in rapid interchange equilibrium and recombine with C, each with different a. With such theory developed, further discussion of the problem and data is possible. For this analysis, credit is largely due to W. B. Kunkel (13), and it was undertaken at the author's suggestion. Initially, the differential equations for multiple carriers had been set up by J. J. Thomson (14), but not solved. Recently, R. B. Holt (15) and his co-workers in microwave breakdown set up the relations and solved them numerically for a single special case. The solution for the upper atmosphere with negative ions and electrons in equilibrium had been set up independently by J. Sayers and D. R. Bates (12). A somewhat analogous study was undertaken by N. E. Bradbury (12), but was not carried to completion. The solution of Sayers and Bates was generalized and extended by W. B. Kunkel and the author (16).

For illustrative purposes, and to emphasize certain inherent properties, a simple case which applies to actual studies will first be set up and solved in elementary fashion. It is assumed that the negative carrier concentration (e.g., of electrons) is n_-, and that two types of positive ions are present, their concentrations at $t = 0$ being n_{A0} and n_{B0}, while that of the electrons is n_{-0}. The value of a_B for electrons recombining with B is very small compared to a_A for the ions A and electrons. It will be assumed that the A and B do not change into each other. Thus, for recombining, ions $n_- > n_A$, and in principle only A recombines. This corresponds to a situation where even when volume ionization makes $n_{-0} = n_{A0} + n_{B0}$, the values of n_- and n_A which recombine are not equal.

To set up the problem, one writes:

(6.7)
$$\frac{dn_B}{dt} = 0, \quad \frac{dn_A}{dt} = - a_A\, n_A\, n_-, \quad \frac{dn_-}{dt} = a_A\, n_A\, n_-.$$

Let $n_- - n_A = \Delta n$. Since $\dfrac{dn_-}{dt} - \dfrac{dn_A}{dt} = \dfrac{d(n_- - n_A)}{dt} = 0,$

(6.8)
$$\frac{d\Delta n}{dt} = 0, \text{ and } \Delta n = \Delta n_0 = n_{-0} - n_{A0} \text{ at } t = 0,$$

$$n_A = n_- - \Delta n_0, \text{ and } \frac{dn_-}{dt} = - a_A\, (n_- - \Delta n_0)\, n_-.$$

If $\Delta n_0 = 0$, this reverts to equation 6.1. If $\Delta n_0 \neq 0$, multiply both sides by Δn_0 and integrate.

This yields:

(6.9)
$$1 - \frac{\Delta n_0}{n_-} = \frac{n_{A0}}{n_{-0}}\, \epsilon^{-a_A \Delta n_0 t},$$

or

(6.10)
$$\frac{1}{n_-} = \frac{1}{\Delta n_0}\left(1 - \frac{n_{A0}}{n_{-0}}\, \epsilon^{-a_A \Delta n_0 t}\right).$$

Equation 6.9 yields equation 6.2 when $\Delta n_0 = 0$. It is to be noted that generally where $\Delta n_0 > 0$, $1/n_-$ plotted against t will not yield a linear graph, as is the case for equation 6.2 where $1/n = 1/n_0 + at$. It is instructive, however, to expand equation 6.9 in series, and to study some numerical examples. Expansion yields

$$(6.11) \qquad \frac{1}{n_-} = \frac{1}{\Delta n_0}\left(1 - \frac{n_{A0}}{n_{-0}} + a_A \frac{n_{A0}}{n_{-0}} \Delta n_0 t + \ldots\right),$$

with $1/n_-$ linear to a first approximation, and of slope

$$(6.12) \qquad \frac{d(1/n_-)}{dt} = a_A \frac{n_{A0}}{n_{-0}} (1 - a_A \Delta n_0 t + \ldots).$$

If then a', the observed value of a, is taken from a plot as $d(1/n_-)/dt$, the value of a' is $a' = a_A (1 - a_A \Delta n_0 t) (n_{A0}/n_{-0})$.

If $a_A \Delta n_0 t << 1$, a' will appear fairly independent of t; but its value will not be the true a_A, but $a' = a_A (n_{A0}/n_{-0})$, which depends on boundary conditions imposed by the experiment where n_{A0}/n_{-0} could vary with pressure.

Again, if Δn_0 is small, so that n_{-0} nearly equals n_{A0}, but if $a_A t$ is large, then a' will decrease with time; and it will depend on n_{A0}/n_{-0} which is near unity. The important fact to notice here is that near equality of n_{A0} and n_{-0}, a' will still vary with time if $a_A t$ is large—a rather surprising observation. For example, under microwave operating conditions, if $n_{-0} = 10^{11}$ and $n_A = (1 - \delta/100) 10^{11}$, $\Delta n_0 = \delta \times 10^9$, $a_A = 10^{-7}$, $t = t_1 \times 10^{-3}$ sec, and $d(1/n_-)/dt \sim a_A (1 - \delta t_1/10) = a'$, a' decreases 10% in 10^{-3} sec, even though Δn_0 is only 1% of n_{-0}.

In the event that $n_{-0} = 10^{11}$, $n_{A0} = 5 \times 10^{10}$, $\Delta n_0 = 5 \times 10^{10}$, $a_A = 10^{-7}$, and $t = 10^{-3} t_1$, then $a_A \Delta n_0 t = 5 \times 10^{-3} t_1$, $d(1/n_-)/dt = a' = 0.5 a_A \epsilon^{-5 \times 10^{-3} t_1} \cdot =. 0.5 a_A = (n_{A0}/n_{-0}) a_A$.

Here there is only 3% variation of a with a variation of t by a factor of 5 about a value of 1×10^{-3} sec, while at the same time the numerical inequality of recombining carriers yields an observed value of a' of half the true coefficient a.

Returning to a solution of the more general problem as set up by Kunkel, the following differential equations apply:

$$(6.13) \qquad dn/dt = - a_1 Mn - a_2 An,$$

$$(6.14) \qquad dM/dt = - a_1 Mn + \beta A,$$

and

$$(6.15) \qquad dA/dt = - a_2 An - \beta A.$$

Here M stands for the concentrations of molecular positive ions. This is one species of ion in the gas which combines with a negative carrier (in this case electrons) in *dissociative* recombination with a coefficient a_1, which is large. The concentration of positive atomic ions recombining *radiatively* with electrons with a coefficient a_2, which is small, is designated as A. For the concentration of free electrons, the negative carrier is n. Since experiment showed that in the inert gases, atomic species A ions formed molecular ions of species M by triple impact in the gas, it must be assumed that A attaches an atom to form M with a probability β in 1 second. The choice of carriers assigned to M, A, and n is not restrictive, for A and M could represent electrons and negative ions, while n could represent a unique positive ion. The quantities M, A, and n are functions of t only, and a_1, a_2, and β are constants.

Now, $(dn/dt) - (dM/dt) - (dA/dt) = 0$, so that it is proper to set

(6.16) $$n - M - A = \delta = n_0 - M_0 - A_0,$$

where n_0, M_0, and A_0 are the concentrations at $t = 0$.

Solutions are not possible for these nonlinear equations in all cases. One solution is possible if $a_2 n << \beta$; that is, if the term in a_2 can be neglected in equation 6.15. For a case studied by Holt and his associates in He, where $a_1 \sim 10^{-8}$, $n < 10^{11}$, and $a_2 < 10^{-10}$, with $\beta \sim 10^3$ or 10^4, the condition is fulfilled and solution yields $A = A_0 \, \epsilon^{-\beta t}$, so that M and A can be eliminated from equation 6.15 and equation 6.13, yielding

(6.17) $$\frac{dn}{dt} = -a_1 n^2 + [(a_1 - a_2) A_0 \, \epsilon^{-\beta t} + a_1 \delta] n.$$

This has a solution:

(6.18) $$1/n = 1/g \left(\frac{1}{n_0} + a_1 \int_0^t g \, dt \right);$$

(6.19) $$g = \exp\left\{ \delta a_1 t + [A_0 (a_1 - a_2)/\beta(1 - \epsilon^{-\beta t})] \right\}.$$

If $a_1 = a_2$, $A = 0$, or $\beta = 0$, this yields

(6.20) $$1/n - 1/\delta = \left[\frac{1}{n_0} - \frac{1}{\delta} \right] \epsilon^{-\delta a_1 t}.$$

This is the equation for two carriers, one of which has an excess concentration δ. When $\delta a_2 t << 1$, this approximates to the relation

(6.21) $$1/n = 1/n_0 - a_1 (1 - \delta/n_0) t,$$

which has already been discussed as equation 6.11.

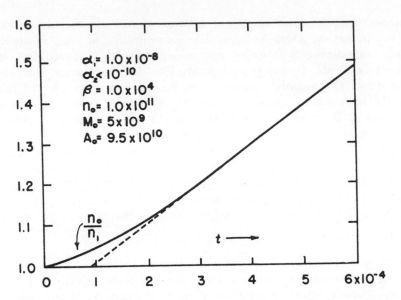

Fig. 6.3. Kunkel's solution of the recombination equation for variation of $1/n$ with t, where two positive ions, A^+ and A_2^+ for example, combine with electrons, A^+ having a low coefficient, while A_2^+ has a fairly high coefficient and A^+ changes to A_2^+ at a rate commensurate with recombination with α. Note the approximate linearity of the plot from 3 to 6×10^{-4} sec, while from 0.2 to 3×10^{-4} sec, the plot is not linear.

The integral of equation 6.18 cannot be evaluated in finite form, but must be expressed as a series. In the usual case $\delta = 0$, this series can be written as

$$(6.22) \quad \int_0^t g\,dt = \left[t - \frac{1}{\beta} \sum_{K=1}^{\infty} \frac{A_0(a_1 - a_2)K}{\beta} \left\{ 1 - \epsilon \frac{-K\beta t}{KK!} \right\} \right] \times \epsilon \left[\frac{A_0(a_1 - a_2)}{\beta} \right].$$

This converges rapidly if $A_0(a_1 - a_2) \overline{<} \beta$, a condition frequently fulfilled, since $A_0 \overline{<} n_0$, and cases are limited to those where $a_2 n_0 << \beta$. If $a_2 << a_1$, then $a_1 A_0 \overline{<} \beta$ is more severe than the previous restriction. If, on the other hand, $A_0(a_1 - a_2) << \beta$, the terms in $K > 1$ may be neglected, and equation 6.18 becomes

$$(6.23) \quad \frac{1}{n} \simeq \frac{1}{n_0} + a_1 t - \frac{A_0(a_1 - a_2)}{\beta} \left[\left(\frac{1}{n_0} + \frac{a_1}{\beta} \right) \left(1 - \epsilon^{-\beta t} - a_1 t\, \epsilon^{-\beta t} \right) \right].$$

This differs from $1/n = (1/n_0) - a_1 t$ only by a small correction term, and is plotted in figure 6.3 for $a_1 = 1 \times 10^{-8}$, $a_2 < 10^{-10}$, $\beta = 1 \times 10^4$, $n_0 = 1 \times 10^{11}$, $M_0 = 5 \times 10^9$, and $A_0 = 9.5 \times 10^{10}$, where n_0/n is plotted against t from 0 to 6×10^{-4} sec (13). Here it is noted that $1/n$ is linear with t for a range from 3 to 6×10^{-4} sec, but shows curvature at lower values. Equation 6.23 has the asymptotic form:

$$(6.24) \qquad \frac{1}{n} \simeq \frac{1}{n_0} - [A_0(a_1 - a_2)/\beta n_0] + a_1 t,$$

so that the intercept of $1/n = 1/n_0$ with the asymptote occurs at $t_1 \simeq A_0(a_1 - a_2)/n_0 a_1 \beta$. Thus, if n_0 is known from measurements, $(A_0/\beta)(1 - a_2/a_1)$ is found immediately.

Since a_1 is given by the slope of equation 6.24, it remains to evaluate A_0 or β separately. With the help of the relation $A = A_0 \epsilon^{-\beta t}$ and equation 6.23, n, $M = n - A$, and thus $(Mn)^{1/2}$, can be plotted directly with the same constants, and lead to the same curves computed by Holt (15) and his associates for this case, using numerical integration. Since a_2 is negligible, the recombination radiation is proportional to Mn, and maximum intensity should occur when $(Mn)^{1/2}$ is a maximum. With the help of relations 6.14 and $A = A_0 \epsilon^{-\beta t}$, and the condition $\delta = n - M - A = n_0 - M_0 - A_0$, it can be shown that the condition for a maximum is

$$(6.25) \qquad \epsilon^{-\beta t} = \left(1 - \frac{\beta}{a_1 M}\right) \frac{A_0}{2n}.$$

This when combined with equation 6.23 results in a complicated transcendental relation among t, β, a_1, n_0, and A_0. Since for maximum M_0, a_1 and t can readily be measured, equation 6.25 yields a second relation between β and A_0.

Kunkel next treated the case where ionization is taking place through reactions such as

$$Hg - He^m \rightarrow Hg^+ + e^- + He, \text{ or}$$

$$He^m + He^m \rightarrow He^+ + e^- + He,$$

that are known to occur in plasmas of inert gases and mixtures. Here only two types of carriers are involved. If diffusion loss is neglected, the equation becomes

$$(6.26) \qquad \frac{dn}{dt} = \frac{dA}{dt} = -anA + q(t).$$

Here $q(t)$ is the production term, and this depends on the time dependence of the ionizing source. Here again $n - A = \delta = n_0 - A_0$. Usually

$\delta = 0$ as one deals with neutral plasma. Allowing δ to have a finite value for generality, and eliminating A,

$$(6.27) \qquad \frac{dn}{dt} = -an^2 + a\delta n + q.$$

Letting $an = dX/X$ leads to

$$(6.28) \qquad \frac{d^2X}{dt^2} - a\delta\frac{dX}{dt} - aqX = 0.$$

A simple case may be considered: If the source decays exponentially, as with the two processes indicated, and metastable removal is not controlled by this process, $q = b\,\epsilon^{-\beta t}$.

Substitution of $\tau = (2/\beta)(ab)^{1/2}\,\epsilon^{-\beta t/2}$ reduces 6.28 to a Bessel-type equation, with a general solution

$$(6.29) \qquad X = \tau^{a\delta/\beta}\left[C_1 I_{a\delta/\beta}(\tau) + C_2 K_{a\delta/\beta}(\tau)\right].$$

For $\delta = 0$,

$$(6.30) \qquad n = \frac{bK_1 - CI_1}{aK_0 - CI_0}\,\epsilon^{-\beta t/2},$$

with

$$(6.31) \qquad C = \frac{(ab)^{1/2} K_1\,(2a^{1/2}b^{1/2}/\beta) - an_0 K_0(2a^{1/2}b^{1/2}/\beta)}{(ab)^{1/2} I_1\,(a^{1/2}b^{1/2}/\beta) - an_0 I_0\,(2a^{1/2}b^{1/2}/\beta)}.$$

This equation is complicated in t, but I_p and K_p can be found in tables, so that $n(t)$ is fairly easy to compute.

If $\tau \ll 1$, which occurs; e.g., $a \sim 10^{-8}$, $\beta = 10^4$, and $b \sim 10^{12}$, so that $\tau < 2 \times 10^{-2}$, equation 6.30 becomes

$$(6.32) \qquad n \simeq \frac{1 - (2a\beta C/\beta^2)\,\epsilon^{-\beta t}}{at + 2a/\beta\,[\log(\beta/a^{1/2}b^{1/2}) - 0.577 + C]},$$

where

$$(6.33) \qquad C \simeq \frac{\beta^2/2a - \beta n_0[\log(\beta/a^{1/2}\beta^{1/2}) - 0.577]}{b - \beta n_0}.$$

If $\beta n_0 \ll b$,

$$(6.34) \qquad C \simeq \frac{\beta}{2an_0} - \log\left[\frac{\beta}{a^{1/2}b^{1/2}}\right] + 0.577 - \frac{b}{2an_0^2},$$

whence equation 6.32 becomes

$$(6.35) \qquad \frac{1}{n} \simeq \frac{1}{n_0} - at - \frac{b}{\beta n_0}\left[\frac{1}{n_0}\left(1 - \epsilon^{-\beta t}\right) - at\,\epsilon^{-\beta t}\right].$$

The Recombination of Ions

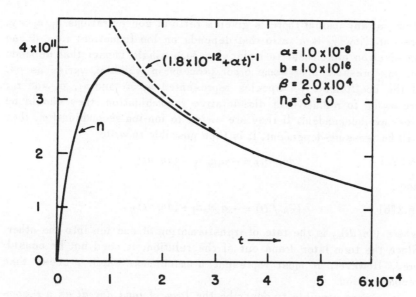

Fig. 6.4. Kunkel's solution for the variation of n when ionization is taking place. The production rate decays exponentially with time, and recombination occurs. The concentration of electrons rises at first, reaches a maximum, and then decays. Such curves have been observed in microwave breakdown owing to metastable action.

This differs only slightly from equation 6.23, and represents a curve analogous to that of figure 6.3.

If $n_0 = 0$, then $C \simeq (\beta^2/2ab) >> 1$, so that

(6.36) $$n \simeq \frac{1 - \epsilon^{-\beta t}}{at - (\beta/b)}.$$

A typical case for growth and decay is shown in figure 6.4, where n is plotted as a $f(t)$, with $a = 1 \times 10^{-8}$, $b = 1 \times 10^{16}$, $\beta = 2 \times 10^4$, and $n_0 = \delta = 0$ (13), (15).

It is now necessary to deduce the Sayers-Bates (12) relations for recombination where, as in the upper atmosphere, two types of carriers of one sign remain in an equilibrium ratio while they recombine with a carrier of the opposite sign (16).

Assume two carrier species present at any one time of concentrations n_1 and n_2. Let these recombine with one type of carrier of opposite sign and concentration n_e, such that $n_e = n_1 + n_2$. Now $n_1 + n_2$ may refer to two positive carriers and n_e to a negative carrier, or n_1 and n_2 can refer to two negative carriers and n_e to one positive carrier. At any pressure, through some dynamic process, rapid interchange between types of ions n_1 and n_2 occurs in a reversible fashion.

Thus, at any instant there is given a ratio of concentrations $n_1/n_2 = \gamma_p$ present. Now γ_p is a ratio that depends on ion formation; i.e., it can be electron attachment to molecules in a single impact that depends on gas pressure p or some other process in which γ_p varies as p^2. If the coefficients for species represented by n_1 and n_2, a_1 and a_2, are owing to radiative or dissociative recombination, they should be pressure-independent. If they are owing to ion-ion recombination, they will be pressure-dependent. It is then possible to write

(6.37a)
$$(dn_1/dt) = - a_1 n_e n_1 - (dn/dt)_{eq}$$

and

(6.37b)
$$(dn_2/dt) = - a_2 n_e n_1 + (dn/dt)_{eq} ,$$

where $(dn/dt)_{eq}$ is the rate of transformation of one ion into the other. Since the term later drops out of the relation, it need not be considered. However, it must represent a much more rapid process than recombination.

It is next possible to describe the loss of ions dn_1/dt as a recombination process with coefficient a_1', which is an observable quantity, so that:

(6.38a)
$$(dn_1/dt) = - a_1' n_1^2 = - a_1 n_e n_1 - (dn/dt)_{eq} ,$$

and likewise for

(6.38b)
$$(dn_2/dt) = - a_2' n_2^2 = - a_2 n_e n_2 + (dn/dt)_{eq} .$$

Since $n_e = n_1 + n_2$, it is also possible to write

(6.39)
$$\frac{dn_e}{dt} = \frac{dn_1}{dt} + \frac{dn_2}{dt} = - a_1 n_e n_1 - a_2 n_e n_2 = - a_e' n_e^2 .$$

Here a_e' is a coefficient for recombination of carriers of concentration n_e, and in which $(dn/dt)_{eq}$ no longer appears.
Now,

(6.40)
$$\gamma_p = \frac{n_2}{n_1}, \quad \frac{dn_2}{dt} = \gamma_p \frac{dn_1}{dt} ,$$

so that

(6.41)
$$a_2' n_2^2 = \gamma_p \, a_1' n_1^2 .$$

Setting

(6.42)
$$\frac{n_1}{n_2} = \frac{1}{\gamma_p} ,$$

(6.43)
$$\frac{n_e}{n_1} = 1 + \gamma_p ,$$

and

(6.44)
$$\frac{n_e}{n_2} = \frac{1 + \gamma_p}{\gamma_n}$$

permits solution of the equations evaluating the three observable coefficients a_1', a_2', and a_e' in terms of the true coefficients a_1, a_2, and γ_p. That is, recombination under the conditions outlined leads to disappearance of the carriers represented by n_1, n_2, and n_e in time, following the simple law 6.2, with $(1/n)$ proportioned to t and yielding three *observable* coefficients, a_1', a_2', and a_e', if measurements of $1/n_1$, $1/n_2$, and $1/n_e$ are possible. These observed coefficients are related to the true coefficients by

(6.45)
$$a_1' = a_1 + \gamma_p a_2 ,$$

(6.46)
$$a_2' = \frac{a_1 + \gamma_p a_2}{\gamma_p} ,$$

and

(6.47)
$$a_e' = \frac{a_1 + \gamma_p a_2}{1 + \gamma_p} ,$$

as seen in reference (16). These relations may be discussed as follows:

Equation 6.45 applies to the condition that n_1 is the measured concentration which will be electrons for the upper atmosphere studies (12), while n_2 refers to negative ions, so that n_e represents the positive ion concentration. If positive ion concentrations of one species could be measured say as n_1, then n_e could be an electron or negative ion concentration, with n_2 a second positive ion.

Equation 6.46 applies when the negative *ion* concentration n_2 is measured, n_e representing the positive ion concentration; or, if n_e is an electron concentration, n_1 and n_2 are positive ions, of which n_2 has its concentration measured.

Equation 6.47 applies when n_e is measured, where the positive ion concentration is n_e, and n_1 and n_2 are two species of negative ions. Actually, it is possible, as in inert gas microwave plasmas, that n_e is the measured electron concentration and n_1 and n_2 are positive ions in some sort of dynamic equilibrium (16).

At present it is only possible to measure electron concentrations by reflection of radio signals from the E layer of the ionosphere, or by cavity behavior in studies with a microwave probing signal. It is assumed that negative ion formation occurs in the upper atmosphere, and that only one positive ion recombines dissociatively with electrons, or directly with negative ions. Equation 6.47 was invoked by the author and Kunkel (16) to account for a pressure-dependent recombination of electrons in H_2 plasmas observed by Varnerin, who assumed that he was dealing with pure H_2. Later work has shown that the H_2 from a Pd leak was not pure, and that the apparent recombination data were falsified by negative ion formation. Great care must be used in interpreting decay of electron densities in microwave techniques, since electron attachment and higher modes of diffusion cause electron-loss curves which may be mistaken for recombination. When so treated, these are quite misleading.

§ 4. The Measurement of the Coefficient of Recombination.

From the relations deduced it is seen that values of a can be determined (a) by the loss of carriers in time, (b) by the growth of carriers in time when production and loss by recombination occur together, and (c) from the equilibrium concentration. The last-named method is not very accurate, since it involves measurement of disparate quantities, "saturation" ion-production current, and the equilibrium number of ions in a given volume. It also involves conditions of measurement that are differently affected by anisotropies. Method (b) has been used on several occasions, by Rümelin (17), by Marshall (18) in the author's laboratory, and in a recent microwave study. In the end most observers have resorted to the method of loss (a), because it gives more direct data and allows of correction for other losses where they occur.

As noted below, the ion concentrations needed have been evaluated by sampling the gas or plasma at two times, separated by a convenient interval.

a) By sweeping the ions out of a known volume V at the two times t_1 and t_2 with high fields, and assuming that the charges qe collected, on being divided by Ve, gave the concentrations n_1 and n_2 corresponding.

b) By inserting probes into the gas and measuring the concentrations of ions n_1 and n_2 at t_1 and t_2 by techniques appropriate to probe theory.

c) By assuming that certain spectral lines, or a continuum, emitted represented the light caused by recombination, and not that caused by imprisoned resonance radiation or secondary interactions. In this case, relative intensities only could be used at the two times t_1 and t_2 after the discharge ceased, by photometer; and now, of course, by

photomultiplier cell. Here absolute electron densities could be measured by probe, or could be calculated from the absolute intensity
of the line at the series limit, with estimates of electron temperature
made from the variation of line intensities with wave length, using
the quantum theory of line emission. The probe measurements roughly
checked the data from spectral lines in Mohler's (19) work.

d) By using Stark-effect broadening of spectral lines in very dense
and luminous plasmas, the density of ions can be determined if the
electron temperature is roughly known (6), (8). If this density is
measured at different times on known lines, the decay in carriers with
time can be estimated.

e) Within certain limits of density, a probing microwave beam in
a cavity can yield fairly good values of electron density through
measurement of the Q of the cavity or its change in resonant frequency (11).

f) Radio echoes from the ionosphere lead to an evaluation of
electron density in that plasma (12).

It must be indicated that the measurement of n by sweeping out
ions cannot apply to dense plasmas, as these are too stiff, so that
this method applies largely to ion concentrations between 10^5 to
10^7 ions per cm^3. The ionizing agencies used to achieve these densities were thus largely α rays, β rays, and X-rays. All these yield
anisotropic carrier distributions, mostly on a microscale. Loss of
carriers by recombination at such concentrations is slow, so that
long time intervals are needed to observe accurately measurable
losses. This precludes study of recombination involving electronic
carriers, because of the rapid loss by diffusion. Thus, such methods
must be confined to negative ion forming gases; e.g., O_2, Cl_2, or any
dirty gas.

Probes can be used only in fairly dense plasmas in excess of 10^{10}
carriers per cm^3, and only when negative carriers are exclusively
electronic and the plasma is not decaying (10). Even then probes
are not too reliable for estimating densities, though the Maxwellian
energy distribution applies between 10^{10} and 10^{12} carriers per cm^3 (20).

The use of emitted light obviously requires that the density of
ionization be such as to yield light sufficiently intense so that the
intensity in single spectral lines, or narrow continua, can be measured. This applies to densities in excess of 10^{10} and up to 10^{17}
ions/cm^3. It is possible that the decline of less dense plasmas could
be studied with photomultipliers. However, high intensities are needed
for absolute measurement of densities of excited atoms. Such studies
have so far been done only on arcs and spark channels (8), (9), (19).

The Stark-effect studies have been confined to ion densities of the order of 10^{15} per cm^3 and greater, up to 10^{17}, since they require high values of n to produce measurable broadening.

The studies of densities in microwave plasmas so far do not extend below 10^8 ions/cm^3, and measurements at densities of more than 10^{11} per cm^3 are now suspect (10), (11). The microwave plasma is generally less troubled by microscale anisotropy. Macroscale anisotropy must be avoided. The method permits of purity control and density measurement for time intervals where significant data can be gathered over limited pressure ranges, even down to low temperatures. These were the studies which called for extension of theory beyond the ideal relation that was until recently applied to all observations.

The question of the time intervals for observation is an important one. Using equation 6.2, it is clear that good measurement requires the data to be taken over the region of significant fall. This means that the time interval $\Delta t = t_1 - t_2$ chosen should be so fixed that n_2/n_1 has values resulting from the condition $n_1 a t \sim 1$, otherwise Δt will require very large values to change n_2/n_1 appreciably, and shorter intervals are desirable. If t_1 and t_2 are in regions where the fall is very steep, Δt cannot be measured accurately. Thus, depending on values of a expected, the quantity $t = 1/(n_1 a)$ around which t_1 and t_2 must lie will vary with the densities n_1 or n_0 achieved. For free electron-atom recombination $a \sim 10^{-12}$, so that unless $n_1 \sim 10^{17}$ the intervals required will be greater than 10^{-5} sec, and in longer intervals the plasma could change appreciably in nature. For ordinary values, such as for ion-ion or dissociative electron-ion recombination, $a \sim 10^{-6}$, which, with n_1 as low as 10^5, makes $\Delta t \sim 1$ sec. This condition in fact made early studies of a in ion-ion recombination difficult, where values of n_1 did not exceed 10^7 ions, until improvements in control and accuracy were achieved. This condition also limits recombination study to intervals of the order of 10^{-2} or more seconds, under which condition secondary reactions of ions in the gas modify the process.

Today it is hardly worth the time to describe the older methods, which were carried out with outmoded techniques and equipment, and usually with impure gases and carriers of indefinite and time-varying character. It suffices to list some of the methods that were used, with references enabling the reader to consult the original paper.

1. Air-blast methods used gas streams which gave a displacement along the x axis in a known time, concentrations being inferred by probe currents at various values of x and hence t. The air was ionized

by X-rays or radioactive substances. These methods suffered from lack of purity control, turbulence, inadequate sampling by probes, etc. They were early used by E. Rutherford, J. S. Townsend, and J. A. McClelland (21).

2. Measurement of equilibrium concentration of ions yielding n_∞, as in equation 6.5, and a measurement of rate of ion production Q by high-field "saturation" currents were carried out by R. K. McClung, H. A. Erikson, and L. L. Hendren, some of the measurements being done with α-particle ionization (22).

3. The measurements, using the rate of increase of ionization in time following equation 6.4, were first used by G. Rümelin (17), who did his timing with a rotating commutator and used gamma-ray ionization. L. C. Marshall (18), in the author's laboratory; and later, J. Sayers (23), both used this method with commutators and X-ray ionization. Marshall and Sayers abandoned the method for the method of loss.

4. In 1896, J. J. Thomson and E. Rutherford (4) first measured a by observation of the variation of an ionization current between parallel plates as the applied field strength was varied, ions being produced at a constant rate Q per cm³ per second. Neglecting diffusion, the creation of ions Q and the loss by recombination and current flow must equal each other, such that $Q = an^2 + (A/V) i/e$, where A is the area of the plates, V the ionized volume, i the current, and e the electron.

Since $i = ne (k_+ + k_-) X$, where n is the concentration, k_+ and k_- are the positive and negative ion mobilities, and X is the field strength; and since $V/A = l$, the distance between electrodes, if I is the "saturation" current evaluating Q when X is very large, then:

$$(6.48) \qquad \frac{a}{e} = \frac{(I - i)(k_+ + k_-)^2 X^2}{i^2 l}.$$

The method was later improved by E. Riecke and G. Mie (4).

5. The loss method was first used by E. Rutherford (24), who ionized air with a flash of X-rays and swept out ions at different intervals t, using a pendulum interrupter. P. Langevin (5) saw the difficulties inherent in the unsteady and unequal X-ray flashes of that time, and devised an ingenious method in which the same flash was sent through two equal condensers, with fields X_1 and X_2 acting. The method by the same flash ionized slabs of gas about 0.2 of the plate separation *thick* as it traversed successively the centers of the condensers. After the X-ray flash a field was put on, driving positive ions say to plate A and negative ions to plate B of each condenser.

If the field X is high, ions are withdrawn so fast that few in the thin, ionized slab can recombine and the "saturation" current can be measured. At lower fields the movements of the slabs of positive and negative ions in opposite directions are slower, and only those ions in a zone $l - (k_+ + k_-) Xt$ thick, where l is the ionized slab thickness, recombine after t. If we designate a quantity ϵ as $\epsilon = a/[4\pi e (k_+ + k_-)]$, solution leads to a number of ions Q collected out of Q_0, given by

$$Q = \frac{X}{4\pi\epsilon} \log \left(1 - \frac{1 - 4\pi\epsilon Q_0}{X} \right).$$

If two fields X_1 and X_2 are used on two condensers, since Q_0 is the same in both condensers, then the charges Q_1 and Q_2 collected are given by

$$X_1 \, \epsilon^{\left(\frac{4\pi\epsilon Q_1}{X_1} - 1 \right)} = X_2 \, \epsilon^{\left(\frac{4\pi\epsilon Q_2}{X_2} - 1 \right)}.$$

Measurement of Q_1 and Q_2 leads to the evaluation of a in terms of

(6.49) $a = \epsilon [4\pi e (k_+ + k_-)]$.

This relation has some theoretical significance, as it represents a calculation of a for ion-ion recombination deduced by P. Langevin, but it is now known only to apply properly at higher pressures. The application of the X-ray flash and the sweep field is again accomplished by pendulum interrupter.

The lack of adequate control of gaseous purity and the lack of correction of losses and errors due to microscale and macroscale diffusion, as well as other inaccuracies inherent in the early techniques, made the results of all these early studies contradictory and of little significance, except as yielding an order of magnitude for the coefficient of ion-ion recombination in air, or soiled and therefore electron-attaching gases. There was evidence, though not clean-cut, that a was a function of age of the ions in the plasma.

Starting in 1924, a series of studies in the author's laboratory by L. C. Marshall (18), O. Luhr (26), and M. E. Gardner (27), with continually improving techniques, under Gardner's careful manipulation eventually led to an evaluation of a, using a commutator method, with X-ray ionization and the loss method. The gas used was O_2, the only pure, electron-attaching gas forming molecular ions and insuring ion-ion recombination. Elimination of diffusive loss to the walls and electrodes, of stray fields during Δt, insurance of saturation collection of ions so far as possible, prevention of inductive effects by

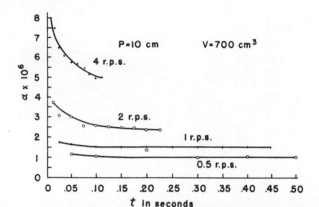

Fig. 6.5. Gardner's observed values of α' as a function of time in O_2. Here flash times are commensurate with recombination times. The individual curves were taken at increasing commutator speeds, thus progressively reducing the diffusion before recombination intervals.

use of a dummy chamber, and a control of constancy of ionization led to reproducible results. Measurements were made, varying temperature and pressure as well as intensity of X-ray ionization within small limits. The measurements were made at different commutator speeds, varying both ionizing flash time and Δt; and thus α', the observed value of α, could be studied over an array of time intervals. In general, α' decreased as Δt and t_1 and t_2 increased because of microscale diffusive effects.

This is seen nicely in figure 6.5, where values of α', as observed over various ionizing flash and recombination times, show α' to decrease as Δt increases. At ages of 0.1 sec the value of α' still. slowly decreased, perhaps because of change in the nature of ions. Details of the method will not be given, as they are adequately described in an earlier book. Gardner's curves for variation of α with pressure and temperature are shown in figures 6.6 and 6.7.

Independently, and nearly simultaneously with Gardner, J. Sayers (23), then at Cambridge, England, carried out a similar study for air. The methods were very closely parallel, except for minor corrections for diffusion, etc. Sayers carried the pressure measurements up to nearly two atmospheres. Sayers' data at longer t and Δt were influenced by change in ion size in air chemically altered as a result of X-radiation.

The measurements of Gardner and Sayers are probably the only valid results on ion-ion recombination, using ion densities of the

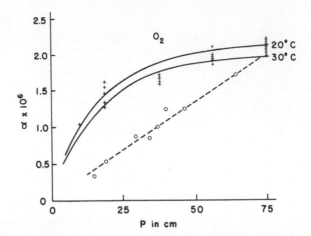

Fig. 6.6. Gardner's values of α in pure O_2 as a function of pressure p in mm of Hg, compared with those computed from J. J. Thomson's theory. Experimental points are crosses. They lie well about the computed curves for 20° and 30° C., the range over which they were observed. The dashed curve shows data from earlier observers, uncorrected for initial recombination, and fitted in absolute value to Gardner's data at 760 mm. This illustrates the unreliability of the earlier data owing to inadequate correction.

order of 10^6 ions/cm³, X-ray ionization, and time intervals Δt and times t ranging from 10^2 to 1 sec. The one defect of both methods lies in the fact that the ionization flash time is commensurate with recombination time; e.g., one-tenth to one-fifth of t for any given commutator speed. This prevents any real test of the influence of diffusion from microanisotropy on the variation of α' with t.

6. The studies of recombination in arc-discharge plasmas fell by chance into a field of investigation that differed from the earlier studies reported, in that they dealt with a study of the recombination of *electrons* with *supposedly atomic ions* in an attempt to verify basic atomic structural theory. The Bohr theory indicated that electrons with kinetic energies $\frac{1}{2}mc^2$ could fall into vacant orbits of the energy-level diagram from the continuum. If ν_x is the frequency of the light radiated when an electron from the zero level falls into some vacant lower-energy level of the neutral atom, then the frequency of the light radiated when an electron of energy $\frac{1}{2}mc^2$ above the zero level falls into the level x will be $h\nu = \frac{1}{2}mc^2 + h\nu_x$. Thus, all lines corresponding to capture into the vacant x orbits of the ion will have frequencies ν which are greater than ν_x by the continuous spectrum of electron energies $\frac{1}{2}mc^2$, modulated by the capture prob-

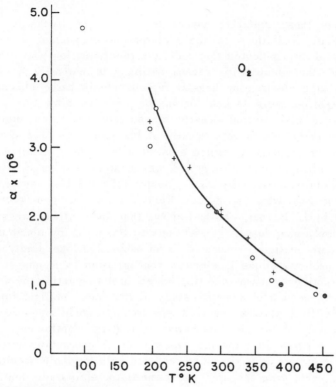

Fig. 6.7. Gardner's values of α in O_2 as a function of temperature at constant density, compared with calculations from Thomson's theory. Gardner's data are crosses, and the data of Phillips and Erikson are circles and circled crosses. Phillips' data are at constant pressure, while Erikson's are at constant density. Absolute values of these workers were adjusted to Gardner's data near $300°$ K. The one point of Erikson's at liquid-air temperature falls badly off the curve. This is doubtless a true deviation caused by clustering at that temperature.

ability from the kinetic-energy states. This probability is greater with smaller $\tfrac{1}{2}mc^2$.

Each of the *capture, or recombination, lines* will have a *continuum*, or broadening, to the short wave-length side. This will be most intense near the line, and will fade out into the ultraviolet. Of course, the lines caused by transitions between states of the neutral atom are not directly involved. However, capture into the higher levels is much more probable than that into lower states. Such lines are in the red, except for broadening by $\tfrac{1}{2}mc^2$. After the capture and emission of continua, the emission of many of the atomic lines appears with no continua in the recombination spectrum.

It was thus natural to associate continua in discharge spectra for capture transitions to the electron-ion recombination process. Because theory indicated that radiative recombination was relatively unlikely, the electron-ion recombination was naturally sought for only in high electron-ion density regions of discharge plasma. The high densities were looked for in the negative glow and positive columns of high current density discharges; i.e., glow discharges with hot cathodes and arcs, mostly at low pressures. The glows described can properly be called arcs. It was in these areas that the studies initiated by C. Kenty (28) on an argon discharge, and later very carefully pursued by F. L. Mohler (19) and his associates on Cs vapor arcs, were carried out. Kenty's work had been preceded by a study by L. Hayner, who had shown that under higher pressures in such discharges, losses of electrons to the walls by ambipolar diffusion were negligible compared to recombination loss. Kenty studied the recombination loss in electron concentration by means of probes after the arc current was cut off. Mohler, first suspecting the accuracy of probes, used a photometric study of the decay of light intensity.

These first studies involved spectrophotometric measurement of the intensity of the glow-discharge light in the continuous spectrum at various times after the arc was cut off. A commutator interrupted the Cs vapor arc in a specially designed bulb by short-circuiting the potential supplying the arc. The commutator also made contacts to probes in the wall, and in the gas at convenient time intervals after cutoff. Slots in the commutator enabled the central portion of the afterglow to be viewed at various times after cutoff. The light was photometered and compared to filtered light from an incandescent filament diffused over a paper surface. Contacts to probes and the viewing slits could be displaced relative to cutoff on the commutator to vary the time. In these arcs, the electron densities were of the order of 10^{12} per cm^3, the electron temperatures were $\sim 1,200°$ K., and a was found to be of the order of 5×10^{-10} cm^3/ion sec.

The data from the probes paralleled those from intensities, and Mohler thereafter used probes to measure electron loss. In the later studies, Mohler also considered the loss of ions by ambipolar diffusion, using a spherical bulb, and with this was able to show· that at 1.5×10^{-2} mm pressure in a given discharge, ambipolar-diffusion loss was ten times that from recombination; while at 0.29 mm the two losses were about equal. Mohler (19) later extended his study to an Hg arc. In these studies, the value of t and of Δt ranged around multiples of a millisecond. At a later date, J. Sayers (29a) also used probes in a dying A arc plasma at 0.1 to 1 mm pressure at 600° and

2,400° K., observing values of the same order as those of Kenty and Mohler. The data obtained by Kenty, Mohler, and others will later be presented in tabular form for discussion.

7. With the advent of photomultipliers and the techniques of World War II, J. D. Craggs and J. M. Meek (6) studied the light emitted in a *spark* channel during breakdown with current flowing and in the afterglow after current ceased. The gases were A and H_2 at about atmospheric pressure. The breakdown was achieved by pulses of appropriate potential, 2 to 4 microseconds in length. Both the potential and the current flow were oscillographically recorded for at least 1 microsecond, and subsequently for longer times. The light emission was first studied with rotating-mirror techniques. This could have been studied more profitably by means of a photomultiplier tube with oscillographic recording. The studies were coupled with calorimetric measurements to give the mean potential drop during current flow. The diameters of the channels were measured by photographs in the visible and ultraviolet. The spectra were also observed. Argon yielded a strong continuum, while H_2 primarily showed Balmer-series lines, much broadened by Stark effect from the neighboring positive ions.

The individual Balmer lines had their intensity measured as a function of time by use of filters and photomultiplier. Ion densities could be estimated by Stark effect in H_2, and by energy balance in the channel in both H_2 and A. The ion densities were initially of the order of 10^{17} per cm³. The channel temperatures were roughly calculated by a Saha equation, and ranged from 10,000° K. and 15,000° K. The spark was confined in a hard glass tube of 3 mm thickness to allow of gas-pressure variation. Current came either from a charged condenser or from artificial transmission lines. The H_2 spark in one case had a channel diameter of 0.15 cm and a peak current density of the order of 40,000 amps/cm².

Subsequently, more careful studies were made on H_2 by Hopwood and Craggs (6). From these it appears that at the peak of emission, ion densities were approximately 2.5×10^{17} per cm³, which represents ionization of all molecules present at constant gas pressure. They associated this with a Saha temperature of 12,000° K. and a recombination coefficient of 2×10^{-12} cm³/ion sec. As the electron temperatures and densities declined with time, the values of the observed coefficient ranged from 2×10^{-12} cm³/ion sec to 1.4×10^{-11} cm³/ion sec.

While Hopwood and Craggs assume thermal equilibrium between electrons and ion plasma in 10^{-6} second in these discharges, the question is an open one. It is most probable that practically all of the molecules of H_2 are dissociated by the spark, for no part of the many-lined spectrum is seen. In H gas of this character, completely ionized and recombining, no secondary reactions or metastable states are encountered. The light of the Balmer lines seen after the first 10^{-7} sec or so can only come from direct electron-exciting impact and from recombination. It is likely that in a microsecond the positive ions and atoms present are in rough thermal equilibrium at an elevated temperature of their own. These will create the shock wave and other manifestations of the spark in the ensuing hundreds of microseconds. The electron energy is initially very high.

It is known that at the electron densities present, Coulomb interactions between electrons will readily insure a Maxwellian energy distribution among electrons. While the lines of the Balmer series initially excited by electron impacts from current flow will have radiated largely in a tenth of a microsecond, the gas is still *electronically very hot*. The absorption of resonance radiation conceivably will prolong the excited state. Some excitations by electron impact will occur. The electrons that cool down can receive energy from excited states by inelastic impacts of the second class and by Coulomb fields. The energy gained by some electrons is at once restored into the Maxwellian distribution of the whole. It is thus doubtful, even in a matter of some microseconds during which these studies were made, whether the electrons *degrade anywhere near to thermal equilibrium with the atoms, as in a Saha equilibrium*.

Finally, as the thermal atomic energy degrades, the recombination of H atoms to make H_2 again injects energy into the gas, some of which goes to the electrons. Thus, the estimate of electron temperatures from a Saha equation is not justified in this analysis. This fact must be borne in mind in the later discussion of the significance of the values of a that is observed in these studies. In any event, it is clear that the method permits of studies of a where it is small, and perhaps under interesting conditions. However, the accuracy of the method hinges on the proper evaluation of n. While the rate of decrease in intensity does give dn/dt, the value of n_0 or its equivalent is not given directly. This can only be had from Stark-effect studies. These studies depend on a theory of Holtsmark for proper interpretation of the ion densities.

At present, there appears to be some doubt cast on the validity of this method in certain discharges, although the author is inclined to be less cautious. With the fallibility of present probe measurements for determining ion or electron concentrations, he is inclined to place more reliance on the Stark-effect analysis. This analysis is possible, however, only at very high ion densities. As will appear later, the data obtained by Craggs, Meek, and Hopwood yield the only certain case of electron-ion recombination. The values of a, though high for the high electron temperatures regarded by theory, may still be correct when the interference of the ionic-force fields at these densities is considered.

§ 5. The Microwave Breakdown Method (11).[3]

The introduction of microwave technique in gas discharges made possible a more accurate study of some fundamental processes in the gases of a gas discharge. With suitably constructed resonance cavities it is possible, over quite a large range in pressure, to suppress secondary processes going on at walls or electrodes, so that they may be neglected. This is accomplished by keeping either the mean free path of the electrons or the oscillation amplitude of the electrons much smaller than the dimensions of the cavity or the gas-discharge container. The main source of production of electrons is thus ionization by electron-atom collisions or metastable atom-atom collisions, and the loss mechanisms are diffusion, recombination, and attachment.

Two features of the microwave technique make this method outstanding relative to older methods. First, in certain cases the electron density may be measured with relatively high accuracy by means of a small probing signal, small enough to have no practical influence on the plasma.[4] Secondly, it is possible to set up the differential equations governing the discharge, solve these exactly for some clear-cut cases, and get relatively good approximations in other cases.

Because of the much higher mobility of the electrons compared with the mobilities of the ions, the ions may be considered stationary and thus give practically no contribution to the high-frequency conductivity. Margenau (29b) has calculated the complex conductivity caused by the electrons in microwave gas discharges, and his results may be expressed by the equation to follow,

---

[3]This section was initially written by the author on the basis of the collected reports of the group associated with Prof. S. C. Brown. Since such a report cannot keep step with the development of this method, Prof. Brown kindly rewrote the section for inclusion here in its most recent form. His cooperation is gratefully acknowledged.

[4]Recent studies by the microwave research group at Massachusetts Institute of Technology, recorded in *Quarterly Progress Report*, item IIc, January 15, 1954, indicate satisfactory agreement between microwave data on electron densities and those from positive ion saturation currents of a probe.

$$(6.50) \qquad \sigma_{\text{compl}} = \int_0^\infty \frac{4\pi v^3}{3} \frac{e^2}{m} \frac{\nu_c - j\omega}{\nu_c^2 + \omega^2} \frac{\partial f(v)}{\partial v} \, dv,$$

where ω is the circular frequency of the microwave field; ν_c is the frequency of collision of the electrons, which in the general case is dependent on the electron velocity v; $f(v)$ is the distribution function of the electrons in velocity space related to the electron density n in the following way:

$$(6.51) \qquad n = \int_0^\infty 4\pi v^2 f(v) \, dv.$$

When ν_c, the frequency of collision, is independent of the velocity of the electron, as is the case with high-energy electrons, e.g., in hydrogen and helium, the complex conductivity may be written simply

$$(6.52) \qquad \sigma_{\text{compl}} = \frac{e^2}{m} \cdot \frac{\nu_c - j\omega}{\nu_c^2 + \omega^2} n.$$

For thermal electrons in most gases, experiment and theory suggest that the collision cross section rather than the collision frequency is more nearly independent of the electron velocity. The complex conductivity for other than constant-collision frequency must be calculated from Margenau's (29b) mobility equations, using experimental values for the collision probability which are usually unknown for thermal energies. Fortunately, the use of microwave frequencies makes ω sufficiently large compared to ν_c for pressures in the mm range for most gases, so that one can assume that the discharge admittance is a pure susceptance, given by

$$(6.53) \qquad \sigma_c = -j \, (e^2/m\omega) \, n.$$

The range of validity of this approximation depends upon the experimental method used. A detailed analysis shows that it is possible for the dissipative part of σ_c to compensate for the error in the susceptive part.

The complex conductivity is in general a function of the electron density; in the simple cases mentioned above it is directly proportional to n. J. C. Slater (29b) has evaluated the influence of a medium with slight conductivity in a cavity at microwave frequencies, and has found the following expression for the change in circular-resonance frequency:

$$(6.54) \qquad -\frac{1}{\omega \epsilon_0} \frac{\int_V \sigma_i X^2 dV}{\int_V X^2 dV} = \frac{\omega}{\omega_0} - \frac{\omega_0}{\omega} \simeq \frac{2\Delta\omega}{\omega_0},$$

where ω_0 is the resonant frequency of the empty cavity; σ_i is the imaginary part of the complex conductivity; ϵ_0 is the permittivity of free space; V is the volume of the cavity; and X is the probing signal, so small as to have no practical influence on the spatial distribution and the energy distribution of the electrons. The formula above is valid only so long as the influence of the conducting medium may be considered as a perturbation of the case when the same cavity contains no conducting medium. This gives the following criterion for the validity of the above formula: $|\sigma| \ll \omega \epsilon_0$; and when the microwave frequency is about 3,000 m.c. and $|\sigma| = e^2/m$, $n \ll 10^{11}$ electrons/cm³.

In the simple case when the cavity contains electrons, such that $\nu_c \ll \omega$, the relative change in circular frequency is

$$(6.55) \qquad \frac{2\Delta\omega}{\omega} = \frac{e^2}{m\omega^2\epsilon_0} \frac{\int_V n X^2 dV}{\int_V X^2 dV}.$$

When the spatial distribution of the electrons and density n and the probing signal X are known, the expression above may be written as

$$(6.56) \qquad \frac{\Delta\omega}{\omega} = \frac{e^2}{m\omega^2\epsilon_0} C\bar{n},$$

where C is a geometrical coefficient and $\bar{n}$ is the average electron density.

Biondi and Brown (7) used this relation between the shift in the resonant frequency and the average electron density to measure ambipolar diffusion and electron-ion recombination in helium. They introduced a cylindrical quartz bottle into a cylindrical cavity, constructed for the TM_{010} mode and a resonant wave length of about 10 cm. The quartz bottle was evacuated, thoroughly outgassed, and filled with a pure gas sample of the desired pressure. The dimensions of the quartz bottle were chosen to be small relative to the dimensions of the cavity, in order to insure a fairly uniform electric field inside the bottle and thus to facilitate the calculation of the geometrical constant C. Power from a pulsed 10-cm magnetron was fed into the cavity, and the gas in the quartz bottle was ionized, so that electron densities of the order of 10^{10} to 10^{11} electrons per cm^3 were reached. The magnetron was on about 250 μ secs, and off about 11,000 μ secs. A small continuous probing signal was sent into the cavity, and the reflected signal was observed on an oscilloscope with a linear sweep and the same repetition rate as the pulsed magnetron. At resonance the probing signal was absorbed more than at nonresonance, and a dip in the trace on the oscilloscope was observed. By changing the frequency of the probing signal, it was thus possible to determine the frequency shift relative to the empty cavity as a function of time, and hence the electron density as a function of time.

With ω of the order of 2×10^{10}, they were able to measure electron densities over the range from 10^8 to 10^{10} electrons per cm^3. These densities are well in the range of ambipolar diffusion. The continuity equation then leads to the following differential equation governing the discharge and the afterglow:

$$(6.57) \qquad D_a \, \nabla^2 n + \nu n - a n^2 - h \nu_c n = \frac{\partial n}{\partial t},$$

where D_a is the ambipolar-diffusion coefficient; ν is the production rate of electrons per electron caused by the electric field; a is the recombination coefficient; ν_c is the frequency of collision of the electrons; and h is the probability of attachment to molecules yielding negative ions. The main purpose of the pulsed magnetron is merely to insure that there is a rather high electron density in the beginning of the decay period. In the decay period, ν is zero if the probing signal is small enough. The differential equation which has to be solved is thus

$$(6.58) \qquad D_a \, \nabla^2 n - a n^2 - h \nu_c n = \frac{\partial n}{\partial t}.$$

Consider first a case when the loss of electrons by ambipolar diffusion dominates, and losses by attachment and recombination are negligible processes. This can usually be arranged by a proper choice of pressure and electron density. Diffusion losses increase with decreasing pressure, and recombination is either independent of pressure or decreasing with decreasing pressure. Thus,

$$(6.59) \qquad D_a \, \nabla^2 n = \frac{\partial n}{\partial t}.$$

The spatial distribution of electrons in the beginning of the decay period is $n_0(x,y,z)$, and the boundary condition is that the electron density go to zero at the walls of the quartz bottle. The solution of the differential equation above is thus most suitably expressed in the form of a series of an orthonormal set of eigen functions $f_i(x,y,z)$, satisfying the differential equation $\nabla^2 f_i - f_i/\Lambda_i^2 = 0$, and the given boundary conditions. Λ_i is a length characteristic of the quartz bottle and the "mode" i, $i = 1 \ldots \ldots \infty$. The solution is then:

$$(6.60) \quad n = \sum n_{0i}\, \epsilon^{-D_a t/\Lambda_i^2} \quad f_i(x,y,z) \quad \text{and} \quad n_{0i} = \int_V n_0 f_i(x,y,z)\, dV.$$

But $\Lambda_1 > \Lambda_2 > \Lambda_3 \ldots \ldots$, which is a property of eigen functions of this kind. The form of the time constant for the different terms in the series then indicates that all higher terms are disappearing with time much faster than the first term, and after a certain time τ of the order of the time constant of the second term, all higher terms are negligible relative to the first term.[5] After the elapse of that time τ, the spatial distribution of electrons is adequately described by only the first term:

$$(6.61) \quad n = n_{01}\, \epsilon^{-D_a t/\Lambda_1^2} \quad f_1(x,y,z).$$

For a cylinder with the radius R and the height H, the first terms are

$$(6.62) \quad \frac{1}{\Lambda_{11}^2} = \left(\frac{\pi}{H}\right)^2 + \left(\frac{2.405}{R}\right)^2 \quad \frac{1}{\Lambda_{22}^2} = \left(\frac{3\pi}{H}\right)^2 + \left(\frac{5.52}{R}\right)^2.$$

For a quartz bottle in the form of a sphere with a radius R, the solution has the form:

$$n = n_{01}\, \frac{1}{N_2}\, \epsilon^{-D_a/\Lambda_1^2}\, \frac{\sin(\pi r/R)}{r},$$

$$\frac{1}{\Lambda_1} = \left(\frac{\pi}{R}\right),$$

and

$$(6.63) \quad \frac{1}{\Lambda_2} = \left(\frac{3\pi}{R}\right),$$

where N_1 and N_2 will be normalizing constants. The average electron density is thus decaying according to the following formula.

[5] Great care must be used in applications to insure that this condition is satisfied, for the appearance of higher modes at once causes observed changes which simulate actions such as attachment or recombination.

$$(6.64) \qquad \bar{n} = \bar{n}_{0_1} \epsilon^{-\left(\frac{D_a}{\Lambda_1^2}\right)t} = n_{0_1} \epsilon^{-t/\tau_1}, \text{ with } \tau_1 = \frac{\Lambda_1^2}{D_a}.$$

The time constant τ_1 is evaluated from the experimentally measured average electron density as a function of time in the decay period as the slope of the straight line in the plot of log $\bar{n}$ against t, and D_a is calculated from this time constant τ_1 and the diffusion length Λ_1, which is determined by the dimensions of the quartz bottle:

$$(6.65) \qquad D_a = \frac{\Lambda_1^2}{\tau_1}.$$

By increasing the pressure it is possible to emphasize the loss of electrons by recombination, and for certain gases the loss of electrons because of attachment is negligible. The differential equation governing the plasma in the decay period is then:

$$(6.1) \qquad \frac{\partial n}{\partial t} = -an^2.$$

If wall effects are negligible and the initial spatial distribution is uniform, the solution of this differential equation is

$$(6.2) \qquad \frac{1}{n} = \frac{1}{n_0} + at.$$

If the initial spatial distribution is not uniform, the greater loss in the high-density regions tends to make the distribution become uniform as the decay proceeds. Thus, if the experimentally measured values of the electron densities as a function of time are plotted as $1/n$ against t, the plot should become a straight line, and this would verify the assumption of uniform density.[6] The slope of this line is then a.

If attachment is the predominant loss mechanism, the differential equation in the decay period is

$$\frac{\partial n}{\partial t} = -h\nu_c n,$$

which equation has the following solution.

---

[6]This is the correct approach. However, there is a natural tendency to forget this possibility and to ascribe the initial curvature to other causes. Since isotropy of charge distribution is not insured in such breakdown, care must be used to insure absence of anisotropy before other explanations are sought.

(6.66 and 5.53) $$n = n_0 \, \epsilon^{-h\nu_c t} \; .$$

Thus, when the density is plotted on a logarithmic scale, there is again a straight line, the slope of which is $h\nu_c$, from which may be calculated the probability of attachment.

In certain cases, when measuring the ambipolar-diffusion coefficient, it is not possible to neglect losses because of recombination, but it is still possible to correct for this term in the differential equation when it is small relative to the diffusion loss term:

(6.67) $$D_a \, \nabla^2 n - an^2 = \frac{\partial n}{\partial t} \, .$$

The assumption is then that

$$D_a \nabla^2 n = - \frac{D_a}{\Lambda_1^2} \, n = - \frac{n}{\eta} \, ,$$

and thus,

$$- \frac{n}{\tau_1} - an^2 = \frac{\partial n}{\partial t} \, ,$$

the solution of which is

(6.68) $$\frac{n}{(1 + a\tau_1 n)} = \frac{n_0 \epsilon^{-\frac{t}{\eta}}}{(1 + a\tau_1 n_0)} \, .$$

If a is known from measurements at higher pressures of the same gas, it is possible by a method of successive approximations to find η from the experimentally determined values of the electron density as a function of time, and thus also the ambipolar-diffusion coefficient D_a when Λ_1 is known.[7]

In the above derivations it has been assumed that the electrons were in thermal equilibrium with the gas in the afterglow period. However, that is not quite true. In the beginning of the decay period the average electron energy is of the order of several electron volts. It may safely be assumed that the high-energy electrons left over from the discharge period are lost almost momentarily in inelastic collision, and thus when calculating the decay of the electron energy, only the energy loss of the elastic collisions must be taken into account. The electrons lose an average of $2m/M$ of this energy at each collision with gas atoms, the rate being faster for molecules.

---

[7] This requires that all anisotropy, higher diffusion modes, and attachment be ruled out.

§5

The rate of energy loss is the energy loss per collision multiplied by ν_c, the collision frequency. Thus,

(6.69)
$$\frac{dn}{dt} = -\nu_c \frac{2m}{M} n,$$

where n is the electron energy.

As this equation already is an approximation, and the decay occurs in a relatively small range down to about 0.04 e.v., it may be assumed that ν_c is constant, and that an average value of ν_c for the energy range in question can be taken:

(6.70)
$$n = n_0 \, \epsilon^{-\left(\nu_c \frac{2m}{M} t\right)}.$$

The time constant τ for the energy decay of the electron is thus determined by the following relation:

(6.71)
$$p\tau = \frac{M}{2m}\left(\frac{p}{\nu_c}\right)_{ave},$$

where $(p/\nu_c)_{ave}$ is constant according to the assumption, and only depends on the gas. For helium, $p\tau$ is 2×10^{-6} (sec-mm Hg); and for hydrogen, $p\tau$ is 3×10^{-6} (sec-mm Hg). This time constant must be compared with the decay time of the electron density measured experimentally. The time constant (for example, in the case of helium) is of the order of 10 μ secs. Thus, if no measurements of electron densities are made earlier than 50 μ secs after the beginning of the decay period, the assumption is well justified that the electrons are in thermal equilibrium with the gas.

As seen, the method has certain advantages over others. First, suitable vessels for calculating ambipolar-diffusion loss can be used, such that corrections for such loss are possible. Again, by varying pressure within reasonable limits, the ambipolar-diffusion coefficient as well as recombination coefficients can be observed. The former yields values of the ion mobility which may serve to identify the ions present, thus rendering interpretation of the recombination process easier. However, for this purpose the plasma had best be analyzed by mass spectrometer to identify ions, since the ions may not be the same at different pressures and ages. Actually, care must still be used, since mass spectroscopy may not reveal less stable ions which mobility detects. An added advantage is that the microwave *breakdown* is achieved in the absence of electrodes and d.c.

ion currents, thus insuring more uniformity of plasma and making achievement of pure gases easier.[8]

By means of the microwave breakdown, uniformity in n, or else a gross calculable anisotropy, can be achieved. There is no microscopic anisotropy. The measurement of the electron density can be achieved in other ways than by measuring the change in resonant frequency, thus affording checks on the accuracy. If the plasma after microwave breakdown is allowed to "cool off" for some 100 microseconds or more, the electrons reach nearly thermal energies, and recombination of thermal electrons can be studied. These afford a real opportunity for comparison of experiment with theory.

Therefore, it is not surprising that the first microwave studies at once revealed some very important facts, and they have gone a long way in clarifying past difficulties. Thus, as the work has progressed, the recombination process, as it occurs even in the inert gases, has been observed to be subject to many complications that no one had foreseen previously. Several pertinent examples may be given: Multiple ion types and changes between types; ion production in "cooled-down" plasma by metastable interaction; and finally, the multiple action of impurities in causing electron attachment, formation of ions with unknown properties, and later complications produced in interpretation of decay curves incident to the presence of higher modes of diffusion, as well as errors introduced when higher electron densities are used. Such complications indicate that the study of recombination by microwave techniques, while most valuable, is still in its infancy.[9]

§ 6. The Mechanism of Recombination, and the Various Recombination Processes.

It begins to be clear from what has gone before that the basic theory of the recombination process was very primitive, and was so oversimplified as not to apply to present-day conditions. Hence, data derived by this means are, to say the least, very difficult of inter-

---

[8]Ironically, this is not always true. In order to avoid losses, quartz-bottles are preferable to glass in microwave cavities. It appears that atomic hydrogen generated by the discharge in H_2 gas reduces (29c) the SiO_2, and thus produces water vapor which seriously attaches electrons, thus vitiating recombination studies unless the quartz has been treated for so many hours as to reduce the inner surface of the bottle.

[9]The first microwave studies were carried out under the most carefully controlled conditions, in order to avoid the various pitfalls mentioned in preceding footnotes. The success of these early studies resulted in greater laxity in later work (7), with its attendant evils, especially in other laboratories.

pretation. It must further be noted that the nature of the earliest experiments—which, because of deficient techniques and impure gases, could only concern themselves with the most effective ion-ion recombination process—again led to an oversimplified mechanism of recombination. This came from the assumption that one ion had merely to wander, or be drawn, into an "encounter" with an opposite ion in order to occasion neutralization or recombination. The indications that all was not right with such a simple notion came early, when an oversimplified theory due to Langevin (25) (now known only to apply at high gas densities) was accepted as correct for nearly twenty-five years, even though Langevin's own early data on a taken by his method indicated serious difficulties. Even the later studies of electron-ion recombination, as observed with probable accuracy by Kenty (28) and by Mohler (19), gave serious concern when attempts were made to correlate the quantum-theoretical predictions with these observations.

Clarification of some of the difficulties associated with ion-ion recombination began with a theory of the process proposed by J. J. Thomson (30) in 1924. This theory appeared to contradict the fundamental postulates of the Langevin theory, but no experimental data were at hand to test it. It thus remained for the experimental data of L. C. Marshall (18), in the author's laboratory in 1928, to indicate that temporal variations in the observed coefficient of recombination could only be interpreted as a diffusion of ion pairs *apart* in time instead of *together*, as Langevin's theory demanded.

S. G. Plimpton (3), from his own excellent earlier measurements in 1913, had independently concluded that the temporal variation of a was caused by diffusion apart of initially close ion pairs. Unfortunately, Plimpton did not realize the significance of this discovery relative to Langevin's theory. In 1928, the author (3) discussed the evidence from Marshall's work with A. Sommerfeld, who analyzed the problem in terms of a Brownian motion of the opposite ions. This analysis clearly indicated the source of Langevin's error, and established the Thomson mechanism as the appropriate mechanism for ion-ion recombination at atmospheric pressure and below. A year later, W. R. Harper (31) independently recognized the error in Langevin's reasoning, and deduced a recombination relation based on diffusive motion, applicable to recombination above one atmosphere in air. This diffusion theory, with a slightly altered constant, amazingly reverted to Langevin's theory.

The studies of O. Luhr (26), following Marshall in the author's laboratory, threw more light on the variation of a with time due to initial microscale anisotropy of paired ions from X-ray ionization. He found that if hydrogen and nitrogen were pure, loss of electrons by diffusion to the walls made recombination measurements impossible in all but electron-attaching gases. From mass-spectroscopic studies he found that the multiple ions observed in air, ranging from N^+ to Hg^+ ions, made impossible any accurate evaluation of a, or intelligent interpretation of the theory of ion-ion recombination measured over 10^{-1} sec. It was thus logical that M. E. Gardner (27), using the techniques developed by N. E. Bradbury for gaseous-purity control in the author's laboratory, should have finally achieved a precision measurement of a for ion-ion recombination in O_2. Gardner carried his measurements from 100 mm to 760 mm pressure and from 200° C. to 450° C. These results led to nearly constant values of a at 1-sec time intervals, and corroborated the Thomson theory in all detail. The values of a obtained by Gardner for O_2 are shown in figures 6.6 and 6.7 (supra).

Quite independently, J. Sayers (3) completed measurements at about the same time, using surprisingly similar techniques in air, going somewhat higher in pressure. He was thus able to note the decline in a with decrease in pressure predicted by Thomson below 760 mm, and a decrease in a with increase in pressure somewhat above one atmosphere.

In 1906, Bragg and Kleeman (2) had called attention to columnar recombination, a special case of microscopic and macroscopic initial anisotropy with alpha-particle ionization. The problem was first analyzed theoretically by G. Jaffé (2) in 1913. It was more completely solved by him in 1929, and the theory was checked against the experimental data of J. Schemel (2), taken in 1928.

In 1939, the author, in his book entitled *Fundamental Processes of Electrical Discharge in Gases*, analyzed the various recombination processes and summarized the theory of the many mechanisms active. That analysis caused G. Jaffé (32) to subject the general problem of the recombination process to an exhaustive study, using a broad, statistical approach. His conclusions showed that theories such as those of J. J. Thomson, W. R. Harper, and P. Langevin were applicable under a limited range of specialized, ideal conditions, and justified the use of the relations under those conditions. He showed that recombination processes generally depend on the relative values of certain basic parameters, viz.: r_0, the average distance of separation of carriers of opposite sign; L or λ, the mean free path of the carriers; and on a d_0, the radius of a sphere of active attraction. The concept of d_0 was initially used by O. W. Richardson (33), but was really properly introduced by J. J. Thomson in his theory of 1924 (30). It represents the distance from the one ion at which the energy of thermal agitation of the opposite ion just equals the potential energy of the ion pair. These three parameters are determined by the nature of ions and ionizing processes, the ambient gas pressure, the density of ionization, peculiarities of the ionizing process leading to anisotropies, and the temperature of the gas.

This generalization of the processes and the clarification which it brought have laid the foundation for a proper, comprehensive discussion of recombination processes that will follow. However, it remained for the post-World War II facilities, using photomultiplier cells, fast oscilloscopes, and microwave breakdown and techniques, to yield further information on the processes. Basically, the advances achieved lay in what may have been the first observations of electron-ion recombination observed by Craggs, Meek, and Hopwood (6) in spark-channel plasmas with 10^{17} electrons/cm^3, using the Balmer lines of H atoms.

The next advance came in part from recombination studies in the ionosphere, where additional theory was developed by J. Sayers (12) and D. R. Bates (12). It laid the foundation for the later insistence by D. R. Bates (7) that large recombination coefficients observed in pure, inert gas plasmas by M. A. Biondi and S. C. Brown (7) were not electron-atom ion recombination, but were dissociative electron-molecular ion recombination. This suspicion was confirmed in inert gas plasmas by the discovery of the existence of molecular inert gas ions. This was achieved in one instance by J. A. Hornbeck and J. P. Molnar (34), and in another by the studies of a microwave group led by R. B. Holt (35), who showed the presence of molecular ions at higher pressures created by atomic ions in triple impact with their own species. Later, more complete data on these processes were furnished by the studies of A. V. Phelps (7) and those of M. A. Biondi (7), (9), who observed the Doppler broadening in the atomic lines of He^+ from dissociative recombination of the He_2^+ molecular ion. The microwave studies also led to the discovery of the multiple carrier recombination, as well as to the more complete analyses of recombination with multiple carriers that were presented earlier.

In order to analyze and present the various recombination processes and their appropriate theoretical interpretation, it is convenient to segregate the phenomena into certain categories and then to apply the most appropriate means of analysis.

It must first be noted that in principle, recombination takes place between two different types of carriers arranged into two subgroups from the viewpoint of the basic mechanism of neutralization. Thus, one may recognize:

I. *Ion-Ion Recombination.*
   A. Between ordinary or small positive and negative ions.
   B. Between large ions or Langevin ions and small ions.

II. *Electron Recombination.*
   A. Atomic ion and electron recombination by *radiative capture.*
   B. Molecular ion and electron by dissociative recombination, or possibly by dielectronic recombination.

Classes I and II can be analyzed most appropriately by different basic approaches. Thus, the mechanics assumed by J. J. Thomson (30) is best suited for discussion of problems of ion-ion recombination; while the electron-ion recombination, especially radiative recombination (process IIA), is best treated in terms of recombination cross sections calculated by wave-mechanical procedures. Actually, theory to date is not able to allow computation of the cross section for the dissociative electron-molecular ion recombination (process IIB). However, it is best considered in terms of a cross section which at present must be inferred from measured values of α and a diffusive approach. There is little of importance to say about large ion-ordinary ion recombination, for it can be treated in terms of elementary theory as a pure diffusive movement of the small ion, with a collision cross section furnished by the physical cross section of the large ion.[10]

Assuming that positive and negative ions are fully formed at a time $t = 0$, the Thomson mechanism in principle involves four basic periods or steps. These are actually complete in detail in only one of the processes, i.e., the recombination of normal positive and negative ions in air and similar gases below 1 atmosphere at relatively low ion densities. However, other cases of recombination are just as conveniently treated by his theory, except that certain of the periods may be absent or modified. The manner in which the Thomson analytical approach is used depends, as indicated, on Jaffé's (32) three critical parameters; average ion separation r_0, mean free path L, and the critical distance d_0, as well as the variations of their

---

[10]Most large, or Langevin, ions carry few charges, and under normal conditions these are of the order of one or two electrons only. Their radii are commensurate with d_0 at 293° K. Thus, the process is merely the diffusive movement of the small ion to d_0, with near certainty of neutralization on impact.

relative magnitudes, deriving from ionizing mechanisms, negative ion formation, density of ionization, gas pressure or density, and temperature. The four steps may be listed as follows:

1. The Diffusive-Approach Period.
2. The Period of Active Attraction within the Sphere of Attraction.
3. The Period of Orbital Encounter.
4. The Period of Charge Transfer.

1. *The Diffusive-Approach Period.*

The carriers of opposite sign, initially separated an average distance r_0, which is relatively great, will not exert attractive forces on each other of sufficient magnitude to alter materially their random thermal motions resulting from molecular impacts. This occurs so long as the Coulomb potential energy e^2/r of the usually univalent carriers is less than $(3/2)kT$, the random energy of thermal agitation of the surrounding molecules and ions in the absence of any imposed electrical field. Consequently, under these conditions the carriers diffuse quite at random. The random motion will continue until, by chance, two ions of opposite charge diffuse to within d_0 of each other, where d_0 is roughly defined by $e^2/d_0 = (3/2)kT$.

2. *The Sphere of Active Attraction and the Period of Active Attraction.*

The sphere of radius d_0 is defined by the condition:

$$e^2/d_0 = (3/2)\,kT$$

or

(6.72)
$$d_0 = (2/3)\,(e^2/kT)$$

about an ion of one sign. It defines a region about the ion *within which* this ion and an ion of opposite sign will have the attractive Coulomb forces of sufficient magnitude to change a random diffusive drift to a more directed movement toward each other. Actually, it is not possible to accomplish an accurate solution of equations for the Brownian movement of carriers with Coulomb forces in the neighborhood of d_0. But roughly speaking, outside of d_0 the ions will experience a retarded type of diffusive random motion which geometrically can be as much apart as together. Just inside d_0 will occur a sort of erratic drift together, which becomes more directed the larger d_0 is relative to r, the distance of separation. It is clear that this directive motion inside d_0 leads more effectively toward what will be an encounter than do motions outside d_0.

The nature of the motion during the period within d_0 will vary, depending on the nature of the mean free path λ or L of carriers relative to d_0. If $d_0 >> \lambda$ or L, then the ions will move together with a velocity $v = e^2/r^2 \, (k_+ + k_-)$. Here e^2/r^2 is the field of one ion active at the other, and k_+ and k_- are the mobilities of the opposite ions. As λ or L becomes more nearly comparable with d_0, the thermal drift velocities, $v = e^2/r^2 \, (k_+ + k_-)$, will not be approached. Greater and greater portions of the movement within d_0 will be without molecular impact. The final motion of the ions will be the execution of parts of their respective orbits about their common center of mass under the Coulomb attractive force. If λ or L is greater than d_0, practically all the motion within d_0 will be the execution of the Coulomb force orbits. These orbits constitute the third period of the process, and fix the nature of the "encounter."

Before going on to discuss the encounter, it should be noted that since the motion near d_0 cannot be accurately defined or solved, there is some difference of opinion as to the most suitable relation fixing d_0. It has been set variously as $e^2/d_0 = (3/2) \, kT$ (30), $e^2/d_0 = 3 \, kt$ (31), and $e^2/d_0 = 6 \, kT$ (36). The author inclines toward the Thomson factor $(3/2) \, kT$, as indicated elsewhere. Irrespective of its exact nature, the important item is the recognition of a sphere of active attraction of about this order of magnitude. It is the distance at which the ions actively move toward each other, thus making a charge transfer more likely. The arrival of the carriers of opposite sign to within d_0 of each other could be chosen as a criterion of the recombination "encounter." However, even though within d_0 the ions move toward each other along orbits, this does not insure that they will effect charge transfer and neutralization. Thus, the orbital encounter must be studied in detail.

3. *The Period of Orbital Encounter.*

If the motion within d_0 were that of two charges in a continuous resisting medium, then a central-impact collision between the carriers at low velocity would be assured. Thus, the chance of charge transfer or neutralization would be high. However, if L is of the order of d_0, so that the carriers have a chance of only one or two *molecular* encounters, or perhaps none within d_0 of each other, then the two carriers, after their last impact with molecules, form a dynamic system, acting on each other with the Coulomb law. In such a system they execute an orbit about their common center of mass. This orbit will be an open hyperbolic one if, at any separation r in the orbit, $\frac{1}{2}mC_1^2$ or $\frac{1}{2}MC^2$ is greater than e^2/r. If the orbit is open, the carriers will separate beyond d_0 after perihelion, and there may have been no charge transfer. This will happen fairly often if L or $\lambda \sim d_0$. If L or

λ is somewhat less than d_0, the molecular impacts will remove so much of the energy e^2/d_0 before the carriers interact freely that in the close encounter at perihelion distance, $\frac{1}{2}mC_1^2$ or $\frac{1}{2}MC^2$ will be less than e^2/r, and the orbits will be elliptical. Such elliptical orbits will continue until the next molecular encounter for either carrier, at which time the energy $\frac{1}{2}mC_1^2$ or $\frac{1}{2}MC^2$ changes and brings the ions closer together, or knocks them apart so that they execute hyperbolic motions and escape beyond d_0.

4. *The Period of Charge Transfer.*

During the period of orbital encounter, whether the electron will transfer from the negative ion to the positive ion, or the electron will be captured into an orbit of the positive ion, will depend on several factors. In a negative ion, the electron sits in a small-potential well of which the depth represents the electron affinity or binding energy $+A$ of the molecule, or atom, for the electron. Undoubtedly, as the positive ion approaches the negative ion, its Coulomb field will distort the energy-level diagram of the negative ion. It is possible that if the positive ion potential well center approaches closely enough to the negative ion during the orbital encounter, the potential barrier of the negative ion will be much lowered. In this event, the electron will spill over to the positive ion and will be captured into an orbit. Since the ionization energy of the positive ion is usually larger than heat of negative ion formation, the energy balance will go to kinetic energy of separation of the neutralized carriers.

On the other hand, if during the orbital encounter the positive ion field slightly lowers the potential barrier about the electron in the negative ion, the electron may tunnel through the barrier and be captured by the positive ion. This tunnel effect is a chance process, with an average or effective time constant τ. If the orbital encounter at a somewhat larger distance r lasts long enough so that the average periods of perihelion T are effectively greater than τ, there will again be a good chance of transfer of charge. The problem of charge transfer between oppositely charged ions can best be treated theoretically as a sort of pseudomolecule formation. During such a state there is a good chance of rearrangement of electrical charge distribution. This may result in neutralization and separation of the two original ions. The heat of neutralization is then shared between them as kinetic energy.

The problem was first attacked by D. R. Bates and H. S. W. Massey (38) in 1943, and was later presented by Bates (38). Here he shows that if the ions X^+ and Y^- approach each other very slowly along their mutual potential-energy curve, they will remain on this curve during the remainder of the encounter and will finally separate as ions. However, if they approach with a finite velocity, there is a probability P of a transition to a lower potential-energy curve of that for the two neutralized initial carriers X and Y occurring at the point of closest approach between X^+-Y^- and X-Y curves. Since this point, which lies at the high-energy knee of the potential curve for X-Y, is passed twice, the probability of separating as neutral atoms is $2P(1-P)$. The probability P can be calculated by quantal methods, as shown by C. Zener (38) and L. Landau (38).

It appears that the larger coefficients do not arise when there is close energy balance, but rather when the process is exothermic by a few e.v. The reason for this is, that when there is close energy balance, the crossing point on the zero-order approximation is located at a greater radial distance, where the interaction is extremely weak: P is almost unity, and thus $2P(1-P)$ is very small. In any case, there is a chance of charge transfer, depending on the circumstances of the encounter and the nature of the ions. Thus, for O_2^- and O_2^+ ions, the low value of A for O_2^- (less than 0.5 volt with E_i for O_2^+ of 12.5 e.v.) should facilitate neutralization, and the cross section in ionic "encounters" for effecting charge transfer may well be quite large. On the other hand, where the ions involved are Cl^- ions and Na^+ ions, the ionization potential of Cl^- being 3.84 e.v., while that for the Na^+ ion is 5.1 e.v., the cross-section transfer could well be quite small. Then only rare orbital encounters will result in charge transfer.

It can be seen from this that even if periods 1, 2, and 3 occur, leading to the fourth period of transfer of charge, on neutralization the cross sections for actual transfer may be small, and carriers will separate in such encounters without neutralization. Thus, the chance that steps 3 and 4 lead to neutralization is not necessarily unity. The chance that carriers, once within d_0, will neutralize each other is represented in a Thomson-like theory by a probability ϵ, which varies with carriers and the parameters L and d_0, i.e., with p and T.

On the basis of these considerations, it is convenient to classify the various recombination processes actually observed and analyzed (as indicated below) with their corresponding coefficients, and afterward to discuss them in detail. First, it is convenient to enumerate the observed processes under headings, shown on the following page.

I. *Electron-Ion Recombination.*

    A. The Volume Coefficient, a_e.

        1. By radiative capture, coefficient a_{er}.

        2. By dissociative capture, coefficient a_{ed}.

        3. By dielectronic capture, coefficient a_{ee}.

    B. Possibly a preferential radiative process with a coefficient a_{ep}.

    C. Wall recombination, consisting of ambipolar diffusion to the walls and recombination on the walls resulting from a relative motion of the ions in two dimensions on the wall surface. Hypothetical coefficient a_w.

II. *Ion-Ion Recombination.*

    A. Preferential recombination at very high pressures in electron-attaching gases. The theory was initially that of P. Langevin (25). It has a coefficient a_L.

    B. Columnar recombination at higher and atmospheric pressures in electron-attaching gases, using heavy-particle ionization which is densely located along narrow channels. The theory was developed by G. Jaffé (2). It has a coefficient a_c which declines greatly with time.

    C. Initial recombination, an initial phase in time preceding what was supposedly volume recombination (3). It is observed in electron-attaching gases at higher (and about atmospheric) pressures, under ionization by fast electrons. There, randomly spaced, well-separated ion pairs are created, with positive and negative ions of the pair lying in close proximity to each other. This distribution with lapse of time after the ionizing act, eventually goes over to a true volume recombination. It has a coefficient a_i which declines with time.

    D. Volume recombination, of which there are at least three mechanisms in different pressure ranges in electron-attaching gases, namely:

        1. High-pressure range, usually above 2 atmospheres, called the "Langevin-Harper process." The theory was evolved by W. R. Harper (31), but the nature of the equation is such that except for a numerical coefficient it can be expressed as the Langevin form. This has a coefficient a_H.

        2. The "Thomson process," proposed by J. J. Thomson (30) in 1924, and the only theory that has all the four periods or steps fully developed. It applies to electron-attaching gases at atmospheric pressure and below. It has a coefficient a_T.

        3. A low-pressure coefficient. This process occurs in electron-attaching gases at truly low pressures, where Thomson's process no longer applies. The coefficient a_σ depends primarily on the cross section for neutralization in a single encounter, and the velocity of the random thermal motion (37).

Following is a detailed discussion of the processes that have been outlined above.

I. *Electron-Ion Recombination.*
I(A). The Volume Coefficient, a_e.

In all gases in which electrons *do not* attach to molecules or atoms to form negative ions, but instead remain free, the recombination process must involve the capture of the free electron by the positive ion. The capture process by the ion may be one of three mechanisms: (1) A radiative mechanism, coefficient a_{er}. (2) A dissociative mechanism (7), coefficient a_{ed}. (3) A dielectronic capture (38) process, coefficient a_{ee}. In these the only differentiating feature is the mechanism of neutralization. As the complicated wave-mechanical theory of the radiative capture, and the as yet only partially developed theory for dissociative capture are not of vital import to what follows, the process will be discussed at this point in terms of only one coefficient; a_e, electron recombination.

The free electrons recombining usually will have been liberated from the parent atoms with some residual energy. This energy is well above the thermal energy of the ambient molecules or atoms. Owing to its small mass and high initial energy, the electron will rapidly diffuse away from the parent atom—by then a positive ion. Thus, the electron escapes to well beyond d_0 from the parent positive ion by the time the electron has collided enough times to have had its energy reduced to thermal values. Even in cases of ionization by a particles in pure, inert gases, the columnar effect will be somewhat reduced by the high velocities of diffusion.

Call r_0 the resulting average distance between ions and electrons. The quantity r_0 can be set equal to $r_0 = \sqrt[3]{1/n_0}$, where n_0 is the initial ion or electron density. If r_0, the average distance between ions and thus between electrons, is much greater than d_0, the first step in the electron-ion recombination will be one of diffusive approach of quite randomly distributed electrons and positive ions. However, the velocity of diffusion of the electrons will be relatively high compared to that of the positive ions. In most cases it will be of the order of a hundred times as fast. Thus, the diffusive phase of the process will be much reduced in time relative to such actions for ions. Once inside the sphere of active attraction, even at relatively high pressures where d_0 is ten or more times the free path λ, the electron will experience largely orbital encounters of the hyperbolic-orbit type about the positive ion. This follows from the small energy losses of electrons on molecular or atomic collision. In these encounters, perihelion distance may be larger than the effective cross section for radiative or dissociative capture.

Thus, in general, the electrons do not have much chance of having their energy e^2/d_0, or excess thermal energy, sufficiently reduced by collisions inside d_0 to prevent escape in hyperbolic orbits. Accordingly, while the high velocity of diffusive motion brings the ions into some "encounter" at a higher rate than is the case for ions, the chance of separation without neutralization is much greater, and the chance of neutralization is much lower.

It is clear that the period of diffusive motion, while less than that for ions, will be of importance in fixing a_e, especially where r_0, the average charge separation, is large compared to d_0. If the cross section for capture of the electron, $Q_c = \pi\sigma_c^2$, is calculated, assuming only a diffusive approach and including the attractive phase, the coefficient of recombination a_e in Q_c, the value of a_e can readily be derived from Q_c. The cross section for capture of the electron by an ion will, by diffusive electron motion, sweep out a volume $\pi\sigma_c^2 \bar{c}_1 dt$ in a time dt. Here $\bar{c}_1$ is the average random velocity of agitation of the electron. There are n such electrons per cm^3, and in the $\pi n\sigma_c^2 \bar{c}_1 dt$ cm^3 of volume swept out in dt by the n electrons, there will be $\pi n^2 \sigma_c^2 \bar{c}_1 dt$ encounters with positive ions. The electron loss by recombination with n positive ions per cm^3 in dt then becomes $dn = \pi\sigma_c^2 \bar{c}_1 n^2 dt = a_e n^2 dt$. Hence,

$$(6.73) \qquad a_e = \pi\sigma_c^2 \bar{c}_1 = Q_c \bar{c}_1 \, .$$

This is the way in which the theoretical physicists have evaluated a_{er} after attempting to evaluate σ_1.

It is also possible to use the radius of the sphere of active attraction of radius d_0, following Thomson's method, and then to compute a value of the capture probability ϵ. The calculation of ϵ on the basis of the combined steps 2, 3, and 4 might be awkward for say, radiative electron capture, as it varies with molecular or atomic species, initial energy of electrons, and the relative value of λ and d_0. This would make the Thomson approach too cumbersome in the study of electron recombination. If a value of ϵ can be conveniently calculated for a_{er} or a_{ed}, reasoning analogous to that given above leads to the expression:

$$dn = -\pi d_0^2 \bar{c}_1 \, \epsilon n^2 dt = -a_e n^2 dt \, ,$$

so that a_e is evaluated as

$$(6.74) \qquad a_e = \pi d_0^2 \bar{c}_1 \, \epsilon \, .$$

If this is not convenient, the relation between the Thomson four-step process and the cross-sectional approach allows ϵ to be computed from

(6.75)
$$\pi d_0^2 \epsilon = Q_c = \pi \sigma_c^2 .$$

I(B). Preferential Electron Recombination, α_{ep}.

It might be expected that at very high pressures, electrons removed from atoms would lose their energy within a distance d_0, the radius of the sphere of active attraction of the parent atom or molecule. In this event, with $\bar{r}_0$ on the average less than d_0, and the electron free path λ much less than d_0, it might be expected that the electron would omit the diffusive approach. Acting then under the influence of the force field of the parent positive ion, it would literally recombine with it. Recombination with $d_0 >> \bar{r}_0 >> L_0$ is called *preferential recombination*. Such ionization and recombination could be detected only by the way in which currents to properly designed electrodes increased as applied sweep fields increased. In some early cosmic-ray studies in chambers, with tens of atmospheres of inert gas, the ion currents collected as a function of sweep fields pointed to such a mechanism. This behavior was later shown to be caused by improperly designed sweep fields (39).

If a gas which does not attach electrons is sufficiently pure at high pressures, the electrons will usually escape from the spheres of active attraction before they lose their energy, and can be "captured." In such gases $\bar{r}_0$ is greater than d_0. Thus, preferential electron-ion recombination cannot occur. N. E. Bradbury (39) discusses preferential recombination from a more general theoretical viewpoint. He arrives at the same conclusion—that preferential electron-ion recombination is not likely to be encountered experimentally. In other cases at high pressures, electrons may be captured by a molecule inside d_0, so that $\bar{r}_0 < d_0$. In this case there will result *preferential ion-ion recombination*, which is actually the process that was originally observed in cosmic-ray studies. The reason is that at high pressure, inert gases in metal containers cannot be pure enough to prevent this attachment.

In the author's earlier book, *Fundamental Processes of Electrical Discharge in Gases*, a peculiar aspect of the ionization process, predicted wave-mechanically by H. Bartels (40), was described under this heading. It now appears that the theory of Bartels was based on a misinterpretation of some work of Bethe, and that the process proposed by him is incorrect. Thus, at this time, preferential electron recombination is a possible but apparently nonexistent process.

I(C). Wall Recombination, q_w.

This phenomenon, as the name implies, has to do with the role of the walls in facilitating recombination. In essence, when the pressures become low in the orders of mm or less, and the density of ionization in the plasma becomes high, the electron diffusion becomes of importance. Under these conditions, especially in the presence of electrical fields maintaining elevated electron energies, the electrons are able to leave the plasma by diffusion to the walls. Arrived there, they are attached to the wall and build up a negative potential; the *wall potential* relative to the plasma. A migration of positive ions to the negative walls sets in, sustained by the wall potential, until the rate of flow of electrons and ions is equal. This leaves a neutral plasma and removes ions and electrons. The characteristics of this process, which is termed *ambipolar diffusion*, can be found in any treatise dealing with diffusion of ions and electrons in plasmas. The subject is also treated in chapter II.

The process is facilitated by the circumstance that the electrons and positive ions, on arrival at the wall, eventually neutralize each other. Neutralization occurs through a *recombination process* of a rather interesting sort. Diffusion of electrons and ions on the wall lies essentially in a plane instead of in three-dimensional space. The limitation of the degrees of random motion speeds up the diffusive phase of the recombination process. However, nothing is known concerning the speed of diffusion along surfaces, but it can be great on glass surfaces. Again, when in such motion ion and electron "encounter" each other within the attractive-force region, the chance of capture and recombination ϵ is near unity. This follows, since the molecules or atoms of the surface are always present as third bodies to take up the liberated energy of neutralization. Thus, there is essentially a *wall recombination process* that is apparently rapid enough to cause no effect on the ambipolar diffusion. The time rate of charge loss is thus set by the ambipolar diffusion to the walls. In consequence, properly speaking, wall recombination does not have a calculable coefficient q_w, though there is a $dn/dt = - a_s n_s^2$ on the *wall surface*, causing loss. The a_s may be so large that n_s, the surface concentration, is less than the 2/3 power of the volume concentration in the gas.

Since the loss from the volume of the gas by ambipolar diffusion is undoubtedly slower than the surface-recombination rate, *the disappearance of the ions from the gas will follow the exponential law of decay characteristic of ambipolar diffusion*, and an a_w cannot be properly evaluated from the exponential decay curve.

II. *Ion-Ion Recombination.*

II(A). Preferential Ion-Ion Recombination at Very High Pressures: The Langevin Law, a_L.

In a very early study of ion recombination, P. Langevin (25) derived an expression for the coefficient of ion-ion recombination on the assumptions given below. He considered the gas to be sufficiently dense to present to *the ions immersed in it* the aspect of a continuous resisting medium. Under such conditions, the energy of thermal impacts of molecules of comparable mass on the ions would not influence their motion, contrary to the assumption made heretofore. On the other hand, each ion of one sign and charge e attracts the nearest oppositely charged ion with a force Xe. The field X is given by the field e/r^2 of the ion of one sign on an oppositely charged ion of charge e, r cm distant. In view of this interaction, each positive ion will at all times move toward the negative ion nearest to it with a uniform relative drift velocity $v = X\ (k_+ + k_-)$. Now if all positive ions are assumed to be fixed, and all negative ions are assumed to be moving toward them with the relative drift velocity $v = X\ (k_+ + k_-)$, it is possible to calculate the rate of loss of ions by recombination.

It must be noted that in such a resistive medium, ions encounter each other, so that neutralization at impact is certain with $\epsilon = 1$. Assume that about each positive ion is drawn an arbitrary sphere of radius S, such that negative ions entering it would be considered effectively and ultimately to reach the positive ion and to be neutralized. At the surface of S the relative velocity of the negative ions is $v = X\ (k_+ + k_-) = (e/S^2)\ (k_+ + k_-)$. This is the speed with which the n negative ions per cm^3 are moving into the positive ions. Thus, nv gives the number of negative ions entering a positive ion sphere per cm^2 per sec. The number of positive ions is n per cm^3. Thus, in 1 cm^3 of gas, the number of negative ions dn flowing into the positive spheres of surface $4\pi S^2$ in a cm^3 of gas in time dt is $4\pi S^2 v dt$. This at once yields the rate of disappearance of ions by recombination as

$$dn/dt = -\ 4\pi S^2 (e/S^2)\ (k_+ + k_-)\ n^2 = -\ 4\pi (k_+ + k_-) e n^2.$$

Langevin's value of a defined as a_L is $dn/dt = -a_L n^2$, so that it is possible to write:

(6.76)
$$a_L = 4\pi e(k_+ + k_-).$$

This theory was apparently accepted without question from 1905 to 1924, as representing the *correct theoretical value for all ion-ion recombination*. Langevin himself showed that the calculated value of a_L was higher by a considerable factor than the value experimentally observed. In fact, his method of measurement of a was designed to evaluate $4\pi e \ (k_+ + k_-)$ more or less directly. To account for the observed values which were less than $4\pi e \ (k_+ + k_-)$, he included a fractional multiplier ϵ in equation 6.76. This quantity ϵ expressed the chance that a given encounter of positive and negative ions will result in neutralization. He and others attempted to calculate ϵ theoretically (33), as did the author and A. F. Joffé in 1927. None of these calculations were properly justified, as they were based on unrealistic assumptions. In fact, some studies went so far as to calculate on theories involving postulates antithetical to the basic picture of Langevin (33). Data at the time were so inaccurate and contradictory that no one noted that the observed decline of a with pressure below 760 mm was contrary to Langevin's theory.

In the dense ionization achieved at, say, 100 atmospheres of gas pressure in air or O_2, $\overline{r_0}$ is less than d_0; for at such pressures, electrons attach to O_2 to give negative ions well within d_0 cm of the positive ion. Under these conditions the dominating force of attraction assumed by Langevin (viz., Xe) is active. Furthermore, at such gas densities the intermolecular force fields and distances are such that the mean free path is very much less than d_0. Ions are struck by many molecules from opposite directions at once, and the gas behaves to the ion virtually as a continuous, viscous medium. The assumptions deduced by Langevin are thus valid, and it is to be expected that the law holds as deduced above.

It is to be noted that the Langevin theory applies strictly so long as there is *no diffusive approach*; i.e., so long as both partners lie inside of d_0. At very high pressures, the considerable loss of the Coulomb energy in molecular encounters within d_0 leads to certain charge transfer at the first encounter. This renders $\epsilon = 1$, and eliminates the fourth step in the process as a time-consuming factor.

It is difficult to understand how Langevin, one of the leading contemporary masters of kinetic-theory analysis, should have gone astray to the extent of applying the theory of equation 6.76 to lower pressures, such as atmospheric. The theory was enunciated very early in Langevin's career as a beginning experimental physicist. The author was assured many years later by Langevin's colleagues, that Langevin had long before recognized his early error, but had never taken the opportunity to correct it in print. Assuming that others also had recognized the mistake, he failed to call attention to it. Had he known that the later workers had thoughtlessly accepted the theory, and guessed the confusion which it caused from 1914 to 1929, it is probable that he would have corrected it.

Preferential ion-ion recombination was independently discovered and named by early workers in cosmic rays (39). When high-pressure chambers were used to study cosmic rays, the recombination of this type was observed through the very high fields needed to draw out the ions and obtain "saturation" currents. This is probably more truly a *recombination* than any other process, since the original electron, as an ion, literally recombines with its parent atom. The existence of this process is manifested only through the fact that fields adequate to cause the ion pairs to separate from within d_0 are very high. Thus, in high, externally imposed fields X, such that with $X \sim e/r^2$ with r less than d_0, the ions in the spherical zone of thickness d_0-r distant from the other partner, that have not recombined, will be swept out to electrodes and measured as survivors.

No proper theory for this mechanism had been evolved until 1940. In that year, N. E. Bradbury (39) set up the outline of a general theory of preferential recombination in an external field X. The theory requires a suitable set of assumptions concerning electron attachment for the solution of a given problem. It has not been worked out in detail, nor was it compared with experiment.

As stated under electron recombination, even in *inert* nonelectron-attaching gases as used at such pressures, the role of preferential ion-ion recombination may be rather great. This follows from the impossibility of adequate purity control with thick metal walls and high pressures, which introduce negative ion forming impurities. It might be added that in cosmic-ray ionization, with the low density of ionization along the path, separate ion *pairs* are at values of r_0 which are very great. In contrast, however, the individual positive and negative ion pairs are separated by much less than d_0. Such ionization is highly anisotropic, and leads to preferential recombination. In fact, at very high pressures there is practically no real volume ion-ion recombination, all recombination being preferential.

II(B). Columnar Recombination, a_c.

In the early studies on the range and ionization by a particles in gases, W. H. Bragg and R. D. Kleeman (2) noted in 1906 that it was much more difficult to obtain what they believed were *saturation* currents with alpha-particle ionization than with other ionizing agencies. It was further noted that achievement of saturation was most difficult when the particle paths were parallel to a uniform electrical field rather than normal to it. Their explanation at that time was in terms of what today is called "preferential recombination." In 1910,

M. Moulin (2) showed that the phenomenon was not preferential recombination, but was to be ascribed to the nonuniform distribution of ions along the α-ray paths.

In 1913, G. Jaffé (2), who had studied conduction currents produced by ionization in liquids, was led to the same conclusion as that of Moulin. He then developed the first part of his famous theory of columnar ionization and recombination. The alpha particle ionizes intensively at the rate of 1,000 ions per mm of path length. The ionized molecules created lie very close to the normally straight-line trajectory of the particle. The initial ionization is probably most intense within a few Å about the nuclear path, and declines radially outward. It is produced by the Coulomb force action of the energetic alpha particle on outer electrons of neighboring atoms. In consequence of the initial high energy (some tens of volts) of the ionized electrons, the electrons will probably diffuse outward. Thus, at the end of 10^{-3} or more of a second, most of the electrons will have attached to give negative ions with O_2 molecules or other impurities within a cylindrical volume, at most some 10^{-2} cm in diameter, about the initial path. In 6 cm of track, an alpha particle will give 6×10^4 ion pairs. As these will be in 1.8×10^{-5} cm^3 of volume, the average ion density, even after 10^{-3} second, will exceed some 3.3×10^9 ions/cm^3. Actually, the density is not uniform along the radius, and the electrons will not have diffused freely. Owing to the high charge densities, ambipolar diffusion will have dragged the positive ions along. For this reason, the estimated density is probably low.

Thus, it was not far amiss for Jaffé to estimate that at the beginning of times open to experimental study (in excess of 10^{-4} second), the positive and negative ions are symmetrically distributed radially about the track axis, with density declining radially outward, following a Gaussian error curve. Even before the time at which a practical measurement can begin, the positive and negative ions will have been disappearing by recombination. Hence, starting from a convenient arbitrary zero of time with the Gaussian distribution, the ions will be diffusing. This will change their density in time, while simultaneously the ions will be disappearing by recombination. For simplicity it must be assumed that recombination will not change the form of the Gaussian distribution curve. Solution of the differential equation gives an expression for the concentration of the ions as a function of distance r from the axis and time t as

$$(6.77) \qquad n = \frac{N_0}{1 + \dfrac{a N_0}{8 \pi D} \log_e \left(\dfrac{4Dt + b^2}{b^2} \right)} \frac{\epsilon^{-\frac{r^2}{(4Dt + b^2)}}}{\pi(4Dt + b^2)}.$$

Here D is the coefficient of diffusion of the ions, and b is a constant related to the *average* displacement r_0 of the Gaussian curve from the column axis given by $r_0 = b\sqrt{\pi}/4$. It is assumed that at $t = 0$,

$$n = (N_0/\pi b^2)\, \epsilon^{-r^2/b^2},$$

r being the distance from the axis column.

If t is very large, the column can approach to nearly a random distribution. Before this occurs, the separate alpha-particle tracks will have expanded radially in time so that they touch and merge. The ions then are probably nearly uniformly distributed in the volume. The recombination from then on follows the relations for normal volume recombination. Both Moulin and Jaffé have shown how the number of ions that have escaped from the columns and columnar recombination can be determined. For liquids, the estimates are quite accurate, even though only 10^{-3} of the ions escape. Each column there is considered to be surrounded by a coaxial cylindrical surface of radius R which is equal to the separation of the two columns. Every ion passing R can be said to have escaped. The escape fraction is given by

$$(6.78) \qquad \frac{N_1}{N_0} = -\int_{\xi_0}^{0} \frac{\epsilon^{-\xi}\, d\xi}{1 + \dfrac{aN_0}{8\pi D} \log \dfrac{\xi_0}{\xi}}.$$

Here, $\xi_0 = R^2/b^2$, and $\xi = R^2/(4Dt + b^2)$. The quantity R^2/b^2 is a ratio that is not particularly critical in its effect on N_1/N_0. Although it does vary with the density of the columns, the densities in the measurable range are usually so nearly of the same order of magnitude that they can be taken as constant. Jaffé shows that with $\xi = 550$, as estimated from his liquid studies and Moulin's studies in gases, values of N_1/N_0 are obtained in satisfactory agreement with theory.

Figure 6.8 gives a good, graphic description of what is occurring. The upper curve N shows the decay of ionization with time, while the curves with Roman numerals below show the densities of ions in the Gaussian curve at the corresponding time periods on the upper curve.

Of more practical interest are the currents that can be derived from alpha-particle ionization in an electrical field. The angle of the alpha-ray trajectories with the field is obviously of importance here. The two extreme cases are for columns perpendicular and parallel to the field. For the perpendicular field the ratio of the escaping ions N_∞ to those initially generated, N_0, (N_∞/N_0), in an electrical field of strength X is given on the following page by

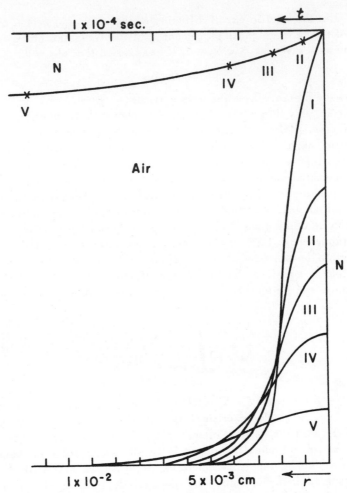

Fig. 6.8. Jaffé's calculated curves for density N of ions in air at various distances r from the axis of an alpha-particle track. The Roman numerals are the distributions at times indicated on the concentration time curve. The time scale, in units of 10^{-4} sec, is at the top; the distance scale in 10^{-2} cm is at the bottom.

(6.79)
$$\left(\frac{N_\infty}{N_0}\right)_X = \frac{1}{1 + \dfrac{aN_0}{8\pi D}\sqrt{\dfrac{\pi}{z}}\,S(z)} \, ,$$

where $z = b^2k^2X^2/2D^2$. The ion mobility is k, and the function $S(z)$ is given by the integral:

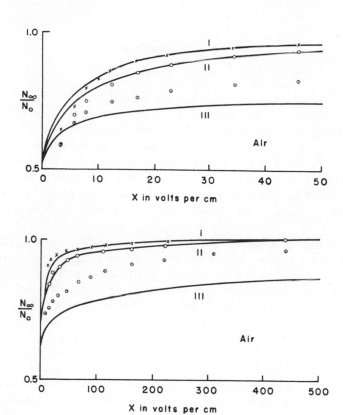

Fig. 6.9. Jaffé's theory of the saturation number of ions withdrawn relative to the initial number of ions for an electrical field X in volts/cm in air at 760 mm, compared to the observed data of Moulin as points. Curves I, II, and III apply to alpha-ray tracks roughly at 90°, 45°, and parallel to the extracting field X.

(6.80)
$$S(z) = \frac{1}{\sqrt{\pi}} \int_0^\infty \frac{\epsilon^{-S}\,dS}{\sqrt{S\left(1 + \dfrac{S}{z}\right)}} \,.$$

If the column makes an angle ϕ with the field, the equations are

(6.81)
$$F(X) = \frac{1}{1 + \dfrac{aN_0}{8\pi D}\sqrt{\dfrac{\pi}{z'}}\,S(z')}$$

and

(6.82)
$$z' = \frac{b^2 k^2 X^2 \sin^2 \phi}{2D^2}.$$

This applies where X and ϕ are not too small.

An indication of the success of this theory is seen in figure 6.9. Here, Moulin's experimental points, or N_∞/N_0 plotted against the field X, with $\phi = 90°$, $45°$, and $0°$, are compared with theory, as shown by curves I, II, III. The deviations are most for the parallel case, since the practical achievement of parallel alpha-ray tracks is virtually impossible. The relations developed disregard the normal recombination during the time of measurement, which even at $X = 1$ volt/cm is 4%.

The theory was not developed further until 1928, when J. Schemel (2) carried on studies with alpha particles in which he measured the coefficient of recombination directly as a function of time. He used the three basic techniques; rate of growth, rate of decay, and equilibrium measurements in his study. This enabled Jaffé (2) to analyze the effect of the diffusive changes in concentration with time on the *apparent coefficient of recombination* revealed by direct measurement. The question is of importance, since it sets a pattern for what will be observed in any set of circumstances in which initial inhomogeneity of charge distribution produces conditions where changes of density caused by diffusion affect measurements of recombination.

In 1928, Jaffé considered the effect of high pressures on the phenomenon, using air, CO_2, H_2, and O_2 from 1 to 6 atmospheres, with potentials of 600 volts and fields nearly parallel to the alpha-particle paths. Schemel's gases were not pure, therefore the electron attachment occurred in H_2 as well as in CO_2, O_2, and air. The experimental points of i_∞/i_0 plotted against potential in volts gave good agreement, as seen in figure 6.10.

In his concluding article, Jaffé derived a more exact relation for the columnar ionization by alpha particles in the absence of a field. Calculations were carried out for two possible orientations of the columns to compare with Schemel's experimental work. Ratios were computed of the observed (or apparent) value a' of the coefficient, relative to the true coefficient a, as a function of time, the true coefficient being invariant with time. A satisfactory qualitative agreement was obtained with Schemel's observed a'/a as a function of time, as shown in figure 6.11 for air. The upper set of curves is from Jaffé's calculations for different flash or ionizing times used by Schemel. The lower set of curves shows those actually observed for

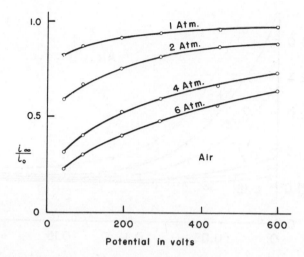

Fig. 6.10. Theoretical calculation of "saturation"-collected ion currents relative to total ions as a function of potential at pressures from 1 to 6 atmospheres in air, as given by Jaffé (full curves), compared to experimental points observed by Schemel.

the same times by Schemel. Some of the needed constants used in Jaffé's calculations had to be taken from Schemel's curves.

It is to be noted that the computed values, in general, decline faster than do those observed. The necessity for relatively long flash times and the lack of adequate control over the variables make more accurate verification impossible. However, agreement is good enough to make it safe to conclude that the mechanism of the process giving an experimental α' varying with time is basically understood, and to apply analogous reasoning to the explanation of other anisotropies affecting recombination leading to a time-varying α'.

II(C). Initial Recombination, α_i.

This phenomenon was probably first noted by G. Rümelin (17) with gamma-ray ionization, for his method was that most capable of revealing it. It showed itself by an initial rapid decline in the value of α' as a function of time, as measured over short intervals of time at varied average times after ionization. He ascribed the decline to electron-ion recombination. It was rediscovered in X-ray ionization by S. G. Plimpton (3), who correctly interpreted its basic character. He assumed that the negative and positive ions are initially distributed in a nonrandom and nonisotropic fashion relative to each other. Thus, if by electron attachment the negative ions are distributed

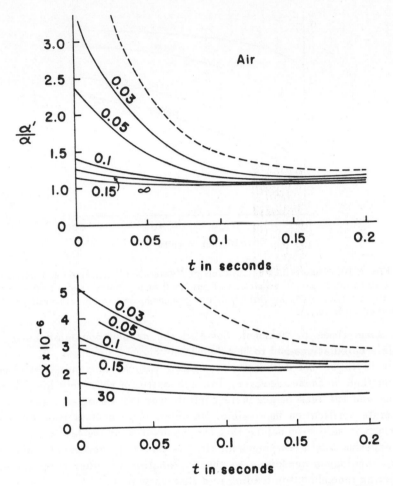

Fig. 6.11. Values of the ratio of the apparent coefficient of recombination α' in columnar recombination relative to the true coefficient α, as computed by Jaffé for air (in upper set of curves) as a function of the time over which recombination was measured. Each curve corresponds to the flash time for alpha-particle ionization. The shorter the flash time, the more rapid and the greater the change in α'/α with time. This clearly indicates the varying coefficient produced when density of carriers varies with time by diffusion as well as recombination. The lower set of curves shows those actually observed for α', as reported by Schemel for air, with the conditions assumed by Jaffé in calculation, so far as these could be equated.

nearer their positive partners in pairs, being separated an average distance r_i, with $r_0 > r_i > d_0$ and $d_0 > L$, recombination will be more rapid corresponding to an effective concentration n' related to r_i, instead of n related to r_0. As time goes on, however, the ions, being outside of d_0 (Plimpton did not know of d_0 at that time), will diffuse to more random distributions, with n' approaching n. Thus, the rate of recombination will appear to decrease to a constant value as t increases and true volume ion-ion recombination occurs. The manner in which the change proceeds will be indicated later. It need merely be noted that Plimpton accepted the initial nonuniformity. He saw that this would decrease with time, and that the a calculated from the method of observation would decline to a steady value when random distribution was achieved by recombination and diffusion. What he did not see was that the diffusion of ions to random distribution was in direct contradiction to the generally accepted theory of Langevin's a.

When Marshall (3), in the author's laboratory, independently confirmed the observations of Plimpton and Rümelin in 1928, the recombination theory of J. J. Thomson (30) was on hand to guide thinking. Thus, the author was quickly able to rule out the electron recombination of Rümelin. He was led to conclude that the decline of a was caused by an *initial nonuniform ion distribution* in pairs, which became more uniform by *diffusion* in time. He further recognized that this was in conformity to Thomson's theory, and that the theory of Langevin was erroneous. In collaboration with A. Sommerfeld (3) he was then able to find the error in Langevin's reasoning as applied to recombination at atmospheric pressure and below in air, and to develop more fully the theory of initial recombination.

Until the advent of the microwave techniques it was impossible, especially at lower densities of ionization, to measure ion densities directly. It is still difficult to measure the densities directly if the carriers are negative and positive ions, and not free electrons and ions. Thus measured usually are the charges q_1 and q_2 collected from a defined volume V at times t_1 and t_2.[11] From now on, q_1 and q_2 will represent *the number of ions*. If the distribution is isotropic, then the concentrations N_1 and N_2 are respectively $N_1 = q_1/V$ and $N_2 = q_2/V$, leading to a recombination coefficient a_{vt} according to equation 6.3b, which reads:

$$(6.83) \qquad a_{vt} = \frac{V}{t_2 - t_1} \left(\frac{1}{q_2} - \frac{1}{q_1} \right).$$

---

[11]In the earlier sections of this chapter, the quantity of charge designated by q, given by $q = ne$, with n the number of ions and e the charge on a univalent ion, could be conveniently used. In that which follows, emphasis will be on the *number* of charges; and to avoid confusion from now on, q will represent *the number of ions*.

On the other hand, if the arrangement of charges is not isotropic, then the charges collected are really in volumes V_1' and V_2', which are less than V. Since the carriers diffuse during the interval $t_2 - t_1$, then in general V_2' will be larger than V_1'. That is, the concentration will have decreased as a function of time owing to diffusion. The true value of the coefficient a_{vt} will then be given by

$$(6.84) \qquad a_{vt} = \frac{1}{t_2 - t_1} \left(\frac{V_2'}{q_2} - \frac{V_1'}{q_1} \right).$$

In the event that $t_2 - t_1$ is so small that $V_2' = V_1' = V'$, for practical purposes the more convenient expression for a_{vt} will be

$$(6.85) \qquad a_{vt} = \frac{V'}{t_2 - t_1} \left(\frac{1}{q_2} - \frac{1}{q_1} \right).$$

The existence of V_2', V_1', and V' is concealed from the observer. In any case, their values are not known, so that in computing the coefficient from observation he will obtain an apparent coefficient, given a_{it}, by

$$(6.86) \qquad a_{it} = \frac{V}{t_2 - t_1} \left(\frac{1}{q_2} - \frac{1}{q_1} \right).$$

Thus, the ratio of the apparent coefficient a_{it} computed from observation and the true coefficient a_{vt} will, from equations 6.85 and 6.86, be related by the expression:

$$(6.87) \qquad a_{vt} = \frac{V'}{V} a_{it} .$$

Now V' is effectively less than V, and V' increases by diffusion from its initial value V_0' asymptotically toward a random isotropic value V. Hence, the observed value a_{it} will decrease either hyperbolically or exponentially from a high value of a_{it} to the true value a_{vt}. This sort of decline is just what was observed by Luhr (26), and by Plimpton, Marshall, Gardner, and Sayers (3), in air and O_2.

The exact evaluation of the decline is difficult. An approximate solution was developed by the author (41), and is presented in full elsewhere. A brief outline will be given in what follows. It can be assumed that as a result of electron attachment in air or O_2, the negative ions at about atmospheric pressure, or below, are well outside of d_0. It can likewise be assumed that the distribution of negative ions in distance x from their parent positive ion is given by $q = q_0 \epsilon^{-x/S}$. Here S is the average value of the distance of separation on electron attachment after, say, $10^{-5} - 10^{-4}$ sec. When t is set equal

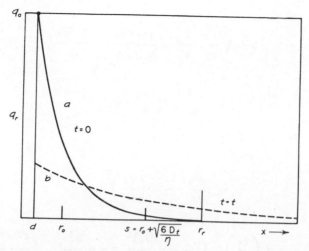

Fig. 6.12. Here is illustrated the value of the average displacement S of the opposite ions with time, owing to diffusion starting from an average separation d.

to 0, as in a measurement, S will be given the value S_0. The distribution about S follows from the locus of electron attachment; viz., the attachment coefficient h, the 'gas pressure, the mean free path L, and the average energy of electron escape and of the gas molecules.

From cloud-track pictures, S may initially be set at 10^{-4} to 10^{-3} cm. It is less than r_r, the average distance between ions in a random distribution, which is $r_r = \sqrt[3]{V/q_0}$. Owing to diffusion in the absence of external fields, S increases with time t, following a relation $S = r_0 + \sqrt{6Dt/\eta}$, which is illustrated in figure 6.12. The quantity η is a diminishing factor caused by Coulomb forces as $S = d_0$. Now those ions in the tail of the distribution law beyond $x = r_r$ at any time will be ions that have random distribution and a normal recombination rate. The number q_r between $x = r_r$ and $x = \infty$ are given by the integral

(6.88)
$$q_r = q_0 \int_{r_r}^{\infty} \frac{1}{S} \epsilon^{-x/S}\, dx.$$

For these ions,

(6.89)
$$\left(\frac{dn}{dt}\right)_n = - \alpha(q_r/V)^2.$$

Between $x = d_0$ and $x = r_r$, the recombination is at a rate:

(6.90)
$$dn_x/dt = \alpha(q_x/V_x')^2.$$

Since

$$r_r = \sqrt[3]{\frac{V}{q_0}}, \quad \frac{V_x'}{V} = \frac{4\pi x^2 dx}{4/3\,\pi r_r^3} = \frac{3x^2 dx}{r_r^3},$$

and

$$q_x = \frac{q_0}{S}\,\epsilon^{-x/S}.$$

Placing

(6.91)
$$\frac{dn_x}{dt} = -a\left(\frac{q_x}{V_x'}\right)^2,$$

$$\frac{dq_x}{dt} = -a\left(\frac{q_x}{V_x'}\right)^2 V_x' = -a\frac{(q_x)^2}{V_x'} = -a\frac{q_0^2 r_r^3}{3S^2 V}\frac{\epsilon^{-2x/S}}{x^2}dx,$$

and combining the recombination events between d_0 and r_r and between r_r and infinity, the complete expression for loss by recombination becomes

$$\frac{dn}{dt} = \frac{1}{V}\frac{dq}{dt} = -\frac{aq_0^2}{V^2}\left[\int_d^{r_r}\frac{r_r^3\,\epsilon^{-2x/S}}{3S^2 x^2}dx + \left\{\int_{r_r}^{\infty}\frac{\epsilon^{-x/S}}{S}dx\right\}^2\right]$$

(6.92)

$$= -an^2\left[\frac{r_r^3}{3S^2}\left\{\int_d^{r_r}\frac{\epsilon^{-2x/S}}{x^2}dx\right\} + \epsilon^{-2r_r/S}\right].$$

Integrating and assigning values consistent with the studies of Gardner, viz., $n = 10^6$ ions/cm^3, $r_r = 10^{-2}$ cm, $a = 2 \times 10^{-6}$, $d = 4 \times 10^{-6}$, $D = 4 \times 10^{-2}$, $\eta = 1$, $r_0 = 2 \times 10^{-5}$ cm, $t > 10^{-3}$ sec (with r_0 of no importance), the value of S is found to be between 1.58×10^{-2} and 5×10^{-1} in times from 10^{-3} to 1 second. This permits the use of only a portion of the expansions yielded by the integral above. It determines the value of dn/dt as

(6.93)
$$\frac{dn}{dt} \simeq -a_{vt}\,n^2\left[\frac{r_r^3\,\epsilon^{-2d/S}}{3S^2 d} + \epsilon^{-2r_r/S}\right].$$

Applied to pure O_2, the definition of a_{it} given above leads to

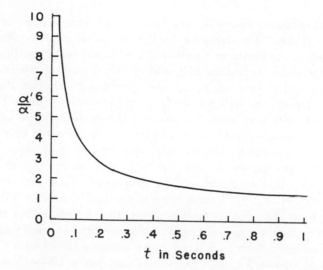

Fig. 6.13. Ratios of the fictitious recombination from anisotropy (a') to the true one (a) as a function of time in O_2, computed from Loeb's equation. This assumes infinitesimally short flash times for ionization.

$$(6.94) \qquad -\frac{1}{n^2}\frac{dn}{dt} = a_{it} = a_{vt}\left[\frac{r_r^3\, \epsilon^{-\frac{2d}{\sqrt{0.24t}}}}{0.72\, td} + \epsilon^{-\frac{2r_r}{\sqrt{0.24t}}}\right].$$

This leads to the simple relation:

$$(6.95) \qquad \frac{a_{it}}{a_{vt}} = \frac{0.347}{t}\,\epsilon^{-\frac{1.63 \times 10^{-5}}{\sqrt{t}}} + \epsilon^{-\frac{0.041}{\sqrt{t}}}.$$

The character of the curve, as derived from this approximate solution for O_2, is shown in figure 6.13. The curves for O_2 observed by Gardner at low pressures in the same time intervals are shown in figure 6.5 (*supra*). The general nature of observed and computed curves is similar. However, there can never be close agreement, because of the rather crude approximations in evaluating concentrations for the anisotropic distribution. More effective in preventing agreement is the circumstance that the curves cannot be measured in such a way as to compare with the assumptions. Thus, the measurements of a in order to give sufficient ions for detectable changes require finite flash times preceding $t = 0$. They must be of the same order of magnitude as $t_2 - t_1$, or even more. Thus, at $t = 0$ the ions are not in the distribution $q = q_0\, \epsilon^{-xr_0}$, but are already in a situation where the portion of random carriers is very large as a result of diffusion during the flash times. This accounts for the series of curves instead of a single curve, as shown by Gardner (3), who had to adjust flash times to correspond to the values of t_1 and t_2. The ratios of the experimentally observed values of a_{it}/a_{vt} are accordingly smaller than those given by theory, as well as changing more slowly with t. The same sort of difficulty was noted between the theory of Jaffé for a_i' relative to a_c in columnar recombination, and Schemel's observed curves.

It should be noted that for otherwise equal conditions, as r_r decreases by use of greater density q_0/V of ionization, r_r approaches r_0, and the value of a_{it} should be decreased. This conclusion was pointed out by A. M. Cravath during Marshall's studies (3). It was confirmed by changing q_0 through absorption filters within the small limits permitted by measurement. A further test of this was carried out by Gardner. Gardner reduced q_0 by a factor of 10 with Cu filters in the path of the X-rays. Theory predicts that a 10-fold decrease in q_0 should produce an effect on a_{vt} equal to that observed with full strength X-rays occurring at flash times ten times greater. Actually, it corresponds to flash times that are fifty times greater. This deviation possibly indicates other weaknesses in the theory.[12]

Reviewing all evidence, it is probable that the initial recombination, as roughly outlined here, will account for the major portion of the changes observed in a' as measured by Gardner and Sayers, especially in the shorter time intervals. The prolongation of the gradual decline of a_{vt}, observed by Gardner in O_2 and by Sayers in air into time intervals of the order of 1 to 2 seconds, probably *cannot* be ascribed to this factor. Some of it can doubtless be accounted for by aging of ions through complex ion formation and change of charge. The value of the recombination coefficient is particularly sensitive to changes in the mass of carriers, such as produced·by change from O_2^+ to Hg^+ ions. In Sayers' work, the ionization of air definitely should have introduced into the measurements this aging factor with change of ion mass, because of the production of nitrogen oxides, etc.

In an extensive and general analysis of the theory of preferential and initial recombination, N. E. Bradbury (39) treated the problem of initial recombination quite generally. He assumed the coefficient to be calculated from data that used the ionized volume V for obtaining concentration, and then he computed the real concentration of ions.

---

[12]Note that the analysis of Jaffé (32) indicates that except in a clearly defined region, a should vary with concentration in Thomson's theory. The data of Marshall, Gardner, and Sayers fall just into the borderline region where a should vary with concentration, as will be seen later.

This involved the length of the β-ray track L_β, the number of ions per cm of track μ, and the number of tracks per cm^3 γ_β. It also involved the average distance between the ions of a pair, r_r, as given by $\theta(r)$. This is the distribution of electrons attached to form negative ions relative to positive ions, calculated from the attachment processes in connection with his study of preferential recombination. The actual volume involved per cm^3 of gas is $L_\beta \gamma_\beta \pi r_r^2$. This volume changes by diffusion and impressed electrical fields. The density of ions is a function of time, given by

$$(6.96) \qquad n_t = \frac{\mu}{\pi[r_r + (4/3)kXt + (\bar{c}\,\lambda t)^{1/2}]^2}.$$

The action of the field is covered by $(4/3)kXt$ and the diffusion by $\overline{c\lambda t}$. From this, Bradbury calculated n_0, the actual number of ions per cm^3 of gas as influenced by recombination, as

$$dn_0/dt = -\,an_t^2\,L_\beta\gamma_\beta\,\pi[r_r + (4/3)\,kXt + (\bar{c}\,\lambda t)^{1/2}]$$

$$(6.97)$$

$$= \frac{a\mu^2\gamma_\beta L_\beta}{\pi[r_r + (4/3)\,kXt + (\bar{c}\,\lambda t)^{1/2}]^2}.$$

This must be integrated over a certain length of time in order to get the loss of ions during the period of initial recombination. This time can be found from equation 6.96 by determining the value of t needed to give the measured macroscopic density. If n_∞ is the concentration, t is obtained from equation 6.96 by putting $n_t = 8n_\infty$. The recombination is then calculated, considering a period of time for initial recombination and then the rest of the time for recombination, following the normal volume process relation. Bradbury then considered the influence of a finite flash time. The very general relations set up enabled the recombination to be computed both with and without a superposed field. No direct comparison was made with any experimental data, nor were any detailed calculations carried out. If sufficient data are at hand in any particular study, the calculations should be carried out. The theory of Bradbury, inspired by the author's original simple formulation, should lead to fair agreement with Gardner's data if flash times are computed. In any case, it seems probable that initial recombination is now adequately accounted for.

II(D). Volume Recombination.

II(D.1). High-Pressure Range: The Langevin-Harper Process, a_H.

It has been noted that in dealing with ion-ion recombination, one condition only was treated; that of preferential ion-ion recombination in which $d_0 >> r_0$ and $d_0 >> L$. Volume recombination, assuming isotropic and random ion distribution, covers all cases where $r_0 >> d_0$ and $d_0 > L$, or $L > d_0$. Currently, the problem of interest is that where $r_0 >> d_0$ and $d_0 > L$. Thus, on the average, the chance of separation of ions once inside the sphere of active attraction is very small, and the chance of recombination ϵ nears unity. This condition corresponds to intermediate pressures in gases attaching electrons readily, and to high pressures where attachment is relatively slow. In air it ranges from above 1 atmosphere up, and ranges similarly for O_2. It is seen that this set of conditions emphasizes the diffusive phase. It considers the process of recombination to be virtually complete, with $\epsilon = 1$, when the ions enter the sphere of active attraction as a result of random diffusion.

The meager experimental data that existed above 1 atmosphere indicated that the value of a varied inversely with pressure. This is precisely the variation predicted by Langevin's a_L. Actually, little importance had been attached to this pressure range in the past. Most interest focused on the value of a at atmospheric pressure and below in air. In the latter pressure range, as has been indicated, the results of Marshall, as interpreted by the author and by Sommerfeld, led to the general acceptance of J. J. Thomson's recombination theory for air and O_2. In order to establish the basic assumption that the ions diffuse randomly until they come within the radius d_0 of the sphere of active attraction of each other, the author and Sommerfeld treated the problem from the point of view of the motion of two Brownian particles acting on each other by Coulomb forces of attraction. This treatment is in contrast to that of using the attractive forces in continuous, homogeneous medium, as postulated by Langevin.

In 1932, W. R. Harper (31), in ignorance of the work of the author and Sommerfeld (36), made a careful analysis of the recombination theory of Langevin. He independently came to the conclusion that diffusion must predominate over an attractive drift together for most of the pressure range studied. Basically, he used an approach in which he set up an expression for the relative radial movement of two opposite ions. This gave the radial velocity of separation as

$$(6.98) \qquad \frac{dr}{dt} = \frac{3(D_+ + D_-)}{r} - \frac{(k_+ + k_-)e}{r^2} \ .$$

Here, D_+ and D_- and k_+ and k_- represent the coefficients of diffusion and the mobilities of positive and negative ions respectively, at a separation r. Diffusion will predominate when r is large. When

r is small, drift of the Langevin type will predominate. At some value of $r = d_{0H}$, dr/dt will be 0. This value of d_{0H} delineates the radius of *Harper's sphere* of active drift together. Its value, in terms of thermal energy following relation 6.72, is set as $d_{0H} = e^2/3kT$. The Brownian movement relations of the author and Sommerfeld yield an analogous expression, $d_{0B} = e^2/6kT$. Thomson has set the radius $d_0 = e^2/(3/2)kT$. It is probable that the value of e^2/DkT derived by Jaffé (32), where D is the dielectric constant (which for gases is near 1.00), is the more correct. However, since all the equations for recombination in current use have been derived on the basis of Thomson's value, which is not far different from Jaffé's equation, Thomson's value will be used for the sake of consistency.

To arrive at Harper's relation for a, i.e., a_H, probably the simplest approach is the rough analysis presented below. A much more accurate analysis is the one given by Jaffé, which is too lengthy for inclusion here. Consider only the diffusive motion of the ions outside of the radius of active drift d_{0H}. Then the square of the separation r of the ions in a time t, owing to random diffusion in three dimensions, is given by

$$(6.99) \qquad r^2 = 6(D_+ + D_-)t + r_0^2.$$

Here, D_+ and D_- are the diffusion coefficients of the positive and negative ions respectively, while r_0^2 is the initial average distance between ions. Differentiation yields

$$(6.100) \qquad \frac{1}{2}\frac{d(r^2)}{dt} = r\frac{dr}{dt} = 3(D_+ + D_-);$$

or better,

$$(6.101) \qquad \frac{dr}{dt} = \frac{3(D_+ + D_-)}{r}$$

as the velocity of radial motion, which is one of separation. To calculate the rate of recombination from this, consider n negative ions in a cm^3 of a gas moving into the spherical surfaces $4\pi r^2$ of the n positive ions per sec at the radial velocity $-dr/dt$. Thus, per cm^3, the relative approach of opposite ions per cm^3 per second dn_r is given by

$$(6.102) \quad \frac{dn_r}{dt} = -4\pi r^2 n^2 \frac{dr}{dt} = -4\pi r^2 n^2 \frac{3(D_+ + D_-)}{r} = -4\pi r\, 3(D_+ + D_-).$$

If ϵ is set equal to unity and $r = d_{0H}$, the quantity dn_r/dt becomes

dn/dt, the rate of loss by recombination of ions. Thus, it is possible to write that

$$\frac{dn}{dt} = - a_H \, n^2 = - 4 d_{0H} \, 3(D_+ + D_-) \, n^2 .$$

This leads to the Harper coefficient of recombination, in the form of

(6.103) $a_H = 4\pi d_{0H} \, 3(D_+ + D_-) .$

According to Jaffé, on the basis of far more general analysis, the coefficient is more correctly:

(6.104) $a_{HJ} = 4\pi d_{0J} f_1 \, (D_+ + D_-) .$

In this event, d_{0J} is set as $d_{0J} = e^2/kT$, and f_1 is a constant very near unity.

Returning to Harper's coefficient, it is proper to introduce his value of d_{0H} into equation 6.103, yielding

(6.105) $a_H = 4\pi (e^2/kT)(D_+ + D_-) .$

But again, in equation 6.105 the relation $k_+/D = e/kT$ as applied to the relative diffusion and mobility coefficients, sets $(D_+ + D_-) = (k_+ + k_-) \, kT/e$, which placed in equation 6.105 leads to the conclusion that

(6.106) $a_H = 4\pi e \, (k_+ + k_-) = a_L .$

This striking result was first noted by Harper, and is discussed in its implications more in detail by Jaffé (32). Despite the fact that the mechanism of the Harper recombination process is a random diffusion, the coefficient which it yields is identical with that of Langevin applying to a different set of conditions; $d_0 >> r_0$ instead of $r_0 >> d_0$, as in the case here assumed. This queer circumstance indicates why Langevin's relation is experimentally observed to hold above 2 atmospheres in air, when it should only hold around 100 atmospheres. Actually, as Jaffé points out, the Langevin and Harper processes are in principle *different*, though leading to the same relation. The coefficients should be equated in the form:

(6.107) $a_H = f_1 a_L .$

Here, f_1 is a constant resulting from averaging processes, which may not differ radically from unity but should be included. In general, it can be said that there is some uncertainty in dealing with Brownian motion in mutual force fields where both partners are acted on by additional random forces. Accordingly, none of the relations and averages are exactly correct. Further discussion of the Harper recombination process will be reserved for the section dealing with the Thomson process and the transition to higher-pressure recombination.

It is important to note that the Langevin-Harper coefficient is proportional to the mobility of the ions. It varies inversely as the gas density, and at constant density it is relatively insensitive to temperature change.

II(D.2). True Volume Recombination: The Thomson Process, a_T.

At atmospheric pressure and below in air, O_2, and most ion-forming gases, with reasonable densities and random isotropic distribution of ions, the conditions encountered are $r_0 >> d_0$, with d_0 ranging from $d_0 > L$ to $L < d_0$. Under these conditions, it is clear that the condition $r_0 >> d_0$ indicates an extensive period of random diffusive approach up to d_0. There then follows an attractive approach with relatively few paths within the sphere of radius d_0. This means that through molecular impacts, the ions have a small chance for loss of the energy e^2/d_0 within d_0, which leads to a closed orbit. In turn, the occasional orbits that do close may not result in electron transfer. Accordingly, there is a finite probability that the "encounter" within d_0 will not lead to recombination. Therefore, a separation and a new diffusive approach will take place in many encounters.

At this point, J. J. Thomson (30) introduced the chance of recombination ϵ. The factor ϵ, calculated in a rough approximation, was the same as another one calculated earlier by O. W. Richardson, that was improperly applied to Langevin's theory. Both relations contained a minor numerical blunder in averaging, subsequently corrected by the author.

In keeping with the concept of the four basic steps of the recombination process, it is easy to derive Thomson's expression in the following fashion. Each of the n negative ions per cm^3, *moving relative to the positive ions* with a random Maxwellian velocity $\sqrt{\bar{c}_+^2 + \bar{c}_-^2}$, sweeps out of a volume

$$\pi d_0^2 \sqrt{\bar{c}_+^2 + \bar{c}_-^2}$$

per second. As there are n positive ions per cm^3, the number of "encounters" dn between positive and negative ions within distances d_0 per cm^3 in a time dt, are given by

(6.108) $$dn = n^2 \pi d_0^2 \sqrt{\bar{c}_+^2 + \bar{c}_-^2}\, dt .$$

Of these encounters, only the fraction ϵ will result in recombination. Hence, the rate of loss of ions by recombination is

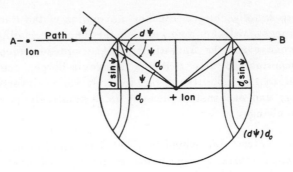

Fig. 6.14. Diagram illustrative of the calculation for a collision of ions with molecules within a distance d_0 of each other.

$$(6.109) \qquad \frac{dn}{dt} = -a_T n^2 = -\pi d_0^2 \, \epsilon \sqrt{\bar{c}_+^2 + \bar{c}_-^2}$$

and

$$(6.110) \qquad a_T = \pi \, d_0^2 \, \epsilon \sqrt{\bar{c}_+^2 + \bar{c}_-^2}.$$

It is next essential to evaluate ϵ. Consider the positive ion at rest in the center of the circle of radius d_0, as seen in figure 6.14. For simplicity, represent the negative ion traversing the sphere along a straight-line path with the *relative* velocity of motion. In the figure it strikes the surface of the sphere of radius d_0 at some point on a zone of radius $d_0 \sin \psi$ and $d_0 d\psi$ wide. Here ψ is the angle subtended by the zone at the center. Actually, the path of relative motion in free space will be curved about the positive ion in the center. This will have the effect of increasing the length of the path within the sphere of active attraction, but the increase will not be too important. Now if the negative ion and the positive ion each have an encounter with a neutral molecule within d_0, it may be assumed that enough of the kinetic energy gained by the system from the field after leaving the outer surface of d_0 will be wiped out, to give the ions a chance to describe closed orbits about their common center of mass.

For simplicity, Thomson considered that *one impact by each of the ions with molecules* within d_0 would so reduce the energy as to lead to closed orbits, and thus to charge transfer. Richardson (33) was not satisfied with this in his treatment, but required more collisions. Comparison with observation indicates that with the crude analysis used, the Thomson assumption leads to adequate agreement with experiment. If the ions do not collide with molecules and shed their energy, they escape from d_0 in open orbits. Then, they must again diffuse at random until they find new partners. The value of ϵ

is thus determined by calculating the average chance of collision of the two ions with a neutral molecule on one of the various paths resulting from the ions striking different zones subtending the angles ψ at the center of the sphere of radius d_0.

The chance of an ion going the path $2d_0 \cos \psi$ at the angle ψ without collision is obviously given by the survival equation $\epsilon^{-(2d_0/L-)\cos \psi}$. Here L_- is the mean free path of the negative ion. The chance of a path of length $2d_0 \cos \psi$ at the angle ψ is given by the ratio of areas of the zone between ψ and $\psi + d\psi$ and the target area of the sphere πd_0^2, multiplied by $\cos \psi$. The multiplication by $\cos \psi$ is needed to give the projection of the zone surface normal to the motion. Thus, the geometrical chance of a path of length $2d_0 \cos \psi$ is

(6.111) $$\frac{2\pi d_0^2 \sin \psi \, d\psi \cos \psi}{\pi d_0^2} = 2 \sin \psi \cos \psi \, d\psi.$$

The chance of escaping collision on a path at angle ψ is given by

(6.112) $$2 \epsilon^{-(2d_0/L_-) \cos \psi} \sin \psi \cos \psi \, d\psi.$$

Integration for all angles from 0 to $\pi/2$ gives the chance for angles. Since $d(\cos \psi) = -\sin \psi \, d\psi$, the chance of escaping collision in d_0 is

(6.113)
$$-2 \int_0^{\frac{\pi}{2}} \epsilon^{-\frac{2d_0 \cos \psi}{L_-}} \cos \psi \, d \cos \psi$$
$$= \frac{2L_-}{2d_0} \left[\frac{L_-}{2d_0} \left\{ 1 - \epsilon^{-\left(\frac{2d_0}{L_-}\right)} \right\} - \epsilon^{-\left(\frac{2d_0}{L_-}\right)} \right].$$

Thus, the chance ω_- that the negative ion will collide within the sphere and thus recombine, is

(6.114) $$\omega_- = 1 - \frac{2L^2}{4d_0^2} \left[1 - \epsilon^{-\frac{2d_0}{L_-}} \left\{ \frac{2d_0}{L_-} + 1 \right\} \right].$$

The chance that a *positive* ion will experience a collision with a molecule within d_0 of a negative ion, is similarly given by

(6.115) $$\omega_+ = 1 - \frac{2L_+^2}{4d_0^2} \left[1 - \epsilon^{-\frac{2d_0}{L_+}} \left\{ \frac{2d_0}{L_+} + 1 \right\} \right].$$

Here, L_+ is the mean free path of the positive ion. The chance that both ions will suffer collision within d_0 is $\omega_- + \omega_+$. However, in adding

$\omega_+ + \omega_-$, the chance of simultaneous impacts $\omega_+\omega_-$ is counted *twice*, so that the correct value of ϵ is given by

(6.116) $$\epsilon = \omega_+ + \omega_- - (\omega_+\omega_-) .$$

Thus, the value of a_T becomes

(6.117) $$a_T = \pi d_0^2 \sqrt{\bar{c}_+^2 + \bar{c}_-^2} \{\omega_+ + \omega_- - (\omega_+\omega_-)\} .$$

A precise evaluation of a_T for a given gas requires knowledge of L_+, L_-, $\bar{c}_+$, and $\bar{c}_-$. If the gas is pure and no aging occurs; e.g., so that k_+ and k_- are known in the gas, L_+ and L_- can be estimated from values of the mobilities. Likewise, since $\bar{c}_+/\bar{c}_- = \sqrt{M_-/M_+}$, the values of these quantities (if known) can play an important role in accurate evaluation of a_T by theory. However, it is usually impossible to evaluate these quantities with much precision over the time intervals needed in studies of ion-ion recombination. It thus suffices for the purpose of discussion to simplify the calculation by using a mean value of L, given by $L = (L_+ + L_-)/2$, and to set $\bar{c}_+^2 + \bar{c}_-^2 = \sqrt{2\bar{c}^2}$, where $\bar{c}$ is an average value. Equation 6.117 then becomes

(6.118) $$a_T = \pi \sqrt{2} \, d_0^2 \, \bar{c} \, (2\omega - \omega^2) ,$$

with

(6.119) $$\omega = \left[1 - \frac{L^2}{2d_0^2} \left\{ 1 - \epsilon^{-\frac{2d_0}{L}} \left(\frac{2d_0}{L} + 1 \right) \right\} \right].$$

The application of this theory for comparison with measurement is facilitated by certain simplifications. The important parameter in evaluating is the variable $x = 2d_0/L$. Accordingly, ω and ϵ may once and for all be calculated as a function of the variable x, and tabulated. To reduce $2d_0/L$ to ready evaluation in terms of stated variables, such as temperature and pressure, it is possible to proceed as follows:

(6.120) $$d_0 = e^2/(3/2)kT = 4.05 \times 10^{-6} (273/T) .$$

Again, the mean free path L may be expressed in terms of the ratio of the particular value to the fictitious standard free path L_A at $0°$ C. and 760 mm pressure of 10^{-5} cm. This gives the true value of L in any case as

(6.121) $$L = 10^{-5} (760/p) (L/L_A) .$$

To get the average L to use in these calculations, the solid elastic mobility equation of Langevin can be invoked. From the observed values of k in the gas in question, solution of

(6.122) $$k = 0.815 (e/M) (L/C) \sqrt{(M + m)/m}$$

TABLE 6.1

Probability Function $\epsilon = 2\omega - \omega^2 = f(x)$, with $\omega = 1 - 2/x^2 \left[1 - e^{-x} (x + 1) \right]$ and $x = 2d_0/L$, as Derived from Thomson's Theory of Ion-Ion Recombination.

x	$2/x^2$	e^{-x}	$\dfrac{f(x)}{\omega}$	$\dfrac{[f(x)]^2}{\omega^2}$	$\dfrac{\epsilon}{2\omega-\omega^2}$
0.2	50.00000	0.818731	0.12385	0.01534	0.23236
0.4	12.50000	0.670320	0.23070	0.05322	0.40818
0.6	5.55556	0.548812	0.32277	0.10418	0.54136
0.8	3.12500	0.449329	0.40248	0.16199	0.64297
1.0	2.00000	0.367879	0.47152	0.22233	0.72071
1.2	1.38889	0.301194	0.53143	0.28242	0.78044
1.4	1.02041	0.246597	0.58350	0.34047	0.82653
1.6	0.78125	0.201897	0.62885	0.39545	0.86225
1.8	0.61729	0.165299	0.66840	0.44676	0.89004
2.0	0.50000	0.135335	0.70300	0.49421	0.91179
2.2	0.41322	0.110803	0.73330	0.53773	0.92887
2.4	0.34722	0.090718	0.75988	0.57742	0.94234
2.6	0.29586	0.074274	0.78325	0.61348	0.95302
2.8	0.25510	0.060810	0.80385	0.64619	0.96151
3.0	0.22222	0.049787	0.82203	0.67573	0.96833
3.5	0.16327	0.030197	0.85892	0.73774	0.98010
4.0	0.12500	0.018316	0.88645	0.78579	0.98711
4.5	0.09876	0.011109	0.90728	0.82316	0.99140
5.0	0.08000	0.006738	0.92350	0.85285	0.99415
5.5	0.06612	0.004087	0.93664	0.87730	0.99598
6.0	0.05556	0.002479	0.94541	0.89380	0.99702
6.5	0.04734	0.001503	0.95319	0.90838	0.99800
7.0	0.04082	0.000912	0.95948	0.92060	0.99836
7.5	0.03556	0.000553	—	—	—
8.0	0.03125	0.000335	0.96884	0.93865	0.99903
9.0	0.02470	0.000123	—	—	—
10.0	0.02000	0.000050	0.98001	0.96042	0.99960

can be made [13] to determine the effective L. The values of e, M, and C are known, and the estimated value of m can make very little error, except in a few cases where m is near M or less than M. Thus, the parameter x can be evaluated as

(6.123) $$x = 0.81 \, (273/T) \, (p/760) \, (L_A/L)$$

for a gas at *constant density*, with p in millimeters of mercury and T in degrees Kelvin. Since $L = L_0 \, (760/p) \, (T/273)$ if density is not constant, the value of x with density variable and pressure constant is given by equation 6.124, on the following page.

[13] Here C is the root-mean-square average velocity of the ions, and hence of the ambient gas, with M the mass of the molecules and m that of the ions.

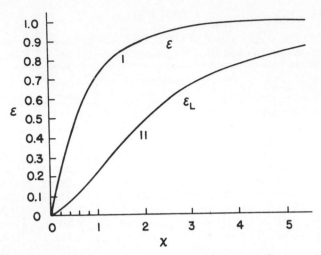

Fig. 6.15. Plot of the calculated value of the chance of separation of ions within d_0 as a result of the failure to lose energy in molecular impacts, plotted against the state-conditioned variable x of equation 6.125.

$$(6.124) \qquad x = 0.81 \ (273/T)^2(p/760) \ (L_A/L) \ .$$

Values of ω, ω^2, and ϵ as a function of x are tabulated in table 6.1 for a commonly useful range of values of x, while ϵ and $[f(x)]^2 = \omega^2 = \epsilon_L$ are plotted as a curve in figure 6.15. It should be pointed out here that in going down to pressures below 0.1 mm, great care must be used in evaluating ϵ, for the reason that the expansion of the expression in x converges slowly under these conditions.

Using the data above, equation 6.118 can be thrown into a convenient form for the calculation of a_T with various values of the constants L, T, m, and p. In this case, m_m will be used for the molecular weight of the ions relative to hydrogen, chosen as 1. With this assignment of m_m, the value of $\pi d_0{}^2 \sqrt{2} \ \bar{c}$, with $\bar{c}$ written as $\bar{c} = 0.922 \sqrt{2} \ \sqrt{2/m_m} \ (1.84 \times 10^5 \sqrt{T/273})$, leads to the relation:

$$(6.125) \qquad a_T = 1.73 \times 10^{-5} \ \left(\frac{273}{T}\right)^{3/2} \ \left(\frac{1}{m_m}\right)^{1/2} \ (2\omega - \omega^2).$$

In this relation, $\epsilon = 2\omega - \omega^2$ is evaluated by means of the curve of figure 6.15 or table 6.1 in terms of values of the argument x, where x is given as above.

As anticipated from the introduction, it is seen that d_0/L is a very important parameter. Furthermore, in view of the sensitivity of d_0 to temperature, a_T will be very sensitive to temperature change, which is not the case in ion mobilities. Likewise, a_T is sensitive to the mass of the ions in a greater measure than is the mobility.

The theory for a_T was put to test by comparison with the results of Gardner in O_2. Very pure O_2 was used, in an all-glass, outgassed chamber with metal electrodes, as it is the best negative ion forming gas. It exhibits least chance of alteration by change of charge, aging, clustering, etc., through complex ion formation with chemical substances formed by X-ray ionization. It is more satisfactory than the halogens, which react with electrodes. This is not the case in more complex electron-attaching gases, such as SO_2 or air. The effects of initial recombination were avoided by using only data on ions in which a' did not change with time. The variations of a with pressure and temperature were studied within controllable limits. Below about 10 cm pressure, the diffusion correction became too large. Above 1 atmosphere, the apparatus was inconvenient to operate. Liquid-air temperatures could not well be achieved.

Results of Erikson, adjusted in absolute value to those of Gardner at higher temperatures, allowed Erikson's (22) relative value at liquid-air temperatures to be used in the analysis. Using equations 6.123 and 6.125, the theoretical values for a_T in O_2 were computed under the following assumptions: The ratio $L_A/L = 5$; $m_m = 64$ or $2M$, with M the molecular weight of the O_2 molecule. [14] The pressure variations, as computed between 20° and 30° C., are drawn as full curves in figure 6.6 (supra, section 4), with a as ordinate and pressure in cm as abscissae. The experimental points were taken between 20° and 30° C., in a room where temperature could not be held very constant during the twelve-hour runs. They are shown as crosses. The results of some of the earlier observations of Langevin (25), Thirkill (42), and Plimpton (3), using older methods and adjusted to agree with Gardner's values at 760 mm, are given as circles. It is seen that they have a linear decrease with pressure. Since these data suffered from initial recombination in varying amounts, as well as numerous other difficulties, they are not too significant. It is seen that Gardner's results fall quite closely along the theoretical curve.

In figure 6.7 (supra, section 4), the theoretical data at constant density are compared for various temperatures from 450° K. to 200° K. Gardner's results in O_2 appear as crosses, while the data of Phillips (43) and Erikson (22) in air are shown as circles and circled crosses.

---

[14] According to recent mobility studies of Varney, the ions observed in O_2 in intervals of 10^{-3} sec are O_2^+, and not O_4^+. The initial negative ion in O_2 is O_2^-. Whether O_4^- forms is not known; but at low X/p, $K_+ = 2.25$ cm2/volt sec, and $K_- = 2.65$ cm2/volt sec. This probably indicates the ions to be O_2^+ and O_2^-.

The data of Erikson were taken at constant density, while those of Phillips were taken at constant pressure. The constant-pressure data do not depart seriously from the constant-density data in this temperature range. Thus, the data are all plotted together, the absolute values having been adjusted to Gardner's at room temperature. It is seen that all data lie along the computed curve for a_T within the limits of accuracy. The departure of the one point at liquid-air temperatures is probably real.

Oxygen at this temperature is near its condensation point. This fact, in connection with the low-temperature mobility studies of the Bristol group, indicates a possible increase in the mass m_m of the ions owing to cluster formation. Using the Thomson value of d_0 and the above assumptions, Gardner got numerical agreement between the computed value of a_T and his observed value. Harper's value for d_0 would have reduced a by a factor of 0.25. If the ions have a mass of 32 instead of 64, the computed a would have been greater by $\sqrt{2}$. Gardner's *observed* value for a_T in O_2 at 20° C. and 760 mm was $2.05 \pm 0.05 \times 10^{-6}$.

Thus, on the basis of absolute values computed on reasonable assumptions for O_2, the Thomson theory is confirmed as much as present-day knowledge permits. More important is the fact that the theory of Thomson for a_T is substantiated by both the pressure and temperature variations of a; at 1 atmosphere and below in O_2, and between 150° and 450° K. Neither the coefficient a_L nor a_H for Langevin and Harper's theories predicts the observed nature of variation in this region.

The theory of Thomson received corroboration almost simultaneously with Gardner's work through the study of J. Sayers (23) in air. The techniques of Sayers were quite similar to those of Gardner (3). Sayers balanced out contact potentials by bias batteries. Gardner, who used homogeneous metals, did not believe this necessary. Sayers' beam occupied the whole volume between the plates; Gardner's did not. Sayers thus corrected for diffusion, a correction which only became important at low ion concentrations. He did not measure a for short time intervals, but used the slope of the reciprocal of concentration plotted against time. From 0.05-0.5 second these were essentially constant. He observed initial recombination in which a_i varied from 6×10^{-6} to 3×10^{-6} in the interval from 10^{-3} to 10^{-1} sec.

The equilibrium concentration method initiated by McClung was used, and gave a value of a of 5.2×10^{-6}, which indicates that this constant is much influenced by initial recombination. Sayers corroborated Marshall and Gardner's observations regarding a reduction

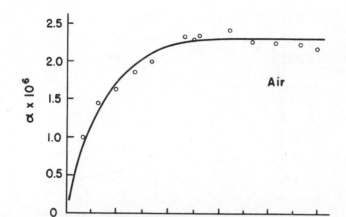

Fig. 6.16. Sayers' curve for α in air as a function of pressure in mm of Hg, represented by points. The full curve represents Thomson's theory for α in this range. Note the departure from Thomson's theory above 1 atmosphere.

in α_i with ion concentration from $\alpha_i = 2.65 \times 10^{-6}$ with 1.5×10^6 ions/cm³, down to 2.3×10^{-6} at 4.4×10^6 ions/cm³. This was attributed by Sayers to the formation of chemical substances (notably O_3) by the X-rays. Using softer X-rays, he observed values as low as 1.65×10^{-6}. Since between 0.1 and 0.5 sec Sayers' curves for α appeared constant, he believed initial recombination to be over at 0.1 sec. This is as it should be. Thus, changes in α were attributed by Sayers to chemical compounds which changed m. This would be expected in air with nitric oxide, etc.

Ozone is not likely to be a factor; unpublished results of Miss E. A. Higley in the author's laboratory showed ion mobilities to be little affected by O_3. The ozone experiments were discontinued following an explosion, owing to the dangerous characteristics of the concentrated gas. However, since Gardner observed the same behavior to a smaller degree when working with pure O_2, where the chemical changes cannot intervene, the chemical interpretation may not account for all of the effect. Gardner investigated α over much larger ranges of t than did Sayers, and observed that the *variation in flash time* produced large changes in the α_i-t curves. He concluded that any *apparent* constancy of α between 0.1 and 0.5 sec was illusory, and was caused by flash-time limitations and plotting. It thus appears that α actually decreased in O_2, even though slowly. Probably the

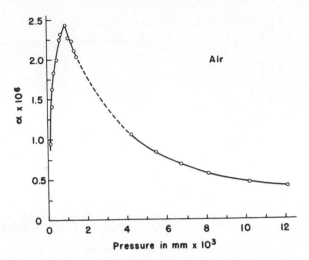

Fig. 6.17. Sayers' data of α in air against pressure to an extended scale. Points beyond 4×10^3 mm are Mächler's values in somewhat impure air. Note that beyond 760 mm the value of α decreases according to the Harper theory, given by the dashed line which connects Sayers' and Mächler's values.

effects observed are due to a combination of initial recombination and chemical actions leading to ionic mass changes.

Sayers extended his measurements in air from 50 to 1,500 mm. Beyond 760 mm the curve for α_T appeared to reach a maximum and then definitely to decline. This is seen in Sayers' curve shown in figure 6.16, where the points lie close along the Thomson curve until about 700 mm, then rise slightly above it and decline below it at 1,500 mm, as would be noted if dashes were drawn through the points. In figure 6.17 are shown the same data plotted to a different scale of ordinates, with Mächler's data on α from 4 atmospheres on up to 12. The decline of Sayers' curve seems to fit nicely as a prolongation of Mächler's (44) curve at higher pressure, even though Mächler's air was far less pure than was Sayers'. The shape of the curve of Sayers and Mächler beyond the hump is just that predicted by the theory of the Langevin-Harper coefficient α_H. Thus, the Thomson mechanism breaks down just beyond 1 atmosphere, with ϵ going to 1. Then a pure diffusive approach characteristic of $d_0 >> L$ sets in at 2 atmospheres.

The Thomson process is analyzed in a more general fashion by Jaffé (32). For the situation in question, $r_0 >> d_0$ and $L >> d_0$, he gives a modification of Thomson's expression in which he accepts $\epsilon = 2\omega - \omega^2 = \phi_2 (d_0/L)$, and derives the relation:

$$(6.126) \quad \alpha_{TJ} = \pi d_0^2 \sqrt{\overline{c_+^2} + \overline{c_-^2}} \; \psi_1 \left[(d_0/L), (d_0/r_0) \right] \phi_2 (d_0/L) .$$

This differs from Thomson's in that it depends on d_0/r_0, i.e., upon *ion concentration*, and gives a marked maximum at $r_0 = L$, as can be shown by the form of $\phi_1[(d_0/L), (d_0/r_0)]$ which is a part of $\psi_1[(d_0/L), (d_0/r_0)]$.

Sufficiently above pressures for which $r_0 >> L$, and for ionization sufficiently weak to make $r_0 >> d_0$, $\psi_1 = 1$. This then gives Thomson's relation:

(6.127) $$a_T = \pi d_0^2 \sqrt{\bar{c}_+^2 + \bar{c}_-^2} \; \phi_2(d_0/L),$$

if $L >> d_0$ and $d_0 >> r_0$.

In discussing the general theory, Jaffé points out that only under the circumstances where Langevin's, Harper's, or Thomson's equation applies, as defined by the criteria given by him, is the coefficient *independent of ion density*. This explains the variation of a with density of ionization, as observed by Marshall, Gardner, and Sayers for atmospheric pressure, which is just on the borderline of changing from the Thomson to the Harper form. This circumstance, plus the influence of initial recombination, adequately accounts for the observed results.

Where L and d_0 become comparable, neither Thomson's nor Harper's theory applies. It might be possible to carry out the rigorous approximations of Jaffé's treatment of a_{TJ} and a_{HJ} until they merge. Actually, the generalized basic expression of Jaffé is not capable of evaluation in this area. The situation is quite analogous to that between the Knudsen and Poiseuille frictional-flow regimes of gases. Jaffé plots all the data on the two sides of the transition region for air much as Sayers did, and shows that theoretically the transition from the Thomson to the Harper relation might be expected to follow the curve.

II(D.3). Volume Ion-Ion Recombination at Very Low Pressures, a_σ.

If $r_0 >> d_0$ and $L >> d_0$, as is the case in the ionosphere, the value of ϵ becomes vanishingly small. Thus, at 6.7×10^{-3} mm pressure, the value of a_T calculates to 10^{-10}. This signifies that the three-body process underlying Thomson's theory is no longer very effective, since the value of a_σ computed for a direct electron transfer of charge after diffusive approach begins to be more likely (37). Accordingly, as multibody collisions of the type envisioned by Thomson become more rare, they will only account for part of the recombination. Assume that for a given ion pair the average radius for charge transfer for ions in a given relative energy range is σ. Then diffusive approach of the n negative ions per cm^3, sweeping out cylinders of cross section $\pi\sigma^2$ and $\sqrt{\bar{c}_+^2 + \bar{c}_-^2}$ cm long per second, will disappear by charge transfer with the n positive ions per cm^3 at the rate in equation 6.128.

TABLE

SUMMARY OF RECOM-

(1) Carrier	(2) Type	(3) Condition of Occurrence	(4) Gas Type	(5) State Variable	(6) Carrier Density
Electron-Ion.	Volume.	$r_0 >> d_0 \gtrless \lambda.$	Inert and pure nonelectron-attaching gases.	10 ats. down. 15,000° K.down.	10^8 to 10^{17} per cm^3.
Electron-Ion.	Preferential.	$d_0 > r_0 >> \lambda.$	Inert and pure nonelectron-attaching gases.	100 ats. 273° K.	10^6 or less per cm^3.
Electron-Ion.	Wall.	$r_0 >> \lambda > d_0.$	Inert and pure nonelectron-attaching gases.	Below 1 mm pressure in confined spaces.	10^8 per cm^3 and up.
Ion-Ion.	Preferential.	$d_0 >> r_0 >> L.$	Electron-at-taching gases O_2, SO_2, Air, Cl_2, etc.Impure inert gases.	100 ats. $\sim 273°$ K. and less.	Generally low (10^6 per cm^3). Notable: $\sim 10^3$.
Ion-Ion.	Columnar.	$r_0 >> d_0 \gtrless L.$ Particle or heavy-particle ionization.	Electron-at-taching gases O_2, SO_2, Air, Cl_2,etc.Impure inert gases.	10 ats. down to 0.01 ats.	Anisotropic. 10^9 to 10^3 about track axis.
Ion-Ion	Initial.	$r_0 >> d_0 \gtrless L.$ β-ray or simi-lar tracks. Sparse ion pairs, ions close.	Electron-at-taching gases O_2, SO_2, Air Cl_2,etc.Impure inert gases.	10 ats. to 0.01 ats.	Anisotropic. 10^8 to 10^3, local pairs.
Ion-Ion.	Volume.	$r_0 >> d_0 >> L.$	Electron-at-taching gases O_2, SO_2, Air, Cl_2,etc.Impure inert gases.	20 ats. to 2 ats. air.	10^{10} and down.
Ion-Ion.	Volume.	$r_0 >> d_0 \gtrless L.$	Electron-at-taching gases O_2, SO_2, Air, Cl_2,etc.Impure inert gases.	1 at. to 10^{-2} mm.	10^{10} and down.
Ion-Ion.	Volume. Low pressure.	$L >> r_0 >> d_0.$	Electron-at-taching gases O_2, SO_2, Air Cl_2,etc.Impure inert gases.	10^{-3} mm down.	All, but usually small ($<< 10^4$).

*All values of α may change with time if one or both partners change character with time.

6.2

BINATION PROCESSES

(7)	(8)	(9)	(10)	(11)
Coefficient*	Theory	Value	Variation	How Studied
$a_{er} = \pi\sigma^2_{er}\,\bar{c}_1$.	Radiative capture quantum-mechanically for σ_{er}.	$\sim 10^{-12}$.	Energy and species.	In arcs; in glows; in spark channels; with microwave breakdown at appropriate pressures.
$a_{ed} = \pi\sigma^2_{ed}\,\bar{c}_1$.	Dissociative capture (Bates elementary theory).	$\sim 10^{-6}$ to 10^{-8}.	Energy and species. $T^{-3/2}$.	
$a_{ee} = \pi\sigma^2_{ee}\,\bar{c}_1$.	Capture to excite two electrons.	10^{-9} to 10^{-12}.	Energy and species.	May have been recently observed by G. H. Dieke.
a_{ep}	Bradbury.	Not known.	Field-dependent.	Not observed.
None. Declines exponentially with time, and thus cannot give an a.	Ambipolar diffusion.	Not known.	Concentration; pressure; ionic mobility; dimensions of chamber.	At lower pressures in discharges, and in microwave breakdown.
a_L.	$a_L = 4\pi e$ $(k_+ + k_-)$. Langevin theory.	10^{-8} and up.	$\propto 1/\rho$ or $1/p$. Varies little with T at constant ρ.	Not usually observed. Could occur in old cosmic-ray studies.
a_c.	Special theory of Jaffé.	10^{-3} on down to 10^{-6}. From $t = 10^{-3}$ to $t = 1$.	$\propto 1/\rho$, or as volume varies with time and density of ions.	Appears with heavy-particle ionization along tracks. Goes to a_H or a_T in time.
a_i	Special theory: Rough—Loeb; Exact— Bradbury.	10^{-4} to 10^{-6}. $t = 10^{-3}$ to 1 sec.	Declines with time from 10^{-3} sec, or varies with ion density. Otherwise like a_H or a_T.	Appears with fast electron ionization. Goes to a_H or a_T in time.
a_H.	$a_H = a_L f_1 = 4\pi e$ $(k_+ + k_-) f_1$ $0 < f_1 < 1$.	10^{-8} to 10^{-6}.	$\propto 1/\rho$ or $1/p$. Varies little with T at constant ρ.	In all gases forming ions above 2 ats. with isotropic ionization.
a_T.	$a_T = \pi d^2_0\,\bar{c}$ $(2\omega - \omega^2)$. Thomson theory.	10^{-6} to 10^{-9}.	Varies $1/T^{3/2}$ and $\sqrt{p}$ roughly. May depend on concentration. Can change with t if ion changes.	Isotropic ionization. All gases where negative ions form by electron attachment.
a_σ	$a_\sigma = \pi\sigma^2_c\,\bar{c}$. σ_c collision cross section for charge transfer.	10^{-10}.	Independent of p. Depends on $\sqrt{T}$.	Occurs at low pressures with large volumes observed in ionosphere.

(6.128) $$dn = -a_\sigma n^2 dt = -\pi\sigma^2 \sqrt{\bar{c}_+^2 + \bar{c}_-^2}\; dt\;.$$

Thus,

(6.129) $$a_\sigma = \pi\sigma^2 \sqrt{\bar{c}_+^2 + \bar{c}_-^2}\;,$$

which defines the low-pressure, volume ion-ion coefficient.

For different ion types and different energies, σ will vary. Since some of these capture cross sections are relatively large, the value of a_σ will become greater than a_T at low pressures. Thus, there will be a gradual change in the value of a, observed as pressure decreases. The a then observed will lose its pressure dependence, becoming dependent only on temperature as it affects σ and $\sqrt{\bar{c}_+^2 + \bar{c}_-^2}$. It is not impossible that the observed a will then vary with time owing to selective recombination, especially in mixed gases. Very little is known about these coefficients experimentally. Measurements are very difficult to make at low pressures, owing to ambipolar diffusion and wall recombination. There is urgent need for this sort of study, as it bears on problems encountered in the upper atmosphere.

It could be expected that σ would be of the order of about 2 Å in most ionic encounters. If this were the case, with $\sqrt{\bar{c}_+^2 + \bar{c}_-^2}$ of the order of 10^5 cm/sec, then a_σ would lie around $1.2 \times 10^{-15} \times 10^5 = 1.2 \times 10^{-10}$, a value that is not unreasonable. On the other hand, for O_2^- and O_2^+, the value of σ could be of the order of 10 Å, which would bring the value down to 3×10^{-9}. This problem can doubtless be solved by wave-mechanical analysis if the ion structures are well known.

§7. The Observed Recombination Coefficients and Their Interpretation.

Following the detailed discussion of the theory of the individual processes of recombination, the information gleaned may be summarized as in table 6.2. Here the carriers involved are tabulated in column 1 for the various types of recombination previously discussed, which are shown in column 2. The relations between r_0, L, and d_0 applying in the various processes are then given in column 3. Next follow gas types in which the different processes may be observed, followed by the values of pressure and temperature usually applying. In column 6 are given the carrier densities at which the various processes may occur. Columns 7 and 8 designate the coefficient and its appropriate theory. Column 9 gives the order of magnitude of values which have been reported in connection with the process, followed by column 10, telling what significant variables other than coefficient apply. The table finishes with column 11, giving the character of the plasma leading to such recombination processes.

TABLE 6.3

The only reliable data currently available on ion-ion recombination in electron-attaching gases at atmospheric pressures. These are data for O_2 and air.

Gas	Observer	Temp.	Pressure	Ion Concen-tration	Age	Value
O_2	Gardner, 1938 (27)	22°C.	760 mm	1×10^6	0.5″	$2.08 \pm 0.05 \times 10^{-6}$
Air	Sayers, 1938 (23)	22°C.	760 mm	1.5×10^6	0.1″	2.65×10^{-6}
				4.4×10^6	0.1″	$2.3 \ \times 10^{-6}$

While this table is of interest in summarizing what has gone before, it may seem incomplete in one aspect: It does not go into the situations arising from the recombination of two or more than one carrier of one sign with a single carrier of the opposite sign, having different values of α for the different carriers. It also does not consider transformation of one of these carriers into the other during the recombination process, nor does it include cases where the two carriers remain in equilibrium while recombination occurs. These are common variants that complicate the experimental evaluation of α and the interpretation of experimental data. Actually, the table is not altered by the omission of these complicating factors, which are usually present in all but the purest gases in even more intricacy than the simple cases cited. The basic processes of recombination remain the same, independent of the multiplicity of carriers.

From what has preceded and from the table, it is also clear that there are very few of the measured values of α that have much significance or importance today. The data from columnar (and perhaps initial) ionization are only illustrative and significant relative to the tracks studied, and to the degree to which achievement of "saturation" currents is of value in measurement with such particles. Actually, only values of α_T for ion-ion recombination have been measured for O_2 and air at 760 mm and 22° C. with sufficient accuracy to warrant their citation. These are the values obtained by Gardner and Sayers, shown in table 6.3.

These values may be extrapolated by means of the Thomson theory with some certainty as to order of magnitude to lower pressures and to higher and lower temperatures. Possibly Sayers' data for air above 1,500 mm Hg may be extrapolated safely up to 10 atmospheres or more following the Langevin-Harper equation. Mächler's (44) data appear to be valid in the region of higher pressures, though the air used was far from clean.

TABLE 6.4

ASSEMBLED DATA ON ELECTRON-ION RECOMBINATION COEFFICIENTS

Gas	Observers	Electron Temp., T_e, in °K.	Pressure, mm Hg	Method Used	α_e in cm³/ion sec	Electron density per cm³	Comments
A	Kenty (28)	3,100°K.	8×10^{-1}	Probes in arc.	2×10^{-10}	10^{13}	Probably rate production of A_2^+.
Cs	Mohler (19)	1,300°K.	$1\text{-}10 \times 10^{-2}$	Optical cont. spectrum Cs arc.	3.6×10^{-10}	1.8×10^{12}	
Cs	Mohler (19)	1,200°K.	$1\text{-}10 \times 10^{-2}$	Probes in arc.	3.4×10^{-10}	1×10^{12}	
Cs	Dandurand and Holt (35)	1,400°K.	0.32 - 0.68	Microwave.	3.5×10^{-7} 1.21×10^{-6}	10^{12}	Gas temperatures respectively 285°K. and 270°K. Immature plasma.
Hg	Mohler (19)	2,000°K.	0.270	Probes in arc.	2.3×10^{-10}	10^{13}	
Hg	Dandurand and Holt (35)	2,000°K.	0.5	Microwave.	5×10^{-9}	10^{12}	Doubtful.
Hg	Biondi (45)	300°K.	1.4-46 mm	Microwave.	$5.1\text{-}14 \times 10^{-7}$	$\sim 10^{9}$	Pressure-dependent. Hg pressure increases with T. Can involve equilibrium between Hg_2 and Hg_3. Exact.
He	Biondi and Brown (7)	300°K.	20-30 mm and below	Microwave breakdown—microwave analysis.	1.7×10^{-8}	10^{10} to 10^{11}	Probably exact.
He	Holt et al. (35)	300°K.	11-27 mm	Microwave breakdown—microwave analysis.	$9.5\text{-}9.8 \times 10^{-8}$	10^{11}	
Ne	Biondi and Brown (7)	410°K. 300°K. 195°K.	5-30 mm	Microwave breakdown—microwave analysis.	2.07×10^{-7}	10^{10} to 10^{11}	Probably exact.
N		300°K.	mm	Microwave breakdown—	1.1×10^{-7}	10^{11}	

Gas	Reference	Temp.	Pressure	Method (microwave analysis)	8×10 (depends on pres.)	10^{11}	Remarks
Ne	Olsen and Huxford (8)	8,300°K.	50-70 mm	Pulsed, overvolted condenser discharge. Stark effect on H_2 lines.	5.3×10^{-14}	10^{17}	Possibly radiative electron-ion recombination.
A	Biondi and Brown (7)	300°K.	20-30 mm	Microwave breakdown—microwave analysis.	3.7×10^{-7}	10^{10}	Argon of doubtful purity.
A	Biondi (45)	300°K.	20-30 mm	Microwave breakdown—microwave analysis.	8.8×10^{-7}	10^{11}	Probably pure.
A	Sayers (29a)	600°K. 1,250°K.	0.1 to 1 mm	Probes in dying arc plasma.	1.12×10^{-9} 4.2×10^{-10}	$>10^{11}$ $>10^{11}$	Constant with pressure. Decreases as $T^{-3/2}$.
A	Holt et al. (35)	300°K.	2 mm 30 mm	Microwave analysis Microwave analysis	5×10^{-7} 1.1×10^{-6}	10^{10} to 10^{11}	
A	Olsen and Huxford (8)	8,300°K.	50-70 mm	Pulsed, overvolted condenser discharge. Stark effect on H_2 lines.	2.5×10^{-13}	10^{16}	Possibly radiative electron-ion recombination.
H	Hopwood and Craggs (6)	12,000°K.	760 mm	Photomult. and oscilloscope in spark channel. Filter for H_α, H_β, H_γ.	1.4×10^{-11}	10^{17}	Probably radiative capture to H^+. Influenced by high Coulomb fields.

TABLE 6.4—Continued

Gas	Observers	Electron Temp., T_e, in °K	Pressure, mm Hg	Method Used	α_e in cm³/ion sec	Electron density per cm³	Comments
H	Hopwood and Craggs (6)	20,000°K.	760 mm	Photomult. and oscilloscope in spark channel. Filter for Hα, Hβ, Hγ.	2×10^{-12}	2.5×10^{17}	Probably radiative capture to H$^+$. Influenced by high Coulomb fields.
H$_2$	Biondi and Brown (7)	300°K.	10-15 mm	Microwave breakdown—microwave analysis.	2.5×10^{-6}	10^{10}	Study incomplete. H$_2$ possibly impure.
H$_2$	Varnerin (46)*	300°K.	3-60 mm	Propagat. const. in microwave plasma.	$\alpha_e = 0.34 \times 10^{-6}$ to 2.5×10^{-6}	$10^9 - 2 \times 10^{10}$	Not a recombination, but electron attachment with O or OH.
H$_2$	Persson (29c)	300°K.	3-60 mm	Microwave breakdown.	0	$\sim 10^{10}$	No dissociative recombination.
N$_2$	Biondi and Brown (7)	300°K.	3-10 mm	Microwave breakdown—microwave analysis.	1.4×10^{-7} at about 5 mm up to 1.9×10^{-7}	10^{10}	Study incomplete.
N$_2$	Bryan (47)	300°K.	6 mm	Microwave breakdown—microwave analysis.	2×10^{-6} 9×10^{-7} 2×10^{-6}	Low power 10^{10}. High power 10^{11}.	Immature plasma.
O$_2$	Biondi and Brown (7)	300°K.	3-20 mm	Microwave breakdown—microwave analysis.	3×10^{-7} to 14×10^{-7}	10^9 to 10^{10}	Dissociative electron or ion-ion recombination. Study incomplete.

*Now recognized as falsified by electron attachment to impurities. With pure H$_2$ no recombination was observed (29c).

The only other data on recombination coefficients which merit discussion are the values observed for electron-ion recombination. All these data have been assembled in table 6.4, which is again self-explanatory. However, the data given therein require considerable comment, and will be discussed in the section to follow.

§ 8. The Dissociative Electron-Ion Recombination Data.

The data shown in table 6.4 merit comment. Wave-mechanical analyses based on hydrogen-like atoms lead to values of a_{er} for radiative capture, which should be of the order of $a_{er} = 2 \times 10^{-12}$ cm^3/ion sec at energies of 0.1 e.v., corresponding to about 900° K. For higher electron energies, the value of a_{er} should decrease with energy according to $a_{er} = 2.0 \times 10^{-12}/V$, with V the electron energy in e.v. These represent the calculated values for hydrogen-like atoms. Calculations indicate that radiative capture for the alkalies, and in fact nearly all monatomic ions, should be in this neighborhood of values.

It is at once observed that practically all values of a_e reported in table 6.4 for monatomic gases are well out of line with these values. Thus, the data from A, Cs, Hg, etc., of Kenty (28), Mohler (19), and others, with electron temperatures of 1,000° K. or more, yielded values of a for supposed radiative recombination that are at least 10^3 times too great. To date these results are unexplained, though there is a possibility that they might be caused by dissociative recombination with $n^+ << n$ at low pressure, where molecule formation governs rate. The data of Hopwood and Craggs (6) for H atoms in spark channels, taken at temperatures estimated to be 12,000° K. (about 1.2 e.v., and possibly higher), come nearest to the classical values. These values may be high by a factor of 10. In this study the ions were certainly H$^+$, and *not* H$_2^+$. The discrepancy with theory for H$^+$ could be accounted for through the influence of ionic-force fields or other factors attributable to the high degree of ionization of the gas in the channel. Some data of Olsen and Huxford (8) for Ne$^+$ and A$^+$ give values $\sim 10^{-14}$ at 1 e.v., but assignment is not certain. The other values in the table are all at least two orders of magnitude high, if not more. At 300° K. most microwave data yield values that are from 10^4 to 10^6 times too high (7). Pressure dependence was noted in some of the gases; a circumstance meriting attention.

It may be added that while some of the earlier high values of the electron-ion recombination coefficients could certainly be ascribed to dissociative recombination, not all of them have been observed under conditions where it was *certain* that the ion that recombined was a molecular ion. More recently, a number of these doubtful cases in inert gases have definitely been shown to be dissociative recombinations of molecular ions with electrons. In these instances, it was possible to show by ingenious techniques that where molecular ions were not permitted to form, the electron loss was all by ambipolar diffusion, and that any coefficient of recombination (of atomic A^+ ions, for example) was of the order of less than 10^{-10} or 10^{-11} cm^3/ion sec (48). The existence of molecular ions does not insure that dissociative electron-ion recombination can occur (29c).

At this point it is essential to suggest two processes for which a can be at least somewhat larger. Both of these processes were suggested by Bates (7) or Bates and Massey (48a). The first is dissociative recombination, the occurrence of which, as will be seen, has been experimentally established. The second is dielectronic recombination. The latter process is one which is the reverse of a phenomenon known as autoionization. If by electron impact two electrons of a given atom are raised to excited states, such that the sum of the energies exceeds the ionization energy, then by internal rearrangement akin to the Auger effect, one electron can fall to the ground state and the other will leave the atom. The inverse of this process would be one in which an electron is captured into the atom, leading to excitation of two electrons in lower states. These can later radiate. W. R. S. Garton (48a), who has studied autoionization spectroscopically, used data on A to calculate the value of a_{ee} for dielectronic recombination for one state of A, using Bates and Massey's relations. This yields $a = 3 \times 10^{-12}$ at 3,000° K., 10^{-10} at 300° K., and 1.5×10^{-9} at 20° K. It is seen that this value is still more nearly of the order of a for radiative capture, though perhaps ten times as large.

In studies dealing with the theory of ion mobilities and the nature of ions, there is merited a lengthy discussion of the peculiar behavior observed in microwave plasma breakdown studies. In this technique, gases contained in clean, outgassed, spherical or cylindrical glass or quartz bulbs in microwave guide systems are broken down by pulses of high-frequency oscillation of adequate amplitude from a pulsed magnetron. The breakdown may continue from some microseconds up to a millisecond, with gas pressures from tenths of a mm up to some 100 mm of Hg. The ion densities that are built up range from 10^8 to 10^{11} or 10^{12} electrons and ions per cm^3. The ionization is so planned that it is relatively uniform over the volume. The ionized plasma is allowed to "cool down" for periods from 10 microseconds to several milliseconds. At any time desired the electron density can be measured by means of a probing signal of low intensity, which may yield the resonant frequency of the plasma, the O of the cavity, or in the later methods, measurements of the complex and real conductivities. The electron density is inferred from these data without disturbing the plasma and without resort to probes. From this it is possible to infer the decay of ionization with time.

In general, this decay of electron density can be accounted for in one of several ways. If the pressures are relatively low (usually below 1 mm) the loss of electrons and ions from the plasma comes through ambipolar diffusion to the walls. This leads to a plot of the logarithm of electron density against time which is linear, and the slope of which gives the characteristic time τ_1 which yields the coefficient of ambipolar diffusion[15] through the relation $D_a = \Lambda_1^2 / \tau_1$. Since this coefficient is essentially the diffusion coefficient of positive ions in the gas, and this quantity is related to the mobility k_+ of the positive ions by the well-known relation $D/k_+ = Ne/p$, with Ne the faraday per cm^3 and p the gas pressure, the dominating ion species active may on occasion be identified by the characteristic k_+. At higher pressures, the loss of electrons may be ascribed to recombination processes, under which circumstances the plot of $1/n$ against time should be linear, the slope yielding the recombination coefficient a.

A third source of electron loss is the attachment of electrons to atoms or molecules to make negative ions. In this event, the decline of density should again be exponential, so that $\log n/n_0 - t$ plots are linear. The rate of attachment is pressure-dependent, and attachment is greater at higher pressures of attaching gas. Thus, attachment like recombination will be more likely to occur at higher pressures. The variation of the coefficient with pressure will depend on the character of the attachment process, and can be used to infer what is happening.[16]

The ambipolar-diffusion coefficient varies inversely with pressure. The negative ion attachment coefficient, as yielded by the characteristic time constant of the exponential, may vary inversely with the attaching impurity; and thus, perhaps in more complicated fashion,

---

[15] The theory for diffusion, including higher modes than the first, indicates that for the higher modes the logarithmic plots are curved in such a fashion as to indicate possible recombination. The higher modes of diffusion, with times τ_2, occur in shorter intervals, and should disappear in longer intervals of observation. Thus, well-cooled plasmas and long intervals $t_2 - t_1$ avoid this complication.

[16] It now appears that extreme precautions must be taken to insure the purity of the gases and the absence of negative ion forming impurities.

with ambient gas pressure, depending on the nature of the contaminating impurity relative to the ambient gas. *A priori*, if only one ion species recombines with an electron, either by radiative or dissociative process, then the coefficient of recombination should not vary with pressure; furthermore, the $1/n$-t plots should be strictly linear over quite a range in values of t.

The first measurements in the inert gases were made by Biondi and Brown (7). There long ionizing pulses were used, and the cool-off period was in the milliseconds. Ion densities were relatively low, i.e., of the order of less than 10^{11} per cm^3. In consequence, they observed very nicely linear plots of $1/n$ against time over long ranges of time, and α was constant. Values for the inert gases were 1.7×10^{-8} for He and 2.07×10^{-7} for Ne. The value was 3.7×10^{-7} for A, which Biondi suspects may not have been pure, as indicated in a conversation with the author. In a later study, Biondi (48) gives 8.8×10^{-7} for A, which is probably the better value. In Ne the values were the same, and constant at 410° K., 300° K., and 195° K.; but at 77° K., while the $1/n$-t plots were linear, α varied with pressure from 2×10^{-7} to 8×10^{-7}, according to a relation of the form $\alpha_a = \alpha_c + A \epsilon^{bp}$; $\alpha_c = 1.94 \times 10^{-7}$; $A = 0.3 \times 10^{-1}$; $b = 0.16/$mm. According to Biondi, the pressure variation could as well have followed some other law, as the range of values was limited.

In ambipolar-diffusion studies at lower pressures, the ions present had been identified as He$^+$, Ne$^+$, and A$^+$. However, mobility studies with mass spectroscope by Holt (35), Hornbeck and Molnar (34), mobility studies of Hornbeck (34), studies of Johnson, McClure, and Holt (35) with microwave discharges using spectroscope and mass spectroscope, and later studies of Biondi and Holstein (48), Biondi (48), and of Phelps (7) with spectroscope and mass spectroscope, as well as of Biondi (9) in He with interferometer, etc., have now clarified the observations of various workers and established what happens.

At the higher pressures in the studies of Biondi and Brown (7), apparently the ions recombining were overwhelmingly molecular ions He$_2^+$, Ne$_2^+$, and A$_2^+$. At appropriate pressures these had been created during the cool-off period largely from triple impacts of He$^+$, Ne$^+$, and A$^+$ with their own species.

However, there are some differences in the creation of these ions and in the dissociative recombination taking place. In He, He$_2^+$ is actually created by two different mechanisms, one of which is within very short times after a field has been applied, accelerating free electrons to higher energies of excitation. These are:

I. *Hornbeck-Molnar process.*

He + (e + > 23 *ev* and < 24.2 *ev*) → He* + e.

He* + He → He$_2^+$ + e + *KE* if collision occurs within 10^{-7} sec.

II. *Holt-Biondi process.*

He$^+$ + 2He → He$_2^+$ + He + *KE*. Triple impact, at higher pressures only.

The latter reaction was proposed by Holt (35) to explain his observations at higher pressures. It was also postulated in 1950 by Bates (7), who calculated the average lifetime of He$^+$ at 25 mm in an attempt to explain the American microwave recombination data. Actual mass-spectrographic studies of the reaction by Phelps (7) indicate that the rate of conversion was 1/3 that predicted theoretically by Bates; i.e., the specific lifetime of He$^+$ at 25 mm was 3×10^{-5} sec.

A spectrographic study of the recombination processes by Biondi and Holstein (48) showed the following facts: In 1-5 mm Hg the square root of the radiation intensity emitted from the afterglow was observed to follow closely the decay of electron density over a considerable range. The visible radiation consisted of *line spectra* from high-level states, $n = 3$, 4, 5, 6; all within 1.5 e.v. of the atomic-ionization potential. For each electron lost, roughly one quantum of radiation is emitted. If dissociative recombination is active in this reaction, the situation is as follows: The heat of dissociation of He$_2^+$ is between 2.2 and 3.1 e.v. If this is so, the energy-level diagrams from which the He$_2^+$ ion dissociates to He + He* require that the electrons cannot come from the lowest energy level of He$_2^+$, but must come from an excited state of He$_2^+$, which lies within 1.5 volts of the ionization potential of 24.5 volts of He, and not at 22.3 or 21.4 volts. The He*, from recombination and dissociation, is excited to within 0.5 to 0.3 e.v. of 24.5 volts. The reaction is then:

$$He_2^{+v} + e \rightarrow He^*(> 23 \ ev) + He .$$

This requires that in the gas studied, the He$_2^{+*v}$, in its excited vibrational state, must last long enough to recombine despite collision frequencies of $\sim 10^7$-10^8 sec with He atoms. This means that the excited vibrational He$_2^+$ ions can suffer of the order of 10^6 collisions without losing the energy of vibration. A study of the theory of such states indicates that for He$_2^{+*v}$, excited to within 0.3 e.v. of the ionization potential, the chance of energy loss is of the order of 10^{-5} per collision. This, taken together with the known existence of the He$_2^+$ ions in these studies and the close correlation of the emission from the lines with electron decay, clinches the assumption of a dissociative recombination in the case in point. In 1953, Biondi (9) announced that the process had been established beyond any question by the observed Doppler broadening of the atomic lines from He*, using interferometric methods.

In the case of Ne, the ions Ne_2^+ at 300° K. were present in the measurement of Biondi. Here again, the square of the electron density fell off as the radiation intensity with one quantum roughly per electron lost. In the Ne the radiating electrons all came from states in the Ne atoms 0.85 or more below the ionization potential. Unfortunately, the energy dissociation of Ne_2^+ is not known, so that quantitative checks cannot be made. However, it seems likely that the Ne_2^+ ions that undergo radiative recombination may all be in the ground-vibrational state.

Furthermore, to prove that the molecular ions are the ones that give the high values of the recombination coefficient in these gases, Biondi (48) performed the following study: In pure A, where A_2^+ ions are largely present at the pressures used, the value of the coefficient of recombination was 8.8×10^{-7} cm^3/ion sec—in fair agreement with previous observation. Then He or Ne was admixed with about 0.1% A. The A atoms were rapidly ionized by He or Ne metastables, giving almost entirely A^+ ions. The density of A^+ ions and atoms was too small to yield any appreciable concentration of A_2^+ ions after sufficient cooling-down periods and use of exciting fields that did not cause breakdown of the He or Ne gas. Thus, the electron decay was entirely caused by the A^+ ions. The decrease in electron density followed an exponential law yielding a coefficient of ambipolar diffusion for A^+ ions in He, which corresponded to a reduced mobility of A^+ ions in He of 22.4 cm^2/volt sec.

This is just what is to be expected for such ions in He when charge exchange does not occur. Within experimental uncertainties in measurement, it can further be concluded that if electrons are lost to recombination with A^+ ions, the coefficient is less than 10^{-3} of that for A_2^+ ions in pure A. If radiative recombination to A^+ had occurred, it could not have been detected, as $\alpha < 10^{-12}$. The radiation intensity decline studies in pure A with the A_2^+ ions gave a value of $\alpha \sim 10^{-6}$. In the He and A mixtures the radiation density of A atoms was at best 10^{-3} of that in pure A. This radiation could have come from some few A_2^+ ions, created in the A-He mixture.

This leaves the question of relatively large values of recombination coefficients in inert gases in the main clearly accounted for by the dissociative recombination of molecular ions. However, it leaves one observation unexplained—namely, the strange pressure variation of a with Ne at 77° K., and the fact that this occurred despite nice linear $1/n-t$ plots over a sufficient range of values of t. This could occur (16) in electron molecular-ion-dissociative recombination if two positive carriers were present in an equilibrium pressure-dependent ratio γ_p, in which event equation 6.47, involving two values of a_1 and a_2 for the ions, leads to a value a_{ed} which varies with γ. Such ion formation is likely at low T.

In the meanwhile, Johnson, McClure, and Holt (35), as well as Holt (35), together with other associates, also studied the electron loss in microwave breakdown of various gases, employing the same general techniques as those used by Biondi and Brown. In addition, spectroscopic and mass-spectroscopic studies were made on the various gases to aid in interpretation. In reading the papers of this group— which will hereafter be alluded to as Holt et al. (35)—since Holt was senior advisor and project-director, certain differences relative to the work of Biondi and Brown must be noted. These workers, in general, used shorter excitation, or breakdown, times for their gases. Their "cooling-off" periods were also materially shorter; e.g., pulse times of the order of 10 microseconds, and cooling-off periods under 100 microseconds. In many cases, electron densities used were higher than those of Biondi; i.e., of the order of 10^{11} to 10^{12} per cm^3.

In reading over the papers, one is impressed by the number of gases studied and the many types of data amassed, leaving an impression that in no case was the study of any one gas so meticulous or exhaustive as were the studies of Biondi and Brown, and later of Biondi. In consequence, it is not surprising that the values obtained for the coefficients by Holt et al. were not in complete agreement with Biondi and Brown's where their studies overlapped. In fact, Holt et al. observed deviations of the linearity of the $1/n-t$ plots, indicating possible variations of a with time. In some cases, a appeared to vary with pressure and intensity of excitation of the gas by microwave pulsing. Finally, two different values of a were observed, such as 5×10^{-7} and 1.1×10^{-6} in argon, dependent on pressure and excitation, while Biondi (48) observed values of 8.8×10^{-7}. In part, the differences must be ascribed to the use by Holt et al. of high electron densities. With such densities, Biondi and Biondi and Brown's collaborators in the measuring techniques (11) had discovered that the ionization of the plasma may not be uniform and the time average electron density is not correctly given by the probing beam because of plasma interaction. Furthermore, higher diffusion modes complicate interpretation of decay curves (29c).

In using short breakdown periods, the various species, such as metastable atoms, are not built up to their more highly developed equilibrium. Thus, Biondi (49) was able to observe and study a considerable ionization and electron-density *increase* by interaction of He metastable atoms in his plasmas, while Holt *et al.* (35) did not build up enough initial concentration of metastable atoms to observe the effect. Again, with short cooling-down periods, not only did electrons in the inert gases fail to reach thermal energies, but mixtures of carriers such as A_2^+ and A^+ coexisted; while in Biondi and Brown's study, the initially created A_2^+ had disappeared by various processes, leaving only A^+ for ambipolar-diffusion studies; and at higher pressures, A_2^+ by triple impact of A^+.

In view of these difficulties, the author is inclined to discount the significance of some of the disturbing findings of Holt *et al.*, and to accept as authentic the more conservative data of Biondi and Brown. However, it is to the credit of Holt *et al.* that they correctly interpreted the data in He which indicated a predominance of He^+ at lower pressures and earlier times and the formation of He_2^+ at higher pressures and larger times from triple impacts of $He^+ + He$. In fact, they calculated the curves for electron densities for a in recombination when He^+ and He_2^+ ions coexisted with electrons, and He^+ was changing to He_2^+. The curves computed were like those observed under the experimental conditions, with parameters chosen to fit.

A very interesting study was recently made in this area by H. N. Olsen and W. S. Huxford (8). They used pulsed, heavy, overvolted current discharges between plane electrodes in an outgassed quartz container of 4 mm diameter with Ne or A gas at 70-30 mm pressure, and on occasion with less than 1% of H_2 gas added. The purpose of the H_2 gas, which did not change the character of the discharge, was to permit an evaluation of *ion densities* by means of the Stark-effect broadening of the lines H_α, H_β, etc., of the Balmer series. Using photomultipliers, spectroscopes, and oscillographic recording, simultaneous observation of potentials, currents, and line intensities as a function of time was possible.

Arc lines, spark lines, and the continuous spectra were separately studied. The discharge patterns for many repeated flashes were all clearly delineated, showing remarkable reproductivity. The Hilger constant-deviation spectroscope permitted traverses of different sections of the spark-broadened lines to be studied, so that time-intensity distribution curves for each section of an H or He line could be plotted. Cross plots at constant times enabled the intensity distribution and broadening at each instant to be determined. Using the corrected

Holtsmark theory, the electron and/or ion densities could be calculated as a function of time for the gas.

The following facts were observed: Ion concentrations in A were
lower than in Ne, even at higher flash energies, despite the lower
ionization potentials and collision cross sections in A. On the other
hand, peak currents were higher in Ne than in A, while breakdown
potentials were lower for Ne than for A. This result is not surprising,
since the electrons begin ionization at lower X/p in A than in Ne;
but their efficiencies are small. Furthermore, the mobilities of ions
and of electrons are lower in A than in Ne.

More interesting is the fact that in these discharges the radiation
peak lagged 5 to 7 microseconds behind the current peak. This again
need not be surprising, since the discharge is an impulsive one in
a highly overvolted gap. The initial breakdown is catastrophic, and
very high fields must collapse as ionization builds up. Large currents
at the high fields can be expected, even before the ion density reaches
its maximum. Currents measured depend on carrier velocity as well
as number, and also on the initially great rate of creation of a plasma
of ions. The electron-drift velocities and energies are high, so that
increase in ionization is exceedingly rapid while the high fields
exist and are collapsing. This pours much energy into the gap at a
very high level. It also removes carriers at a high speed while fields
are high.

During high fields and currents, the carriers are removed by the
current. When these losses decline toward 0, the ionization density
rises in consequence of the stored energy with increased efficiency
of lower-energy electrons. Since most efficient ionization and excitation occur as the carrier energy comes down to near the ionization
threshold, it is not surprising to see that the ionization and radiation
continue to increase for some time after current peak may have passed.
Radiation rise due to excitation may even lag behind the peak of
ionization.

The current rose to a peak in Ne in some 1.5 μ sec at 3×10^3
ampere and declined to $1/5$ by 5 μ sec, while in A the rise to a peak
took 4 μ sec with about 1,000-ampere peak value, falling to $1/5$ in
15 μ sec. The *ion concentrations* rose to a peak in some 7 μ sec in
Ne, and in 10 μ sec in A. The intensity of the continua at 4,000,
7,000, and 9,000 Å in both gases closely paralleled the ion concentrations in rise, having peaks at 5 and 7 μ sec in Ne and A, but fell
much more rapidly. Ion concentrations[17] at peak in Ne were 3×10^{17},

[17]It must be recognized that breakdown at these energies may have been
nearly as complete as in the spark channels. In the work of Hopwood and

and in A about 1.2×10^{17} per cm³. More interesting, perhaps, are the times to peak value in the gases for specific lines. The 4,806 Å line in A and the 4,413 Å line in Ne, both *spark lines*, rose to a peak in around 5 μ secs; i.e., at the peak of ionization. The arc lines 8,408 Å in A and 6,383 Å in Ne peaked at 10 μ sec, and were associated with recombination lagging behind the peak of ionization. The H_α and H_β lines in hydrogen showed very broad peaks somewhere around 10-12 μ secs.

It is noted that the lines requiring high energy show the sharpest peaks, and were the first to reach a maximum intensity. These are lines excited by electron impacts that radiate at once. Thus, the spark lines show maxima near the current peak, while the arc lines reach a maximum well after the current peak has passed. The arc lines, at least in part, result from recombination. Since ionization and excitation of low-energy lines continue for a considerable time because of the degradation of energy and its consequent "temperature ionization," the ionization continues. In 5 to 7 μ sec the current has fallen to zero, and the rate of ionization begins to equal the rate of loss by recombination and by ambipolar diffusion to the walls, which at these densities and temperatures is not negligible. This time represents the peak of ionization.

The continua which decline with electron concentration can be due to electron deceleration in the field of the ions, "bremsstrahlung" (free-free transition), or to recombination. The nature of the ratio of the electron concentration to the continuum at each stage in the discharge shows that *ion* and *electron* concentrations build up together while the discharge builds up, and that relative temperatures do not change materially during the period. *Where the plasma is decaying, the intensity of the continua falls off more rapidly than the concentration.* This precludes recombination as the major cause for decline of continua. The only factor that can decrease the radiation in this way is the decrease in electron and ion temperatures. As the temperature decreases there must result a decrease in the energetic free-free transitions yielding continua. Thus, the free-free transition deceleration radiation should decrease with relative rapidity, while more electron-ion radiative recombination will occur as electron energies decrease.

A careful study of the problem indicates that if the electron temperature at peak is 10,600° K., and falls to 8,300° K. in 30 μ secs,

Craggs (6), gas pressure p was constant and temperature was adiabatically high. Here gas density is constant in the volume, and both T and p are adiabatically high.

the bremsstrahlung (free-free transition) will account for the main portion of the continuum and its decline. The recombination is occurring all the time, but is least during the intense portion of the flash owing to high electron temperatures. From the *decay in intensity of the arc lines*, which were only a few per cent of the total reduction, extending from 15 μ sec to 30, the coefficients of recombination were computed to be 2.5×10^{-13} cm^3/ion sec in A, and 5.3×10^{-14} cm^3/ion sec in Ne. Such recombination could therefore contribute little to the continuum. The values of the coefficients were fairly constant, indicating only a slow decline of electron temperatures in the decaying plasma.

In discussing these results, it is to be noted that the situation here differs materially from that in the study of H_2 by Craggs and Meek (6). There recombination was studied between H^+ and electrons in the intensely ionized H gas, again using Stark-effect broadening. Pressure was 760 mm, and density was as high as the elevated channel *gas temperature* admitted; perhaps 2,000° K. Recombination was enhanced by the high fields of the ions, despite electron temperatures of 12,000° K. When Craggs and Meek looked at spark channels in A, they were confused by the considerably longer duration of afterglows and continua—paralleling the data of Olsen and Huxford—and made no analyses. The discharge study of Olsen and Huxford, while yielding the same order of number density of ions, used initial pressures of about 0.1 atmosphere and constant density. Gas temperature was probably not so high as in the channels of Hopwood and Craggs. H_2 was present to less than 1% of the inert gas, and was used purely to measure ion densities, often being omitted entirely.

It is clear that with the inert gases, the problem is exceedingly complex. The absorption and imprisonment of resonant radiation, and the action of metastable atoms in these gases, contrasted to the simplicity existing with completely dissociated H gas, kept electron temperatures high in the gas for far longer times through inelastic impacts of the second class. This is indicated by the increase in ionization with current flow, and the prolongation of the continua caused by bremsstrahlung. While ion densities in this study were high, the chance was small for the cumulative formation of molecular ions of inert gases by triple impacts in any great quantity in the 10 to 40 μ secs of observation.

At the elevated electron temperatures, formation of molecular ions by the Hornbeck-Molnar process is less likely. It is not known to what extent the H_2 present interfered with the creation of A_2^+ and Ne_2^+ by destroying the metastables or excited states. It could *not* have been serious, because the lines without H_2 behaved just as did those with it. Thus, in these gases at the times used, in contrast to the long delays at the same pressures in cold gases, as used by Biondi and Brown (7), little or no A_2^+ and Ne_2^+ was present to give dissociative recombination. Thus, Olsen and Huxford argue that the only electron loss was by ambipolar diffusion and electron-ion radiative recombination of A^+ and Ne^+. If there was no recreation of excited states of Ne and A by electron impacts, causing new radiative emission, any decline in the intensity of arc lines in intervals of 10 to 30 microseconds had to be ascribed to reduction in electron and ion densities by recombination.

The curves plotted for $1/n$ against time in μ sec from 15-30 μ secs appear linear, but over small ranges of t. That for A is less steep between 10-15 μ secs than later; i.e., it is curved. The values for a observed are $a = 2.5 \times 10^{-13}$ for A and 3×10^{-14} for Ne, with electron temperatures of the order of 8,300° K. This would indicate *radiative* recombination under these conditions.[18] No correction was made for ambipolar diffusion, though some calculation that was not reported may have indicated it to be negligible.

While there is probably little question as to the origin of the lines or the general conclusions drawn in this study, and while radiative electron-ion recombination is observed, with coefficients which are reasonably in line with wave-mechanical theory, some care must be used in accepting these interpretations. In the first place, the retarded decline of the intensity in the arc-spectral lines, attributed to recombination, could result from the continued excitation of those states by electron impact unless electron temperatures as low as 8,300° K. were certainly established. While (as the authors seem to assume) electron loss by ambipolar diffusion to the walls at most 2 mm away, in the observed time intervals at the 50- or 20-mm pressure, is negligible compared to the loss to recombination, this may not be the case. With the small ranges of t to yield linear plots of $1/n$ against t, the variation could as well be that for ambipolar diffusion. Finally, it is quite possible that the existence of enough molecular ions to give the slow decline of electrons by dissociative attachment, leading to arc lines of the inert gases, could have yielded the curvature seen in A. Thus, at this time the interpretation of these results is submitted, as are also the following interpretations on recombination, as suggestive and tentative but by no means proved.

It is now of interest to regard the data on the molecular gases

---

[18]Of course, if small amounts of A_2^+ and He_2^+ were present, they could have yielded a dissociative electron-ion recombination with very small calculated coefficients.

H_2, N_2, O_2, and on arc plasmas with A, Cs, and Hg, as well as Hg by microwave study. In discussing these studies, it is urgent to indicate that the ionization and excitation products in pulsed microwave discharges of milliseconds duration, arc currents as used by Mohler, and flashbulb breakdown currents such as used by Olsen and Huxford, are not those to be expected from appearance-potential studies. The broad spectrum of electron energies in most of these breakdown studies, the prolonged ionization, and especially the very high electron densities from 10^{10} to 10^{17}, produce carriers of all kinds. For example, while O^+ ions should not readily appear compared to O_2^+ ions, since the appearance potential is much higher for the former on a Franck and Hertz type study, considerable O^+ may be expected in microwave breakdown. The reason is that O_2 dissociates at some 5.09 e.v., and in a microwave breakdown with 10^{11} electrons and ions, there will be quite a concentration of dissociated O atoms capable of ionization by subsequent impacts. Likewise, the metastable atoms, etc., also accumulate; and even the imprisonment of resonance radiation makes certain some further ionization and excitation of these by impact of electrons of low energy.

Beginning with the work on H_2, a very peculiar situation is presented. As previously indicated, Craggs, Meek, and Hopwood (6) observed what was probably a true radiative electron-ion recombination yielding the Balmer series, with 100% dissociation and ionization in a spark channel. At these high Stark-effect fields, the coefficient was probably increased by a factor of 10 or 100 to 10^{-11}, instead of 10^{-12} or 10^{-13}. If the decline of electrons by recombination is to be conveniently measured in microseconds, then the value of n_e must be of the order of 10^{17}. On the other hand, if a microwave plasma is used, with observing times in the milliseconds, the ion density must be of the order 10^{14}. Of course, this is greater than densities safely studied by these techniques. It will be noted that the presumed radiative electron-ion recombination of A^+ and He^+ with $a \sim 10^{-13}$ required 10^{17} electron per cm^3. It will then be unlikely that true electron-ion recombination of a radiative sort will be observable with microwave techniques. Dissociative electron-molecular ion recombination with coefficients a of more than 10^{-8} will, however, be readily measured.

In the work of Biondi and Brown (7), the microwave discharge vessel was a thoroughly outgassed quartz bottle. In the studies on *inert gases*, such a container had shown no evidence of contaminating the gases during the discharge. In Varnerin's (46) work, the vessel was a silver-plated Kovar tube with a glass window at one end sealed to the Kovar frame, and a quarter wave-length block of quartz at the

other end to prevent ionization. All-metal stopcocks and other precautions were used to prevent contamination. The H_2 came through
a Pd leak, while that of Biondi and Brown was spectroscopically
pure H_2. Varnerin had some trouble in achieving purity with his system. With their method, Biondi and Brown found a single value of
$a = 2.5 \times 10^{-6}$ for H_2 between 1 and 10 mm pressure. Varnerin observed
values ranging from 0.34 to 2.5×10^{-6} following an S-shaped curve
of the initial form $a_p = a_0 + 0.0026\ p^2$, with p in mm. Above 20 mm
the curve flattened out to the same value as that of Biondi and Brown
at 45 mm pressure.

Varnerin was inclined to account for this behavior in terms of
equation 6.45, assuming a dynamic equilibrium to be maintained between H^- ions and electrons recombining with single positive ions.
Now the H^- ion is not an ion that forms in the gas through attachment
of electrons to H_2 dissociatively, or to H atoms. It is a rarely observed ion, created by grazing incidence of H^+ or H_2^+ ions of some
100 volts or more energy on a metal surface. According to W. H.
Bennett and P. F. Darby (50), the ion is created in considerable
quantity in discharges in H_2O through dissociation of H_2O in a polar
phase. Thus, assuming the H_2 of Varnerin to be pure, and accepting
his data as representing a true recombination, the author and W. B.
Kunkel (16) showed that a curve shaped like the one reported by
Varnerin would be expected through equation 6.47, assuming that
H_2^+ and H_3^+ ions were in dynamic equilibrium and that they had values
of a corresponding to the values 0.34 and 2.5×10^{-6} in recombination
with electrons. In this case, if the ratio of H_3^+ to H_2^+ was due to triple
impact between H_2 and H^+, with an H_2 molecule in labile equilibrium,
the ratio $\gamma = n_2/n_e$ of equation 6.47 would have to be proportional
to p^2. Agreement in the general shape of the curve calculated with
Varnerin's observed curve was significant, but a higher power variation with p than the second seemed to be indicated.

Fortunately, K. B. Persson (29c), who later worked at Massachusetts
Institute of Technology on the same problem as Varnerin, using the
more conventional microwave techniques with the quartz flask, ran
into some interesting facts, reported at the Sixth Conference on
Gaseous Electronics in 1953. First, he found that the Pd leak gave
O_2-contaminated H_2. Secondly, he discovered that running the micro-
discharge in the initially pure H_2 in the quartz flask liberated a large
amount of H_2O. Baking did not remove the O_2, and only prolonged
discharge for days with fresh H_2 in the quartz flask eventually reduced
the contamination so that measurements could be made in pure H_2.
He also noted that great care had to be taken to avoid distortions

produced by the confusion of higher modes of ambipolar diffusion with a recombination when this was small. This hazard was well known to Biondi and Brown (7), and was carefully eliminated in their work; while it may not have been avoided in the work of Holt *et al.* (35).

On removing all H_2O and O_2 impurities, Persson was *unable to observe any recombination* in H_2. This is a most significant discovery.

It is at once clear that Biondi and Brown's preliminary study, and Varnerin's work in particular, were complicated by the presence of H_2O vapor in the H_2. In the last analysis, this must have come from the action of the H produced in the prolonged microwave breakdown in reducing the SiO_2 of the quartz to either a lower silicon oxide or to Si, and creating water vapor. On prolonged treatment, the effective wall surface of the vessel was so far reduced—for example, to SiO— as to be ineffective in creating much H_2O. The use of Pd leaks by the author's students had never yielded pure H_2. Pure H_2 is best prepared electrolytically; and after drying, acid removal, etc., it should be passed through long tubes of O_2-free Cu metal at 300° C., and over liquid-air traps. In the author's laboratory, such H_2 was always used in thoroughly outgassed, borosilicate glass vessels. Ordinary discharge did not appear to produce contamination from the glass, and the most sensitive criteria indicated the H_2 to be pure. However, the glass never received the intensive action of H, such as that produced in a microwave discharge. Therefore, it is still an open question whether borosilicate glasses are better than quartz, but it is suspected that they are. In microwave cavity work, however, quartz is far preferable to glasses, since these absorb so much energy and heat up.

Leaving aside the question of *prevention* of contamination, it is of interest to see how this might have given the results observed by Biondi and Brown and by Varnerin. The microwave discharge in H_2 initially produces H^+, H_2^+, and later, by triple-body impact, H_3^+, from H_2 and H^+ or from H_2^+ and H. At the pressures used, the predominating ions after a millisecond would be H_2^+ and H_3^+, with most of the H^+ gone. The negative carriers in Persson's pure H_2 were only electrons. Under these conditions a was observed to be 0, and since radiative recombination could not be observed at these carrier densities, no dissociative recombination could have occurred. This observation is very significant, for it shows that the existence of molecular ions and even molecular ion complexes like H_3^+ does not insure a dissociative recombination with slow electrons.

In the impure H_2, the presence of H_2O vapor insured the existence of some H^- ions, as observed by Bennett. Bradbury (51) inferred that at an electron energy above 5.4 e.v., electrons attached dissociatively to H_2O to form OH^- ions and H. No doubt O^- ions were present in Varnerin's H_2 as well. The H^- ions formed from H_2O were not in any exchange relation to the free electrons, as assumed by Varnerin. The relatively high heats of formation of OH^- and O^- also precluded such action. Furthermore, most of the formation of these ions occurred during the breakdown period before the electrons had cooled off. What percentage of the negative ions consisted of H^-, OH^-, and O^- is not known; but if the contamination was even as much as 1% of the H_2 pressure present, it is hardly probable that these ions constituted any large fraction of the negative carriers present. These negative ionic carriers obviously recombined with H_2^+ and H_3^+ in *pressure-dependent, ion-ion recombination* reactions at the pressures noted.

The creation of these carriers does not figure significantly in electron loss during the recombination period. The presence of negative ionic carriers—ions that formed during the breakdown period—serves to remove positive ions during the recombination period, but scarcely affects the measured electron concentration. There is no clue in this action of the H_2O as to what is reducing electron concentration during recombination intervals. It thus becomes very difficult to account for the apparent recombination, observed by Biondi and Brown and by Varnerin through electron loss, in any fashion other than ascribing it to a *negative ion formation by attachment of free electrons to water-vapor or O_2 molecules.*

Such action, which seemed to be pressure-dependent, was observed by Bradbury (51) to occur with cross sections of the order of 10^{-20} cm^2 for low-energy electrons. However, Bradbury's data on H_2O are not very accurate, and their significance is not clear. If the decline was a loss of electrons to make H_2O^- ions, the quantity of H_2O vapor must have been fairly large. It is also queer that the electron loss in the studies of Biondi and Brown and of Varnerin, even with water vapor present, should have yielded linear $1/n$-t plots if an electron attachment occurred.

Thus, while it is clear that the decline of electrons in the microwave plasmas of Biondi and Brown and of Varnerin are associated with the presence of unknown amounts of water vapor in the H_2, the interpretation of their data in terms of this circumstance is not clear, and this phase of the study in soiled H_2 merits further investigation.

However, it is both significant and satisfying to note that in pure H_2, with largely H_2^+ and H_3^+ ions, dissociative recombination with electrons of thermal energy *does not* occur.

The studies of α in pure N_2 are as yet in their preliminary stages. In the first place, purity of N_2 is hard to achieve. Prepared from the air by liquefaction methods, contamination with perhaps 1% A is certain, and this is hard to remove. CO_2, O_2, and H_2O are effectively removed. Prepared from NaN_3 or one of the other azides, the presence of amines, H, and NH_3 can be feared; though O_2 and H_2O are effectively "gettered" by Na. When Na and N_2 gas are exposed to ionizing action, there is present some form of volatile and readily ionized compound of sufficient vapor pressure to increase ionization coefficients by 17% at high X/p, and to show marked photon absorption in some regions (52). Chemically prepared from solution, N_2 should be reasonably pure if properly dried and purified, including passage over O_2-free Cu at 300° C.

There is no guarantee that the N_2 used was pure, either in Biondi and Brown's work or in that of Holt's group. The most reliable value is that of Biondi and Brown (7), where there was a pressure variation with α ranging from 1.4 to 1.9×10^{-7} cm³/ion sec. This could indicate some negative ion forming impurity, which is not probable. Neither N_2 nor N forms negative ions. In N_2 gas the ions initially formed are N_2^+ and N^+. R. N. Varney (53), in mobility studies at different X/p, noted an initial ion N_2^+, the mobility of which was low because of charge-exchange reactions. The other ion noted had a mobility which identified it as probably N_4^+. O. Luhr (54), with mass spectroscope, from a discharge in pure N_2 at 0.2 mm pressure, observed considerable N^+, three times as much N_2^+, some N_3^+, and more N_4^+. At the higher pressures it is probable that the older ions at low X/p were largely N_4^+ and N_3^+, while at lower pressures and higher X/p the ions were largely N^+ and N_2^+, with the latter predominating for obvious reasons.

In recombination studies it is possible, but not certain, that electrons *might* recombine dissociatively with either N_2^+, N_3^+, or N_4^+, but especially with the latter. Varney has evidence that in certain ranges of energy, N_2^+ and N_4^+ are in dynamic equilibrium. Thus, relations such as those invoked by the author and Kunkel (16) for recombination in H_2 for Varnerin's work (represented by equation 6.47), with α proportional to p, could be applicable. The values of X/p for such equilibria were higher than those corresponding to microwave plasma. If dynamic equilibrium occurred, it would account for a pressure variation such as observed. No definite conclusions can be drawn on the basis of the present preliminary results.

The results in O_2 probably present no problem as regards purity (7). O_2 can be taken from a tank, and after removing CO_2 and other obvious impurities, condensed in liquid air. Successive fractional distillation yields very pure O_2. If needed, it can be produced by heating $KMnO_4$ (*not* $KClO_3$, under any circumstances). O. Luhr (54) has shown, however, that no matter how pure the O_2, if a discharge using N_2 is first run in a tube that later will contain O_2, the N_2 will be removed from electrodes by the O_2 discharge, yielding NO^+ and N_2O^+. It is unlikely that such action complicated this study. The O_2 distilled over liquid air was thus very pure. The only data in O_2 are the preliminary results of Biondi and Brown (7). A pressure-dependent a, ranging from 3×10^{-7} to 14×10^{-7} cm^3/ion sec, was inferred from the decrease of electron densities. O. Luhr, at his low pressures, observed a few O^+ ions, but mostly O_2^+ ions. No O_3^+ or O_4^+ ions were observed. Varney (53), using pulsed breakdown techniques, observed only one ion in O_2. The value of its drift velocity identified it as probably O_2^+, which suffers momentum loss due to charge exchange.

There is, of course, electron loss to negative ion formation. Two negative ions can form. One is a stable ion O^- of energy of binding 1.45 e.v., created only by electrons in excess of 3 e.v. energy by a dissociative attachment process with O_2 (55). The cross section for this reaction is large, and there is no question that in the microwave plasma, while the discharge is on, as many as half of the electrons created are attached to give O^- ions. After the discharge ceases, with $\sim 10^{11}$ electrons per cm^3, the radiation density and the cooling electrons in the plasma may effectively reionize some of these negative ions, restoring electron concentration in some measure. The balance of the O^- ions will undergo ion-ion recombination with O_2^+ ions, the coefficient of which is a relatively large one which increases as pressure increases in the range used. There is also possible a slower formation of O_2^- ions, which at 8 to 25 mm Hg may not lead to a serious loss. The binding energy for the electrons in O_2^- is less than 0.5 e.v., and it is a question whether in plasmas radiatively as hot as the plasmas used, the O_2^- ions are permanently stable. They could be in a labile equilibrium with electrons with radiation, with $\gamma_p \propto p$.

Strangely enough, while the electron disappearance in O_2 was largely due to attachment according to Biondi (7), the value of the cross section was of the order of 1.2×10^{-22} cm^2. This is far less than that for the Bradbury-Bloch process for O_2, which is about 6×10^{-20} cm^2. Whether a reduced Bradbury-Bloch coefficient could appear as a result of detachment is not clear. It is thus very unlikely that the dissociative attachment forming O^- ions plays any role in the disappearance of electrons in the cooled-down plasma, though it is instrumental in determining the initial relative concentrations n_-, n_+,

TABLE 6.5

Summary of Recombination Data from Arc Plasmas

Observers	Energy	Pressure, mm Hg	α_e	n_e	Comments
IN ARGON					
Kenty	0.4 e.v.	0.8	2×10^{-10}	7×10^{12}	
Sayers	0.07 e.v.	0.1-1 mm	1.12×10^{-9}	10^{11}	Independent of p. Varies as $T^{-3/2}$.
	0.14 e.v.	0.1-1 mm	4.2×10^{-10}	10^{11}	
Biondi	0.35 e.v.	20-30 mm	8.8×10^{-7}	10^{11}	Microwave.
IN MERCURY					
Mohler	0.23 e.v.	0.27	2.3×10^{-10}	10^{12}	
Dandurand and Holt	0.23 e.v.	0.5	5×10^{-9}	10^{12}	
Biondi	0.035 e.v.	1.4-46 mm	$5.1-14 \times 10^{-7}$	10^9	Microwave. Pressure-dependent.
IN CESIUM					
Mohler	0.140 e.v.	$(1 \text{ to } 10) \times 10^{-2}$	3.4×10^{-10}	10^{12}	
Dandurand and Holt	0.16 e.v.	0.32-0.68	3.5×10^{-7} 1.45×10^{-6}	10^{12}	Microwave. Gas at 285° and 270° K.

and n_e. The coefficient of recombination observed by Biondi and Brown may have been a dissociative recombination of electrons with O_2^+ ions (the chief ion present). Such a process has an α that is *not* pressure-dependent, and so is ruled out. The measurement of this coefficient is complicated by the following factors.

1. n_e is reduced by a slow attachment, or negative ion forming process, yielding an unknown negative ion, with an apparent cross section $\sim 10^{-22}$ cm^2.

2. n_O is greater initially (perhaps as great) as n_e, since many n_O ions were formed in the plasma from free electrons..

3. n_O is still being altered by ion-ion recombination with O_2^+, while n_e is also being reduced by dissociative recombination with O_2^+.

4. It is possible that the Bradbury-Bloch attachment yields a reversible equilibrium with O_2^- ions and electrons. This would lead to

a possible pressure-dependent α, since n_e and $n_{O_2^-}$ recombine with a single type of O_2^+ ion, and γ_p is pressure-dependent. This is the process visualized in the E layer. Whether such an equilibrium negative ion formation would appear as an observable one in the attachment study of Biondi is a question.

In this case it is seen that it is again impossible at this time, with the preliminary data, reasonably to account for the presence of a pressure-dependent electron-ion recombination.

It is now of interest to discuss the values of a observed by Kenty, Mohler, and Sayers in arcs, and to associate them with the microwave breakdown values at relatively lower electron temperature. Reference to table 6.4 (*supra*) will indicate that the data appearing in table 6.5 apply in this case.

Certain features stand out clearly. The electron temperatures in the arc studies were generally higher than those in microwave studies, and the pressures were generally lower. Correlated with these associations are the very small values of a' from arc studies, and the correspondingly large values from microwave breakdown. At first sight, it would be logical to ascribe the difference in values to a very rapid decrease of the coefficient for dissociative recombination with electron energy. For radiative recombination, it was assumed from theory that a varied as $1/E$ where E was the energy in e.v.

D. R. Bates (7) has developed a rough theory of the process which evaluates a_{ed} as a function of electron temperature. It has the form:

$$a_{ed} = 2.1 \times 10^{-16} \left\{ \frac{r}{T^{3/2}} (r_A + r_s) \right\}$$

(6.130)

$$\int_G \epsilon^{-\frac{E}{kT}} f(E)dE \ \text{cm}^3/\text{ion sec}.$$

Here, r is the ratio of the statistical weight of A_2^* to A_2^+; E is the electron energy; $f(E)$ is the familiar Franck-Condon factor, measuring the degree of overlap between the nuclear wave functions concerned in the initial transitions; r_A is the averaged characteristic time associated with autoionization, i.e., the reversal of $A_2^+ + e \overset{\leftarrow}{\to} A_2^*$; and r_s is the averaged time for the effective separation to occur. Estimates of r by Bates place r relatively high if a number of excited states occur; he suggests 10. He estimates $r_A \sim 10^{-13}$ sec and r_s to be of the same order, as velocities are 10^5 cm/sec and less then 10^{-8} cm is involved. The integral depends on the details of the potential curves. It will be small unless $f(E)$ is appreciable for low E_s, but in favorable circumstances it can equal the numerical value of $2kT$ when expressed in e.v. With these possibilities, at 250° K. $\alpha_{ed} \sim 10^{-7}$, which is good. Here it is seen that α_{ed} varies at $T^{-3/2}$. This value fits in with data obtained by Sayers, and extrapolates from his data reasonably well to Kenty's value yielding 0.8×10^{-10}. It is clear that the difference in electron temperature, or energy, between thermal and some 0.5 e.v., will not account for the differences in α by several orders of magnitude.

In Cs there is near equality of electron energy, but a 10-fold pressure difference between Mohler's conditions and those of Dandurand and Holt, with Mohler's values of α as 3.4×10^{-10} as against 3.5×10^{-7} or more for the latter. There is one other difference between microwave and probe, or light-intensity, measurements; the probes measure local electron concentrations far from the walls, while the microwave studies measure the over-all decline of electron densities throughout the volume. Thus, in microwave studies, ambipolar-diffusion loss figures, and must be corrected for at all times; whereas with the probes, it is only after some time that the loss reaches the probe. Hence (for example, with Kenty's arrangements), despite the fact that ambipolar-diffusion loss probably equaled recombination loss in rate, it is doubtful whether diffusion loss materially altered the concentration near his probe. Study of the light intensity, if the light emission comes from recombination, reveals that this intensity does decrease in proportion to the density of the recombining ions averaged over the emitting volume. If the microwave plasma is not isotropically ionized, and if higher modes of diffusion occur, the changes of carrier density observed can lead to falsified values of the recombination coefficient deduced. For reasons indicated, the plasmas created in relatively short ionization periods and studied after 100 microseconds' aging, as in Hg by Dandurand and Holt, could have given values of α that are in doubt; and the same may apply to the Cs studies, even though light intensity was observed. The errors caused by "green" plasmas could well lead to high apparent values of the recombination coefficient.

It is now essential to consider the cause for the discrepancy between the low values of α in the arcs and the higher values at higher pressures and lower energy in microwave breakdown. For the purpose of discussion it is best to choose A gas, about which much is known. As indicated elsewhere, recombination with a coefficient $\alpha \sim 10^{-6}$ in the inert gases is known to be a dissociative recombination of molecular ions such as A_2^+ ions with electrons; the coefficient for radiative recombination of A^+, for example, being computed as $\sim 10^{-13}$ at 0.4

e.v. Now in microwave plasmas in 2-4 milliseconds at 10 to 20 mm pressure, the A^+ ions have all transformed to A_2^+ ions by triple impact, so that $n_e = n_{A_2^+}$. However, in the arcs at 0.8 to 10^{-2} mm, the transformation of A^+ and A_2^+, or the existence only of A_2^+ and electrons, is not assured. Thus, when a is computed from equation 6.2, assuming $n_e = n_+ = n$ in equation 6.1, the value of loss indicated by a $1/n-t$ plot will not give the true a, since with $n_+ < n_e$, $dn/dt = a n_+ n_e$, and the situation can become quite complex. Now there are two processes by which A_2^+ ions are formed, giving an electron for each A_2^+ formed. One of these is the Hornbeck-Molnar process:

(1) $A^{*14.01} + A \rightarrow A_2^+ + e$.

The other is the triple-impact process suggested by Holt:

(2) $A^+ + 2A \rightarrow A_2^+ + A$.

Fortunately, a great deal is known about these processes, so that calculations can be made. Thus, for process 1 at an $X/p = 30$, there are 2.5 photons created with energies capable of forming A_2^+ ions on impact with neutral atoms. The product of cross section σ_m for formation of A_2^+ in collision, and the lifetime τ of the active state for this process at an $X/p = 30$ is 1×10^{-22}. Hence, if $\sigma_m = 10^{-16}$ cm^2, τ is 10^{-6} sec. The critical pressure p_c at which collision frequency $1/z$ is about equal to τ, above which the formation of A_2^+ is independent of pressure, is 8 mm Hg. Thus, below 8 mm pressure, the ratio of atomic to molecular ions produced in A becomes pressure-dependent, varying directly as p below 8 mm. For example, in Kenty's study the ratio of A_2^+/A^+ would have been of the order of 2.5×10^{-1} if Kenty's ions had been created at an $X/p \sim 30$. In Kenty's low-voltage, hot-cathode, high-current arc of 15.5 volts, X/p was certainly less than 15, and ionization was by cumulative impact by an energy distribution of average energy 2.5 e.v. Hence, it is probable that far less than 2.5 photons were produced per A^+ ion; and even at a conservative guess, $n_{A_2^+}/n_{A^+} < 0.1$.

At this point it is perhaps of value to digress and present some of Kenty's findings in detail, since his very careful and complete study sheds much light on what transpired, and makes it profitable to direct further inquiry into the formation processes of A_2^+.

The very careful measurements of Kenty indicate that the afterglow spectrum was very different from that of the arc and that the light came largely from very highly excited A atoms. No continuum was observed. That the light did not come from electron excitation was shown by the absence in the afterglow of the D lines from traces of Na present in the discharge. Metastable action was also excluded by careful use of admixtures with H_2, which did not change the after-glow but quenched metastable atoms very effectively. Application of small potentials, increasing electron energy in the arc plasma, at once quenched the afterglow which resumed at its previous level once the potential was removed. This and other controls indicated that the recombination effectively only occurred after the electrons had cooled, from 2.5 to 0.4 e.v., and that recombination was rapidly decreased as energies rose above this.

The actual data on recombination were taken with probes in which n_e decreased from 7×10^{12} per cm^3 to 2×10^{12} per cm^3 in the interval from 2.5×10^{-4} to 2.5×10^{-3}, seen after cutoff, with electron energy constant at 0.4 e.v. Ambipolar-diffusion loss was estimated as being about equal to recombination loss, but not corrected for. The $1/n\text{-}t$ plot was "approximately a straight line." The value of $a = 2 \times 10^{-10}$ derived was not corrected for diffusion loss, so that on this count it could be high by a factor of 2, according to Kenty. Since Kenty meas-ured local densities with probes, ambipolar diffusion under his ex-perimental conditions need not have lowered local carrier densities near the probe in his time intervals. Thus, correction for diffusion is not warranted, while it would be if microwave probes had been used. Kenty also rightfully recognized the fact that since the probes were on intermittently, this may have changed ion concentrations. The steady arc currents observed with intermittent probes gave n_e twice as large as with steady probes, considering the ratio of times during which the probe was connected. He drew currents in excess of 10^{-7} ampere to his probes. This may have introduced uncertainty by another factor of 2, according to Kenty. It is now recognized that probes in a decaying plasma do not give reliable values of electron densities. Thus, Kenty was justified in estimating that a could be 10^{-10} as well as 2×10^{-10}.

One fact emerges clearly from the spectra observed: Kenty was observing a dissociative electron recombination of A_2^+ with electrons, yielding the initially highly excited states of A which created the A_2^+, and there was thus no evidence of the continua associated with capture into the higher levels of A to be expected from radiative capture. It is also evident from his observation that even this recom-bination process is very sensitive to electron energy, though *how* sensitive cannot be decided from these measurements.

It is now necessary to investigate the effect of disparate numbers of A_2^+ and A^+, and thus of electrons on the value of a deduced. Kenty assumed that radiative capture occurred, and that $n_{A^+} = n_e$, such that his a was determined from equation 6.2. Actually, after the arc was cut off, there were n_e electrons and probably 0.1 n_e or less A_2^+ ions that could recombine with an a roughly 1×10^{-6}. In addition, through triple impacts at these pressures, A^+ could have increased, or at least could have compensated for the losses of the initial A_2^+ by triple impact. Both conditions will yield an apparent a' calculated from equation 6.2, which is less than that which really exists. The effects of these two actions must be considered separately.

The value of a' when there is an initial difference in concentration of recombining partners is treated by the solution of equation 6.10, which reads:

$$(6.10) \qquad \frac{1}{n_e} = \frac{1}{\Delta n_0} \left(1 - \frac{n_{A0}}{n_{e0}} \epsilon^{-a\Delta n_0 t} \right) ,$$

so that

$$a' = d(1/n_e)/dt = a(n_{A0}/n_{e0}) \epsilon^{-a\Delta n_0 t} .$$

In this equation, as applied to Kenty's study, $a \sim 10^{-7}$, $t \sim 10^{-4}$, $\Delta n_0 \sim 9 \times 10^{11}$, $n_{A0} = 1 \times 10^{11}$, and $n_{e0} = 10^{-12}$, such that in the interval of observation, a' would be vanishingly small. This physically means that owing to the high electron concentration, the n_{A0} ions would have largely recombined in $t < 10^{-4}$ sec. Had t been 1.1×10^{-5} sec, then the $1/n_e$ - t plot would not have been linear, and an $a' = 3.7 \times 10^{-8}$ would have been observed.

Thus, it must be concluded that in this and other similar studies, disparity caused by the Hornbeck-Molnar process would not have yielded the observations. It then is necessary to consider the recombination resulting from the production of A_2^+ or similar ions in three-body impacts. This situation has been analyzed by the author and W. B. Kunkel. Probably the easiest approach to the calculation of the production of molecules such as A_2^+ by collisions of A^+ with two atoms, can be to use the J. J. Thomson treatment for the collision of two atoms occurring within a critical distance of association σ of the ion. D. R. Bates also uses the approach in some of his calculations (7). Equation 6.119 expresses this as a quantity ω, given by

$$\omega = 1 - \frac{2\lambda^2}{4\sigma^2} \left[1 - \epsilon^{-\frac{2\sigma}{\lambda}} \left(\frac{2\sigma}{\lambda} + 1 \right) \right] ,$$

which can be simplified if $\sigma/\lambda << 1$ by expansion of the exponential in series to read:

$$(6.131) \qquad \omega = 1 - \frac{\lambda^2}{2\sigma^2} \left(\frac{2\sigma^2}{\lambda^2} - \frac{8\sigma^3}{3\lambda^3} \right) = (4/3)\,(\sigma/\lambda).$$

The molecular free path $\lambda = 1/\sqrt{2}\pi\sigma_0{}^2 n$, whence $\omega = (4\pi\sqrt{2}/3)\,\sigma_0{}^2\sigma n$. The collision frequency z for the molecules of the gas within σ of the ion then becomes

$$z = \sqrt{2}\,\pi\sigma^2\,\bar{c}\,n\,\omega = (8/3)\,\pi^2\,\bar{c}\,\sigma^3\sigma_0^2 n^2 = V_\sigma z_0,$$

with $V_\sigma = (4\pi/3)\,\sigma^3$, the volume of the collision radius σ around an ion, and $z_0 = 2\pi\sigma_0{}^2 cn^2$, which is the collision frequency per cm^3 for the atoms. It is then possible to set down the analogue of equations 6.13 through 6.15, applicable to this situation for creation of molecular ions of concentration M from ions in triple impacts with atoms A and loss of molecular ions and electrons by dissociative recombination. Thus,

$$(6.15) \qquad\qquad \frac{dM}{dt} = zA - aMn,$$

$$(6.14) \qquad\qquad \frac{dA}{dt} = -a_1 An - zA,$$

and

$$(6.13) \qquad\qquad \frac{dn_e}{dt} = -a_1 n - aMn,$$

with n_e the electron concentration. Since $a_1 \sim 10^{-12}$, the term $a_1 An$ at once drops out.

In order to further simplify the equations applicable to this problem, exemplary values for the case of A gas will be given. The constants here used can be readily changed to more correct values as data become available. For convenience, the values to be used are as follows:

$\bar{c} = 3 \times 10^4$ cm/sec.

$\sigma_0 = 3 \times 10^{-8}$ cm.

$\sigma = 1 \times 10^{-7}$ cm, arbitrarily but realistically chosen.

$n = 3.6 \times 10^{13}\,p$, where p is the pressure in microns,
   i.e., 10^{-3} mm of Hg.

This makes $z = 5.7 \times 10^{-4}\,p^2$, with p in microns.

Now Kenty used $n_0 \sim 10^{13}$ ions/cm^3, $n_{e0} \simeq A_0 \simeq 10^{13}$: also, $M_0 \ll n_{e0}$.

At 0.4 e.v., a for A_2^+ from Biondi's value will be $\sim 3 \times 10^{-8}$ cm^2/ion sec; $a' \sim 10^{-12}$. Equations 6.13, 6.14, and thus 6.15, simplify to:

$$\frac{dM}{dt} = + zA - aMn_e,$$

(6.132)
$$\frac{dA}{dt} = - zA,$$

$$\frac{dn_e}{dt} = - aMn_e.$$

Furthermore,

$$n_e = M + A, \ M = n_e - A, \ A = A_0 \, \epsilon^{-zt}$$

at $t = 0$,

$$\frac{dM_0}{dt} = 0, \text{ or } M_0 = \frac{z}{a}\frac{A_0}{n_{e0}} = \frac{z}{a}\frac{n_{e0} - M_0}{n_{e0}},$$

and

(6.133)
$$M_0 = \frac{z}{a} - \frac{z}{an_{e0}} M_0, \ M_0 = \frac{z/a}{1+(z/an_{e0})} = \frac{zn_{e0}}{an_{e0} + z},$$

so that

(6.134)
$$M \simeq \frac{z}{a} \text{ if } an_{0e} \gg z \, ;$$

(6.135)
$$\frac{dn}{dt} = - an_e^2 + a A_0 \, \epsilon^{\frac{zt}{n_e}} \, ;$$

(6.136)
$$\frac{1}{n} = \frac{1}{g}\left(\frac{1}{n_{e0}} + a \int_0^t g dt\right) ;$$

with

(6.137)
$$g = \epsilon^{\frac{aA_0}{z}}\left(1 - \epsilon^{-zt}\right)$$

and

(6.138)
$$\int_0^t g dt = \left(t - \frac{1}{z} \sum_{K=1}^{\infty} \frac{1 - \epsilon^{-Kzt}}{KK!}\right)\epsilon^{\frac{aA_0}{z}} .$$

For $a A_0 > z$ this does not converge rapidly, so that it is not a useful solution. However, it is exact so far as the assumptions hold.

If $aA_0 >> z$, the initial steady state is $dM/dt = 0$, i.e., $M_0 = z/a << A_0$, so that

(6.139) $$M << A, \quad \text{or} \quad A \simeq n_e, \quad \text{and} \quad \frac{dn_e}{dt} \simeq zn_e,$$

with

(6.140) $$n_e = n_{e0}\, \epsilon^{-zt}.$$

Thus, the decline in electron concentration is no longer completely covered by recombination; this, as before, occurring so rapidly that the rate of disappearance of electrons in time depends on the rate of formation of molecules from atoms. As noted, this gives a decline of the number of electrons which follows an exponential curve. Actually, the effect of the recombinative process will cause a slower rise, so that a plot of n/n_0 against t will *not* be exponential, but will rise somewhat more slowly. Thus, over a limited range of t, with the scatter of experimental points as observed in all these studies, the n_{0e}/n_e - t curves will give "approximately a straight line." Thus, from an approximate slope of the line using equation 6.1, as was done in all these studies, setting

(6.141) $$\frac{dn_e}{dt} = -a' n_e^2,$$

when in reality,

(6.142) $$\frac{dn_e}{dt} \simeq -zn,$$

(6.143) $$\frac{dn_e}{dt} = -a' n_e^2 \simeq -zn_e, \quad a' = \frac{z}{n_e}.$$

Using $z = 5.7 \times 10^{-4}\, p^2$ at $p = 1,000\ \mu$, as in Kenty's study, then

$$aA_0 = 3 \times 10^{-8} \times 10^{13} = 3 \times 10^5 >> z = 570.$$

Hence, it is possible to assume that $a' = 570/10^{13} = 5.7 \times 10^{-10}$, which is in reasonably good agreement with Kenty's values.

The case of Cs observed in arcs by Mohler is somewhat more complicated. He studied the afterglow in the yellow "continuum" and measured a supposed a_{er} of the order of 5×10^{-10} which, corrected for an estimated loss by ambipolar diffusion, was reduced to 3.5×10^{-10}. A later study gave similar values, using probes with pressures ranging from 10 to 110 microns and using various ways for correcting for diffusion loss. The range of values of time was not very great, and with the scatter of points the plots of $1/n$-t were never certainly linear. Furthermore, at the low pressures used, it is surprising that the corrections for diffusion should not have been far greater. It might be mentioned that ambipolar-diffusion loss, observed by Dandurand and Holt at low pressures such as used by Mohler, gave very low values for the reduced mobility of Cs ions, 0.065 cm^2/volt sec, when the normal reduced mobility of such ions is ~ 1.3. This would reduce diffusion loss in Mohler's work to the values he used in correction of his data.

However, there is a great deal of doubt about the significance of all these data in Cs, because of the complex character of the actions occurring. Studies of Mohler (56) on the photoionization of Cs vapor show that considerable photoionization occurs above wave lengths corresponding to 3.86 e.v., the ionization potential. The ionization potential of Cs_2 is 3.17 e.v. The heat of dissociation of $Cs_2 = 0.35$ e.v., and that of $Cs_2^+ \rightarrow Cs + Cs$ is 1.02 e.v. Thus, several reactions are possible:

1. $Cs^{*\,3.19} + Cs \qquad \rightarrow Cs_2^+ + e + 0.02\ ev \propto p$ and l.
2. $Cs^{*\,2.72} + Cs^{*\,2.72} \rightarrow Cs_2^+ + e + 1.65\ ev \propto l^2$.
3. $Cs^{*\,2.72} + Cs \qquad \rightarrow Cs_2^+ + e + 0.61\ ev \propto p$ and l.

Thus, in an excited plasma it is clear that the formation of molecular ions is quite possible. The attachment reaction $Cs^+ + 2Cs \rightarrow Cs_2^+ + Cs + 1.02\ ev$ is also energetically very likely if pressures are adequate. Thus, it would seem natural to expect formation of Cs_2^+ and dissociative recombination with electrons. However, the situation is not so simple as this.

Dandurand and Holt, with microwave techniques from 680 to 2,600 microns, observed pressure-dependent coefficients ranging from 3.5×10^{-7} to 1.45×10^{-6}, the electron densities being 10^{12} and electron energies 0.23 e.v. Their spectroscopic observations indicate that while in the discharge the light is chiefly the line spectrum of Cs, in the afterglow the spectrum is purely a molecular band spectrum which perhaps can be associated with Mohler's yellow "continuum." There appears also to be much infrared. There is little doubt about the electron loss observed by them being primarily due to recombination, following fairly linear plots for $1/n$ against t. At lower pressures, loss is largely by ambipolar diffusion. The light emission rises to a maximum, beginning to rise 30 microseconds after cutoff and peaking at 80 microseconds. There is also strong indication that the recombination is dependent on Cs_2^+ molecule formation. Dandurand

and Holt postulate that the recombination is one of molecular Cs_2^+ ions with electrons, with capture into highly excited states of Cs_2, yielding the infrared followed by a subsequent band emission. The strong pressure dependence also indicates molecule formation. The reaction postulated by Dandurand and Holt was that

$$Cs_2^+ + e \to Cs_2^* + h\nu_R \to Cs_2 + h\nu.$$

It is unlikely that the radiative capture to a molecular state could yield the cross sections observed. One might be tempted, however, to postulate the following mechanism, in view of the notorious readiness with which molecular ions and possibly molecules form in Cs.

$$Cs^+ + 2Cs \to Cs_2^+ + Cs, \text{ or } Cs^{*1} + Cs \to Cs_2^+ + e.$$

$$Cs_2^+ + e \to Cs^{*2} + Cs^{*2}, \text{ or } Cs^* + Cs + KE.$$

$$Cs^* + 2Cs \to Cs_2^* + Cs \to 3Cs + h\nu.$$

That is, it is postulated that Cs ions or higher excited states of Cs in triple or single impact yield the Cs_2^+ ion, which recombines dissociatively with a cross section of the order observed, yielding perhaps two less highly excited atoms. These also rapidly form excited molecules in triple impacts at higher pressures, so that little atomic line emission is seen. The molecular ions then radiate. This will be especially true if the resonance radiation in Cs is readily trapped, so that much of it does not escape, thus facilitating recombination of such states of molecular ions. This applies especially to pressures well above 1 mm.

Mohler's values of a' would then be compatible with the data of Dandurand and Holt only if the rate of recombination were again governed by the formation rate of Cs_2^+, which alone removes electrons. If this were to occur with Mohler's data, then the cross sections for the triple impacts forming Cs_2^+ would have to be larger than those used for A_2^+ formation.

For Cs, assume $c = 2.5 \times 10^4$, $\sigma_0 = 10^{-7}$, $\sigma = 3 \times 10^{-7}$, and $n_e = 3 \times 10^{-13} p^2$, yielding $z = 10^{-1} p^2$. Here again, $A_0 = 10^{12}$, $a = 1 \times 10^{-6}$, $aA_0 = 10^6$, while $p \sim 30$, so that $z = 90$ and, at 30 μ pressure, $a' = 90/10^{12} = 9 \times 10^{-11}$. Actually, Mohler observed values around 3×10^{-10} which showed some pressure dependence.

It must here be noted that in general Mohler's corrections for ambipolar diffusion were probably inadequate, so that his values of a in Cs may be inexact by more than he estimated. In Mohler's optical studies he used from 46 to 110 μ pressure. He later estimated that his loss was 0.6 to 0.7 due to recombination, and 0.4 to 0.3 due to diffusion. In this event his values of a' were 3.6×10^{-10} and z became of the order of 1,000; $a' = 1,000/10^{12} = 10^{-9}$.

It can be concluded from the foregoing that owing to the inaccuracy of the corrections for diffusion, the agreement of the assumed larger cross sections for the triple impact give reasonable agreement with observation. However, it must be recognized that while molecular ion formation is undoubtedly involved in the Cs recombination, the exact mechanisms are not clear, and await further study for classification.

In the case of Hg^+ ions there is little difficulty. Biondi has established dissociative recombination as the active process at higher pressures, as will be seen. At lower pressures and at somewhat higher pressures, Dandurand and Holt observed no recombination—all plots of n against t indicated exponential decay. This can surely in part be ascribed to their use of immature plasmas and high electron temperatures and densities, leading to higher diffusion modes and other difficulties. Their assumption that the exponential decay is due to Hg ion formation by electron attachment was incorrect, for Hg does not form negative ions and their pure Hg was free from contamination. Only line spectra were observed optically, in agreement with the dissociative recombination hypothesis.

The data of Mohler were taken at 270 microns, where ambipolar-diffusion loss was small. If we use much the same cross sections for Hg as for A, though $\bar{c}$ is decreased and σ_0 is no doubt larger, setting $A_0 = 10^{12}$, $a = 5 \times 10^{-7}$, $aA = 5 \times 10^5$, and $z = 10^{-3} p^2$, $z = 73$ and $a' = 73/10^{12} = 7.3 \times 10^{-10}$, which is perhaps high; but accurate data for z are not so easy to compute as they are for A. Thus again, Mohler's low values are accounted for. This interpretation is rendered more plausible as a result of the beautiful data of Biondi (57), which came as part of a more exhaustive study of ions and metastable atoms in Hg afterglows; and it fittingly concludes this chapter. The study was made in He-Hg mixtures, to insure thermal electrons and to reduce diffusion loss. Here, definite evidence of a loss of Hg ions to recombination indicated by the pressure and temperature behaviors that Hg_2^+ ions were being created in a three-body impact from Hg^+, according to

$$Hg^+ + 2\,Hg \rightarrow Hg_2^+ + Hg.$$

The rate of this reaction is of the same order of magnitude as that measured for the formation of He_2^+ from He^+ by triple impact, as observed by Phelps and Brown (7).

The Hg_2^+ then removes electrons by dissociative recombination, according to

$$Hg_2^+ + e \rightarrow Hg^* + Hg.$$

There was *no indication* of formation of Hg^- ions, as is to be expected, since it has been shown by W. H. Bennett, R. H. Sloane, and others that despite Arnot's work, Hg^- ions do not form, and that such ions appear to be energetically unstable.

If pressure is high enough after a millisecond, all ions might be expected to be Hg_2^+. Then equation 6.2 is applicable, and $1/n$ is proportional to t. Biondi's observed electron density fell off in a nice linear fashion over a range of t from 0.5 to 5×10^{-3} sec at 4.16 mm of Hg. However, as pressures *increased*, the value of a_{ed} increased *linearly* from 5.1×10^{-7} to 15×10^{-7} between 1.4 mm and 46 mm, the temperature being increased from 407° K. to 505° K.

Using relation 6.47, and assuming that the Hg_2^+ adds an Hg atom according to the reaction

$$Hg_2^+ + 2\,Hg \rightarrow Hg_3^+ - Hg,$$

with Hg_3^+ having a weak binding energy compared to kT. Then,

$$a'_{ed} = \frac{a_2 - a_3\,\gamma_p}{1 - \gamma_p},$$

where a'_{ed} is the observed coefficient and a_{2e} and a_{3e} are the true values for Hg_2^+ and Hg_3^+, respectively.

If $\gamma_p = Kn$, with K the equilibrium constant, and if n is the concentration of Hg atoms, a'_{ed} varies linearly with p when $Kn \ll 1$. At values of $Kn \gg 1$, the observed a_{ed} approaches a_3 as a limit. Unfortunately, measurements could not be carried above 50 mm, so that the inflection and saturation could not be observed. If a_{3e} were known, the binding energy of Hg_3^+ could be found. The intercept of the curve for a'_{ed} as a function of p yielded a_{2e} for Hg_2^+ as 5.5×10^{-7} cm³/ion sec, with electrons at about 400° K. The value of a_{2e} is of the same order as that for Ne_2^+ and A_2^+. It does not agree with Dandurand and Holt's value, as they failed to insure that $n_e = n_{Hg_2^+}$.

It should be added that Biondi also observed the reaction

$$Hg^m + Hg^m \rightarrow Hg^+ + e + Hg$$

between metastable atoms of Hg, one in the 6^3P_2 state at 5.47 e.v., and the other in the 6^3P_0 state at 4.67 e.v. Here, Hg vapor was used without He. The rise of a curve was analogous to that deduced by Kunkel in equation 6.36. It is interesting to note that the metastable interaction does not yield molecular ions, as Arnot supposed. The growth and decay curve rose to a peak of 10^9 electrons in about 0.2 $\times$

10^{-3} sec. A value of the cross section for de-excitation of the $^3P_2$ state of $\sigma_d = 8 \times 10^{-17}$ cm^2 good to 10% was obtained. The diffusion coefficient $D_m N = 1.5 \times 10^{18}$ for this state, and is of the same order of magnitude as for the $^3P_0$ state, which lies around 1.7×10^{18}.

BIBLIOGRAPHY TO CHAPTER VI

(1) For a summary of the early studies of recombination of ions, see J. J. Thomson and G. P. Thomson, *Conduction of Electricity through Gases*, third edition, Cambridge University Press, 1928, vol. I, pp. 19 ff.; also, L. B. Loeb, *Fundamental Processes of Electrical Discharge in Gases*, John Wiley & Sons, New York, 1939, chap. II.

(2) W. H. Bragg and R. D. Kleeman, Phil. Mag. *11*, 466, 1906; R. D. Kleeman, Phil. Mag. *12*, 273, 1906; M. Moulin, Ann. Chim. Phys. *21*, 550, 1910; Ann. Chim. Phys. *22*, 26, 1911; G. Jaffé, Le Radium *10*, 126, 1913; G. Jaffé, Ann. Phys. *85*, 137, 1928; J. Schemel, Ann. d. Physik. *85*, 137, 1928.

(3) S. G. Plimpton, Phil. Mag. *25*, 65, 1913; L. C. Marshall, Phys. Rev. *34*, 618, 1929; L. B. Loeb and L. C. Marshall, Jour. Franklin Inst. *208*, 371, 1929; M. E. Gardner, Phys. Rev. *53*, 75, 1938; J. Sayers, Proc. Roy. Soc. *A169*, 83, 1938; N. E. Bradbury, Terrest. Mag. and Ats. Elect. *43*, 55, 1938.

(4) J. J. Thomson and E. Rutherford, Phil. Mag. *42*, 392, 1896; E. Riecke, Ann. d. Physik *12*, 814, 1903; G. Mie, Ann. d. Physik *13*, 857, 1904.

(5) P. Langevin, Ann. Chim. Phys. *28*, 289, 443, 1903.

(6) J. D. Craggs and J. M. Meek, Proc. Roy. Soc. *A180*, 241, 1946; W. Hopwood and J. D. Craggs, Proc. Phys. Soc. Lon. *59*, 755, 771, 1947.

(7) D. R. Bates, Phys. Rev. *77*, 718, 1950; Phys. Rev. *78*, 492, 1950; M. A. Biondi and S. C. Brown, Phys. Rev. *75*, 1700, 1949; Phys. Rev. *76*, 1697, 1949; M. A. Biondi and T. Holstein, Phys. Rev. *82*, 962, 1951; M. A. Biondi, Phys. Rev. *83*, 1078, 1951; A. V. Phelps and S. C. Brown, Phys. Rev. *86*, 102, 1952; M. A. Biondi, Phys. Rev. *90*, 730, 1953; M. A. Biondi, Phys. Rev. *88*, 660, 1952.

(8) H. N. Olsen and W. S. Huxford, Phys. Rev. *87*, 922, 1952.

(9) M. A. Biondi, Sixth Conference on Gaseous Electronics, Washington, D.C., October 22-24, 1953, paper C4.

(10) L. Malter and E. O. Johnson, Phys. Rev. *80*, 58, 1950.

(11) See ref. (7) under Biondi. Also, S. C. Brown and D. J. Rose, "Measuring the Properties of Ionized Gases at High Frequencies," Jour. App. Phys. *23*, 711, 719, 1028, 1952.

(12) J. J. Thomson, *Conduction of Electricity through Gases*, third edition, Cambridge University Press, 1928, vol. I, p. 20; E. V. Appleton and J. Sayers, Jour. U.R.S.I. *78*, 272, 1938; D. R. Bates, R. H. Buckingham,

and H. S. W. Massey, Proc. Roy. Soc. *A170*, 322, 1939; D. R. Bates
and H. S. W. Massey, Proc. Roy. Soc. *A187*, 261, 1946; N. E. Bradbury,
Terrest. Mag. and Ats. Elect., March, 1948, p. 55.

(13) W. B. Kunkel, Phys. Rev. *84*, 218, 1951.

(14) J. J. Thomson, *Conduction of Electricity through Gases*, third edition,
Cambridge University Press, 1928, vol. I, p. 20.

(15) R. A. Johnson, B. T. McClure, and R. B. Holt, Phys. Rev. *80*, 376,
1950.

(16) L. B. Loeb and W. B. Kunkel, Phys. Rev. *85*, 493, 1952.

(17) G. Rümelin, Phys. Zeits. *9*, 657, 1908; Ann. d. Physik *43*, 821, 1914.

(18) L. C. Marshall, Phys. Rev. *34*, 618, 1929.

(19) F. L. Mohler and C. Boeckner, Bur. Stand. Jour. Res. *2*, 489, 1929;
C. Boeckner, Bur. Stand. Jour. Res. *6*, 277, 1931; F. L. Mohler, Bur.
Stand. Jour. Res. *10*, 771, 1933; Bur. Stand. Jour. Res. *19*, 447, 559,
1937.

(20) J. H. Cahn, Phys. Rev. *75*, 293, 1949.

(21) E. Rutherford, Phil. Mag. *44*, 422, 1897; J. S. Townsend, Phil. Trans.
Roy. Soc. *A193*, 144, 1899; J. A. McClelland, Phil. Mag. *46*, 29, 1898.

(22) R. K. McClung, Phil. Mag. *3*, 283, 1902; H. A. Erikson, Phys. Rev. *27*,
473, 1908; L. L. Hendren, Phys. Rev. *21*, 314, 1905.

(23) J. Sayers, Proc. Roy. Soc. *A169*, 83, 1938.

(24) E. Rutherford, Phil. Mag. *47*, 109, 1899.

(25) P. Langevin, Ann. Chim. Phys. *28*, 289, 433, 1903.

(26) O. Luhr, Phys. Rev. *35*, 1394, 1930; Phys. Rev. *36*, 24, 1930; Phys.
Rev. *37*, 998, 1931; Phys. Rev. *44*, 459, 1933.

(27) M. E. Gardner, Phys. Rev. *53*, 75, 1938.

(28) C. Kenty, Phys. Rev. *34*, 624, 1928.

(29a) J. Sayers, Conference on Physics of Ionized Gases, Univ. Coll. Lon.,
auspices of Warren Research Fund, Royal Society, April, 1953; report
circulated September, 1953, p. 29.

(29b) H. Margenau, Phys. Rev. *69*, 508, 1946; J. C. Slater, *Microwave Electronics*, D. Van Nostrand, New York, 1950, chap. V; J. C. Slater, Rev.
Mod. Phys. *18*, 481, 1946.

(29c) K. B. Persson, Sixth Conference on Gaseous Electronics, Washington,
D.C., October 22-24, 1953. Added paper after program was printed.

(30) J. J. Thomson, Phil. Mag. *47*, 337, 1924.

(31) W. R. Harper, Proc. Camb. Phil. Soc. *28*, 219, 1932; Proc. Camb. Phil.
Soc. *31*, 430, 1935; Phil. Mag. *18*, 97, 1934; Phil. Mag. *20*, 740, 1935.

(32) G. Jaffé, Phys. Rev. *58*, 968, 1940; Phys. Rev. *59*, 652, 1941.

(33) O. W. Richardson, Phil. Mag. *10*, 242, 1905.

(34) J. A. Hornbeck and J. P. Molnar, Phys. Rev. *84*, 621, 1951; J. A. Hornbeck, Phys. Rev. *80*, 297, 1950; Phys. Rev. *83*, 374, 1951.

(35) R. B. Holt, J. M. Richardson, B. Haviland, and B. T. McClure, Phys.
Rev. *77*, 239, 1950; R. A. Johnson, B. T. McClure, and R. B. Holt,
Phys. Rev. *80*, 376, 1950; P. Dandurand and R. B. Holt, Phys. Rev.
82, 278, 818, 1951; A. Redfield and R. B. Holt, Phys. Rev. *82*, 874,
1951.

(36) L. B. Loeb and L. C. Marshall, Jour. Franklin Inst. *208*, 371, 1929.

(37) L. B. Loeb, *Fundamental Processes of Electrical Discharge in Gases*,
John Wiley & Sons, New York, 1939, pp. 130 ff.

(38) D. R. Bates and H. S. W. Massey, Phil. Trans. Roy. Soc. *A239*, 269, 1946; D. R. Bates, Conf. Phys. Ionized Gases, Univ. Coll. Lon., April, 1953, p. 34; C. Zener, Proc. Roy. Soc. *A137*, 696, 1932; L. Landau, Phys. Zeits. d. Sowjetunion *2*, 46, 1932.

(39) I. S. Bowen, Phys. Rev. *41*, 24, 1932; R. A. Millikan, Phys. Rev. *39*, 397, 1932; N. E. Bradbury, Jour. App. Phys. *11*, 267, 1940.

(40) H. Bartels, Zeits. f. Phys. *105*, 704, 1937.

(41) L. B. Loeb, *Fundamental Processes of Electrical Discharge in Gases*, John Wiley & Sons, New York, 1939, pp. 131 ff.

(42) H. Thirkill, Proc. Roy. Soc. *A88*, 490, 1913.

(43) P. Phillips, Proc. Roy. Soc. *A33*, 246, 1910.

(44) W. Mächler, Zeits. f. Phys. *104*, 1, 1936; P. Kraus, Ann. d. Physik *29*, 449, 1937.

(45) M. A. Biondi, Phys. Rev. *90*, 730, 1953.

(46) L. J. Varnerin, Jr., Phys. Rev. *84*, 563, 1951.

(47) R. B. Bryan, Third Conference on Gaseous Electronics, New York, October 19-21, 1950, paper A2.

(48) M. A. Biondi and T. Holstein, Phys. Rev. *82*, 962, 1951; M. A. Biondi, Phys. Rev. *83*, 1078, 1951.

(48a) D. R. Bates and H. S. W. Massey, Rep. Prog. Phys. *9*, 67, 1943; W. R. S. Garton, Conf. Phys. Ionized Gases, Univ. Coll. Lon., April, 1953, p. 90.

(49) M. A. Biondi, Phys. Rev. *88*, 660, 1952.

(50) W. H. Bennett and P. F. Darby, Phys. Rev. *49*, 97, 1936.

(51) N. E. Bradbury, and Bradbury and Tatel, Jour. Chem. Phys. *2*, 827, 835, 840, 1934.

(52) W. E. Bowls, Phys. Rev. *53*, 293, 1938; F. Ehrenkrantz, Phys. Rev. *55*, 219, 1939.

(53) R. N. Varney, Phys. Rev. *89*, 708, 1953.

(54) O. Luhr, Phys. Rev. *44*, 459, 1933.

(55) M. A. Harrison and R. Geballe, Phys. Rev. *85*, 372, 1952; *91*, 1, 1953.

(56) P. D. Foote and F. L. Mohler, Phys. Rev. *26*, 185, 1925; Phys. Rev. *27*, 37, 1926; F. L. Mohler, Phys. Rev. *31*, 187, 1928; F. L. Mohler and C. Boeckner, Bur. Stand. Jour. Res. *2*, 489, 1929.

(57) M. A. Biondi, Phys. Rev. *90*, 730, 1953.

Chapter VII

ELECTRICAL CONDUCTION IN GASES BELOW

IONIZATION BY COLLISION

§ 1. Introduction.

Thus far in the text, only the various component fundamental factors in gaseous conduction have been presented. It is next of interest to discuss the effect of these factors on conduction currents in gases where the field-to-pressure ratio, X/p, is so low as not to produce ionization by electron impact. Such a discussion will bring out certain limiting factors common to all discharge studies, which in the absence of complicating agencies clearly reveal their nature. Thus, for instance, it is not appreciated that in studies of conductivity the familiar Ohm's law, derived from metallic conduction, is a special limiting relation which is rarely encountered in the general conduction problems. The law happens to apply in metals, owing to the enormous numbers of electrons which are virtually free and the immobile nature of the ions in the lattice. Such conditions do not exist in gases, except to a first-order approximation at very low ratios of field strength to pressure, X/p. In the other extreme of the X/p ratio, below the ionization range, another expected limiting condition is only approximated. It is only natural to expect that with the mobile carriers a relatively low field-to-pressure ratio would serve to remove carriers as fast as they are generated. The measurement under such conditions would reveal a "saturation" current.

From the earliest studies on, it was believed that all the carriers generated were being collected at relatively low X/p values. This subtle error was made more plausible through the circumstance that plots of currents against field strength to a given scale give the visual impression of leveling off to an apparent "saturation" value at the scale employed. Replotting to a new scale of abscissae, with higher numerical values for a given ordinate distance, at once reveals the illusion resulting from the initial plot. In consequence, the supposed "saturation" value of the current taken from a single scale plot can lead to the use of entirely erroneous values. As will be indicated by the equations to be derived, the true *mathematical* saturation of a conduction current is only approached at infinite values of X/p. *Practical* values of 0.99 of the saturation value might be expected to be reached at reasonable values of X/p. However, owing to factors which will presently appear, even such "practical saturation" is, in some cases, not achieved at fields close to breakdown. This requires great care in the interpretation of results. It further requires that special measurements be made to establish the true value of the background current caused by a pre-existing ionization when attempts are made to study breakdown currents at higher values of X/p.

The factors that hinder the achievement of saturation current measurements and influence the current-X/p relations observed, may be summarized as follows:

a) Geometrical factors affecting the generation and collection of carriers. These, owing to the initial directions of the emitted carrier velocity vectors in vacuum, or owing to diffusive motion in a gas, escape through the boundaries limiting the collecting region and are not registered as current.

b) The superposition of random diffusive motions of carriers in a gas onto the directed, field-induced motion causes a loss of carriers by return to the electrode of origin. This occurs because diffusion is independent of the field, and retrograde diffusive currents return some carriers to the originating electrode.

c) Even in vacuum, in the absence of geometrical factors, when carrier densities become high, space-charge fields caused by a local accumulation of carriers can considerably limit and generally influence the current-potential relationships. Such space-charge effects can be even more effective in the retarded motion caused by gases.

d) When carriers of both signs are being produced in a volume of gas (omitting any disturbance by diffusion or geometrical factors, but allowing a loss of carriers by some agency, such as a recombination, and permitting a difference in mobility of the carriers to exist), there appear other limitations on the currents observed. The conditions resulting also yield characteristic current-potential relationships connected with space-charge accumulations. The forms of the resulting potential and field distributions are equally illustrative. They furnish a valuable background for comparison with conditions observed in gaseous discharges. These four current-regulating agencies will be discussed briefly in what follows.

§ 2. The Geometrically Conditioned Saturation Current.

Consider a plane parallel electrode system, consisting of circular plates A and B of radius R separated by a distance d, with suitable guard rings to maintain uniformity of field. From the lower plate A, carriers (electrons, for example) are uniformly liberated over the surface area πR^2 by photo effect, with light of a single wave length. Assuming for simplicity no energy loss in escaping from the surface, beyond that of overcoming the work function, these electrons will be assumed to emerge with the same velocity v_0 isotropically directed in all directions with the normal to the surface. It is seen that with a given ratio $\delta = d/R$ between separation and radius, the electrons emitted with no field across the plates will be intercepted only in part by the collecting electrode B of radius R, and thus register as current. The rest of the electrons will reach the guard ring or escape out of the system altogether if they emerge at a sufficiently small grazing angle with plate A. It is assumed that current densities are sufficiently low so that no space-charge effects occur.

Superposition of a field X between A and B, with B positive and A negative, will cause an acceleration of magnitude $a = Xe/m$ of the electrons toward B. Thus, the initially linear trajectories will become parabolic relative to the lines of force. Electrons which were escaping to the guard ring or beyond in the absence of the field will begin to reach B when X is applied. The current collected by B will accordingly increase from some initial value i_0 to some larger value i, dependent on the values of v_0, e/m, δ, and X. As the field X approaches indefinitely large values, it is clear that the current collected by B will approach the total current emitted by A. This current is the true "saturation" current i. It is possible to set up the equations for the calculation of the current at any field X as a function of e/m, X, δ, R, and v_0, which will range in value from i_0 at $X = 0$ to i at $X = \infty$. The relations for the solutions of the problem were set up by W. R. Haseltine and integrated by Leslie Cook (1). The setting up of·the relations and the solution thereof are presented elsewhere.

Illustrative results of the study are summarized in the two curves for $f = i/i_\infty$ at values of $\delta = 0.1$ and $\delta = 1$ in figure 7.1. In this figure the quantity f is plotted as ordinate against the parameter γ given by $\gamma = (Xe/2m)\,(R/v_0^2\delta)$. If the current had been measured in a system with a value of v_0 of 1 e.v., with $R = 5$ cm, $\delta = 1$, the quantity $\gamma = 1.22\,X$, with X expressed in volts per cm, the values of X needed for the values of the f recorded are shown above the axis in the figure of abscissae. Since actual numerical values of the field X (which will vary with circumstances) are of less interest than the principles involved, it is more appropriate to note that when $\delta = 1$, geometrical loss alone is serious. In that case, i_0 when $X = 0$ is less than 0.4, and at $\gamma = 9$ the curve *appears* to have reached the saturation values of i_∞; but the scale of ordinates indicates the value of i at this point

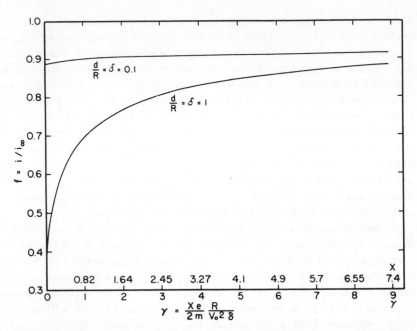

Fig. 7.1. Curves computed by Haseltine and Cook of current collected by anode in parallel plane geometry for electrons liberated in vacuum from the cathode relative to the total emission $f = i/i_\infty$ as a function of a parameter $\gamma = (Xe/2m)(R/v_0^2 \delta)$, where X is the applied field. Note that in no case does f approach unity, although when $d/R = \delta = 0.1$ the curve appears "saturated."

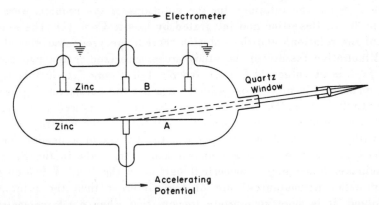

Fig. 7.2. Bradbury's device for studying the back-diffusion loss of photoelectrons liberated in a gas. This uses a zinc cathode, with electrons collected at the anode.

to be only 0.87 i_∞. It must especially be noted that even if $\delta = 0.1$ with $i_0 = 0.89$, the curve has an appreciable slope at $\gamma = 9$, and i_0 is still only 0.93 i_∞. Thus, *great caution must be used* in accepting a visually flattening conduction curve as indicating a saturation value i_∞, or $f = 1$.

It is always best to replot such curves to a more intensive scale and then draw conclusions. By reducing δ and liberating carriers only in the center of the plate B, the geometrical loss in the simple case above can be much reduced. Even then achievement of values of $i = 0.99\ i_\infty$, or $f = 0.99$, is rare. It may be added that if total emission from the cathode alone is desired, the current from the cathode can be measured and coupled with a measurement of current collected at the anode. The loss can then be determined for a given situation.

§ 3. The Diffusive Effects on Currents in a Gas. The Photoelectric Current of Low Density in Gases.

One of the earliest studies of conduction currents in gases was that of the photoelectric current liberated from the cathode plate in a plane parallel electrode system in the presence of gases. This particular system has contemporary applicability in that it is one of the most satisfactory means of obtaining negative carriers in gases or electrons for mobility studies, and electrons for studies of ionization by collision in gases. It therefore merits study, aside from its illustrative value in the present discussion. Figure 7.2 shows a pair of Zn electrodes forming a plane parallel electrode system with guard rings in an all-glass chamber. This chamber is capable of being baked out and of being filled with very pure gases. Fields from accumulation of static charges on the glass walls may be prevented by using monel metal screening next to the walls or by lightly coating the glass with evaporated metal or aquadag. Ultraviolet light from a quartz lens may be focused on the center of the plate systems through the quartz window shown. The upper Zn electrode B is at ground potential through a high resistor.[1] It may have its current measured by using a quadrant electrometer as a null instrument. A potentiometer at the ungrounded end of the resistor may be used to counteract the potential drop in the resistor given by the ionization current. A field X is placed across the plates by applying a negative potential V to the lower plate A by means of a battery or potentiometer, the positive pole of which is grounded. By evacuating the glass system, the photo-

---

[1] An alternative method uses an anode perforated with many small holes (200 of 0.2 mm diameter), and lets light from a quartz window behind the anode strike the cathode normally.

electric vacuum current can be determined as a function of the applied potential V. If the ratio d/R of the gap length to the radius of the illuminated spot on A is small, the current should be nearly saturated and constant at low values of X. If geometrical loss is to be avoided, the current from the cathode should be measured, and not that collected by the anode.

A fairly accurate determination of the energy distribution of the emitted photoelectrons is achieved by having the light fall on a small Zn sphere surrounded by a hollow, spherical Zn shell, the light being admitted through a small hole in the shell and in plate A. The hole in A is so placed that the spot of light on A strikes the hole; the current can then be measured as desired. By means of a retarding potential curve, this arrangement allows of an evaluation of the average energy of the emerging photoelectrons, $\frac{1}{2}m\bar{v}_0^2 = \bar{V}e$, with $\bar{V}$ the average value of the retarding potential. Thus, $\bar{V}$ evaluates $\bar{v}_0$, and the accuracy of the current studies to be made later in the presence of gases is predicated on the absence of any contact potentials between electrodes. This further implies that both surface work functions and the value of i_0, the vacuum photoelectric current, are unaffected by the alteration of the Zn surface through the action of the gas. Avoidance of such difficulties requires the use of appropriate control studies, which need not now be considered.

The gases used may be gases not attaching electrons, or they may be gases forming negative ions, as desired. The photoelectric current densities are to be considered so low that space-charge effects do not intervene. In general, starting with a clean Zn surface, if the gas to be used is admitted, the plate is illuminated with ultraviolet light for a time, and then the gas is pumped out to about 10^{-2} to 10^{-3} mm, the "vacuum" current i_0 measured at this time will remain relatively unchanged on the further admission of gas in subsequent studies. With this preparatory treatment of the surface, it can be assumed that normally the value of i_0 is constant, whether the pressure of gas used is 10^{-3} mm or 760 mm, provided that the gas used is not too reactive chemically.[2]

Assuming now that a stable cathode with constant illumination and i_0 is achieved, it will be noted that on admitting gas to any appreciable pressure p, the current i observed for a given potential V will be much lower than i_0. This current will be lower, the higher the pressure p of gas admitted. The current at constant p will increase

---

[2] Recent studies of J. K. Theobald in the author's laboratory (to be presented later) indicate that stabilization of surfaces is difficult, requiring bombardment by positive ions in a glow discharge.

with the potential V of the applied field. Thus, owing to some action of the gas, even if electrons remain free, the current i at any given potential will be observed to be much less than i_0; a circumstance that merits study.

This very circumstance so interested J. J. Thomson that in 1906 he derived a rather rough relation to account for it (2). The theory, although it indicated a diminution of current i so that i/i_0 was less than unity and varied with X/p, failed to account for the magnitude of the effect observed. In 1926, R. E. Woolsey (3), using an all-metal chamber in the author's laboratory, reinvestigated the problem. He showed that the observed deviations from Thomson's theory (as the theory was then interpreted) involved orders of magnitude, and that disagreement with theory was serious indeed. He also showed that what had been taken for saturation currents were not such in reality, and that it appeared to be impossible to obtain saturation currents at any appreciable pressures. In 1931, I. Langmuir (4) encountered difficulties related to this phenomenon at lower pressures, and attempted an explanation. His theory was correctly based on the assumption of a diffusive loss of electrons to the cathode, as was Thomson's. On the other hand, Langmuir based his analysis on an early study of G. Hertz (5) which showed the importance of diffusion in such currents. Hertz's pioneering relation had unfortunately neglected f, the fractional energy loss on electron impact. This circumstance gave Langmuir a theory which fitted well below 1 mm pressure, but was very unsatisfactory at 100 mm.

The unsatisfactory nature of Langmuir's theory induced N. E. Bradbury (6) to undertake measurements with the more modern type of arrangement described in figure 7.2. At that time Bradbury did not include the device for measuring $\bar{v}_0$. The data so obtained, with a reinterpretation of the significance of Thomson's symbols by the author, were then shown to follow the theory satisfactorily. In fact, the agreement was so good that Bradbury later employed the method to evaluate roughly the electron mobilities in attachment studies (7). The theory of Thomson admittedly is somewhat weak, and the errors owing to contact potentials, etc., in the evaluation of $\bar{v}_0$ limit the accuracy to no better than 10% or 20% in the mobilities so obtained. Subsequently, Young and Bradbury attempted to derive a more correct equation, using wave-mechanical procedures (8). A. M. Cravath (9) pointed out, however, that the problem is essentially a purely classical diffusion problem of a very complicated sort, and is not amenable to wave-mechanical treatment. Therefore, the simple Thomson theory still stands as the most useful solution.

In principle, the current i_0 of $n_0 e$ photoelectrons liberated per cm^2 per sec in the absence of a gas is reduced to the observed value $i = ne$, owing to the action of the gas molecules in "reflecting" a fraction of the emitted photoelectrons back to the cathode. Properly speaking, the effect of the gas molecules or atoms on the emitted electrons is not a reflection. Owing to their velocities of agitation at the time of emission, the electrons, despite the directed drift velocity caused by the field, execute random motions of diffusion on which the drift is superposed. As G. Hertz (5) showed in 1925, such diffusive motions may not be neglected in the study of currents. In regions where the random velocity of the electrons is high, the drift velocity is low (as seen in chapter III), while the diffusion is increased by the same circumstance. In fact, equation 3.3 says that the relation between mobility and diffusion coefficient is $k_e/D = e/\eta kT$. Here η is the Townsend multiplier. This gives the factor by which the energy of the electrons is greater than $(3/2)kT$, the thermal energy of the molecules. Hence, the greater is ηkT owing to whatever cause, the greater is D/k_e in proportion. Since diffusion is isotropic in space, its displacements are backward toward the cathode as well as lateral, or toward the anode. Thus, the diffusive loss back toward the cathode depends on D. This increases with electron energy, and may become quite important relative to the current induced by the field, which is dependent on k_e, thus making the errors indicated by Hertz even more serious.

The reasoning used by Thomson in deriving his relation follows. Consider n_0 electrons of charge e emitted per cm^2 per second from the cathode A. Impacts of these electrons with gas molecules, and diffusive motion, result in building up a density of n electrons per cm^3 near A. The density n is obviously not constant outward from A toward the anode B. If the field is uniform, it is probably quite constant over most of the path toward B. Close to the cathode A, in virtue of the emission of n_0 electrons per cm^2 per second and the diffusive return current, the density will not be uniform, but will be greater near A. If for simplicity it is assumed that the density of electrons is uniform and of average value n right up to the cathode surface, the following reasoning is permitted: The field $X = V/d$ draws the n electrons per cm^3 across from A to B with a drift velocity $\bar{v} = k_e X$, k_e being the electron mobility over most of the gap. This is determined by the average energy of the electrons in the gas under an imposed ratio of X/p.

It is assumed that both d, the gap length, and pressure p are so large that electrons have lost any initial velocity of emission v_0, and have gained the terminal energy appropriate to the field (as seen in chapter IV) long before the anode is reached. This drift of electrons yields a current density $j = ne k_e X$, which is measured at the collector plate B. Meanwhile, photoelectric action liberates a current density $j_0 = n_0 e$ of electrons from A. Of these, owing to the high value of $\bar{v}_0$, the average velocity of emission, a number of electrons return to the cathode A by diffusion. It is to be noted that the electron velocity $\bar{v}_0$ is high compared to the velocity of thermal motion of the molecules encountered. The electrons will gain energy from the field as they advance toward the anode. They will thus at first tend to reduce $\bar{v}_0$ by collisions to $(3/2)kT$ of the gas molecules; but before this loss can go too far, the field X will in many cases again raise the random velocity to that of field equilibrium. The diffusive loss to the cathode is greatest right near the cathode. Thus, with the elasticity of electron impact, the velocity $\bar{v}_0$ will largely govern diffusive loss and will be used.

According to equation 4.84, the number of electrons returning per cm^2 per second to A is $n\bar{v}_0/4$. The net current received by plate B is then $j = nek_e X = j_0 - n\bar{v}_0 e/4 = n_0 e - n\bar{v}_0 e/4$. Since $j = nek_e X$, $n = j/ek_e X$, and $j = n_0 e - j\bar{v}_0/4k_e X$, it follows that

(7.1)
$$j = \frac{n_0 e k_e X}{\bar{v}_0 + 4 k_e X}.$$

Since $k_e = (760/p) K_e$, with K_e the reduced electron mobility, the relations become

$$j = \frac{3{,}040 \, n_0 \, e \, K_e \, (X/p)}{\bar{v}_0 + 3{,}040 \, K_e (X/p)} = \frac{3{,}040 \, j_0 (X/p) \, K_e}{\bar{v}_0 + 3{,}040 \, K_e \, (X/p)},$$

or

(7.2)
$$j/j_0 = \frac{3{,}040 \, (X/p) \, K_e}{\bar{v}_0 + 3{,}040 \, (X/p) \, K_e}.$$

This derivation (and the final form of the equation) differs slightly from that given by Thomson. At the time he derived it he assumed that the random electron velocity near the cathode was that given by thermal equilibrium with gas molecules, viz.: C_1 determined by $\frac{1}{2}mC_1^2 = (3/2)kT$. Here T is the gas temperature, and the average velocity $\bar{c}_1$ is related to the root-mean-square velocity C_1 by means of the relation $C_1 = \bar{c}_1 \sqrt{3\pi/8}$ for a Maxwellian velocity distribution. Thus, he replaced $\bar{v}_0$ in equation 7.2 by C_1, and put the divisor of C_1 as $\sqrt{6\pi}$ in place of 4. It was this interpretation of $\bar{v}_0$ that was responsible for the most glaring failure of the equation. Again it must be noted that in the body of the gas, well beyond the cathode, the mobility is governed by a *random velocity* which is a function of X/p, and is generally well above that set in thermal equilibrium by $(3/2)kT$. This non-Maxwellian velocity distribution, with its average velocity equivalent to $\sqrt{\eta}$ times as great as $\sqrt{3kT/m}$, plays no role in determining diffusive loss. On the other hand, this random velocity does determine k_e, and thus j, over most of the gap. It is actually the average velocity $\bar{v}_0$ of emission of the electrons by the ultraviolet light from the Zn that, in the neighborhood of the cathode, before it is reduced by some hundreds of impacts with gas molecules or increased by action of the field X, determines the major element of the back-diffusive loss. It was the recognition of this situation by the author in 1931 that at once gave Bradbury the chance to verify the observed curves by comparison with theory.

To evaluate $\bar{v}_0$, it must be recognized that the electrons liberated by light, principally[3] of a limited range in frequency about a value ν, will emerge from the surface of work function ϕe (expressed in ergs if $h\nu$ is in ergs, or in e.v. if $h\nu$ is in equivalent e.v.) at all angles, with a maximum residual energy of agitation v_0, theoretically given by Einstein's law. This reads $\frac{1}{2}mv_0{}^2 = h\nu - \phi e$, where m is the electronic mass and h is the Planck constant. Actually, the energies of the emergent electrons are not all equal to $\frac{1}{2}mv_0{}^2$, which is the maximum possible for the given frequency. It appears that, using a concentric spherical condenser so that angular distributions are avoided, the retarding potential method shows the photoelectrons to emerge with a distribution of energies such that the average energy $\frac{1}{2}m\bar{v}_0{}^2 = 0.6 \, (h\nu - \phi e)$. Thus the velocity $\bar{v}_0$ to use in the equation is derived from $\bar{v}_0 = \sqrt{1.2 \, (h\nu - \phi e)/m}$. As an example, if the photoelectrons are liberated from Zn having $\phi e = 3.57$ e.v., and the line 2,537 Å from a quartz mercury arc is used, which gives $h\nu = 4.9$ e.v., the maximum energy is 1.29 e.v. and the average energy is 0.77 e.v.

It is clear that the equation using the evaluated average $\bar{v}_0$ cannot be correlated with any Maxwellian energy distribution. Since the photoelectric energy distribution is not Maxwellian, the relation of $\sqrt{\bar{v}_0{}^2}$ from observation to $\bar{v}_0$ in the equation is not known, and use of the factor $\sqrt{6\pi}$ in place of 4 to convert $\bar{c}$ to $\sqrt{C^2}$ is not justified. The error involved is probably far less than that resulting from setting the electron density n as going right to the cathode, which is inherent in this method.

---

[3] Usually, the light yielding i_0 will come in a limited range of wave lengths, giving an average frequency ν. If precision is required, the average energy of emission can be found by a retarding potential curve. For discussion, a single frequency ν will be assumed.

In testing the equation, Bradbury preferred to observe j and $\bar{v}_0$, and from these and the values of X/p to infer the values of K_e. The reason was that the values of K_e were not at that time consistently known over the extended range of variables required. Accordingly, the *computation* of the j/j_0 curves as a function of X/p was not convenient. Bradbury's computed values of K_e fitted well to the earlier observed values of Townsend and of the author where they overlapped. As stated, Bradbury later used the relation above to evaluate K_e in his attachment studies, and estimated these to be good to about 10%, or at worst, 20%. Later, Bradbury and Nielsen (10) directly evaluated K_e, and the theory has now been more generally tested by J. K. Theobald (28). Added support for use of the relation at that time also came from the studies of Kruithoff and Penning (11) in Ne and Ne-A mixtures.

Returning to the equation, it is seen that j/j_0 is a rather involved function of X/p. At very low X/p, K_e is nearly constant with X/p, and $\bar{v}_0$ is very much greater than $3{,}040\,K_e(X/p)$, and is constant. Thus, in this region, near the origin, Ohm's law is approximated at constant p, and the rise from $j/j_0 = 0$ is linear. As X/p increases, K_e begins to decline, and at higher X/p, K_e is proportional to the $\sqrt{p/X}$. Hence, as X/p gets quite large, so that $3{,}040\,K_e(X/p)$ is comparable with $\bar{v}_0$, the j/j_0 varies somewhat as the $\sqrt{X/p}$, as noted in the curves. At very high values of X/p, the quantity $3{,}040\,K_e(X/p)$ can become larger than $\bar{v}_0$, at which point j/j_0 approaches unity and the current saturates. In most gases, before saturation is approached, X/p has reached values for ionization by collision, so that saturation can never be achieved experimentally.

It must be noted that the theory is limited, and its interpretation requires care. As derived, it depends on a steady drift velocity $v = K_e X$, with electrons in equilibrium with X over most of the gap length d. It also requires that the region next to the cathode in which back diffusion is largely active be limited, and that the energy of the carriers on emission be little changed by impacts with molecules or by the field in this region. However, the energy must be lost rapidly, so that K_e is not changed by $\bar{v}_0$. As X/p increases and p decreases, the rate of energy gain and width of the diffusion zone near the cathode increase. Thus, eventually a value of X/p will be reached at which the diffusion velocity will no longer be determined by $\bar{v}_0 = \sqrt{1.2\,(h\nu - \phi e)/m}$, and will remain constant. The value of $\bar{v}_0$ will be influenced by the energy gain in the field while still within diffusive range of the cathode. Thus, in a gas with highly elastic impacts, such as A at 1 mm pressure, with X ranging from 10 to 100, the energy gain per electron free path in the field direction is of the order of

0.1 to 1 electron volt. Hence, with a $\bar{v}_0$ of 0.6 e.v., the diffusion will be affected by energy gain from the field, and j/j_0 will no longer be governed solely by $h\nu$ and ϕe.

To explore the situation, assume the extreme case that the energy near the cathode is that given by the equilibrium value of the energy distribution in the field. The simple Compton theory of electron mobilities then gives

$$K_e = A(f^{1/4}/\sigma) \sqrt{p/X} \text{ and } \bar{v}_0 = B\sqrt{X/p} \ (f^{1/4}/\sigma) \ .$$

Here f is the fractional loss of energy per collision and σ is the collision cross section for electrons. By placing these in equation 7.3, it is possible to write

$$(7.3) \qquad j/j_0 = \frac{3{,}040 \ A(f^{1/4}/\sigma) \ \sqrt{X/p}}{B(f^{1/4}/\sigma) \ \sqrt{X/p}) + 3{,}040 \ A(f^{1/4}/\sigma) \ \sqrt{X/p}} \ .$$

It is seen that in this extreme case, j/j_0 ceases to depend on X/p, and remains constant at a value less than unity. It is further seen that j/j_0 here is independent of any variation in Ramsauer cross section with X/p, for the collision radius cancels out. If at any point between the constant $\bar{v}_0$ and the strict dependence of energy, and thus $\bar{v}_0$ on X/p, there is a range of X/p values where the $\bar{v}_0$ term increases faster than the $K_e(X/p)$ term, the value of j/j_0 will decrease. Such behavior is not inconceivable.

Molnar (12) states that in A near 1.5 mm pressure, and with X from 6 to 60 volts per cm, a dip in the values of j/j_0 was observed. Probably a corrected Langmuir type of theory should apply in this region. It is also possible that Molnar's data were falsified by space-charge effects resulting from his heavy currents i_0 of the order of 10^{-8} ampere. In any event, the very restricted region of applicability of Thomson's theory must be noted, in view of its assumptions. It appears through its form *to apply as an empirical relation* to observed regions of p and X/p where *the theory is not justified*. In part, the deviations observed by Molnar were not even serious.

In view of the importance of back diffusion in cathode action in discharges, the problem was studied anew by J. K. Theobald (28) in the author's laboratory. Plane parallel nickel disc electrodes 3 cm in diameter and 1 cm apart were placed in a borosilicate glass chamber with monel metal screening, as shown in figure 7.3. Light from a quartz mercury arc, provided with filters as needed, entered at grazing incidence through a quartz window from the side, illuminating 0.5 cm^2 of the center of the lower electrode E. This electrode served as cathode, was earthed through a high resistance, and connected to

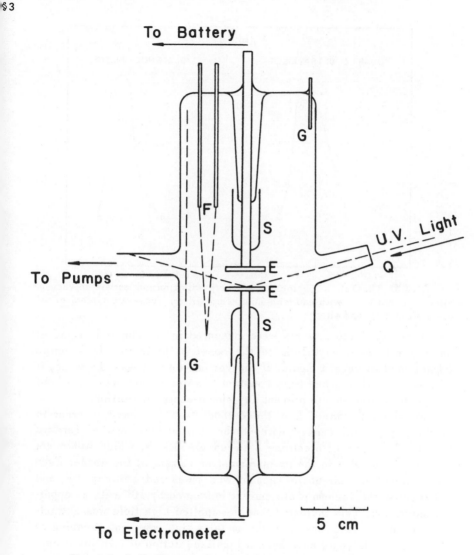

Fig. 7.3. J. K. Theobald's tube for the study of back diffusion.

an electrometer acting as a null instrument with potentiometer compensation. The chamber was provided with a hairpin W filament F for heating the electrodes by bombardment, and insulating stems to the leads were protected by sputtering shields S from evaporated metals created in outgassing. Potential was supplied to the anode. The tube was outgassed in an oven at 450° C., and the electrodes were outgassed at red heat by electron bombardment from the filament

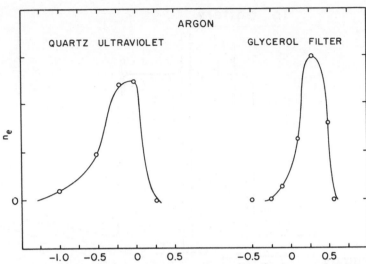

Fig. 7.4. Theobald's photoelectron energy-distribution curves in vacuum after exposure to A, with and without glycerol filter. These are typical of all gases except O_2 and air.

for 48 hours. Photo currents were measured in vacuum and in gas at an X/p ranging from 0.1 up to the onset of ionization by electron impact, and in vacuum again. If the vacuum current was the same, it was assumed that i_0 had been constant. The photo currents were kept below 10^{-11} amp/cm² to prevent any space-charge distortion.

The electron current from the cathode was measured in order to evaluate the total current without the geometrical loss of carriers by lateral escape of electrons between electrodes, which would not have been included in the measurement of current at the anode. Even then, when the current in vacuum was measured between 100 and 1,000 volts, the vacuum photo current increased by 10% with no apparent saturation. This indicated that the applied high field was extracting low-energy electrons from the metal which were not escaping at low fields. This could have been a localized action at emitting irregularities on the surface, such as observed in photoemission by Lawrence and Linford, or some similar action. Since all that was needed in these studies was the value of i_0 at the given X used, the vacuum photo current appropriate to the field was taken to represent the total emission in the presence of gas *at that field*.

After outgassing, the cathode required no treatment to give uniform results in A and N_2 gases. H_2, air, and O_2 produced changes in photosensitivity which slowly disappeared when the tube stood evacuated to 10^{-6} mm. To stabilize the surfaces, ion bombardment by heavy glow

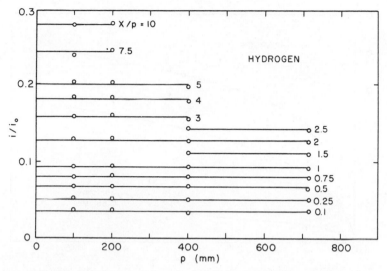

Fig. 7.5. Theobald's proof that back-diffusion loss is a function of X/p only, and not of p as well. Each line is for a different X/p.

discharges was employed, bombarding the cathode with positive ions. Bombardment with O_2 produced an initially high photosensitivity, which decreased to a low value in about a day. Retarding potential studies in vacuum for all gases to yield the mean electron energy and to check for contact potential differences between the initially similar electrodes indicated fictitiously high electron energies from the sensitive O_2 surfaces, while rough checks with filters indicated a photoelectric emission threshold of 2,300 Å. The photo effect in this case, and the peculiar high-energy distribution, can no doubt be ascribed to a patchy surface and localized areas of superposed field emission by the Malter (29) effect from the oxide layers produced by positive ion bombardment.

Hydrogen bombardment gave a satisfactory cathode surface. Two energy distributions of photoelectrons were achieved by filtering the quartz arc light through glycerol, cutting out wave lengths shorter than 2,300 Å, giving a mean energy of 0.2 e.v.; and by using the arc light through quartz, which gave an asymmetric distribution toward higher energies with a mean energy of 0.6 e.v. These are shown in figure 7.4. Other filters were altered by the ultraviolet light, so that transmission was not constant over the time needed for measurement.

Attempts to use low work function alkali metals were unsuccessful. Potassium gave good stability and retarding potential data, but the currents in A had an almost linear current-voltage characteristic.

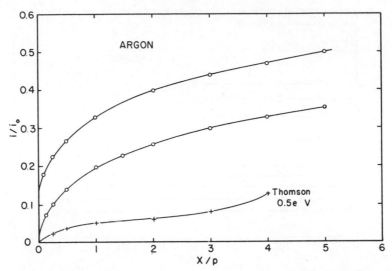

Fig. 7.6. Typical i/i_0 curves of Theobald in A gas for two photoelectron energy distributions. The values calculated from Thomson's theory corresponding to the data used are shown by the curve with crosses.

This no doubt was caused by conditions applying to low X/p with K_e nearly constant, and a very high value of initial emission velocity $\bar{v}_0$. Under the circumstances, Theobald did not attempt to use the alkali surfaces, especially as he at that time attributed the linearity of the curves to negative ion formation of some sort, which is unlikely but not entirely ruled out.

Figure 7.4 shows the energy-distribution curves for the direct ultraviolet and the glycerol-filtered ultraviolet in A, which are representative of all gases except air and O_2, where the Malter effect causes spurious distributions. The change in work function due to H_2 bombardment was too small to be revealed by these crude measurements. In other metals it ranged around 0.5 volt relative to an A- or N_2-bombarded surface. In any event, the energy distribution was not notably affected. Thus, the very large increase in photoelectric emission caused by H_2 appears to have been an increase in the effective area of photoemission, or better, increase in the number of sensitive regions for photoemission, and not due to a decrease in work function. The reproducibility of the vacuum current was only within a few per cent, so that the slopes of the retarding potential curves can give only approximate energy distributions. The error in contact potential determinations from the curves is about 0.1 volt. Contact potential varied with cathode history, and variations were not corre-

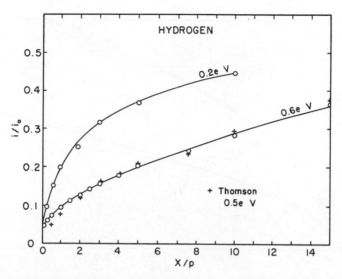

Fig. 7.7. Typical i/i_0 curves of Theobald in a molecular gas H_2 at two energies of electron emission. Thomson's theory, shown by crosses for 0.5 e.v., fits surprisingly well.

lated with changes in emission, since in general these depend on the gross average for a surface, while the emission depends on the most active centers.

One of the most immediate questions to answer relative to the Thomson theory is whether the effect is influenced by pressure independently of X/p. Such would be the case if photoemission, i.e., i_0, were influenced by pressure. Figure 7.5 shows a series of values of i/i_0 plotted against pressure in H_2 gas for X/p ranging from 0.1 to 10. This is typical of all gases studied. It is noted that i/i_0 is a function of X/p alone. In all this work pressures were such that an electron free path was small compared to the gap length. From such plots average values of i/i_0 were taken and plotted against X/p for the two energy distributions in figures 7.6 and 7.7, for A and H_2. Points computed from Thomson's equation, using Nielsen's (30) drift velocities assuming $\bar{v}_0 = 0.5$ e.v., are shown as crosses for the two gases. It is noted that the curve rises more rapidly with the smaller $\bar{v}_0$, and that in A the Thomson data fall far short of theory, while in H_2 the fit is remarkable. In N_2 gas (which is not shown) it is fairly close. The nature of the curves for N_2 and H_2 at low X/p is shown for the two values of v_0 in figure 7.8. Here the agreement is striking, despite the differences in drift velocity. The curve for i/i_0 in O_2 is shown in figure 7.9. The vertical lines show the spread of data in air.

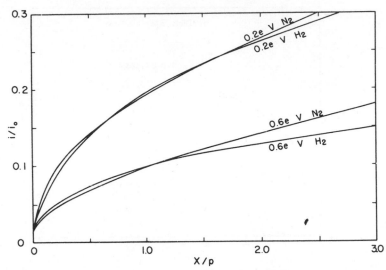

Fig. 7.8. Curves for i/i_0 at low X/p in N_2 and H_2 at two energies of electron emission, after Theobald. Note how closely the curves fall on top of each other for these two molecular gases.

The reason for this rather remarkable agreement with a theory as fallible as that of Thomson in the gases H_2 and N_2 lies in the circumstance that the electrons are emitted with energies not far from the equilibrium values in molecular gases, and have approximately the equilibrium drift velocity on emission. Thus, the data yield the correct value of n near the cathode. In A the emitted electrons have energies much lower than the equilibrium energies in the gas. Near the cathode they have drift velocities that are much higher than those out in the gas. It is true that the electrons gain energy from the field, but not rapidly enough to reduce drift velocity and increase n near the cathode. Thus, i/i_0 is higher than predicted by the Thomson equation, as more electrons with reduced n escape loss by back diffusion. The equation should fit fairly well in A for secondary electrons produced by inert gas positive ions or metastable bombardment of the cathode. These electrons escape with mean energies of several volts. Then the drift velocity values corresponding to X/p are low, n is high, and the loss is great, but correctly estimated.

The energy dependence of back diffusion also indicates in general that if two processes of equal efficiency at the cathode are producing secondary electrons in the discharge, the mechanism producing the lower electron energy will play the dominant role in the discharge, since the electron loss by back diffusion will be least.

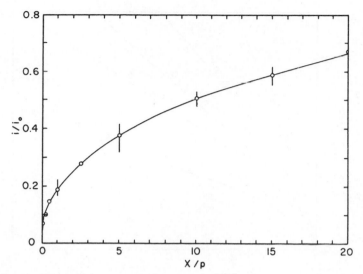

Fig. 7.9. Theobald's curves for i/i_0 as a $f(X/p)$ in O_2, with photoelectric energies not known. The vertical lines represent the spread of data in air at the same values of X/p.

The curves for argon show that electrons are not in equilibrium with the field in the zone of back diffusion, for the upcurving in the Thomson curve caused by inelastic impacts at $X/p>2$ is not seen in the observed curves.

These data indicate what is needed in a proper equation to correct for back diffusion. Thomson's equation, with Nielsen's values of drift velocity, will give values of the right order of magnitude in all cases with better accuracy if the emissive energy of the secondary electrons is reasonably close to the equilibrium energy at the value of X/p effective in the zone of back diffusion. The disagreement in the case of A is about as extreme as can be expected, and leads to a factor of about 5. Fast secondary electrons will lose energy more rapidly in He and N_2 than in A, but more slowly in Kr and Xe. On the other hand, in the molecular gases the loss of energy is rapid indeed, and the energy of the emitted electrons will be appreciably lowered before electrons leave the zone of back diffusion.

In order to make approximate data available for correcting values of secondary emission observed in a given gas at a given X/p, figures 7.10 and 7.11 have been prepared. They show the variation of i/i_0 with the reciprocal of the emissive energy, as estimated from the observed data at 0.2 and 0.6 e.v. and the Thomson equation at higher energies, for A and H_2 respectively. Choosing the emissive energy

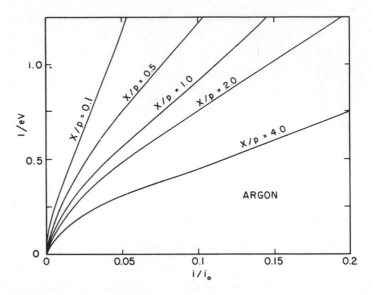

Fig. 7.10. Theobald's curves for calculating i/i_0 at various values of X/p for different values of energy of electron emission at the cathode in A and other inert gases. In these the values of the reciprocal of electron energy in e.v. are plotted as ordinates against i/i_0 as abscissae for X/p in A, ranging from 0.1 to 4.0. These curves should yield values correct within a factor of 2.

applicable to a given situation and the curve for the X/p in question, the value of i/i_0 may be read from the curves. These curves should give values good to a factor of 2 for molecular gases and inert gases respectively, for secondary electrons of known initial average energies. So far, these curves have proved to be quite useful, and have led to reasonable reductions for the secondary coefficients observed at the Ni cathodes of Lauer and Huber for H_2, N_2, and A.

In the commonly met case of gases which attach electrons, the theory as given must be used only after considerable study. With many electron-attaching gases it is not even certain that j_0 will remain constant with gas filling, pressure change, and time. Control measurements of j_0 in vacuum should be made before and after each run at a given pressure. Certainly Zn would not be a good surface to use, Ni or Pt being better in the presence of O_2. More important is the circumstance that with ion formation by electron attachment in the gas, the situation is complicated. Near the cathode, the n_0 electrons/cm² per second are emitted at a velocity v_0, or C_1, and there is an ion concentration; but the value of n may be modified as a result of space-charge accumulations. A rough estimate of what happens can

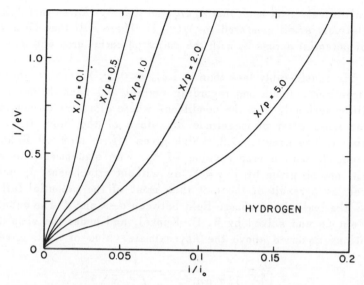

Fig. 7.11. Theobald's curves for calculating i/i_0 at various values of X/p for different values of average energy of electron emission in molecular gases, plotted similarly to those in figure 7.10.

be had by assuming that the average electron attaches to form an ion at a distance $\bar{x}$ from the cathode, given as $\bar{x} = mk_e^2 X_e/0.75\ eh$ by equation 5.5, with h the coefficient of attachment. Then continuity of current flow in the gap indicates that $j = en_e k_e X_e = en_i k_i X_i$, where the subscripts e and i refer to the values of the concentrations n, mobilities k, and field X obtaining over the regions from cathode to $\bar{x}$ where electrons are free, and $\bar{x}$ to d where the ions move. Thus, these quantities are altered owing to space charges and resulting fields which are no longer uniform and given by $X = V/d$, but are X_e from 0 to $\bar{x}$, and X_i from $\bar{x}$ to d. It is accordingly possible to write $X_e\bar{x} + (d-\bar{x})X_i = Xd = V$.

It is at once clear that the basic assumptions of J. J. Thomson no longer apply if space charges are present, and the situation becomes one of combined sections 3 and 4 of this chapter; i.e., back diffusion and space-charge limitation. It is seen that $n_e X_e/n_i X_i = k_i/k_e$, in which the values of $k_e \sim 10^3\ k_i$. Thus, the electron density and the drop in potential are small from 0 to $\bar{x}$, and the analogous quantities are high from $\bar{x}$ to d for ions. Solution is possible, using $dX_e/dx = 4\pi n_e e$ from 0 to $\bar{x}$, and $dX_i/dx = 4\pi n_i e$ from $\bar{x}$ to d, with dX_i/dx never greater than dX_e/dx. Solution of the involved algebraic expressions is not simple, as the space charges, and hence X_e and X_i, vary with

x. Qualitatively it is seen that $n_e < n_i$ and that $X_e < X_i$, so that $X_e \bar{x}$ will be relatively small compared to $X_i (d - \bar{x})$. There will thus be a small fall of potential across $\bar{x}$, with the major potential drop acting across $d - \bar{x}$.

If $\bar{x}$ is considerably less than d, i.e., $\bar{x} < 0.2d$, but $\bar{x} >> \lambda$, the electron free path, conditions regarding current and back diffusion will not differ seriously from the conditions where electrons do not attach for the same order of magnitude of values of the field. It is then possible to use equation 7.2, which gives j/j_0 in terms of $\bar{v}_0$ and X_e as deduced, with a proper value of X_0. With attachment, however, X_e will not be given by $V/d = X$, as without attachment. X_e will be reduced as a result of the fact that most of the potential fall lies across the ionic space-charge field between $d - \bar{x}$ and d. The equations were set up and solved by W. B. Kunkel, and under the simplifying conditions assumed above the approximate value of X_e is given by

$$(7.4) \qquad X_e \simeq \frac{9}{32\,\pi} \frac{k_i}{e\,n_e\,k_e} \; \frac{V^2}{d^3 \left(1 - \dfrac{\bar{x}}{d}\right)^3}.$$

With $n_e = 10^5$ electrons/cm^3 and $k_e/k_i = 10^3$, with d in the order of cm X_e, this becomes

$$X_e \simeq 2.0 \frac{V^2}{d^2} \; \frac{1}{d \left(1 - \dfrac{\bar{x}}{d}\right)^3} = \frac{2 X^3}{d \left(1 - \dfrac{\bar{x}}{d}\right)^3}.$$

Here V is the applied potential, and $V/d = X$. If X is set as 0.33 e.s.u. or 100 volts/cm, with $d = 1$ cm and $\bar{x} = 0.1d$, $X_e = 66$ volts/cm or $X_e = 2X/3$. Thus, equation 7.2 would be applied with an (X_e/p) of two-thirds the value of the potential, and thus X/p, applied across the gap. The values of j/j_0 would be correspondingly lowered below the values with no attachment for the same X/p, V, d, and p where electrons do not attach. The current density for electrons in air at 66 volts/cm at 760 mm pressure, with 10^5 ions/cm^3, is about 3×10^{-9} amp/cm^2.

It is seen that at lower electron-current densities the attachment will not seriously alter the currents where no attachment takes place, unless very low fields are involved. This seems to have been the case in the comparison of curves in air and pure N_2, and is to be attributed to the high electron velocities, which make n_e relatively low for current densities used in electrometric measurement. At larger current densities, as used in galvanometric studies of j, there will be observable effects. In fact, Theobald's recent data for air and N_2, fulfilling these conditions, indicate no essential effect of attachment.

The application of the Thomson theory has been extended to coaxial cylindrical electrode geometry with a nonuniform field, by C. W. Rice (13). Underlying assumptions parallel the derivation here given. The generalization of field conditions gave greater latitude, so that solution extends from space-charge limitation to back diffusion. The general validity of the theory with the limitations cited was verified for protons and electrons from thermionic sources near atmospheric pressure. The equation deduced for cylinders of inner and outer radii r_1 and r_2 reads

$$(7.5) \qquad V = \frac{C_1}{\sqrt{6\pi}\,k_e} \frac{j}{(j_0 - j)}\, r_1 \log_e \frac{r_2}{r_1}$$

for electrons. Here C_1 is the root-mean-square velocity of thermal agitation of thermionic electrons. It appears that thermal sources for carriers were used in this study. The relation can be rearranged to take the form

$$(7.6) \qquad j = \frac{A_1 V}{B_1 + V} = \frac{A_2 (X/p)}{B_2 + X/p}.$$

This is the same form as that of equation 7.2.

The theory is most useful in many studies of electron multiplication by ionization by collision in gases, for the following reason: In such measurements, electrons photoelectrically generated from a cathode must be used to give the initial electron current of which ionization is to be studied. Such current densities in gases, as indicated above, owing to $\bar{r}_0$ at liberation, are not the original current density j_0 liberated by the light, but have a value j dependent on X/p, given by equation 7.2 in the case of plane parallel electrodes. For many gases studied the X/p required to make $j/j_0 = 0.99$ is so large that ionization by collision increasing the i observed sets in at values below this. Thus, it is extremely difficult as X/p is increased to know whether the observed increase in j/j_0 indicated by observation is caused by incipient ionization by collision or by the Thomson relation. To get values of the quantity j/j_0 beyond the point where ionization begins, so that j may be subtracted from the total observed current density J to give j_i, where $j_i = J - j$ is the contribution caused by ionization, it is convenient to know j. Under some simple conditions in uniform fields, the theory for the multiplication of current by ionization permits j_i and j to be evaluated from two observations of J at different gap lengths. Where fields are not uniform or complications ensue, this is not possible.

From the theory of equation 7.2 it should be possible from K_e and $\bar{v}_0$ to calculate j. Owing to inaccuracies inherent in the derivations, such calculation, with estimates of $\bar{v}_0$, etc., would be of no help in precision measurement. However, the *theory*, either for the plane parallel or for the coaxial geometry, gives the *form of the relation* for j/j_0 as that of equation 7.6. Thus, for plane parallel electrodes, equation 7.2 indicates that $j/j_0 = [Af(X/p)]/[B + Af(X/p)]$, generally; and at high X/p for electrons, as in the present instance, $f(X/p)$ is of the form $\sqrt{X/p}$. If p and gap length d (or r_1 and r_2) are constant for either the plane parallel geometry or coaxial cylindrical geometry,

$$(7.6) \qquad\qquad j = \frac{A_1 V}{B_1 + V}.$$

Then, where X is increased by change in applied potential V, j should be given by equation 7.6 so long as B_1 is sensibly constant. Since $V = A_1(V/j) - B_1$, by plotting V against V/j, both A_1 and B_1 in a given limited range of V or X/p are determined. Then, with A_1 and B_1 determined where ionization by collision does not occur, i.e., where $j_i = 0$ and $J = j$, the curve may be extrapolated into the values at V beyond ionization and used to evaluate j and. thus j_i. This procedure made it possible for G. W. Johnson to study electron multiplication in coaxial field geometry where Townsend's theory of j did not apply (14). There will of course be an error as soon as B_1 begins to vary with V. In general, the extrapolation is over limited ranges of V. The error in the slowly changing j is relatively small, since j_i increases very rapidly with V.

§ 4. The Space-Charge Limited Current.

In all cases where ions of one sign of charge are generated at a high rate in a region, and the fields active are unable to remove them rapidly enough so that the volume density of charges $\rho = ne$ becomes appreciable, the lines of electrical force emanating from these charges can become comparable in density to those of the imposed electrical fields. Under such circumstances, the electrical field X is altered along a given direction x to the extent that $dX/dx = d^2V/dx^2 = 4\pi\rho = 4\pi ne$. It is seen that such a condition implies that any imposed uniform field $X = dV/dx$ existing previously is no longer constant, by virtue of the space charges. Accordingly, not only is the potential fall no longer linear, but the field X varies with distance along the direction in which it was previously constant. Such changes in field strength will influence the local carrier velocity v, and thus will profoundly alter conduction currents in gases.

In practice, except for conduction at very low current densities (i.e., low carrier densities in gases), there are no observed discharge currents in which $dV/dx = X$ is constant and the carrier velocity $v = kX$ is uniform along the whole current path. To indicate the order of magnitudes involved, it should be noted that 10^6 electronic charges per cm^3 lying in a slab 1 cm thick normal to a uniform field of strength X will add or subtract a field contribution of 1.64 volts/cm to the field traversing the slab. This is an appreciable field distortion for fields commonly used in gaseous ion studies. If the density of 10^6 carriers per cm^3 is to be generated by a current of electrons having a velocity corresponding to 1 e.v. of energy, the current density required is 8.8×10^{-6} ampere per cm^2. If this same density is to be caused by Na^+ ions of velocity corresponding to 1 e.v. of energy, the density is 4.2×10^{-7} ampere per cm^2. Such current densities of ions and electrons are readily achieved from thermionic sources.

In fact, if it is desired to achieve current densities of any magnitude whatsoever from sources emitting ions of one sign *only*, the resultant field distortion requires considerable potential to overcome the space-charge limitations on current flow. In consequence, where tubes giving large currents are needed, resort is had to *gaseous discharges* where the simultaneous presence of negative and positive carriers reduces the space-charge limitations. However, even in systems in which gaseous breakdown furnishes both positive and negative carriers, differences in mobilities, especially when carriers are electrons and positive ions, lead to the building up of space-charge regions which limit and control the current. These are found most frequently near the electrodes. It is thus essential that the effect of such space charges be studied in order that the phenomena may be understood. By all odds the simplest example is that of the thermionic vacuum current between plane parallel electrodes in a uniform field. The study of this will at the same time lay the foundation for discussion of the balanced space-charge detector which is of importance in many discharge studies.

Imagine electrons emitted uniformly over the cathode plate of a plane parallel plate condenser of unlimited radius R compared to the plate distance d. This ideally insures a uniform field and permits neglect of motion parallel to the plates and equipotential surfaces. The velocity of emission of the electrons at the cathode may initially be considered zero. The electrons are emitted at considerable density, say of the order of 10^8 to 10^{10} per cm^3. The anode plate is at $+E$ volts relative to the cathode, which is at ground potential. Were the electrons not emitted, the potential would rise from zero to $+E$ at

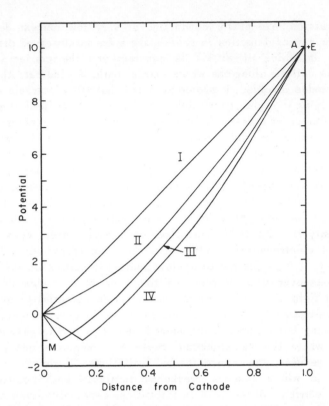

Fig. 7.12. Potential distribution across a uniform field gap as influenced by space charges from electrons in vacuum. Curve *I* shows uniform potential fall from anode *A* to cathode for a 1-cm gap with distance and potential 0 at the cathode. Curve *II* shows space-charge distorted distribution with 0 velocity of electron emission. Curves *III* and *IV* show distribution, with $E = 10$ volts, velocity of emission 1 volt, and current-density ratios at saturation of 5 and 1 respectively, as computed by Langmuir. Note potential troughs for curves *III* and *IV*.

the anode d cm away along the straight line *I* of figure 7.12. In this case the field X is given by $X = dV/dx = E/d$, where x is the distance along X from the cathode. However, since there are n electrons per cm³, the charge density is $ne = \rho$. There will thus be subtracted from the field the change in X in one cm of length along x, which is $dX/dx = 4\pi\rho$ lines. Since the field strength X is given at any point by $X = dV/dx$, it follows that $d^2V/dx^2 = 4\pi\rho$. This is the elementary form of Poisson's equation applicable to the situation above.

In consequence of the field acting on the electrons, there is a current density of j amp/cm². If ρ is the charge density at any point and the velocity is v, $j = v\rho$. At any point in a vacuum distant x cm from the cathode, the electron velocity is given by the potential V through which it has fallen; namely, $\frac{1}{2}mv^2 = Ve$. Thus, $v = \sqrt{2Ve/m}$ and $\rho = j/\sqrt{2Ve/m}$. It then follows that $d^2V/dx^2 = 4\pi j\sqrt{m/2Ve}$. This is integrated readily by multiplying both sides of the equation by $2dV/dx$, which yields

$$2\frac{dV}{dx}\left(\frac{d^2V}{dx^2}\right) = 8\pi j \sqrt{\frac{m}{2e}}\;\frac{dV}{V^{\frac{1}{2}}dx}.$$

This relation must be integrated from $(dV/dx)_0$ at $x = 0$ and $V = 0$, and dV/dx at x where V has the value V. Integration yields

$$\left[\left(\frac{dV}{dx}\right)^2\right]_{\left(\frac{dV}{dx}\right)_0}^{\left(\frac{dV}{dx}\right)} = 8\pi j \sqrt{\frac{2m}{e}}\;\left[V^{\frac{1}{2}}\right]_0^V.$$

The value of $(dV/dx)_0$ may be set equal to zero. The justification for this assertion is not obvious, even though $V = 0$ at $x = 0$, for rough reasoning leads to a paradox. More rigorous derivations in the limit justify this assumption. Thus, the relation becomes

$$\left(\frac{dV}{dx}\right)^2 = 8\pi j \sqrt{\frac{2m}{e}}\;V^{\frac{1}{2}},$$

leading to the relation

$$\frac{dV}{V^{\frac{1}{4}}} = \sqrt{8\pi j \sqrt{\frac{2m}{e}}}\;dx,$$

which is open to a second integration from $V = 0$ at $x = 0$ to $V = E$ at $x = d$. This yields

$$\frac{4}{3}E^{\frac{3}{4}} = \sqrt{8\pi j \sqrt{2m/e}}\;d,\text{ or }\frac{16}{9}E^{3/2} = 8\pi j \sqrt{2m/e}\;d^2.$$

Accordingly, the current density for a space-charge limited electron flow is

(7.7) $$j = \frac{1}{9\pi}\sqrt{\frac{2e}{m}}\;\frac{E^{3/2}}{d^2} = 2.33 \times 10^{-6}\frac{E^{3/2}}{d^2}\text{ amp/cm}^2.$$

This is the famous relation first deduced by C. D. Child in 1911 (15). In 1913, I. Langmuir independently derived the same relation for electron currents in vacuum (16).

The relation at once indicates that the space-charge potential acts to hold the current back, and that j is proportional to $E^{3/2}$ and to $1/d^2$. If j is constant, the E required to maintain constancy is proportional to $d^{4/3}$. Stated in another way, this says that if j is constant across the space, the potential V needed to maintain it rises as the 4/3 power of the gap length. This leads to a variation of potential with distance from the cathode, that rises as shown by curve II, figure 7.12. In other words, the potential begins to rise more slowly near the origin than the rise of linear slope in the absence of space charge. In recompense, however, this curve has a steeper rise as the anode is approached.

The common-sense explanation of distribution of potential is that owing to the repulsive effect which the charge of the electrons on the anode side of the gap exerts on the newly emitted electrons, the latter electrons are densest at the cathode. Thus, they effectively project the low-potential value of the cathode out into the gap, lowering the potential below the linear rise of curve I. In consequence, the potential must rise more steeply near the anode. The tangent to the potential curve at any point x is the field strength dV/dx. For a fixed value of j it can be computed at any value of V, or of the distance x corresponding to that value of V. Since

$$(7.8) \qquad X_V = \left(\frac{dV}{dx}\right)_V = 8\pi j\sqrt{\frac{2m}{e}}\, V^{\frac{1}{4}},$$

it is seen that X_V is proportional to the fourth root of the potential at each point. Now V is proportional to $x^{4/3}$, as seen above; therefore, the field X is proportional to the cube root of the distance from the cathode, viz., $X \propto x^{1/3}$. This makes the *slope* of the potential curve, or the *field strength*, which is zero at $x = 0$, rise very rapidly at first and then more and more slowly as x approaches d, at which point it still has a finite value.

The space-charge limited current is not confined to electrons. Heated Kunsman catalysts, certain fused glasses having alkali ions, or jets of alkali atoms fired at a hot surface having a work function greater than the ionizing potential of the atoms, emit copious quantities of the appropriate positive ions (17). The currents from these sources are space-charge limited, and limitation sets in at lower current densities because of the sluggishness of movement of the relatively massive ions. The equations as deduced for electrons apply to ions, except that now the relation $\frac{1}{2}mv^2 = Ve$ for electrons must be replaced by $\frac{1}{2}Mv_i^2 = Ve\bar{v}$ for ions. Since ions of valence greater than unity have a multiple charge equal to their valence $\bar{v}$, the relations deduced must substitute $\bar{v}e/M$ for the ions in place of e/m for the electrons. Since M (the mass of the ion) can be expressed in terms of M_1 (the molecular weight of the ion) by taking the actual mass of an atom of unit atomic weight into the constant term, the relation written for electrons transforms into the relation

(7.9) $$j_i = 5.402 \times 10^{-8} \sqrt{\frac{\bar{v}}{M_1}} \frac{E^{3/2}}{d^2} \quad \text{amp/cm}^2$$

for positive ions. This relation limits the currents of ions drawn from a source (17). It is because of this limitation that in the separation of isotopes, the ion sources in mass spectrographs are not thermionic, but use the plasmas from arc discharges where the current is not space-charge limited, as it is partially neutralized by electrons.

From equations 7.7 and 7.9 it might be thought that j would increase indefinitely with E. This is of course impossible, since the number of electrons or carriers emitted is limited to the saturation current density j_0. These limitations depend on the processes involved, e.g., how many Na atoms strike 1 cm² of surface per second. In the example of the thermionic electronic vacuum current, the maximum current density possible is given by the Richardson thermionic equation, as modified by the wave mechanics. In this, the saturation current density is

(7.10) $$j_s = \frac{4\pi m e k^2}{h^3} DT^2 \epsilon^{-b/T} = AT^2 \epsilon^{-b/T}.$$

Here h is Planck's constant, k the gas constant per atom, m and e pertain to the electron, D is a surface-reflection coefficient, and b is a constant depending on the work function of the surface. The quantity A lies between 60.2 and 120.4 amp/cm² degree², except where surface contamination changes it in one sense or the other. However, the value of j_s is primarily dependent on the work function and T. It would thus be expected that j should follow equation 7.7 up to a value of E at which $j = j_s$, and then remain constant, as shown in curve A of figure 7.13. In practice, the curve observed starts at slightly negative values of E, and parallels the theoretical curve pretty well, as shown in curve B. Actually, as it approaches j_s in value, it rounds off and reaches j_s asymptotically.

The explanation of these deviations obviously stems from departures from the ideal conditions assumed in the interest of theoretical simplicity. For one thing, the electrons are not emitted with $v_0 = 0$. They are emitted at all angles, and with a *nearly* Maxwellian energy distribution about a mean velocity C_1, related to the temperature T

§4

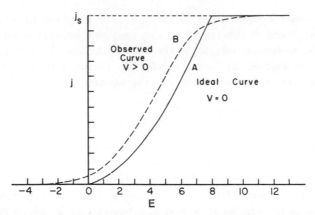

Fig. 7.13. Curves for current density in a space-charge limited vacuum electron current from a hot cathode, plotted against potential. Curve A is the ideal curve, showing saturation. The real curve B shows a little current at negative values of E, from the velocity distribution, and a gradual transition to saturation at higher potentials.

of emission from the filament. It is clear that under these conditions electrons will escape from the cathode, even if it is at zero potential. In fact, since $\tfrac{1}{2}mC_1^2 = (3/2)kT = - V_1e$, the *average* electron emitted normally to the cathode will escape against a retarding potential $-V_1$. Since there are electrons faster than the average in the distribution, the number of which declines exponentially with the value of the velocity, an exponentially decreasing number of electrons emitted normally will have velocities requiring higher values of $-V$. Thus, the rise of current will occur at more negative values of V, and will increase exponentially at first, having an appreciable value at $V = 0$. As the number of electrons of very high energy is vanishingly small, the currents are sensibly zero for potentials of a very few volts negative. This applies to very hot cathode emitters as well, since, for example, electrons at 2,400° K. have a mean electron energy of only 0.24 e.v. Because of the geometrical considerations, the initial velocity of electron emission with an energy distribution, together with the random direction of electron emergence, will reduce the increase of current as j approaches j_s relative to that for directly accelerated electrons. It will also require higher values of E to yield saturation than called for by the $E^{3/2}$ power law. The reasons for this will become clearer in detail when the influence of an initial velocity is considered.

The problem of initial velocities has been studied by I. Langmuir, W. Schottky, P. S. Epstein, P. C. Fry (18), and many others at later times. It is treated in a comprehensive fashion in Langmuir and Compton's article on electrical discharge in gases (19), to which the reader is referred for a complete analysis. The principles involved in the changes produced as a result of initial velocities of emission v_0 are of sufficient importance to require presentation here. For simplicity, assume that all the electrons are emitted with the average velocity component $\bar{v}_0$ that is *normal* to the surface of the cathode. Space-charge limitation of current can only operate if these escaping electrons are held back by a negative electron space-charge field out in the gap. This field forces the electrons emitted with the initial velocity back toward the cathode. Thus, in consequence of the space charge, when the electrons are emitted with an initial velocity $\bar{v}_0$, there must exist at some plane x_0 distant from the cathode a negative potential of such magnitude as to reduce the electrons of velocity $\bar{v}_0$ to zero velocity. Accordingly, at x_0 the potential must be $-V_0$, defined by the relation $V_0 = \frac{1}{2}m\bar{v}_0{}^2$. Then the electrons, instead of starting from the cathode with zero velocity, as initially assumed, start from x_0 at *zero velocity*. The equation derived may therefore be deduced as before, if referred to x_0 as the initiating surface. The quantities V and x are then measured from values V_0 and x_0, with $(dV/dx)_0 = 0$ at x_0 as origin. Under these circumstances, the current density from the cathode is j_0, a return current density $j_0 - j$ flows *back* to the cathode in view of the space charge, and the net current density flowing is j, as before. The density of the space charge between zero and x_0 is that which would be caused by a current $2j_0 - j$ in one direction. Between the cathode and the minimum the potential distribution is given by

$$(7.11) \qquad 2j_0 - j = 2.334 \times 10^{-6} \frac{V_0^{3/2}}{x^2} .$$

On the anode side of the minimum,

$$(7.12) \qquad j = 2.334 \times 10^{-6} \frac{V_a^{3/2}}{x_a^2} ,$$

if $V_a = E + V_0$ and $x = x_0 + x_a$. These relations may be combined to give

$$(7.13) \qquad x_0 = \frac{x}{1 + \left(1 + \dfrac{V}{V_0}\right)^{3/4} \left(2\dfrac{j_0}{j} - 1\right)^{1/2}} ;$$

and if $V \gg V_0$,

$$(7.14) \qquad \frac{x_0}{x} = \left(\frac{V_0}{V}\right)^{\frac{3}{4}} \left(\frac{j}{2j_0 - j}\right)^{\frac{1}{2}}.$$

The curves *III* and *IV* of figure 7.12 were computed by Langmuir, using $V = 10$ volts, $V_0 = 1$ volt, $x = 1$ cm and j_0/j being taken as 5 for curve *III* and 1 for curve *IV*. The important feature of these curves is the *negative potential trough* of depth $-V_0$ in the two cases at 0.07 d and 0.14 d from the cathode. Beyond V_0 the potentials rise to E more rapidly than in the absence of a velocity of emission. The interesting feature to notice is that the minimum at x_0 acts like a *new source*, with $v = 0$ at x_0, and sending a current density $j_0 - j$ back to the cathode. The effect of the velocity *distribution* in emission and the random direction of emission is to round off and broaden the minimum at x_0, as well as to round off and extend the approach to the value of j_0. This more complicated problem, with distribution of velocities and random emission, is treated in detail in Langmuir's article. The analysis in that article is also carried over to other geometrical arrangements, including coaxial cylinders. Since the principles are adequately covered in what has gone before, it is not profitable to cover material which should more appropriately be taken from the original source.

§ 5. The Effect of Positive Ions on the Space-Charge Limited Electron Current and the Space-Charge Limited Ion Detector.

If a negative electronic space charge exists in a region, thus limiting the current flow, the current will be influenced by any agent altering the space-charge density. Thus, if by some means positive ions are introduced into a region of electron space charge, in effect neutralizing some of the electron space charge, the charge being reduced will permit more current to flow. The effectiveness of positive ions in accomplishing this action is much greater than that owing to the charge which they carry. Positive ions, being more massive than electrons, will move much more slowly in a given field. Langmuir showed that for plane parallel electrodes, the positive ions are effective in reducing an electronic space charge in proportion to their density, multiplied by the ratio $\sqrt{1,836 \, M_1}$ to unity (20). Here M_1 is the molecular weight of the positive ions. This follows at once, since the velocities of two particles for the same energy vary inversely as the square root of their molecular weights. Thus, even with plane parallel geometry, each Hg^+ ion will effectively neutralize 600 electrons of the space charge, while an He^+ ion can neutralize 85 electrons.

In the coaxial cylindrical geometry, the effectiveness of the positive ions is much greater, as shown by K. H. Kingdon (20). This circumstance has many useful applications, probably the most useful one being the *space-charge ion detector*, or Kingdon cage. Such a detector can be developed by using an electron space charge in vacuum, the positive ions being shot into the space charge, altering the space-charge limited current. The device can also be used to detect rare ionizing events *in a gas* with accuracy and certainty (21), (22), (23). Attempts to detect the electrons produced are often falsified by secondary electrons released from surfaces. In such application, the gas to be ionized is present in the cylinder with the space-charge limited electron current. Then ions produced in the gas—e.g., by photoelectric action, by impact of positive ions, or by impact of fast atoms on gas atoms—will furnish one electron and one positive ion per ionized atom. In the 10^8 or more electrons per cm^3 of electron space-charge density, the electrons created (including spurious ones) pass unnoticed. On the other hand, the positive ions simultaneously created, with their multiple neutralizing power, are registered by effective increase in current and indicate a true ionization in the gas. Such positive ions in the gas can be created only by ionization of the gas, and are not emitted by other agencies or by ion bombardment of the walls. This circumstance alone makes the study of this phenomenon worth while.

Consider a coaxial cylindrical system with central cathode a fine wire of radius r, and the outer cylinder with a radius R of some 1 to 2 cm. The cylinder is L cm long, and its ends can be closed off with perforated caps, having openings for the wire and a hole for the ionizing agency near the outer cylinder. If desired, the ends may be left open. The gas must be present at relatively low pressure to give the most effective results. The central cathode of radius r is heated to electron-emitting temperature and maintained at *constant* temperature. The electrons emitted are driven by a weak field of a few volts to the positive outer cylinder. The circuit is closed, so that the current can be measured. The electron current to the outer cylinder is thus space-charge limited. If on generation the positive ion is at rest near the outer cylinder wall R, the ion will be drawn radially into the wire of radius r, requiring a time of transit in the ratio of $\sqrt{1,836\ M_1}$ to unity greater than an electron. It thus effectively neutralizes $\sqrt{1,836\ M_1}$ electrons of the space charge. However, at the least, the positive ions in a gas will have random thermal energies in the gas, and in many other cases may have much higher energies. In consequence of collisions with molecules, irrespective of energy, the ions will have components of motion transverse to the radius of the system. Thus, in general, while the field draws the positive ion into the wire cathode, the collisions and resulting transverse velocity components will cause the ion to enter orbits about the cathode, only a few of which strike the surface. Such orbits will continue indefinitely until the ion suffers collisions with gas molecules under such conditions as to lose energy and transverse motion near the filament. When this occurs, the ion will be captured by the cathode.

G. W. Hull (24) has determined the conditions to be fulfilled in order that the ion may miss the filament. The relations deduced ignore the motion caused by the magnetic field of the filament current. These fields are usually weak, and can be ignored in a rough study. The condition set is that at every point the potential V should be less than a value V_0 defined by the relation $eV_0 = \frac{1}{2}Mv_0^2 (R/r)^2$. Here $\frac{1}{2}Mv_0^2$ is the energy of the positive ion, R and r are the radii of the outer and inner cylinders, and e is the electron. Thus, the larger are R/r, v_0, and M, the greater is the value of V at a point in the field likely to be less than V_0. Eventually, the value of V will exceed V_0. All positive ions of energy $\frac{1}{2}Mv_0^2$, lying inside a cylinder of radius corresponding to the point where $V = V_0$, will escape capture and have to make a new approach. Hence, at appropriately large values of v_0 and R/r, the positive ions can move around the wire many times before capture, and neutralize the negative space charge. The electrons coming from the hot filament, even when scattered by occasional collisions of gas molecules, will move to the outer cylinder and, except for the few that are reflected from the wall, all will reach it. It thus transpires that the hundredfold effectiveness of a single positive ion in regard to electron space charge is increased another hundredfold. In general, then, the presence of positive ions can be very effective, and equivalent to from 10^2 to 10^4 electrons in reducing space-charge limitation. If the filament cylinder can be run quite hot, without deterioration or fluctuation, the negative space-charge sheath may develop a potential trough which will be still more effective in the presence of positive ions. This indicates why not only the space-charge detector is possible, but why in addition many circuits needing to pass heavier currents use gas-filled tubes. Such, for example, are the thyratrons, used in place of thermionic vacuum tubes, where positive ions created help to neutralize the space charges.

F. L. Mohler (21), who was attempting to study photoelectric ionization in gases, was among the very first to use the space-charge detector for ion detection. Since it was almost impossible to prevent scattering of the ultraviolet light to electrode and walls, causing effective secondary emission of electrons which falsified observation, the detection of the feeble photoionization in the body of the gas presented a difficult problem. By using the creation of *positive ions produced in the gas*, only the ionization of the gas was detected.

The positive ions can effectively reduce the number of space-charge electrons by a factor of the order of 10^4 in the coaxial geometry at relatively low gas pressures. Thus, it is clear that the creation of some 10^3 photoelectrically produced ions in 1 cm³ of the gas will effectively neutralize some 10^7 electrons of the space charge, while the accompanying 10^3 electrons created are of no consequence. If the space-charge density lies around 10^9 ions, then the effective space-charge density will be reduced 1%, an effect readily detected by changes in current. There will thus be a change in the space-charge limited current which will depend on the number of ions produced. As used by Mohler, there was a single cylindrical system, with the light beam traversing the space between the coaxial cylinders along their length parallel to the axis near the outer wall. The device worked well, except that the background current "drifted" badly, owing to assumed small current changes that were ascribed to temperature changes of the filament. This drift necessitated checking of the current reading without light.

E. O. Lawrence and N. L. Edlefsen (21) improved this method by placing two identical cylinders with their filaments in series in the same envelope. One of these cylinders was a balancing dummy space-charge system. The same small potential was placed between the filament wires and outer cylinders, giving a similar space-charge limited current in each case. The cylinders had caps on the ends with orifices for the central wire filament. The measuring cylinder also had an entrance and exit hole for the ionizing light; the other had none. The two cylinders were connected, in order to make two arms of a resistance bridge circuit. Thus, in the absence of ultra-violet light, the bridge could be balanced with a detecting galvanometer reading zero. Any fluctuations in heater current of the filaments caused compensating charges in the two chambers, so that balance was not disturbed and a large amount of drift was eliminated. The current registered was caused by the effective reduction in resistance of the illuminated cylinder when ionization occurred. This could be calibrated in terms of the positive ionization created. Direct calibration was possible by replacing the light by a beam of electrons of known energy whose ionization efficiency in the gas was known.

In attempting to adapt the system to the study of ionization of a gas by fast positive ions, R. N. Varney (23) found that placing the two filaments in parallel across a constant-potential source gave greater stability, and thus sensitivity. He later investigated the question of the factors yielding greatest efficiency. The sources of loss of positive ions may be listed as follows:

1. Absorption by the cathode wire.
2. Escape from the ends of the cylinder.
3. Electron-ion recombination.
4. Collisions with gas molecules, leading to loss of energy and capture by the wire.

The gradual drift of the ions in the magnetic field about the wire, as well as diffusion with cylinders of large ratio of R/L, leads to loss of electrons from the ends. This is reduced by using end caps which, however, distort the radial field in their vicinity. The filaments should be indirectly heated, since the iR drop down the filament causes ions to drift to one end. Such central cathodes unfortunately have a large radius r, which is not desirable. Pulsing of heating current and calibration when the current is not on will reduce drift by the field. Electron-ion recombination at the low gas pressures causes some loss, but it is small. Obviously, the effect of increasing gas pressure in causing loss of positive ions, while at the same time increasing by its presence the number of ions formed, indicates that the choice of the correct pressure is critical for optimum sensitivity. Loss of ions through the ends of the cylinders by the filament holes of the caps increases as pressure decreases. According to Kingdon's measurements, the optimum neutralizing efficiency for ions in He gas with 35 volts on the anode was near 2×10^{-5} mm pressure, where one positive ion was equivalent to 2.6×10^4 electrons. The ions roughly made 200 trips at 2×10^{-4} mm pressure. Varney found that higher filament temperatures increased the effectiveness, and the author suggested that with the low anode potentials used, the effect was caused by the accumulation of positive ions in the electron space-charge trough.

The problem of actual efficiency in detection, and of its improvement, has been worked on for a long time. Before World War II, the limit appeared to have been reached with the detection of some 10^2 to 10^3 ions. The chief limitation was "background noise," or fluctuations in the space-charge detectors, the origin and control of which were difficult to determine. Developments since the war have appeared to indicate greater ultimate sensitivity than dreamed of before. R. N. Varney and others have investigated the factors limiting the sensitivity of the *balanced* space-charge detectors. The single space-charge detectors used by Mohler gave disturbances and undesirable drifts, for various reasons that were not then clearly recognized, except that they came from changes in filament emission with time. Lawrence and Edlefsen, as well as Varney, originally ascribed these changes to current fluctuations in the filament, which altered the temperature by minute amounts, thus changing the space-charge emissions by larger amounts. By using two such emitters, housed in the same container and subject to all changes in condition, including changes in filament current, the major difficulties of that period were eliminated by balancing the fluctuations of one detecting cylinder against its twin dummy cylinder.

It now appears that while some drift may have been caused by current changes, the drifts were actually caused to a great extent by changes in filament emission which *were not due to fluctuations of current* in the filament. They were caused instead by changes in the filament work function with time, or by actual spurious positive ion generation in the counting cylinder, produced by the presence of small quantities of various types of impurities, or by background radiation. Balancing cylinders under such conditions, if both cylinders are in the same glass envelope, eliminates these drifts and makes work easier.

The modern techniques for gas purification and outgassing electrodes have made it possible to show that *single cylinders exhibit no drift* if made of clean, outgassed outer tantalum with outgassed tungsten, or oxide-coated filaments indirectly heated as central cylinders. Under such conditions, the limitations on sensitivity are caused primarily by background noise. These are fluctuations caused by statistical fluctuations in electron emission from the filaments. The use of two tubes, therefore, increases rather than reduces background. Thus, by using clean, outgassed tubes and electrodes, Varney (25) obtained better results when the dummy space-charge cylinder was replaced by a constant, accurate, suitable high resistance in the bridge circuit. The bridge needs complete rebalancing, however, if gas pressure is changed in the detector. This is not so important with the dummy cylinder in the same envelope.

Further improvements are possible by modulating the positive ion generating source (e.g., photon beam, positive ion beam, etc.) in one cylinder, with a suitable square-wave pulse technique at a suitable high repeat rate. This will generate a fluctuating ion balance current in the bridge, which can be amplified by a suitable electronic amplifier circuit. Such an arrangement naturally lowers the background noise to signal ratio. It is possible that in this fashion the sensitivity could be increased by a factor of 100. Under these conditions, fluctuations of the order of 10^6 electrons in the space charge can be produced by a single positive ion. This should make possible the detection of the production of single, or at least very few, positive ions, possibly of the order of 10 per cm^3.

With a balanced space-charge detector without modulation, G. L. Weissler (26) believed that 40 positive ions created at one time were detected. Still further advances appear possible, since in these studies Weissler and his associates discovered that the magnitude of the neutralizing space-charge action of a positive ion is equivalent to the number of ions liberated in a Geiger counter pulse. Such ionic disturbances can be picked up by a counter circuit and observed with an oscilloscope. This led to the introduction of a single coaxial space-charge cylinder detector with hot filament, as a *counting tube*. The hot filament and cylinder operate in a gas at low pressure in the space-charge limited region. When the cylinder was placed in series with a pulse transformer, or a 1-megohm resistor, an oscilloscope placed across the resistor was able to pick up single pulses. These pulses apparently came from the ionization of impurity molecules in the He gas filling within the cylinder. With this method, it was hoped that the detector could ultimately be used to detect and count the appearance of single positive ions. It proved, however, that the detector used this way was critically sensitive to the location of ion generation. Since the sensitive volume was too small, the method has been abandoned.

§ 6. Currents with Volume Ionization and Ion Recombination in a Gas (27).

It is desirable, after having studied the special cases preceding, to consider the case of a conduction current in a gas in which carriers of both signs are produced at a given rate, and are removed by the fields and some other source of loss. In practice, most currents generated in gaseous discharges have these essential elements, viz., a uniform rate of generation of carriers in equal numbers from the gas, the extraction of these by electrodes yielding a current, and the subsidiary loss of carriers by some agency throughout the volume of the gas. In actual discharges, the ions are generated primarily by electron impact. The loss of ions occurs in part by recombination, as here assumed, but often in greater measure by ambipolar diffusion to the walls. In some discharges, such as arcs, electrons are generated from an electrode. In most conduction currents studied, negative carriers are chiefly electrons of high mobility, while positive carriers are slower positive ions. The solution of equations in which, for example, loss by diffusion replaces loss by recombination and charge generation is not uniform throughout the volume, is too involved to serve as an example. Thus, it will be advantageous to consider a much less complicated situation. This simplified current problem, despite its idealizations, will lead to solutions so similar to conditions in actual discharges that its derivation is justified at this place.

Assume that the electrodes are infinite parallel plates giving a uniform[4] field of length l with a potential V across the plates. Let the field, in the absence of any current, be $X_p = V/l$, and be along the x axis. Neglect any lateral diffusion, as well as diffusion along x. If desired, current could be collected over a small section of one plate by cutting a thin, circular slot around that area. The gas is uniformly ionized by some external agency, such as X-rays, so that q ions are created per cm^3 per sec for any cm^3 of the volume. The ions move toward their appropriate electrodes with mobilities k_+ and k_- in the fields generated. The ions will recombine at a rate given by an_+n_-, where a is the coefficient of recombination. Once the ionization begins, the ions are created and move to the electrodes with different velocities. This will alter the uniform field distribution between the electrodes through the creation of space charges, which will be most prominent near the electrodes. Near the anode, the positive ions created in the volume near it are being withdrawn by the current, while the current brings in negative ions. Near the cathode, the situation is reversed. If the ions have different mobilities, it is clear that the space charges at the two electrodes will differ. Thus, it must be expected that, in consequence of the current flow, the fields will no longer be uniform, and the current will vary with potential in a manner which does not follow Ohm's law. To solve the problem, it is necessary to set up and solve the differential equation appropriate to the situation. Needless to say, the equation and its solution will not be so simple as that for the space-charge limited electron current.

Call n_+ and n_- the concentrations of positive and negative ions, i.e., the numbers of these ions per cm^3 at any point in the gas. The drift velocities of the ions are $v_+ = k_+X$ and $v_- = k_-X$, where X is the field at any point in the gas. The ions are generated at the rate of q per cm^3 per second. The loss by recombination per cm^3 is an_+n_-. The net volume density of electrification at any point is ρ, and is given by

(7.15)
$$(n_+ - n_-)\, e = \rho.$$

[4] The theory given here is a condensed version of a fuller treatment given by J. J. Thomson (27), and the reader is referred to the original for details.

Poisson's equation then states that

$$(7.16) \qquad \frac{d^2V}{dx^2} = \frac{dX}{dx} = 4\pi \, (n_+ - n_-) \, e \, .$$

The current density j at any point is given by

$$(7.17) \qquad j = e \, k_+ \, X \, n_+ + e \, k_- \, X \, n_- .$$

These relations may be rearranged to read

$$(7.18) \qquad n_+ e = \frac{1}{k_+ + k_-} \left\{ \frac{j}{X} + \frac{k_-}{4\pi} \, \frac{dX}{dx} \right\}$$

and

$$(7.19) \qquad n_- e = \frac{1}{k_+ + k_-} \left\{ \frac{j}{X} - \frac{k_+}{4\pi} \, \frac{dX}{dx} \right\}.$$

In the stationary state in any cm³ of the gas, as many ions must be created per second as are lost by recombination and by current movement of ions across 1 cm² normal to the flow. It thus follows that

$$(7.20) \qquad \frac{d \, (n_+ k_+ X)}{dx} = q - a n_+ n_-$$

and

$$(7.21) \qquad -\frac{d(n_- k_- X)}{dx} = q - a n_+ n_- .$$

These equations may be transformed to yield the differential equation governing the process, which reads

$$(7.22) \qquad \frac{d^2X^2}{dx^2} = 8\pi e \, (q - a n_+ n_-) \left(\frac{1}{k_+} + \frac{1}{k_-} \right).$$

This equation yields information as to the field distribution. If $q - a n_+ n_-$ is positive, so that d^2X^2/dx^2 is positive; that is, if production is greater than loss by recombination, the curve of X^2 as a function of x is convex to the axis of x. If it is negative, recombination is in excess of ionization, the sign is negative, and X^2 is concave to the axis of x. Insert into equation 7.22 the values of en_+ and en_-, given by equations 7.18 and 7.19. This yields

$$(7.23) \qquad \begin{aligned} \frac{d^2X^2}{dx^2} = 8\pi e \left(\frac{1}{k_+} + \frac{1}{k_-} \right) & \left\{ q - \frac{a}{e^2 X^2 (k_+ + k_-)^2} \right. \\ & \left. \left(j + \frac{k_-}{8\pi} \, \frac{dX^2}{dx} \right) \left(j - \frac{k_+}{8\pi} \, \frac{dX^2}{dx} \right) \right\}. \end{aligned}$$

This equation has a general solution, which can be found by changing variables if q is constant. Call $X^2 = y$ and $dy/dx = p$, and for simplicity, let $k_+ = k_- = k$. The equation then reads

$$(7.24) \qquad p\frac{dp}{dy} = \frac{16\pi e}{k}\left\{q - \frac{a}{4e^2 k^2 y}\left(j^2 - \frac{k^2 p^2}{64\pi^2}\right)\right\} .$$

Equation 7.24 integrates to

$$(7.25) \qquad \frac{k^2 p^2}{64\pi^2} - j^2 = \frac{q\,e\,k\,y}{2\pi\left(1 - \dfrac{a}{8\pi e k}\right)} + Cy^{\frac{a}{8\pi e k}}$$

The quantity C is a constant of integration.

This relation determines the ratio of the field X_0 (midway between the plates) relative to X_1 (that near the plates), which is symmetrical for anode and cathode, since $k_+ = k_- = k$. Furthermore, dX/dx and p are zero at the center. Since $k_+ = k_-$, and the q and a processes take equal numbers of positive and negative charges in or out respectively, it is obvious that in the center the net space charge between the plates is zero. This makes $d^2X/dx^2 = 0$ in that region. In consequence,

$$(7.26) \qquad X_0^2 = \frac{aj^2}{4e^2 k^2 q}$$

and

$$(7.27) \qquad \frac{-X_0^2\,(4k^2 e^2 q/a)}{1 - (a/8\pi ek)} = CX_0^{\frac{a}{4\pi ek}}$$

At the positive plate, the anode $n_+ = 0$ as ions are repelled from it and none are created beyond its boundary to replace those that move away. At the negative plate, the cathode $n_- = 0$ for similar reasons. Thus, at both plates $n_+ n_- = 0$, and recombination does not occur. Since, in general, the solution gives

$$(7.28) \qquad n_+ n_- = \frac{1}{4k^2 e^2 X^2}\left(j^2 - \frac{k^2 p^2}{64\pi^2}\right),$$

it is possible to evaluate X_1, the field at either plate. The value is

$$(7.29) \qquad \frac{-X_1^2\,\dfrac{qek}{2\pi}}{1 - \dfrac{a}{8\pi ek}} = CX_1^{\frac{a}{4\pi ek}} .$$

This gives the ratio X_0/X_1, in the form of

(7.30)
$$\frac{8\pi e k}{a} = \left(\frac{X_0}{X_1}\right)^{\left(\frac{a}{4\pi e k} -2\right)}$$

Designating $8\pi e k/a$ as a quantity β, it follows that

(7.31)
$$\frac{X_0^2}{X_1^2} = \beta^{\frac{\beta}{1-\beta}}$$

As β goes from 0 to ∞, the quantity $\beta\beta/(1-\beta)$ decreases from 1 to zero. This means that X_1/X_0 is always unity, or greater than unity. Put in another way, the mid-gap field is lower than the field at the electrodes. In the case of few ions or vanishingly small current, $X_1 = X_0$, with $X_0 = X_p$ the uniform static field in the absence of ionization. Again, β depends on k/a, and is independent of q or j, so that the ratio of the fields depends on k and a, but not on q or j. For air at n.t.p., k in e.s.u. is 520, $a = 1.6 \times 10^{-6},[5]$ $e = 4.8 \times 10^{-10}$ e.s.u., and β has a value of 3.9. Since k is proportional to $1/p$, while a decreases more rapidly than proportional to p below 1 atmosphere (as seen in chapter VI), the quantity β will decrease very rapidly with pressure increase. Thus, at a few mm of mercury, β is very large. If β is about 4, as indicated for air at n.t.p., $X_1/X_0 = 4^{2/3} = 2.51$. At lower pressures, setting $\beta \propto 1/p^2$, X_1/X_0 is approximately given by $X_1/X_0 = \beta^{1/2}$, and X_1/X_0 varies approximately as $1/p$. That is, the greater the mobility and the lower the recombination rate, the greater the potential gradient at the electrodes relative to that in mid-gap.

The accurate potential, as a function of distance x from cathode to anode, can be calculated by evaluating the integral $\int X dx$ given by the equations from $x = 0$ at the anode to $x = l$ at the cathode l cm distant. These integrations are difficult and tedious to perform. The potential distribution can be sufficiently delineated by breaking the gap into three regions: the first extending from $x = 0$ at the anode to $x = \lambda_1$; the second extending from $x = \lambda_1$ to $x = l - \lambda_2$; and the third extending from $x = l - \lambda_2$ to l at the cathode. At the anode the field has the value X_1, and at λ_1 the field has fallen approximately to X_0. From $x = \lambda_1$ to $x = l - \lambda_2$ the field is sensibly constant, and equal to X_0. In the region $x = l - \lambda_2$ to $x = l$ the field rises from X_0 to X_1 at the cathode.

[5]This is Thomson's earlier value, used by him in this study. The correct value is given in chapter VI.

Electrical Conduction in Gases below Ionization by Collision

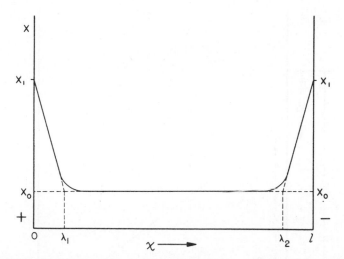

Fig. 7.14. Variation of the electrical field X across the uniform field gap in the absence of ions, as modified by a current in which q ions are created per cm^3 per second and ions are lost in the volume by recombination, as calculated to a first approximation by J. J. Thomson when positive and negative ion mobilities are equal. Note that the fields X_1 are high at the electrodes because of space charges, and low and constant at X_0 over the main parts.

The justification for doing this comes from the fact that the disturbance at the electrodes giving the fields X_1 cannot extend far into the gap. If l has any appreciable value, the long central section will have nearly a uniform field X_0, and it is only in the short distances λ_1 and λ_2 near anode and cathode that X reaches the high values approaching X_1. In the distances λ_1 and λ_2, where X changes from X_1 to X_0, the change is certainly not linear, but can be set sensibly so for convenience if λ_1 and λ_2 are short. The values of λ_1 and λ_2 may roughly be computed. The current density j is caused by positive and negative ions moving in opposite directions and passing normal to a cm^2 area. At the anode it is due to negative ions only, and at the cathode it is due to positive ions only. At the anode (j/e) $k_-/(k_+ + k_-)$ negative ions arrive per cm^2 per second, and at the cathode (j/e) $k_+/(k_+ + k_-)$ positive ions arrive per cm^2 per second. If, as assumed here, $k_+ = k_- = k$, then $j/e(k/2k)$ ions arrive per second at each electrode. At the anode these can only come from the quantity q created in the volume 1 cm^2 and λ_1 cm long. This makes $q\lambda_1 = (j/e)$ $(k/2k) = j/2e$, so that

(7.32) $$\lambda_1 = j/2eq .$$

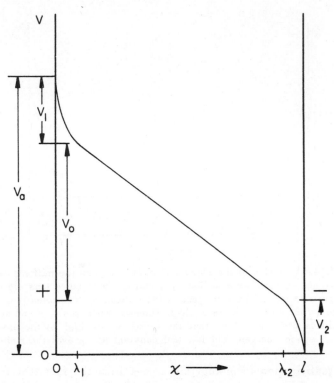

Fig. 7.15. The potential distribution resulting from the conditions in figure 7.14 is shown here, with anode at the origin and cathode l cm distant. Note the potential falls V_1 and V_2 at the electrodes, caused by space charge.

Likewise,

(7.33) $$\lambda_2 = j/2eq \ .$$

Since at the electrodes, $n_+ n_- = 0$, there is no recombination, so that X_1 and X_2 are produced by the space charges of negative ions at the anode and positive ions at the cathode. Between λ_1 and λ_2, where the field is X_0, the positive and negative ions are moving past each other, $n_+ n_-$ has a finite value, and recombination is occurring. Presumably, the rate of recombination just compensates for q, so that the density remains constant and n_+ equals n_-.

In practice, the idealized potential falls do not occur. The fall from X_1 at the electrodes to X_0 at λ_1 and λ_2 is not linear, and the fields X_1 gradually and continuously fall to X_0 over more of the gap than was ideally pictured. The simple picture of the variation of X with distance is illustrated in figure 7.14, where $k_+ = k_-$. The potential

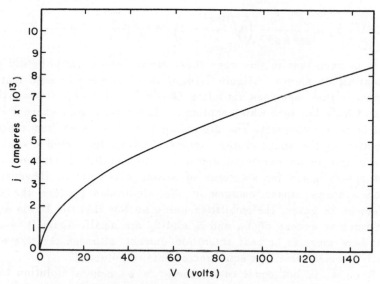

Fig. 7.16. Current-potential relation resulting from the conditions
described in figure 7.14, as evaluated by J. J. Thomson.

distribution resulting from these assumptions is shown in figure 7.15,
where the anode is at a potential V_a above the cathode at ground.
Then V_a is composed of the following terms, as indicated in figure
7.15:

(7.34) $\lambda_1 X_1 + [l - (\lambda_1 + \lambda_2)] X_0 + X_2 \lambda_2 = V_1 + V_0 + V_2 = V_a$.

Since $k_+ = k_- = k$, $V_1 = V_2$ and $\lambda_1 = \lambda_2$. Considering the solution
arrived at in equation 7.31, relation 7.34, on inserting equations 7.32
and 7.33, becomes

$$V_a = 2\lambda_1 X_1 + (l - 2\lambda_1) X_0 =$$

(7.35)

$$\frac{j}{qe} X_0 \frac{1}{\sqrt{\beta\left(\frac{\beta}{1-\beta}\right)}} + \left(l - \frac{j}{qe}\right) X_0 = X_0 \frac{j}{qe}\left(\frac{1}{\sqrt{\beta\left(\frac{\beta}{1-\beta}\right)}} - 1\right) + X_0 l.$$

For large values of β, $\beta^{\beta/(1-\beta)}$ approaches $1/\beta$, with $\beta = 8\pi ek/a$.
This enables the relation between current density and potential applied
to be deduced in the form shown by equation 7.36, to follow.

$$(7.36) \qquad V_a = \frac{j^2 \sqrt{a}}{2e^2 k q^{3/2}} \left(\sqrt{\frac{8\pi e k}{a}} - 1 \right) + \frac{j\sqrt{a}}{2ekq^{1/2}} \, l = A j^2 + B j \, .$$

It is seen that in this case the current j rises parabolically with potential, as shown in figure 7.16. It is of interest to note that the current in this case does not follow Ohm's law, $V_a = Bj$, although there is an Ohm's law term which applies to the center region where $X = X_0$, and is nearly constant. The disturbing term Aj^2 comes from the contribution of the space-charge regions. In fact, as stated elsewhere, Ohm's law is an exception applicable to metallic conduction only, and approximated for solutions of strong electrolytes. However, in such systems, space charges at the electrodes produce the same effect as in gases, the mobilities being so low that the fields X_1 are not much in excess of X_0, and λ_1 and λ_2 are small. Again it is clear that here *there is no real saturation current*, although the rise eventually becomes small for equal increments of potential.

When k_+ is not equal to k_-, there is no general solution to the equations, but a particular solution may be found from the following relations, as shown by J. J. Thomson. The relations read

$$(7.37) \qquad n_1 = n_2 = (q/a)^{1/2}$$

when the steady state is reached.

$$(7.38) \qquad k_+ n_+ X e = \frac{k_+}{k_+ + k_-} j \, ,$$

$$(7.39) \qquad k_- n_- X e = \frac{k_-}{k_+ + k_-} j \, ,$$

and

$$(7.40) \qquad X = \left(\frac{a}{q} \right)^{1/2} \frac{j}{e(k_+ + k_-)} \, .$$

This solution corresponds to a constant value of the electric field between the plates, and indicates that the fraction of the current density j carried by the carriers is proportional to their mobility. Obviously, the assumption of a constant field between the plates corresponds to that in the center of the gap only. There are corrections for the fields near the electrodes. Certain simplifications result by assuming (as for the case where $k_+ = k_-$) that the changes in X with distance are confined to regions λ_1 and λ_2 close to the electrodes, and that in these regions recombination does not occur. Simplifica-

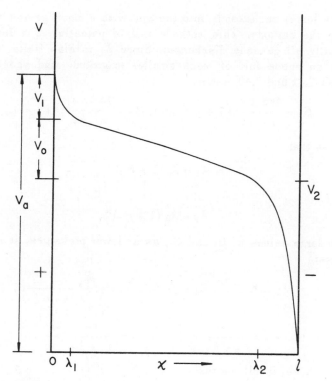

Fig. 7.17. The distribution of potential calculated for the conditions set forth in figure 7.14, assuming that electrons are the negative carriers and that their mobility is far greater than that of the positive ions.

tions resulting from these assumptions lead to solutions for the fields X_1 and X_2 near the anode and cathode relative to the field X_0 in the center. These read

$$(7.41) \qquad X_1 = X_0 \left\{ 1 + \frac{4\pi e}{a} \frac{k_+}{k_-} \left(k_+ + k_- \right) \right\}^{\frac{1}{2}}$$

and

$$(7.42) \qquad X_2 = X_0 \left\{ 1 + \frac{4\pi e}{a} \frac{k_-}{k_+} \left(k_+ + k_- \right) \right\}^{\frac{1}{2}}$$

In this event, X_1 and X_2 are determined largely by the ratio of k_-/k_+. If the mobility of the negative carriers is that of electrons, $k_- >> k_+$, i.e., $(k_-/k_+) \sim 100$, then X_2 is very much greater than X_1. Thus, the distribution of potential across the gap is roughly indicated by figure 7.17. There it is seen that the cathode fall of potential is not only large, but extends into the gap with a much greater value of λ_2 from the cathode. This cathode fall of potential is a feature of practically all gaseous discharges. Since X_1 is also finite, there is always an anode fall of much smaller magnitude and scope. From relations 7.41 and 7.42, setting

$$\beta_+ = \frac{4\pi e}{a} \frac{k_+}{k_-} (k_+ + k_-) \quad \text{and} \quad \beta_- = \frac{4\pi e}{a} \frac{k_-}{k_+} (k_+ + k_-),$$

it follows that

(7.43)
$$X_1 = X_0 (1 + \beta_+)^{1/2}$$

and

(7.44)
$$X_2 = X_0 (1 + \beta_-)^{1/2}.$$

With large values of β_+ and β_-, as at lower pressures, it is possible to set

$$X_1 = X_0 \beta_+^{1/2}, \quad X_2 = X_0 \beta_-^{1/2}, \quad X_0 = \sqrt{\frac{q}{a}} \frac{j}{(k_+ + k_-)},$$

(7.45)
$$\lambda_+ = \frac{k_+}{k_+ + k_-} \frac{j}{qe}, \quad \text{and} \quad \lambda_- = \frac{k_-}{k_+ + k_-} \frac{j}{qe}.$$

From these, it follows that

(7.46)
$$V_1 = \frac{1}{2} \frac{a^{1/2}}{e^2 q^{3/2}} \frac{j^2 k_+}{(k_+ + k_-)^2}$$

$$\left\{ (1 + \beta_+)^{1/2} + \frac{1}{\sqrt{\beta_+}} \log_e (\sqrt{\beta_+} + \sqrt{1 + \beta_+}) \right\}$$

and

(7.47)
$$V_2 = \frac{1}{2} \frac{a^{1/2}}{e^2 q^{3/2}} \frac{j^2 k_-}{(k_+ + k_-)^2}$$

$$\left\{ (1 + \beta_-)^{1/2} + \frac{1}{\sqrt{\beta_-}} \log_e (\sqrt{\beta_-} + \sqrt{1 + \beta_-}) \right\}.$$

For large β_+ and β_-, these yield approximately

(7.48)
$$V_1 = \frac{\sqrt{\pi} j^2}{k_-^2} \left\{ \frac{k_+ k_-}{qe(k_+ + k_-)} \right\}^{3/2}$$

and

(7.49)
$$V_2 = \frac{\sqrt{\pi}\,j^2}{k_+^2}\left\{\frac{k_+\,k_-}{qe\,(k_+ + k_-)}\right\}^{3/2}.$$

The last relation indicates that roughly, $V_1/V_2 = k_+^2/k_-^2$. This means that the cathode and anode drops are in the order of the squares of the ratios of the mobilities. In actual cases these extreme simplifications do not apply, and cathode falls run from 10^2 to 10^3 volts, while anode falls generally are around 10 volts. However, it should be pointed out that conditions in glow discharges, for example, are more involved in that the cathode falls have to do with the electron-generating mechanism, while the anode falls must furnish positive ions by other than an external X-ray source. Thus, the anode falls of potential must equal the ionization potential of the gas. It is further to be observed that in these considerations diffusion has been omitted. Diffusion (as indicated in section 3) exerts a considerable influence, especially with discharge electrons where these electrons have energies of the order of 10 e.v. Ion velocities may vary as $X^{1/2}$ and k as $X^{-1/2}$ at high fields. These changes have the effect of lowering the cathode fall while increasing the anode fall.

Continuing the discussion of the ideal case above, since k_+ and k_- vary inversely *with* pressure, while q varies directly *as* pressure, V_1 and V_2 will vary inversely as the square root of the pressure. The variation of j with V_a will follow the same general trend as in the case where $k_+ = k_-$. The result of the difference of mobility on the distribution of potential in the gap from V_a at the anode to zero at the cathode is shown in figure 7.17. It may be added that the solutions here presented have been taken from J. J. Thomson's classical text, third edition (27). In that book the problem is treated more extensively for various cases, such as currents with different degrees of saturation, for the negative carriers being electrons, and for the case where diffusion is included. The effect of diffusion at fields below ionization is small. These studies are of principally academic interest, as they do not bear much on the more general problems of discharge. There is thus no place for them at this point.

The approximate theory for the current was tested experimentally by H. Seeman in 1912, and agrees with observation. It is thus seen that the theory not only fits the observations, but that it indicates some very important general properties of electrical conduction currents in gases. These comprise not only the anode and cathode drops of potential, but the form of the current-potential characteristic which will be referred to in other connections. With this information it is possible to consider what happens when fields reach values where electrons can ionize by impact.

BIBLIOGRAPHY TO CHAPTER VII

(1) L. B. Loeb, *Fundamental Processes of Electrical Discharge in Gases*, John Wiley & Sons, New York, 1939, pp. 306 ff.

(2) J. J. Thomson, *Conduction of Electricity through Gases*, third edition, vol. 1, Cambridge University Press, 1928, p. 466.

(3) R. E. Woolsey, Master's thesis, University of California, 1926.

(4) I. Langmuir, Phys. Rev. *38*, 1656, 1931.

(5) G. Hertz, Zeits. f. Phys. *32*, 298, 1925.

(6) N. E. Bradbury, Phys. Rev. *40*, 980, 1932.

(7) N. E. Bradbury, Phys. Rev. *44*, 885, 1933.

(8) L. A. Young and N. E. Bradbury, Phys. Rev. *43*, 34, 1933.

(9) A. M. Cravath, private correspondence with Loeb and Bradbury, 1933.

(10) N. E. Bradbury and R. A. Nielsen, Phys. Rev. *49*, 388, 1935.

(11) A. A. Kruithoff and F. M. Penning, Physica *4*, 434, 1936.

(12) J. P. Molnar, private communication to the author, summer, 1950.

(13) C. W. Rice, Phys. Rev. *70*, 228, 1946.

(14) G. W. Johnson, Phys. Rev. *73*, 284, 1948.

(15) C. D. Child, Phys. Rev. *32*, 492, 1911.

(16) I. Langmuir, Phys. Rev. *2*, 450, 1913.

(17) P. Keck and L. B. Loeb, Rev. Sci. Inst. *4*, 486, 1933.

(18) I. Langmuir, Phys. Rev. *21*, 419, 1923; W. Schottky, Phys. Zeits. *15*, 526, 624, 1914; P. S. Epstein, Verh. d. Deutsch. Phys. Gesell. *21*, 85, 1919; P. C. Fry, Phys. Rev. *17*, 441, 1921; *22*, 445, 1923.

(19) I. Langmuir and K. T. Compton, Rev. Mod. Phys. *3*, 191, 1931.

(20) I. Langmuir, Phys. Rev. *33*, 954, 1929; K. H. Kingdon, Phys. Rev. *21*, 408, 1923.

(21) F. L. Mohler and R. L. Chenault, Phys. Rev. *27*, 30, 1927; P. D. Foote and F. L. Mohler, Phys. Rev. *26*, 195, 1925; E. O. Lawrence and N. L. Edlefsen, Phys. Rev. *34*, 233, 1929.

(22) A. Rostagni, Phys. Rev. *53*, 729, 1938.

(23) R. N. Varney, Phys. Rev. *53*, 732, 1938; *47*, 483, 1935; *50*, 159, 1936.

(24) G. W. Hull, Phys. Rev. *18*, 31, 1921.

(25) R. N. Varney, private communication to the author, 1949.

(26) G. L. Weissler and N. Wainfan, Third Conference on Gaseous Electronics, New York, October 19-21, 1950, paper D2.

(27) J. J. Thomson, *Conduction of Electricity through Gases*, third edition, vol. 1, Cambridge University Press, 1928, pp. 139 ff.

(28) J. K. Theobald, Jour. App. Phys. *24*, 123, 1953.

(29) L. Malter, Phys. Rev. *49*, 879, 1936.

(30) R. A. Nielsen, Phys. Rev. *50*, 950, 1936; N. E. Bradbury, Phys. Rev. *49*, 388, 1936; *51*, 69, 1937.

Chapter VIII

IONIZATION BY COLLISION OF ELECTRONS IN A GAS—
TOWNSEND'S FIRST COEFFICIENT

---

§ 1. Introduction.

At the turn of the twentieth century, not long after the establish-
ment of the conductivity produced in gases by X-rays and other
external agencies, but after the fundamental studies on ion mobilities,
diffusion coefficients, and recombination, J. S. Townsend began a
series of investigations that were to lay the foundation for the future
analysis of all gaseous discharges (1). At that time the variation of
current in a plane parallel gap in an ionized gas as field strength,
$X = V/x$, increases at a given pressure, was well known. Around 1899
it was also known that if the field strength X at a given pressure p
was increased beyond the apparent saturation current value, there
would set in, at some critical value of X and pressure p, a further
rapid increase of current (2). This increase would ultimately lead to
a breakdown of the gap, in the form of a spark. The critical value
of X and p would depend on the nature of the gas used, and would be
characteristic of it.

The current plotted against field strength, as it might be observed
for the photoelectric current from the cathode in a plane parallel gap
in air at atmospheric pressure, is shown in figure 8.1. Between the
origin and the point A is seen the region discussed in section 3 of
chapter VII, ultimately yielding a "saturation" current i_0. Beyond A
is seen an exponential rise of current, starting at i_0, which terminates
in a spark at B. Townsend investigated this section of the curve,
between A and B. His method of investigation was to illuminate the
cathode in a plane parallel condenser system with ultraviolet light,
either through a partly silvered, transparent quartz anode plate, or
through small perforations in the metal anode (1). Adjusting the values
of the ratio X/p to be in the region AB seen in figure 8.1, Townsend
measured the current at a fixed field strength X and pressure p as he
varied the distance x between the plates. To keep the field constant
at a given value, the applied potential V across the plates, separated
x cm, was altered to keep $V/x = X$ a constant. In varying x at constant
X/p, Townsend observed that as x increased for a given value of
X/p, the current i appeared to increase exponentially with x.

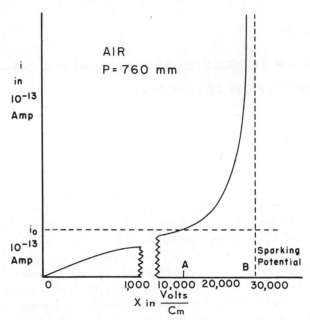

Fig. 8.1. Current as a function of field strength X at constant pressure in a plane parallel (Townsend) gap, with an initial photoelectric current liberated from the cathode by ultraviolet light. The scale of field strengths and currents is highly compressed. The current increase, following the Thomson back-diffusion relation, applies at lower fields. Above 20,000 volts/cm in air, some slight multiplication of ions sets in. It leads to a rapid increase of current, with a spark at 30,000 volts/cm.

A curve for i as a function of x, as might be observed for air at a value of X/p somewhere around 25 kv per cm at 760 mm pressure, is shown in figure 8.2. The form of variation of i relative to the "saturation" current i_0 is seen to resemble an exponential curve. To determine the form of this curve, Townsend, in his pioneering study, plotted $\log_e i$ against distance x. In so doing, he obtained a linear plot of $\log_e i$ against x, which intercepted the axis of ordinates at $x = 0$ at the value of the photoelectric current i_0 at that value of X/p.

A typical set of such plots at various values of X/p is shown in figure 8.3. If, instead, $\log_e (i/i_0)$ is plotted against x, the plot shows a straight line passing through the origin. Townsend next observed that the slope of this line had a constant value a for a given value of X/p in a given gas, and that a increased consistently at constant p as X/p increased. This experiment, therefore, indicated that $i = i_0 \epsilon^{ax}$, and that $\log_e i/i_0 = ax$, with a at a given pressure a quantity which increased with X/p.

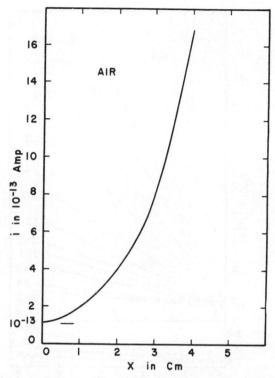

Fig. 8.2. A typical Townsend curve of current, plotted against distance between plates at constant field strength, is shown for an initial current i_0 of 10^{-13} ampere without multiplication. Its exponential rise is strongly indicated.

Townsend proceeded to analyze this increase of simple analytical form by making the assumption that when X/p reached suitable values in a gas, the photoelectrically liberated electrons[1] from the cathode acquired enough energy from the field to enable them to ionize neutral atoms or molecules by impact. In this way they create further electrons, and leave behind the residues of the atoms or molecules as

[1]Actually, it was not known in 1900 that electrons were free in gases at high X and low p (1). Thus, Townsend originally assumed that the ionization was caused by negative ions. At some point before his studies of the electron velocities and energies in gases were carried out in 1913, probably as early as 1910, Townsend recognized that the ionization was caused by electrons, and modified his thinking accordingly. In this presentation of Townsend's work, the earlier misconception will be avoided. It should be added that since these early studies assumed negative *ions* to ionize in a gas, it was logical for Townsend, in studying the secondary ionization phenomena in gases contemporaneously, to assume that positive ions could likewise ionize gases at impact, perhaps at somewhat higher values of X/p.

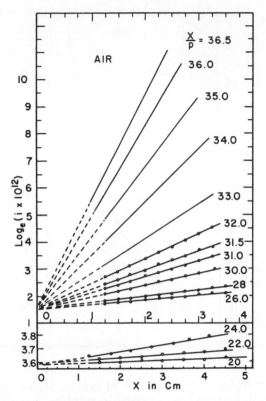

Fig. 8.3. Townsend plots of $\log_e i/i_0$ against plate separation x at various ratios of field strength to pressure in air, beginning at X/p about 20, as observed by F. H. Sanders. The slope of the curve gives α, and its intercept on the axis of ordinates gives i_0.

positive ions. If it is assumed that in advancing 1 cm in the gas in the direction of the field X, a single electron creates α new electrons and positive ions, then the increase in ions dn, caused by n electrons in advancing a distance dx, is given by the relation

$$(8.1) \qquad dn = \alpha n \ dx .$$

Integrating this relation between $n = n_0$ at $x = 0$, and $n = n$ at $x = x$, i.e., setting

$$\int_{n_0}^{n} \frac{dn}{n} = \alpha \int_{0}^{x} dx ,$$

there results the important relation to follow.

(8.2) $$\log_e \frac{n}{n_0} = ax \quad \text{and} \quad n = n_0 \, \epsilon^{ax}.$$

If both sides of this relation are multiplied by the electronic charge e, calling $ne = i$ and $n_0 e = i_0$, the experimentally observed relation of Townsend,

(8.3) $$i = i_0 \, \epsilon^{ax},$$

is at once obtained.

Thus, it is clear that a represents the number of new electrons and positive ions created by a single electron traversing 1 cm of path in the field direction in a gas at appropriately high X/p. It is called the *first Townsend coefficient*. Its reciprocal $1/a$ represents the *average* distance required to be traversed by an electron to make a new ion pair in a field of appropriately high X/p, i.e., the ionizing free path. The ϵ^{ax} electrons created by one electron in advancing x cm in a uniform field direction are today termed an *electron avalanche*.

If the field X is not uniform along x, as will later be seen, a will vary with the field X, and thus with distance x traversed along X. In this event, the avalanche must be computed from

$$\int_{\epsilon}^{b} a \, dx$$

Here a varies with distance x, since the field X is a function of x. The constants a and b are the limits of x between which the integration is to be taken. In evaluating the avalanche in a nonuniform, as in a uniform field, it must be assumed that at every point in the field X, the variation of x with X is such that the electrons achieve an equilibrium energy appropriate to the value of X. Where this does not occur throughout X, then the electron multiplication must be measured directly, and a may not be used (3). It should be pointed out in this connection that even in a uniform field the electron does not achieve its energy, and hence its value of a, at once on leaving the cathode. As indicated in chapter IV, the electron must traverse a certain distance [2] in order to achieve its terminal energy u_t. Generally, if pressures are relatively high and X is not too great, equilibrium is achieved in

---

[2] It should also be recognized that while the ionization by direct impact may proceed across the gap with the velocity of the electron swarm (ionization acts consume little time), at times most of the ions may be produced by secondary effects (Hale, Penning, or Hornbeck-Molnar effects), with some microseconds' delay. These will not be detected in Townsend measurement, but will appear with high time resolution.

distances much less than $1/a$. When such is not the case, the correction must be made for this circumstance, as was done by A. A. Kruithoff and F. M. Penning in their measurements of a (4). Neglect of this correction probably led to serious errors in the past. It is believed that the downward trend of a/p as a function of X/p at high X/p, noted by some observers, may be ascribed to failure to achieve equilibrium before measurement (5).

Probably one more characteristic of a affecting its action should be noted at this point. The events leading to ionization by collision are governed in considerable measure by *chance*. Regard a single electron moving in a field in a gas. The accidents of random collision and deflection when moving in a field after traversing the *average* distance to get the terminal energy will usually leave the electron with more or less than the most probable energy. As time goes on, individual electrons change their energy status, but the population of states remains constant in the distribution once an equilibrium is reached. Eventually, as the cloud of electrons advances along X, many electrons gain the ionizing energy. Some do so in fewer paths; some, in more paths. Once an electron has this energy, there is a *chance* that it will ionize an atom or molecule on impact as soon as it gets this energy. On the other hand, even having the energy, it may not ionize for many impacts later, and may lose the energy before doing so. Thus, by luck, an electron may get the ionizing energy short of the critical average distance in the field, and ionize at once. An "unlucky" electron will go quite some distance before it ionizes. Thus, each individual electron in its ionizing behavior, as viewed over many successive events, will fluctuate considerably relative to the mean behavior. Accordingly, the a measured is the *average value* for a large number of electrons over large distances compared to $1/a$.

Since individual electrons in their ionization leading to an avalanche ϵ^{ax} can fluctuate above and below the mean represented by ax, so the number of electrons in individual avalanches ϵ^{ax}, under constant conditions, is also likely to fluctuate among different avalanches at the same X, x, and p. This was first recognized by the author, and the statistical fluctuations in the value of ϵ^{ax} have been deduced by R. J. Wijsman (6). Thus, it must be borne in mind at all times that a and ϵ^{ax} represent *average values* under a given set of conditions, and that in the behavior of a given electron, ionization may occur short of or beyond the average distance $1/a$; also, that a given electron avalanche may be greater or less than ϵ^{ax}. Wijsman showed that if $\bar{n}$ is the average number of electrons in the avalanche after traversing a distance x, which is $\bar{n} = \epsilon^{ax}$, then the chance of an

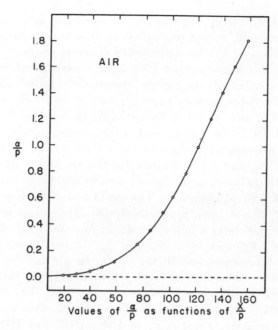

Fig. 8.4. Curve for a/p as a single-valued function of X/p, as observed in air by F. H. Sanders, following Townsend's techniques.

electron avalanche containing n electrons, if $\bar{n}$ is large, is given by

(8.4)
$$P(n, x) = \frac{1}{\bar{n}} \epsilon^{[-n/\bar{n}]} .$$

This indicates relatively large fluctuations about the average.

It is clear that this first Townsend coefficient is an exceedingly important parameter in the study of the avalanche formation that must precede any gaseous breakdown.

Townsend's next step was to study the variation of a as a function of the quantity X/p in a given gas. That is, by increasing the field X at a given pressure p, he measured the increase in slope of the $\log i/i_0$ curves, or a. He found that while a fell on a consistent curve as X was increased for a given p, the curves for a, as a function of X/p at different values of p, did not coincide. Further study showed that if instead of a the quantity a/p were plotted as a function of X/p, all the experimental points fell on a smooth, continuous curve. Hence, a/p in any given gas is a unique function of X/p. Such a curve is shown in figure 8.4.

Upon this discovery, Townsend, in the ensuing years, with the aid of his students, turned to evaluating this very important quantity α/p as a function of X/p for a number of different gases.

The work was begun around 1900 by Townsend, and between then and 1904 a number of his papers appeared, covering air, H_2, CO_2, H_2O, and HCl. Subsequently, papers appeared by H. E. Hurst on CO_2 and N_2 in 1906, and on A and He by E. W. B. Gill and F. B. Pidduck in 1908 and 1912 (7). Later, work with greater gaseous purity and techniques appropriate to its time was done by T. L. R. Ayers in 1923, on H_2, N_2, and A (7). Finally, in the era of all-glass or quartz systems with bake-out and high-frequency discharge cleanup techniques, work was published by Townsend and McCallum on pure Ne and He in 1928 and 1934, respectively (8). These last measurements began to overlap later studies, made in Aachen by M. Paavola and K. Masch in 1929 and 1932 (9), and by A. Jodelbauer (9) in 1934; also, by F. H. Sanders and D. Q. Posin, on air and N_2 at low X/p, in the author's laboratory in 1932, 1933, and 1936 (10). Simultaneously, studies on very pure inert gases, Ne, A, Kr, Xe, and mixtures, were undertaken by A. A. Kruithoff and F. M. Penning at Philips Research Laboratory, Eindhoven, in 1936, 1937, and 1940 (4), while W. E. Bowls and D. H. Hale (11) studied pure N_2 and H_2 in the author's laboratory in 1937 and 1938, respectively. Later studies were carried out in 1939 and 1940 by W. S. Huxford and R. W. Engstrom (12), and by Huxford (5), on pure A. In 1951, R. Geballe and M. A. Harrison (11) measured α at low X/p in O_2 and other gases in the presence of electron attachment.

It is clear that the early work, begun before high-potential sources other than stacks of small accumulators were available, before the time of the mercury-vapor pump, and before Pyrex glass and out-gassing techniques were known, was defective to the extent of yielding untrustworthy values, and thus limiting the interpretations derived from them. The interpretations suffered also from the fact that inferences were drawn and theory developed before the time of the Bohr atom, and before elastic electron impacts, excitation functions, and ionization functions were known. The experimental techniques of all groups improved with facilities, and it appears that the later determinations of the Townsend group fit well into the results of their contemporary workers.

With this introduction, it is proper to leave the discussion of the basic phenomena of ionization by collision, and proceed to consider the methods of observation, the data, the resulting later developments, and their theoretical interpretation.

§ 2. The Experimental Evaluation of the Townsend Coefficients.

The primary objective of the evaluation of the coefficient a/p as a function of X/p is probably the acquisition of data needed in the study and analysis of gaseous discharge phenomena in the gases commonly used. The secondary objective is the accumulation of enough data on gases of known atomic and molecular properties to facilitate development of a suitable theory of the process. Both these objectives imply the evaluation of a/p as a function of X/p over as great a range of X/p as possible. They also require evaluation in gases of established purity, as used in the various discharge studies, to which basic atomic data are applicable. The gases of utmost interest at this time are probably the inert gases, He, Ne, A, Kr, and Xe, and the common, more permanent molecular gases, H_2, N_2, O_2, and perhaps CO_2. The mixture called air, while subject to change in composition by chemical reactions produced by discharge, enters into so many discharges by its omnipresence that in a relatively pure state, data must be obtained on it. Perhaps values should also be obtained for at least one of the halogens, e.g., Cl_2. It would be desirable to have the constants for a few of the more standard mixtures used in Geiger counters, such as A and CH_4 or C_2H_5OH. Data in H_2 and air, contaminated with H_2O, or H_2O and C_2H_5OH, such as used in cloud chambers, possibly have some value. Studies have been made on Ne, contaminated with varying amounts of A, in which the atoms are ionized by Ne metastables. These studies, like those dealing with mercury- and sodium-contaminated gases, are of value in indicating the effectiveness and role of impurities in changing the a/p-X/p curves.

In the design of equipment for actual measurement, there are basically two schools of thought as to the best direct method. One of these advocates the use of larger electrode separation and ultraviolet illumination of the cathode from the side at grazing incidence. The other illuminates the cathode through perforations in the anode, and employs smaller electrode separation.

Until 1929-1931, there had been no satisfactory data[3] on a/p for very low values of X/p. Data were urgently needed for air around an X/p from 30 to 40, which covers the sparking thresholds for air in different gaps and around atmospheric pressure. This same lack of adequate, consistent data over the whole range of values was in part responsible for the acceptance and use of an imperfect theory of the

---

[3] The work of Ayers in N_2 (7), done in 1923, did cover a very large range, but appears to have been faulty, as his data do not consistently agree with work done later with better facilities.

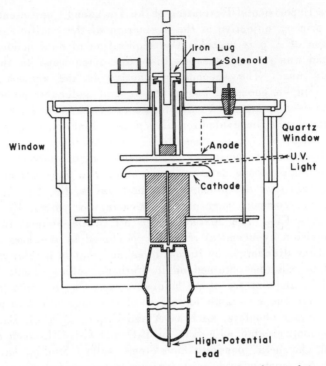

Fig. 8.5. Sanders and Posin's all-metal chamber for studying α/p at low values of X/p and large plate separation.

mechanism well beyond the time when it should have been discarded. Low values of X/p mean lower X or higher p. Under these conditions, α/p is very low. Thus, to get measurable increases in current, larger pressures or longer distances x are needed. Such conditions generally require high potentials, electrodes of larger diameter, and possibly some sacrifice of gaseous purity. Thus, work was commenced in the author's laboratory in 1929 (10), (11), using the larger plate separation. This has some advantages.

Where plate separations of the order of 1 cm and up are used, many corrections can be avoided, and precision of measurement is more readily achieved. The use of larger separations permits the creation of the i_0 electrons needed, by a beam of ultraviolet light admitted through a quartz window in the side of the chamber. The beam strikes the center of the parallel plate system at grazing incidence, and then on reflection escapes through an appropriate window on the other side of the chamber. With larger plate separation, no corrections are needed to compensate for the distance taken by the electrons to acquire the terminal energy u_t, except at very low p and high X/p. Currents i_0 need not be large. With the high potentials used, contact potentials are unimportant. This general procedure has been used in the author's laboratory, whence it was adopted from other ion studies (10), (11).

The all-metal chamber used by Sanders for precision study of a/p in air at low X/p is shown in figure 8.5. The same apparatus, with all-metal chamber and large electrodes, was also used by D. Q. Posin, who covered a very large range in X/p for N_2, which, aside from mercury pollution, was soiled by the use of a metal chamber. Both gases were, through ignorance, mercury-contaminated, *as was equally true of all the other work on air,* since before 1935 the importance of the influence of small traces of certain impurities on the values of a/p was not recognized (11). The recognition came simultaneously in the several different laboratories working in the field at about this time. It is very doubtful if air will be seriously contaminated in a clean, well-dried, all-metal chamber if care is taken to preclude H_2O vapor, and particularly Hg contamination, which is serious.[4] Needless to say, the study of pure N_2 requires an outgassed glass chamber and "getters." The adaptation of the author's technique to pure gases, such as N_2 and H_2, is illustrated in figure 8.6, which depicts the apparatus used by D. H. Hale (11), who covered quite a large range in H_2. His values at low X/p are not too consistent, as is to be expected with his smaller plate diameter and more limited separation.

The other school of thought in these measurements (as indicated) has followed Townsend's basic technique (1). In this the plate separation is small, from 0.1 cm to 1.5 cm. The anode consists of a metal plate, perforated by many small holes. A. A. Kruithoff (4), on his 5-cm radius circular anode, used silvered quartz plates with alternate strips unsilvered, or else semitransparent silvered quartz plates or gauzes of very fine mesh, stretched tight on a ring. The cathode used by Kruithoff was a plane parallel plate opposite the perforated anode, as shown in figure 8.7, depicting Kruithoff's chamber. The ultraviolet light entered through a quartz window back of the anode. In the early days the light came from a spark. Later, quartz mercury arcs were used. Kruithoff and Penning (4), desiring a very strong photo current which could be read on a galvanometer, used a *hot cathode* quartz mercury arc in which the output could be controlled. The ultraviolet

---

[4]This is attested by recent mass-spectrographic analyses of gases, including argon, used in Sanders' original chamber by L. H. Fisher and G. A. Kachickas (13), where the gas appeared exceptionally clean. Recently, Westinghouse techniques have yielded very pure argon in a baked metal chamber.

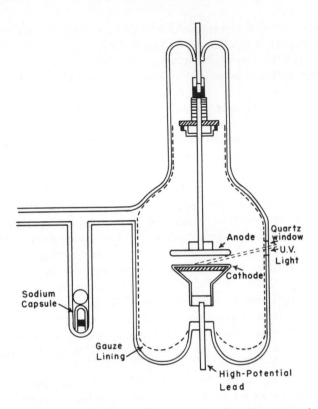

Fig. 8.6. Bowls and Hale's modified chamber for observing α/p at larger plate separations in pure gases, in glass chambers with outgassed electrodes.

efficiency was monitored by a photoelectric cell with an electrode of the same material (fine copper) as the cathode used. The heat from this lamp was so great that the light passed through two optical plates back of the anode between which there was a chamber through which cooling water circulated. With such illumination and cathode material, Kruithoff's cathode sometimes showed "photoelectric fatigue," for which correction had to be made. No such "fatigue" appears when using clean Ni or Pt with moderate illumination, with perhaps the exception of "unstabilized" cathodes in O_2. In some cases in the author's laboratory (11) where Na was present, the cathodes were so photosensitive that the chamber was placed in the dark, and light from an ordinary electric light globe with glass envelope was used to give i_0.

All workers surrounded the two plates at a suitable distance, either with a conducting metal film on the glass walls, a thin metal shield,

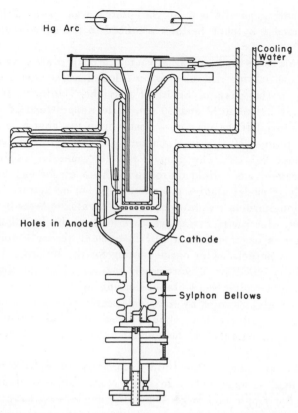

Hg Arc

Cooling Water

Holes in Anode

Cathode

Sylphon Bellows

Fig. 8.7. Kruithoff's modification of Townsend's original technique for measuring α/p in very pure inert gases, using short gaps and transparent anode.

or a metal gauze which was grounded between glass walls and plates to keep static charges from stray electrons from accumulating on the glass walls, thus distorting the field. In one study this shield was at mid-potential relative to cathode instead of ground (4). Distortions from the static charges, observed in the author's laboratory, were serious unless precautions were taken. In practically all later work the plate distance was changed by turning a screw nut resting on the supporting frame and acting on a threaded stem holding the anode or the cathode, depending on whether the illumination was from the side or through the perforated anode. The nut was rotated from without the chamber by an electromagnet acting on an iron lug fastened to the nut. If desired, the iron lug could be enclosed in a sealed glass container and fastened to the nut by tungsten wires sealed into the glass. Usually, parallelism of the plates was insured by guides. Kruithoff used a sylphon bellows attached to the stem supporting his cathode (4).

Distances were read by cathetometer through plate-glass or quartz windows from outside the tube, or by fiducial marks and a micrometer screw, as in the case of Kruithoff's sylphon bellows. If the plate diameter lies between 20 and 30 cm, plate separations of up to 7 cm may be employed if the current i_0 comes from the central cm^2 of plate area. For plates 10 cm in diameter, plate separations should not exceed about 2.5 cm. The grounded walls must be sufficiently far away to prevent much field distortion. These errors can be detected by electrolytic model studies to perhaps 1%, but no better.

Ionization currents i were measured with galvanometer by Kruithoff. A quadrant electrometer was used in the author's laboratory. An electrometer is best used as a null instrument across a constant high resistance, a potentiometer compensating for the iR drop. Townsend's group usually used an electrometer and an electrostatic induction balance (7), in which the suitable compensating potential was intro-duced to the electrometer by a potentiometer acting on the electrom-eter through a suitable low-capacity, nonleaking air condenser. This technique is excellent, and has advantages over the high-resistance method.

Potential sources for the field X formerly came from many banks of small lead storage cells. In later years, stabilized high-voltage sets with low ripple and large smoothing condensers have been used.

All operations require care in measuring and checking the current i_0. Even if the arc is constant, the current i_0 may change with time, owing to "fatigue" effects. It will certainly change with X or X/p, since (as was shown in chapter VII, section 3) photoelectric currents in gases near 760 mm are *not* "saturated," even for values of X/p, where a begins to be appreciable. It is desirable to evaluate and check i_0 at various times during a measurement, even if the source is monitored by photocell. This can, in essence, be done in one of two ways. The log i-x curves may be plotted and extrapolated back to $x = 0$, at which point the intercept on the log i axis gives log i_0. It is more convenient to proceed to evaluate a and i_0 from the relation

$$(8.5) \qquad \frac{\log i_1 - \log i_0}{x_1} = a = \frac{\log i_2 - \log i_0}{x_2}.$$

Since X/p is constant, two measurements of i as i_1 and i_2 at values of x set equal to x_1 and x_2 will give both a and i_0.

The methods of reducing the data used varied among the different groups, depending on the nature of data required, i.e., whether or not the second coefficient was also to be evaluated, and on the number of corrections required. Sanders and Posin used relatively simple and direct calculations (10), while the calculations of Kruithoff and Penning were more elaborate, requiring much more correction (4). This difference in data came in part from Kruithoff and Penning's use of very small gaps with low potentials, where the distance δ for gaining terminal energy had to be subtracted from their values of x. High values of i_0, involving "photo fatigue," also necessitated correction.

One procedure that was always resorted to in the author's work, as well as that of Kruithoff and Penning, was *to enclose the quartz arc completely in a well-vented glass vessel*. The paths taken by the beam of ultraviolet light, where they passed outside of the glass vessel, were also surrounded with glass tubing. All the air in the glass system circulated and was vented *outside* of the room. These precautions, when engaged in prolonged series of runs using ultraviolet light, are urgently needed to protect the eyes of the workers, and to avoid exposing the workers to the high ozone concentrations produced by the ultraviolet light in free air. Ozone, contrary to popular belief, is a very irritating substance if inhaled for any length of time, leading to chronic laryngitis, and predisposing exposed personnel to more serious respiratory infections.

Electrode and other metals used inside the chambers should be as light as possible compatible with rigidity, so that they can be heated by induction furnace and readily outgassed. The best metals to use are nickel, platinum, tungsten, and tantalum, although tungsten should be avoided if O_2 is used. Monel metal, and perhaps copper, brass, and zinc, should not be used, as these volatilize under heating. The electrodes should be polished with rouge or SnO_2, and can be cleaned by using volatile grease solvents, such as CCl_4, and *later*, acetone, or nondenatured, pure, 95% grain alcohol (C_2H_5OH) and distilled water. If Hg contamination is suspected, dilute HNO_3 may be used before polishing, followed by much rinsing with distilled water. Once the electrodes are inside the chamber they may show some oxidation, resulting from the glass blowing. After pumping and baking out the assembly, H_2 can be introduced and the assembly heated to 300° C. for several hours, while clean dry H_2 (preferably from a tank) flows through.

Gases prepared by electrolysis or by the "wet" chemical techniques require exceptionally careful purifying techniques as these, owing to entrained impurities, are very hard to free from contamination. Tank gases, passed over finely divided hot metal (Cu) and metal oxide tubes, if appropriate, then through $CaCl_2$ and P_2O_5 traps for drying, and finally through liquid-air or other low-temperature traps, have by various sensitive tests revealed themselves to be the best. *Under no circumstances* should HF or HCl be put into a glass system to clean it. The halogens are hard to get rid of. Especially, the fluorides of silicon and boron from borosilicate glass can never be removed from a glass system, once they get in, and these ruin discharge studies. Glass may be cleaned by fat solvents, acetone, water, and a cleaning mixture of concentrated $H_2SO_4 + Na_2CrO_4$, but must be rinsed many times with distilled H_2O. Metals oxidize with the H_2SO_4. The later steps in the cleanup of the electrodes then require heating by induction or electron bombardment on the pumps, to 900° C., and bakeout of the whole glass system at 400° C. for several hours. To remove the final traces of gas from electrodes, the best procedure is to bombard the electrodes in turn as cathodes with a low-pressure glow discharge of N_2, A, or one of the inert gases. Prolonged bombardment produces sputtered deposits that may lead to current leaks. Repeated rinsing with clean gases following repeated discharges aids in the final purification. Electron bombardment of metal electrodes heats them, but does *not* outgas them. Outgassing can only be achieved by making the electrode the cathode, using appropriate heavy positive ions of an inert or neutral gas. Best are A or N_2. H_2 reduces oxide films, but is absorbed and re-emitted for hours afterward. It alters the work function.

The purification of the gases follows different techniques, depending on the gases used. For O_2, N_2, and H_2, the best procedure is to use tank gases, with properly heated glass tubes containing powdered metals, such as Cu, Ca, Ba, Mg—and for some gases, CuO, to remove H_2—for removing disturbing gases. Gas circulated over arcs or really hot Ca, Ba, or Mg, without an intervening cold trap, may coat electrodes with these metals or their oxides. With O_2, the gas should be passed through a heated tube of CuO to remove the last traces of H_2, followed by $CaCl_2$, P_2O_5, and cooling traps. O_2 can be liquefied in liquid air or N_2 at adequate pressures, and then fractionated. Pure O_2 can be prepared by heating $KMnO_4$. It *cannot* be prepared pure by heating $KClO_3$. Pure N_2 is best taken from tanks. That prepared from NaN_3 is free from O_2. However, NaN_3 comes from *organic diazotization procedures*, and is always contaminated with C and H. Thus, N_2 from the heating of NaN_3 is full of traces of $CH_3NH_2NH_3$ and other "junk," as ion-mobility studies show, while *it appears spectroscopically clean.*[5]

Townsend and McCallum believed final cleanup to be achieved in He and Ne by a high-frequency glow discharge (8). Perhaps, at correct frequency and pressure, this operated to outgas the glass walls and electrodes. Usually, "getters" of the type of Mg, Ba, Cs, or "batalum," distilled into tubes, will remove the last traces of O_2 and H_2O, which are always troublemakers, as they keep coming out from the walls and electrodes for hours. Care must be used to insure that these metals are clean by successive distillation, and that they do not contaminate or distill onto electrodes. The use of Na as a "getter" with N_2 and H_2 is questionable, as it appears to form volatile compounds, giving very strong photoelectric or metastable ionization and absorption in certain spectral regions. With A, on the other hand, Na causes no trouble. Heating or flashing W filaments that have previously been flashed and outgassed has been shown by mass spectrograph in Huber's work (49) to introduce 1% of O_2 into pure N_2. Best of all "getters" is thin, corrugated, oxygen-free copper, hot or cold, as shown by D. Alpert (50).

Actually, the word "purity" requires interpretation in terms of the gas and its desired properties. Mercury, while not considered as a serious foreign gas, is a very nasty contaminant for studies of a/p. It alloys with some electrodes, and has a vapor pressure of 10^{-3} mm at $20°$ C. It distills around the apparatus during bakeouts, and cannot be surely removed unless the whole assembly is rinsed out with dilute HNO_3. Hg vapor is bad in gases of high ionizing potential, such as H_2, N_2, A, Ne, etc., as it is ionized by excited and especially metastable states. Hg yields electrons to most positive ions in gases—thus, after 10^{-3} sec, all positive ions may be Hg^+.

Again, traces of A, in which the ionization potential is about 15.95 e.v., in Ne, where the first excited metastable state is at 16.6 e.v., constitute a very serious contaminant. Similarly, traces of Ne would disturb He, but a trace of He in Ne would not cause any trouble. Separation of heavier impurities from inert gases by continued glow discharge, which removes the heavier atoms to the cathode region, is very effective, according to R. Rietz and G. Dieke (51). Recent spectroscopic observations in the author's laboratory show that 0.5% of N_2 in He contributes virtually all of the light in the positive column of a glow discharge at low pressure.

[5]Spectroscopic cleanliness is very illusory, because of the masking action of many gases. Mass-spectrographic analysis may be better, but there is no sure general test for traces of impurity.

Whether to use mercury-vapor pumps or the newer oil-diffusion pumps is a question. The vapor pressure of the oils used in such pumps is less than that of Hg, and there is presumably less chance of contamination by these organics. In theory, this is correct. However, all diffusion pumps sooner or later have electrical discharges of static types, or kick-back discharges at low pressure from the leak-testers, etc., used on the apparatus. These electrical discharges, as well as heating, break down the heavy oils, and lighter, more volatile hydrocarbons are formed that contaminate the system. The author has never known an oil-pumping system that does not ultimately foul the glass tubes and traps connected to it with greasy organic deposits. He believes Hg can better be controlled by putting liquid-air traps and suitable cutoffs between all Hg gauges and pumps than by taking chances with organic oil-diffusion pumps. Hg does not undergo alteration by discharges or prolonged heating.

The use of thermionic sources of electrons in place of photoelectrons in these measurements is not recommended, since these all introduce density gradients of an unpredictable sort, so that the values of X/p, or its equivalent in density, are not accurately known.

One more precaution must be borne in mind. If large electrode distances x are used, the photoelectric current *density*, $j_0 = i_0/A$, where A is the area illuminated, must be kept down. It was discovered by Posin, using up to 5 cm of plate separation in N_2, that if j_0 is greater than 10^{-13} amp/cm^2, the cumulative ionization at larger a is such that a considerable ion space charge builds up between the electrodes (10), (14). This leads to curved portions at the upper ends of the otherwise linear log i/i_0-x plots. These curvings yield spurious values of the second coefficient γ. With small values of x, Kruithoff and Penning could tolerate a value of j_0 of the order of 3×10^{-10} ampere/cm^2, with, however, some space-charge distortion. In these cases j got up to 3×10^{-8} amp/cm^2, and the values of γ were distorted, while a was little changed.

§ 3. The Form of the a/p-X/p Curves, and the η Efficiency Function.

In general, since a/p is what is sought for in tables and curves of data, it is natural to express (or plot) a/p against X/p to a linear scale in values of a/p. This shows the functional shape of the curve. For extended ranges, such as those observed, these plots are impractical. Plots of log a/p against log X/p are useful, but data are not accurate. For use, curves of sections of a/p values against X/p in cogent regions are best. Thus, it is advisable to present the data for a/p as a $f(X/p)$ in tables, with X/p expressed as volts per cm per mm Hg pressure of gas.

In plotting their results for a/p as a function of X/p, the Philips group (4), (15) uses a notation and procedure which have certain useful properties, and lead to valuable interpretations, especially in regard to breakdown. In this, a is replaced by a quantity which is a divided by X, viz.,

(8.6) $$\eta = a/X.$$

That is, in place of setting $di = iadx$, they set $di = i\eta dV$. Accordingly, on integration, in place of $i = i_0 \epsilon^{ax}$ they write

(8.7) $$i = i_0 \epsilon^{\eta V}.$$

The expression first appears to have been noted by J. Stoletow in 1901 (16). It was later used by J. J. Thomson to a limited extent (17). It is extensively discussed and used by von Engel and Steenbeck (18). In all of these cases, not $\eta = a/X$, but $1/\eta = X/a$, is used. This gives a chance to calculate the volts per ion pair in Townsend ionization for comparison with that by ionization by fast electrons. The valuable properties of η in relation to spark breakdown are clearly indicated by von Engel and Steenbeck, and are exploited to the full by the Philips research group (15). Where ionizing efficiency is of import, this is the function to use. Where number of ions is required, the a/p function of Townsend is most convenient.

Thus, $\eta V = ax$, and for a plane parallel gap where the field $X = V/x$, $\eta = a/X$. In order to evaluate a from η, the latter is merely multiplied by the field strength X. Where the electrons require a distance x_0 to gain their equilibrium energy in such a measure that x_0 cannot be neglected, the equation used is

(8.8) $$i = i_0 \epsilon^{a(x-x_0)} = i_0 \epsilon^{\eta(V-V_0)}.$$

The quantity

(8.9) $$\eta = a/X = (a/p)/(X/p)$$

represents *the ions per cm created per unit of energy available from the electrical field*. As such, it is of paramount interest in discussion of *ionizing efficiency*, which involves the sparking potential. Thus, both expressions (a and η) for the first coefficient have their usefulness.

The a/p-X/p curves, either directly plotted or to log-log scales, have a characteristic "S" shape, rising from an asymptote, then

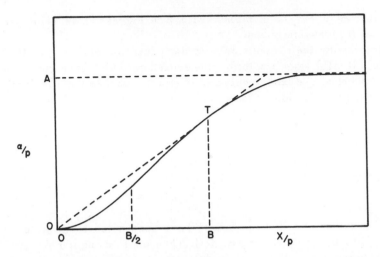

Fig. 8.8. Characteristic curve for α/p, plotted against X/p over an extended range of X/p values. Note that the scale of plotting for real curves of α/p is so compressed near the origin that it does not indicate that α/p has zero values out to considerable values of X/p, e.g., 20 in air, 10 in H_2, and 2 in A. Real α/p curves do *not* start at the origin. Illusions from this scale of plotting have led to serious complications. However, in the interest of saving space, the curve here shown is that corresponding to an analytical form $\alpha/p = A\ \epsilon^{-Bp/X}$.

passing through a point of inflection to an apparent "saturation" value, as in figure 8.8. In contrast, the quantity η plotted on the log-log scale has generally a uniform shape, rising steeply at low X/p, *reaching a peak, and then declining.*

As will later become clear, owing to the change of electron-energy distributions with X/p, there is really no single or unique functional relation covering the whole range of the α/p-X/p curves for any gas. There does exist a semiempirical, single functional relation which *simulates* observed forms. This was originally deduced by Townsend (19) on inaccurate and primitive theory before the ionization potentials were discovered. The relation has been justified in some correct, modern approximations *for limited ranges* of X/p, as by von Engel and Steenbeck (20) for high X/p, and by Druyvesteyn and Penning (21) for inert gases at a low range of X/p. While this expression, because of its general form, *can be made to approximate* sections of the α/p-X/p curve by judicious choice of constants, *it is not generally applicable over the whole curve* for any gas. It is, however, a single, continuous function over the X/p range that has the general "S" shape and other superficial properties of the observed curves, and serves

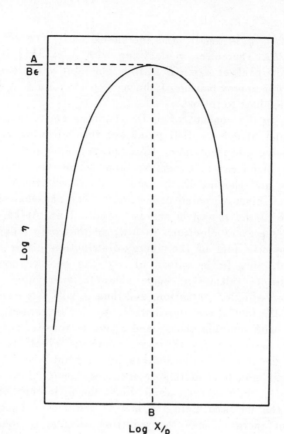

Fig. 8.9. Characteristic curve for $\log \eta = \log (\alpha/X)$ against $\log X/p$, as it appears from experiment. This curve was drawn from the relation $\eta = (Ap/X)$ $\epsilon^{-Bp/X}$, in order to conserve space in discussion.

as a convenience in guiding discussion of the effects of the α/p-X/p curves on sparking and otherwise. It is thus instructive and useful to apply it *with full recognition of its limited accuracy of fit*. The expression reads

$$(8.10) \qquad \alpha/p = A \, \epsilon^{-Bp/X} .$$

This starts at *zero* when $X/p = 0$, rises asymptotically and more slowly to a point of inflection at $B/2$, and then slowly approaches A as X/p increases indefinitely, as shown in figure 8.8. The expression, in terms of η, is

$$(8.11) \qquad \eta = \frac{\alpha}{X} = \frac{A}{X} \, p \, \epsilon^{-Bp/X} .$$

At low X/p, η is small, and increases until $X/p = B$, at which point $\eta = A/Be$. Thereafter, η declines with X/p. This is shown in figure 8.9. The peak at $X/p = B$ is flat, but rapidly decreases beyond $X/p = 2B$. This approximation of the η-X/p function will be used in various discussions to follow.

Returning to the concept of η, Druyvesteyn and Penning (15) and von Engel and Steenbeck (18) point out the following properties of the η-X/p curve just mentioned. These properties apply to pure gases and to some mixed gases, excepting those where ionization by metastable atoms and photons in the gas leads to additional ionization, as in the coefficient α', noted in section 6. The physical significance of the shape of the α/p-X/p curves is not clear. At very low X/p, the average energy of electrons is low, so that only those electrons in the asymptotic foot of the energy-distribution curve can ionize. As indicated, only finite values of α/p can be measured, and the curve appears to initiate at some characteristic value of X/p for each gas. Accordingly, ionization, and thus α, will rise asymptotically from zero at the foot of the distribution. As X/p increases, the number of electrons with ionizing energy and above increases, but probability of ionization at impact by the more energetic electrons decreases. Eventually, the rate of ionization reaches a point where it is proportional to X/p, and beyond this it increases more slowly with X/p. The quantity η, representing, as it does, the efficiency of ionization relative to the imposed field, is low at lower X/p because of the high ratio of energy losses to excitation relative to ionization. As X/p increases, this loss decreases relative to ionization, and η approaches higher values. As X/p still further increases, the electrons continue to gain energy, which is not lost to ionization, as the probability of ionization ultimately decreases with increase in electron energy. At the point where the electrons gain energy faster than they can dissipate it in ionization, they ultimately deliver the excess energy to the anode. Hence, the value of η decreases as X/p increases.

In this region of X/p, the electrons are *no longer in equilibrium* with the field X. The value of α/p is then a function of distance x as well as X/p; for as x increases, the average electron energy increases with decreasing η, and α/p decreases with increased energy and decreased probability of ionization. The effect is not observed in uniform fields, as the study of α is limited to short ranges of x.

Thus, the peak of the η-X/p curve represents the point of most efficient ionization, and the point where electrons cease to remain in equilibrium with the field. It is of interest to relate this point to

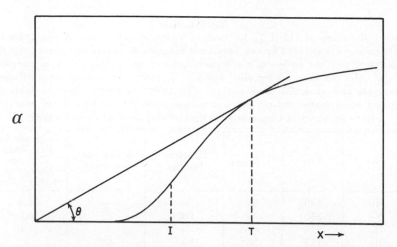

Fig. 8.10. Curve of a/p as a function of X/p, as it really might appear with construction for locating the point of maximum efficiency of ionization. $\eta = a/X$ at constant p is constant along the tangent from the origin to the curve.

properties of the a/p-X/p curve. At constant p, assume that a is plotted against the field X. Such a curve is shown in figure 8.10. The point of inflection is seen at I. Let a straight line be drawn from the *origin* tangent to the a/p curve. This point of tangency is labeled T. The quantity $\eta = a/X$ is constant along the straight line. At all points on the a/p-X/p curve, the quantity $\eta = a/X$ is less than the ratio set by the tangent straight line, except at T. Thus, the point of tangency of a straight line from the origin to the a/p-X/p curve gives the value of a, which divided by the corresponding value of X, gives η_{max}, the *maximum value* of η. This diagram clearly shows geometrically how the shape of the η-X/p curve is related to the a/p-X/p curve, and identifies the peak of the former with the tangent to the latter. This is indicated by von Engel and Steenbeck (18), who note that $\tan \theta = a/X = (a/p)/(X/p)$.

It can now be stated that when sparking theory is considered, it will be found that there are two points of utmost importance for the theory of breakdown, both being properties of this a/p-X/p or η-X/p relation. If there are no complicating factors in the ionization by collision, such as those involving two ionizing mechanisms acting simultaneously (i.e., an a and an a', as for Ne with 0.001% A), the *peak* of the η-X/p curve. or the point of tangency on the a/p-X/p curve, fixes the minimum sparking potential (4) if the second coefficient γ is sensibly constant with X/p. Again, the point of inflection

§3

TABLE 8.1

Table of values of $(1/\eta)_{max}$ for various gases at the value $(X/p)_{max}$ for the field strength X divided by the Townsend function α, giving the volts potential difference to yield an ion at maximum efficiency in the gas. This is compared to the volts per ion pair for slow and fast electrons at various most efficient energies, and at 4,000 volts energy. The effect of energy loss to inelastic impacts ·in excitation by the electron swarm, with its distribution of energies, is to be noted in comparison to that of electrons of unique energy.

Gas	X/p	$(1/\eta)_{max}$	Electron Energy	Volts per Ion Pair	Volts per Ion Pair When Electron Energy is 4,000 Volts
Air	340	68	—	—	32.4
N_2	350	75	100	35	36.0
O_2	270	—	—	—	31.0
He	125	70	100	62	—
CO_2	400	62	—	—	—
A	170	45	100	63	—
			200	68	29 ± 1
Ne	65	60	100	50	—
			75	63	43 ± 8

of the α/p-X/p curves fixes the point below which space-charge accumulations facilitate sparking and above which they impede it, as will be shown later in this chapter. This was simultaneously noted by von Engel and Steenbeck (22), and by the author's group (14). In the simple Townsend approximation used in equations 8.10 and 8.11, the inflection occurs at $B/2$, and T occurs at B, as seen in figure 8.8. It is perhaps of interest to note that from data current in 1932, von Engel and Steenbeck calculated $(1/\eta)_{max}$ in terms of electron volts per ion pair (18). This may be compared with the number of volts per ion pair required by electrons of energy in excess of 4,000 volts and of around 100 volts on the same gases, as seen in table 8.1.

Very recently it has been observed that in truly clean gases, like He and Ne, the energy to create an ion may be still higher than reported here. Past data gave values that were too high through secondary ionization by metastable states. Thus, comparison of $(1/\eta)_{max}$ with volts per ion pair by fast electrons cannot be too significant. In general, $(1/\eta)_{max}$ should be less than the value for fast electrons in a gas. This comes from the inevitable losses to excitation and elastic impacts at low energies.

The decrease in η at high X/p leads to an increase of observed ionization in highly divergent fields above that given by use of $\epsilon \int \alpha dx$, as will be seen. With this, it is possible to leave the Philips treatment, and to state that this is used in their publications to replace

a. Otherwise, it is of no interest until the sparking potentials are discussed.

§ 4. Indirect Evaluations of the First Coefficient.

Aside from the direct evaluation of a, which has just been discussed, use at times has been made of Townsend's sparking criterion for evaluating a, and its counterpart, the second coefficient. The development of the *theory* underlying the sparking criterion, which has been and still continues to be applied to the evaluations of the first and second Townsend coefficients, finds no place here. In order to present the method at this appropriate point, it will be assumed that beyond the primary mechanism involving a, a spark occurs when a second coefficient γ reaches some critical value in combination with the critical value of a.

For simplicity, assume that the secondary mechanism is the liberation of secondary electrons by impact of the positive ions from an avalanche on the cathode. If the chance that a positive ion can liberate one electron from the cathode on impact is γ, then Townsend assumed that if

$$(8.12) \qquad \gamma_s (\epsilon^{\alpha_s x_s} - 1) = 1,$$

a spark would ensue. Usually, $\epsilon^{a_s x_s}$ is so large that $\epsilon^{a_s x_s} >> 1$, and the condition is set more briefly that

$$(8.13) \qquad \gamma_s \, \epsilon^{\alpha_s x_s} = 1.$$

Here, a_s, x_s, and γ_s are the values of these quantities, observed when the spark across the gap of length x_s occurs. It is now convenient to invoke the terminology introduced by the Philips group; namely, the quantity $\eta_s = a_s/X_s$. If this is used, since for a uniform gap $X_s = V_s/x_s$, it is permitted to write $\eta_s = a_s x_s/V_s$, or $\eta_s V_s = a_s x_s$. Hence, the Townsend sparking criterion becomes

$$(8.14) \qquad \gamma_s \, \epsilon^{\eta_s V_s} = 1.$$

It is at once clear that if the sparking voltage at a given X_s, V_s, and pressure p is observed, η_s is given if γ_s is known, and vice versa. If $1/\eta_s$ is plotted against X_s/p, both to a logarithmic scale, and if V_s is plotted against X_s/p to the same scale, the curves will parallel each other, and the vertical distance between the two curves for any value of X_s/p will give the value of $1/\gamma_s$ (23). This procedure for evaluating either η_s or γ_s was first used by O. Klemperer, and by Townsend and McCallum, all in 1928. It was later used by Penning and Addink in 1934, and by R. Schöfer in 1938 (24). It has been employed at various other times, occasionally yielding results that were quite confusingly erroneous (25). The procedure is of very questionable value, as will be indicated. Why it should be used for a or η when such a relatively simple and precise direct method is at hand, is not readily understood. The same applies to an evaluation of a γ, where one actually exists, for γ can also be directly determined, simultaneously with a. It is true that an accurate evaluation of a or γ requires setting up an apparatus for the purpose and making measurements, but if these quantities are needed, they should be directly and accurately determined. Even if the values are required under conditions where a spark passes, the methods outlined above will yield these data *right up to spark breakdown.*

Actually, the use of this inferior method has been for diverse purposes. It has been used to check sparking theory and results as a by-product of sparking-potential measurements. It has been carried out for convenience, in ignorance of its inherent uncertainty. Finally, it is suspected that it has been used as an easy, quick method, or a method of last resort, to gain an order-of-magnitude value of a *secondary* coefficient from the supposedly relatively simple measurement of a sparking potential V_s. The method is unacceptable, except for the crudest information, for the following reasons.

1. While it is true that, in general, most sparking or breakdown thresholds are given by a generic expression of the form $f_2 \, \epsilon^{\int a \, dx} = 1$, or $f_2 \, \epsilon^{\int \eta_s \, dV_s} = 1$, where f_2 represents some sort of function expressing secondary ionization, the observed value of V_s may not represent a real threshold of this sort. This is true for many cases where the cathode is at the high potential, and a cleanup or conditioning by low-order discharge yields unstable, uncontrollable overvolting of the cathode (26). The value of V_s here is absolutely meaningless. In many discharges starting from the anode, the streamer process of breakdown does not fit into any such simple expression with a simple value f_2, so that the lumping into an expression of a single constant such as f_2 is inadequate (26). Finally, the secondary mechanisms are very diverse, as will be seen later, and often minute or unknown changes in gas or electrode conditions will change the mechanism involving a γ to one involving a photo effect at the cathode, or vice versa. Thus, unless a given discharge condition is known to depend on a definite and clearly defined secondary mechanism, thereby justifying the use of an equation such as 8.14, the method is not valid at all. As a good example of this sort of error, C. G. Miller and the author (27) inferred the most asinine values for γ from V_s for a negative wire corona discharge.

2. Again, the method is good for evaluating a γ or f_2 only if $a/p =$

$f(X/p)$, or if $\eta = f_1(X/p)$ is known, and vice versa. This means that data must be taken from some direct measurements of one or the other function. But there is no assurance that the values of these quantities for γ or f_2 and a/p or η *are the same in the two sets of measurements* for V_s and γ or a/p. For example, Penning and Addink used the values of γ for Ne obtained by Townsend and McCallum to evaluate η, and yet they initially undertook the measurements of V_s, as *they were not confident of Townsend and McCallum's data on Ne*. In later studies, Penning abandoned the method, and his associate, Kruithoff, discovered in the direct studies how utterly capricious were the values of γ and f_2 for a cathode. Not only are these values of γ a function of the past history of the cathode, but they vary with strong illumination and during a measurement, and are not even uniform over the surface of the same cathode. This alone makes the method questionable, since no two workers can assume that γ for their cathodes was the same.

Perhaps, assuming that data were adequate and theory applied, this method has one advantage. Sparks will pass at spots of the highest γ or f_2 on the surface. Thus, values of γ, obtained from sparking data with good values of a/p or η, will yield the values of γ *for the points of highest γ on the surface*. These can be compared with the *average* values yielded by the more legitimate methods. However, if the method is used to evaluate a/p and η, and the values of γ or f_2 from the legitimate methods in some other study are used, then the values of η or a/p so computed will be high; for the sparks passed at only the spots of high γ, while low average values were used for computation of a/p.

3. The third criticism lies in the question of accuracy alone. Even where V_s can be described in terms of a clean-cut phenomenon, not dependent on cathode cleanup to an unknown degree, etc., neither sparking-potential measurements nor threshold measurements of V_s are much more accurate than 2%. Under rare conditions, accuracy of such thresholds can perhaps approach 1%, and often may be no better than 3% to 5%. Now the solution of the equation for η_s, assuming γ_s to be known, depends on the accuracy of the value of V_s. Thus, if V_s is 2% low, η_s will appear 2% high. This error in a_s is not too serious, except that it associates an $X_s/p = V_s/pX_s$ which is 2% low with an a_s/p which is 2% high, thus giving a systematic offset error of 4% in a table. Usually, the method is not utilized to evaluate an η_s or a_s/p, but is used to evaluate a second coefficient; namely, γ_s. Here the error can be serious indeed; for regarding the variation of a/p with X/p in the region $a/p = A(X/p)^2$, it is quite clear that the evaluation of a V_s which is 2% in error would give the exponent in

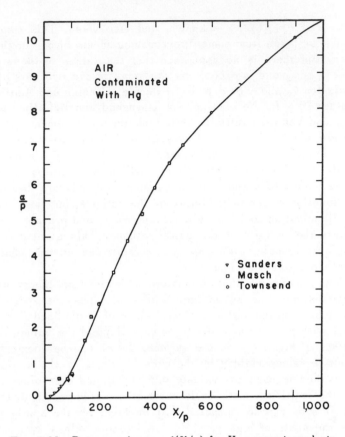

Fig. 8.11. Data on α/p as a $f(X/p)$ for Hg-contaminated air,
as given by Sanders, Masch, and Townsend.

$\epsilon^{\alpha_s x_s}$ an error of 4%. Thus, a small error in V_s could produce a serious change in the value of $\epsilon^{\eta_s V_s}$ or $\epsilon^{\alpha_s x_s}$. This would then yield quite an error in γ if $\epsilon^{\eta_s V_s}$ were in a sensitive range of values of the exponent. In the region where $\alpha/p = A \epsilon^{BX/p}$, $\epsilon^{\alpha x}$ varies as exp $xpA \epsilon^{BX/p}$, so that very small changes in V_s or X_s can make radical changes in the value of γ inferred.

It is for this reason that with several values of V_s from different observers on the same gas to choose from, it is possible to adopt the value of γ inferred from relation 8.14 to fit any favored theory. This is the reason why numerical agreement with sparking theory and coefficients is virtually of no value in establishing the relative merits of any theory.

Accordingly, the author wishes once and for all to warn workers

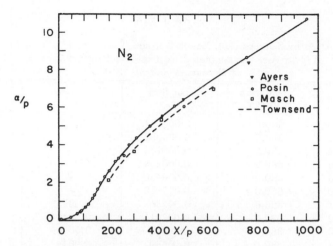

Fig. 8.12. Data of Posin, Masch, and Ayers for a/p
as a $f(X/p)$ in Hg-contaminated N_2.

against using this method for any but the crudest estimates. He has
seen the most fallacious data and conclusions, published and unpublished, derived from this "sloppy" technique. However, where a and
γ are measured on the same gas as V_s, the value of γ computed from a
and V_s can be compared with the average γ observed, to see how much
γ, for points on the surface, exceeds the average value.

§ 5. Measured Values of the First Townsend Coefficients in Pure Gases.

From what has preceded, it is quite clear that most of the determinations of a antedating 1930 are of little value in practical applications to discharge calculations. Furthermore, the range in X/p
values covered in these early studies was not adequate to be of great
weight in clarifying the theoretical interpretation.

Probably, the first step in the amelioration of this situation came
from the evaluations of a/p as a function of X/p in air, N_2, and O_2
at lower values of X/p, which began about 1930. These evaluations
consisted of the work of M. Paavola and his successor, K. Masch (9),
using techniques analogous to Townsend's in quasi-glass chambers,
in the laboratory of Rogowski at Aachen. Independently, studies of
the same character were begun by F. H. Sanders in 1929 on air, succeeded by D. Q. Posin in 1933 (10) on N_2, using large metal chambers,
with the techniques initiated in the author's laboratory. All of these
studies were made on reasonably pure, dry air, contaminated with
the saturation pressure of Hg vapor at 22° C. The data of Sanders

§ 5

TABLE 8.2

Values of a/p by Sanders (10), Masch (9), and Townsend (7), as a Function of
X/p in Air, Contaminated with the Equilibrium Pressure
of Mercury Vapor at $22°$ C.

X/p	Sanders p in mm	Sanders a/p	Masch a/p	Townsend a/p
20	380.0	0.000034	—	—
22	380.0	0.000052	—	—
24	380.0	0.000134	—	—
26	380.0	0.000234	—	—
28	380.0	0.000430	—	—
30	380.0	0.000910	—	—
31	380.0	0.00136	0.00152	—
32	380.0	0.00201	0.00204	—
33	380.0	0.00305	0.00309	—
34	380.0	0.00459	0.0044	—
35	—	—	0.0059	—
36	380.0	0.00820	0.0076	—
38	—	—	0.0120	—
40	25.0	0.0167	0.0168	—
45	—	—	0.0335	—
50	9.95	0.0554	0.057	—
60	4.90	0.127	0.130	—
70	1.0	0.224	0.235	—
80	0.98	0.340	0.365	—
90	0.97	0.491	0.51	—
100	0.96	0.637	0.68	0.72
110	0.975	0.806	0.85	—
120	0.975	1.007	1.05	—
130	0.973	1.236	1.23	—
140	0.950	1.477	1.40	—
150	0.990	1.602	1.60	—
160	1.0	1.758	1.83	—
180	—	—	2.25	—
200	—	—	2.60	2.6
250	—	—	3.50	—
300	—	—	4.36	4.4
350	—	—	5.10	—
400	—	—	5.80	5.82
450	—	—	6.5	—
500	—	—	7.0	7.0
600	—	—	—	7.9
700	—	—	—	8.7
800	—	—	—	9.3
900	—	—	—	10.0
1,000	—	—	—	10.5

TABLE 8.3

Values of a/p for Mercury-contaminated N_2 as a Function of X/p,
as Given by Ayers (7), Masch (9), and Posin (10)

X/p	a/p			Pres. Used Posin	X/p	a/p			Pres. Used Posin
	Ayers	Masch	Posin			Ayers	Masch	Posin	
10	0.0110	–	–	–	120	–	0.80	0.95000	1.000
15	.0170	–	–	–	125	0.850	–	–	–
20	.0239	–	0.000087	700.0	127	–	–	1.13500	0.490
25	.0305	0.00009	–	–	130	–	0.98	–	–
26	–	.00022	.000258	500.0	137	–	–	1.272	.425
27	–	.00041	–	–	140	–	1.15	1.400	.720
28	–	.00060	.000456	500.0	142	–	–	1.451	.345
29	–	.00081	–	–	150	1.32	1.32	–	–
30	.0382	.00112	.000911	250.0	156	–	–	1.635	.420
31	–	.00150	–	–	160	–	1.50	–	–
32	–	.00190	.00199	250.0	166	–	–	2.020	.290
33	–	.00245	–	–	175	1.84	–	–	–
34	–	.00315	.00281	250.0	176	–	–	2.350	.425
35	–	.00385	.00305	250.0	180	–	1.95	–	–
36	–	.00475	.00441	250.0	196	–	–	2.522	.230
38	–	.0071	.00521	150.0	200	2.50	2.25	–	–
40	.0550	.0100	.00734	100.0	215	–	–	3.07	.330
44	–	–	.01070	100.0	230	–	–	3.20	.25
45	–	.0208	.01353	100.0	250	–	3.15	3.50	.25
50	.0820	.0373	–	–	270	–	–	4.0	.25
59	–	–	.09340	0.985	300	4.10	3.90	–	–
60	.121	.087	–	–	310	–	–	4.40	.18
68	–	–	.14500	0.985	350	–	4.55	4.93	.18
70	–	.162	–	–	400	5.43	5.2	5.50	.14
78	–	–	.28300	0.635	450	–	5.7	6.0	.125
80	.257	.260	–	–	500	6.29	6.1	6.23	.125
88	–	–	.41200	0.635	750	7.91	–	8.78	.075
90	–	.375	–	–	1,000	9.02	–	10.8	.075
100	.471	.505	.70000	–	2,000	11.24	–	–	–
108	–	–	.72900	–	3,000	12.10	–	–	–
110	–	.65	.73000	–					

covered the range from $X/p = 20$ to $X/p = 160$, and probably are the best results in this range. At lower X/p, the data of Masch scatter, but straddle the more consistent data of Sanders. The data of Townsend in air, going back many years, appear to be consistent with those of Masch. They extend the curve to $X/p = 1,000$ (7). The data enumerated constitute the only values for that important medium, air.

As the air in all these studies was contaminated with saturated Hg vapor at room temperature, they are doubtless, at higher X/p, some

TABLE 8.4

Values of α/p for Mercury-contaminated O_2 as
a Function of X/p, According to Masch (9)

X/p	Masch α/p	X/p	Masch α/p
31	0.0011	90	0.79
32	0.00335	100	0.97
33	0.0072	110	1.16
34	0.0128	120	1.37
35	0.0206	130	1.55
36	0.0285	140	1.75
38	0.0465	150	1.93
40	0.064	160	2.13
45	0.105	180	2.48
50	0.153	200	2.85
60	0.280	300	3.65
70	0.435	350	4.4
80	0.61		

10% higher than the values for the same air when free of Hg. They
are reproduced in table 8.2 for Hg-contaminated air, and are plotted
as α/p against X/p in figure 8.11. Figure 8.4 shows the asymptotic
rise of α/p as a function of X/p, as obtained by Sanders. Plotting
this rise from $X/p = 20$ to $X/p = 40$, the rise can be seen to be well
represented by an exponential law of the form $\alpha/p = 2.07 \times 10^{-8}$
$\epsilon^{0.35\,X/p}$. This sort of rise was also observed by Posin in relatively
pure N_2, contaminated with Hg, in the range of $X/p = 20$ to $X/p = 40$.
This circumstance is of great interest, as will later be seen.

The data for N_2 obtained by Posin (10), Masch (9), and in 1923
by Ayers (7), are shown in table 8.3, and plotted in figure 8.12. Again,
Masch's data seem more erratic, but straddle Posin's data nearly all
the way up. The data of Ayers at low X/p are high, and begin at
very low X/p. They agree with no other data in that region. Likewise,
at high X/p, his values depart from Posin's. As seen on the curve
of figure 8.12, the dashed curve of Townsend is below that of Posin,
and agrees better with Masch's data than with Posin's. It is believed
that Ayers' N_2, prepared in a wet reaction and dried by H_2SO_4, P_2O_5,
etc., was possibly less pure than that of Masch or Posin. All samples
of N_2 were Hg-contaminated from the mercury gauges alone. In general,
all these data show the same trend and the same shape, and differ
only in smaller details.

Table 8.4 gives the values observed by Masch (9) for O_2 with Hg
contamination. Masch, in these observations, noted a rather sharp

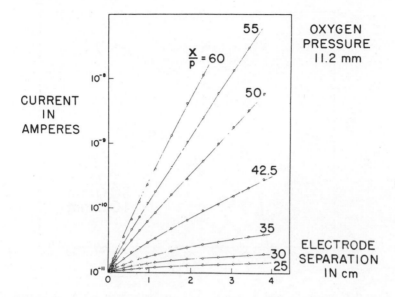

Fig. 8.13. Geballe and Harrison's curves for log i/i_0, plotted against gap length x in O_2 with electron attachment at $X/p = 60$. Note the curvature.

decline in a/p as a $f(X/p)$ at low values of X/p, which he ascribed to loss of electrons by attachment. However, he did nothing about correcting this condition. His range of values of gap length x was furthermore too limited to direct his attention to the fact that the log i/i_0-x curves ceased to be linear at small values of x for low X/p. Recent studies of R. Geballe and M. A. Harrison (11) showed these features. In consequence, as shown in chapter V, equations were derived for evaluating both a and the attachments per cm distance in the field direction. Their results for η/p and a/p for air, O_2, and certain other electron-attracting gases, including CCl_4, freon 12, CF_3SF_5, SF_6, $SiCl_4$, isopentane, and a few values in pure H_2 and N_2, are given in tables 5.1, 5.2, and 5.3. Figure 8.13 gives Geballe and Harrison's plots of log i/i_0 against x for O_2, showing the curvature at low X/p and small x caused by attachment. Figure 8.14 shows Geballe and Harrison's values for a/p as a $f(X/p)$, plotted for O_2, in comparison to those of Masch.

Before this time, Townsend had evolved a theory for a/p as a $f(X/p)$ in which the form of the expression is given by equation 8.10:

$$a/p = A \, \epsilon^{-pB/X}.$$

For the range of values covered by Townsend's curves in air and

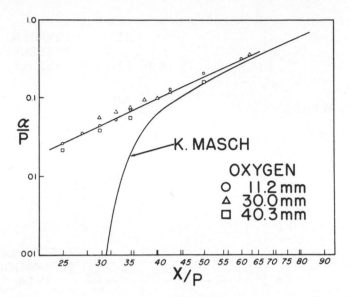

Fig. 8.14. Geballe and Harrison's curves for α/p as a $f(X/p)$ in pure O_2 where attachment occurs. Note that Masch's data fall off badly at low X/p, owing to failure to correct for attachment.

in N_2, the plot of log α/p against p/X is fairly linear. However, Masch (9) observed that while such linearity applied for higher values of X/p, the plots for lower X/p over larger ranges of X/p were curved. The *deceptively slight* curvature resulting from Masch's scale of plotting deceived him into believing that he had substantiated the theory. Actually, as seen, *it is not permissible to make judgments on such easily mistaken visual impressions, which depend on the scale of plotting.* Thus, it is not strange that on closer scrutiny[6] the extensive data of Sanders and Posin yield for the low range of X/p values a functional form for α/p given by $A\ \epsilon^{BX/p}$, and *not $A\ \epsilon^{-Bp/X}$.* Posin was furthermore able to represent the values of α/p as a function of X/p over the whole range for N_2 by essentially *four different functional forms*, each holding over different sections of the range. The justification for these empirical expressions over the regions covered is shown in the curves of figures 8.15, 8.16, and 8.17. The equations inferred from the data read:

(8.15) X/p 20-38, $\alpha/p = 5.76 \times 10^{-7}\ \epsilon^{0.245\ X/p}$.

---

[6]Here again caution is urged, as Sanders and Posin's data were in air and N_2 contaminated with Hg. This could have altered the shape of the curves, as Hg is ionized by excited N_2 and O_2 states. However, at 760 mm, the Hg contamination would have been $1.5 \times 10^{-4}\%$, which probably is not very effective.

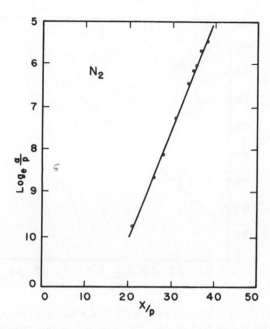

Fig. 8.15. Posin's data for α/p as a $f(X/p)$ for mercury-contaminated N_2, from $X/p = 20$ to $X/p = 40$, plotted as log α/p against X/p, showing the true rise of α/p as a positive exponential one with X/p, and not according to Townsend's equation.

(8.16) X/p 44-176, $\alpha/p = 1.17 \times 10^{-4} (X/p - 32.2)^2$.

          X/p 176-200, $\alpha/p =$ proportional to X/p, linear through the point of inflection.

(8.17) X/p 200-1,000, $(\alpha/p + 3.65)^2 = 0.21 X/p$.

Leaving aside the doubtful derivation of the expression

(8.10) $$\alpha/p = A \epsilon^{-Bp/x},$$

it is interesting to note that superficially the quantity $\epsilon^{-Bp/X}$, plotted as a function of X/p, has the peculiar, S-shaped form *starting at the origin*, characteristic of the observed curves of α/p. The rise is asymptotic from *zero at the origin*, undergoes a point of inflection at $X/p = B/2$, and flattens out at higher X/p. By adjusting constants A and B, it is possible to adapt $A \epsilon^{-Bp/X}$ to almost any *section of* the observed α/p-X/p curves. But *there is not a single observed curve that fits this function all the way along*. The point of inflection may coincide, but high or low X/p values will not. It does not fit at the foot for the lowest X/p, where the function may vary as $A \epsilon^{BX/p}$,

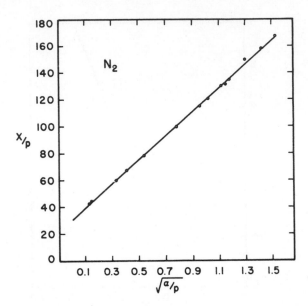

Fig. 8.16. Posin's data in N_2, from $X/p = 44$ to $X/p = 176$, plotted as X/p against the square root of α/p, showing that in this region α/p varies as $(X/p)^2$.

Theoretically, equation 8.10 can be derived as an approximation at very high X/p, where it fits best. Where a single analytical function is desired for generalized discussion of functional forms over a large range of X/p, as in a study of sparking relations, equation 8.10 may legitimately be used for discussion, as done by Steenbeck (20).

Similar analyses of empirical relations fitting sections of the curves may be applied to the curves for α/p as a function of X/p for all gases. Such piecemeal analysis of the curves leaves no doubt that the functional form of α/p, in terms of X/p, is of a most complicated nature. In fact, it is impossible to fit any single analytical function to the curves observed. Thus, the expression of Townsend and the doubtful theory on which it is based are applicable to only a section of the observed curves. Later theoretical studies bear out the fact that no single analytical function can be made to fit the curves. The reason for this is quite simple. The value of α/p depends on the number of the electrons in the swarm in a given field X at a pressure in a gas that have the energy necessary to ionize the gas molecules, and on the chance that they will ionize on a given impact if they have this energy. As shown in chapter VI, the form of the energy-distribution curve depends critically on the way in which the

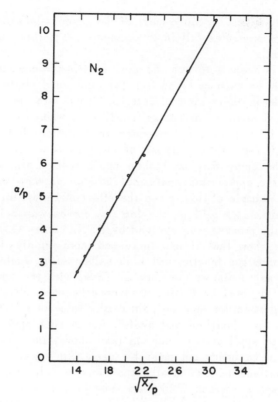

Fig. 8.17. Posin's data in N_2 for α/p, plotted against the X/p from $X/p = 200$ to $X/p = 1,000$, showing that in this region α/p varies sensibly as $\sqrt{X/p}$.

Ramsauer free paths for the electrons in the gas vary with electron energy. This means that as X/p changes and the average energy of the electron swarm in the gas changes, the shape of the distribution law, *particularly in regard to the shape of its asymptotic foot on the high-energy side*, changes radically. Since the value of α/p depends critically on the integral of the foot of these distribution functions from the ionization energy on out, it is clear that the form of the α/p curve will change with X/p as the analytical form of the distribution law changes.

Thus, the important contribution of the studies of α/p at this time was to establish the general S-shaped form of the α/p-X/p curves, and the fact that *it could not be represented by any single analytical function.* It also demonstrated a rate of increase of α/p with X/p that was very high at low values, and before the point of inflection still varied rapidly with X/p. Since most of the gaseous-breakdown thresh-olds at higher pressures fall in this range of X/p, this has important consequences.

Where it is desired to use the data on a/p for computations, the values should be used as taken from the tables and plotted to a con-venient scale in the region of interest. There are times, however, in the general study of discharge conditions, where for the purpose of analysis it is desired to introduce an analytical form for a/p as a function of X/p for the purpose of integration or extrapolation. In this case the curve may be broken up into segments, as done by Posin, and *the appropriate analytical function in that range may be used.* As an example of this, when the effect of heavy initial electron current densities $j_0 = i_0/A$ on the log i/i_0 curves was being studied, a theory of the process was evolved by R. N. Varney (14). In this he was able to show that if a/p increased more rapidly than linearly with X/p, large gap lengths and high values of j_0 would build up a space such as to distort the curves. Thus, with the functional ap-proximations devised by Posin, it at once becomes clear up to what value of X/p attention must be paid to the value of j_0. The treatment by Posin is then justified and useful. For a much more generalized discussion in applications such as that above, the Townsend form $A \, \epsilon^{-Bp/X}$ can be used, but must be used with caution. By its use Steenbeck arrived at essentially the same conclusions as Varney concerning space charges (22). Care must be taken in such usage to prevent misconceptions.

On the other hand, experience prompts that a warning be issued in this connection. If any function is plotted to an exaggerated scale, distortion of the curve can be such that *visual* impressions will lead to definite misuse of the curves. Thus, by expanding the scale of abscissae to emphasize the region about the point of inflection of the a/p - X/p curve, the scale of the plot masks the exponential rise and the upper arm of the "S." In consequence, the curve for a/p as a function of X/p can be made to *appear to be essentially a linear relation*, with only small curvatures near its ends. Such an improper plot was actually used to justify the use of a linear form of the curve in a certain theoretical approximation by Wilkinson (28), leading to erroneous conclusions. Since the linear range is actually very limited, the introduction of a linear approximation over a long range led to completely incorrect conclusions concerning a discharge mechanism. Whenever such a temptation arises, one should resort to the expedient of breaking the curve up into sections and solving for the correct form of an approximate law over limited regions, adopted by Sanders and Posin. The limits of the approximation are then clearly defined.

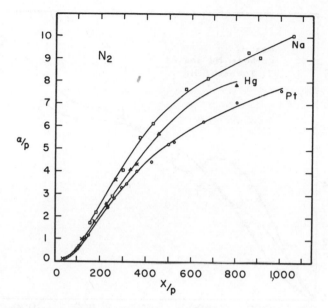

Fig. 8.18. Bowls's values of a/p as a $f(X/p)$ in pure N_2, in N_2 contaminated with Hg vapor at 22° C., and in pure N_2 with Na distilled into the apparatus. Hg vapor increases a/p about 17% at the highest X/p above that for pure N_2. The Na produces some volatile compound with N_2 that is readily ionized by photons from N_2; increase, 25%.

Following this development, it became clear from various angles of approach that traces of impurities might alter the values of the first coefficient. F. M. Penning had arrived at this conclusion from studies on the thresholds for various types of breakdown and in fact, his first approach to a study of the coefficients, together with C. C. J. Addink (24) in 1934, came from a study of breakdown thresholds in pure and contaminated inert gases, notably neon. In the author's laboratory, the desire for more data on the *second* coefficient, because of the suspiciously uniform values of earlier observers, prompted consideration of purer gases (11). On observing the cathode of Posin with grazing-incidence illumination, fine droplets of Hg were noted, indicating a mercury-coated cathode. This condition was recognized as probably more important in its effect on the second coefficient.

Toward this end, the author in 1935 suggested to W. E. Bowls that he repeat Posin's work on N_2 in an all-glass, outgassed system with Pt cathode in the absence of Hg (11). After completing this, Bowls was to distill Na metal into the tube to change the work function of the cathode, and again observe the second coefficient. To the author's satisfaction, Bowls reported in 1937 that in carrying out this program

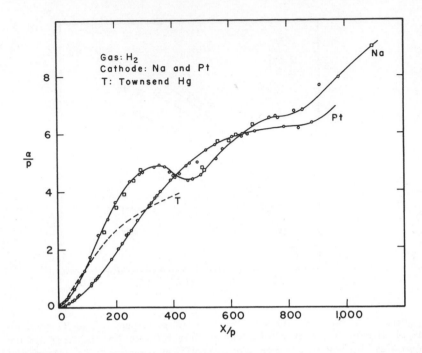

Fig. 8.19. Hale's curves for α/p as a $f(X/p)$ in pure H_2. Note that Townsend's curves, contaminated with Hg vapor, lie above Hale's for most of their course. Use of Na gives a volatile, very strongly photoionized impurity in the H_2. This gives the double maxima for α/p. This effect is a new phenomenon, akin to the action of traces of A in Ne, called the "Penning effect." The upcurving of both α/p curves around $X/p = 1,000$ is spurious, and is caused by failure of electrons to gain equilibrium in the gap used.

in the apparatus of figure 8.6, he had been *unable to duplicate the values of Posin* in N_2. In fact, his observed values fell 17% below Posin's at the highest X/p, as seen in figure 8.18. At the suggestion of the author, Bowls then distilled one small droplet of Hg into his clean tube (11). He at once duplicated Posin's points over the range of X/p covered. Thereafter, outgassing at 400° C. for four days failed completely to clean up the Hg, and the apparatus was dismantled and treated with dilute HNO_3. On reassembly, the values of α/p returned to their initial low state. The work of Bowls on N_2 was followed up by D. H. Hale (11) in 1938-1939, using H_2 with Pt and Na cathodes. His curves for α/p were even more striking, especially with Na present. The results of Bowls and Hale are listed in tables 8.5 and 8.6, and the curves are shown to a small scale in figures 8.18 and 8.19.

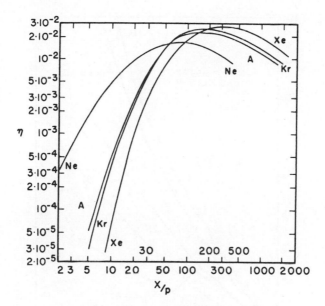

Fig. 8.20. Kruithoff and Penning's curves for log η, plotted against log X/p, for Ne, A, Kr, and Xe.

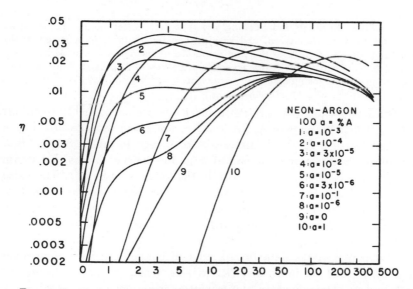

Fig. 8.21. Kruithoff and Penning's curves for log η, plotted against log X/p, for pure Ne, pure A, and mixtures, indicated by the figures on the curves. Note the double maxima associated with the Penning effect.

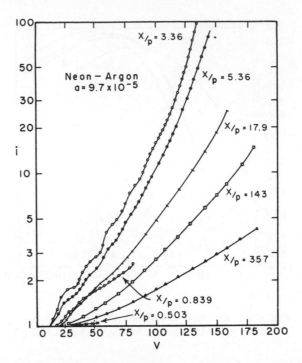

Fig. 8.22. Kruithoff and Penning's curves for current against potential at constant field X, pressure p, and varying gap length in x, in mixtures of Ne and $9.7 \times 10^{-5}\%$ of A. Note the fine structure of the curves, caused by low V and x. Several curves are drawn for various values of X/p used. Note that the rise is most rapid for intermediate values of X/p. (*See page 698.*)

The studies of A. A. Kruithoff and F. M. Penning, and of Kruithoff (4) in 1936-1940, on pure A, Kr, and Xe, are given in table 8.7. Those for pure Ne, and for Ne-A mixtures, are shown in tables 8.8 and 8.9. These are in terms of η instead of a/p, for the pure gases. To obtain a/p, it is only necessary to multiply the value of η by X/p. The same data are shown for these gases, plotted as log η against log X/p, in figures 8.20 and 8.21. Data on a/p for pure He by Townsend and McCallum (8) are given in table 8.10, and shown plotted as η in figure 8.24.

Discussion of the data in mixtures of gases, and with contamination by Hg and Na in H_2 and N_2, will be found in section 6, as will certain data obtained where electron attachment occurs.

The one gas for which no *extensive* reliable data exist is He. This gas was initially studied by the Townsend group at a time before purity control was adequate. This, like Ne, is one of the most dif-

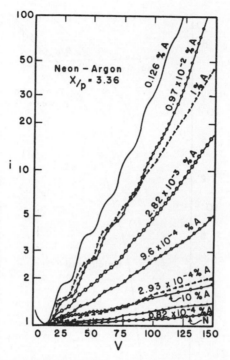

Fig. 8.23. Kruithoff and Penning's curves for Ne-A mixtures at $X/p = 3.36$, the optimum value of figure 8.22. Here percentages of A are varied. The most effective value is 0.126% A. Note the diffusion current at small V and x, starting at zero, caused by the velocity of emission of electrons and its decline as x increases before X becomes high. The curves in pure Ne are very low on this scale of plotting. (See page 698.)

ficult gases to study as with its high excitation potentials it is affected by traces of impurity in the same way as Ne.[7] It is urgent that good data be obtained on He, as it is the *one gas* for which the theoretical deductions on energy distributions are *adequate* to enable a proper calculation of a/p as a $f(X/p)$ to be made (30). This calculation has recently been accomplished by S. H. Dunlop (48) in the Emeléus group at Belfast. Adopting modern techniques, Townsend and McCallum (8) obtained values in pure Ne in 1928, and in pure He in 1934. The data in Ne deviate slightly from those of Kruithoff and Penning (4) at higher X/p, in a direction indicating minor contamination. Their data in He are shown in figure 8.24, together with

---

[7]It is possible that today, with the purification of He in a glow discharge (51), or using He from superfluid leakage of liquid He II (53), good measurement could be made by using Alpert vacuum techniques (52).

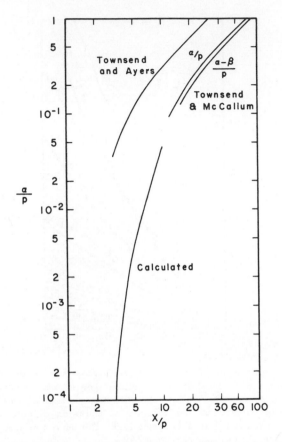

Fig. 8.24. Townsend and McCallum's curves for log a/p, plotted against X/p, for He gas. The data of Townsend and Ayers are shown, together with Dúnlop's calculated curves. Note the excellent agreement obtained between theory and the later observations.

those computed by Dunlop. It is seen that their data appear not to be seriously off, although the range covered is inadequate for a direct comparison.

Just prior to World War II, W. S. Huxford (5) and R. W. Engstrom (12) studied the current in pure A with Ba and Cs-Ag-O photosensitive electrodes. The values for a/p in A of both investigations, where they overlapped those of Kruithoff and Penning, lay well on the latter's curves, with, however, considerable more dispersion. Huxford (5), in his earlier paper, reported an eventual decline in a/p, with the highest values of X/p beyond the range of Kruithoff and Penning's data. This was not confirmed in the later work of Engstrom, and it

TABLE 8.5

Bowls's Values of α/p as a $f(X/p)$ for Pure, Mercury-free N_2

X/p	α/p	X/p	α/p
59	0.1189 ± 0.0073	250	2.68 ± 0.11
65	0.2128 ± 0.0067	290	3.378 ± 0.068
78	0.297 ± 0.015	320	3.58 ± 0.11
94	0.4047 ± 0.0066	350	3.96 ± 0.14
115	0.6120 ± 0.013	440	4.372 ± 0.080
140	0.961 ± 0.032	500	5.163 ± 0.085
160	1.196 ± 0.072	530	5.19 ± 0.27
195	1.898 ± 0.059	660	6.203 ± 0.008
198	1.993 ± 0.093	800	7.19 ± 0.40
215	2.215 ± 0.30	1,000	7.58 ± 0.18

TABLE 8.6

Hale's Values of α/p as a $f(X/p)$ for Pure, Mercury-free H_2

X/p	p (mm)	α	α/p	X/p	p (mm)	α	α/p
22.7	17.60	0.715	0.041	252.6	0.475	1.310	2.757
24.0	12.50	0.500	0.040	271.4	0.468	1.369	2.928
30.6	8.50	1.045	0.123	277.9	0.475	1.459	3.071
32.3	9.30	1.200	0.129	299.0	0.475	1.520	3.200
45.5	7.70	1.320	0.172	306.4	0.360	1.177	3.268
52.3	4.20	1.000	0.238	328.4	0.335	1.280	3.820
61.9	3.23	1.076	0.334	337.4	0.290	1.120	3.870
68.6	5.10	2.000	0.392	362.0	0.355	1.342	4.010
74.7	1.02	0.809	0.444	392.6	0.270	1.160	4.290
85.0	1.13	0.654	0.578	424.0	0.283	1.263	4.463
100.0	1.20	0.943	0.785	448.0	0.250	1.184	4.736
130.4	1.15	1.144	0.995	452.0	0.270	1.280	4.750
136.2	0.94	1.020	1.085	481.0	0.283	1.378	4.870
144.7	0.76	0.850	1.119	516.0	0.283	1.473	5.210
146.0	1.15	1.411	1.220	536.0	0.250	1.323	5.290
153.8	0.91	1.053	1.157	600.0	0.190	1.100	5.810
164.7	0.668	0.907	1.358	663.5	0.190	1.149	6.050
175.8	0.910	1.543	1.690	694.5	0.190	1.159	6.120
209.6	0.668	1.374	2.056	787.8	0.165	1.032	6.260
219.7	0.910	2.044	2.245	833.5	0.120	0.730	6.180
228.0	0.475	1.193	2.380	867.0	0.120	0.757	6.300
240.0	0.450	1.163	2.540	916.7	0.120	0.805	6.700

has generally been assumed to have been spurious, caused by failure of the electrons to achieve equilibrium in the field. The data of these workers on α/p will not be reported, but considerable attention will be paid to their evaluation of the second coefficient.

TABLE 8.7

Kruithoff's Data on $\eta = \alpha/X$ as a $f(X/p)$ for Pure
A, Kr, and Xe, Reduced to $0°$ C.

X/p $V/\mathrm{cm}\times\mathrm{mm}$	Argon 100	Krypton 100	Xenon 100	X/p $V/\mathrm{cm}\times\mathrm{mm}$	Argon 100	Krypton 100	Xenon 100
2.0	—	—	—	60	1.546	1.545	1.110
2.2	—	—	—	70	1.695	1.711	1.315
2.5	—	—	—	80	1.805	1.838	1.497
2.8	—	—	—	90	1.894	1.946	1.664
3.2	—	—	—	100	1.977	2.035	1.804
3.6	—	—	—	120	2.079	2.193	2.000
4.0	—	—	—	140	2.142	2.288	2.152
4.5	—	—	—	160	2.177	2.354	2.280
5.0	0.0048	0.0031	—	180	2.204	2.399	2.384
5.5	0.0067	0.0044	—	200	2.213	2.417	2.470
6	0.0093	0.0061	—	240	2.199	2.416	2.577
7	0.0161	0.0110	—	280	1.154	2.383	2.635
8	0.0259	0.0180	0.0024	320	1.097	2.343	2.645
9	0.0384	0.0281	0.0040	360	2.036	2.294	2.622
10	0.0576	0.0414	0.0064	400	1.975	2.236	2.600
11	0.0805	0.0587	0.0098	450	1.891	2.159	2.565
12	0.1075	0.0789	0.0143	500	1.814	2.089	2.505
14	0.171	0.132	0.0275	600	1.672	1.951	2.417
16	0.240	0.198	0.0476	700	1.540	1.815	2.298
18	0.311	0.270	0.0749	800	1.423	1.690	2.184
20	0.383	0.345	0.1091	900	1.320	1.573	2.074
22	0.454	0.422	0.1478	1,000	1.228	1.467	1.977
25	0.561	0.535	0.2136	1,200	1.074	1.284	1.795
28	0.672	0.644	0.2869	1,400	0.952	1.138	1.637
32	0.816	0.782	0.395	1,600	0.854	1.019	1.495
36	0.939	0.917	0.506	1,800	—	0.922	1.377
40	1.076	1.045	0.619	2,000	—	0.839	1.267
45	1.220	1.191	0.754	2,400	—	—	1.087
50	1.343	1.321	0.882				

The data of Bowls and of Hale in pure N_2 and pure H_2 are not too satisfactory, in that they do not accurately cover a large enough range of X/p. This arises from reduced electrode diameter and range of spacing. The few values of Geballe and Harrison, shown in table 5.2, do not agree at all with the data of Bowls and of Hale. The data on air and O_2 with mercury contamination are unsatisfactory, and work on these gases, covering a limited range of X/p, should be repeated, covering especially the lower X/p values, even though the data of Geballe and Harrison should be good over a limited range. It is probable that better and more extensive data on pure O_2 are of importance. Finally, the gases used in cloud chambers, and particularly a few of the more standard mixtures used in Geiger counters, merit being studied. Until they are, the endless futile controversies of the counter "gadgeteers," who cannot spend the time to take basic data, will bedevil the literature indefinitely.

It is probable that the methods of measurement of the first Townsend coefficient are now so clearly established as to present no controversial issues. The need for accurate data on standard gases has, in recent years, become great, because of the many industrial applications of gaseous discharge mechanisms. Therefore, it would appear proper for future studies to be made at the U. S. Bureau of Standards, or at some other standards laboratory, since there is no particular incentive to doing this sort of work on the part of the research workers who are currently studying gaseous breakdown.

§ 6. Discussion of Observations, Including Augmentation of a by Processes Other than Direct-Impact Ionization.

A. *Effect of Ionizable Impurities; the Penning and the Hale Effects.*

It is now of interest to discuss certain details of the later observations, beginning with those of Bowls, Hale, and Penning. Referring to figure 8.18, showing the data of Bowls in pure N_2, the first curve, labeled Pt, is that for a very clean, mercury-free tube, with Pt electrodes. It is seen that a/p is low. The result obtained when a minute globule of Hg was distilled into the tube is shown in the curve marked Hg. The data of Posin, Townsend, and Masch agree with the Hg curve. Some of Posin's points are indicated by crosses, while those of Bowls are triangles. In this curve, at 1 mm pressure, the Hg was present roughly to 0.1%; but it was much less in percentage at higher pressures. It is seen that the presence of Hg raises a/p by 17% at the top of the curve. The ionization potential of Hg is 10.4 volts, and that of N_2 is 15.5 volts, with many excited and some metastable levels in N_2 between 6.14 and 15.5 volts. Metastable levels occur at 6.14 and 9.77 volts, and perhaps higher, while dissociation occurs at 9.6 volts.

R. S. Mullikan has found that 10.4 volts can be transferred by active N_2. An atom of N combining with an excited atom gives a molecule excited to 11.5 volts which may be metastable. Calculation shows that at $X/p = 100$, with a Maxwellian energy distribution, the direct ionization of the Hg present by electron impact could increase a/p by 1%. It is thus clear why the presence of Hg increases a/p, since it takes energy of excitation of N_2 molecules and converts it to

§6

TABLE 8.8

Kruithoff's Data on α/p as a $f(X/p)$ for Pure Ne, Reduced to $0°$ C.,
Compared to Townsend and McCallum's Values

X/p	Kruithoff α/p	Towsend and McCallum α/p	X/p	Kruithoff α/p	Townsend and McCallum α/p
2.0	6.5×10^{-4}	—	22	0.225	—
2.2	7.9×10^{-4}	—	25	0.276	0.34
2.5	0.00115	—	28	0.328	—
2.8	0.00157	—	30	—	0.43
3.2	0.0023	—	32	0.398	—
3.6	0.0032	—	36	0.469	—
4.0	0.0042	—	40	0.540	0.63
4.5	0.0059	—	45	0.629	—
5.0	0.0080	—	50	0.715	0.80
5.5	0.0104	—	60	0.882	0.99
6.0	0.0133	—	70	1.027	—
7.0	0.0204	—	80	1.198	1.29
7.5	—	0.30	90	1.348	—
8.0	0.0290	—	100	1.493	1.57
9.0	0.0398	—	120	1.757	1.79
10.0	0.0501	0.058	140	1.999	—
11.0	0.0622	—	160	2.219	2.19
12.0	0.0748	—	180	2.453	—
12.5	—	0.108	200	2.596	2.53
14.0	0.1016	—	240	2.890	—
15.0	—	0.152	280	3.156	—
16.0	0.1302	—	320	3.309	—
18.0	0.1607	—	360	3.452	—
20.0	0.1924	0.240	400	3.560	—

ionization of Hg atoms. To get rid of this Hg contamination, Bowls ultimately had to disassemble his tube and treat all parts with dilute HNO_3. It may be added that the curve for the second Townsend coefficient with Hg contamination was typical of all the curves previously observed, and gave values of γ of the same order of magnitude. The curves with Hg absent were quite different.

In order to change the work function of the cathode, besides contaminating it with Hg, Bowls distilled some very pure Na metal into the tube. To his surprise, the curve for α/p lay even *higher* than with Hg contamination above the curve for pure N_2. This appears strange indeed, since Na is supposed to have a vapor pressure of 10^{-10} at $22°$ C. It is clear, however, that the increase in α/p to a maximum of 25% above the pure N_2 at high X/p can only be ascribed to an

Kannuluk and Penning's values of $\eta = \alpha/X$ as a $f(X/p)$ in Ne-A Mixtures, Reduced to 0° C., for Various Quantities of A
(Mean Values of $100\eta = 100\,\alpha/X$)

% Argon	0	10^{-4}	3.10^{-4}	10^{-3}	3.10^{-3}	0.01	0.1	1	10	100
0.5	—	0.008	0.021	0.050	0.095	0.146	0.048	—	—	—
0.6	—	0.026	0.065	0.158	0.298	0.461	0.309	0.021	—	—
0.7	—	0.051	0.125	0.302	0.569	0.879	0.75	0.068	—	—
0.8	—	0.076	0.185	0.444	0.835	1.28	1.26	0.148	—	—
0.9	—	0.097	0.237	0.568	1.07	1.65	1.68	0.263	—	—
1.0	—	0.116	0.281	0.670	1.26	1.94	1.99	0.408	—	—
1.2	—	0.146	0.347	0.827	1.55	2.38	2.54	0.76	0.0113	—
1.5	—	0.175	0.410	0.969	1.81	2.79	2.97	1.24	0.0385	—
2.0	0.033	0.203	0.461	1.07	2.00	3.07	3.43	1.88	0.105	0.0095
2.5	0.046	0.221	0.484	1.11	2.06	3.15	3.67	2.27	0.201	0.0259
3.0	0.064	0.238	0.498	1.12	2.06	3.14	3.71	2.58	0.319	0.0576
4.0	0.106	0.272	0.522	1.12	2.01	3.05	3.70	2.93	0.590	0.108
5.0	0.159	0.313	0.546	1.10	1.94	2.91	3.64	3.11	0.852	0.203
6.0	0.221	0.358	0.575	1.09	1.87	2.78	3.56	3.22	1.12	0.383
8.0	0.362	0.476	0.664	1.11	1.77	2.56	3.33	3.23	1.50	0.56
10.0	0.501	0.607	0.768	1.15	1.73	2.40	3.22	3.20	1.77	0.74
12.0	0.623	0.728	0.851	1.18	1.69	2.27	2.98	3.14	1.94	1.08
15.0	0.772	0.866	0.963	1.24	1.65	2.13	2.79	3.07	2.18	1.36
20.0	0.962	1.06	1.11	1.32	1.58	2.01	2.58	2.97	2.37	1.71
25.0	1.103	1.17	1.23	1.38	1.57	1.93	2.43	2.87	2.50	1.99
30.0	1.210	1.27	1.31	1.43	1.56	1.88	2.30	2.80	2.58	2.18
40.0	1.351	1.37	1.41	1.48	1.58	1.81	2.15	2.67	2.63	2.23
50.0	1.430	1.44	1.46	1.51	1.57	1.75	2.06	2.58	2.63	2.19
70.0	1.482	1.48	1.49	1.51	1.54	1.66	1.93	2.32	2.54	2.13
100.0	1.493	1.49	1.49	1.49	1.49	1.53	1.79	2.08	2.38	1.97
150.0	1.406	1.41	1.41	1.41	1.43	1.46	1.60	1.77	2.08	
200.0	1.298	1.30	1.30	1.30	1.31	1.34	1.42	1.55	1.79	
250.0	1.182	1.18	1.18	1.18	1.20	1.22	1.27	1.36	—	
300.0	1.073	1.08	1.08	1.08	1.09	1.11	1.15	1.22	—	
400.0	0.890	0.89	0.89	0.89	0.89	0.89	0.90	0.93	—	

TABLE 8.10

Townsend and McCallum's (8) Values of
a/p as a $f(X/p)$ for Pure He

X/p	a/p
12	0.095
25	0.29
32.5	0.413
50.0	0.675
60.0	0.76
97	1.11

easily ionizable gaseous impurity, present to at least the same extent
as the Hg. The conclusion drawn is that the action of the ionization
currents on the Na and N_2 present created some rather volatile compound of Na, perhaps one of the azides. It is not impossible that
traces of H_2 present coming from walls might form $NaNH_3$, or similar
volatile compounds. That a compound is formed which absorbs active
photons produced by electron impact near the anode in N_2, is shown
by the fact that with Na and Hg the very high photoelectric peak
from excited N_2 on the pure Pt cathode is wiped out, even though
the Na-coated Pt surface is far more photoelectrically sensitive to
light than is Pt. This photon absorption by the Na and Hg content
of the gas goes to increasing a/p at the cost of a second coefficient.
What the compound is, and that such compounds form under discharge
conditions with Na, is a problem meriting spectroscopic study.

The action of excited states in ionizing atoms of lower ionizing
potentials is, of course, an example of the very important inelastic
impacts of the second class, discovered by James Franck and G.
Cario. Its importance in changing the value of a was first noted by
F. M. Penning in the work on Ne-A mixtures to be reported. There
the metastable states were responsible for the action. This phenomenon is called the "Penning effect," in honor of its distinguished
discoverer. That photoelectric ionization of certain easily ionizable
impurities occurs as an effective process, was undoubtedly present
in Bowls's work with a sodium-coated cathode. It was only the later
observations by Hale of decreases in photon γ at the cathode, with
simultaneous increases of a above that in pure H_2, that clearly indicated the increased ionization to differ from the Penning effect. This
photoelectric increase in a by means of ionizable impurities should
thus be called the "Hale effect."

It should be stated at this point that where photoelectric action in the gas, and metastable action in the gas, produce the ionization of impurities near the scene of creation of the photons and metastables by the avalanche impacts, the effect will be reflected by equation 8.3, viz., $n = n_0 \epsilon^{ax}$. The action causes an increase in a by addition of a quantity Δa, such that $a + \Delta a = a'$, with a' on occasion much greater than a. If, however, the metastables, and notably the photons, produce their effects near the cathode, then the resulting relations are of the form

$$(8.18) \qquad n = n_0 \, \epsilon^{ax} \Big/ \Big[1 - f\theta g \, \epsilon^{(a-\mu)x} \Big],$$

and the second coefficient, in this case $f\theta g$, becomes important.

Reference to figure 8.19 for Pt and Na, or NaH-coated electrodes in H_2, shows these effects even more strikingly. The curve marked Pt shows the values for pure H_2 with a Pt electrode in the absence of Hg. The data obtained by Ayers, which should have applied to pure H_2 from a Pd tube, are shown in the short, dashed curve. Obviously, the failure to flame and bake out the glass vessel used by Ayers gives higher values for lower X/p than Hale observed in materially purer H_2, using liquid-air freezing.*

The curve marked Na is that obtained by using H_2 into which Na has been distilled. The circles are for a pure Na cathode; those with squares are for one that is photoelectrically supersensitive, with a coating of NaH. This coating was formed by running a glow discharge in H_2, with Na in the tube. Here again is evidence of a volatile Na compound that is highly ionized by avalanche photons from the neighborhood of the anode. The peak in a/p coincides with a trough in the γ curve, indicating an absorption of gas photons around $X/p = 250$ *to ionize the gas* near the photon source, instead of liberating photoelectrons from the cathode. There is also a second peak, at X/p around 700 to 800, which is again reflected in a dip in the secondary electron emission from the cathode. Obviously, the active constituent *in the gas* is being ionized by two groups of photons, or by quenching of their excited emitters, which appear with the electrons at two different values of X/p. In pure H_2 there is no such behavior. It may be added that these data on the behavior of Na were corroborated in 1939 by results of F. Ehrenkrantz (29) on the effects of Na on sparking potentials in A, N_2, and H_2, with and without Na. In A, where *no volatile Na compounds form*, and only γ for the cathode surface is affected by Na, the lowering of V_s is only 8%. With N_2 and H_2, the lowering of the sparking potential is so great that it can only be

---

*Rose confirmed this for low X/p.

ascribed to changes in α/p as well as in γ. This was confirmed by very heavy predischarge currents before sparking with Na in N_2 and H_2, but not in A. Conversion of all the Na to NaH by prolonged sparking, or by heating the cathode to 600° C. and the gas in the gap to above 300°, destroyed the effect of Na. It must also be noted that the curve for α/p as a function of X/p where this effect occurs has two points of tangency with the line from the origin instead of one, and some lines from the origin cut the curve in four places.

Analogous tendencies, produced by mixing a more easily ionized gas with a less readily ionized one, are seen in the work of Kruithoff and Penning, which will be presented in some detail.

Kruithoff and Penning (4), in making their measurements, used a procedure that was somewhat different from that conventionally used. They had a monitored, steady photoelectric source i_0. They kept the field strength X constant at a constant p. They did not plot i against x, but instead plotted i against V, the potential used. This is equivalent to plotting i against x, for $V/x = X$ is constant in the uniform field, and as x increases, V increases. It must be noted that they began their measurements of x at close proximity between anode and cathode, using a very small x and a correspondingly low V and low p. This brought out details that would not be noted at larger values of x, and that the group in the Philips laboratory had been interested in observing for other reasons.

Figure 8.22 shows the results in Ne + 0.01% A, with curves for several values of X/p. Figure 8.23 shows a similar set of curves for $X/p = 3.36$, and different percentages of A in Ne. The curve for 100% pure Ne is seen in figure 8.23 as the lowest flat curve, rising at a value of $V = 21$, the ionizing potential of Ne. Thus, until electrons go a distance x, corresponding to $V = 21$ volts, such that they can acquire an energy of 21 volts, Ne is not ionized and $i = i_0$. On the other hand, if a trace of A is present with an ionization potential of 15.86 volts, the current begins to rise at lower values. With 0.01% A present, the chance is very small that the A will be ionized directly by impact with the electrons that have 15.86 e.v. of energy. On the other hand, Ne is excited beginning at 16.6 e.v., and the excited atoms, especially the metastable state at 16.6 e.v., can readily ionize A. Thus, the sharp rise observed at 16.6 e.v. is caused by the ionization of the trace of A present by the Ne metastables.

The rise of current by this process is rapid. As x, and thus V, further increases, there is no great increase in current until the distance x_2 is reached, at which V is 33.2 or 2(16.6) e.v. At this point, the average electron that has excited the Ne once will have regained the ionizing energy after the second distance x equivalent to 16.6 volts has been traversed. As noted, the initial spread of energy of the photoelectrons in i_0, plus the statistical nature of the ionizing acts, rounds out the sharp corners of the steps at x_1, x_2, and x_3. As V and x increase further to 3, 4, and 5 times 16.6 volts, the dispersion of the phenomena gradually erases the sharp peaks. Thus, when the curves are observed at distances x of some 10 ionizing free paths, or 166 volts, the discontinuities begin to disappear, and the standard, smooth Townsend curves result. It is seen that when using data in this region, corrections for contact potentials, etc., are in order. The greater is X/p, as seen in figure 8.22, the more rapidly the curves smooth out. This comes from the fact that at high X/p the potential difference over a free path is relatively high. Thus, in a few free paths the electrons gain an energy greater than the ionization potential of Ne. Hence, direct ionization of Ne is greater, and excitation and indirect ionization by excited states are less common. The steps disappear, and efficiency of ionization is less, because ionizing efficiency decreases as electron energy gets higher.

As the concentration of argon increases from the order of $10^{-3}\%$, where the rarity of argon atoms yields only a small increase in ionization, the ionization observed increases with concentration. This increase continues until about 0.12% A. Thereafter, the argon atoms become so numerous that they are ionized and excited directly at potentials below and near the excitation potential of neon. They reduce the average energy of the electron swarm, reduce the excitation of neon, and increase the excitation of argon atoms, which do not contribute to the ionization. Thus, the discontinuities decrease and the currents decrease as the argon concentration exceeds 1%. Direct ionization of argon does not count until really high argon concentrations are reached, and then is not so effective as the metastable action. It is particularly of interest to note how much i, and thus α, is increased over that in pure neon with 0.12% A.

One very interesting feature of the curves of figure 8.23 is the initial decline of current from zero to 16.6 volts. In that region little or no excitation of Ne can occur, and only a few electrons lose energy to argon or ionize it, as it is too dilute. But as V increases, x also increases. The photoelectrons are emitted from the cathode with some one volt of initial energy. Consequently, even in a gas at zero potential, if x is small enough, electrons will leave the cathode and reach the anode. As the distance x increases with V at constant X, the *back diffusion* of the electrons to the cathode increases, so that fewer and fewer of the electrons reach the anode. Since the field is then constant as x increases, more and more scattering molecules are interposed between anode and cathode without a compensating increase in the field to draw the electrons across. Hence, it is not strange that when x reaches some value dependent on X, the electrons cease to cross, and the current begins to increase only when ionization sets in.

The use of A atoms in Ne or He, or of Hg in A, Ne, and He, to give ionization below energies at which A, Ne, or He are ionized by direct electron impact, may be invoked to create ions cumulatively in quantity, with no electron-energy loss to excitation. The action is produced directly, by converting the energy given to metastable atoms of the appropriate inert gas at low X/p to ionization of the sparse population of the admixed gas, e.g., A in Ne, or He or Hg in A, Ne, or He. As noted in the curves discussed, the action of the small amount of readily ionized admixture increases the value of a materially. Such action can be detected in spark discharges by marked lowering of the sparking threshold, which is effectively reduced on illumination by light from the inert gas being used. In one set of experiments on microwave breakdown, S. C. Brown and A. D. MacDonald (45) used Hg to quench He metastables, in order to observe the action of ionization without the dual loss of electron energy to excitation and ionization of He. The gas used for this purpose was characterized by the symbol Heg.

In view of the importance of the Penning effect, attempts have been made to measure the cross sections for ionization of A by Ne and He metastables. The first attempt was that of A. A. Kruithoff and M. J. Druyvesteyn (46). Actually, they only succeeded in measuring the ratio of the cross section σ_i for ionization of A by Ne metastables to σ_d for de-excitation of Ne metastables in impacts with normal Ne atoms. The value of the ratio inferred was $\sigma_i/\sigma_d = 4.1 \times 10^4$.

More recently, M. A. Biondi (47) has evaluated these quantities separately, under the nicely controlled conditions in microwave breakdown. His direct values for cross sections σ_i for A in He and Ne, and of σ_d in He and Ne, are shown in table 8.11.

The ratio σ_i/σ_d for A in Ne is 2.9×10^3, which is 0.1 that reported by Kruithoff and Druyvesteyn, as observed under more difficult conditions. Their value of σ_d could not well have been higher, as it is doubtful if the purity of their Ne exceeded the purity of Biondi's. Their error must have lain in an overestimate of σ_i.

B. *Indirect Ionization by Associative Processes, and Related Effects.*
The Penning and Hale processes, which act to increase a by mechanisms other than direct-impact ionization, are not the only

TABLE 8.11

Cross Sections for Ionization of A by He and Ne Metastables and for
De-excitation of He and Ne Metastables, According to Biondi (47)

Parent Gas	Gas Ionized	Ionization σ_i in cm^2	Destroying Gas	Destruction σ_d in cm^2
He	A	9×10^{-17}	He	9.6×10^{-21}
—	Hg	1.4×10^{-14}	—	—
Ne	A	2.6×10^{-16}	Ne	8.9×10^{-20}

processes of this sort. It has recently been discovered that a number
of associative processes, some of which involve and destroy metastable states even in pure gases, may contribute to the value of α,
sometimes in a measure equal in magnitude to the direct ionization.
These processes were first noted in studies in photoionization, where
positive ions were detected at photon energies below the ionization
threshold. The very large cross sections for such processes were,
however, not discovered until the microwave techniques, accompanied
by mass-spectrographic and mobility determinations, made this possible. These processes may be listed as follows:

Applicable to Inert and Monatomic Gases with Metastable States.

(1) $B + [e + \frac{1}{2}mv^2 = (E_i - \lesssim 3\ ev)] = B^* + e$. $B^* + B \to B_2^+ + e$.

(Hornbeck-Molnar process)

(2) $B^m + B^m$ (usually $^3P_2$ states) $\to B^+ + B + e$.

Applicable to All Gases.

(3) $B^* + B \to B_2^+ + e$, if $E_{i_{B_2}} < E_{e_{B^*}} + E_{B_2}$.   (Mohler process)

Two other reactions of importance at higher pressures, not directly
leading to ionization and increase in α, but changing carriers or qualities of active photons, should be listed in this connection:

(4) $B^+ + 2B \to B_2^+ + B$.   (Molecular ion formation)

$B_2^+ + e \to B^* + B \to 2B + h\nu$.   (Recombination and delayed photon emission)

(5) $B^m + 2B \to B_2^* + B \to 3B + h\nu$.   (Delayed photon emission—Colli-Facchini effect)

Reaction 4 leads to creation of faster ions, and results in a delayed line emission; it also *removes* carriers by recombination. Reaction 5 removes metastable atoms, and yields photons foreign to gas

B, which are not absorbed and can reach the electrodes, while B^* photons are absorbed and delayed.

Before proceeding to discuss reactions 1, 2, and 3 in detail, some general remarks must be made. First, the measurements of a are made statically on a steady-state process, where the temporal sequence of events, even with delays of a millisecond, plays no role. All that is measured is the *total* value of a. If, however, extra electrons are created through the Hale, Penning, Hornbeck-Molnar, metastable interaction, or Mohler process, then the measured a is composed of a by direct-impact ionization, and a by secondary interactions; i.e., $a = a_1 + a'$. Now a' can range from n times a_1 with n large, as in the Penning effect, through equality, as in the Hornbeck-Molnar effect at its optimum, down to small fractions of a_1, as in the Hale effect. In addition, a will not essentially act just at the site of creation of the agent producing this effect, but may be diffused by motion of the carrier or dispersion of the photons, etc. Thus, the effect of such action will be to diffuse the ionization spatially along the avalanche path, so that the assumption that $n_x = n_0\, \epsilon^{ax}$ may not strictly hold, since electrons created by photon action nearer the cathode will have more progeny, while those nearer the anode will have less progeny.

If the dispersion is really large, the effect takes on a character more akin to a cathode action, since most creation is within a few free paths of the anode. This action, in an extreme case, could be such that it is no longer proper to write that $a = a_1 + a'$, where a is measured from $n = n_0\, \epsilon^{ax}$. Such extreme action usually is not observed, as an a' merely produces a change in the second coefficient, γ.

More important is the fact that the ionization produced by a' is temporally delayed relative to the creation of electrons by direct impact. In the static studies of a this is of no great importance. In dynamic studies of breakdown processes, where the direct ionization events are resolved on the oscilloscope screen, a_1 will only be noted there, and the delayed effects of a' will show up in a lagging current pulse and delayed secondary-effect pulses, stemming from retarded arrival of the ions or photons. If a' is comparable with a_1, the effect will be to give an avalanche pulse which is diffused in time, and yields an average time of advance which is greater than the electron-transit time. If the delays are short, the apparent avalanche-crossing time may be of the order of twice the electron-transit time. Otherwise, the delay will act to alter the shape of the section of the oscilloscope pattern associated with ion movement in the gap.

Potentially much more serious than diffusion in space and time is the possibility that a' is pressure-dependent; for it must be noted that reactions 1, 2, and 3 depend on collisions with neutral atoms during the lifetime of various types of states. Reactions 1 and 3 should vary as pressure below a critical pressure where collision time is equal to the average lifetime of the excited state. They also depend on the amount of excitation, while reaction 2 depends on the square of the excitation and on the collision frequency of the metastable states compared to their lifetime. If this gas is pure enough, reaction 2 and reaction 4 are the ones that remove metastable states, so that these reactions vary with pressure even if the concentration of metastables is independent of pressure, since collisions of type 4, which remove metastables, increase with pressure relative to those of reaction 2.

However, as has been noted so far, measurement has shown that a/p is a $f(X/p)$ only, and is not independently a function of p. The reason for this observation is that the critical pressure is low, so that while in many reactions, such as the Penning process and the Hornbeck-Molnar process, a'/a_1 is of the order of or greater than unity, measurement of a is limited in the range of p that can be used, because of the limitations of the length of uniform-field gap lengths and the relatively low values of a, except at higher X/p. Thus, as will be shown in detail in the case of the Hornbeck-Molnar process, all measurement has been conducted in regions of pressure where a/p is independent of pressure. However, since this may not always be true, this contingency must be borne in mind and watched for.

It is now proper to consider the Hornbeck-Molnar process and the resulting Hornbeck paradox (54). Accompanying the creation of a electrons per cm advance in the field direction by electron impact in avalanches, there are created in the gases many excited states of atoms. Among the excited states in the inert gas group atoms He, Ne, and A, there are quite a number lying within 1.5 to 0.3 e.v. of the respective ionization potentials. Many metastable atoms are also produced. On collision with neutral atoms, these excited states, lasting some 10^{-7} sec or more, produce *molecular* ions and electrons. Furthermore, in time two He metastable atoms can get together and yield He^+ ions and electrons. The first process occurs very rapidly, $\sim 10^{-7}$ sec, while the second process requires perhaps a millisecond to materialize. Both processes are pressure-dependent; the fast process becomes so when the collision frequency is of the order of or less than 10^7 per sec. Of interest here is the fast process. Now the quantity ω, which represents the number of excited atoms within 1.5 e.v. of ionization created per cm advance of the electron, will under some conditions be commensurate with a. The ratio $f = \omega/a$ will vary with electron energy, and thus as X/p varies. It will start with values greater than unity when the average electron energy is below the ionizing potential, and will decline rapidly as the average energy exceeds the ionizing potential.

Using pulsed discharges, J. A. Hornbeck has recently evaluated what amounts to $\omega/a = f$ in three inert gases; He, Ne, and A. Electrons n_0 in number, liberated by a light pulse of short duration in a Townsend gap of length d, moved to the anode, yielding avalanches. These created atomic and molecular ions by two processes; one by direct ionization, the other indirect, by excited atoms, as indicated above. The number of ions formed is then:

$$\text{Atomic ions} = n_0 \, a_i \, \epsilon^{(a_i + a_m)d}.$$

$$\text{Molecular ions} = n_0 \, a_m \, \epsilon^{(a_i + a_m)d}.$$

Here, a_i is the number of atomic ions formed per cm per electron, and a_m is the number of molecular ions formed per cm per electron.

The absorption by the anode of electrons released from the cathode by positive ions arriving at one molecular ion transit time and at one atomic ion transit time, gives discontinuities in the pulse seen by the oscillograph. Each discontinuity is proportional to the rate of arrival of the positive ions, and to the secondary emission coefficients γ_m and γ_i for the molecular and atomic ions, as seen in chapter 9.

Let Δm be the measured discontinuity at one molecular ion transit time and Δi that at one atomic ion transit time. Then,

and

$$\Delta m \propto \gamma_m \, a_m \, v_m \, \epsilon^{(a_i + a_m)d}$$

$$\Delta i \propto \gamma_i \, a_i \, v_i \, \epsilon^{(a_i + a_m)d},$$

with v_m and v_i the respective drift velocities. Thus, it is possible to set

$$\frac{\Delta m}{\Delta i} = \frac{\gamma_m}{\gamma_i} \, \frac{a_m}{a_i} \, \frac{v_m}{v_i} \, .$$

Now

$$v_m = d/T_m \text{ and } v_i = d/T_i,$$

whence

$$\frac{T_m}{T_i} \frac{\Delta m}{\Delta i} = \frac{\gamma_m}{\gamma_i} \frac{a_m}{a_i} .$$

Here T_m and T_i are the two observed transit times. Now γ_m/γ_i is not accurately known for the two types of ions, except for He_2^+ and He^+ on W at low energies. This value, recently observed by H. D. Hagstrum, is about $\gamma_m/\gamma_i = 0.6$, i.e., molecular ions are approximately half as effective as atomic ions at this sort of liberation. The ratio may vary with the ions, but since the energy available, forming He_2^+, Ne_2^+, and A_2^+, is close to 0.8 or more of the ionization value for He, Ne, and A, the estimate is reasonable and may be used as a basis for discussion. Thus,

$$\frac{1}{0.6} \frac{T_m}{T_i} \frac{\Delta m}{\Delta i} = \phi = \frac{a_m}{a_i},$$

which is open to experimental evaluation. However, a_m must be expressed in terms of the process of formation from excited atoms and impacts with molecules.

Now

$$a_m = \omega \left[\frac{\text{Probability } A^* \to A^+}{\text{Probability that excited atoms decay} + \text{probability that ion forms}} \right].$$

The denominator of the bracket is unity. Call r the mean lifetime of A^*. Let $\bar{c}$ be the random atomic velocity, σ_m the cross section for ion formation from A^*, and σ_d the cross section for destruction of excited atoms, and let N be the number of molecules per cm³. Then the expression above reduces to

$$a_m = [\omega] \left[\frac{\sigma_m \bar{c} N}{1/r + (\sigma_m + \sigma_d) \bar{c} N} \right]$$

and

$$\phi = \frac{a_m}{a_i} = \frac{\omega}{a_i} \left[\frac{N}{\dfrac{1}{\sigma_m \bar{c} r} + \left\{ \dfrac{\sigma_m + \sigma_d}{\sigma_m} \right\} N} \right].$$

Now $\omega/a = f$ depends only on the velocity distribution and average energy of the electron swarm, and is, as noted, a function of X/p. The constants σ_m, σ_d, and r are atomic properties of the gas in question. The number N is related to the normalized pressure p, in that $N = N_1 p$, with N_1 the number of molecules per cm³ at 1 mm. For convenience, set a critical pressure in mm at which $(1/Z)$, the reciprocal of the collision frequency in the gas, is equal to or commensurate with r. As

$$z = \sigma_m \, \bar{c} \, N_c = \sigma_m \, \bar{c} \, N_1 \, p_c = 1/r,$$

$$p_c = 1/(\sigma_m \, \bar{c} \, N_1 \, r),$$

with N_1 the number of molecules per cm³ at 1 mm pressure. Then if σ_d is set equal to zero, as in any case it is small, it is possible to cancel out N_1, and to evaluate ϕ as

$$\phi = \frac{a_m}{a_i} = f \left(\frac{p}{p_c + p} \right) \text{ or } \frac{1}{\phi} = \frac{a_i}{a_m} = \frac{1}{f} (1 + p_c/p).$$

Thus, $1/\phi$ is measured from $\Delta i T_i / 0.6 \ T_m \Delta m$ as a function of p at constant X/p, and is plotted in the form of $1/\phi$ against $1/p$. A rough linear plot was obtained for each X/p, even though the points scattered badly. The slope of the plot gave $\omega/a = f$, and the intercept and the slope gave p_c. If the value of p_c is known, together with c and N_1, the quantity $\sigma_m r$ can be computed. If $p \gg p_c$, ϕ is independent of p. All excited states form molecular ions, and the result is that $a = a_{obs} = (a_m + a_i)$ is increased over a_i, but there is no pressure dependence, and a_{obs}/p is a function of X/p alone. If $p_c \gg p$, then $1/\phi$ varies linearly with p_c, but so few molecular ions form that a is not altered above a_i, and $a/p = f(X/p)$.

Actually, the observed slopes and intercepts of the lines vary with X/p, as one would expect, so that $p \sim p_c$. At low X/p, the observed first Townsend coefficient, $a_{obs} = a = (a_m + a_i)$, will have a/p vary with X/p and with pressure p, a fact which is not considered in the Townsend theory, and is quite surprising. Before drawing conclusions, it is best to give results of the measurements as derived from experiment and from the rough theory given. (Table 8.12.)

The decrease in f with X/p is in the expected direction, reasonable in magnitude, and the values are sensible. They furnish useful exemplary data for discussion of many processes.

Next it is worth noting that the values of $\sigma_m r$ are roughly 0.5 and 0.9×10^{-22} cm² sec. If atomic-collision cross sections are of atomic magnitude, i.e., 10^{-16} cm², then r is of the order of 10^{-6} sec. If now the collision cross section is of such a magnitude that $1/z$ is comparable with r, the ratio ϕ will be pressure-dependent, and the observed $a = (a_m + a_i) = a_i (1 + \phi)$ will have a/p depend on pressure and on X/p. The experimental observations leading to the evaluation of $\sigma_m r$ actually yielded the pressure p_c at which this occurs, as 4 mm, 10 mm, and 8 mm in He, Ne, and A. If in A, $\phi = 1$, then $a = a_i (1 + \phi)$,

TABLE 8.12

Hornbeck Values for $\sigma_m \tau$, p_c, and $f = \omega/\alpha$, for the Creation of Molecular Ions
of the Inert Gases He, Ne, and A by the Hornbeck-Molnar Process

Gas	X/p	$\sigma_m \tau$ in cm^2 sec	p_c mm Hg	$f = \omega/\alpha$
He	12	0.43×10^{-22}	4	1.0
	14	0.61×10^{-22}	4	0.7
		ave. 0.5×10^{-22}		
Ne	15	0.68×10^{-22}	10	0.6
	20	0.34×10^{-22}	10	0.4
		ave. 0.5×10^{-22}		
A	30	0.98×10^{-22}	8	2.5
	35	0.85×10^{-22}	8	2.0
	40	0.79×10^{-22}	8	1.6
		ave. 0.9×10^{-22}		

so that at least one-half of the value of α observed will vary rather
rapidly with p. At an X/p of 30, this occurs at about 6 mm pressure.
Thus, if α were measured in A at $X/p = 30$ and a $p \sim 5$ mm, both α
and η would vary with p as well as X/p. Experimental studies on α
and η in inert gases were all done with the Townsend techniques,
and gap distance x was 1 cm and less. If in such a study $X/p = 30$
with $p = 10$ mm, then $X = 300$ volts/cm and $V = 300$ volts. In varying
x at constant $X/p = 30$ to evaluate α, p could not have been less
than 10 mm, since at $x = 0.1$, V would have been less than 30 volts,
and terminal energies would hardly have been achieved.

It is therefore probable that practically all data on α were taken
with p well above p_c, so that the *Hornbeck anomaly* of a Townsend
coefficient varying with p and X/p has not been observed. If the
author's technique is used, with longer x and lower p, it is possible
that data on α/p will appear in which α/p is a function of p and X/p
in these inert gases.

It should be recognized that the variation of α/p with p and X/p
violates the principle of similitude, and would alter the famous
Paschen's law, which says that the sparking potential is a function
of pd for the gap only, and not of p and pd. That the Hornbeck anomaly
has not been observed in measurements of sparking potential V_s as
a function of pd, can only mean that V_s, in the region of X/p between
12 and 40 in the gases He, Ne, and A, has been carried out primarily
above 10 mm pressure. This happens to be a correct deduction, for

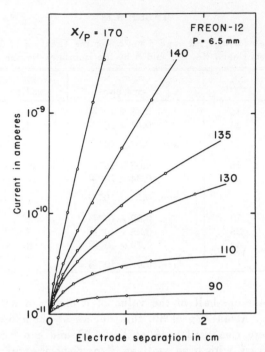

Fig. 8.25. Curves of Geballe and Harrison for log i/i_0 against plate separation in freon 12, showing curvature caused by attachment η in an exaggerated form.

observation of a spark breakdown in A at $X/p = 30$ would require a large product pd, such that pressures used would be quite large. In fact, the minimum sparking potential in all of these gases is never below 95 volts, and pd_m is in the region of 1 mm × cm, which means that X/p will be at least 100. Thus, long before breakdown at X/p as low as 40 is observed, p will be near 100 mm.

Accordingly, it is unlikely that the Hornbeck anomaly will affect observed values of sparking potential, and Paschen's law will be obeyed as observed. With care, the anomaly should be discovered in a pressure variation of a/p, but in long gaps only.

§ 7. Measurements of the First Coefficient a in Gases Where Electrons Attach to Form Negative Ions.

Recently, in an endeavor to account for the spark-suppressant properties of CF_3SF_5, R. Geballe and M. A. Harrison (11) attempted to measure a in this gas. Electrodes were copper, 9 cm in diameter, in a 5-liter flask. Ultraviolet light struck the cathode through 400

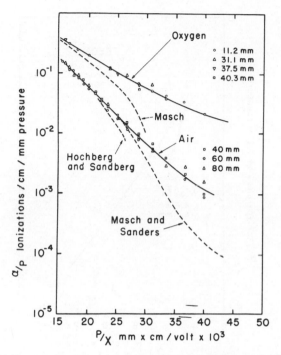

Fig. 8.26. Curves for a/p as a $f(p/X)$ for air and O_2, after Geballe and Harrison, compared with the data of Masch and Sanders and of Hochberg and Sandberg (9).

holes in the anode within a circle of 2 cm diameter. The plate distance could be varied from 1 mm to 40 mm. The log i/i_0 curves plotted against d for a fixed X/p were not linear in this gas. Log i/i_0 had low values at small d, which increased faster than linearly with d, but ultimately flattened out to fairly good lines at higher values of X/p before rising again. This action was ascribed to electron loss from the avalanches by attachment to form negative ions. To test this further, Geballe and Harrison investigated pure O_2 and pure H_2. In O_2 they varied d, with large plates from 0.5 mm up to 40 mm, at pressures from 11 to 40 mm Hg, with X/p 27.5 to 75 volts per cm per mm.

Curves for log i/i_0 in O_2 and freon 12 are shown in figures 8.13 and 8.25. The curves for H_2 gave strictly linear plots, as for other observers, but the values of a were quite low. In O_2, however, the curves were of the form noted in CF_3SF_5 and freon 12, except that the curvatures were not so pronounced. The initial rises were pronounced at low X/p and high p, but became imperceptible above

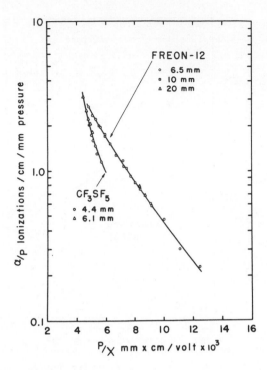

Fig. 8.27.   Curves for α/p as a $f(p/X)$ for freon 12 and CF_3SF_5, according to Geballe and Harrison.

$X/p = 65$ at the pressures used. Neither Masch nor Sanders had observed these nonlinear log i/i_0-x plots, because of the limited ranges of x used. Masch did note a very sharp drop in his α/p-X/p curves at low X/p, and attributed this to attachment, but did not investigate further. In air, both the Masch and Sanders curves for α/p as a $f(X/p)$ show a drop of such form that it would not have been noticed. These deviations are shown in figure 8.26, where α/p is plotted to logarithmic scale against p/X, so that deviations at low X/p are exaggerated. There it is seen that at higher X/p, the values of Geballe and Harrison do not differ seriously from earlier data on the scale of plotting used. Figure 8.27 shows the values of α/p as a $f(p/X)$ for freon 12 and CF_3SF_5.

To analyze the data, Geballe and Harrison proceed as indicated below, following an earlier theory of J. J. Thomson. It is assumed that electrons create new electrons at the rate of α per cm advance in the field direction. It is also assumed that an electron may attach to make a negative ion at the rate of η per cm advance in the field direction. Once attached, the electron still yields part of the current, but is unable to create further electrons. The existing values of X/p are such that the negative ions, in this instance O^- ions, do not lose the electrons in molecular impacts. As will be noted later, the ions are formed by dissociative attachment on impact of electrons of more than 3.61 e.v. of energy on O_2 molecules. The heat of dissociation of O_2 is 5.06 e.v., and the energy of O^- formation is 1.45 e.v. Call n_e the number of electrons at any point x, and n_i the number of ions at any point x. Let n_{e0} electrons leave the cathode by external photoelectric action at the cathode per second, i.e., at $x = 0$. Then, following the procedure of Townsend, it is possible to write

(8.18a) $$dn_e = n_e\, a\, dx - n_e\, \eta\, dx = n_e\, (a - \eta)\, dx$$

and

(8.18b) $$dn_i = n_e\, \eta\, dx .$$

Then,

(8.18c) $$\log \frac{n_e}{n_{e0}} = (a - \eta)\, x , \quad \text{so that} \quad n_e = n_{e0}\, \epsilon^{(a - \eta)\, x}$$

and

(8.18d) $$dn_i = n_{e0}\, \epsilon^{(a - \eta)\, x}\, dx .$$

Now, $n_i = 0$ at $x = 0$, and $n_i = n_i$ at $x = d$.
Thus,

$$n_i \Big]_0^{n_i} = \frac{n_{e0}}{a - \eta} \left[\epsilon^{(a - \eta)\, x} \right]_0^d$$

and

(8.18e) $$n_i = \frac{n_{e0}\, \eta}{a - \eta} \left[\epsilon^{(a - \eta)\, d} - 1 \right] .$$

The total current to the anode is then $n = n_e + n_i$, so that

(8.18f) $$n = n_{e0}\, \epsilon^{(a - \eta)\, d} + \frac{n_{e0}\, \eta}{a - \eta}\, \epsilon^{(a - \eta)\, d} - \frac{n_{e0}\, \eta}{a - \eta}$$

$$= \frac{(a - \eta)\, n_{e0}\, \epsilon^{(a - \eta)\, d}}{a - \eta} + \frac{n_{e0}\, \eta}{a - \eta}\, \epsilon^{(a - \eta)\, d} - \frac{n_{e0}\, \eta}{a - \eta} .$$

As shown in the equation to follow, this makes

(8.18g) $$n = \frac{n_{e0}}{a-\eta}\left[a\,\epsilon^{(a-\eta)d} - \eta\right],$$

so that the ratio of the currents is

(8.18h) $$\frac{i}{i_0} = \frac{1}{a-\eta}\left[a\,\epsilon^{(a-\eta)d} - \eta\right].$$

Typical observed curves for $\log i$ as a function of d in O_2 at various X/p are shown in figure 8.13. The curves can be fitted by equation 8.18h, and yield at once values of a and η. The values of a as a function of X/p are shown plotted as $\log a/p$ against p/X, together with Masch's data, in figure 8.26. At $X/p > 65$, where attachment ceases to be important, the curves of Masch and of Geballe and Harrison are fairly close together. The values of η/p observed as a function of X/p are shown in figure 5.11. They lead to a coefficient of attachment h which is nearly constant with electron energy. This attachment sets in roughly at an energy of 2.6 e.v., with $h = 2 \times 10^{-4}$. Since the true average electron energies in O_2, as related to X/p, are not too accurately known, the agreement with onset of a dissociative attachment at 3.61 e.v. is quite good.

Before closing the discussion of this method, certain peculiarities of these equations and their bearing on measurement must be pointed out. Ordinarily, a is measured by evaluating the slope of the log i/i_0 - x plots, assuming that $n = n_0\,\epsilon^{ax}$. Now the plots of $\log i/i_0$ for equation 8.18h are nonlinear. If $a \gg \eta$, the deviation from linearity is hard to detect, as seen in figure 8.28 for air, where only the data below 1 cm show a distinct curvature. Even if there is more curvature, as in O_2, if conditions as to avoidance of fluctuation of potential and i_0 are not ideal, so as to reduce scatter, curvature will be hard to detect if the *range* of values of X is limited to large values, even when a is only slightly larger than η. In this case, the additive terms in the equations are negligible, and the coefficient deduced will be $a - \eta$. If d, because of experimental limitations, is confined to small values (a few mm), deviations will hardly be apparent. The slope of the straight line drawn through the experimental points will, in this case, have no simple interpretation. It is apparent, then, that good stability and a long *range* of values of x are needed to evaluate a and η properly.

§ 8. **Theoretical Evaluation of a/p as a Function of X/p.**

It is quite natural that the first attempt at a theoretical evaluation of a/p should have been made by Townsend (19). At the time, the

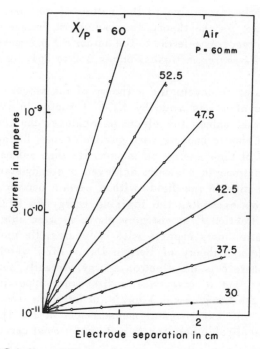

Fig. 8.28. Geballe and Harrison's curves for log i/i_0 against x in air.

experimental data were limited in range to the higher values of X/p, and the Bohr atom and the Franck and Hertz experiments still lay in the future. Thus, it is not strange that the theory should have been deficient in some respects. It was notable in two respects. In the first place, it recognized the existence of some critical *ionization threshold* or *potential*, and *endeavored to evaluate this long before the measurements of Franck and Hertz*. Secondly, although faulty in its deduction, it led to an analytical form

$$(8.10) \qquad a/p = A \, \epsilon^{-\dfrac{BE_i}{X/p}},$$

which closely resembles a relation that was later more rigorously deduced by von Engel and Steenbeck for high X/p (20). Thus, it is not strange that it can be fitted to the upper curved section of the range in X/p. However, the evaluation of the ionization potential E_i from the experimental curves, owing to the rather primitive underlying theory, *was not successful*. These values of E_i derived by the theory were from 30% to 50% higher than the present accepted values, and were particularly insensitive to the nature of the gas, which is not really the case. As the theory does not merit further discussion at this point, the reader is referred to the author's *Fundamental Processes of Electrical Discharge in Gases*, pages 358 to 361, for more detailed discussion.

The first step in developing a theory of the process on the basis of the nuclear atom was made by K. T. Compton in 1917-1918 (31). He assumed that unless the electrons achieved the ionizing energy E_i, they made elastic impacts with gas molecules, losing only a fraction $f = 2m/M$ of their energy on impact. He then assumed that eventually the electrons in a swarm achieved a steady-state Maxwellian energy distribution in the field, with a certain number in the swarm having energies exceeding the ionizing energy E_i. Of these, he assumed that a fraction P_i at energies above E_i were able to ionize the atoms in kinetic-theory impacts with molecules. He took the expression for P_i from a theory of Bergen Davis (32), which placed $P_i = (E - E_i)/E$, where E is the electron energy. Actually, this assumption is not correct, but it *resembles* a first-order approximation to the rising part of the Compton-van Voorhis, or later, the Tate-Smith curves (33), derived from experimental measurement of P_i. The correct approximation, applicable between E_i and $3E_i$ for most curves, reads

$$(8.19) \qquad P_i = \beta\,(E - E_i) = \beta_1 \left(\frac{E - E_i}{E_i} \right).$$

With the theory cited above, Compton was able to get a reasonable fit with the observed values of α/p in He, obtained over a limited range by E. W. B. Gill and F. B. Pidduck (7). These early values of α/p in He were obtained on He of questionable purity, as the later data of Townsend and McCallum showed. Compton's theory marked a great step in advance. However, besides employing the inaccurate value of P_i of Bergen Davis, it was defective in several ways, in that it neglected inelastic impacts to excitation, it assumed a Maxwellian energy distribution, and it antedated the knowledge of the Ramsauer electronic free paths.

The next attempt was made by F. M. Penning (34) in 1926, using the basic theory developed in 1925 by G. Hertz. Penning neglected the loss of energy in elastic impacts; recognized, but did not apply, losses to excitation; used Ne gas, since the Ramsauer free paths are constant there; and used the Compton-van Voorhis ionization probability. The theory was adequate in its time, but was still too primitive to lead to satisfactory conclusions.

With the advance in knowledge of the electron-energy distributions in a field in a gas, it is not surprising that the next attempt at evaluation should have come from one of the pioneers in establishing these distributions. In 1932, M. J. Druyvesteyn (35) attempted to derive a theory. In doing this, he was hampered by inadequate knowledge of the electron cross sections for the excitation of Ne. Assuming his distribution law with an arbitrary constant involving the unknown factor, he used Townsend and McCallum's data (8) on a/p in Ne to evaluate the constant. These data permitted Druyvesteyn to analyze the wall current observed in the positive column of a neon glow-discharge tube. The computation, based on the constant calculated from a/p, yielded reasonable results, so that Druyvesteyn concluded that his theory lay in the right direction. When the measurements on excitational cross sections for Ne and other gases by Maier-Leibnitz became available, Druyvesteyn directly derived the relation for the energy distribution in fields above that at which ionization by collisions in Ne set in. Thus, in 1936, he obtained fairly good agreement (35) with Townsend and McCallum's values in Ne, for which his assumption of constant Ramsauer free paths was valid.

Apparently, simultaneously with Druyvesteyn's 1932 attempt, von Engel and Steenbeck (20) in their book used a direct, classical kinetic-theory approach to the evaluation of a/p as a $f(X/p)$. Their treatment, in outline, was the same as was later successfully and more generally developed by Emeléus, Lunt, and Meek (36). Assuming a Maxwellian energy distribution, von Engel and Steenbeck *calculate* the energy and electron-drift velocities in a fashion similar to that used by K. T. Compton in chapter III. Using the fractional loss of energy f, and assuming high values of X/p, they approximate the earlier equation 8.10, deduced by Townsend.[8] This relation, using the observed ionization potentials, approximates some of the observed curves for high X/p in inert gases.

In 1936, K. G. Emeléus, R. W. Lunt, and C. A. Meek (36) developed a general theory for the evaluation of the first Townsend coefficient along classical kinetic-theory lines.[9] This theory permits the insertion of the appropriate energy-distribution function, as well as the observed values of P_i, expressed in functional form. It requires, as well, the data on the electron-drift velocity. Thus, from the calculated energy distribution $f(E)$ for any given X/p range, the values of P_i,

---

[8] They recognized the error in Townsend's deduction.

[9] Contemporaneously, F. E. Null (20) developed a similar analysis, but did not leave the distribution function unspecified.

and the drift velocity v, a/p can be computed. It contains relatively few assumptions, and constitutes the most satisfactory general theory, as it pushes the theoretical assumptions troubling Compton back into the experimental evaluation of $f(E)$, P_i, and v. Beyond this, probably the only superior theory would be the complete, esoteric, kinetic-theory analysis, based on the methods outlined in Chapman and Cowling's theory for nonequilibrium gases (I.53). This analysis has not been undertaken to date, and may present formidable mathematical difficulties.

The analysis developed by Eméleus, Lunt, and Meek was applied by them to the calculation of a/p as a function of X/p, using the data they had at hand. These were data obtained by Townsend and his school on the electron-drift velocity and the average electron energy, assuming Maxwell's distribution law and a distribution law shortly before derived by Townsend, which is a peculiar version of the Druyvesteyn distribution law, discussed in chapter IV. The values of P_i were taken from Compton and van Voorhis, and all values were correlated with X/p, using the values of the average energy $\eta(3/2)kT$, evaluated by Townsend's group for the gases air, N_2, H_2, and A. Considering the fact that the Maxwellian distribution law is *generally not applicable*, the agreement between theory and experiment observed in the intermediate range of X/p values is remarkably good for air, N_2, and H_2. In the more extreme ranges of X/p, high and low, agreement is not good. In argon, where the energy distribution is known to be far from Maxwellian, the theory deviates by orders of magnitude. The general character of the relation, as well as the agreement obtained, makes this approach to a theoretical evaluation the one to be developed in this section.

Later developments follow logically on the theory of Eméleus, Lunt, and Meek. In 1937, J. A. Smit (30) had developed a general theory for the calculation of the energy-distribution function, if excitation, ionization, and Ramsauer free-path variation were known. He applied this to the calculation for the distribution of energy in He at X/p values of 3, 4, 6, and 10. In 1948, S. H. Dunlop (30), in Eméleus' laboratory, extended the calculations of Smit to values of X/p of 3, 4, 5, 6, 8, and 10, and to the higher values of average energy. With these data, and suitable values of P_i and v from the Tate-Smith curves and the data of Bradbury and Nielsen and of Townsend, he calculated the curve of figure 8.24 for a/p as a $f(X/p)$, which, on extrapolation, appears to agree well with Townsend and McCallum's data.

Still further pursuing the studies, H. D. Deas and K. G. Eméleus (37) have recently reversed the procedure, in that they used observed data of a/p as a function of X/p, of P_i, and of v, to determine the *electron-energy distribution law*. Actually, the law may not be evaluated uniquely or directly; but by using various assumed forms of the law, it is possible to decide which one is the most suitable, used within the observed range of values of X/p. The conclusions reached in this study will be discussed after the theory of Eméleus, Lunt, and Meek has been presented in detail.

By definition, the quantity a represents the number of *new* electrons created by one electron in advancing one cm in the field direction. In one second, the electron advances v cm in the field direction, in virtue of its drift velocity. Thus, the number of new electrons created per second by one electron is $a v$. In one second, owing to its random drift velocity c, an electron covers a zigzag path of c cm in the gas. Now all electrons having a velocity greater than the root-mean-square velocity C_i, corresponding to the ionizing energy $E_i = \frac{1}{2}mC_i^2$, will be able to ionize. The chance that an electron will ionize in traversing one cm of random motion in the gas is P_i. This quantity can be evaluated experimentally from the ionizing cross section as a function of its velocity c. Such studies have been made by Compton and van Voorhis, and later by Tate and Smith.

Let $P_i(c)$ represent the chance of ionizing in one cm of random path in the gas at one mm of gas pressure. In one second, at a pressure of p mm, the electron with energy above E_i will make $pcP_i(c)$ electrons. Now the chance that an electron has a velocity c is given as $f(c)dc$, where $f(c)$ is the *form* of the energy-distribution law existing in the gas at the value of X/p assumed. If the number of impacts per second that can ionize is multiplied by the chance that they have a velocity c, the quantity $pcP_i(c) f(c)dc$ represents the number of ions created by electrons of velocity c per second,[10] provided c is greater than C_i. The total number of electrons created per second in this fashion is the integral of the individual velocity regimes, from C_i to infinity. It is thus possible to write that

$$(8.20) \qquad\qquad av = p \int_{C_i}^{\infty} c\, P_i\,(c)\, f\,(c)\, dc.$$

---

[10]It should be noted that C_i is the critical r.m.s. average value of the ionizing velocity. The average velocity corresponding to C_i is represented by $\bar{c}_i$.

Since v may be expressed in terms of the electron mobility, $v = k_e X = (760/p) K_e X$, where K_e is the reduced electron mobility and is itself a function of X/p, the relation 8.20 may be written:

$$(8.21) \quad a/p = \frac{I}{v} \int_{c_i}^{\infty} c \, P_i(c) f(c) \, dc = \frac{1}{760 \, (X/p) \, K_e} \int_{c_i}^{\infty} c \, P_i(c) f(c) \, dc \, .$$

It is also possible to express c in terms of equivalent electron volts of energy by setting $\frac{1}{2}mC^2 = Ve/300$, with V expressed in volts. Thus, in a more convenient form, it is possible by means of $c = \sqrt{2e/300m} \, \sqrt{V}$, to write

$$a/p = \frac{\sqrt{\dfrac{2e}{300\,m}}}{v} \int_{E_i}^{\infty} V^{\frac{1}{2}} \, P(V) \, F(V) \, dV$$

or

$$(8.22) \qquad a/p = \frac{\sqrt{\dfrac{2e}{300\,m}}}{760 \, K_e(X/p)} \int_{E_i}^{\infty} V^{\frac{1}{2}} \, P(V) \, F(V) \, dV \, .$$

Here V is the electron energy expressed in volts, and E_i is the ionization potential in volts.

For most gases used, v or K_e is given by measurements of Bradbury and Nielsen or of the Townsend group, where the gases are clean, as indicated in chapter III. The quantity $P_i(V)$ can be approximated for most gases in the range of X/p used from the linear rising portion of the Tate-Smith curves (33) by the analytical form:

$$(8.19) \qquad\qquad P(V) = \beta (V - E_i) \cdot$$

This holds from E_i to $3E_i$, with β a characteristic of each gas. This leaves only $F(V)$ undetermined. Where $F(V)$ is known, as Dunlop (30) has shown, it is possible to compute a/p at once.

The results of the studies of Emeléus, Lunt, and Meek for H_2 and for air are indicated in tables 8.13 and 8.14. There it is seen that with a Maxwellian energy distribution in these gases, the theory is in relatively good agreement with observation between values of X/p of about 20 and 200. At lower values of X/p, the agreement is not so satisfactory. For argon, the values computed were from two to four orders of magnitude too high when the Maxwellian distribution was assumed. The deviation for argon is not unexpected, for in this range of values of electron energies, the Ramsauer free paths in A,

TABLE 8.13

Emeléus, Lunt, and Meek's Calculations of α/p as a $f(X/p)$ in H_2

$\overline{V}$ Ave. Energy in Volts	X/p	Drift Velocity $v \times 10^{-7}$	Calculated α/p	Observed α/p	$\dfrac{\text{Calculated}}{\text{Observed}}$
2	13	0.47	0.0004	0.015	0.027
3	21	0.73	0.015	0.027	0.55
4	31.5	1.20	0.089	0.090	0.99
5	43.5	1.82	0.23	0.26	0.88
6	57.5	2.63	0.40	0.50	0.80
7	72.5	3.62	0.57	0.81	0.70
8	88	4.62	0.77	1.12	0.69
9	105	5.75	0.95	1.45	0.65
10	123	6.98	1.10	1.75	0.63
12	161	9.50	1.33	2.24	0.59
14	203	12.30	1.47	2.66	0.55

TABLE 8.14

Emeléus, Lunt, and Meek's Calculations of α/p as a $f(X/p)$ in Air

$\overline{V}$ Ave. Energy in Volts	X/p	Drift Velocity $v \times 10^{-7}$	Calculated α/p	Observed α/p	$\dfrac{\text{Calculated}}{\text{Observed}}$
2	20	0.90	0.0002	—	—
3	36	1.35	0.011	0.012	0.93
4	55	1.84	0.074	0.077	0.96
5	75	2.25	0.24	0.29	0.84
6	100	2.70	0.53	0.72	0.74
7	130	3.19	0.92	1.33	0.69
8	163	3.74	1.39	1.95	0.71
9	198	4.23	1.90	2.60	0.73
10	239	4.73	2.44	3.33	0.73
12	334	5.78	3.59	4.86	0.74
14	455	6.62	4.88	6.48	0.76
16	595	7.58	6.14	7.87	0.78

Kr, and Xe undergo violent fluctuations, and especially such as to give a distribution law with very few electrons in the high-energy portion.

These conclusions are further amplified by the study of the form of the distribution law by means of the observed variation of α/p as a function of X/p, together with data on v and $P(V)$, by H. D. Deas and K. G. Emeléus (37). In this study, they used the Maxwellian energy distribution and the Druyvesteyn distribution laws for diatomic gases, air, H_2, and N_2. The data on a/p used were those of Sanders for air, Posin and Bowls for N_2, and Hale for H_2. The use of the Druyvesteyn law for all these gases gives values that are lower than those obtained with a Maxwellian distribution. In theory, at large values of the average electron energy $\bar{E}$, the Maxwellian and Druyvesteyn forms converge toward asymptotic values, $7.3 \times 10^7 \ v^{-1} \ b\bar{E}^{3/2}$, and $6.7 \times 10^7 \ v^{-1} \ b\bar{E}^3$, respectively, in which the Maxwellian constant is slightly larger. At very low X/p, however, the value of a/p falls off much more rapidly in the Druyvesteyn law, as might be expected from its functional form. Thus, the observed values of a/p in all cases fall between the two laws, somewhat favoring the Maxwellian form relative to the Druyvesteyn form. However, the values a/p, $\bar{E}$, and v are not too accurate, so that conclusions must not be pushed too far.

It is probable that the distribution is slightly off a Maxwellian in the direction of the Druyvesteyn law at very low X/p, but is *not* of the Druyvesteyn form. At higher X/p, the values derived from both the Maxwellian and Druyvesteyn laws bracket the observed data. However, the data are too crude to distinguish the form of the laws, since the difference in the laws makes relatively small changes in a/p only. It should be added that the reason for the relatively closer adherence to the Maxwellian energy form for the diatomic gases lies in the relatively slow change in Ramsauer free paths with energy for these molecules, and probably to a larger extent in the onset of inelastic impacts to vibration or excitation at low electron energies. In O_2, excitation sets in near 1.62 e.v., and in N_2, by at least 4.2 e.v. In the inert gases, these impacts do not set in until energies near 10 e.v. are reached. Such inelastic impacts will act to reduce the cumulative influences of the variation of electron free paths with energy.

In the case of He, the variation of the Ramsauer free paths with energy is such as to prolong the asymptotic foot of the distribution curve to high energies. As the computations of Smit and of Dunlop take this into account, agreement between experiment and theory is probably as good as the experimental data permit.

In Ne, the distribution of energies in the range of X/p below excitation is sensibly the Druyvesteyn distribution, and the calculations should agree with experiment if the distribution is not upset by inelastic impacts. The studies of Druyvesteyn (35) and of Smit (IV.10) on energy distributions led Druyvesteyn (21) to set up an approximation to the Smit relation for electron-energy distribution when excitation and ionization occur. This may be seen in the equation to follow.

$$f(E) = C \; \epsilon^{\left\{ - \frac{[3K_h(E_2)]^{\frac{1}{2}} \, E}{Xe\lambda} \right\}}.$$

In this, $K_h(E_2)$ is a constant probability of excitation at an average energy $E_2 = E_e + 2/3 \, (E_i - E_e)$, with E_i the ionization energy, E_e the excitation energy, λ the free path, and X the field strength. Using this, the number of ionizations per cm^3 per sec is given by

$$j_i = \int_{E_i}^{\infty} f(E) \left(\frac{2E}{m} \right)^{\frac{1}{2}} \frac{K_i(E)}{\lambda} \, dE,$$

in which $K_i(E)$ is the probability of ionization. Druyvesteyn and Penning set the drift velocity v as $v = 0.655 \, (Xe\lambda)/(m\bar{E})^{\frac{1}{2}}$, with $\bar{E}$ the average electron energy. This leads to an expression for $\eta = a/X$,

$$\eta = \frac{j_i}{X \int_0^{\infty} j(E) \, dE} = \frac{3}{\lambda^2 eX^2} \frac{\int_{E_i}^{\infty} E^{\frac{1}{2}} f(E) \, K_i(E) \, dE}{\int_0^{\infty} \frac{f(E) \, dE}{E^{\frac{1}{2}}}},$$

which, except for some constants, is in essence the same as the equation of Eméleus, Lunt, and Meek.

Druyvesteyn and Penning prefer, however, to use an energy-balance equation which they assert is less sensitive to the form of the distribution law than is the latter method. It is clear that in the methods cited, the value of η or a depends critically on the form of the tail of the distribution law, and this is seriously altered by the Ramsauer free paths. However, the average energy is not so seriously altered, as noted in chapter IV. Actually, the advantage is illusory, for the same inaccuracy is introduced more subtly in that the multipliers are average, or fixed, values of the energy or potential into probabilities of excitation and ionization which vary with energy. The energy-balance equation used by Druyvesteyn and Penning reads

(8.23) $\qquad 1 = \eta \, E_i + \sum_n \xi_{hn} \, V_{hn} + \sum_n \xi_{vn} \, V_{vn} + Kf\bar{V} + \eta\bar{V}.$

In this relation, n designates the different excitational states, e.g., $n = 1$, 2, 3, etc., for the first, second, third, etc., level. Here ξ_{h1} represents the coefficient of excitation of the first level per volt, ξ_{v1}, that of the first coefficient for vibrational excitation per volt, etc., while V_{h1}, V_{v1}, etc., represent the excitation potentials corresponding to the states. The quantity $\bar{V}$ is the average potential in volts corresponding to the energy, i.e., $\bar{V} = \bar{E}/e$. The quantity f is the fractional loss of energy per impact in elastic impacts, e.g., $(8/3)$ (m/M), and K represents the elastic-collision frequency per volt with E_i, the ionization potential. If the various quantities are known, η

can be computed. Omitting the vibrational losses for the inert gases, and considering the elastic losses as negligible at the higher X/p used, it is possible, from existing data and by using certain approximations, to compute η for Ne and A. The values of $\bar{V}$ or their equivalent $\bar{E}$ can be computed from the distribution law given. They can also be taken from measurements of the Townsend group (III.1), (III.4). This is achieved by a simplified form of equation 8.23, that reads

$$(8.24) \qquad \eta = \frac{1}{V_i} \left[1 + r + \frac{\bar{E}}{E_i} \right].$$

The ratio r of excitation to ionization is defined by

$$r = \sum_n \xi_{hn} \, V_{hn}/\eta V_i.$$

The distribution law used is $F(E) = $ constant for $E < E_h$, and above E_h, the distribution is that given above. The quantities K_h and K_i are taken as

$$(8.25) \qquad K_h = a_h \frac{E - E_h}{(E \, E_h)^{\frac{1}{2}}} \text{ and } K_i = a_i \frac{E - E_i}{(E \, E_i)^{\frac{1}{2}}},$$

which makes r read

$$(8.26) \qquad r = \frac{a_h}{a_i} \left(\frac{E_h}{E_i} \right)^{\frac{1}{2}} \epsilon^{\left[\frac{(3K)^{\frac{1}{2}}}{Xe\lambda} (E_h - E_i) \right]} = \frac{a_h}{a_i} \left(\frac{E_h}{E_i} \right)^{\frac{1}{2}} \epsilon^{\left[\frac{C p_0}{X} \right]}.$$

The average energy $\bar{E}$ is then

$$(8.27) \qquad \bar{E} = \frac{E_h}{2[1 + Xe\lambda/(3K)^{\frac{1}{2}} E_h]} \left[1 + \frac{2Xe\lambda}{(3K)^{\frac{1}{2}} E_h} + \frac{2X^2 e^2 \lambda^2}{3K E_h^2} \right].$$

With these relations, the value of η for Ne was calculated between $X/p = 5$ and $X/p = 30$. For small values of X/p, less than 30 in Ne, the expression for η reduces to

$$(8.28) \qquad \eta = \frac{a_i}{a_h V_i} \epsilon^{-\frac{C p_0}{X}}.$$

This has

$$C = (3K)^{\frac{1}{2}} (E_i - E_h)/\lambda p_0.$$

It should be noted that where $(3K)^{\frac{1}{2}}$ appears in the relations above, it applies to the $K_h(E_2)$, the excitation probability at the peculiar mean energy, used by Druyvesteyn and Penning in their distribution

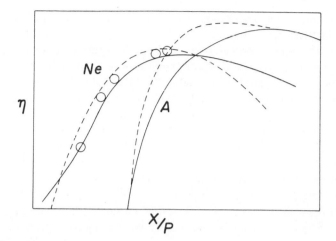

Fig. 8.29. The calculated values of log η plotted against log X/p for Ne and A, as given by Druyvesteyn and Penning from the former's theory. Experimental values are the full lines. The approximate equation gives the dashed lines, and the more accurate computation from the energy-balance equation in Ne gives the circles.

law above. The symbolism $K_h(E_2)$ has been omitted, and K used for simplicity.

Equation 8.28 has the same form as the original relation of Townsend. The experimental values of η for Ne and A are shown in a log η - log X/p plot as full lines in figure 8.29. The curves from equation 8.28 are dashed lines, and those computed for Ne from the energy-balance equation 8.24 in detail are the circles. The agreement is called "satisfactory" by Druyvesteyn and Penning (21). When it is recalled that this is a log-log plot, a "satisfactory" agreement is illusory, differences being really large. In form, the computed and observed curves show a *similar trend*, since they cross or touch in a couple of points. Likewise, curves computed for A show a similar trend relative to observation. Actually, the disagreement is of the order of a factor of 2 or more in spots. Agreement is not even good at low X/p for Ne. The type of agreement gotten by Eméleus, Lunt, and Meek is better, except in A. The type of agreement illustrates only too emphatically the care required in interpreting functional agreement from superficial observation of curves.[11] Druyvesteyn and Penning apparently did not attempt to use their relation of the type

[11] That which constitutes a satisfactory agreement depends on the individual objectives or standards, which are partly aesthetic, and are therefore not open to debate.

of Emeléus, Lunt, and Meek, since their energy distribution was not sufficiently accurate.

Actually, while the relation outlined is applicable to the solution of the problem, it is quite clear that the approximations made in computation are not particularly fortunate. Variable Ramsauer free paths are not used for argon. Probably, the loss of energy to elastic impacts can be neglected, as was done.

The relations cited, especially 8.24 in this analysis, have been used by Druyvesteyn and Penning in an inverse sense, in that other data were computed, *assuming the theory and approximations correct*, and using observed values of η. In this work, E_i, V_{hn}, and V_{vn} were known, and f was set as $(8/3)$ (m/M), which is good for inert gases. The values of η were the observed values. The average electron energy $\bar{E}$, or expressed in volts, $\bar{V}$, was computed. For N_2 and H_2, the quantities f were not known, but were computed by combining the energy-loss determinations of the Townsend school with those for the efficiency Q_{vi} of vibrational excitation, as observed by Harries and Ramien. With these data, Druyvesteyn and Penning (21), (38) calculated a set of curves for f, the percentage of energy lost to elastic impacts, to vibrational excitation, electronic excitation, ionization, and increased kinetic energy, as a function of X/p. Interesting as these relations may be, and desirable as it is to have such data, the author has no faith in the *quantitative accuracy* of these computed curves. With the very bad actual agreement (factor of 2) of η, computed from such data where known, the results derived from the inverse process, and the sketchy values of Harries and Ramien (III.17), for example, are highly questionable. On the other hand, *the curves are of academic interest* in that *they yield very useful information on the type of relations between processes*. Such data are urgently needed in discharge studies. The author has no quarrel with the basic theory or the objectives. However, he believes that Druyvesteyn and Penning pushed very uncertain data beyond their accuracy in deriving those particular curves. He warns against basing any conclusions on quantitative data derived from the curves. The curves given for Ne (Ne + 1% A), A, N_2, and H_2 are shown in figures 8.30 and 8.31, and will be referred to later.

As indicated above, in regard to the evaluations of η or a/p in Ne, the author must agree with Deas and Emeléus (37) that experiment and theory appear still to be somewhat inadequately reconciled, as seems also to be true for A. This deficiency is probably owing to the considerable uncertainty in the form of the distribution law at values of X/p, where inelastic impacts with varying Ramsauer free

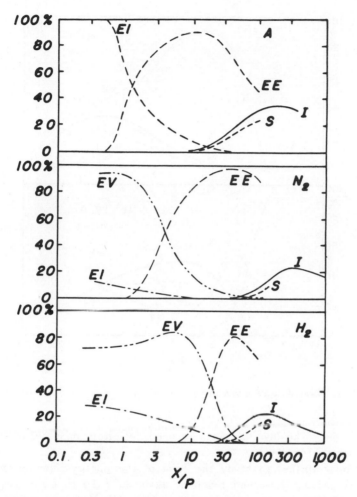

Fig. 8.30. Approximate computed curves showing the percentage of electron energy at any given X/p for A, N_2, and H_2 gases going to various actions. El = loss to elastic impacts. EE = excitation of electronic levels, leading to light emission and metastable states. I = ionization by direct impact. S represents the average kinetic energy of the electrons, viz., their "temperature." EV = energy going to excitation of vibrational levels. The fraction of energy is given in per cent. S comes from Townsend's studies, and is reasonably good. The other computed values can be off by as much as a factor of 2.

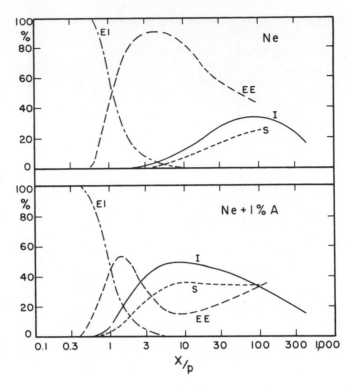

Fig. 8.31. Same data as given in figure 8.30, but for Ne, and Ne with 1% A.

paths occur. The laws obtained or used definitely admit of too many high-energy electrons.

In order further to study the form of the energy-distribution law in inert gases, Deas and Eméléus assumed $F(V)$ to have the form $A_n V^{1/2} \epsilon^{-(R_n V)^n}$, with n ranging from 3 to 10 in Ne. Here,

$$R_n = \Gamma\left(\frac{5}{2n}\right) \Big/ \bar{E}\Gamma\left(\frac{3}{2n}\right) \quad \text{and} \quad An = nR_n^{3/2} \Big/ \Gamma\left(\frac{3}{2n}\right).$$

They used V. A. Bailey's 1924 data (III.4) for $\bar{E}$ and v as functions of X/p, and Kruithoff and Penning's data for a/p. It was found impossible to get agreement between theory and experiment for any single constant value of n. At an X/p of 1.7, the best agreement was for a value of n between 9 and 10, and at an X/p of 6.7, the agreement was best when n lay between 6 and 7. They do not believe that the situation would have been much improved if better values had been used for $\bar{E}$ and v. Thus, at the present time there appears to be no suitable distribution function $F(V)$ which yields correct variations of a/p as a function of X/p for the inert gases Ne, A, Kr, and Xe. The results that have been obtained indicate a marked paucity of electrons with energies much above the mean energy, indicating that the functions fall off rapidly with energy above the mean. It is likely, as indicated by the work of Harriet Allen and of Domenick Barbiere, that this results from inelastic impacts to excitation and ionization which cannot well be included in the theory without a much more detailed analysis. It would seem best to attempt a Smit (IV.10) or Holstein (IV.14) calculation for the energy distribution in A and Ne over the range of observed values of X/p, and with this to make a proper calculation for a/p as a $f(X/p)$, as was done for He by Dunlop. This has been achieved over limited ranges of X/p by Barbiere, in a study carried out under Theodore Holstein (IV.21). The energy distributions obtained are shown in chapter IV, part one.

It may be said in conclusion that while doubtless a more complete calculation for a/p as a $f(X/p)$, using the methods of analysis for nonequilibrium gases, might lead to more satisfactory results, the direct kinetic-theory approach, as first used by von Engel and Steenbeck and later generalized by Emeléus, Lunt, and Meek, is sufficiently good for most purposes. Needed now are proper data on the average energies $\bar{E}$ in the common gases as a function of X/p, proper energy-distribution laws at these values of X/p, and consistent values of v and of a/p in gases of the same degree of purity. With these data, it is believed that satisfactory agreement can be achieved between theory and experiment, as is the case for He.

§ 9. Ionization by Collision in Nonuniform Fields.

As indicated earlier, where the electrical fields cease to be uniform, the magnitude of the electron avalanche is no longer given by $i = i_0 \, \epsilon^{ax}$, for a/p is a function of X/p, and in a nonuniform field X is a function of distance x from some reference point in the field. Thus, if i_0 electrons are generated at the surface of an inner cathode cylinder of radius a, in a coaxial cylindrical electrode system, the current i to the outer anode cylinder of radius b will be given by

(8.29)
$$i = i_0 \, \epsilon^{\int_a^b a \, dx} .$$

Now $a = pf(X/p)$, and at constant p, the field X as a function of the distance x from the axis of the system is given by

(8.30)
$$X_x = \frac{V}{2x \, \log_e b/a}$$

in this geometrical arrangement. Thus, to solve the problem and evaluate i/i_0, a must be written as

$$a = pf \left(\frac{V}{2\, px \log_e b/a} \right) ,$$

so that

(8.31) $i/i_0 = \exp \int_a^b pf \left[V/(2\, px \log_e b/a) \right] dx .$

If the analytical form of the function f is known, as is often the case over a limited range of values, then the integration can be performed. If the functional form is not known, resort must be had to a graphical integration of the quantity. In this event, the experimentally observed curve a/p as a $f(X/p)$ is available. With p constant, a curve can be plotted for a as a function of X. From equation 8.30 or similar relations, the field X, over the region of values of X needed, may be plotted against x for various values of x. With these two curves, the values of a and x may be read off for a given chosen value of X. By plotting the a-x curve so derived and calculating the area under it between $x = a$ and $x = b$, the integral is determined. It is of interest to note that in very many applications, such as would occur for the cylindrical geometry, with a small and b large, X decreases so rapidly with x that it is usually of no interest to integrate over the whole range from $x = a$ to $x = b$. The quantity a decreases very rapidly with X, and will be sensibly zero at some value of $x = x_c$ which is much less than b, which may then be used as a practical limit of integration.

Recently, E. E. Dodd (39) has found a relatively simple means of performing the integration applicable to certain geometries, including coaxial cylinders. The use of the Townsend integral, so long as the electrons are in equilibrium with the field X, has certain consequences in divergent fields, one of which should be mentioned, as it generally affects discharges in a characteristic fashion. Since only electrons ionize the gas by impact in discharge fields, while positive ions in time scales of microseconds are relatively immobile, there will be a difference in the character of the positive ion distributions left behind by the nimble electrons, depending on the sense of the field X.

If the small inner electrode radius a is the cathode, the cloud of i_0 electrons, together with their avalanches, moves outward. Now the electrons ionize cumulatively, and while at the cathode a, X is very high, so that a is high, there are few collisions near a, and ionization is slow. As the electrons advance, X becomes less, but i_0 will have been increased exponentially to i by ionizing impacts, so that the

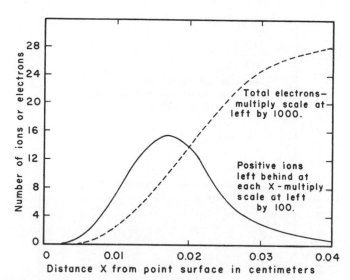

Fig. 8.32. Curve for cumulative ionization i/i_0 as a function of distance x from the cathode of small radius, as for air with coaxial cylinders, or point to plane geometry shown as dashed. The curve for distribution of ionization by collision (i.e., positive) is the full curve. Contrast this with figure 8.33.

rate of ionization is greater. Finally, as x increases toward x_c still more, X declines rapidly, and a falls to zero. Hence, despite the many electrons at $x = x_c$, there is virtually no more ionization by collision. Thus, while the *total number of electrons* increases from a to x according to the integral

(8.29)
$$i = i_0 \, \epsilon^{\int_a^x a\,dx} ,$$

as x increases, reaching a maximum at $x = -x_c$, the rate of ionization and the distribution of the relatively immobile positive ions along x represent the derivative, $d(i/i_0)/dx$ of i/i_0, which is a curve with a peak lying between a and x_c. This is shown in figure 8.32, and is a rather important feature of many nonuniform field processes where the cathode has the high field.

If now the inner cylinder of radius a is made the anode, the electrons being liberated from inside the cathode cylinder of radius b, the situation is altered. The electrons move in toward a, and begin ionizing toward a from x_c on. The number of electrons increases as x decreases, and the last ionizing acts take place when nearly all electrons are $1/a$ cm from cylinder a in the highest field X_a at a. Thus, *the ionization is most effective right near the anode*. Here again, the ionization is given by the equation to follow.

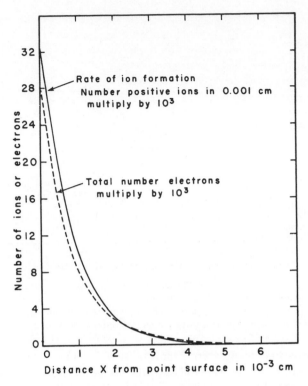

Fig. 8.33. Curves similar to those of figure 8.32,
with the anode of small radius.

$$(8.29) \qquad i/i_0 = \epsilon^{\int_{x_c}^{a} - a\,dx},$$

and *the value of this integral is the same as before.* That is, *the total number of electrons is the same, irrespective of the sense of motion,* since the algebraic signs reverse with the limits of integration. On the other hand,

$$(i/i_0)\, x = \epsilon^{\int_{x_c}^{x} - a\,dx}$$

increases as x decreases, and the curve for the number of electrons increases exponentially as x decreases to $x = a$. This curve is shown in figure 8.33.

It is to be noted that in this case $d(i/i_0)/dx$ is also an exponential, and is greatest at $x = a$, decreasing monotonically from $x = a$ to sensibly zero at $x = x_c$. Thus, the positive ions in this arrangement are placed along an exponential curve with maximum at the anode, and going to zero at $x = x_c$. This differs materially from the reverse case of electron motion *from* the inner cathode, and in actual discharges is responsible for a marked difference in behavior of the utmost consequence. Basically, the creation of positive ions at the *anode* surface when a is anode acts as an inhibitor to further ionization, for as these ions move *from* the anode, *they diffuse the anode field* and reduce X. Actually, the positive ions close to the anode *should enhance the field between cathode and anode* in the gap. This action is slightly reduced by their electrical image field in the conducting anode. When they move out into the gap a very little, they reduce the field between themselves and a (in the critical region of high X), and enhance X in mid-gap. Such conditions near a discharge threshold can act to extinguish or suppress a discharge. On the contrary, the cloud of positive ions created at some distance from electrode a when it is the cathode, enhance the cathode field by space charge. This action facilitates ionization and leads to an inherent instability of such cathodes, tending toward autocatalytic breakdown. Under appropriate conditions both these actions appear, though there are exceptions.

One more remark must be made at this point. It has been observed that when electrons are generated from a cathode in a gas, back diffusion tends to reduce the current i_0. The effect is particularly serious, as seen in chapter VII, for photoelectrons. Now there is a very interesting circumstance connected with back diffusion in divergent fields, the importance of which was first indicated in work to be described presently. Consider the negative cathode wire of relatively small radius a in the coaxial system discussed, and impose a strong field, such as would give finite values of a at the surface. The value of X/p at the surface may be very high, especially if the space charge of the positive ions created intervenes. Thus, even if the energy of the photoelectrons at emergence is 1 volt, and if the pressure is not very low, back diffusion will be relatively small compared to a plane cathode in uniform field, for the directed surface field is high and directed away from the surface, while at the cathode the electron energy is only 1 volt, contrasted to an equilibrium electron energy of 10 volts. The geometry is also somewhat against return diffusion if a is small, especially by the time the electron has advanced to once or twice $1/a$ and multiplied itself.

The positive ion space charge aids in reducing back diffusion. Thus, loss to back diffusion is less under these conditions. Now consider the reverse case of the same wire of small radius a as *anode.* The electrons drawn to it from *b* will have been continuously increasing their energy, and will have been multiplying themselves. Arrived near the anode, they will have received considerable incre- ments of energy in the last ionizing free paths, thus having gained a high random energy (of the order of 10 or more volts) relative to the energy gain over one free path. They will thus diffuse away from the anode as well as toward it, despite the high, directed field. They also will have created the maximum number of positive ions within $1/a$ of the anode surface. This positive space charge, if dense, will by its image field slightly act to reduce electron escape to the anode. Thus, while at first glance it would be expected that the electrons, after their last ionizing acts, *would at once go into the anode* in a gas, they do not do so. Those that have dissipated all or most of their high energy by ionization near the anode will be picked up by the anode field and absorbed. Those still having high energy and that are still capable of ionizing will, owing to their energy, the positive space charge created, and favorable geometry, continue to move diffusively near the anode until their energy has been largely spent in ionization. They will then be absorbed. Thus, *little of the ionizing energy gained from the field is lost.* This circumstance acts to produce the following effect, *except at very low pressures.* The total number of electrons i created in a gap by a current i_0 is practi- cally the same, despite very high fields X_a on the inner electrode, whether the i_0 electrons move from a as cathode or move to a as anode. At first sight this seems strange, as the electrons moving to a as anode do not get their full energy from the field until they practi- cally arrive at a. If they went to the anode directly from a distance $1/a$, they would dissipate an appreciable fraction of the field energy without ionization, a fraction which the electrons leaving the same electrode a as cathode would not have lost. Thus, the ratio i/i_0 would be expected to be less with a the anode than with a the cathode. In practice, the two are so nearly equal as to appear the same until the pressures fall well below 1 mm. At the lower pressures, the ratio i/i_0 for a as the cathode is some 10% greater than when a is the anode (40).

So far, discussion has been limited to the situation where the divergent fields and pressures are such that the electron everywhere has the energy appropriate to the value of X at which it finds itself. Under such conditions, a varies with distance x in the same measure as X does. Thus, the integrations and setting $i/i_0 = \epsilon^{\int a dx}$ are justified. While it is logical to expect that this will not always hold, serious consideration had not been formerly given to this contingency. In their excellent book, von Engel and Steenbeck (41), as well as W. Rogowski (41), had assumed that in the Crookes dark space in the glow discharge, the values of X/p were such that a/p followed the values of X. The rapidly changing character of the positive space-charge field of the Crookes dark space should have suggested caution in the use of this assumption. Actually, such doubts were expressed by Druyvesteyn and Penning in 1940 (21). On the basis of the functional form of a/p as a $f(X/p)$, a very complete theory of the glow discharge had been derived by von Engel and Steenbeck and by Rogowski, which at first gave fortuitously good agreement with experiment. Later data, however, seemed to indicate that something was wrong.[12]

P. L. Morton in 1938 had set up the very complete, intricate, third-order, nonlinear differential equation for the glow discharge at Massachusetts Institute of Technology, with the hope of solving it by the aid of their newly developed analyzer. When he began to look up the constants, including the Townsend coefficients, prior to solution, he was struck with the divergence of the Crookes dark-space field, and became convinced that the ionization in the Crookes dark space was such that a, as derived from a uniform field, could not remain in step with X and thus with position x. Under such conditions, it was impossible to use the $\epsilon^{\int a\,dx}$. Accordingly, Morton stated that it was possible that the true ion multiplication in the Crookes dark space could be much greater, or much less, than that given by $\epsilon^{\int a\,dx}$, where a was the conventional uniform-field function. When this was brought to the author's attention in a seminar at which Morton described his work, it was suggested that Morton test this by comparing i/i_0 in a coaxial cylindrical gap at various values of X/p and p with the calculated values of $\epsilon^{\int a\,dx}$ from Hale's data on H_2. Morton (40) undertook the measurements for his doctoral dissertation under the author's direction. In the meanwhile, G. L. Weissler and L. H. Fisher (42), studying the values of i/i_0 in confocal paraboloid gaps, had observed that the calculated i/i_0 from the field using $\epsilon^{\int a\,dx}$ was considerably *less* than the observed values in their gaps. Morton's investigation showed that his surmise had been correct, and that the currents i/i_0, under conditions of high X and low p in nonuniform field gaps, differed by several hundred per cent from those given by $\epsilon^{\int a\,dx}$. Morton's studies were later carried farther by G. W. Johnson (40), to higher pressures for H_2 and air. The reader is referred to the original papers for experimental details.

---

[12]The conditions in the Crookes dark space of the glow discharge were recently investigated by R. P. Stein (44), and still later by R. W. Warren (published in 1955), both in the author's laboratory. These workers have thrown much light on this situation.

Morton used coaxial cylinders with an all-glass, outgassed system, and H_2 gas that was mercury-free and comparable in purity with Hale's. Two inner cylinders of different radii a_1 and a_2 were used, with a fixed outer cylinder of radius b. Ultraviolet light through a quartz window and a gauze window in the anode struck the electrodes a_1 and a_2 to give i_0. Both inner and outer cylinders were used as cathode. Morton's work, especially at higher pressures, suffered from the inability to estimate i_0 above the point where cumulative ionization set in when back diffusion became bad. Johnson was fortunate in that just as he began his work, C. W. Rice (43) had solved the J. J. Thomson relation for currents with back diffusion in the case of coaxial cylindrical geometry. Morton measured i, i_0, the applied potential V, and the pressure p. The ratio i/i_0 was plotted against V for the small and large cathode cylinders of radii a_1 and a_2. At low pressures, above a potential of 25 volts, which is somewhat in excess of the ionizing potential 15.4 volts, the curves indicated that the electrons gained their energy in the high-field region near the cathodes. If they subsequently had sufficient impacts, they expended this energy in producing ions on their way to the anode. At the low pressures used, there was not much opportunity for cumulative ionization. In that event, the plots of i/i_0 against V had a curvature concave to the axis of abscissae. The distances from b to a_1 and to a_2 differed only 10%, and the voltage V was constant. Thus, the two sets of curves for a_1 and a_2 were nearly the same. At higher pressures, the curves again started at some 25 volts, but were *convex* to the axis of abscissae. This indicated cumulative ionization, since the electrons could have several ionizing impacts before they left the high field. In this case, as might be expected with the same potential V, the small electrode a_1 with its initial higher field was far more efficient at producing electrons than was a_2. These curves were not otherwise significant for the point of interest.

Cross plots were made of i/i_0 against *pressure* for constant values of V. These proved to be very interesting. One of these is illustrated in figure 8.34, where $V = 150$ volts and p ranges from 0.01 to 10 mm; with $a_1 = 0.16$ cm, $a_2 = 0.51$ cm, and $b = 4.42$ cm. It is at once noted that these curves exhibit a maximum at about 0.4 and 0.3 mm pressure for a_1 and a_2, respectively. On the same plot are shown the calculated values for $\epsilon^{\int a\,dx}$, using Hale's values for a/p. The effect is quite striking, since for electrode a_1 the values of $\epsilon^{\int a\,dx}$ are one-sixth as great as the observed values of i/i_0. This is in agreement with the findings of Weissler and Fisher on the confocal paraboloids. However, the values of i/i_0 were very low at low pressures, and again

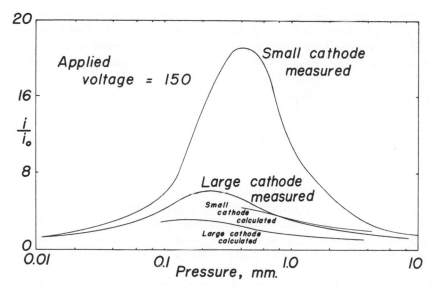

Fig. 8.34. Morton's curves for i/i_0 in H_2 as a function of pressure in mm Hg at high X/p, in cylindrical geometry, with small wire cathodes. The curves, using integrals of Townsend's first coefficient, are compared to the measured values.

fell to low values which asymptotically approached $\epsilon^{\int \alpha dx}$ at around 10 mm pressure.

The interpretation is relatively simple. At very low pressures, the electrons are directly accelerated in the high fields; they suffer few impacts, and gain energies near to those appropriate to the potential difference which they have traversed. Having gained the maximum energy on passing through the distance x_c as applied to Townsend's a, they expend this energy, producing ionization between x_c and b. At very low pressures, they meet very few molecules, even between x_c and b, and so they plunge into the anode b with most of their energy and produce few ions. As pressure increases, the electrons may lose some energy in impacts with molecules between a_1 or a_2 and x_c, but still have high energy. This they expend very effectively in ionizing between x_c and b, as they then meet enough molecules. An electron which has plenty of energy, say some 150 volts, will produce ions on the average at the rate of an ion for every 25 to 35 volts, depending on the gas. Thus, ionization would be at a maximum if the electrons gained most of the 150 volts and spent it all between x_c and b in making ions. As pressure further increases, the electrons, getting up energy between a_1 or a_2 and x_c, lose energy to elastic and exciting

impacts. Thus, beyond x_c they have not their full energy appropriate
to the fall of potential, but p is then great enough, so that they lose
all their energy in ionization between x_c and b and before they reach
the anode at b. Thus, i/i_0 declines, eventually reaching a condition
where the electrons collide often enough in the high-field region to
get the energy appropriate to equilibrium with X/p, and thus reach
the value of a, calculated on statistical grounds. It is seen that with
the losses to elastic and exciting impacts, the ionizing efficiency
shown by a is low compared to that where the energy is gained rapidly
with no loss, and spent in ionization and excitation after being
acquired.

Contrary to expectations and to the *initial interpretation* given to
the data by Morton and the author, the *inapplicability* of the Townsend
coefficient a, as measured in a uniform field, to the evaluation of
i/i_0 in equation 8.29, *is not caused by the gradient of the field*. The
more complete data of Johnson, as will be seen later, clearly indicate

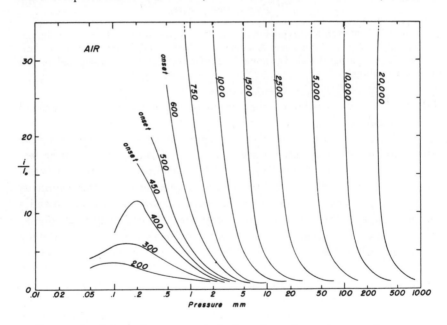

Fig. 8.35. Johnson's sequence of i/i_0 values for various maximum potentials at the small cylindrical cathode as a function of pressure in mm of Hg,
for mercury-free air. Note the peaks at low pressure, analogous to Morton's up
to 400 volts, and the curves terminating in secondary mechanisms and discharge at higher pressures. Note the shift in the peaks as potential increases.
The pressure at which the highest peaks occur represents the minimum sparking potential in air.

that the deviations from equation 8.29 set in just above values of X/p at which $\eta = a/X$ is a maximum, or just above the tangent to the a/p-X/p curve by a line from the origin. That is, deviations set in when the values of η decline and where a no longer is in equilibrium with the field, but varies with x. In the uniform-field evaluations of a/p or η, this lack of equilibrium is not readily detected, except by the decline of η. It is only in *nonuniform fields*, under conditions where the excess electron energy from high X/p can be converted to ionization in low-field regions, that the presence of such excess energy is directly manifest. It then leads to *more* ionization than the use of the uniform-field values of x with inefficient processes would lead one to calculate.

Johnson carried the work of Morton to its logical conclusion for air and for pure H_2, especially in the regions of higher pressures. He determined i_0 from the relation of C. W. Rice (43) that the photo-electric current i_0 from a cylinder such as a_1 or a_2, with back diffusion, is given by an equation of the form

$$i_0 = AV/(V + B).$$

By measuring i_0 as a function of V below and up to the region of ionization by electron impact, it is possible to evaluate A and B for the apparatus at the pressures used. Then, from the value of V used where ionization by collisions occurs, it is possible to compute the extrapolated underlying i_0 with sufficient accuracy for this problem. [13]

On this basis, Johnson got data for the cross plots of i/i_0 against p in mm (shown in figure 8.35), for dry, mercury-free air, for X ranging from 200 to 20,000 volts per cm at the cathode surface, as indicated by the number on each curve. Johnson confirmed Morton's peaks, and the fact that they shifted toward lower pressures as the value of V, or $(X/p)_{max}$, at the cathode was lowered. The highest peaks in H_2 and air were found *to represent the pressure for each gas at which the minimum sparking potential was observed*. At the time observed this circumstance appeared interesting, but there was no clearly defined reason for such behavior. However, the action is to be expected, on the basis of the discussion connected with the ionizing efficiency function of the Philips group. The study indicates

---

[13] Actually, at very low values of p and high X/p, the Thomson theory, as well as Rice's relation inferred from it, is inaccurate. At high values of X/p and low p, extrapolation presents no problem. At the higher pressures where it was used by Johnson, it was good enough for purposes of extrapolation as a semiempirical relation.

that, except for the influence of the variation of the second Townsend coefficient γ, the maximum of the $\eta - X/p$ curve, or the point of tangency of the straight line from the origin with the $a/p - X/p$ curve, marks the value of X/p for most efficient ionization by the electrons, and this, at constant γ, fixes the *minimum sparking potential*. The *peak* of the $\eta - X/p$ curve thus *marks the transition* from the lower values of X/p, where electrons are in equilibrium with the field, to those where, because of falling efficient ionization, energy is lost to the anode.

The shift of the peaks to lower pressure also becomes clear. The peaks are associated with the point of linear tangency to the $a/p - X/p$ curve. The point of tangency for a given gas occurs at one particular value, $X/p = (X/p)_T$. If V, and thus $(X/p)_{max}$, at the surface of the cathode is reduced, then a lower p is required to increase X/p to its critical value $(X/p)_T$. It must thus be emphasized that in nonuniform fields above $(X/p)_T$ in value, it is not correct to employ, or base conclusions on, ionization computed by the use of the *uniform field values* for a/p.

The correct physical interpretation of the $V - p$ curves for *nonequilibrium* in the field has been given in the discussion of Morton's $V - p$ curves. Townsend's a values above $(X/p)_T$ are not equilibrium values, and the electrons have more energy than manifested by their ionization. They are nonequilibrium values as measured in *uniform fields* over long gaps. The values of a/p will vary with gap length in such fields. Their available excess in energy is not divulged in uniform fields until they expend it at the anode. It then appears only in a decline of η with X/p. In *nonuniform fields*, however, the excess energy can be converted to ionization, which is then greater than expected from uniform field values of a. The purpose of these studies was to locate the region where electrons ceased to be in equilibrium with the field, and thus where $\epsilon^{\int a dx}$ ceased to give the ions observed. It is gratifying that study with nonuniform fields designed to indicate this should have so clearly indicated that the point where this occurs is one easily located on the $\eta - X/p$ or $a/p - X/p$ curves, and is associated with the minimum sparking potential. Thus, where η begins to decrease marks the value of X/p above which energy is not effectively spent in ionization, energy is lost to the anode, and the ionization observed rises above that given by the Townsend integral, with uniform field values of a above $(X/p)_T$.

Regarding figure 8.35, it is noted that above a certain potential, e.g., at 450 volts, the i/i_0 curve rises to what would be a peak, but terminates in a discharge (corona or spark) at a certain minimum

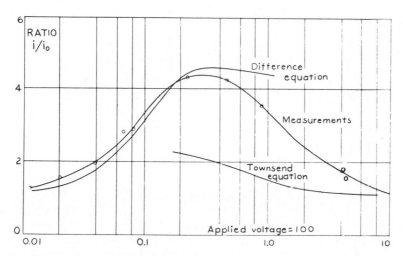

Fig. 8.36. Morton's measured i/i_0 values as a function of p for H_2 at 100 volts (shown as the curve with points), compared to the calculated values by the difference equation for low p and the Townsend integral. Note that the crude difference-equation approximation is surprisingly good below 0.2 mm. At higher pressures approximations are inexact for large sequences of collisions, because of cumulative error. The Townsend integrals are low, but begin to apply above 10 mm.

pressure. This is not surprising, for with the fixed distances in this geometry, above a minimum pressure or pd, corresponding to the minimum sparking potential, secondary processes leading to a spark can occur. As soon as V_{min} at $(X/p)_T$ is exceeded, a spark results in these measurements. Thus, the peak in the i/i_0 curves is not achieved beyond a given V and a given p, determined by $(X/p)_T$. This was brought out by Johnson.

Morton, working largely at lower pressures, next proceeded to study the ionization produced for pressures in the region of the peak and below, i.e., in the region where the Townsend function for uniform fields fails. To do this he took the equations for gain and loss of electrons in an electrical field in a gas, essentially as set up by Smit and used by Dunlop (30) in calculating an α. Under these non-uniform field conditions the problem becomes very complex. At lower pressures it is possible to solve the complex relations, knowing the coefficients for excitation and ionization, by a step-by-step method. In this the range of each of the independent variables is divided into small intervals, and the density of the electrons in the intervals is calculated successively. This allows of approximations and simplification, and leads to a solution which is valid up to 1 mm pressure

§ 9

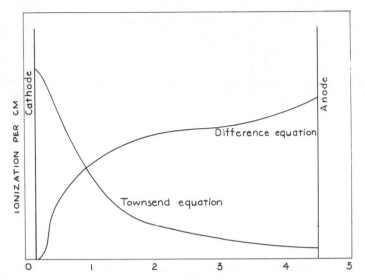

Fig. 8.37. The equivalent of Townsend's $\alpha \times 1$ cm, as computed from Morton's difference equation for coaxial cylinders, compared to the values of Townsend's $\alpha \times 1$ cm at various distances from the cathode at 0.160 mm pressure.

for a 100-volt curve. The Tate-Smith curves (33) for H_2 gave the probability of ionization P_i. For high-energy electrons, one-half the energy losses were attributed to ionization. Below 30 volts, one-fourth the losses were ascribed by Morton to ionization. These assumptions were based on the fact that fast electrons make 1 pair of ions at 16 volts for every 33 volts of energy at higher energies. Below this more energy goes to excitation. The function g, representing the average value of the cosine of the angle between electron path and field direction, was assumed to be given by $\cos (\pi/2) (1 - \omega/\omega_x)$, where ω is the energy of the electrons and ω_x is the energy appropriate to the potential difference from a to x. This empirical expression is of the right form and magnitude, and does not differ much from one for high-energy electrons that have made few collisions. It is not good at low electron energies and high pressures.

The results of this calculation are shown, compared to observation, in figure 8.36. It is seen that the difference relation deduced by Morton follows the observed curve with remarkable fidelity until 0.2 mm pressure is reached. Beyond this it gives too much ionization, and the method is not valid. Figure 8.37 is even more significant, as it shows an essential difference between the ionization and the equilibrium ionization assumed for the Townsend coefficient. In this figure the ionization per unit distance in the coaxial field is given, as predicted by the difference equation and by the Townsend coefficient. It is seen that the ionization, and likewise the excitation at 0.160 mm pressure in H_2 as predicted by the equilibrium a process, is most intense *at the cathode surface*, and is low at the anode. With the difference equation there is zero ionization at the cathode, as the electrons must get out to some distance to get 16 volts of energy. Then it rises as the electrons gain energy in the few free paths in the high field. At this low pressure the rest of the distance in the low field is devoted to ionization. It is seen that the integral of the difference-equation curve is going to be larger than that of the Townsend curve, as reflected by the comparison of i/i_0 with $\epsilon^{\int a dx}$ in that region of V and p.

It should be remarked that the plot of ionization against distance from the cathode shows precisely the sort of variation actually observed in glow discharges, where potential measurements, ionization, and luminosity show a high field at the cathode, low ionization and excitation at the cathode (the Crookes dark space), with a maximum of ionization and luminosity and very low field in the negative glow.[14] Certainly, the uniform field integral $\epsilon^{\int a dx}$ cannot be applied there. It should be added that this applies as well to conditions at high pressure if X is great enough. Thus, in negative corona, from a 1-mm point in air at 760 mm, X is around 100 kv, so that $X/p \sim 130$ with no space-charge distortion. The corona shows a Crookes dark space and negative glow. Actually, because of space charges of positive ions, the field may be four or five times the value of 130 volts/cm per mm Hg, which places it in the Morton regime.

Another illustrative relationship is that depicted in figure 8.38, where the energy distribution of the electrons reaching the anode at different pressures is shown. In it are plotted the number of electrons per e.v. that reach the anode against the available energy of 100 e.v. used in calculation. It is seen that at 0.01 mm pressure the number of electrons getting to the anode with 100 volts is very high, accounting for the low i/i_0, but at 0.08 mm most electrons have less than 40 volts when they reach the anode. It is important that these conditions applying to high X and low pressure be appreciated, so that proper interpretation may be made of phenomena under such circumstances in the future.

Having shown that the quantity a/p as a function of X/p derived

---

[14] Recent studies of the field in the Crookes dark space of glow discharges, by R. P. Stein in the author's laboratory, give strong support to such ionization functions in the low-pressure discharges.

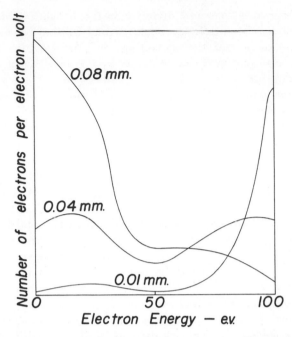

Fig. 8.38. Morton's calculations of electron-energy distribution, using the difference equation for H_2 at three pressures with 100 volts on the cathode.

from equilibrium conditions in a uniform field cannot be applied to calculations of i/i_0 when a field is divergent and equilibrium is not achieved, the problem is now to determine i/i_0, so that the value of i/i_0 can be applied to practical problems. Toward this end, G. W. Johnson (40) made an exhaustive study for two mercury-free gases, H_2 and air. Analysis of the data showed that if for this geometry $(1/a) (1/p) \log_e (i/i_0)$ was plotted against $(X/p)_{max}$, where $(X/p)_{max} = V/2 \ ap \ \log_e (b/a)$, the surface field of the small electrode, all the data fell on a single curve. This single curve did not extend into the Morton regime beyond the first peak at the minimum sparking potential in these measurements. At *pressures* corresponding to and below the one associated with the minimum sparking potential of figure 8.35, the single function appeared to fail. Instead, at that pressure and at each succeeding lower pressure, the curves of $(1/a) (1/p) \log_e (i/i_0)$ were displaced to lower values. These deviations occurred in H_2 at 0.55 mm and in air at 0.2 mm. This deviation may have been due to the circumstance that the electrons were getting to the anode with some of their ionizing energy left, i.e., the electrode spacing was too close below this pressure. In consequence, the ionization would have been less than expected.

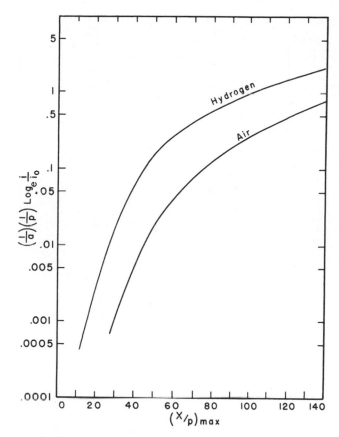

Fig. 8.39. Johnson's data on ion multiplication in coaxial cylindrical fields for H_2 and air represented by a quantity $(1/a)\,(1/p)\,\log_e\,(i/i_0)$, plotted against $(X/p)_{max}$, the maximum field at the cathode, from 0 to 140 volts/cm per mm Hg.

It is unfortunate that the data could not have been obtained in this region with a larger value of b, to see whether this supposition was correct. If it was correct, then the convenient single-function representation may apply over all the very important regime where $\epsilon \int a\,dx$ cannot be used. At present it applies only to a part of that region. If, however, the departure from the single-functioned curve is caused by the appearance of the Morton regime and not by inadequate apparatus, a careful study of i/i_0 in this region must be made, to enable some sort of functional form of more general applicability to be set up by which i/i_0 can be evaluated for any set of electrodes in the same geometrical configuration.

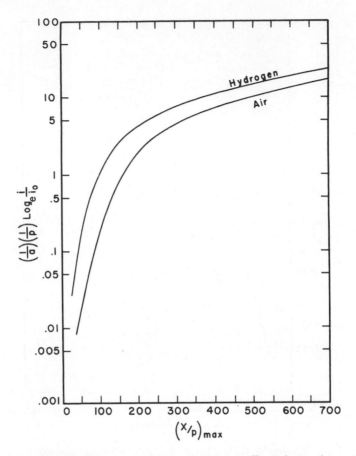

Fig. 8.40. Continuation of Johnson's data for H_2 and air, shown in figure 8.39, for $(X/p)_{max}$ from 100 to 700 volts/cm per mm Hg.

The general curves obtained by Johnson for air and H_2 are reproduced in figures 8.39 and 8.40. Insofar as they apply down to 0.2 mm in air at fields of 400 volts/cm and above, and 0.55 mm in H_2 at fields of 300 volts/cm and above, they certainly cover some of the region where i/i_0 is materially greater than $\epsilon^{\int a dx}$, and thus can be used in some situations.

Both Morton and Johnson observed that if the polarity was reversed on their cylinders, so that the outer cylinder b was the cathode, the ratio i/i_0 was nearly the same as when the cylinder a was the cathode. This result at first appears surprising in the region where electrons gain energy rapidly in the high-field region. As shown earlier in this section, it is to be expected on the basis of diffusion. At Johnson's

TABLE 8.15

Values of a'/p, Computed from Johnson's Coaxial Cylinder Data and
Sanders' Values of a/p in Uniform Field Geometry in Air

$(X/p)_{max}$	a'/p	a/p Observed	Ratio $\dfrac{a'/p}{(a/p)\ Obs.}$
60	0.127	0.127	1.00
80	0.330	0.340	0.97
100	0.600	0.637	0.94
200	2.53	2.60	0.96
300	3.50	4.36	0.78
400	5.15	5.80	0.89
500	7.7	7.0	1.1
600	9.8	7.9	1.24
700	12.0	8.7	1.38
800	12.2	9.3	1.31
900	12.0	10.0	1.20
1,000	12.0	10.5	1.14

lowest pressures the negative cylinder a gave i/i_0 only 10% higher
than negative cylinder b.

Johnson then proceeded to show that the same relations shown in
figures 8.39 and 8.40 apply to confocal paraboloid geometry as used
by Weissler and Fisher, since here again X varies inversely as the
first power of x. Thus, if in place of a, the radius of the inner cylinder, the focal length of the smaller paraboloid is used, the relations
above apply to within 10%. Whether this or some other relation holds
for fields that vary at a different rate, is not known. A study should
be made with concentric spheres where the field varies differently.

Johnson made an attempt to compare his values of i/i_0 at higher
pressures with those computed from the Townsend integral $\epsilon^{\int a dx}$, as
had Morton. Unfortunately, the data of Hale on H_2 in this region were
not accurate enough over the ranges needed to yield a satisfactory
integration. Johnson did not wish to use Sanders' data derived from
mercury-contaminated air for comparison. To get around these difficulties, on the advice of Dr. J. Weinberg, Johnson differentiated his
curves, and subjecting them to the proper functional analysis, he
derived values of a'/p, his equivalent of Townsend's a/p, to compare
with the uniform-field values of Hale in H_2. Johnson compared the
values of a'/p for air to those of Bowls in N_2 because he was afraid
of the mercury-contaminated air data. On reconsideration of Sanders'
data, the author has used the data of Sanders, Masch, and Townsend
on mercury-contaminated air for comparison with Johnson's a'/p for

TABLE 8.16

Values of α'/p, Computed from Johnson's Coaxial Cylinder Data
and Hale's Values of α/p in Uniform Field Geometry in H_2

$(X/p)_{max}$	α'/p	α/p Observed	Ratio $\dfrac{\alpha'/p}{(\alpha/p)\text{ Obs.}}$
30	0.057	0.080	1.40
35	0.106	0.100	1.06
45	0.266	0.120	1.57
60	0.520	0.31	1.08
100	1.06	0.71	1.50
200	3.60	1.95	1.85
300	5.00	3.30	1.52
400	6.00	4.30	1.40
500	5.90	5.05	1.17
600	6.00	5.80	1.03

pure air. These data should have values of α some 10% to 20% high at higher X/p compared to those for pure air, because of the Hg contamination. The comparison is shown in tables 8.15 and 8.16, for air and H_2, respectively.

The results in H_2 are inconclusive, since Hale's data vary too much. On the other hand, the trend in air is very interesting. In mercury-contaminated air, α/p should be high compared with α'/p, where X/p is so low that Townsend's α can be used. The value of α/p in contaminated air should increase in value relative to pure, mercury-free air as X/p goes up and p goes down. This trend is clearly seen up to an X/p of 300. Johnson's α'/p begins to *increase* relative to α/p at $(X/p)_{max} = 400$. Despite the increase in α/p at higher X/p and lower p, it is clear that α'/p is increasing faster, as Morton's findings indicate it must, above the initial $X/p = 400$ in air. The region where the increase occurs in air is seen from the curves of figure 8.35 to be roughly above X/p about 400. The failure of the ratio to increase indefinitely is probably owing to the decrease in the $(1/a)\,(1/p)$ $\log_e\,i/i_0 - X/p$ curves observed by Johnson as pressures get too low— which, it is hoped, is an instrumental weakness.

Enough has been said about this phenomenon to indicate that there is a problem at lower pressures and higher X/p when it comes to using the Townsend integrals and equilibrium uniform-field values of α, the first coefficient in nonuniform fields. The difficulty stems from the fact that at high X, low p, and high X/p, the electrons do not have enough impacts to get into equilibrium with the field, and thus to have a distribution yielding an equilibrium a. It is important tc note that, as first pointed out by Dr. J. Weinberg, this phenomenon appears to depend on X/p, and *not* on the gradient of X over a free path, as others had supposed. Strangely enough, the failure of a sets in at relatively low X/p ratios in air, i.e., about 400. In this region, the electrons find it difficult to gain equilibrium with the field, and start to have energies somewhat more in keeping with the potentials they have fallen through. Thus, they have energy to deliver to the anode that is not spent in ionization unless the distance is very long. This point of transition is the point of tangency in the a/p-X/p curves, or the peak of the η-X/p curves, as it should be. Beyond this, values of η decrease with X/p, since the electrons move too fast to lose energy to the molecules and to ionize as effectively as they did before.

Since electrons gain more energy from the field than they can dissipate, the longer the path in the gas in a uniform field, the more the excess energy. As this increases, losses to ionization still further decrease. Thus, η beyond its peak should not only decrease with X/p, but for a fixed X/p, slowly decrease as gap length x increases. The range of distances over which η has been studied is too short to have revealed this condition. If gaps become too short or the pressures become too low, as is the case in some of the studies of a/p around an $X/p = 1,000$, even the values of a/p would decrease as X/p increases, since energy is gained very rapidly, and electrons would cross with too few collisions to increase ionization.

When the fields are nonuniform, so that us pressures get low the electrons above $X/p = 400$ are gaining energy appropriate to the potential drop instead of remaining in equilibrium with X, owing to rapidly decreasing geometrical fields, they forge ahead into regions where X/p is lower before they have dissipated their energy. They will thus produce excessive ionization. The effects then become noticeable, as Morton showed, in an increase of i/i_0 above $\epsilon^{\int a dx}$. When pressures get so low that geometrical dimensions become relatively too small, so that there is no chance of dissipating the energy in ionization, these overenergized electrons lose their energy at the anode and the ion production falls.

The only effect of geometry leading to field gradients of importance in these matters is first to permit the nonequilibrium energy gain in high-field regions to be used for ionization in low-field regions where an a equilibrium would have dissipated it in higher-field regions. Secondly, the only influence of distances, as the pressures and numbers of impacts get too small, is to cause the electrons to dissipate the energy at electrodes instead of in gaseous ionization. Thus, while the nonequilibrium is a matter of X/p alone, it is manifest through enhanced ionization in field gradients or diminished ionization with such gradients at low pressures and short gaps. When this occurs, it is essential to note that the distribution of ionization will always be different from that predicted by the Townsend integral. Thus, the appearance near a cathode of a dark space with a negative glow beyond indicates a nonequilibrium ionization.[15] If the ionization continues right up to the cathode as a maximum in a divergent field, Townsend equilibrium exists. Where nonequilibrium exists, care must be taken not to use $\epsilon^{\int \alpha dx}$ to calculate i/i_0. The field condition should be simulated, using a proper electrode arrangement with voltages, pressures, and i/i_0 measured as a function of V and p. Only in this way can correct values of i/i_0 for use in theoretical studies be obtained. In this matter, the study of Johnson has shown the general procedure.

BIBLIOGRAPHY TO CHAPTER VIII

(1) J. S. Townsend, Nature 62, 340, 1900; Phil. Mag. 1, 198, 1901; Electrician 3, April, 1903. Also, *Electricity in Gases*, Oxford University Press, 1914, chapter VIII. Also, *Electrons in Gases*, Hutchinson's, London, 1947.

(2) J. Stoletow, Jour. Phys. 9, 468, 1890; H. Kreusler, Verh. d. Deutsch. Phys. Gesell. 17, 86, 1898; E. von Schweidler, Wien. Ber. 18, 273, 1899.

(3) See section 7 of this chapter.

(4) A. A. Kruithoff and F. M. Penning, Physica 3, 515, 1936; 4, 430, 1937; 5, 203, 1938; A. A. Kruithoff, Physica 7, 519, 1940.

(5) W. S. Huxford, Phys. Rev. 55, 754, 1939.

(6) R. J. Wijsman, Phys. Rev. 75, 833, 1949.

(7) J. S. Townsend, Phil. Mag. 3, 557, 1902; 6, 389, 598, 1903; 8, 738, 1904; H. E. Hurst, Phil. Mag. 11, 535, 1906; E. W. B. Gill and F. B. Pidduck, Phil. Mag. 16, 280, 1908; 23, 837, 1912; T. L. R. Ayers, Phil. Mag. 45, 353, 1923; J. S. Townsend, *Electrons in Gases*, Hutchinson's, London, 1947.

---

[15] There is one exception to this generalization that occurs at very low pressures at lower fields, where the electrons have to fall through the excitation or ionization potential before the luminosity or ionization begins. This situation occurs in visible distances only for very pure, inert gases, Ne and He, and at low voltages and low pressures. It is not to be confused with the situation discussed above.

(8) J. S. Townsend and S. P. McCallum, Phil. Mag. 5, 695, 1928; 6, 857, 1928; 17, 678, 1934.

(9) M. Paavola, Arch. f. Elektrotech. 22, 443, 1929; K. Masch, Arch. f. Elektrotech. 26, 589, 1932; A. Jodelbauer, Zeits. f. Phys. 92, 116, 1934; B. M. Hochberg and E. J. Sandberg, Compt. Rend. Acad. Sci. URSS 53, 511, 1946.

(10) F. H. Sanders, Phys. Rev. 41, 667, 1932; 44, 1020, 1933; D. Q. Posin, Phys. Rev. 50, 650, 1936.

(11) W. E. Bowls, Phys. Rev. 53, 293, 1938; D. H. Hale, Phys. Rev. 54, 241, 1938; 56, 815, 1939; R. Geballe and F. S. Linn, Phys. Rev. 21, 592, 1950; R. Geballe and M. A. Harrison, Phys. Rev. 85, 372, 1952; 91, 1, 1953.

(12) W. S. Huxford and R. W. Engstrom, Phys. Rev. 68, 67, 1940.

(13) L. H. Fisher and G. A. Kachickas, Phys. Rev. 79, 32, 1950; and with B. Bederson, Phys. Rev. 81, 109, 1951. Analyses of these gases were made by J. A. Hornbeck of Bell Laboratories, and reported to the author in a private communication in February, 1951.

(14) R. N. Varney, H. J. White, L. B. Loeb, and D. Q. Posin, Phys. Rev. 48, 818, 1935.

(15) M. J. Druyvesteyn and F. M. Penning, Rev. Mod. Phys. 32, 97, 1940.

(16) J. Stoletow, Phil. Mag. 1, 198, 1901.

(17) J. J. Thomson, Conduction of Electricity through Gases, second edition, Cambridge University Press, 1906, pp. 484 ff.

(18) A. von Engel and M. Steenbeck, Elektrische Gasentladungen, Julius Springer, Berlin, 1932, vol. I, pp. 93 and 100 ff.

(19) L. B. Loeb, Fundamental Processes of Electrical Discharge in Gases, John Wiley & Sons, New York, 1939, chapter VIII, section 4, pp. 358 ff.

(20) A. von Engel and M. Steenbeck, Elektrische Gasentladungen, Julius Springer, Berlin, 1932, vol. I, pp. 89, 184, 191. Also, F. E. Null, Phys. Rev. 47, 301, 1935.

(21) M. J. Druyvesteyn and F. M. Penning, Rev. Mod. Phys. 12, 102, 1940.

(22) A. von Engel and M. Steenbeck, Elektrische Gasentladungen, Julius Springer, Berlin, 1934, vol. II, pp. 51 ff.

(23) M. J. Druyvesteyn and F. M. Penning, Rev. Mod. Phys. 12, 112, 1940.

(24) O. Klemperer, Zeits. f. Phys. 52, 650, 1928; J. S. Townsend and S. P. McCallum, Phil. Mag. 5, 695, 1928; 6, 857, 1928; 17, 678, 1934; F. M. Penning and C. C. J. Addink, Physica 1, 1007, 1934; R. Schöfer, Zeits. f. Phys. 110, 21, 1938.

(25) A. P. LaRocque and H. Jacobs, Phys. Rev. 74, 163, 1948; Jour. App. Phys. 18, 199, 1947.

(26) L. B. Loeb, Phys. Rev. 76, 255, 1949; L. B. Loeb and R. J. Wijsman, Jour. App. Phys. 19, 797, 1948.

(27) C. G. Miller and L. B. Loeb, Jour. App. Phys. 22, 504, 621, 742, 1951.

(28) D. R. Wilkinson, Phys. Rev. 74, 1417, 1948.

(29) F. Ehrenkrantz, Phys. Rev. 55, 219, 1939.

(30) J. A. Smit, Physica 3, 543, 1937; S. H. Dunlop, Nature 164, 452, 1949.

(31) K. T. Compton, Phys. Rev. 7, 489, 501, 509, 1916; 8, 449, 1917; K. T. Compton and J. M. Benade, Phys. Rev. 11, 234, 1918.

(32) Bergen Davis, Phys. Rev. 24, 93, 1907; 5, 118, 1915.

(33) K. T. Compton and C. C. van Voorhis, Phys. Rev. 26, 436, 1925; 27,

724, 1926; J. T. Tate and P. T. Smith, Phys. Rev. *39*, 270, 1932; P. T. Smith, Phys. Rev. *36*, 1293, 1930.

(34) F. M. Penning, Zeits. f. Phys. *40*, 4, 1926.

(35) M. J. Druyvesteyn, Phys. Zeits. *33*, 836, 1932; Physica *3*, 65, 1936; *4*, 440, 1937.

(36) K. G. Emeléus, R. W. Lunt, and C. A. Meek, Proc. Roy. Soc. *A156*, 394, 1936.

(37) H. D. Deas and K. G. Emeléus, Phil. Mag. *11*, 460, 1949.

(38) F. M. Penning, Physica *4*, 286, 1938.

(39) E. E. Dodd, Phys. Rev. *78*, 620, 1950.

(40) P. L. Morton, Phys. Rev. *70*, 358, 1946; G. W. Johnson, Phys. Rev. *73*, 284, 1948.

(41) A. von Engel and M. Steenbeck, *Elektrische Gasentladungen*, Julius Springer, Berlin, 1934, vol. II, p. 79. Also, W. Rogowski, Arch. f. Elektrotech. *26*, 643, 1932.

(42) G. L. Weissler and L. H. Fisher, Phys. Rev. *66*, 95, 1944.

(43) C. W. Rice, Phys. Rev. *70*, 228, 1946.

(44) R. P. Stein, Phys. Rev. *89*, 134, 1953.

(45) S. C. Brown and A. D. MacDonald, Phys. Rev. *75*, 411, 1949.

(46) A. A. Kruithoff and M. J. Druyvesteyn, Physica *4*, 482, 1937.

(47) M. A. Biondi, Phys. Rev. *35*, 653, 1951.

(48) S. H. Dunlop and K. G. Emeléus, Brit. Jour. App. Phys. *2*, 163, 1951.

(49) E. Huber, Phys. Rev., January 15, 1955.

(50) D. Alpert, Westinghouse Res. Lab. scientific paper No. 1744, June 8, 1953.

(51) R. Rietz and G. Dieke, Jour. App. Phys. *25*, 196, 1954.

(52) D. Alpert, Jour. App. Phys. *24*, 860, 1953; *25*, 202, 1954.

(53) M. A. Biondi, Rev. Sci. Inst. *22*, 535, 1951.

(54) J. A. Hornbeck, Phys. Rev. *84*, 1072(L), 1951.

Chapter IX

THE SECOND TOWNSEND COEFFICIENT

---

§1. Introduction.

In his early investigations on the first coefficient a, Townsend extended his measurements of a to higher values of X/p. It then appeared that while at lower values of x the log i/i_0-x plots were linear, they began to curve upward as x was increased to higher values. This is nicely illustrated in Sanders' (VIII.10) plot for log i/i_0 against x in air for X/p above 110, as shown in figure 9.1. Below $X/p = 110$, Sanders had observed that the plots were strictly linear. They could be extended either to the 7-cm limit of plate separation, or else to a point short of this at which a spark occurred. In all the low X/p cases, the measurement of i/i_0 with increasing x terminated as a spark while still in the linear region. The appearance of the spark at large x for small X/p with only a linear log i/i_0-x plot was somewhat of a mystery at the time, and for some years later. It was at first ascribed to fluctuation in the high-tension source. However, it was also observed by Posin (VIII.10), and later by Bowls (VIII.11) and Hale (VIII.11), where the potential control appeared to be stable.

Since it was believed that the failure to observe curvature was not caused by instrumental deficiency, this failure was ascribed by the author and Meek (1), about 1940, to a property of the newly discovered streamer mechanism of spark breakdown. The vast improvements in postwar techniques, including the use of fast oscilloscopic study as well as electronic stability control, has led to much new information concerning this situation which must be reviewed briefly. First were observations in breakdown of asymmetrical gaps, indicating that these breakdowns, some caused by photoionization in the gap leading to anode streamers and burst pulses, and others to more conventional current types, were preceded by self-sustaining Townsend discharges of low order, involving a γ mechanism (2). This conclusion was followed by the investigations of L. H. Fisher (3) and his students on the formative time lags of sparks in air and other gases going from overvoltages to within 0.05% of the sparking threshold. These studies required highly stabilized potential sources and the addition of a highly steady-step pulse to yield the sparking potential needed. The

751

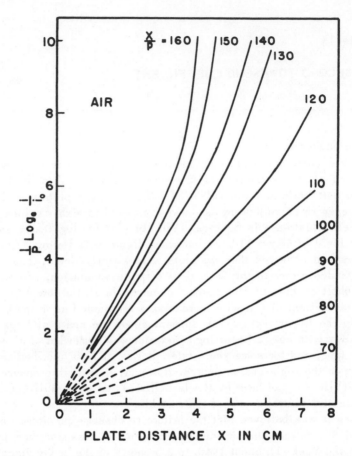

Fig. 9.1. Sanders' curves of log i/i_0, plotted against plate separation x in air for various values of X/p. Note the upcurving caused by secondary action above $X/p = 110$. The curves at lower X/p terminate in sparks at appropriately great values of x, without any upcurving. With more highly stabilized potential sources, this may not always occur.

change in time lag from 10^{-7} sec for overvoltages from $2\frac{1}{2}\%$ in air to 100 microseconds at about 0.05% in air, with longer lags in A, which required in excess of 100% overvoltage to bring in the short time lags, indicated clearly that the streamer breakdown of Meek's theory with 10^{-7} sec of time lag required a higher threshold ($\sim 10^7$ ions at anode) than the low-order Townsend discharge.

The author (4) and Fisher (3) indicated that the Townsend discharge created a space-charge distortion of the gap, which, in conformity with the independently derived theories of M. Steenbeck (5), and of R. N. Varney, H. J. White, L. B. Loeb, and D. Q. Posin (6), leads to lowering of the sparking threshold, and in the pressure ranges used by Fisher, to a streamer spark. This interpretation was dramatically substantiated in 1954 by H. W. Bandel (7), who measured the current growth in the time lags of about 60 microseconds near threshold in air, as described by Fisher. The growth of the Townsend discharge from 3 microseconds and a microampere to 3×10^{-4} amperes at about 40 microseconds, followed by the hyperexponential rise in current by space-charge accumulation to 10^{-2} ampere, ending in the streamer spark within a microsecond or so after passing 10^{-2} ampere, has been theoretically calculated in conformity with established constants. The value of γ, which initially was probably a slightly delayed photon γ_p at the brass cathode, from observation was 1.5×10^{-5}, at $p = 722$ mm of air, with $X_s/p = 28.5$ kv/cm, Sanders' data being used. The analysis of Bandel further leaves no doubt that the space charge leading to the spark occupies the whole uniform high-field electrode area, while the spark is the filamentary spark characteristic of a streamer.

It will be clear that except for well-overvolted gaps in most gases studied, the threshold is not that given by the theory of Meek (1) or of Raether (1), but is set by a Townsend discharge with cathode γ, which builds up a space charge leading to a mid-gap streamer spark, as observed in cloud chambers by Raether (1), and currently with photomultiplier by G. G. Hudson in the author's laboratory. With this information, it is gratifying to note that F. Llewellyn Jones and A. B. Parker, and J. Dutton, S. C. Haydon, and F. Llewellyn Jones (8), with sufficiently stabilized sources, have succeeded in observing an upcurving of the $\log i/i_0$-x curves in gaps of from 1 mm to 2.5-5 cm in air and in slightly contaminated N_2 cylinder gas (no outgassing of the apparatus above $100°$ C., silicone grease seals, oil-diffusion pumps, and no liquid-air traps), for X/p values from $X/p = 39$ to 45. The values of γ derived in N_2 for Ni cathodes ranged from 1.3 to 3.7×10^{-4}. At first it was considered that these upcurvings might have been caused by the field distortion initiated by field-intensified cathode current densities $j = i_0/A$, where A is the area illuminated. However, these workers varied the currents i_0 over some range without observing visually any change in upcurving. On the basis of these results, they generally discredited the accumulated data and theory of space-charge distortion on the $\log i/i_0$-x curves. Since these authors have nowhere quoted the work of Steenbeck or of Varney, White, Loeb, and Posin, and have always referred to the current i_0, but not to current density j_0, it appears that they were unaware that it is not the current i_0, but $j_0 = i_0/A$ and the gap length d, or the field amplification, that cause this phenomenon. Thus, contrary to their claims, they have not disproved anything by these observations.

Fortunately for all concerned, Crowe, Bragg, and Thomas (9) recently have correctly applied the calculations on space-charge distortion by j_0 to the data and work of F. Llewellyn Jones and his students (8), and have shown that except for their highest current values (not used in the measurements of γ), those workers were below the space-charge distortion limit. It should further be pointed out that with the very short distances of upcurving shown in this work, any critical evaluation of an ω/a or a γ, and a decision as to whether it is or is not distorted by space charge, cannot be made, as these short bits of curves can be approximated by almost the desired functional form.

In any event, it is now reasonably clear that at threshold (in contrast to overvoltage), breakdown in uniform field geometry is initiated by a low-order Townsend discharge, operating with a cathode γ mechanism and leading to an ultimate spark by space-charge formation throughout the gap, which may terminate as a mid-gap streamer spark. There is thus a low value of γ, which should be observable at the ends of the log i/i_0-x curves with highly stabilized sources and low current densities $j_0 = i_0/A$.

It is now essential to focus attention on the upcurving as noted by Townsend (VIII.7), assuming that it is general. It must be added in passing (as noted above) that not all upcurving at larger x may be of the special kind studied by Townsend. In 1934, Posin discovered that a spurious upcurving will be observed with larger values of x if the photoelectric current density $j_0 = i_0/A$ is too great (VIII.14). This condition was fortunately avoided by Townsend and all the earlier workers. It must be guarded against in future study with stronger sources of j_0, and greater gap lengths.

It happens that the upcurving observed by Townsend (VIII.7) was a genuine phenomenon, setting in at higher X/p as x increased. It appeared to enhance the avalanche-intensified currents $i = i_0\ \epsilon^{\alpha x}$ beyond the value caused by ionization by electron impact and the initial i_0 alone. This circumstance at once suggested to Townsend that some process began to set in at high X/p, the action of which lay in supplementing i_0 through some *secondary process*. Such a process would have to come from actions accompanying the creation of $i_0\ \epsilon^{\alpha x}$ electrons and positive ions. In casting about for some secondary mechanism, at the time of the discovery between 1899 and 1903, Townsend was naturally influenced by the current belief that α was caused by ionization by *negative ions*. It was thus quite natural for Townsend to attribute the increase of current in the upcurved portions of the log i/i_0-x curves to the ionization of the gas by the ϵ^{ax} positive ions created in the avalanche as they moved toward the cathode in the field. This concept was quite plausible at this time, since it was observed that positive ions usually had lower mobilities than negative ions. Thus, it was not surprising that the negative ions appeared to ionize by impact at lower X/p than positive ions.

When Townsend concluded (about 1910) that the negative carrier causing a was probably the free electron, it was still the current belief among physicists that the positive ions would ionize by impact at higher X/p. This theory persisted until well after 1920. The experiments of J. Franck and E. von Bahr (10) and others indicated such action, notwithstanding the negative data of W. F. Horton and A. C. Davies (10). In consequence, Townsend assumed that a positive ion could create β new electrons and positive ions in advancing 1 cm in the field direction. In order to analyze the consequences of the assumption of β, it may be assumed, as before, that n_0 photoelectrons leave a cm^2 of cathode in a plane parallel electrode system with the anode d cm distant. Consider a slab of gas dx cm thick and x cm from the cathode. Let p positive ions be created per square cm of area between the cathode and the plane slab dx thick at x cm from the cathode by *positive and negative ions*. Let q be the number of such ions generated per cm^2 in the distance d-x remaining between dx and the *anode*. If n_0 electrons are initially liberated per cm^2 from the cathode, the number of electrons arriving at the anode is

(9.1) $$n = n_0 + p + q$$

electrons. In dx, there are generated per cm^2, $(n_0 + p)adx + q\beta dx$ ions. Thus, dp, the increase of ions in dx, is

(9.2) $$dp = (n_0 + p)\,adx + q\beta dx\,.$$

From equation 9.1, $q = n - n_0 - p$, so that dp/dx becomes

(9.3) $$dp/dx = (n_0 + p)\,a + \beta(n - n_0 - p) = (n_0 + p)(a - \beta) + n\beta\,.$$

Separation of variables in equation 9.3 yields

$$\frac{dp}{(n_0 + p) + n\beta/(a - \beta)} = (a - \beta)\,dx\,,$$

which in turn, on integration, gives

$$\log_e\left[(n_0 + p) + \frac{n\beta}{a - \beta}\right] = x(a - \beta) + \log_e A$$

or, as in the equation to follow,

$$(9.4) \qquad n_0 + p = A\,\epsilon^{(a-\beta)x} - n\beta/(a-\beta).$$

Since $p = 0$ at $x = 0$, the constant A becomes $A = n_0 - n\beta/(a-\beta)$. At $x = d$, $n = n_0 + p$. Thus, it follows that

$$n = \left(n_0 + \frac{n\beta}{a-\beta}\right)\epsilon^{(a-\beta)d} - n\beta/(a-\beta),$$

yielding

$$n\left[1 + \frac{\beta}{a-\beta} - \frac{\beta}{a-\beta}\,\epsilon^{(a-\beta)d}\right] = n_0\,\epsilon^{(a-\beta)d}$$

or

$$(9.5) \qquad n = n_0\,\frac{(a-\beta)\,\epsilon^{(a-\beta)d}}{a - \beta\,\epsilon^{(a-\beta)d}}.$$

Multiplying n and n_0 by the electron e for any plate distance $d = x$, the equation becomes

$$(9.6) \qquad i = i_0\,\frac{(a-\beta)\,\epsilon^{(a-\beta)x}}{a - \beta\,\epsilon^{(a-\beta)x}}.$$

This is Townsend's famous equation for the current when a and β mechanisms are simultaneously active. It is the *generic prototype equation for simultaneous action of primary and secondary coefficients*, and thus for the extension of the log i/i_0-x curves to higher values of X/p and x. As such, it sets the pattern for later theory and for the development of a proper equation for breakdown. For this reason, its importance cannot be overlooked.

Townsend at once applied this equation to the analysis of the curved portions of the log i/i_0-x plots at high X/p. With three values of i for three values of x, it was possible to evaluate i_0, a, and β. However, since the linear portions of the plots of log i/i_0 at lower x easily yielded a value of a and i_0, it was possible, with these values and the observed values of i, i_0, x, and a at a longer x, to solve for β. This was done, and values of β were measured. These values of β/p were again found to be a unique function of X/p. The upcurved portions of the log i/i_0-x curves were relatively short. Thus, the evaluation of β was not too accurate, nor could the accuracy of the agreement between observed curves and theory be properly tested. The rough values of β observed were small, and were limited to a relatively small range of values of X/p in most cases. The values obtained ranged from 0.01 at lower X/p, and rose asymptotically, monotonically, and more rapidly than linearly with X/p to about 0.2 in the gases N_2, H_2, and air. The values were not appreciable below $X/p \sim 100$ in N_2 and air under test conditions before 1947, where a spark preceded the upcurving. Since the curved portions of the plots were short in any case, so that the accuracy of observation was not great, the fit obtained to the observed curves by relation 9.6 was of necessity encouraging, but by no means critical or significant. Such agreement served to establish the theory and its assumed underlying mechanism. The theory early received further strong support from another aspect. If equation 9.6 is regarded, it will be noted that i/i_0 becomes indefinitely great when the denominator vanishes, i.e., when

$$(9.7) \qquad \qquad a = \beta \; \epsilon^{(a-\beta)x}.$$

Townsend set this condition of indefinite increase as the threshold for a spark, or electrical, breakdown. Thus, with a given x, if curves of a/p and β/p as a function of X/p are available, it becomes relatively easy to find a value of X/p designated as X/p for sparking at which relation 9.7 is satisfied. The value of X_s so observed multiplied by x gives V_s, the *sparking potential*. Roughly, V_s may be directly determined by experiment in the same apparatus, and compared with V_s calculated as above. The agreement so obtained by Townsend lay quite successfully within the accuracy of the observations. This seemed still further to justify the conclusions. Thus, with his intuitive genius, Townsend succeeded in deriving still another prototype equation; that for gaseous breakdown. This was destined to serve in later years as the generic relation for many such processes. Finally, to clinch the arguments in favor of this particular secondary mechanism, there were observed a number of discharge conditions, such as those from isolated positive points and wires, in which it appeared that breakdown could only occur by *some secondary mechanism in the gas*. At that time, ionization by positive ions *appeared* to be the only logical mechanism.

It will be seen that from the circumstance of the upcurving of the log i/i_0-x curves at higher X/p, Townsend was logically led to a theory introducing the concept of a secondary ionizing mechanism, characterized by a second coefficient β, attributed to a specific mechanism in the gas. This led to an equation for the process that was in sensible agreement with observation. From this new equation for the current ratio i/i_0, he derived a concept of the threshold for gaseous breakdown that was in sensible agreement with observation, thus relating the first and second coefficients to a breakdown threshold condition. He also pointed out a most essential requirement for break-

downs from positive points and wires. While these relations and concepts were derived in relation to a particular assumed mechanism,
their significance extends far beyond the particular mechanism assumed. Thus, quite independently of any mechanism, Townsend established the principles of the primary ionizing process and the first
coefficient a, a secondary ionization process and a corresponding
second coefficient, and finally, the relation of these to the upcurving
of the observed $\log i/i_0$-x plots and to the threshold for gaseous breakdown. These principles are basic to an understanding of all gaseous
discharges, and will doubtless be used in improved and modified form
as long as discharges are studied.

It is no discredit to the genius of Townsend, nor does it detract
from his great contribution, that some thirty years later physicists
experimentally established beyond the shadow of a doubt that the
particular mechanism initially invoked by Townsend, i.e., *ionization
by collision by positive ions in gases*, cannot occur in gases under
ordinary breakdown conditions (11). The values of X/p involved in
most gaseous discharges are *not exceptionally high*. Positive ions,
colliding with atoms and molecules in the gas, on the average lose
of the order of 30% of their energy at each impact. Thus, the chance
is exceedingly remote of such ions achieving as much as 10 volts
average energy with the X/p values existing in discharge. It has been
observed that ionization of atoms or molecules by positive ions in a
gas actually requires *at a minimum* some 70 volts of energy. This low
energy is observed only for certain ion-gas atom combinations that
exhibit special resonance properties (12).

Ions studied in molecular gases appear to require in the hundreds
of volts of energy to ionize the gas. Collisions of fast neutral atoms
derived from charge exchange ionize at somewhat lower energies.
Assuming, for the sake of argument, that a most rare ion or neutral atom
by chance should achieve an ionizing energy, its chance of producing
ionization before it lost the energy would also be remote; for even at
the *ionizing threshold*, the cross section for ionization by positive
ion impact is very small compared to ordinary elastic impacts with
atoms. These latter, in their impacts, would reduce the high energy
of the ion before it achieved ionization. It is true that canal-ray
studies demonstrate the ionization by positive ions in gases. Here,
as in the region close to the cathode in low-pressure glow discharges,
ions have energies in the hundreds of volts. Thus, in such discharges,
with $X/p > 1,000$, with heavy ion currents near the cathode, there is
evidence of ion-impact ionization. Breakdown in gases where X/p is
in excess of 1,000, i.e., below the minimum sparking potential, may

have some ionization by positive ions which will be subordinated to more efficient mechanisms.

Further, it is hardly to be expected that Townsend could have foreseen that with the theoretical and experimental advances following on the heels of the Bohr atom, new atomic properties producing effective secondary mechanisms would come to light. Again, these newly discovered properties, when considered as secondary mechanisms, most strangely yielded relations for the current ratio i/i_0 that differed so little in general form from the equation deduced for Townsend's β mechanism that experimental data are not of sufficient accuracy to distinguish between them. In consequence, these new expressions involving known possible mechanisms also yielded threshold expressions for gaseous breakdown. Owing to mathematical properties inherent in all these equations, and to the experimental inaccuracy of threshold evaluations, agreement between experiment and theory again did not permit distinguishing between the β mechanism and the new ones. Finally, in 1934, evidence was obtained from discharges themselves that indicated *an ionizing mechanism in the gas, other than ionization by positive ions,* which accounted for the positive wire and point discharges, as Geiger counter action and streamer breakdown now eloquently attest (13).

Today, it is therefore essential to look anew at the possible secondary mechanisms, and to apply the basic principles of Townsend to their exploitation. This will furnish the objective of the succeeding sections.

Before closing this section, a few more matters require clarification. In the preceding paragraphs, certain positive and dogmatic statements have been made. This applies especially to the eradication of ionization by positive ions in a gas as an active mechanism in common discharges. It is doubtful if all discharge physicists will accept these statements. However, the question has been adequately discussed in the author's book, *Fundamental Processes of Electrical Discharge in Gases,* and in a later paper by Varney, Loeb, and Haseltine (11). The author leaves to the interested reader the task of looking up the literature and making his decision, and to the future to resolve any further doubts.

This text will proceed on the assumption that the β mechanism is not operative. In justice to Townsend, it must be pointed out that he recognized and, it is believed, first proposed one of the accepted, and perhaps most emphasized, alternate secondary mechanisms. That is, Townsend proposed that *positive ions* from the avalanche $\epsilon^{\alpha x}$, moving to the cathode in the field and *striking the cathode,* might liberate secondary electrons from it. This sort of action of positive ions had early been observed in radioactivity from alpha-ray and canal-ray impact on metals. Thus, Townsend proposed a secondary mechanism in which each positive ion had a chance γ of liberating an electron from the cathode on impact. He derived the equation for the process (14), which will be presented later, in section 3. For some reason, he seems not to have done much with it in the intervening years. Probably, since the quantity β seemed to suit all purposes and accounted for some obscure phenomena, he saw no special need for γ.

§2. The Possible Secondary Mechanisms Active in Gaseous Breakdown.

It is possible to segregate the principal proper secondary mechanisms active in gaseous breakdown into certain categories, as indicated by the author (13).

A. *Mechanisms Active at the Cathode in All Geometries.*
1. Secondary electron liberation by impact of positive ions on the cathode. (Coefficient γ_i.)
2. Secondary electron liberation by photoelectric action at the cathode. (Coefficient γ_p.)
3. Secondary electron liberation by action of metastable or active atomic and molecular states diffusing to the cathode. (Coefficient γ_m.)

B(1). *Mechanisms Active in the Gas in Uniform Field Geometry.*
1. Ionization by positive ions in the gas. This mechanism, as indicated, is not very important under most breakdown conditions in gases. (Coefficient β.)
2. Photoelectric ionization in the gas by photons produced in the primary avalanche.
3. Ionization by impacts of the second class, i.e., by excited atoms or molecules or metastable states of these in the gas.

B(2). *Photoionization in the Gas in Asymmetrical or Nonuniform Fields; Anode Mechanisms.*
1. If the coefficient of absorption for photoionizing action is of the order of 10 cm^{-1} (ionizing free path 1 mm), breakdown characterized by spread over the anode surface occurs. (Burst-pulse or Geiger counter actions.)
2. If the coefficient of absorption for photoionizing action is of the order of 100 cm^{-1} or less with appropriate geometry, a self-sustaining process projects radially into the gap by photo-

ionization and space-charge action leading to breakdown. (Streamer action.)

The preceding categories are further detailed below.

A. In regard to the cathode active mechanisms, these all lead to a type of breakdown that is characteristic of the state of the cathode and the nature of the agency active. As a group, they lead to what are now described as classical Townsend discharges. They are associated with very characteristic time intervals, resulting from the transit time of the agencies, ions, photons, or metastable atoms from the region of the anode, where the intensive ionization occurs. The secondary electrons liberated are all subject to loss to the cathode by back diffusion at low X/p. They all lead to the same type of equations of breakdown, except that while *all* ions reach the cathode, photons and metastable states are subject to geometrical attenuation through the solid angle subtended by the cathode at the anode. Photons are further subject to attenuation by absorption and perhaps by delay in the gas in transit, while metastable states are subject to destruction by impacts in the gas. The effects can all appear simultaneously, and will be difficult to segregate by static measurements such as Townsend's, while they will be segregated by dynamic techniques with oscilloscopic analysis.

B(1). The agencies active in the gas in uniform fields require some discussion relative to principal locus of occurrence in the gap and the field geometry.

1. In a sense, if ionization by positive ions occurs in a uniform field in the gas, this action will simulate a cathode mechanism more than that of photons and second-class impacts. While positive ions ionize all across the gap from the anode where they were first largely created, if β is effective they will by cumulative effect produce many of their electrons near the cathode where they can simulate a cathode mechanism. It will thus not be strange to note a formal similarity between the relations for β/a and γ.

2. In regard to the action of photons in the gas, it will be noted that if the absorption coefficient μ for photoionizing radiations in the gas is such that $1/\mu$ is of the order of $1/a$ or less, the new electrons will be produced in the gas nearly *in situ*. Such electrons cannot contribute as secondary agencies to the buildup of a breakdown in a uniform field. All they do is to augment the value of a, so that the a measured with $i = i_0\, \epsilon^{ax}$ will be $i = i_0\, \epsilon^{a'x}$, with $a' = a + f\xi$, where f is the number of photons created per ion pair, and ξ is the fraction ionizing near the region of their origin. If $1/\mu$ approaches the distance

from anode to cathode, and the value of $h\nu$ exceeds ϕe, the work function of the surface, the action will be a cathode γ_p action. As detailed analysis will later show, the effectiveness of intermediate values of $1/\hat{\mu}$ in uniform field geometry is trifling. The action where $1/\mu$ is comparable with $1/a$ in uniform field geometry was first clearly observed by D. H. Hale in hydrogen, and might be termed the "Hale effect."

3. The action of metastable states, having an energy greater than some component present in small amount in a vehicular gas, will act to cause increased ionization *in situ* near the point of origin in an avalanche. Such action was first noted by F. M. Penning and A. A. Kruithoff, in Ne with 0.1% or less of argon, where the first Townsend coefficient was found to be increased by a factor as high as 20 at a given potential relative to the pure vehicular gas. This is known as the "Penning effect," in honor of its distinguished discoverer. A somewhat similar action occurs whereby inert gas atoms excited to within some 1.5 volts or less of their ionizing potential will collide within 10^{-7} second with a neutral atom, yielding a molecular, inert gas ion and an electron. This action, called the "Hornbeck-Molnar effect" after the discoverers, has been observed to increase a by 100% under proper conditions. Many delayed reactions have been observed, by which such states interacting yield atomic ions. These actions at lower pressures may lead to pressure-dependent values of a. All act to delay and diffuse avalanches slightly. It is only where the metastables are not destroyed and can reach the cathode that they produce a γ_m. In the intermediate region, such actions are of no interest.[1] Thus, more generally, photon or metastable action in the gas in uniform field geometry primarily either only increases a or yields a cathode γ mechanism.

B(2). In asymmetrical or nonuniform fields, however, photoelectric action in the gas becomes a very important secondary action, leading to breakdown in the high-field anode regions or in high space-charge, distorted fields in mid-gap. Two types of action may result.

1. If $1/\mu$ is of the order of 0.1 cm, then a self-sustaining discharge by photoionization in the gas will propagate over the anode surface at high speed. This is the process present in fast, self-

---

[1]In his analysis of metastable atoms as a secondary mechanism, shown in section 15, J. P. Molnar derived relations in which the ionization by metastable atoms in the gas through the positive ions can be regarded as a secondary mechanism acting on the cathode; i.e., as a sort of γ mechanism. He did not get any experimental data on the effect. Observations of Penning, Bowls, and Hale indicate that in Townsend-type measurements, it appears segregated in a.

quenching Geiger counters and in the burst-pulse corona in air at higher pressures.

2. If $1/\mu \sim 10^{-2}$ cm, and/or geometrical conditions are favorable, when fields are adequate, a discharge propagating at high speed by space-charge distortion and photoionization in the gas will proceed as a *streamer* normally from the anode, or will occur in mid-gap in a space-charge distorted gap. This can lead to a spark.

The breakdowns caused by 1 and 2 will have thresholds at lower fields than some cathode mechanisms in asymmetrical gaps. Such secondary mechanisms cannot be ignored.

C. Beyond the categories of secondary mechanisms indicated above, further actions should be considered.

1. There is nothing to prevent several mechanisms being active at the same time. This is particularly true of the cathode mechanisms. In fact, in the same gap with the same gas, the breakdown condition will be determined by one mechanism at higher pressures and a different one at lower pressures. It can also happen, by changing the time scale of observation, that as many as three different breakdown thresholds, determined by the three cathode mechanisms, will be observed.

2. In addition to the principal actions (A 1, 2, and 3, and B(2) 1 and 2), there are other actions that are not strictly secondary mechanisms, sometimes associated with conventional forms of gaseous breakdown. These, in the initial absence of gas, lead to breakdowns of their own. These are actions caused by very high, localized fields at points on cathodes, which merit understanding. They are:

a) Field emission of electrons from metal cathodes, often improperly invoked as secondary agents in discharges.

b) Spurious currents from specks of charged insulators on cathode surfaces, sometimes called Malter, or Paetow, effect (32).

3. There must also be discussed a phenomenon occurring in a Townsend type of static measurement of α and γ in which the log $i/i_0\text{-}x$ curves show an upcurving that might be ascribed to a γ mechanism, but is a result of space-charge distortion in the gap resulting from too large a photoelectric current density $j_0 = i_0/A$, when current amplification owing to a large x becomes adequate. It can lead to a spark with a low or inappreciable γ, which is not causing the upcurving of the log $i/i_0\text{-}x$ curves.

In what follows, it is proposed to consider the mechanisms outlined above in several sequentially numbered sections.

§ 3. Liberation of Electrons at the Cathode by Positive Ion Bombardment.

It had early been noted that positive ions were able to liberate electrons from surfaces on impact, and the subject has been studied extensively (15). Most investigations have been made with positive ions of considerable energy. Recent studies of H. D. Hagstrum, and of J. H. Parker, Jr., in the author's laboratory, indicate that some ions of practically zero kinetic energy can liberate electrons from metal surfaces (15). Studies of W. J. Jackson (15), using the alkali ions Na^+ and K^+, in which the ionization potential was less than the work function of the surfaces investigated, showed that given adequate kinetic energy, even these ions could liberate electrons from any metal surfaces. If given some 10^3 volts of energy, the probability of secondary emission by alkali ions on then *supposedly* degassed surfaces rose to the order of unity, and became vanishingly small at lower energies of the order of 100 volts.

Since this chapter was first written, experimental vacuum techniques and ion sources have developed to a point where really reliable studies of γ_i on clean and gas-coated surfaces at high and low ion energies are possible. Recently, H. D. Hagstrum at Bell Laboratories and J. H. Parker, Jr., in the author's laboratory have made studies of considerable interest. These studies have also aided materially in developing theory. In view of the very great importance of electron liberation by positive ion impact in many cathode-conditioned discharges, the recent data of Parker and of Hagstrum will be given *in extenso*.

Parker used a Finkelstein ion source consisting of a hot cathode electron beam from a disc cathode at the end of a discharge tube, coaxial cylindrical anode cylinder, and a negative disc repeller plate opposite the cathode with a hole for ion extraction in its center. The gas pressure was low, of the order of 10^{-4} mm, and a coaxial magnetic field and repeller plate caused the electron paths to spiral back and forth, such that ionization was at a maximum. By suitable control of potentials used the ionization could be kept within such bounds that only singly ionized atoms or molecules were produced. This source yields ions of down to 2 volts energy spread when properly decelerated. The ion energies thus ranged from 2 to 200 volts in the study, and beam intensities with focusing were of the order of 10^{-8} ampere.

These ions struck targets of Ta and Pt which could be thoroughly outgassed. The Alpert vacuum techniques were used, with pressures down to 10^{-9} mm or better of background gas. Ions of A^+ were used on clean surfaces, and on surfaces contaminated with A, H_2, N_2, and

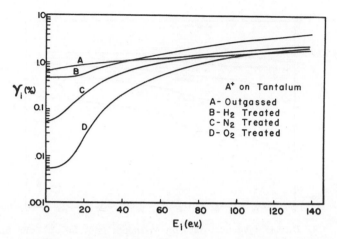

Fig. 9.2. Parker's vacuum data on γ_i in per cent for A^+ ions on flashed Ta, from 2 to 150 e.v., for clean surfaces and for surfaces contaminated by various gases.

O_2. Ions of hydrogen, nitrogen, and oxygen could be used on the surfaces coated with the parent gas. Hagstrum also used superb vacuum techniques and beams of ions of known mass, using differential pumping and a magnetic mass spectrograph. Measured in Parker's work were the secondary electron emissions per positive ion impact in per cent as a function of electron energy, from 2 volts to about 150 volts.

The results for A^+ on flashed Ta are shown in figure 9.2. Curve A is representative of the data after heating and flashing the Ta target to 1,400° C. Data were reproducible on different days to ± 5%. The drift in γ_i after flash was slow and small. With target cold it was 20% in 1 hour and only 30% after 24 hours. As the tube had A gas present at less than 10^{-4} mm, the drift could have been caused by A. Since the impurity of the A was less than 5×10^{-3}%, the partial pressure of impurities was less than 10^{-9} mm. Use of a different tube and target arrangement in which measurements could be made within 25 seconds after flashing confirmed the slow drift, and indicated that no major coating occurred subsequent to flashing except that associated with the slow drift. The conclusion was that flashing did not remove a basic gas film from the Ta surface, and that the later decrease in γ_i with time was caused by the adsorption of some gas with low sticking coefficient on the already coated Ta surface. Fortunately, Hagstrum, working with He^+ ions on Ta, had previously been forced to conclude that there is a basic gas film on Ta that is not removed on flashing to 1,475° C., but enters into the metal and returns to the surface on

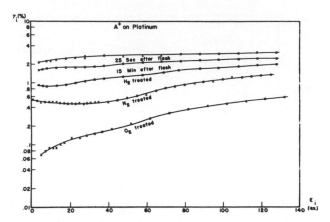

Fig. 9.3. Parker's vacuum data on γ_i in per cent for A^+ ions on flashed Pt, from 2 to 150 e.v., for clean surfaces and for surfaces contaminated by exposure to certain gases for a few minutes.

cooling. Thus, the curve A is for gas-covered Ta, and any large change in γ_i after flash results from the addition to the already coated surface of a few less tightly bound atoms. To check the conclusions, γ_i for He^+ ions on flashed Ta was tried over the energy range of 10 to 150 e.v., where it was essentially constant, and found to be 13%; while Hagstrum had observed 14% for the same conditions.

The data for A^+ on flashed Ta of figure 9.2 may be compared with the data of Molnar from dynamic studies of γ_i on Ta at various values of X/p and p, in which γ_i ranged from 0.5% to 2.0%. The value here observed was 0.7%. Molnar's data depended critically on accurate values of Townsend's first coefficient in A, which are difficult to measure with the requisite precision.

The effects of gas treatment are shown by curves B, C, and D of figure 9.2. When measurements were started after each gas treatment (usually, just exposure to the gas; occasionally, cathode bombardment by the ions of the gas), the value of γ_i at lower energies drifted slowly upward. This was probably caused by a cleanup of the adsorbed atoms. Note that the gas-contaminated surfaces had γ_i lowered by factors of 10 to 100 respectively for N_2 and O_2, for low-energy A^+ ions. While at higher energies the values of γ_i all rose to values near those for the flashed surfaces above, perhaps 70 volts energy, H_2 lowered γ_i only slightly at low energies, but at higher energies appeared to increase γ_i above that for the flashed surfaces. These actions *in part* are to be anticipated from changes in work function by the gases. O_2 raises work functions by at least 1 volt, while bombardment with H^+

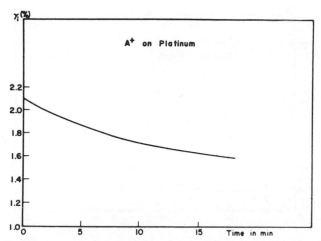

Fig. 9.4. Parker's data for γ_i of A^+ ions on Pt as a function of time in minutes, exposed only to *background* gas from the pure A gas leaking from the source at 10^{-4} mm.

ions lowers work functions perhaps 0.5 volt (11). At low energies it is clear that the A^+ interacts only with the surface layers, and so reflects the secondary emitting properties of these, while at higher energy, for O_2 and N_2 on Ta, the A^+ ions penetrate to the surface and yield an emission characteristic of pure Ta.

The results for A^+ incident on Pt are shown in figure 9.3. Each point represents a measurement made 25 seconds after the target was flashed to 1,400° C. With Pt a large drift .in γ_i with time was observed to occur after the flash, which is shown for A^+ ions in figure 9.4. This is also to be noted in the curve labeled "15 minutes after flash" in figure 9.3. After 24 hours the cold target had γ_i reduced to 33% of that 25 seconds after flashing. No doubt the flashing did not completely clean the surface, but the major portion of it was cleaned. The decrease in γ_i could have come from a trace of residual impurity in the chamber, or from some impurity in the A which was adsorbed as rapidly as the atoms struck the clean and reactive Pt surface.

With Pt the surface was treated with a gas through a 5-minute exposure without glow discharge. The gas was then pumped out for 10 minutes, and the measurement began after 15 minutes. However, in all cases gas treatment was far more effective in changing γ_i than was background impurity. It is again noted that at lower ion energies the lowering of γ_i was greatest, and that as the energy of the ions increased, the values of γ_i increased. With Pt, however, in contrast to Ta, values of γ_i did not all rise toward the same value of flashed

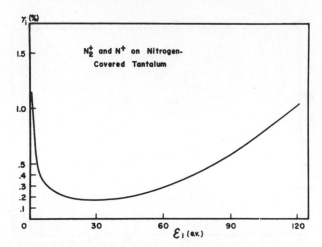

Fig. 9.5. Parker's data for nitrogen ions on nitrogen-coated tantalum.
Note the unusual initial decrease in γ_i with energy.

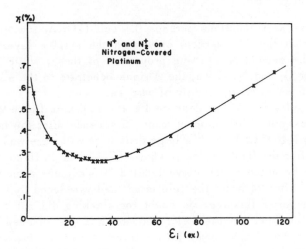

Fig. 9.6. Parker's data for nitrogen ions on nitrogen-coated platinum.

Pt as energy was raised, each gas tending toward a characteristic
lower value of its own. Again O_2 caused the greatest decrease, N_2
next, and H_2 next. The values of γ_i increased with time under continuous bombardment at constant energy, as with Ta, indicating some
cleanup. Bombardment of the Pt with N_2^+ ions to condition it only
decreased γ_i about 10% below that caused by simple 5-minute exposure
of flashed Pt to N_2. The difference between the behavior of Ta and
Pt films was that the A^+ ions at higher energies were readily able to

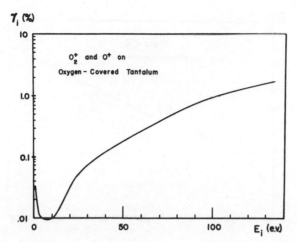

Fig. 9.7. Parker's data for oxygen ions on oxygen-coated tantalum.

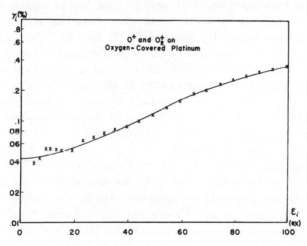

Fig. 9.8. Parker's data for oxygen ions on oxygen-coated platinum.

penetrate the loosely bound additional gas film on Ta, while with Pt the film produced by the gases covered the whole surface, and could not be penetrated readily by the faster A^+ ions.

From a practical point of view, the action of ions from molecular gases on surfaces is of more interest. Here, ions from N_2 gas, presumably mostly N_2^+ with some N^+ ions, were tried on these surfaces. The results are shown for Ta and Pt respectively, in figures 9.5 and 9.6. It is seen that the value of $\gamma_i \simeq 1\%$ at low ion energies falls to about 0.2% at energies of around 20 volts, and rises again, as with

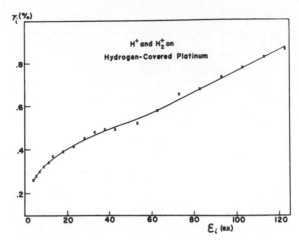

Fig. 9.9. Parker's data for hydrogen ions on hydrogen-coated platinum.

A^+ ions, at high energies. This decline from higher values of γ_i at low energies is real, and is shown by no other gas. The values of γ_i above 30 volts are not materially different for A^+ ions on N_2-coated surfaces. Such action is not unexpected, since the ionization potentials of N_2^+, N^+, and A^+ are not very different. The value of γ_i here observed is consistent with those of Huber (49) in the author's laboratory. Using pulsed nitrogen discharges in coaxial cylindrical geometry, γ_i for N_4^+ ions on clean Ni surfaces from 700 mm of N_2 pressure down at thermal ion energies, when corrected by Theobald's factor for back diffusion, was observed to be close to 2%.

The data for O_2^+ and O^+ ions on O_2-treated Ta and Pt are shown respectively in figures 9.7 and 9.8. The initial decrease in γ_i for Ta at low energies can well be spurious. Again, the values of γ_i for O_2^+ ions on O_2-treated Ta and Pt are not too different from those of A^+ ions on O_2-coated surfaces, although the ionization potentials of O_2 and O are somewhat less than for A, but apparently not critically so.

The data for H_2^+ and H^+ ions on H_2-covered Pt are shown in figure 9.9. The curve lies well below that for A^+ on H_2-treated Pt. Hydrogen ions on Ta were not studied. These data on H_2-coated Pt are in reasonable agreement with the observations of Hale shown in figure 9.22 (section 12), using the Townsend method, in which there was a strong γ at low X/p for Pt that was obviously a photoelectric γ_p, and a measurable γ_i appeared to come only at higher values of X/p. Likewise, E. J. Lauer, using pulsed coaxial cylindrical geometry with Ni cathodes in H_2 at pressures from 650 mm down to 100 mm at thermal ion energies, observed only a γ_p of the order of 0.1% to 1%, corrected

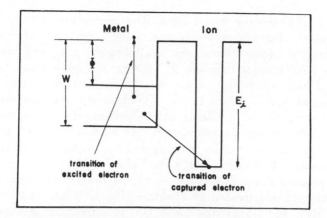

Fig. 9.10. Parker's diagram for one-step (Auger) mechanism
of potential ion liberation.

for back diffusion. Thus, γ_i for Lauer must have been less than $10^{-2}\%$.
In Lauer's work, and especially in Hale's, the Ni could well have
been heavily coated with H_2 owing to higher pressures, and in Hale's
by positive ion bombardment.

In interpreting the theory, it is unfortunate that most earlier studies
were done with the very energetic ions of He at 24.5 e.v. and of Ne
at 21.5 e.v. Thus, early theory emphasized a two-step capture process,
which can also be accompanied by a single-step process. For most
ions, such as A^+, with ionization potential of 16 e.v. or less, and
surfaces with work functions of the order of 5 e.v. or more, only the
single-step process occurs. Thus, while the theoretical interpretations
of the γ_i processes are fairly clear qualitatively, they are not as yet
on a sound quantitative basis. The theoretical interpretations of the
observations of Parker that follow are those that were concisely for-
mulated by Parker in his paper, in collaboration with the author.

♦　♦　♦　♦　♦

In principle, the mechanism can best be pictured in terms of the
schematic energy-level diagram of figure 9.10. Here the levels of
electrons in the metal and approaching ion are depicted as for infinite
separation. Actually, as the ion approaches the metal, its interaction
with the metal alters the levels somewhat. It is seen that what happens is that an electron in the Fermi band is captured into the ground
state of the ion, and then another metallic electron is excited to an

energy level above the Fermi band. The energy *available* to the excited electron depends on the region of the band from which the captured electron comes. Thus, the available energies can range from E_i to ϕe for the upper limit and E_i to W for the lower limit, where E_i is the ionization potential of the ion, ϕe is the work function, and W is the height of the surface barrier. On close approach the interaction energy decreases the available lower-limit energy, while the upper-limit available energy is unchanged. The method by which the effect of these interactions can be investigated has recently been independently developed by Hagstrum (15) and Varnerin (15).

The process described above is termed the *direct* process, originally proposed and treated by Shekhter (15). Oliphant and Moon (15), Massey (15), and Cobas and Lamb (15) proposed and treated a two-stage process. In this the ion is first neutralized to an excited state by resonance capture of a metallic electron. From this state the atom subsequently decays to the ground state with excitation of a second metallic electron. The process active with A^+ ions is only the direct process, since the values of ϕe for the surface used are greater than the difference between the lowest excited state and the ionization potential of A.

Now if part of the range of levels that may be occupied by the excited electron lies above the surface barrier, then those of the electrons in these levels that are directed toward the surface and are not reflected at the surface barrier are able to escape. The condition that the upper limit of the range of possible occupied levels lies above the surface barrier is that $E_i > 2\phi e$.

It is seen, then, that if ϕe increases because of surface contamination, the number of excited electrons in levels above the surface barrier will be less, and thus γ_i will be decreased. It is thus essential to regard work functions and change in work function as gases are adsorbed. No work-function data were obtained in these studies. However, Oatley (16) and others have found that H_2 *decreases* the work function of Pt slightly, while O_2 increases ϕe by at least a volt. Weissler (16) has studied the changes in work function of surfaces of W and Ag after bombardment with hydrogen, nitrogen, and oxygen ions. Quite uniformly, bombardment with A^+ or N_2^+ ions cleaned up the surface and restored the work function nearly to its normal value, while H_2 decreased the work function by a few tenths of a volt, and O_2 increased it by the order of a volt or more. No data on Ta are available. On the other hand, Bosworth and Rideal (16) report that H_2, N_2, and O_2 films *all* increase the work function of W. Doubtless, the conditions of formation and the nature of the films differed from those of Weissler and others. Accepting Oatley and Weissler's conclusions, it appears that there must be another action causing a reduction in γ_i besides that of an increase in ϕe. This is borne out by the following data. Hagstrum (15), whose Ta was in the same state as that used here, observed a work function of 4.9 volts, and the Ta had a gas film on it. As observed in this study, flashing the Pt target removed most of the active gas films, so that the work function of the Pt used was not less than the accepted work functions of clean Pt of value 5.3 volts. In consequence, if the value of the work function alone determines γ_i, the γ_i for Ta should be greater than that for Pt. Actually, the reverse is true, as noted. Again Hagstrum observed that for He^+ ions on Mo, after the background gas had formed a monolayer on the target, γ_i was lowered by 30%, while ϕe had not changed by more than 0.1 volt.

A guess as to the nature of this action comes from Hagstrum's observation that the energy distribution of electrons from the gas-covered surface had more slow electrons than that from the clean surface. This indicates that the probability of the excited electron occupying a low level in the range of levels available to it is greater for the gas-covered surface than for the clean one. Such a condition would obviously also lower γ_i. The process active may be crudely envisioned as follows: With a clean surface neutralization involves direct interaction with only one electron of the Fermi band. With a covered surface, it could well involve two, for the electrons causing neutralization can come from a local state produced by an adsorbed gas atom. In general, since such a local level does not lie in the Fermi band, it will be refilled after neutralization by a metallic electron. Such a two-step process could well act to lower the energy available to the excited electron.

Thus, gas coatings not only lower γ_i by raising ϕe, but also lower γ_i by reducing the *available* energy for excitation by a more complicated neutralization process. If the *lowering* of ϕe, for instance by H_2 treatment, is small, the value of γ_i can still be decreased by H_2 films because of reduction of available escape energy. Likewise, clean Pt could yield a higher γ_i despite its 0.4-volt higher value of ϕe relative to Ta, as Ta has a gas film at its surface.

That γ_i increases with ion energy is not surprising, since kinetic liberation superposes on potential for all surfaces. For gas-treated surfaces the observed increase of γ_i with energy is greater than for clean surfaces. This is to be expected, for aside from some "cleanup" of the film by high-energy bombardment, more of the high-energy ions penetrate the gas film and interact directly with metallic electrons;

i.e., the interaction time with the local gas surface states is decreased relative to that with the lattice.

The initial decrease in γ_i with ion energy, observed *only* with nitrogen ions, can be accounted for by the very high energy of association of N atoms to form N_2 molecules. Thus, in addition to the neutralization energy of N^+ ions, these can react at the surface to yield N_2 at 9.6 e.v., and this energy may be available for electron liberation. Such a reaction may take place for slowly moving, low-energy ions, and may decrease as ion energy increases.

♦ ♦ ♦ ♦ ♦

H. D. Hagstrum (15) began his studies at about the same time as the studies ending in Parker's work were begun in the author's laboratory. With his own skill, together with the exceptional facilities available in the Bell Laboratories, Hagstrum has carried on a series of investigations for different ions on various metals, aimed primarily at the behavior of clean surfaces and to develop the basic theory. He used a more conventional ion source than Parker's, consisting of a magnetic field deflector. This did not enable him to go below 10 volts of ion energy. However, it gave him control of the ion species used, and permitted energy-distribution curves of the electrons to be studied. He varied ion energies from 10 to 1,000 volts. His vacuum techniques were equal to or slightly superior to Parker's, as he was concerned with cleanliness of surfaces, and by differential pumping maintained lower pressures in his measuring chamber, as he was not interested in gassy surfaces. Much time was spent in studying the adsorption or formation of gas films by known or background gases as a function of time and pressure. These films could be studied by flashing his target to high temperatures and measuring Δp, the pressure increase in a known volume owing to the gas released.

His studies have been reported largely in two published papers and two subsequent theoretical papers, first published as abstracts and now appearing in their final form (15). Studied were clean Mo surfaces with He^+, He^{++}, and He_2^+ ions, similar surfaces using "monolayers" of He gas, and Ta surfaces which could be flashed clean, but always reformed some monolayer from gas dissolved in Ta with He^+, He^{++}, and He_2^+ ions. Finally, clean W was studied, with He^+, Ne^+, A^+, Kr^+, and Xe^+ ions from 10 to 1,000 volts, as well as He^{++}, Ne^{++}, Ne^{+++}, A^{++}, and A^{+++}; Kr with from II to IV charges, and Xe with from II to V charges.

TABLE 9.1

Properties of Ions and Metals Involved in Secondary
Emission Studies, after Hagstrum

Ion or State	Energy in e.v.	For Metals		
		ϕe	$\triangle$ Width Cond. Band	Depth Potential Well
He^+	24.58	Mo 4.27	~ 6.5	~ 10.8
He^{++}	78.98	Ta 4.9	–	–
He_2^+	16.8	(not clean)		
He^m	19.81	W 4.6	~ 6.3	~ 10.9
He. $E_i - E_m = \epsilon.$	4.77			
Ne^+	21.559	$\phi e = W_A - \triangle^-$		
Ne^m	16.6			
A^+	15.756			
A^m	11.57			
Kr^+	13.996			
Kr^m	9.9			
Xe^+	12.127			
Xe^m	8.3			

Before proceeding to give results in detail, the data assembled in table 9.1 are perhaps in order. These have to do with the ion energies and work functions involved.

It must next be noted that for all ions for which $E_i > 2\phi e$, it was recognized that electron liberation for low-energy ions was, in virtue of the potential energy of the ion, "potential" liberation. However, alkali ions with $E_i < 2\phi e$ at appropriate kinetic energies were earlier supposed to liberate electrons by a kinetic or "thermal" process. In Parker and Hagstrum's work, only potential liberation is considered.

As suggested in Parker's work, there are two assumed liberation processes. Originally, Oliphant, and after him most other workers, considered a two-stage process by which an electron in the Fermi level was captured into the metastable state of the atom, and then the metastable state interacted with metallic electrons and by impacts of the second class liberated an electron from the Fermi band. This two-stage process has been assumed general for energetic ions like He, though it was recognized that less energetic states could only liberate by a single-stage process. Thus, Parker recognized that A^+ on Ta liberated only by the one-step process.

The more extensive investigations of Hagstrum now indicate that the two-stage, resonance-capture process is a rare occurrence, applicable only to He^+ on Mo and to a limited extent, perhaps 9%, for

Ne on W. Otherwise, all liberation so far accurately studied is by the one-step process. The processes are characterized as follows by Hagstrum.

A. *Direct Single-Step (Auger) Capture Process.*

This has been pictured in Parker's discussion, preceding. It occurs if $\epsilon = E_i - E_m$ is less than ϕe, which prohibits an electron being captured into the metastable level directly. If $\epsilon > \phi e$ the single-step process can still occur. The two-step process may not be likely unless a state is isoenergetic with the top of the filled band in the metal. This applies so far only for He$^+$ on Mo, and to a less extent for Ne$^+$ on W. The single-step process is accordingly the *common* process.

The maximum and minimum energies of emission in this mechanism are given below.

Maximum energy: $E_i - 2\phi e$.
Minimum energy: $E_i - W_A$.

For He$^+$ on W, $\epsilon = 4.77$, $\phi e = 4.6$, $E_i - 2\phi e = 15.4$, and $E_i - W_A = 13.7$. In this process, theory places the probability of emission as of the order of 0.1.

B. *Induced Resonance Capture; a Two-Step Process.*

This occurs if $\epsilon > \phi e$, and if the metastable level is isoenergetic with the top of the filled band in the metal. This applies to the ^3S state of He$^+$ on Mo. In this case the energies are bounded by maximum energy.

Minimum energy: $E_i - \epsilon - W_A$.
Maximum energy: $E_i - \epsilon - \phi e$.

For He$^+$ on Mo, this is 9 e.v. minimum and 15.5 e.v. maximum. Concerning this process for He, the probability of capture of an electron at 3.5 Å with 25-volt He$^+$ ions is unity, and becomes unity at 4 to 5 Å from the surface for 10-volt He$^+$. Theory indicates that the chance of no electron exchange relative to exchange at the surface is 0.05. The process cannot occur for He on Ta.

It appears that Mo will adsorb monolayers of He. Thus, with Mo, both clean surfaces and surfaces of Mo with monolayers of inert gases are formed. Ta, as stated, provides its own monolayer from dissolved gas, and is never gas-free, but is clean. W, properly outgassed and maintained at background pressures of 10^{-10} mm of residual gas, remained clean for thirty minutes or more. This applied also to the surfaces of Ta and Mo in regard to foreign gases.

TABLE 9.2

Hagstrum's Values of γ_i for Various Ions on Clean or
Slightly Gassy Surfaces of Mo, Ta, and W

Ion	Surface	γ_i at 10 Volts	γ_i at 1,000 Volts
He^{++}	Monolayer He on Mo	0.8	0.9
He^{++}	Pure Mo	0.72	$\sim$0.72
He^{+}	Pure Mo	0.25	$\sim$0.25
He^{+}	Monolayer He on Mo	0.15	0.25
He_2^{+}	Monolayer He on Mo	0.13	—
He^{++}	Ta(unknown monolayer)	0.6	0.9
He^{+}	Ta(unknown monolayer)	0.14	0.20
He_2^{+}	Ta(unknown monolayer)	0.10	—
		Extrapolated to 0.1 Volt	
He^{+}	W pure	0.295	0.27
Ne^{+}	W pure	0.213	0.25
A^{+}	W pure	0.095	0.11
Kr^{+}	W pure	0.0475	0.06
Xe^{+}	W pure	0.019	0.019
		At 200 Volts	
He^{++}	W pure	0.74	0.82
Ne^{++}	W pure	0.72	0.70
Ne^{+++}	W pure	1.82	1.6
A^{++}	W pure	0.42	0.36
A^{+++}	W pure	1.2	1.08
Kr^{++}	W pure	0.32	0.27
Kr^{+++}	W pure	1.32	0.76
Kr^{++++}	W pure	2.16	1.90
Xe^{++}	W pure	0.24	0.18
Xe^{+++}	W pure	0.81	0.69
Xe^{++++}	W pure	1.64	1.41
Xe^{+++++}	W pure	2.84	2.46

With background pressures of 10^{-6} mm, a monolayer of N_2 forms on W in 0.66 sec. Hagstrum also shows that the monolayer of N_2 on W is 98% pure N_2 if He is present, and 92% pure N_2 with Ne present. The H_2 monolayer has one-third the atoms of the N_2 layer. Adsorption of a monolayer of H_2 reduced γ_i with He^+ by 10%, and γ_i with Ne^+ by 18%. Adsorption of a monolayer of N_2 reduced γ_i for He^+ by 18%, and γ_i for Ne^+ by 23%. These studies were made for ions of 200 volts energy on W. In general, the adsorption of H_2 or N_2 reduced the relative number of fast electrons ejected by He^+ and Ne^+.

The data obtained from various inert gas ions on surfaces may be summarized as in table 9.2.

The following conclusions may at once be drawn.

§3

1. In conformity with Parker, but contrary to practically all of the earlier work, Hagstrum finds γ_i, caused by either the single-step (Auger) or the two-step process, to be virtually independent of the ion energy on clean metal surfaces from 10 to 1,000 volts.

2. There is some indication that for surfaces with monolayers of gas, as in Parker's work, there will be a gradual increase in γ_i with energy up to 1,000 volts. Since the surfaces of Oliphant (15) and previous workers were contaminated, it is possible to account for the difference as being caused by gas films. The effect of really thick gas layers on W will be mentioned later.

3. The values of γ_i for He^{++}, He^+, and He_2^+ on both Mo and Ta surfaces were roughly in the order of energies available after neutralization, namely, $E_i - 2\phi e$ for each type of ion. This signifies that the emission is almost all caused by the potential energy of the ions. The constancy of γ_i up to 1,000 volts further indicates that the process is one based on potential, not kinetic, energy.

4. He^{++} can liberate by two possible mechanisms. The first is neutralization in steps which could yield a γ_i of 0.7. The other is direct ejection by capture into a low level and ionization by electron impact. Fast electrons of the order of 70 volts would have a probability of ejection of about 0.7, so that no conclusion can be drawn. Since no electrons are emitted by these ions with energies greater than 40 volts, it appears that the stepwise neutralization is the more likely.

5. One of the important observations for all clean surfaces was that reflection of ions or neutral metastables from the surface at low energies at normal impact was negligibly small, i.e., less than 1%. As energies increased from 40 to 1,000 volts, the fraction reflected increased to some per cent for such surfaces.

6. With no reflection, and the chance of capture or liberation within the surface of near unity, the value of the probability of emission P_e, and thus of γ_i, should be equal to or greater than 0.5 if the neutralization occurs outside of the barrier. If liberated inside the barrier, the probability of emission is $\lesssim 0.5$. Thus, since γ_i, even for the He^+ ions with resonance capture from Mo, is only 0.25, and for the Auger process is only of the order of 0.1, there must be attrition of the electrons liberated inside the barrier by reflection at the surface.

Hagstrum assumes that only those electrons incident at an angle $\theta > \theta_c$ with the surface can escape. The value of θ_c can be calculated by the relation

$$\cos \theta_c = \left(\frac{W_A}{E_K}\right)^{\frac{1}{2}} \quad \text{with} \quad E_K = E_i - \epsilon.$$

TABLE 9.3

Energy Limits of Electrons on Clean and Gassy Surfaces of Mo and Ta
Emitted at Different Ion Energies, as Observed by Hagstrum

Ion	Ion Energy in Volts	Surface Condition	One Group		Two Groups	
			Minimum Energy	Maximum Energy	Minimum Energy	Maximum Energy
He^+	40	Clean Mo	0	16	—	—
He^+	40	Mo + He layer	0	10	—	—
He^+	200	Clean Mo	0	9	9	16
He^+	200	Mo + He layer	Many slow	—	Less fast	—
He^+	1,000	Clean Mo	0	9	9	20
He^+	1,000	Mo + He layer	0	8(Many)	Very few	20
He^{++}	200	Clean Mo	0	16	16	30
He^+	40	Ta + own layer	0	6(Weak cutoff peak)	—	15 (Sharp)
He^+	1,000	Ta + own layer	A few electrons $> E_i - 2\phi e$			
He_2^+	1,000	Ta + own layer	A few electrons $> E_i - 2\phi e$			
He^{++}	1,000	Ta + own layer	Tailing off toward > 20 volts.			

Thus, P_{escape} or P_e becomes

$$(9.8) \quad P_e = \frac{1}{4\pi} \int_0^{\theta_c} 2\pi \sin\theta \, d\theta = \frac{1}{2}(1 - \cos\theta_c) = \frac{1}{2}\left(1 - \frac{W_A}{E_K}\right)^{\frac{1}{2}}.$$

Since γ_i is the product of the resonance-captured electrons and P_e, it is possible to calculate γ_i for He^+ on clean Mo to lie between 0.13 and 0.18. Since the γ_i observed is 0.25, a considerable fraction of the electrons start inside the barrier, but some are outside. Thus, γ_i is lowered because a considerable fraction of the resonance-captured atoms penetrate the barrier before releasing the electron.

Since all of the single-step (Auger) process liberations require neutralization or capture within the barrier, the values for γ_i by this process will have around 0.1 and below.

The ion He_2^+ neutralizes inside the barrier and dissociates into true normal He atoms. The energy by which the He_2^+ state lies above the repulsive potential for He_2 at the same nuclear level is recovered and used to extract the neutralizing electron and to excite the ejected electron.

7. Hagstrum was able to make retarding potential studies of the emitted electrons, using a plane opposing the plane of the emitting foil. This geometry has the disadvantage that electrons emitted with low energy at more grazing angles may appear to be less energetic than they really are. Thus, they give many more electrons around 0 energy than are really emitted. Such curves were obtained with Mo

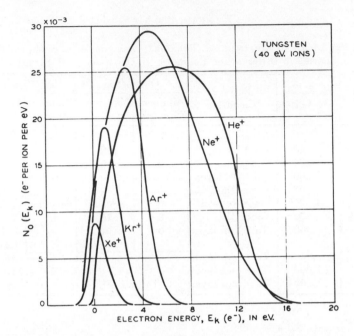

Fig. 9.11. Hagstrum's energy-distribution curves of 40-e.v. inert gas
ions on W as number of electrons per ion per e.v.

and Ta for 40, 200, and 1,000 volt ions. The curves were corrected
for contact potentials and differentiated to give the electron-energy
distribution. The results are reported in table 9.3.

Similar data for the variously singly charged ions of 40 volts energy
on clean W are shown in figure 9.11.

8. The energy distributions of the emitted electrons for He^+ on pure
Mo are like those observed for metastables in the work of Oliphant and
of Greene (15). They are contrary in two aspects to those observed
by Oliphant for He^+ ions on Mo.

First, Oliphant's curves for He^+ showed no electrons of zero energy,
while those of Hagstrum and of Greene for He^m have electrons of 0
energy. Instead, Oliphant's ion curves cut off sharply at 1.9 volts.
His curves showed a peak at 20 not observed by Hagstrum. Both of
these limits fitted the theory of Oliphant with the data then at hand
on Mo. It is probable that Oliphant's curves were not properly corrected for contact potentials, thus giving no electrons with zero energy.
The extension of Oliphant's curve to 20 volts indicates admixture of
He^{++} ions not suspected by Oliphant in his beam.

9. Quite generally, the effect of gas films, both on Ta and mono-layers of He on Mo, was to reduce the number of fast secondaries relative to clean metal and to give many more slow electrons. It is probable that for He^+ on clean Mo, there should not have been many slow electrons. The presence of these in Hagstrum's study was owing to the repulsion of the electrons at grazing emergence by the plane parallel retard field, these electrons with increasing retarding potential registering as slow electrons. The effect of gas layers seems to be to retard and extract energy from the escaping electrons.

10. The maximum velocity of secondary electrons at 15.5 volts is consistent with the two-stage resonance-capture process. The 9-volt electrons were clearly noted for the He^+ on pure Mo above 200 volts.

11. In some cases there are a very few electrons ejected, with more than the energy limit expected. This is caused by the distortion of the lattice and its energy levels on close approach of the ion. The faster the ion, the more the distortion before capture.

12. For the different ions on clean W, where monolayers do not form with inert gases, the only ion showing resonant capture and the two-step process is Ne^+, and this occurs only to the extent of 9%.

13. Only He^+ and Ne^+ have sufficient excess energy so that all the electrons, if properly directed, can leave the metal. For A^+, Kr^+, and Xe^+, only electrons from the top 50, 40, and 25% respectively of the filled level have a chance to escape.

14. There are minor variations of γ_i with ion energy for these various processes, which are shown in figure 9.12, kindly supplied by Hagstrum. They are largely the effects of broadening the energy distribution in virtue of the uncertainty principle as the ion is neutralized closer and closer to the metal surface with increased energy. This action can be made to account for an initial drop in the γ_i energy curve for He^+, and rises in the A^+, Kr^+, and Xe^+ curves. A rise for He^+ at higher energies may be the result of a new mechanism coming in. Ne^+ ions rise at first with energy through an increase of the proportion of the resonant capture with faster ions. In any case, these changes are relatively minor.

15. Careful comparison between the emission γ_i for the two isotopic Ne ions showed very little difference, indicating that no material difference is produced which might be associated with a temperature effect.

16. The energy-distribution curves plotted as the number of electrons of a given energy in electrons per ion per electron volt are shown as furnished the author by Hagstrum in figure 9.11. The negative ordinates in energy need not cause concern. These are caused

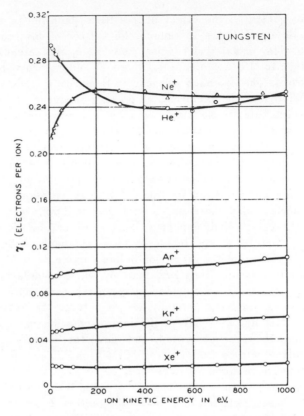

Fig. 9.12. Hagstrum's curves of γ_i for singly charged
inert gas ions on W as a function of energy.

by the fringing magnetic fields, and the effect is greater on the electrons from heavier ions. Correction for this would start all curves at
0 energy. Note in particular the higher-energy ends and the differences
in Ne+ and He+, owing to the presence of two-step capture in Ne to
9%. Careful study of the feet of the energy-distribution curves shows
that the asymptotic portions result from the distortions produced close
to the lattice.

17. Hagstrum has kindly provided the data shown in table 9.2 and
in figure 9.13 for the values of γ_i for the multiply charged ions of He,
Ne, A, Kr, and Xe on W, from roughly 200 to 1,000 volts. It is to be
noted that from He++ on, multiply charged ions have γ_i decrease as
energy increases. Considering the complexity of the energy-exchange
and neutralization processes, this increased inefficiency of liberation
with impact energy and velocity of penetration need not be surprising.

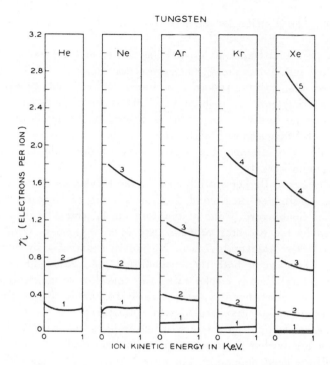

Fig. 9.13. Hagstrum's data for emission of electrons at energies from 200 to 1,000 e.v. for multiply charged inert gas ions on clean W.

18. In a private communication, Hagstrum gives some data on very dirty surfaces. Thus, a W surface was placed in vacuum after simple mechanical cleaning and grease removal by proper solvents. For contaminated W, the value for the He⁺ ion ranged from 0.15 at 10 e.v. to 0.72 at 1,000 e.v., while for He⁺ on clean W, the values ranged from 0.24 to 0.29.

19. The effect of contamination on the energy distribution of the ejected electrons was equally startling. For the contaminated W, the width of the electron distribution at half maximum was about 20% of the width of the distribution at half maximum for the clean surfaces shown in figure 9.11. The maximum kinetic energy for the electron distribution on the dirty surface seems to be about half the maximum kinetic energy for the clean surface. The peak of the distribution is correspondingly higher.

20. Heating such a target to 500° C. is ineffective on such a film. This shows the importance of proper cleaning and outgassing. Heating the surface to 900° C. does have the effect of greatly improving the

situation. The distribution then is like that of W with some monolayer on it.

It is seen that Hagstrum's work has done much to clarify the basic principles underlying the γ_i mechanism for clean surfaces. It is also clear that his results, reported in items 18, 19, and 20 above, bear on the earlier work. It is urgent at this point that γ_i be studied for alkali ions on really clean surfaces before much clarification on the concept of "temperature" liberation can be undertaken. It will thus be necessary to discuss the earlier work in the light of the work of Hagstrum and Parker.

In contrast to Parker's study, where the thickness of the gas layers was not determined on Pt and Ta, the studies of Hagstrum show the effects of monolayers. None of the data on W, which like Ta liberates electrons by the one-step process, are in disagreement with Parker's findings, where thicker layers of N_2 and H_2 reduced γ_i by much larger factors. The data of both these observers are good, and in principle complementary; Parker emphasizing the very low energies and heavier gas coatings corresponding more closely to conditions of clean electrodes in pure gas discharges, while Hagstrum was more interested in definable physical parameters of use in physical theory.

There are further comments that should be made. It is to be noted that while γ_i must depend on the work function of the surface, it must also depend on other factors connected with surface structure; i.e., the existence of surface states created either by adsorption of external gases or vapors, or owing to internal dissolved contaminants, and on clean surface of metal on crystal planes and orientations. It is also quite clear that from a molecular viewpoint, in no sense is the optically smooth, clean, outgassed surface homogeneous. Structural surface irregularities are of two orders of magnitude greater than the basic lattice dimensions, even for the smoothest of surfaces, as shown in many electron microscope pictures and in the field-emission studies of W. P. Dyke and others.

At very best, a cleaned surface will have elevated and depressed local layers of many lattice units. Superimposed on these is the orientation of crystallites or preferred crystallographic directions relative to the surface. Thus, the surface of a nonoriented, microcrystalline substance will have all sorts of crystal planes exposed, unless exacting special precautions are taken to orient the surface structures. As thermionic, field-emission, and now even the sputtering studies of Wehner show, such different axes have wide individual differences in work function, thermionic emission, and photoelectric emission, and have different sputtering rates. In fact, Wehner (17) has shown that by sputtering, a cleaner-cut surface etch may be achieved, emphasizing certain exposed crystal planes, than by chemical etch. Further, in sputtering, some crystal faces grow, while others erode. Since the routine procedures for cleaning surfaces are heating by electron bombardment or by induction furnace (best, by ionic bombardment, preferably with inert gas ions, using the surface as cathode), it is seen that surface structures of a patchy character can be altered (1) by recrystallization; (2) by movement of impurities from inside or by deposit of coated filament products from outside; and (3) by etching and crystal growth through sputtering, etc. It should also be noted that bombardment of surfaces of electrodes by gaseous ions (1) can create chemically relatively stable surface layers with suitable atoms or molecules; (2) can produce gas film coatings on the surface from occasional isolated atoms at preferred points, in thickness through monolayers up; and (3) will drive into the electrode structure a considerable number of atoms of the bombarding gas.

The data from glass cleanup studies in tubes, including the pumping action of the Alpert (18) vacuum gauges, indicate that at least one in the order of 10^4 ions incident upon the surface does not escape as a gas atom after neutralization, but remains *ab*sorbed in the electrode. These can usually only be removed by prolonged intense heating or by bombardment by another gas type. Gases like H_2 are in fact sufficiently soluble so that they diffuse through the whole metal, and are exceedingly hard to remove. Mass-spectrographic studies of Luhr (19) show that even N_2 is hard to remove. Other routine gases, such as O_2 and the halogens, form very thick layers. In consequence, as a rule the surfaces are thoroughly patchy. It can thus be concluded that neither work function measurements nor direct γ_i or γ_p measurements do more than give an over-all *average* description of the surface state.

Careful sparking-potential measurements may, from the sparking threshold observed, yield values of γ characteristic of those centers or points of highest effective emission if a is known with sufficient accuracy. However, it now appears that even for high-pressure sparks, the threshold is set by a low-order Townsend discharge acting through a γ_p which over the whole cathode builds up a space-charge distortion leading to a streamer spark. Thus, it is not a single point or a very few points of highest γ that set the threshold, but an aggregate of a *sufficient number* of such points *all over the cathode surface* that succeed in building up the space charge.

Even then, the character of all surfaces will be such that the adsorbed surface states will be in limited areas or regions of preferred orientation, and owing to the irregularity of the smoothest surfaces, the calculation leading to the concept of a *monolayer* is not too significant. Hence, if crystallographic surfaces comprising less than 10% of the real physical undulatory surface adsorb, for example, He atoms, a monolayer takes on a significance quite different from that calculated in number of He atoms per cm^2 of geometrical surface of optical smoothness, calculated in terms of the cross section of an individual He atom. Thus, actually the value of γ_i, even in the most uniform, simple surface structures, may come from only a small fraction of the total surface, presenting exposed planes of a certain sort; γ_i for the other regions being so low as to be inappreciable.

Again, by the same token, a photoelectric γ_p will emanate from centers created in one fashion or another, and may be quite different in character, behavior, and variation of efficiency with surface conditioning relative to γ_i. This is entirely aside from any photon absorption by the gas. Examples of such differences must be cited. Thus, Lauer observed a photon γ_p on a clean Ni surface in H$_2$ gas with cathode at low X/p, while he could detect no γ_i within an order of magnitude or more of the γ_p value. Pure A showed slightly delayed γ_p action from radiations of 1,250 Å of A$_2$ which were not absorbed in A gas, but had a low but definite γ_i on Ni at low X/p (26). Again, Parker observed that addition of an H$_2$ layer to Pt lowered γ_i for slow A$^+$ ions by a factor of 2. For H$^+$ and H$_2^+$ ions on Pt, an increase in ion energy raised γ_i by a factor of 5 at 200 volts.

In contrast, Theobald (20) found that after a glow discharge in H$_2$ with Pt as cathode, the value of the vacuum photo current between 2,300 and 2,537 Å was increased by a factor of the order of 100, though the change in energy of emitted photoelectrons was negligible. This indicates that the H$_2$ had multiplied the number of photoelectrically active centers initially with a certain threshold owing to γ_p. by a factor of 100 without altering the value of the work function involved. Likewise, bombardment of Pt with O$_2$ gave an unstable increase in photoemission which decayed on standing, while O$_2$ on Pt lowered γ_i for A$^+$ ions by a factor of 10^2 at low energies ($\sim$ 2 volts), and for O$_2^+$ and O$^+$ ions, lowered γ_i by a factor of 10 over the range of 2 and 200 volts. These data are sufficient to warn the reader against the earlier simpler generalizations that γ_i and γ_p might be similar because of their association with the work function, which is seen to be indeed a rather vague term for agencies acting in detail with areas of lattice dimensions on the surfaces.

At this point it is perhaps of importance to discuss briefly the conclusions drawn by various workers, beginning with Oliphant and

Moon, on electron liberation at higher energies of ion impact, originally described as a "temperature" type of emission. It had been noted almost universally that γ_i appeared to increase with ion energy from lower values at around 40 volts up to higher values when ion energies reached around 1,000 e.v., at which γ_i appeared to be near unity. Now it will be noted that for *clean* surfaces, or surfaces of Ta, with its characteristic layer from inside the metal, neither Hagstrum nor Parker observed any appreciable changes of γ_i with ion energy. With monolayers of N_2, H_2, and He, Hagstrum observed a decrease in γ_i of some 10% to 20%, and Parker observed really marked reduction of γ_i for gases like H_2, N_2, and O_2 by 1 to 2 orders of magnitude where thicker films formed. In all these cases, for Ta Parker found increases in γ_i which rapidly increased in value from 2 e.v. of ion-impact energy to near vacuum values when the ion energy reached 100 e.v. and thereafter remained constant, while in Pt the values increased to those characteristic for each gas from 2 e.v. to 100 e.v., and thereafter increased more slowly. He also noted that the bombardment by the ion beam was sputtering gas layers from the surfaces in increasing measure as ion energy increased. Parker's increases of γ_i with ion energies are consistent with Hagstrum's observations and conclusions, and are not to be associated too closely with increases at higher energies that had been observed by earlier workers.

Later observations of Hagstrum on clean W with a range of inert gas ions confirm this generalization, and permit some explanation of minor variations of γ_i with kinetic energy of ion impact. With He^+ alone, above 400 e.v. there was indication of a new process of electron liberation connected with energy or velocity. All these observations clearly indicate that below 1,000 e.v. there is little electron liberation by kinetic ion impact ("temperature" liberation) for clean metal surfaces. Both Hagstrum's data, with his change in energy distribution resulting from gas films, and Parker's data, definitely indicate that surface gas films decrease γ_i for ions of very low energy, and that increase of γ_i with ion energies appears *not* to stem from change in the recognized potential mechanism of liberation, but merely arises in some fashion through the penetration of more ions to interaction with the metal lattice and electrons. That is, for a range of from 2 to 100 e.v., the increased ion energy merely permits more ions to capture, by resonance or directly, electrons from the lattice, leading to potential emission. In fact, it is not illogical to assume that for a thick gas layer the slow ions may capture electrons from surface states of the gas layer, and thus lead to an inefficient mechanism of neutralization so far as γ_i goes.

§ 3

As energy increases, the ions tend to displace the gas atoms along the surface, or sputter them off, thus being more frequently able to interact directly with the surface. Since the energy of the adsorbed surface gas layers is certainly not much more than some 5 e.v. or less, the increase in kinetic energy of the ions to values of the order of 20 e.v. should materially improve the situation. The alteration of the energy distribution of emitted electrons with gas films can in this case be ascribed in part to energy losses of escaping electrons in the gas films, and perhaps at lower energies to the fact that with gas films the inefficient liberation of electrons from the surface states, leading to stepwise degradation of the energy, results in many more slow electrons.

It is also clear that in all of the earlier studies done with the vacuum techniques used before World War II, the target had *at least* "monolayers," and usually thicker layers, of background-impurity gases on them unless the electrodes were *quite hot* at the time of study. In all cases, gas films of varying degrees of thickness and tenacity on different metals were dealt with. There is nothing in the work of Parker or Hagstrum to show that for such films, as ion energy increases from 100 to 1,000 volts, γ_i may not increase in the fashion observed by Oliphant and Moon, Jackson, Greene, and by Chaudhri and Kahn (15). However, for really dirty W, Hagstrum has shown that with He^+ the value of γ_i rises continuously from low value to 0.72 at 1,000 volts, and that narrow energy distributions appear, akin to those observed by Oliphant. The increased emission was always accompanied by greater and greater quantities of slow or "thermal" electrons emitted from the gassy surfaces, as noted by Hagstrum.

In order properly to discuss the action, a brief reference is required to the earlier excellent pioneering studies of Oliphant and Moon, and to the subsequent studies of others, including the work of Greene and of Chaudhri and Kahn, which followed along the same general line. Some of the measurements of Oliphant and Moon suffered from unrecognized contact potential differences, since they found no electrons of energies below 1.9 e.v. This, while consistent with their theory, is inconsistent with the later data of Greene and of Hagstrum. They also found electrons of 20 volts for He^+ on Mo, which is energetically unlikely, as Hagstrum showed for clean Mo surfaces where the energy limit is 16.6 volts for the two-step process. These electrons probably came from the presence of He^{++} ions, as Hagstrum's data show.

Oliphant and Moon did not go to low ion energies, the lowest values being not less than 40 e.v. and more often 60. Thus, many of

Parker's data and some of Hagstrum's were not accessible to them. They did observe γ_i for He$^+$ on Mo of the order of 0.2 for 200-e.v. ions. Increasing energies to 500 e.v. yielded a slow increase in γ_i, which became 0.8 or 0.9 when 1,000 e.v. was reached. The change in γ_i was accompanied by a change in form of the electron-energy distribution, which perhaps indicated a second mechanism of "thermal" origin. The changes were, in general, quite like the changes observed by Hagstrum for change in distribution with monolayer gas-coated surfaces. The numbers of electrons with low energy increased, or better, *appeared*. Suspecting that a different mechanism was setting in, Oliphant and Moon investigated the emission of electrons by impact of *alkali* ions on Pt, where γ_i is less than ϕe, so that potential emission could not appear. This decreased the emission from their clean, outgassed surfaces. The value of γ_i was generally less than 1% unless the kinetic energy was very high. The retarding potential curves were quite different from those of the inert gas atoms. They shifted in value with ion energy and had many electrons of low energy. Logarithmic plots of electron current against retarding potential were linear. This suggested some sort of an emission of electrons having a Maxwellian energy distribution. The slope of the plots yielded the "temperatures" of the emitted electrons. The average electron energies varied with the target used, being 10,000° K. for an Al target (i.e., about 1.16 e.v.), and 66,000° K. or 7.7 e.v. for a Pt target for 600-volt K$^+$ ions. Chaudhri and Kahn extended these "temperature" studies, using Ni and Mo targets, both gassy and degassed (note that all targets were gassy by Hagstrum standards), with neutral atoms of K and Hg with energies in the order of 1,500 to 2,500 volts. The electrons emitted had distributions similar to those of Oliphant and Moon, with "temperatures" varying from 30,000° K. (3.48 e.v.) to 45,000° K. (5.22 e.v.).

The studies of D. Greene (15) in Emeléus' laboratory repeated Oliphant and Moon's studies in He, but also used metastable atoms of Ne and A and ions of H$_2$ and H. The general techniques were similar to those of Oliphant and Moon. Degassing was carried out, but all measurements were made with a background gas pressure of unknown nature, around 10^6 mm. Thus, after outgassing, as in all measurements prior to those of Hagstrum and Parker, the film of background gas formed in less than a minute. The metastables were created by grazing incidence of ion beams on channels of metals forming the beam. Since Greene created his metastable beams by such a process, he was duly conscious of the very high percentage of reflection of the neutralized metastable atoms on walls. He thus investigated this aspect of the metastables in connection with the secondary emission by them from surfaces. He observed that even for normal incidence, at between approximately 300 and 1,100 volts, neutral particles (largely metastable atoms) suffered reflection at the surface. The effect was greatest for argon metastables, and ranged from about 0.75 at 300 volts, decreasing to 0.48 at 1,100 volts. Helium was next, and led to values ranging from 0.6 at 500 volts to 0.52 at 1,100 volts. The effect was lowest in hydrogen, ranging from 0.33 at 500 volts to 0.15 at 1,000 volts. Thus, he attributed the observed lowering of γ_i with He to the reduction of the fraction of the neutralized ions that *penetrate* from unity by a factor 0.4, the incident number. This, at low energies, would have given an electron emission γ_i of 0.2 instead of the theoretical 0.5. As seen, however, neither Hagstrum nor Parker observed any such amount of reflection on really clean surfaces, and Hagstrum accounts for the reduction in γ_i by surface reflection of internal electrons.

Aside from this reflection, which had not been anticipated or observed by Oliphant and Moon, the metastable atoms of Ne and A were similar in behavior to those in He observed by them. The data from A indicated the presence of some of the assumed "temperature" emission of Oliphant and Moon in addition to the Auger emission, since with the small margins of energy to spare with A, the other emission mechanisms also became important. Greene's work in H_2 showed that *much* of the emission was of the thermal type, but evidence of emission from excited states of H_2 was also observed. In the case of H_2 ions, it is clear that Greene's Mo surfaces were heavily gas-contaminated. Greene's observed limits of energy of emission for the three gases on Mo are shown in table 9.4.

The difficulty with the lower limit in He may lie in the value of the bottom of the Fermi level chosen. Actually, as was shown by Hagstrum, the lower limit to the energy should be 0, as observed, indicating that contact potentials were adequately corrected for.

It is clear that the work of Oliphant and Moon, Greene, and Jackson (15) with alkali ions of high energy on really gassy surfaces yielding electrons with peaked energy distributions superficially resembling a thermal process, discloses a second common and important liberation mechanism of unknown nature that is not directly a potential emission process. An Office of Naval Research report of June, 1954, by H. W. Berry and R. C. Abbott at Syracuse University, clarifies the issue. They attribute the initial "thermal" emission theory of the higher-energy kinetic process to P. Kapitza (Phil. Mag. *45*, 989, 1923), and indicate that similar considerations have also been applied to sputtering of cathode atoms by ion impact. More recently, C. H. Townes

TABLE 9.4

D. Greene's Data for Interaction of Metastable Atoms
of He, Ne, and A on Gassy Molybdenum

	Helium	Neon	Argon
E_m	19.8	16.5	11.5
ϕe	4.4	4.4	4.4
Excess available energy	15.4	12.1	7.1
Observed upper limit	15.0	12.0	7.0
Lower limit if			
$\quad W_A = 17.9$ for Mo	1.9	0	0
Observed minimum	0	0	0

(Phys. Rev. 65, 319, 1944), showed that high temperatures over volumes with diameters of several angstroms are possible under low-energy ion impact. It is not evident how this can lead to an electron-velocity distribution characteristic of this small region among electrons which have mean free paths several hundred times longer than the region. The semilogarithmic plots of the various workers are thus misleading in indicating some sort of an equilibrium "temperature" distribution.

Berry and Abbott undertook a study of *kinetic* liberation using fast neutral He atoms in the ground state. Energies ranged from 300 to 3,500 volts on hot targets (1,500° K.) of W with about a monolayer of O gas and on targets with thick layers of adsorbed gases. Pressures before admission of He were 7×10^{-7} mm Hg. Reflection of fast He$^+$ ions was investigated at 30° angle of incidence with the normal on W. From 500 to 2,000 volts, reflection from targets at 1,300° K. was less than 0.1% of the incident beams.

Results with neutral atoms and ions indicated that neutral atoms gave practically no emission below 300 e.v. on hot W, whereas He$^+$ ions gave around 0.16 electrons per ion. The numbers for both slowly increased along a parabola-like curve, tending toward values of around 0.42 and 0.5 for neutral He and He$^+$ ions respectively at 3,500 e.v. The cold, gas-coated targets indicated currents extrapolating to 0 around 100 e.v. for neutrals and to perhaps 0.16 for He$^+$ ions. At 3,500 e.v. the He atoms on gassy surfaces yielded 0.98 and the He$^+$ ions yielded 0.92 electrons per atom or per ion. If differences between neutral atoms and ion yields are taken, it appears that the potential component of the ion yield was essentially constant to 2,000 e.v., declining to 0.09 at 3,000 e.v. The rise of the kinetic yield was at first almost linear with energy, leveling to 0.42 at 3,000 e.v. With the beam at 30° to the normal with the target, the normal energy component was 0.75 of the beam energy. The neutral atom yield on cleaner and on gassy surfaces was not constant as velocity increased. There were eight times as many electrons per atom from gassy surfaces at 500 e.v. and only 2.3 times as many at 3,000 e.v. Thus, with sufficient energy, even the thin adsorbed gas films on heated targets contribute, while at lower energies more gas is needed.

The decrease in the yield for *ions* on gassy targets relative to that for neutral atoms could be caused by the effect of gas noted and interpreted by Parker in the potential liberation process. It must further be ascribed to a smaller efficiency of ions relative to neutral atoms in the kinetic liberation. Such an action is not unexpected.

Since yields of gassy surfaces for ions and neutrals at high energy are of the order of 0.42, while potential liberation by ions is low, it is clear that in the liberation process the neutral atom or fast ion must create as many as two or three ions in passing through the gas layer. These several ions can then each liberate an electron by the potential process. With a thick gas layer on the target it is not impossible that the He^+ ion or neutral will ionize one or two atoms of the layer, and that the neutral itself will be ionized. Ionization by such a process with many ions of low potential energy would give increased yields of electrons with a common general shape that did not vary sensibly with ion-impact energy and with many slow electrons, as observed.

R. N. Varney, Rostagni, and others (12) have observed ionization of gases by fast neutral atoms and by ions. The mechanism is that of a pseudomolecule formation in which the atoms are ionized on separation. As a rule, ionization yields in such processes require high energy, and in general are more effective for neutral atoms than for ions and atoms. In consequence, Varney suggested to Berry and Abbott that as velocity and energy of the He^+ ion increase, the ion has less chance of neutralization before it enters the gas layer, and thus has less chance of ionizing within it. It has also been suggested by W. Walcher, who noted that secondary emission is high for electronegative gases bound in a metal, that the electron bound to the negative surface ion might be liberated by impact. It is further known that bombardment of gassy surfaces of metals by ions above 200 e.v. energy will liberate some negative ions of the gas film from the surface.

It is believed that this excellent contribution once and for all lays the ghost of "temperature" as a factor in kinetic liberation. It also points the way to a reasonable explanation of the high yields from gassy surfaces bombarded by high-energy ions.

One more ion is of interest because of its omnipresence in the past. Mixed beams of He^+ and Hg^+ were observed by Oliphant and Moon through contamination from the diffusion pumps. The Hg^+ ions increased the numbers of electrons of near zero energies, and decreased the total emission as well. Hg^+ has an ionization potential of only 10.36 e.v., and thus for most surfaces used would be a very poor potential emitter. Its metastable levels are particularly low in value, $\sim$ 5 e.v. If there is any thermal-type liberation phenomenon, it would be less effective by virtue of the inertia of Hg^+. It is also likely to coat many metals, especially those like Ag, Cu, etc., with which it amalgamates or alloys. Thus, if Hg is a poor secondary emitter, it will reduce γ_i on this score. In measurements of γ_i in gases where Hg contamination is present to its equilibrium vapor pressure at the apparatus temperature, it is doubtful whether the value of γ_i observed is in any way related to vehicular gas, and perhaps even to the cathode. By charge exchange in any Townsend-like γ_i measurement, practically every ion created near the anode will have been degraded to Hg^+ on reaching the cathode. Thus, γ_i measurements of all early workers showed essentially the same set of values as a function of X/p, since contamination from mercury-vapor diffusion pumps and McLeod gauges was active. Once Hg gets into an apparatus, it can only be removed by washing with dilute HNO_3. It cannot be removed by degassing.

It should also be added that there is one more contaminant that will reduce γ_i from any surface, and that is a carbon deposit. Reactions in gases where carbon atoms are liberated in virtue of the discharge will quickly reduce γ_i from the cathode to negligible values, and in fact such reduction where C contamination can occur is a very sensitive test for carbon deposition. With this, enough has been stated to proceed to discuss the effect of such a process in electron emission.

The Effect of γ_i on the Field-Intensified Photoelectric Current.

The character of the effect of the γ_i secondary process on the current, as deduced by Townsend, is the following (22). Consider, as before, the plane parallel condenser with anode x cm from the cathode and a current $i_0 = n_0 e$ electrons per cm^2 emitted from the cathode by an external agency. These n_0 electrons emitted per cm^2 of cathode per second have each created an avalanche of $\epsilon^{\alpha x}$ electrons and positive ions on arrival at the anode. The positive ions move with their proper mobility back toward the cathode. On arrival, assume that each ion has a chance γ_i of liberating an electron from the cathode by impact. It is advisable to note here that γ_i should perhaps be broken into two factors, γ_c and ν, thus:

$$(9.9) \qquad\qquad \gamma_i = \gamma_c\, \nu.$$

Here, γ_c is the chance that the ion will liberate an electron from the cathode, and ν is the chance that the electron will not be returned to the cathode by back diffusion. γ_c depends on the condition of the cathode, the nature of the ions, and their energy. ν, as shown in chapter VII, varies with X/p and the energy of electron emission.[2] The newly created $\gamma_i\,\epsilon^{\alpha x}$ secondary electrons per avalanche add to the initial n_0 electrons being emitted from the cathode by external agency. They thus augment the total number of electrons leaving the cathode to n_0' and those arriving at the anode to n. Accordingly, the secondary action liberates $n_0' - n_0$ electrons from the cathode, and the number of electrons created *in the gas* by avalanches is $n - n_0'$. Thus, it is possible to set $n_0' = n_0 + \gamma_i(n - n_0')$ and $n_0' = (n_0 + \gamma_i n)/(1 + \gamma_i)$. Now the n_0' avalanches yield $n_0'\,\epsilon^{\alpha x}$ electrons at the anode; therefore $n = n_0'\,\epsilon^{\alpha x}$, so that $n = \epsilon^{\alpha x}\,(n_0 + \gamma_i)/(1 + \gamma_i)$. From this, it follows that

$$n\left(1 + \gamma_i - \gamma_i\,\epsilon^{\alpha x}\right) = n_0\,\epsilon^{\alpha x}$$

and

$$(9.10) \qquad\qquad n = n_0\,\frac{\epsilon^{\alpha x}}{1 - \gamma_i\left(\epsilon^{\alpha x} - 1\right)}.$$

Multiplying both sides of equation 9.10 by the electron yields the first of the relations for secondary action at the cathode as

$$(9.11) \qquad\qquad i/i_0 = \frac{\epsilon^{\alpha x}}{1 - \gamma_i\left(\epsilon^{\alpha x} - 1\right)}.$$

If γ_i is set equal to

$$(9.12) \qquad\qquad \gamma_i = \beta'/(a - \beta'),$$

where β' is an appropriate constant, it follows that equation 9.11 takes the form

$$(9.13) \qquad\qquad i/i_0 = \frac{(a - \beta')\,\epsilon^{\alpha x}}{a - \beta'\,\epsilon^{\alpha x}}.$$

---

[2]In some analyses it is desirable to segregate the cathode characteristic mechanism from the variation with discharge variables, such as ν. At other times, simplicity makes the use of a collected coefficient γ_i desirable.

This differs only slightly from Townsend's relation, deduced in section 1, which reads

(9.6)
$$i/i_0 = \frac{(a - \beta) \; \epsilon^{(a-\beta)x}}{a - \beta \; \epsilon^{(a-\beta)x}}.$$

Within the accuracy of the data from the log i/i_0 curves, the differences are not significant.

§4. Liberation of Electrons at the Cathode by Photons Produced by the Avalanches.

It has long been recognized that electron impacts in the gas at higher X/p, aside from ionizing the atoms or molecules, can excite large numbers of them to emit radiation. Unfortunately, the quantitative data on yields relative to ionization are not known. They vary rapidly with average electron energy and thus with X/p in some regions. Estimates such as those made by Penning (VIII.34) and Druyvesteyn (VIII.21), and shown in figures 8.30 and 8.31, are indicative. As the data are too sketchy to give real values, quantitative conclusions should not be inferred through their use. Practically all gases, except perhaps the vapors of the alkali and alkaline earth atoms, have electronic excitation energies lying above some 5 or 6 volts.[3] With the exception of the inert gases, the alkaline earth atoms, and some molecules like N_2 and O_2 which have metastable states of long duration, the excited states radiate according to an expression $N = N_0 \; \epsilon^{-t/\tau}$. Here τ represents the average lifetime of the excited state. These lifetimes can be measured in various ways, and range in value from 10^{-10} to 10^{-7} second.

Unless X/p is very high, with the corresponding average electron energy much in excess of 7 e.v., it is probable that the number of excited atoms created per cm path ω, or in Druyvesteyn and Penning's notation, $\zeta_{he} V$, in any gas will exceed a by a factor

(9.14)
$$f = \omega/a ,$$

which might reach 10 or more. This factor will vary with X/p. It will be very high when X/p and a are relatively low, and will decrease rather rapidly when X/p is high, as indicated quasi-schematically in figures 8.30 and 8.31. As with the positive ions, most of these photons will be *created near the anode*. At least half of them will be radiated with a component of their path in the direction of the cathode. Of

---

[3]Exceptions to this would be atomic gaseous forms of substances normally molecular; e.g., O atoms, S atoms, and some of the halogens. Normally, these are not considered common gases.

these, a fraction will miss the cathode and escape from between the plates. Another fraction will be absorbed by the gas atoms and molecules in the x cm between electrodes. Some of the absorbed photons will cause photoionization of impurities; others will be degraded by fluorescent processes. Others of the absorbing agencies will reradiate the light in all directions by *resonant scattering*, so that again half goes to the anode and half to the cathode. If the absorption and reradiation continue for many repetitions, the phenomenon is called "imprisonment of resonance radiation" (23). This has two effects. It reduces in some measure, by geometrical factors, the light that ultimately is received by the cathode. It may also delay the arrival at the cathode.

One more possibility exists, as in A. The imprisoned state may degrade to a near-by $^3P_2$ metastable state. At appropriate pressures, this state, by triple impact with A atoms, gives A_2^* excited molecules that appear slightly metastable and radiate to the ground state, giving photons at 1,250 Å that appear 4 microseconds and upward later. These are not absorbed, and yield a delayed γ_p on Ni. While most of the directly radiated light from the initially excited atoms reaches the cathode in about 10^{-7} second or less, the imprisoned resonance radiation will continue to arrive at the cathode for perhaps as long as 10^{-4} second, thus being diffused in time of arrival as well as delayed. Sojourns of radiations of this type for this length of time in the gas are favorable to certain other secondary actions. They lead, for example, to ionization by formation of excited molecular ions from appropriately excited atoms. They can also lead to the ionization of impurities of lower ionization potential by the excited atoms.

In any event, many of the photons created in some gases on reaching the cathode will be able to liberate photoelectrons from the surface. The work functions ϕe of most metallic surfaces, unless badly contaminated, are under 6 electron volts, but usually not below 4 volts. Thus, possibly some 10 $\epsilon^{\alpha x}$ photons are produced per avalanche. These are attenuated by a geometrical factor $0 < g < 0.5$, depending on electrode geometry. They are still further reduced by an absorption coefficient of equivalent value μ, which varies with the wave length and removes them at the rate $\epsilon^{-\mu x}$ by absorption. Despite such losses, it is clear that a considerable number of photons could reach the cathode. The coefficient μ will vary over wide limits with wave length and gas (13), (24). In general, it will have large ranges of values where it is small. The photons arrive in time intervals ranging from 10^{-7} sec or less for those not undergoing imprisonment, to 10^{-4} sec for those badly trapped. Arrived at the cathode, only a relatively small fraction θ are absorbed by the metal, and release photoelectrons from the metal which escape into the gas against the surface barriers and back diffusion. Since back diffusion varies with X/p as well as gas type, it is segregated from the symbol θ by some workers. Thus, what was designated as θ perhaps should be written as

$$(9.15) \qquad\qquad \theta = \psi\nu.$$

Here ψ is the fraction of photons liberating electrons from the cathode, and ν is the fraction of these escaping loss by back diffusion. The quantities ψ, irrespective of back diffusion, are not large,[4] and may range in value from 10^{-1} to 10^{-4}. Back diffusion ν at higher pressures will still further reduce θ, since it can range from 1 to 10^{-2} or less. However, since $f \, \epsilon^{\alpha x}$ can range around 10^6 to 10^8 it is clear that $\theta g \, \epsilon^{-\mu x}$ can be as large as 10^{-7} to 10^{-9} and still yield values of $f \, \epsilon^{\alpha x} \, \epsilon^{-\mu x} \, \theta g$ which are 0.1, and thus quite effective.

Strangely enough, this mechanism was not regarded as a very important contributing factor in gaseous discharges and breakdown for many years. This was probably because it did not appear prominently in the evaluations of β, and because the relative values of $\theta g \, \epsilon^{-\mu x}$ were considered to exceed $f \, \epsilon^{\alpha x}$ by a considerable margin. This mechanism should have been considered important from 1917 on. At that time, Bergen Davis and F. S. Goucher (24) showed that most of the data in the Franck-Hertz type of measurements were falsified by secondary photoelectrons liberated from metal surfaces by photons preceding or accompanying ionization.

C. Kenty (24) recognized the importance of the process in his measurements. It reappeared very prominently in the measurements of the secondary coefficient by Bowls in N_2 and Hale in H_2 (VIII.11), especially with Na-coated cathodes, but for some strange reason was notable by its absence with Hg-coated cathodes. The dynamic studies of discharges by von Gugelberg (25) in Switzerland in 1946 showed that it was important in some cases. Recent studies in the author's laboratory appear to place this mechanism in its proper place in the category of discharge mechanisms (VIII.26), (VIII.27). It occurs prominently in very many breakdown phenomena in leading to self-sustaining discharges of low order, of which the relations to the more dramatic breakdowns are just being realized. In this capacity it gives what might be termed a "conditioning" discharge that prepares surfaces through positive ion bombardment or space-charge accumulation leading to a very high γ_i, resulting in complete breakdown (27). These

---

[4]For short wave lengths (400 to 900 Å) on some surfaces, efficiencies can perhaps be as high as 0.2. Usually, they are lower (17).

discharges are much more frequent than previously suspected. The mechanism must now be classed as a frequent and important one, even though it only leads indirectly to the impressive breakdowns (2).

There are not very many direct data on this mechanism, and the results will vary widely in different gases, with wave lengths, and with the cathode materials and their condition. The photoelectric emission θ will depend on the work function ϕe of the surface, the wave length λ fixing ψ, the gas pressure governing μ, and X/p governing back diffusion ν. It will be very high for substances of low work function, such as the alkalies Na, K, etc., alkali hydrides like NaH, and for various composite surfaces, such as BaO and Cs-Ag-O. The shorter the wave lengths, the greater the emission. High values of X/p reduce loss to back diffusion. Some oxides of common electrode materials, such as Cu, Ni, Fe, etc., appear to have relatively poor emission, though Ni with an adsorbed O film has good emission. H_2O has a very poor secondary emission, while ice is about as good as CuO above 1,300 Å, and is $\sim 10^4$ that for liquid water, as shown by Oblensky (24).

Probably the most complicating feature is the variable value of the absorption coefficient of the gas. In inert and atomic gases, it is high for resonance electronic transitions. It is also very high in most gases from 400 to 700 Å. Too few data exist between 2,500 and 1,000 Å, e.g., 5 to 10 e.v., where the effects are most important. In molecular gases, the absorption occurs over bands, and is more extensive. With pressure or temperature broadening of the lines, the absorption is further increased. This leads to whole areas of a spectrum having a high μ, with intervening intervals with a low μ, as shown by Schneider and by Weissler and Po Lee (24). For example, O_2 appears to show rapidly fluctuating strong absorption in the very short wave-length ultraviolet capable of photoionizing the gas, while at longer wave lengths, yielding photoelectrons from metal surfaces of work function about 5 e.v., it is possibly more transparent, with considerable delay (VIII.27). Obviously, a gas will be likely to be more opaque to radiations of its own molecules or atoms, for absorption is strictly a resonance phenomenon. Absorbing cross sections are very small for sharp lines, but become larger for broadened lines. Further evidences of such action will be discussed in connection with the work of Bowls and Hale. These conditions in a measure complicate the development of a proper theory, as will be seen.

To analyze the problem, it may be assumed, as before, that n_0 electrons are liberated per second per cm^2 from a cathode by some external source. Assume that the avalanche of ϵ^{ax} electrons is accompanied by $f \, \epsilon^{ax}$ photons capable of liberating electrons from the cathode, i.e., photons of $h\nu > \phi e$, with ϕe the work function of the cathode. These photons are in a large measure produced relatively near the anode. Let z be the number of photons that reach the cathode, and of these let a fraction $\theta = \psi\nu$ liberate electrons from the cathode under existing conditions of X/p. Thus, the total number of electrons leaving the cathode is

$$(9.16) \qquad n_0' = n_0 + \theta z .$$

Now z is influenced by the geometrical factor g, which represents the fraction of photons geometrically capable of reaching the cathode because they are headed for it. For a parallel plate system with plate radius much greater than the distance between them, g should be nearly 0.5. If resonance entrapment is prominent, g will be less than 0.5. If there is much entrapment, g appears to approach about 0.4. The value of g is also influenced by the optical reflections from cathode and anode (23). For coaxial cylindrical geometry, with length large compared to radius and negative outer cylinder with *small anode radius* (Geiger counter geometry), g is nearly unity. In the same geometry, *with the small central wire as cathode*, g may be small indeed. z is further determined by the absorption coefficient μ. As this varies for different wave lengths, it is essential, in the interest of simplicity, to work with a single rough average value applicable to the most effective wave-length region.

Let p be the number of new electrons created by avalanches between the cathode and some variable distance x from the cathode. Thus, at x there are $p + n_0'$ electrons. These, in passing through a distance dx, will create by collision dz photons, which are destined to reach the cathode and there produce new photoelectrons. In order to estimate dz, it is necessary to introduce a new concept. This represents the number of active photons produced per electron per cm path in the field direction, which will be designated by the symbol ω. It corresponds to the $\zeta_{he} V$ of Druyvesteyn and Penning (VIII.21). Thus, dz becomes

$$(9.17) \qquad dz = (n_0' + p) \, g \, \epsilon^{-\mu x} \, \omega dx.$$

The classical Townsend picture for the primary process indicates that $dp = (n_0' + p)adx$. At the cathode, with $x = 0$, $n_0' = p$, and integration between 0 and x leads to

$$(9.18) \qquad n_0' + p = n_0' \, \epsilon^{ax} ,$$

so that

$$(9.19) \qquad p = n_0' \left(\epsilon^{ax} - 1 \right) .$$

Accordingly, dz becomes

(9.20)
$$dz = n_0' \, \epsilon^{ax} \, g\omega \, \epsilon^{-\mu x} \, dx .$$

Integration for z yields the relation

(9.21)
$$z = \left(\frac{n_0' \, \omega}{a - \mu} \right) g \, \epsilon^{(a-\mu)x} + c .$$

As $z = 0$ at $x = 0$, c becomes $c = -n_0' \omega g / a$, making z:

(9.22)
$$z = \frac{n_0' \, \omega g}{a - \mu} \left[\epsilon^{(a-\mu)x} - 1 \right] .$$

Introducing the value of z into $n_0' = n_0 + \theta z$, there results

(9.23)
$$n_0' = n_0 + n_0' \left(\frac{\theta \omega g}{a - \mu} \right) \left[\epsilon^{(a-\mu)x} - 1 \right] .$$

Since $n = n_0' \, \epsilon^{ax}$, this yields

(9.24)
$$n = \frac{n_0 \, \epsilon^{ax}}{1 - \dfrac{\theta \omega g}{(a-\mu)} \left[\epsilon^{(a-\mu)x} - 1 \right]} .$$

If this is multiplied by the electron, there results the equivalent current equation:

(9.25)
$$i/i_0 = \frac{\epsilon^{ax}}{1 - \dfrac{\theta \omega g}{(a-\mu)} \left[\epsilon^{(a-\mu)x} - 1 \right]} .$$

If there are several different values of μ involved, probably related to different values of ω and θ, then the ratio of total current i to i_0 will represent the summation of the separate components of i contributed by each value of μ with its associated values of ω and θ. It may be noted that the absorption coefficient μ acts effectively to reduce the value of the first Townsend coefficient, yielding an effective coefficient $(a - \mu)$. If $\mu = a$, then no photons reach the cathode, and the relation reverts to the original Townsend equation 8.3 for a primary process.

Neglecting for the instant the value of μ, when $a >> \mu$, as is often the case, it is to be noted that as regards secondary action the probability γ_i for electron liberation by positive ion impact at the cathode is replaced by $\omega \theta g / a$ in the relation:

(9.26)
$$i/i_0 = \frac{\epsilon^{ax}}{1 - \dfrac{\omega \theta g}{a}\left(\epsilon^{ax} - 1\right)}.$$

Thus is demonstrated the close parallelism between these two cathode-active coefficients, which was discussed in section 2. This makes it difficult to interpret data obtained by the Townsend method.

Now g is a geometrically calculable dimensionless ratio, while $\theta = \psi\nu$ is a fraction expressing an average value of the probability of electron liberation from the cathode, which is a statistical process. This leaves a ratio ω/a representing the average number of active photons per electron cm path in the field direction relative to the similar quantity a representing ions produced in 1 cm. This ω/a is nothing more than a fraction:

(9.14)
$$f = \omega/a,$$

which is the average value representing the chance that an active photon will be produced per avalanche ion. It is then permitted to write, as shown on page 798, that in an avalanche the number of active photons is given by

$$n_p = f\,\epsilon^{ax} = \frac{\omega}{a}\,\epsilon^{ax}.$$

This quantity n_p, multiplied by g, θ, and $\epsilon^{-\mu x}$, then gives the number of secondary electrons liberated per avalanche as

(9.27)
$$\frac{g\theta\omega}{(a-\mu)}\left[\epsilon^{(a-\mu)x} - 1\right]$$

In expression 9.27 just deduced, and in equation 9.25, it is noted that the exact expression reads $[\epsilon^{(a-\mu)x} - 1]$. The unity deducted represents the initial external electron starting the avalanche, which is not accompanied by secondary effects. In most cases ϵ^{ax} or $\epsilon^{(a-\mu)x}$ is so much larger than unity that this quantity can effectively be neglected. Mathematically, it is essential to include it when ϵ^{ax} is not much greater than unity.

§ 5. Ionization by Photons in the Gas in Uniform Field Geometry.

For many years the possibility that photons ionize effectively in the gas was ignored. The reason for this was that until about 1925 no very good or certain data could be obtained experimentally that indicated photoelectric ionization to occur in gases. It was theoretically expected, but the absorption cross sections $Q = \pi\sigma^2$ given by

§5

(9.28) $\epsilon^{-\mu x} = \epsilon^{-\pi\sigma^2 N_1 p x}$

were so small relative to the effectiveness of photoelectric liberation
from surfaces of metal that the action was deemed negligible. The
reason for this was that gases usually studied were at relatively low
pressure, and when high pressures were used the absorption coefficient was so large that the phenomena were not noted.

The work of Williamson, F. L. Mohler, and later of E. O. Lawrence
and N. L. Edlefsen (13), (28), established the existence of the phenomenon. These workers also discovered appreciable photoelectric
ionization of gases by radiations *below the threshold* of the ionization
potential E_i for the gas. The appearance of such ions was ascribed
to ionization by molecule formation by reactions between excited
atoms, by ionization of existing molecules of associated forms, and
by ionization of impurities. Recent studies have shown that such
actions can have large cross sections.

There is *no gas* in which a discharge is passing which sooner
or later is not ionized by radiations coming from its own species.
All gases having metastable states will form these, and they will be
photoionized by the photons present.[5] Thus, He has a metastable
state at 19.5 volts. Its ionization potential is 24.5 volts. Radiations
of energies in excess of 5 volts present in the discharge will cause
ionization of these states. Excited states make molecules that are
ionized in the process. Thus, two Hg atoms excited to the metastable
state 6^3P_2 of 5.47 volts will form an Hg^+ ion of ionization potential
10.44 volts. He excited to 23 e.v. on impact with an He atom yields
He_2^+ of ionization potential 18.8 volts. Two He^m metastables $^3P_2$ on
impact form He^+ and an electron.

In molecular gases, such as H_2 and N_2, dissociation occurs at
4.36 and 9.6 volts, respectively. The discharge produces much dissociation. The ionization potentials of the molecular and atomic
forms always differ sufficiently so that excited states of one form
can ionize the other. For example, in H_2, E_i is 15.4 volts, while for
H it is 10.13 volts. In all mixed or impure gases, photoelectric ionization of one constituent by radiations from another can be expected.
For O_2^+ and O^+, the potentials are 12.2 and 13.55 volts, respectively,
and photons from high states of O readily ionize.

---

[5] Recent evidence of C. Kenty (29) in his studies of the mechanisms in the
A-Hg mixtures used in fluorescent tubes, indicates that in these arcs or
glows, densities of the metastable Hg states 6^3P_2 and 6^3P_0 are commensurate
with and even greater than those of electrons; viz., $\sim 10^{11}$ per cm^3, with
6^3P_2 predominating. Such gases will certainly act to photons like gases of
low ionization potential.

Thus, with the observation of photoelectric ionization by numerous workers and the evaluation of the cross sections for these processes, which are of the order of 10^{-20} to 10^{-22} compared to ionization cross sections by electron impact of the order of 10^{-18} to 10^{-19}, these phenomena could no longer be ignored. It was, however, quite a surprise when the nearly simultaneous but independent studies of A. M. Cravath and C. Dechène (13) in 1934 respectively revealed that the light emitted in corona or spark discharge effectively ionized air at atmospheric pressure. In fact, Cravath observed the amount of ionization from the gas and from a superficially oxidized Cu plate to be comparable. The absorption coefficients of the active photons observed by Cravath were of the order of 10 cm^{-1}. Dechène, with sparks, observed values ranging from about 7 cm^{-1} to smaller values of the order of 2 cm^{-1} in air. He also observed that as the thickness of the air traversed increased, the absorption coefficients were progressively decreased by filtering action and absorption.

Of course, photoionization in gases by discharges had been known somewhat earlier. Most of these observations were made at materially lower pressures, such as those of H. Greiner (13), in Geiger counters and other cases. The work of Cravath and Dechène was impressive, as it indicated that the phenomenon was present in air at atmospheric pressures, and was capable of producing quantitatively notable yields. The values of the coefficient μ observed by Greiner in Geiger counters, in C. T. R. Wilson cloud chambers by H. Raether and his students, and by many others, vary considerably (13). The use of the concept of photoionization as active in propagating discharges at higher pressures appears to have come independently from Flegler and Raether in 1935 (30) and by Cravath, the author, and R. R. Wilson later in 1935 and early 1936 (30). The mechanisms are quantitatively little known.

In most gases, direct photoelectric ionization requires photons of high energy. While the absorption coefficients are known for wave lengths that pass through quartz and fluorite and contribute much to photoelectric emission from surfaces, this is not the case for those photons ionizing gases. Thus, the wave length of a photon ionizing at 10 volts is 1,236 Å, compared to the 2,536 Å for the 4.9-volt Hg resonance line. Since most gases are ionized above 10 volts, say between 10 and 16 e.v., the wave length of the photons active will lie between 824 and 1,236 Å. Virtually nothing is known about the absorption coefficients and absorbing cross sections at these energies, though currently several investigations are under way. It is known that O_2 has very rapidly varying values of μ, ranging from the order of 10 cm^{-1} at $1,000$ Å to 100 or 500 cm^{-1} at various points around 600 to 800 Å. The quantity f_g for such photons is also completely unknown for the gases employed. At high X/p, where a is fairly large, this quantity can also be large. No attempt has been made to measure these quantities or the photoelectronic yields in the gas from known avalanche production, though this quantity might well be measurable. Accordingly, it is only possible to derive the theory in simplified general terms, and to draw general conclusions.

The theory for this process may be simply derived if it is recognized that most of the ions are produced in the last two or three ionizing free paths from the anode. Thus, if $1/a$ is small compared to the gap length x in the plane parallel electrode system previously considered, it can be assumed that the

$$(9.29) \qquad f_g n = \omega_g n / a$$

photons created accompanying the n electrons and positive ions produced near the anode originate in this region. Here ω_g is the equivalent of a in regard to the number of photons created per cm path in the field direction. The subscript g applied to the ω indicates photons capable to ionizing *in the gas*. Actually, the photons originate all along the avalanche path, and thus are perhaps not quite so effective as the assumed concentration near the anode would make them. The error will be different depending on the value of μ and the absorption distance relative to x. The n electrons are composed of two parts; the $n_0 \, \epsilon^{ax}$ electrons coming from avalanches initiated at the cathode by external agencies, and the p electrons and ions created in the gas by photoelectrons there produced. These yield their own avalanches in proceeding to the anode. Thus, it is possible to set

$$(9.30) \qquad n = n_0 \, \epsilon^{ax} + p .$$

To calculate p, choose a slab of thickness dy at a distance y from the anode. The $f_g n$ photons created near the anode, diminished by the geometrical factor g, which is here nearly 0.5, will penetrate to the depth y and be absorbed to the extent $-\mu \, \epsilon^{-\mu y} dy$ in the thickness dy. Of these, a fraction ξ will produce photoelectrons. Thus, in dy there will be produced $-f_g g n \xi \mu \, \epsilon^{-\mu y} dy$ electrons. In proceeding to the anode the distance y, these will produce ϵ^{ay} electrons and ions. Thus, dp, the contribution of dy to the ions arrived at the anode, is

$$(9.31) \qquad dp = - g f_g n \xi \mu \, \epsilon^{-(a-\mu)y} \, dy .$$

The quantity p sought to compute the current is the integral of dp from $y = 0$ at the anode to $y = x$ at the cathode. Thus,

$$p = + ngf_g \, \xi \mu \int_0^x \epsilon^{(a-\mu)y} \, dy \, ,$$

which yields

$$p = ngf_g \, \xi \, \frac{\mu}{a-\mu} \left[\epsilon^{(a-\mu)x} - 1 \right].$$

Accordingly, it is possible to write

(9.32)
$$n = n_0 \, \epsilon^{ax} + ngf_g \, \xi \, \frac{\mu}{a-\mu} \left[\epsilon^{(a-\mu)x} - 1 \right].$$

Solution for n/n_0 and multiplication by the electron yields the expression:

(9.33)
$$i/i_0 = \frac{\epsilon^{ax}}{1 - gf_g \xi \, \dfrac{\mu}{a-\mu} \left[\epsilon^{(a-\mu)x} - 1 \right]} \, .$$

In form, this relation resembles the relations for cathode-liberated electrons, as indicated in section 2. The value of g is about 0.5, and $f_g = \omega_g/a$ can be of the order of unity. It may also be greater or less but not much more than an order of magnitude either way. The quantity ξ will probably be considerably less than unity, say $10^{-4} < \xi < 10^{-2}$. The critical quantity is obviously $a - \mu$. In air at atmospheric pressure near the sparking threshold, a is of the order of 17, with $x = 1$ cm. It is noted that in air Cravath found, under corona-discharge conditions, a value of μ of 10 cm^{-1}, and with filtering Dechène observed values ranging from 2 to 7. On the other hand, μ can be very large, and thus larger than a. If $\mu = 0$, then the denominator becomes unity. Thus, equation 9.33 reverts to Townsend's original equation 8.3, with no secondary action present.

If μ approaches a, the denominator of equation 9.33 slowly approaches the value

(9.34)
$$1 - gf_g \xi \mu x,$$

achieved at the point where $a = \mu$. Assuming a to have been about 17 and $x = 1$, μ will be 17 and the whole denominator of equation 9.33 will be close to the value unity, unless f_g is of the order of 10 and ξ is of the order of 10^{-2} or larger. Such values are not common.

If x is large and $a - \mu$ is of the order of 10 to 15, the quantity

(9.35)
$$gf_g \, \xi \, \frac{\mu}{a-\mu} \left[\epsilon^{(a-\mu)x} - 1 \right]$$

might approach unity, making the denominator of equation 9.33 small. Then i/i_0 will show an increase. If μ is greater than a, the denominator in equation 9.33 becomes

$$1 - gf_g \; \xi \; \frac{-\mu}{\mu - a}\left[\epsilon^{-(\mu - a)x} - 1\right].$$

If $x = 1$ and $\mu - a = 10$, the quantity $\epsilon^{-(\mu-a)x}$ becomes small compared to unity. The denominator of equation 9.33 then becomes sensibly:

(9.36) $$1 - gf_g \; \xi \; \frac{\mu}{\mu - a}.$$

This again will not materially differ from unity unless f_g and ξ are relatively large. Very large values of μ (around 100) will be even less effective in causing an appreciable decrease in the denominator of equation 9.33. In consequence, unless the production of photons through f_g is of the order of 1 to 10 and ξ is of the order of 10^{-2}, which is large, *photoionization in the gas will not be very effective* except in the region where $a - \mu$ has such values that $\epsilon^{(a-\mu)x}$ can be of the order of f_g. The cases where this will occur may be quite rare. It is clear that this mechanism as derived is not one to prove of much interest. It must be noted, however, that the assumption used in the deduction involved liberation of photons, mostly near the anode, and treated the problem essentially like a cathode mechanism. This accounts for the form of equation 9.33.

However, if an extreme assumption had been made that μ was, for example, of the order of $10a$, and if $f_g\xi$ had a value of the order of 10^{-1} or 10^{-2}, then the photoionization would parallel the ionization by impact in the gas. At each point in the gas, $nf_g\xi$ new electrons would have supplemented ax. The geometrical factor g will be unity with $\mu = 10a$. In this event, the measurement would have revealed that $i = i_0 \, \epsilon^{a'x}$, with

(9.37) $$a' = a(1 + f_g\xi).$$

Such behavior has been observed by Bowls and Hale (VIII.11) with N_2 and H_2, contaminated by Hg or Na vapors.

In the other extreme, where μ is small compared to a and where $1/\mu$ becomes comparable with x, the relation does *not* revert back to equation 8.3, as indicated from the strict algebraic interpretation of equation 9.33. In this event, very short wave-length photons from the avalanche reach the cathode, and equation 9.25 applies. It must be added that in nonuniform fields, i.e., with anode wire and large outer cathode cylinder where ions are created in a narrow zone of high field near the wire, if $1/\mu > \delta$, the width of the ionizing zone, photoionization is very effective, and acts as if electrons came from a γ_p with short transit times. It leads to the Geiger counter-like discharges about the anode, which are *not* cathode but anode actions.

Summarizing, it can be stated that photoionization in the gas does not afford an important *conventional* secondary mechanism. However, in asymmetrical gaps or with heavy space-charge field distortion, and with strong anode fields, photoelectric ionization of the gas leads to new mechanisms (frequently anode mechanisms) that lead to electrical breakdown. The basic forms of the breakdown relations, by lumping complicated coefficients, again resemble the generic Townsend relation.

§ 6. The Action of Metastable Atoms at the Cathode.

The investigations of the secondary liberation of electrons by impact of slower positive ions on the cathode, as well as observations of C. Kenty (24) and others involving discharges where *metastable atoms* were present, indicated that such atoms should, by impact on the cathode, cause the emission of secondary electrons (15). Theoretically, if the energy of the metastable state is higher than the work function of the cathode, the metastables will liberate electrons from the metal (see page 798), as with the positive ions, theory and measurement indicate relatively high efficiencies.

There is one difference in the action of the metastable atom in contrast to the ion. The *metastable atoms* must succeed in *diffusing* to the cathode, while *all positive ions are drawn* to the cathode by the field. Furthermore, the positive ions moving under a field arrive at the cathode rather promptly, while the diffusion of the metastable atoms is a much slower process. It would be unnecessarily tedious at this point to derive formally the accurate equations for the secondary action produced by metastables at the cathode. The problem has been treated by W. Rogowski and by R. W. Engstrom and W. S. Huxford (31) in a most important pioneering investigation. It will be further treated quite completely in connection with the dynamic studies of J. P. Molnar.

It is clear that except for the time delay of diffusive arrival of the metastable atoms at the cathode, and the relatively greater loss of these by diffusion to the anode and between the plates, as well as by *destruction in the gas* (sometimes leading to ions in the gas), the action is closely similar to that of impact of positive ions of low energy. Thus, a fraction of the metastables that arrive liberate electrons from the cathode. These then progress in the gas to the anode, augmenting i_0. The metastables, like the ions, are largely produced near the anode, so that the diffusive loss is great. Hence, it is to be expected that in the relation for i/i_0 with metastables, action at the cathode will be of the form:

$$(9.38) \qquad i/i_0 = \frac{\epsilon^{ax}}{1 - \gamma_m \ (\epsilon^{ax} - 1)},$$

which is actually the form deduced and used in study. This differs from equation 9.11 only in that γ_m for metastables replaces γ_i, the value for positive ion impact. In this circumstance, measurements of the $\log i/i_0$-x curves in a gas with metastables will yield a relation:

$$(9.39) \qquad i/i_0 = \frac{\epsilon^{ax}}{1 - \gamma(\epsilon^{ax} - 1)}.$$

In this case, the observed γ is composite, consisting of

$$(9.40) \qquad \gamma = \gamma_i + \gamma_m.$$

Thus, some appropriate means of segregating γ_m and γ_i must be found.

To evaluate γ_m, it will be noted that there must be assumed a rate of metastable atom production by electrons per cm advance in the field direction, to be designated as ω_m. Then, as before, it is possible to set

$$(9.41) \qquad \frac{\omega_m}{a} = f_m,$$

where f_m is the fraction of metastables produced per ion of the avalanche. Again, there is a geometrical factor g, depending on how many metastables diffuse to the cathode relative to those created.[6] Finally, it must be assumed that a fraction,

$$(9.42) \qquad \theta_m = \psi_m \nu,$$

of the metastables striking the cathode succeed in liberating an electron from it. Thus,

$$(9.43) \qquad \gamma_m = \theta_m g \frac{\omega_m}{a} = \theta_m g f_m.$$

Equation 9.39 now takes the more complete form:

---

[6]This will be less than a half, as it contains implicitly the fraction of metastables lost by destruction *in the gas*. Strictly, the g used above should be $g_1 \ \epsilon^{-\mu_m x}$, where μ_m is the "absorption coefficient" for destruction of metastables by gas-molecule impact.

$$(9.44) \qquad i/i_0 = \frac{\epsilon^{ax}}{1 - (\gamma_i + \theta_m f_m g)(\epsilon^{ax} - 1)} .$$

The quantity g entails not only the true geometrical loss of metastables inherent in diffusion, which will be less than but near 0.5, but the loss to destruction of metastables by impact with gas molecules or impurities.* Where the loss results in ionization in the gas, as with A in Ne, then γ_m is reduced but a' is increased. There is nothing of particular importance in regard to this equation. In the event that for some reason metastable reaction predominates, $\theta_m f_m g$ will be larger than γ_i, and the increase of i/i_0 will be largely owing to this mechanism.

The reason for "lumping" the metastable action with positive ion action in the same relation lies in the similarity of the processes. If the condition of the cathode is such that $\theta_m f_m g$ has a finite value, γ_i will also be finite and probably larger. The reason for this in a single gas is that while f_m is perhaps large, g for metastables is usually quite small, with $g = 1$ for positive ions. Again, the ionizing potential E_i is greater than the metastable threshold E_m, so that the *a priori* probability for electron liberation (i.e., ψ_i) could be greater than ψ_m. It must thus be expected that $\gamma_i > \gamma_m = f_m g \psi_m \nu = f_m g \theta_m$, and that the change in the i/i_0 curves by these actions will not permit the two to be separated.

However, since ions move directly from near the anode to the cathode with a velocity $v = kX$, while the metastables merely diffuse to the cathode (a much slower process), the metastable action will show a temporal delay over the action of positive ions. It thus remains for studies involving time lags in the secondary processes to distinguish between the two actions. This thought apparently first came to R. W. Engstrom and W. S. Huxford (31), who applied techniques for this purpose as early as 1939. In this way, it was observed that θ_m for one cathode in A was of the order of 0.4 when γ_i lay between 0.1 and 0.4. This was the forerunner of the later development of dynamic methods for differentiating between the action of photons, metastables, and positive ion impact.

§ 7. Ionization by Metastable and Excited Atoms in the Gas.

It was shown by James Franck and G. Cario in 1928 that metastable atoms of excitation potential E_{mA} in gas A greater than the ionization potential E_{iB} of another gaseous species B could, on encounter with a probability P_{AB}, ionize atom B. Thus, in certain mixed gases only,

*See footnote 6 on preceding page.

where metastable atoms can form, it is possible for a secondary mechanism produced by metastable atoms to act in the gas. It can also occur when excited atoms of gas A encounter atoms of gas B where E_{eA} is greater than E_{iB}. Since metastable atoms have a relatively long life compared to excited atoms, these are much more likely to produce the ionization noted. Still, if resonance radiation is imprisoned in gas A, then ionization of gas B by excited atoms A can occur in detectable measure.

The phenomenon can be described by an expression analogous to the expression for photoionization *in the gas*. There will be a quantity f_m, or perhaps f_{eA}, representing the ratio of the metastable or excited states and the electrons created in the avalanche. The creation of these states will be greatest nearer the anode. There will be a geometrical loss factor g akin to that for metastables moving to the cathode. The metastables will have to diffuse to the region of the cathode to yield an effective γ type of secondary mechanism. With imprisonment of resonance radiation, the diffusion toward the cathode region is about the same as the diffusion of the metastables.

It appears in actual practice that if the gas A is contaminated with atoms or molecules of gas B to a sufficient extent to produce much ionization of B, the metastables and excited states will not have a chance to diffuse very far from the location of excitation. Thus, most of the ion production by this process will occur *very close to the point of excitation of the metastable atoms*. If conditions are such that the metastable atoms survive long enough to go to the cathode *area*, they will give a γ_m by acting on the cathode rather than an ionization *in the gas*. That is, either this process is one that is quite exclusive and will act effectively on the cathode directly (γ_m), or it will act *in the gas* shortly after formation. In the latter event it leads to an augmented primary process 8.3, with

$$(9.45) \qquad\qquad a' = a(1 + f_{mA}\, \xi_B).$$

This phenomenon has been effectively observed by Kruithoff and Penning in Ne-A mixtures (VIII.4). It is called by some the "Penning effect." Data on cross sections, etc., are given in section 6 of chapter VIII. In that study the value of γ may have been increased by the Ne metastables. The increase in a through the A atoms of low concentration indicates that the argon is ionized effectively very near where the Ne metastables were formed. Thus, ξ_B seems to be very large, resulting in an increased a and decreased γ. In any case, the accuracy of the data on the log i/i_0-x curves or the i-V curves is not such as to indicate much intermediate action. The γ determinations in the mixture relative to pure Ne indicate a decreased γ between X/p of 1 and 10 for the mixture. Pure Ne, on the contrary, shows a nearly constant value. This suggests that possibly in pure Ne, γ is largely metastable γ_m at the cathode for low X/p and γ_i at high X/p. In mixtures, γ_m is prevented and only γ_i appears.

The change in α has been described in detail in chapter VIII. If too much A is present, the argon is ionized and excited directly by the avalanche electrons. This reduces the chances of creating metastable Ne at the lower potentials and X/p values. If the concentration of A is too low, the few A atoms are ionized, but the number is small, and Ne metastables get a chance to diffuse to the cathode, α' decreases, and γ_m increases. The optimum concentration must depend on f_{mA}, ξ_B, and the values of X/p and p, as well as on E_{mA} and E_{iB}. The most effective observed concentration of A in Ne was 0.1%. In this case the current i was increased to seven times that in pure A and forty times that of pure Ne at 75 volts.

It is clear that the action of metastable atoms in the gas is almost entirely confined to effectively increasing α to α', in which event the theory has been adequately covered. Otherwise, the gas is so clean that the metastables produce little ionization in the gas, in which case they diffuse to the cathode and give a γ_m, which has also been discussed effectively. While some rare cases may occur where the metastables act *in the gas near the cathode*, the rarity of the process and the fact that it would *simulate* a γ_m make it hardly worth while to develop the equations in detail at this point. These possibilities have been adequately canvassed by J. P. Molnar, and will be presented more at length elsewhere. In any case, neither action of metastables appears to be of prime importance in leading to gaseous breakdown. Metastable action doubtless aids in breakdown and increases γ or α (25). The notable effect of metastables in breakdown studies and industrial application is that they furnish a secondary mechanism with a *long time delay*. They thus influence many phenomena by adding persistence of initiating electrons to complicate the discharges.

§ 8. The Joint Action of Photoelectric Ionization at the Cathode and Secondary Electron Liberation by Positive Ion Impact on the Cathode.

The combination of secondary cathode mechanisms 1, 2, and perhaps 3, might be considered of interest, inasmuch as a cathode surface may, and usually will, have the ability to liberate photoelectrons as well as electrons on positive ion impact. It might be expected in general that the photo effect would predominate at lower X/p, while the γ mechanism would predominate at higher X/p. However, both may be present. More frequently, the photoelectric mechanism may offer the lower threshold for a discharge, which will produce the conditioning for an increase in γ by this means or through space charge.

Under these conditions, it is not unreasonable to neglect μ relative to a, and to combine the actions[7] of relations 9.11 and 9.25 as

$$(9.46) \qquad i/i_0 = \frac{\epsilon^{ax}}{1 - [\gamma_i + \theta fg] (\epsilon^{ax} - 1)} .$$

Actually, this was done in 1940 by A. A. Kruithoff (VIII.4), in his study of the gases A, Kr, and Xe. There he wrote that

$$(9.11) \qquad i/i_0 = \frac{\epsilon^{ax}}{1 - \gamma(\epsilon^{ax} - 1)} ,$$

with

$$(9.47) \qquad \gamma = z(\gamma_i + gf\theta),$$

which, in the notation of this text, reads

$$(9.48) \qquad \gamma = \nu(\gamma_c + gf\psi).$$

This device of multiplying γ_c and ψ by ν to give γ_i and θ has some merit, in that ν represents the loss of emitted electrons to the cathode by back diffusion, which is common to both actions. It varies with X/p and energy of electron emission. γ_c varies with the nature of the ions, positive ion energy, and the surface condition of the cathode. The quantity f depends on the gas and on X/p, while g depends on geometry, and ψ depends on the cathode surface and work function ϕe, as well as qualities of photons.

In Kruithoff's studies, he set

$$(9.49) \qquad \nu = \{(X/p)/500\}^q .$$

Neglecting diffusion and absorption of radiation, he evaluated q as

$$(9.50) \qquad q = \frac{1}{2}\left(1 - \frac{x}{\sqrt{r^2 + x^2}}\right).$$

Here x was the electrode spacing, and r the radius of the circular

---

[7]Since γ can be on occasion be composed of γ_m and γ_i, perhaps this relation should replace γ_i by $\gamma = \gamma_i + \gamma_m$, as indicated in section 6. Actually, unless dynamic methods are used, if metastable-forming gaseous species are present, there is no way of differentiating γ_i from γ_m. This is not quite the case for the photon action to be discussed.

electrodes. In this way Kruithoff was able to reproduce some of his curves for γ, as observed for Kr, with $q = 0.72$, $\gamma_i = 0.004$, and $g\theta = 0.0029$, for a copper cathode in one state. In another state of the cathode, the values were $\gamma_i = 0.022$ and $g\theta = 0.0011$. This serves to show in general how such relations with mixed coefficients can be used. Under discharge conditions, usually one mechanism or the other predominates, with the photoelectric process prominent at low X/p and γ_i prominent at high X/p.

More recently, J. K. Theobald (20) has measured back diffusion in the author's laboratory. He has shown that it is strictly dependent on X/p, and depends on energy of electrons emitted and on gas type. General relations have been developed for correction for inert and molecular gases. This is discussed in detail in chapter VII.

§ 9. Field Emission as a Secondary Mechanism.

Strictly speaking, the emission of electrons from a surface owing to a high surface field should not be classed as a secondary mechanism. Furthermore, field emission of electrons does not *necessarily* directly follow as a result of actions accompanying the primary process at any pressures. It is also affected by geometrical configurations combined with potential in the gap at low pressures. In gaseous *discharges* at any pressures, considerable multiplication of electrons in the gap and the creation of heavy space charges in virtue of the differences in mobility of electrons and positive ions under suitable conditions build up gross fields at the cathode surface in excess of 10^6 volts per cm. Such fields are sufficient to cause field emission. Probably, there are a few cases where the primary process alone is able to produce enough ions of itself to lead to field emission. This occurs in the Malter, or Paetow, effect if insulating films are on the cathode (32). Field emission, however, must be considered among these processes, as it is often invoked, and it does play a role in the initiation and perhaps in the maintenance of some discharges. It certainly appears as a modifying breakdown mechanism at electrodes in gases for very small gaps and very high pressures.

The distribution of electrons in the positive ionic lattices of metals leads to surface-potential barriers holding electrons within the metal. The potentials affecting the electrons in the conduction band of the metals range from some tenths of a volt for composite and alkali metal surfaces subject to the infrared, to some 2.5 volts on more common metals, and extending beyond 7 volts for oxygen-contaminated Pt. They represent the work function ϕe of the metals in thermionic and photoelectric liberation. For the degenerate electrons, the potentials

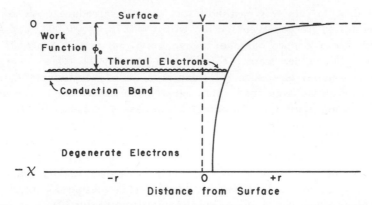

Fig. 9.14. Potential diagram showing conditions at the surface of a metallic conductor. The outside is at zero potential, and the electrons lie in a potential trough of depth $^-\chi$ inside the surface to the left of zero. The shape of the potential barrier is shown by the full-line curve at the right. The conduction band at the upper limit of the degenerate electrons at height μ above $^-\chi$ is shown. Above it are the conduction thermal electrons in the unfilled band. The work function ϕe is clearly indicated.

to raise them to the top of the barrier may be much larger and of the order of up to 20 volts. The way in which the image forces of electronic charges fall off with distance from the metal surface leads to fields of the order of 10^8 volts per centimeter near the surface, decreasing as the distance from the surface increases.

The potential diagram of a metal surface relative to distance from the surface, showing conduction band, degenerate, and thermal electron bands is seen in figure 9.14. If now an appropriate field of the opposite sign produced by neighboring conductors or by a suitable positive space charge is applied, the height of the barrier will be reduced by the overlapping field. What is more important, the potential barrier is reduced in thickness.

The effect of the externally applied field on the natural potential barrier of a metal is illustrated in figure 9.15. This situation in theory makes possible two types of action. The lowering of the barrier with a potential trough of lower value from the positive space-charge field adjoining should permit electrons in the top of the conduction band to get enough energy from the thermal-energy distribution to jump the barrier. That is, the field should lower the "effective" work function ϕe.

The energy to get electrons out in this case comes from thermal energy and the electron energies with zero or more kinetic energy. It cools the metal in escaping. The process will facilitate photoelectric liberation in certain wave-length regions, and should increase

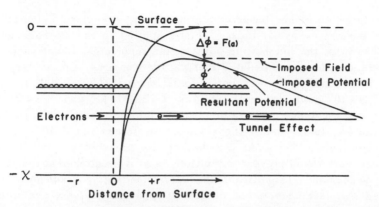

Fig. 9.15. Potential diagram showing the effect of the superposed external field, given by the sloping line at the right, starting at V. The reduction $\Delta\phi$ of the work function barrier is shown, as well as the new function ϕ'. The tunnel effect for a level of degenerate electrons is also shown.

the *thermionic emission*, since the threshold has been lowered. This concept was initially put forward and developed by O. W. Richardson and W. Schottky (33). It is known as the "Richardson-Schottky theory." The so-called field-emission current is then merely an enhanced photoelectric current, of density:

$$(9.51) \qquad j = \frac{2\pi k^2 m e}{h^3} \; T^2 \, \epsilon^{-\frac{(\phi \, - \sqrt{X_s}\,)e}{kT}}.$$

Here X_s is the applied surface field. This theory was tested by a study of the increase in thermionic "saturation" current as a function of field strength at different temperatures, and supposely verified for clean metal surfaces up to 10^6 volts/cm by W. S. Pforte and N. A. de Bruyne in 1928 (33). Its photoelectric counterpart was tested in a preliminary fashion by E. O. Lawrence and L. B. Linford (33), who observed an increase in the photoelectric threshold of some hundreds of Å in wave length with relatively low applied fields (limit 6×10^4 volts/cm), and the magnitude of the shift was in keeping with the $\sqrt{X_s}$ prediction.

At ordinary temperatures, the thermionic emission being small, this effect is negligible in regard to yielding values of j_0 which can furnish a secondary mechanism. According to Schottky, for Na and W the applied fields to cause measurable j_0 would be 9×10^7 and 2.8×10^8 volts/cm, respectively, at room temperatures. Since the mechanism is thermionic, it is *strongly* temperature-dependent, and should become very large at higher temperatures and field strengths. Calculations have been made by R. Holm (34) and applied to the mechanisms in the hearth of the low boiling point metal vapor arcs. Under such circumstances, he has calculated that $j = 10^4$ amp/cm^2. The arc currents observed can thus be accounted for if $\phi e = 3$, T is 1,300° K., and $X_s = 2.3 \times 10^7$ volts/cm; or if $\phi e = 4.5$, $T = 2,000°$ K., and $X_s = 4.2 \times 10^7$ volts/cm. At these temperatures, many of the metal surfaces considered are fluid. Whether the electrostatic forces would disrupt such surfaces before emission, or whether the pressure of positive ion bombardment would prevent disruption, is still a matter of speculation. The mechanism is significant and very important *if it can be established that this phenomenon occurs at such temperatures and fields.* Unfortunately, there is no evidence to support this.

The discovery of the so-called "vacuum spark" established that there were rather heavy field-emission currents leading to breakdown when surface fields exceeded some 10^6 volts/cm at room temperatures for clean, outgassed, and fairly smooth metal surfaces (35). If the surfaces are machined and not outgassed, such currents and breakdown appear to occur at gross fields as low as 4×10^5 volts/cm. The investigation of this process, systematically studied as the "vacuum spark," probably first by R. A. Millikan and his students, and later by J. E. Lilienfeld and others, revealed that it initiated with a field emission which up to 1,500° C. was *not* temperature-dependent (35). The phenomenon was theoretically described in 1928 in terms of the wave-mechanical theory of metals by numerous theoretical physicists, including W. V. Houston, J. R. Oppenheimer, L. Nordheim, and R. H. Fowler (36). The theory in its accepted form was that of Fowler and Nordheim, and is called the "Fowler-Nordheim theory." The corrected form of the equation, including the image force field, as given by Sommerfeld and Bethe, reads:

$$(9.52) \quad j = 1.55 \times 10^{-6} \, \frac{X^2}{\phi} \, \epsilon^{\frac{6.8 \times 10^7 \phi^{3/2}}{X}} \, \psi \left(\frac{3.62 \times 10^{-4} \sqrt{X}}{\phi} \right).$$

The term $\psi(3.62 \times 10^{-4}\sqrt{X})/\phi$ comes from a table of values computed by these authors, and corrects for the image force. The mechanism envisioned by this theory applies to *all* electrons in the distribution. It assumes that in virtue of the *narrowing* of the potential barrier by the external field, the electrons of appropriate wave length have a chance of diffracting around the potential barrier and thus leaking out. The diffraction concept appears in later years to have been replaced by the concept that the electrons "tunnel" through the barrier. The chance of tunneling depends primarily on the thickness of the barrier and its height. This, however, applies to all the electrons, degenerate and thermal alike, and *is independent of temperature.* Since the degenerate electrons outnumber thermal electrons ~ 100 to 1, electrons emitted will generally be degenerate electrons, many from near the top of the Fermi distribution. When these electrons emerge, they emerge at the level which they had inside the barrier.

The currents observed for "conditioned," cleaned, and outgassed wires, with most of the smaller points of roughness melted off, occur at notably lower applied potentials and hence calculated fields than the theory requires. For $\phi e = 4.5$, as with W, X for a detectable current should be of the order of 2 or 3×10^7 volts/cm. Actually, as stated, the phenomenon is observed to set in at 4×10^4 volts/cm for gassy, irregular surfaces, and 10^6 volts/cm for clean, outgassed W surfaces.

Schottky (33) accounted for this disagreement on the assumption of small points or molecular roughnesses on the surfaces. At such points, the values of X are larger than are the continuous metal surface fields for the geometrical form from which X was computed. Schottky set $X_p = \beta X$, where X_p is the point field and X the assumed gross field. If the irregularity is a hemispherical boss on a surface which to the boss appears infinitely plane, the value of β is 3. A second, much smaller boss on the surface of the first boss would again yield a β of 3. Thus, if a roughness has such dimensions as would be indicated by this geometry, X_p could be roughly ten times the value given by the calculated field X. If the ratio of radii of the small boss on the larger boss must be of the order of 10, to fulfill the "infinite plane" condition imposed, then on the wires used *it is not possible to ascribe lowering of more than an order of magnitude to this factor.* An optically smooth surface has irregularities not much more than 2×10^{-5} cm, and the boss on the boss would make the small boss already 2×10^{-7}, which is only 10 atomic diameters. That removal of small points was a factor was demonstrated by Millikan and Roether (35), who reached fields of the order of 10^7 volts per cm by progressively "burning off" smaller and smaller points through a carefully graded series of vacuum sparks with increasing voltage. On machined surfaces, obviously the roughness is of the order of 10^{-3} cm, and the lowering by a factor of 10^2 from 10^8 to 10^6 volts/cm is possible.

The discussion so far has focused on pure, smooth metal surfaces of a single constituent. With composite surfaces, such as thoriated tungsten, Pt + Na, Pt + NaH, BaO, Cs on W, or Cs-Ag-O surfaces, and dirty or gassy surfaces, the values of ϕe and thus of X may be much lower. With such surfaces, interpretation must be made with due caution, for coating of a whole surface may not imply the coating of a point, and vice versa. For example, coating W with Ba resulted in decreased values of ϕe over those of the W surface, but the active area for emission decreased. In 1928, one observer, C. del Rosario (37), had not been able to obtain field emission at all under conditions observed by other workers. C. C. Chambers (37) found that the rigorous heat treatment and vacuum conditions had left no points for emission on del Rosario's wires. A. J. Ahearn (37), using thoriated tungsten, even further confirmed N. A. de Bruyne's conclusions (33) that *field* currents were independent of temperature up to the point where these currents were completely masked by thermionic emission. The field currents observed were independent of the degree of thoriation, again indicating that the emission was from points where chance thoriation did not conform to average values for the surface. Ahearn also suggested that the vacuum spark might arise by the concentration of the current in small points, raising these to near the melting point, with disruption of the liquid surface by electrostatic forces, thus leading to a vapor cloud and a spark.

In 1936, E. W. Müller (38) started a train of studies, some of which confused the situation, but his techniques ultimately led to clarification. He investigated field emission as a function of the work function ϕe of the metal, and also in regard to the energy distribution of emitted electrons. With composite surfaces, and emission from points of unknown work function or crystallites of substances on the surfaces, he arrived at the erroneous conclusion that the field emission varied with ϕ^3 instead of $\phi^{3/2}$, as wave mechanics predicted on the Fowler-Nordheim theory. His studies of the energy distribution of emitted electrons indicated conclusively that these came from the Fermi level, and not from the thermal conduction band. The point *was not cooled* by field-emission currents, as it would have been with thermal electrons. He surrounded the cathode wire by a perforated anode cylinder (W helix), with approximately 10,000 volts between it and the wire. An outer W cylindrical electrode could be lowered to suitable negative potentials relative to the wire helix anode to act as a retarding field. The field-emitted electrons could *not* reach the outer cylinder against the potential unless the outer cylinder was at 9,995 volts, or 5 volts positive to the inner W wire. The current to the outer cylinder saturated at 10 volts positive. From the potential diagram of figure 9.16, it is seen that this means that the electrons came from the Fermi level between 5 and 10 volts below the barrier.

These experiments were later confirmed by J. E. Henderson and his associates (39), with 5 volts as the work function of the collector.

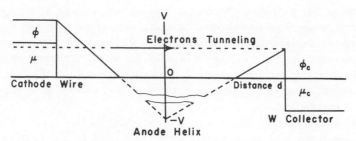

Fig. 9.16. Potential diagram illustrating Müller's arrangement for proving that field-emission electrons come from the Fermi level.

If these had been conduction electrons, they would have begun to be collected at −10,000 volts on the collector. Abbott and Henderson (39) showed that the log j-$1/X$ plot curved, as indicated by the X^2 term in equation 9.52. However, their points made the quantity vary as X^4, and not X^2. This was not in contradiction to theory, since the theory envisages a constant field over the whole uniform surface, while the emitting point has its own high field, which is unknown.

In 1936, W. Shockley and R. P. Johnson (40) conceived of a most ingenious device for studying the thermionic emission from a wire. The wire was surrounded by an open helix of fine wire, and this in turn was surrounded by the cylindrical wall of the glass envelope, coated with fluorescent material. The thermionic electrons radiating from regions on the wire diverged to give a magnified image on the screen of the wire surface in terms of electron emission. The magnification was in the ratio of the wire radius to that of the glass cylinder.

Müller applied this device to field emission. He used a point of W etched with $NaNO_2$, surrounded by a cylindrical anode, with the fluorescent screen 10 cm distant opposite the point and normal to the cylinder axis. Magnification from the 1-micron point was 10^5, and the applied potential was 10^4 volts. For the untreated point, field emission came from sharp lines on the crystal. Strong heating led to more uniform emission. Some regions of the point failed to emit, leaving dark patches on the screen. With single crystals of W used as points, the dark patches could be identified with the 110, 211, and 100 crystal planes, the first being darkest and the others less so. Similar pictures were obtained with Mo points, which also have a body-centered, cubical, crystalline lattice. The admission of O_2 poisoned the Mo crystal preferentially on the 100 plane. Heating removed the O_2. Ni and Cu had the 111 plane a nonemitter. These points were unstable, as they could not properly be outgassed. Thoriation indicated the thorium to reside on relatively small portions of the surface.

The smoothing pattern on heating a W point was caused by a migration of the W away from the sharply etched plane edges over the surface. Studies of surface-migration rates as a function of temperature for different metals and coatings can thus be made. Evaporation of Ba atoms onto the surface caused nonemitting areas to emit, indicating that nonemission was a property of the area and not owing to a depression of the surface.

The techniques of Müller were extended by R. O. Jenkins (41) and his co-workers, and are currently being exploited by W. P. Dyke (42). Jenkins, in addition, is the author of the most comprehensive recent review of the field-emission problem. He observed that on heating an etched, shaped point in a high field, the shape of the surface altered to a new state of minimum potential energy with the field present. The changes in shape were studied in silhouette by electron microscope. Shaping of the Ni point in the field changed the pattern. In Ni, the nonemitting planes are the 110, 100, 111, and 113 planes. Heating to 1,120° K. caused strong building up on the 111 plane. If too much field was applied, the point disrupted. This agrees with Ahearn's explanation of the vacuum spark from fine field points. Nonemitting areas were ascribed by Jenkins to deactivation by O_2.

In 1940, R. H. Haefer (41) used the electron microscope to determine the shape of the points. Using these data, giving area and radius of the true emitting agent whose work function he knew, he was able to verify the predictions of the Fowler-Nordheim theory quantitatively. He also proved that the variation with work function was $\phi^{3/2}$, as the theory requires, using Ba, K, and Cs layers, as well as pure W.

The recent studies of Dyke (42), using the method outlined, but with pulsed fields of the order of 10^8 volts/cm, are most revealing. When such voltage pulses were applied to cold emitters for a few microseconds, current densities as high as 10^9 amp/cm^2 were drawn from the emitters. These were sharpened W wires with approximate hemispherically capped tips of radius 10^{-5} cm. The areas of emission could be estimated from the image size on a Müller tube. Electron-microscopic examination of the points gave the shape factor. The current density was approximately that predicted by the Fowler-Nordheim theory. The effects of space charge near the emitter must thus have been small in view of this agreement. When the applied field reached the calculated value of 1.4×10^8 volts/cm for W, the emitter was generally damaged by the passage of a brief but brilliant metallic arc in vacuum. One emitter sustained such an arc for a microsecond without damage.

Dyke and his associates next extended their investigations into regions where the current density from field emission reached values at which space-charge distortion acts to limit the current. This should be indicated by a departure of the linear log j-$(10^8/\beta V)$ plots obtained where the Fowler-Nordheim equation applies. Since damage to the point can occur in this region, the pulsed microwave discharge technique was employed so that the point could not overheat. The space-charge distortion should appear at a critical value of the current density $j = j_c$, of the order of 6×10^6 amp/cm^2. Calculations and experiment can be carried out up to densities $j > 4 \times 10^7$ amps/cm^2, at which value resistive heating occurs in the point. The appearance of space-charge current limitation can also be noted in the Müller patterns for the single crystal point, for as soon as space-charge limitation occurs, the space-charge cloud interaction diffuses and starts to smear out the clear-cut Müller pattern. To study the effect of space-charge limitation, the Fowler-Nordheim and space-charge limitation equations are used to eliminate the current density between them. Thus, the space-charge limitation equations for the geometry of the point field read:

$$(9.53) \qquad (2\,KJV^{\frac{1}{2}} - X_0^2)(4\,KJV^{\frac{1}{2}} + X_0^2)^{\frac{1}{2}} = 6\,K^2J^2d - X_0^3 ,$$

with $K = 2\pi(2m/e)^{\frac{1}{2}}$ and $J = cX_0^2\,\epsilon^{-b/X_0}$, the Fowler-Nordheim equation, letting J represent the current density.

This yields

$$4\,KcV^{3/2}\,\epsilon^{-(b/X_0)-3V} = 9\,K^2c^2X_0^2d^2\,\epsilon^{(2b/X_0)} - 3\,X_0d ,$$

so that

$$(9.54) \qquad (3.9 \times 10^{-1}/\phi)\,V^{3/2}\,\epsilon^{-(b/X_0)-V}$$
$$= (25.8 \times 10^{-2}/\phi^2)\,X_0d^2\,\epsilon^{-\left(\frac{2b}{X_0}\right)} - X_0d ,$$

using ϕ in electron volts, V in volts and X in volts/cm.

If one sets $X = V/d$ and $X = \beta V$, where β is the geometrical shape factor, it is possible to plot the value of $\log_{10} j$ in amps/cm^2 against $10^8/\beta V$ as the dot-dashed curve DB in figure 9.17. The plot for $\log_{10} j$ against $10^8/\beta V$, where no space-charge limitation occurs, is the straight line AC, which extrapolates to E. The curve, calculated for a point with area $A = 6.3 \times 10^{-9}$ cm^2 and $\beta = 4 \times 10^{-3}$ cm^{-1}, is shown as the solid curve ACD of figure 9.17, for lower-potential d.c. and

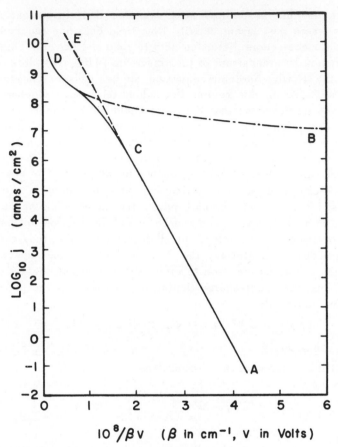

Fig. 9.17. Dyke's calculated curve for space-charge limitation BD, and for unmodified field emission $A\,C\,E$, and the experimental curve $A\,C\,D$ obtained with pulsed discharge.

high-potential pulsed discharge with W point. It will be seen that in fact, in the region around $j_c = 6 \times 10^6$ amp/cm², the linear plot of lower fields departs from linearity and presently joins the space-charge limited current to follow the curve $B\,D$. In figure 9.18 are shown calculated curves for the same phenomenon, assuming different values of ϕe, from 4.35 to 5.0.

However, as the pulsed currents were pushed higher, the point eventually broke down to a short power arc in the microsecond duration of the pulse. Experience with this breakdown phenomenon and observations of the Müller patterns showed that this breakdown must be associated with the resistive heating of the point by the heavy current drawn. Using the pulsed technique, the values of the field

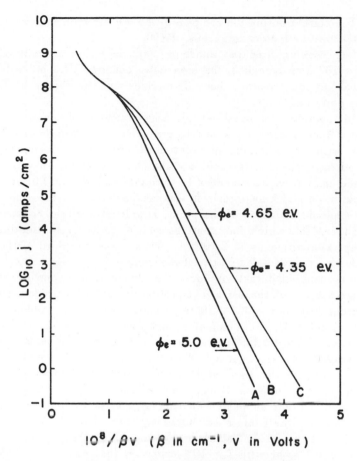

Fig. 9.18. Dyke's calculated curves of field-emission current
for three values of the work function ϕe.

X, the current density j, the value of the work function, and the sparking potential could be determined. Contrary to previous beliefs and
findings for high-potential vacuum-spark breakdown, the breakdown
always occurred when a critical value of $j \sim 10^8$ amps/cm² appropriate
to the W point was reached. Thus, for a given point, breakdown was
predictable. To lay the ghosts of pre-existing theories, certain points
were carefully established.

1. There was *no* bombardment of the cathode by material from the
anode.

2. The breakdown was independent of *applied* potential between
$5 < V < 60$ kv if $j \sim 10^{-8}$ was *not* exceeded. This was contrary to
the larger-scale breakdown findings of Trump and van de Graaf (43).

3. The current during the arc phase was greater than that preceding the breakdown by factors in excess of 100.

4. Ion crossing from the anode or cathode was not involved, as once $j \sim 10^8$ was exceeded, the breakdown occurred with pulse length less than an ion crossing time. This rules out the theory of Trump and van de Graaf.

5. Micrographs and oscilloscopic measurements of i and V could be made. When a current reached to the value of around 9×10^{-2} amp for the order of magnitude of point used, the value of current was observed to increase with time, and the Müller pattern, already fuzzy by space charge, was surrounded by a ring of emission. This occurred at about $j = 6 \times 10^7$ amp/cm². It was suspected that this ring came from thermionic emission of the point, largely at a slight constriction behind the point, which was near the melting point of W. Heating the point by external means to 2,100° K. when j was one-third of that for ring appearance, produced no tilt of the ring.

It was concluded that, in fact, the phenomenon occurring was a resistive heating of the narrowest portion of the point produced when the current rose to near 8.7×10^6 amp/cm². This heating added thermionic emission to the field emission, and produced the ring.

Increase in current further increased heating until the melting point of W at 3,000° K. was reached. With this, of course W vaporizes appreciably, and in the light of Bennett's theory (44) of self-focusing streams, once a unipolar beam, such as an electron beam, reaches an adequate current value and encounters a mass of ionizable vapor, it can stabilize itself into a self-focusing beam. This is obviously the mechanism of the vacuum-spark breakdown. Once the current reaches a value of 0.1 amp, with $j \sim 10^8$ amp/cm², the regenerative heating of the point begins. With W this results in raising the point to 3,000° K., the melting temperature of W metal in the microsecond of pulse application. Once the W starts to melt, the vapor jet leaving the surface can become ionized by the field-emission electron current and thermionic current beam. This at once leads to the self-focusing beam proposed by W. H. Bennett (44), with an ultimate arc current of the order of 40-100 amps.

To establish the question of the melting of the point, Dyke and his associates computed the average current density needed to raise a number of their observed points to 3,000° K. by resistive heating of the point in the microsecond and even less of the applied pulses. A study of seven such events revealed the computed resistive-heating current density and the observed current density in each case to agree with each other within a factor of 2, current densities ranging between

3×10^7 and 1×10^8 amp/cm². Considering the difficulties with form factor for the different points, the agreement is striking. Thus, it is established that vacuum-current breakdown arises from a field-emission current density at small points that leads to melting and vaporization of the point, yielding an arc probably by the mechanism of self-focusing streams (44). With various surfaces and under different conditions, the potentials, etc., can vary by considerable margins as ϕe, β, and other factors change. However, before the self-focusing stream mechanism may be applied, this phenomenon must be quantitatively developed, theoretically and by experiment, so that it can be established that the currents observed fulfill the criteria in the vacuum-spark breakdown.

Unexplained as yet are the low values of the vacuum-spark breakdown observed with machined surfaces and surfaces of massive metal, which cannot be outgassed or cleaned. The observed gross fields are of the order of 4×10^5 volts/cm, and might at a maximum be between 4×10^6 and 4×10^7 for surface irregularities. With gassy surfaces, ϕe may be low, and gas formation with heavy positive ion beams from the gassy anode can lead to ready spark-over. Some experimental study should be made with such surfaces, as these are the ones that cause flash-over in various technical installations and limit development of devices.

Attention should be called to studies of E. W. Haworth and L. H. Germer (45), of the Bell Laboratories, on breakdown produced through the closing of gaps with potentials applied. On pure, noble metals, when the fields reach values for field emission, the gap will arc over if the circuit conditions permit growth of current at a rate of 10^8 amperes per second. In this breakdown a pit forms on the anode, and the current density is of the order of 10^8 amp per cm². The breakdown starts presumably as a field emission from the cathode. If the cathode is covered with a film of grease, carbon, or organic material, MgO dust, etc., a field-emission triggered arc will result if the rate of current rise is 5×10^4 amp/sec. The pit then forms on the cathode. Current densities are also high.

Haworth has shown that if a film of dirt is present on the cathode that is a nonconductor, and a field is placed across a gap of up to several mm, the system will go to arc-over at surprisingly low potentials if positive ions are sprayed on the insulator. Here the low potentials preclude any direct field emission from the clean metal surface. Layers of various sorts were used, especially the calcium stearate layers prepared by the Blodgett techniques, in which the thickness could be controlled. When positive ions reach the outer surface of such a film, fields of *very high value* can build up across the nonconducting film. These will lead to field emission from the cathode of such magnitude as to create gas ions from the film and cause breakdown from gassy anodes, opposite, by liberation of gas. How far these studies throw any light on field emission leading to arc-over in more commercial systems, is still unknown. It is noted, however, that they all involve field emission initially, with ion actions later. One criterion as to whether they can lead to an arc appears to be the possible rate of rise of current. This indicates that the breakdown represents a very high rate of local energy input and high current densities in order to liberate the vapors needed.

It is, however, incorrect to use this mechanism as a "catchall" for any current in discharges where the mechanisms are *not* known. In the past, attempts were made by many workers to account for the electron emission from the cathode sustaining the glow discharge and low boiling point metal vapor arc by means of a field emission. If the unbiased observer attempts to compute j under these conditions, making reasonable assumptions concerning ϕe and X, the values of j are *many orders of magnitude too low* on the basis of the Fowler-Nordheim theory. In the case of a glow discharge, the assumption is not needed, as values of γ are adequate and the field-emission hypothesis is gratuitous. For the arc, the earlier estimates of j now appear to be even more inadequate, since j in many such arcs appears to reach the fantastic value of from 10^5 to 10^6 amps per cm^2. Such densities do occur in field emission from ultrafine points that lead to arcs. They probably do not figure in the sustaining mechanism. Perhaps more reasonable values of j in arcs can be obtained by the use of the Richardson-Schottky equation. There is, however, no experimental indication that this mechanism is applicable at higher fields. It may be remarked that such phenomena as field emission require, in general, an organized surface with clearly defined potential barrier. It is very questionable whether any such condition exists at arc cathodes of low boiling point metals.

§ 10. The Secondary Electron Liberation by Charged Insulating Dusts; the Malter, or Paetow, Effect.

This chapter requires the brief mention of a spurious type of secondary emission. It had been noted that various types of discharge tubes, stressed to the breakdown threshold in plane parallel gaps and Geiger counters, seemed to show continued and spurious discharges without the external triggering ionizing events, once an initial gas discharge had passed through the tube. In many cases the spurious counts might continue for hours after the initial discharge. These spurious discharges were associated primarily with very fine particles of insulating materials on the cathode. Substances that worked best were MgO, Al_2O_3, SiO_2, and the like. The particles most active were perhaps 10^{-4} or 10^{-5} cm in diameter. The effect was first studied by Malter (32), more extensively in regard to triggering effects by Paetow (32), in connection with Geiger counters, and more recently in detail as a source of electrons at low potentials by Jacobs (32).

In its simplest form, it was believed that after a discharge the anode side of the insulating particle lying on the cathode intercepted positive ions, thus charging the surface away from the cathode up to a high positive potential. Fields across the insulator were then of the order of 10^6 and more volts/cm because of the small thickness. This was assumed to call forth a field emission from the cathode which would continue to flow until the surfaces of the insulators were discharged. Thus, dusty Geiger counters discharged from time to time, triggered by the field-emitted electrons, each discharge of the counter placing a fresh positive charge on the dust particles. Ultimately, electrical and mechanical actions removed the dust from the cathode, and the spurious counts ceased (46).

The work of Jacobs in particular has shown that the actions are really much more involved. He also showed that the phenomenon could be made to yield a continuous current of electrons at low potential, giving a self-sustaining discharge. In high vacuum a gun with an Mg pellet which could be evaporated was placed opposite a metal cylinder that was outgassed and clean. At an appropriate time the pellet was heated and evaporated with a small amount of O_2 in the tube. This gave a uniform deposit of MgO on a cm^2 of cylinder surface. On the far side of this cylinder was a BaO cathode gun and a coarse grid. When the oxide-coated filament had been activated after forming the MgO, the metal cylinder was rotated opposite the BaO filament gun and grid by an internal iron lug and external magnet. The filament was heated and a beam of electrons i_0 of about 1 microampere current was shot at the MgO layer at about 150 volts. These electrons knocked secondary electrons out of the MgO with the secondary emission of MgO electrons greater than the current i_0 from the BaO cathode gun. This left the outside of the MgO layer positively charged, with a field between metal cylinder and grid driving electrons to the grid. Thus, the potential on the grid side of the MgO soon reached that of the grid, which was about 100 volts positive to the metal cylinder. When this occurred the positive potential of 100 volts was across the 10^{-4} cm diameter particles of MgO. At this point a self-sustaining discharge set in, yielding currents of the orders of milliamperes from the metal cylinder and MgO layer through the grid for about 1 microampere of current from the BaO cathode gun. With proper disposition of the potentials, the discharge could be made self-sustaining, with no current from the BaO gun, once the MgO was charged. In this state the MgO layer was luminous, emitting spectral lines from excited states of MgO. The discharge continued indefinitely.

Many studies revealed that to get such a discharge, the MgO surface had to consist of more or less isolated or very loosely packed small pellets, and not of a uniform layer. Use of various metals for the cylinder and the variation of the secondary emission from the layer as potential varied, indicated that field emission from the metal was *not* the primary source of electron emission. It was shown that the high field across the small gaps between particles in vacuum and metal backing accelerated electrons emitted from the metal to a point where the MgO was ionized cumulatively by electron impact. Acceleration of electrons *in* the MgO did not produce this effect, but it required the porous MgO so that the electrons liberated could accelerate and ionize again. The discharge became self-sustaining across the insulator as soon as the avalanches ϵ^{ad} in the porous MgO produced enough *photons* so that the γ_p in the backing metal gave $\gamma_p \, \epsilon^{ad} = 1$. If the fields and currents were not adequate to produce the photons and the field amplification, then the discharge was not self-sustaining, so that the BaO gun current i_0 was needed.

In actual discharge tubes, obviously the action of dust will not be so extensive, elaborate, or long sustained. However, through the initial charging up of proper oxide dust specks on the cathode by antecedent discharges that plasters them with positive ions, currents produced by some slight field emission, but mostly by cumulative ionization and photon γ_p through the particles, will yield spurious electron bursts which can spoil otherwise well-planned experiments. Thus, avoidance of dust and proper choice of abrasives on cathode surfaces are indicated.

§ 11. The Apparent Second Coefficient Resulting from Space-Charge Distortion Owing to Heavy Current Densities.

It is now necessary to consider another activity observed in Townsend gaps which of itself is not a strictly secondary mechanism. It is, however, an activity which can act to alter conditions so that secondary mechanisms otherwise not active may become important. It is also an activity which manifests itself by an upcurving of the $\log i/i_0$-x curves that *superficially simulates a secondary action* and thus falsifies data. However, it does not yield very consistent values of γ as a function of X/p, and was, in fact, discovered by this circumstance. It was noted by D. Q. Posin (VIII.10), in his studies of the second coefficient in N_2, that there were upcurvings of the log i/i_0-x plot that did not seem to yield a systematic set of values of γ as X/p increased. Sanders (VIII.10) and Paavola (VIII.9) had also noted such erratic evaluation of β following Townsend's original theory. In a brilliant analysis of the trouble, Posin inferred that it occurred when the externally stimulated photoelectric current density $j_0 = i_0/A$ exceeded certain values and the gap length x approached to near 5 cm. The matter was discussed, and ultimately R. N. Varney, with the aid of H. J. White, the author, and Posin, developed the theory (VIII.14). In principle, the upcurving is caused by an accumulation of positive ion space charges near the cathode. These result from cumulative ionization in the primary process when j_0 is large enough, a/p varies properly with X/p, and distances x are sufficiently great.

The analysis assumes the usual plane parallel electrode system and a plate separation d. The distance x is a variable which will be used along the field direction from the cathode. The applied potential at the anode is V_d, and $V_d/d = X$, the undistorted field in the gap. At any point in the gas the electron current is $i_- = i_0\,\epsilon^{ax}$, and that at the anode is $i_0\,\epsilon^{ad}$. The condition of continuity of current flow states that $i = i_+ + i_- = i_0\,\epsilon^{ad}$. This leads to the value for the positive ion current i_+ as $i_+ = i_0\,(\epsilon^{ad} - \epsilon^{ax})$. Poisson's equation states that $d^2V/dx^2 = -4\,\pi(\rho_+ - \rho_-)$. Since current density j is given by $j = \rho v$, the velocity v is $v = kx$, and $X = -(dV/dx)$, it is possible to set

$$(9.55) \qquad \frac{d\left(\dfrac{dV}{dx}\right)}{dx} = -\frac{4\pi j_0}{dV/dx}\left[\frac{\epsilon^{ad} - \epsilon^{ax}}{k_+} - \frac{\epsilon^{ax}}{k_-}\right].$$

Here j_0 is the electron current density at the cathode, and k_+ and k_- are the positive ion and electron mobilities, respectively.

Since k_- is $10^3\,k_+$, $1/k_-$ may be neglected relative to $1/k_+$, yielding

$$(9.56) \qquad \frac{dV}{dx}\,\frac{d\left(\dfrac{dV}{dx}\right)}{dx} = \frac{4\pi j_0}{k_+}\left(\epsilon^{ad} - \epsilon^{ax}\right).$$

Now a/p is a function of X/p, or at constant p, $a = f(X)$. The expression $i = i_0\,\epsilon^{ax}$ was written for the initially uniform field. If the field is not uniform, this simple relation may not be used, and the expressions

$$\epsilon^{\int_0^x a\,dx} \quad \text{and} \quad \epsilon^{\int_0^d a\,dx}$$

replace ϵ^{ax} and ϵ^{ad} for the uniform field. This alters equation 9.56 to

(9.57)
$$X\,\frac{dX}{dx} = \frac{dV}{dx}\,\frac{d\left(\dfrac{dV}{dx}\right)}{dx} = -\frac{4\pi j_0}{k_+}\left(\epsilon^{\int_0^d a\,dx} - \epsilon^{\int_0^x a\,dx}\right).$$

To solve this relation, set $\int_0^x a\,dx = u$, and $du/dx = a$. Replace $j_0 \epsilon^{\int_0^d a\,dx}$ by its equivalent j, so that

(9.58)
$$aX\,dX = \frac{4\pi}{k_+}\,(j_0\,\epsilon^u - j)\,du\,.$$

While j is dependent on u and X, in any particular measurement in which d and X are not changed j will be a constant, for it is not a function of x. Thus,

(9.59)
$$\int_{X_0}^X a\,X\,dX = \frac{4\pi}{k_+}\int_0^u (j_0\,\epsilon^u - j)\,du\,.$$

In N_2, between $X/p = 40$ and $X/p = 180$, Posin showed that roughly $a/p = A'(X/p)^2$, or $a = AX^2$. Placing this value of a in equation 9.59,

(9.60)
$$\int_{X_0}^X aX\,dX = A\int_{X_0}^X X^3\,dX\,,$$

which makes

$$\frac{A}{4}\,(X^4 - X_0^4) = \frac{4\pi}{k_+}\,(j_0\,\epsilon^u - ju - j_0)$$

or

(9.61)
$$X^4 = \frac{16\pi}{A\,k_+}\,(j_0\,\epsilon^u - ju - j_0) + X_0^4\,.$$

To evaluate j and X_0, it is possible to use $du/dx = AX^2$, so that

$$\int_0^{\log_e j/j_0}\frac{du}{AX^2} = \int_0^d dx \quad \text{and} \quad X = -\,dV/dx\,,$$

so that

$$\int_0^d X\,dX = -\int_0^{V_d} dV.$$

Since $dx = du/AX^2$, it follows that

(9.62)
$$\int_0^{\log_e j/j_0} \frac{du}{AX} = V_d = X_A\,d,$$

where X_A is the applied field. Using the value of X defined,

(9.63)
$$\int_0^{\log_e j/j_0} \frac{du}{\left[\dfrac{16\pi}{Ak_+}(j_0\,\epsilon^u - ju - j_0) + X_0^4\right]^{1/4}} = Ad$$

and

(9.64)
$$\int_0^{\log_e j/j_0} \frac{du}{\left[\dfrac{16\pi}{Ak_+}(j_0\,\epsilon^u - ju - j_0) + X_0^4\right]^{1/4}} = AX_A d.$$

These two equations, 9.63 and 9.64, must be solved in the following manner: Given a value of j_0, the applied field X, and of d, find the corresponding values of j (or j/j_0) and X_0. What is wanted is j as a function of d. This must be done by trial and error, using numerical integration on an assumed or tried value of X_0 and j, and seeing if X_A and d are obtained correctly.

A sample calculation was made as follows: $j_0 = 1.75 \times 10^{-11}$ amp, $X_A = 120$ volts/cm, and $p = 1$ mm. The value of α for the undistorted field was 1.00. Plotting $\log j/j_0$ against d showed that at $d = 7.96$ cm $\log j/j_0 = 8$, and at $d = 8.6$ cm the slope of $\log j/j_0$-d curves became infinite. This indicated an indeterminacy, leading to an increase in current beyond all measure. Such condition can lead to rearrangement of space charges consistent with a self-sustaining discharge, i.e., a spark.

This particular variation was discovered with an assumed $f(X/p) = A(X/p)^2$. If the functional form is different, a new solution must be made. Thus, the increase in α comes from a field distorted by space charge, and this depends on the functional relation $\alpha/p = f(X/p)$. If α/p increases faster than linearly with X/p, then it can be shown in a simple way that $\log j/j_0$ will increase above its value when the field is undistorted. If α/p increases more slowly than linearly with X/p, the space charge can no longer suffice to give an apparent large value of α, but must give a smaller value. The reader is referred to the original text for the formal proof of this assertion (VIII.14), (VIII.22).

The conclusions to be drawn are then: Depending on the number of molecules present in a given spark gap, with sufficient illumination a value of X/p causing α to take on measurable values will give rise to a positive ion space-charge accumulation in the gas of such magnitude as materially to distort the field and the curves of $\log i/i_0$ plotted against gap length. These distortions resemble the upcurving caused by a real secondary action, except that values of β inferred from the data increase markedly along the curve. Effectively, this means that the apparent value of β or γ derived from such data is not a function of the applied uniform field alone, but varies with gap length, since space charges increase with x. It is very important to note that such an increase in apparent α can lead to field changes in the gap of such a nature that they lead to an indefinitely great increase in current i. In themselves, as will be seen later, such indefinite increases in current do not properly represent a spark-breakdown criterion. However, there is nothing to prevent such large space-charge and current increases from leading to a breakdown or discharge, with an effective real secondary mechanism active.

This situation may explain some of the sparks observed at the end of the $\log i/i_0$-x curves at lower X/p by Sanders, Posin, and F. Llewellyn Jones and A. B. Parker (8).

It is clear that the space-charge accumulation by this mechanism is so slow that i has a very large formative time lag. These effects can only occur if $\alpha/p = f(X/p)$ varies more rapidly than proportional to X/p. Such values are found in the lower X/p ranges of all gases *up to the point of inflection* of the α/p-X/p curves. It must be pointed out that quite independently, at about the same time, A. von Engel and M. Steenbeck (VIII.22), (55), in developing the equation for the Townsend discharge, studied the increase in current in a Townsend gap. Using as $\alpha/p = f(X/p)$ the Townsend relation

(8.10) $$\alpha/p = A \ \epsilon^{-Bp/X},$$

it was found that below the point of inflection of the curve at $X/p = B/2$, the space charge would cause α to increase and thus increase i or j. Above the point of inflection, where α/p changes more slowly than proportional to X/p, this will not occur. This very important conclusion was thus simultaneously arrived at in different connections (VIII.14), (VIII.22). This conclusion has been directly confirmed through oscilloscopic time analysis of growth of sparks in uniform field geometry near threshold by H. W. Bandel in the author's laboratory, in which the growth of current was quantitatively verified by use of this theory (7).

The complete solution of the equation in the region where $f(X/p) = A(X/p)^2$ in N_2 enables a quantitative check of this theory to be made. Measurable upcurving should occur in the log i/i_0 curves at $X/p = 120$ when $j_0 = 2 \times 10^{-11}$ amp/cm^2 at a plate distance of $d = 7.5$ cm with a spark appearing at $d = 8.1$ cm. With 10^{-15} amp/cm^2, a true constant γ was observed, while at $X/p = 120$ and j_0 estimated as 10^{-12} amp/cm^2, a space-charge distortion of the log i/i_0-x curves was observed.

One more comment should be made at this point. The phenomena described here depend on the concentration of ions, since space charge and j_0 are concentration effects. Under such circumstances it is not to be expected that the much-quoted principle of similitude applies. This principle has for one of its important consequences the fact that the sparking potential is a function of pd, where p is the pressure and d is the gap length. This, it is seen, makes the breakdown a function of the total number of molecules or atoms across the gap. Here the total number do not play a role except to the extent that they must be adequate. Added to this is the condition that ion concentration, or the density of ionization, must be adequate. Since, in general, space charges and ion concentrations govern most discharge conditions, the principle of similitude is of little value. It is a first-order approximation only in the more or less classical Townsend regions.

§ 12. The Values of the Second Coefficients Observed by Townsend's Method, and Their Interpretation.

As indicated, there are several possible secondary mechanisms. Of these, the first one proposed (ionization by positive ions in the gas) appears unlikely under most discharge conditions. Fortuitously, it will be noted that all of the secondary processes lead to relations for i/i_0 of form so similar that the limited lengths of the curved portions of the log i/i_0-x plots, together with their limited accuracy, make it nearly if not completely impossible to differentiate between them. Thus, it was possible for W. E. Bowls to evaluate both a consistent β/p and a γ for his curves in N_2, with and without Hg and Na contamination on the cathode (VIII.11). The curves are shown in figures 9.19 and 9.20. The same was found to be true by Hale (VIII.11) and others. Obviously, the functions are different, so that different numerical values and to some extent variations of these might be expected. However, both fit the data sufficiently well, so that no differentiation can be made.

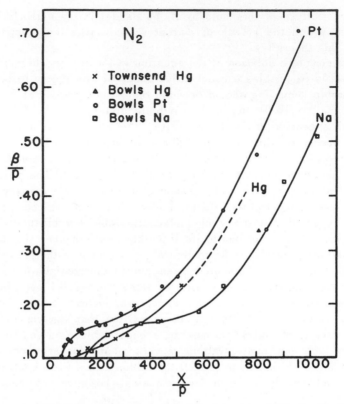

Fig. 9.19. The data of Bowls on β/p as a function of X/p for Hg-covered Pt, pure Pt, and Na-covered Pt in pure N_2 gas. Note the conventional monotonic rise for γ with Hg-coated cathode, coinciding with Townsend's values. Note the presence of photoelectric peaks once Hg vapor was absent and photons reached Pt and Na-covered Pt surfaces.

Analysis relative to the probable mechanisms active is even less satisfactory. As will be seen by inspection of equations 9.11, 9.24, and 9.44, covering the action of positive ions, photons, and metastable atoms at the cathode—the most likely mechanisms—all lead to an expression that to a first approximation may be "lumped" into one constant, γ, in the form of

$$(9.65) \qquad \gamma = \nu(\psi_i + f_m \psi_m g_m + \psi f g) = (\gamma_i + f_m \gamma_m g_m + \theta f g) ,$$

which multiplies into $(\epsilon^{ax} - 1)$. Thus, dimensionally and functionally, the cathode actions with coefficients γ_i, $\theta \omega g/a = f \theta g$, and $\theta_m f_m g_m$ can additively merge in producing a single composite quantity that experiment evaluates. The photoelectric ionization at the cathode does

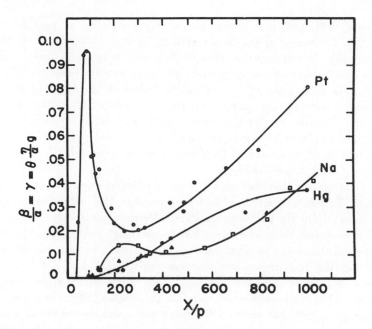

Fig. 9.20. The same curves of Bowls as in figure 9.19, with $\gamma \equiv \beta/a$ plotted against X/p. Note the strong photo effect on pure Pt in absence of Hg. Note the Hg curve, with small values and no photo effect. The ions were possibly larger Hg^+, which gives a notably low γ_i on Hg surfaces.

have a modification, including the absorption coefficient μ, where this is great enough. In fact, we shall see that this allows identification of the photoelectric part relative to γ_i when γ is plotted against p and X/p.

The effective photoelectric ionization *in the gas* has such characteristically different nature that its action is always easily separated, not only by its dependence on the gas and its changes in a', but by its anode localization. In fact, where the action at the cathode occurs in mixed or impure gases, the changes in a' and those of θfg have such interrelations that they can be identified and segregated as a function of μ.

In the early days only β/p was solved for. The gases were Hg-contaminated, leading to more or less uniform values of β/p, since the cathodes were Hg-coated and the ions were largely Hg^+ ions. Apparently, γ_p is very low on Hg-coated surfaces. Thus, for many years no distinction could be made. The early determinations of β by Townsend (VIII.1), (VIII.7) and his students revealed that the β/p inferred from their data ranged from values beginning at a low X/p

at about 0.01 and increasing either exponentially or parabolically with X/p to values of the order of 0.2. In any case, the rise of the inferred β/p values as a function of X/p was monotonic. They started from a small value at low X/p, and rose more rapidly than proportional to X/p. As this group of investigators believed that the phenomenon was one involving the gas, they paid no attention to the cathode material. The rise of β/p was most rapid, and set in at lower values of X/p in He, with H_2 next, followed by relatively impure A and N_2, air, and CO_2 in succession. CO_2 began at an X/p of 800 and rose up to $\beta/p = 0.1$ at $X/p = 1,400$.

It must be recalled that in all these earlier studies the gases were undoubtedly contaminated with Hg, and thus the cathodes probably were essentially Hg cathodes and ions (largely ineffective Hg^+ ions), as Oliphant and Moon observed for γ_i with Hg^+ (15). This statement will be substantiated in what follows. In addition to this experimental situation, the techniques for gaseous purification had not been adequately developed and the necessity for such purification was not obvious. Thus, not only were data on β/p using different.electrodes *strangely uniform*, but up to 1920 even the sparking-potential studies had revealed values of V_s that were strangely insensitive to cathode work function. This still more confirmed the earlier workers in their belief in the β mechanism.

While Townsend (VIII.1), (VIII.7) and J. J. Thomson (VIII.17) had conceived of the γ mechanism at an early date, there was no indication from these results that it played a role, so that the possibility of a dependence on the cathode material was overlooked.

The first workers to call attention to a possible cathode mechanism were G. Holst and E. Oosterhuis, between 1921 and 1923 (47). They were led to it when observing "negative striations" near the cathode in a neon discharge. The dark space next to the cathode led them to conclude that the electrons came from the cathode and not from the gas. The same workers, in 1920, also observed that in inert gases, the cathode *material* had a great influence on the sparking potential. This also indicated a γ mechanism, and one in which the positive ions required only low energies. The secondary emission of electrons by slow, positive ions was thus investigated quite independently by M. L. E. Oliphant and by Oliphant and P. B. Moon (15) at the Cavendish Laboratory in England, and by F. M. Penning (15) at the Philips Laboratories at the suggestion of Holst, beginning in 1929 and 1930, respectively. The dependence of the sparking potential on cathode material, noted by Holst and Oosterhuis, was confirmed in 1929 by L. J. Neuman and in 1937 by F. Ehrenkrantz (47). Other investigators, notably James Taylor (48), considered the liberation of electrons by positive ions to be a photoelectric action at the cathode. These proposals were all made between the years 1926 and 1928, antedating the studies of Oliphant and Moon. Thus, beginning around 1930 with positive results by Oliphant, Moon, and Penning, the cathode phenomena began to be considered as important secondary mechanisms. Most of these data, which began to point toward cathode mechanisms, came to light with the improvements in the achievement of gas purity. It was no accident that the first data in this direction should come to light in the Philips Laboratories, where industrial applications of inert gases required the development of such techniques to a high degree.

Quite independently, the author concluded from the data and operating conditions of Sanders and Posin that probably all previous values of γ had been obtained on sensibly the same surfaces. That is, he was inclined to believe that Hg-contaminated surfaces in which secondary response in a γ to the action of *different gaseous ions* was nicely reflected in the previous data on β/p, irrespective of where it had been measured.[8] Accordingly, W. E. Bowls was given the task of restudying N_2, using an all-outgassed system with Pt and Na-coated Pt electrodes, *carefully excluding all Hg vapor*. This technique at once paid dividends in the most striking fashion. Bowls's curves for β/p are shown in figure 9.19. It is there seen first that the curves of β/p, with essentially the *same gas*, except for minor contaminations, differ materially from each other, not only in their starting value in regard to X/p, but in their *shape* as well. They are no longer monotonic, except possibly for the Hg-coated cathode. Since these data, together with the work mentioned above, all pointed to a γ mechanism and *not* to a β/p mechanism, the data were used to calculate a γ instead of a β/p. In virtue of equation 9.12, this can be roughly accomplished without difficulty by taking the ratio of β/p to a/p at the same X/p. The results are valid within the accuracy of the log i/i_0-x curves. In Hale's (VIII.11) continuation of these studies with H_2, he made direct calculations for γ instead of using the approximation of Bowls.

It is seen from figure 9.20 that the data on γ are even more revealing than those for β/p. For pure, uncontaminated N_2 and a Pt surface, it is seen that at low X/p there is a prominent peak of values, with $\gamma = 0.095$ at an X/p of near 80. The value of γ falls to about 0.02 at

---

[8]Actually, the effect of Hg on such surfaces may not have been nearly so important as the effect of Hg vapor in converting all ions of higher energy to inefficient Hg^+ ions of low γ on any surfaces.

an X/p of 250 and rises thereafter parabolically to about 0.07 at an X/p of 1,000. It is first perhaps of interest to guess at what happens to photons and ionization as X/p increases. Some helpfully suggestive data, doubtful as to quantitative accuracy, have been derived for N_2 by F. M. Penning (VIII.38) and M. J. Druyvesteyn (VIII.21), indicating that electronic *excitation* of N_2 reaches a peak at an X/p of about 30, but is still large though declining at $X/p = 100$. The work function of Pt, such as Bowls used, could be some 5 to 6.5 volts. All of the photons created at lower X/p, where the peak occurs, may not be active in liberating electrons from the cathode, so that the peak of photoliberation may require higher X/p. It must be noted that ν is also raised as X/p increases. Theobald's data for N_2 indicate that above $X/p \sim 50$, ν should be about 0.8. Thus, it would take an X/p of perhaps 30 to create photons that act on Pt. At $X/p = 100$ the ionization by electron impact is rising, and according to Penning's curves $f = \omega/a = 9$. Data do not permit of evaluating f at $X/p = 250$, but a rough guess could place it at a lower value of 3, at $X/p = 300$. When X/p reaches 1,000, f probably will have decreased to around 0.5 to 1, while $\psi\nu$ is increasing. It was originally concluded that Bowls's peak at $X/p = 100$ was due primarily to a photoelectric effect, and that he should have used equation 9.48, with the observed γ given by $\gamma = \gamma_i + f\theta g$.

However, recent data from dynamic studies may alter this picture. Huber (49) observed for pure N_2 that there was no γ_p. The γ_i observed for identified N_4^+ ions at about thermal energies on outgassed Ni, which led to self-sustaining corona, had a value of around 2×10^{-2}, corrected for back diffusion. Since Bowls's value for γ at $X/p \sim 100$ is reduced by a factor of only 0.8 by back diffusion, the results should be comparable. Huber observed that with 0.1% of impurity, such as O_2, γ_i was reduced by a factor of 5 and a weak γ_p peak occurred. Bowls's N_2 was presumably as pure as that of Huber. Huber's techniques would *not* have revealed a delayed γ_p of considerable magnitude, caused by photons entrapped as resonance radiation. J. H. Parker, Jr. (49) discovered for N_2^+ and N^+ ions, on Pt coated with N_2, that γ_i was $\sim 10^{-2}$ at 2 e.v. ion energy, and $\sim 2 \times 10^{-3}$ at 30 e.v. The ion energies of Bowls, even at $X/p \sim 200$, were not more than 0.1 e.v., and his ions no doubt were N_2^+ at these values of X/p, as shown by Varney.

It is hard to account for the high value of $\gamma = 0.09$ observed by Bowls. Values of γ from the Townsend method of study are critically dependent on an accurate evaluation of a/p as a function of X/p. In this regard, no experimental evaluation of a/p so far is adequate to give accurate values. Bowls's data on α/p at lower X/p are not too good through the small range of distance x available with his method. As to the reality of his peak at low X/p, there is no doubt. Absolute values of γ are in doubt. However, if there is a photon γ_p at $X/p \sim 80$, which is larger than Huber's measured value of γ_i, then it is a much-delayed photon γ_p by some sort of resonance radiation or through secondary radiations in N_2. There is one difference between Huber's conditions and those of Bowls; namely, that Huber worked at from 600 to 50 mm pressure, while Bowls worked at pressures well below Huber's, so that much of the absorption in her observations was not active. It is impossible at this time to correlate the various observations, and the original assumption that the first peak is due to a γ_p while the later rise is due to a γ_i will have to stand.

The introduction of a droplet of Hg into the system, which at once amalgamated with the Pt surface so that it could only be removed by HNO_3, altered the whole picture. It is seen by reference to figure 9.20 that the monotonic curve appears for β/p and/or γ, first observed by Townsend and later also noted by Posin in N_2. There is no photoelectric peak, even though at an $X/p = 100$ in the N_2, there is still the same production of photons with an $f\theta g$. The 0.1 per cent of Hg cannot have altered f very much. However, the value of γ was changed for the surface by the Hg in a manner unknown, and the ions were perhaps largely Hg^+. For *pure* Hg, ϕe is 4.53 e.v., but it is possible that the Hg-coated Pt could have a higher value. Oliphant and Moon report such action of Hg on γ_i with He^+ ions. Aside from this factor, however, it is clear from the marked *increase* in α/p of 0.5 to 0.7 at an X/p of 100, noted by Bowls with Hg, that the 0.1% of Hg vapor present is being photoionized by these photons and N_2 metastables present *near the scene of their creation* in the gas. Hence, the value of μ must be so high that taken in conjunction with a possible *increase* in ϕe for the amalgamated surface, the value of $f\theta g$ is sensibly 0. That the value of ϕe may be increased above 5 to 6.5, and γ may be reduced by the Hg, is seen in the observation that Hg reduces γ_i at an X/p between 800 and 1,100 by about 0.5. It must be added, however, that this reduction could also be ascribed in some measure to the circumstance that all of the ions striking the surface are Hg^+. Hg has an ionization potential so low compared to N^+ and N_2^+ ions that the action of photoionization, together with charge transfer, produces a large proportion of Hg^+ ions by the time the ions arrive at the cathode. For Hg^+ ions on an Hg surface, the value of γ_i is very low. In any case, it may be concluded that μ is increased by the Hg, perhaps ϕe is raised, and the ions arriving at the cathode are the inefficient Hg^+ ions, so that the whole mechanism is shifted with a trace of Hg. It must further be added that in N_2 there are metastable states that conceivably could contribute to γ by $f_m \theta_m g_m$, and that Hg vapor definitely destroys some of these.

The data obtained in Na are in a measure still more revealing. It appears that in N_2 and H_2, but *not* in A, Na in the presence of ionization produces an exceedingly easily ionized gas or vapor, present to 10^{-3} mm or more of vapor pressure. Na and NaH apparently are solids, with vapor pressures around 10^{-10} mm of Hg, which thus cannot cause the effect. No one appears to know what the compounds are, but both sparking data and these measurements indicate, from values of a as well as γ, the presence of such a substance. In addition, Na distilled into the chamber settles on the electrodes, as these are cold and are good heat conductors. The alkali metal surface has an exceedingly low photoelectric threshold, and thus ϕe is around 1.8 to 3 volts. This makes the surface so active that i_0 is obtained by shining the dimmed light of an ordinary light bulb onto the cathode in a darkened room to prevent too much photoemission and additional emission from the Na condensed on the glass walls. The surface of NaH, created by making the cathode the negative electrode in a glow discharge in H_2 for some time, is even more sensitive. In Bowls's work in N_2, the surprising thing is that with ϕe of the order of 1.8 to 3 volts in N_2, with Na at an $X/p = 100$, there was no appreciable value of $f\theta g$ observed at all at the point where in pure N_2 the photoexcitation at energies above 5 volts yielded intense values of $f\theta g$.

Reference to the curve of figure 8.18 for the first coefficient a/p indicates that with Na in the chamber, a/p is increased some 25% or more over that with pure N_2 and the Pt electrode. Accordingly, as with Hg vapor, the volatile Na compound apparently *absorbs all active photons* as they are created in the avalanche *to ionize itself*, thus leading to an enhanced first coefficient a'. This leaves virtually no photons to produce a cathode emission. The relatively low ionizing potential of the gas-produced ions $(Na_x N_x)^+$, or even Na^+ ions, makes these very ineffective in knocking electrons out of the Na surface of the cathode. Thus, γ_i is about zero. Between $X/p = 100$ and $X/p = 300$, there appear to be some photons that get through the gas to produce a low photoelectric peak of value $f\theta g = 0.01$ at an X/p of 250. At higher X/p, as the photons of greater energy are absorbed by the N_2 gas (as with pure N_2), this peak declines. Were it not for the high value of μ for the photons at X/p of 250 in N_2 and $(Na_x N_x)$, the peak would doubtless be higher.

From the extrapolated slope of the curve with Na above an X/p

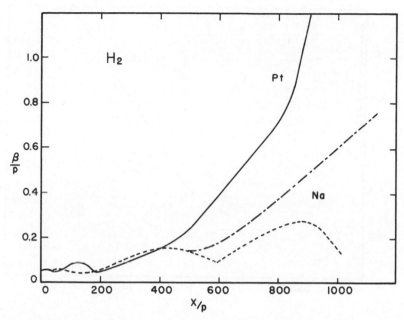

Fig. 9.21. Hale's curves for β/p for pure Pt and Na, and NaH-coated Pt in H_2. Here some volatile, photoionizable impurity was present to absorb some photons.

of 500, it appears that the N_2^+ and N^+ ions are able to liberate some electrons from the surface on impact, beginning at an X/p of 400. At low X/p, most ions are N_4^+, or may be Na^+. At high X/p and low p, $N_2^!$ ions may get through. Ionization of N_2 and N is so intense at this point that ions capable of giving a good γ_i reach the cathode. The value of γ, however, does not reach much above 0.04, even at high X/p. This might indicate that while ϕe was low and the energy of the N^+ and N_2^+ ions was high, secondary electron emission by positive ion bombardment may not always show a maximum when photoelectric action does show it.

Analogous data were obtained by Hale (VIII.11) in H_2, with pure Pt, Na, and NaH-coated cathodes. As with N_2, the presence of Na made a volatile, easily ionized gas available to contaminate the H_2. Hale computed an approximate $\beta g = \beta/\alpha$ from Townsend's theory applied to his i/i_0 curves. He also computed γ directly from his data through equation 9.26. The curves are shown in figures 9.21 and 9.22 for comparison. It is seen that as might be expected, the more accurate direct calculation of γ gives a much more clearly cut curve in regard to fine structure.

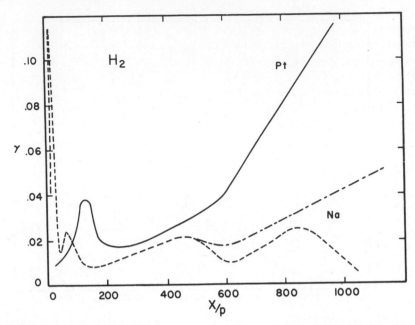

Fig. 9.22. Hale's curves for γ_c as a function of X/p for pure H_2, calculated from the same data as in figure 9.21. Note the very marked photo peaks with pure Pt and Na-coated Pt.

Concerning the quantities a and ω or f in H_2, as derived by Penning and shown in figure 8.30, excitation reaches a rather sharp peak of 0.8 at X/p around 50, with a relative ionization of 0.06 and f, thus about 10 or slightly more. At $X/p = 100$, f has dropped to perhaps 3, and at $X/p = 300$ it is near 1. The work function of Pt is probably around 5.0 in H_2, and the ionization potentials for H_2 and H, the gaseous forms present, are 15.37 and 13.54 volts, respectively. At low X/p and high p, the ions in H_2 are H_3^+, with low γ_i. Hale's observations yield appreciable values of a/p at an X/p of 10, and γ appears to be detectable at an X/p of 32. The values of γ do not rise to the anticipated peak at the height of f at an X/p of 50. Instead, γ, or better, $f\theta g$, rises to a broad peak of 0.04 at an X/p of about 140, and falls sharply to a minimum at around $X/p = 200$.

Parker found γ_i for H_2-covered Pt at low energies of H^+ and H_2^+ ions to be 2×10^{-3}, which rose to 4×10^{-3} at 20 volts and more slowly thereafter. Lauer observed a γ_p for H_2^+ and H_3^+ ions from 150 to 100 mm. Even when corrected for back diffusion, this varied from 1.4×10^{-2} at 100 mm to 1.3×10^{-3} at 150 mm. Absorption thus plays a role. In Hale's work, p was much lower. Lauer got no γ_i in H_2, but his ions were all H_3^+. This indicates quite definitely that there is some strong local absorption of the photoelectrically active frequencies above 5 volts in the neighborhood of the most effective excitation of the gas at an X/p of 50. Since this is pure H_2, there should be no effect giving an a'. These are the only data on a in pure H_2.

Above an X/p of 100 the absorption decreases, so that some photons get through. Thereafter, the photon effect at the cathode practically ceases in H_2 for higher X/p, probably because of absorption. The remaining portions of the curves appear to represent secondary electron liberation by positive ions of two classes, judging from the change in slope. This could represent secondary emission by H_2^+, which might be ineffective because of its molecular state for the first slope, and a more effective secondary liberation by H^+, setting in at an $X/p = 400$. Here the currents are large, with much dissociation of H_2, and the H^+ ions have plenty of energy. At any rate, there appear to be two processes of electron liberation by positive ion bombardment, and some photoelectric ionization reduced by the absorption of gas. The average coefficient is not materially different from that of N_2.

Addition of the Na or NaH to the cathode reduced ϕe to 1.8 and put in a photoionizable gas. There resulted an appreciable value of a' at $X/p = 5.85$, which was 0.318 with a value of γ of 0.04. At an X/p of 8.65 there appeared a very high peak for γ of 0.114, as seen in figure 9.22, which fell off sharply to a low value of near 0.01 at an $X/p = 25$. This was followed by a series of low peaks, none being higher than 0.02 at X/p values of 50, 450, and 850, with lows less than 0.01 at X/p values of 150 and 600. The curve for Na paralleled that for NaH, except that it showed indications of a γ starting above $X/p = 600$, while NaH showed only peaks. In this case also, the curve for a/p shows structure. In the region of the peak for γ at X/p around 8.65, no special effect on a/p is noted. However, in the region of $X/p = 150$, where the first large trough in γ appears, a/p with Na reaches its maximum value above that for pure H_2. This indicates much absorption of photons to ionize the (Na_xH_x) impurity present.[9]

At around $X/p = 500$, where γ shows a peak, there is a sharp dip in the a/p value, even below that in pure H_2. This indicates that the photons of shorter wave length are getting through to the cathode and are not ionizing the impurity. Similar increases in a/p with depression in γ are noted around an X/p of 600, with a rise to a peak in γ at an X/p of about 850, where a/p shows a dip in value. It thus appears that with NaH, the surface is highly active photoelectrically. Thus, for the very long wave-length, low-energy photons that can

[9]This is the first observation of the "Hale effect."

liberate electrons from the NaH surface, enough are produced at low values of X/p to give a peak at about 8.65. However, when X/p exceeds this value very much, the photons are of shorter wave length on the average, and these are selectively absorbed by (Na_xH_x), the gas present. This gives the high values of α/p and generally low values of γ_p, or better, of $f\theta g$. Apparently, the absorption spectrum of the complex (Na_xH_x) is very complicated, with bands at X/p corresponding to the average excitation at 50, 150, 100, and 1,000. Possibly, NaH has its idiosyncrasies as a photoelectric emitter. It appears at no point to yield electrons by positive ion bombardment, i.e., a value of γ_i. Here again, all H_2^+ and H^+ ions may be converted to ineffective $(Na_xN_x)^+$ or Na^+ ions which cannot liberate electrons from the surface to yield a γ_i. It may be that this accounts for its peaks of photoelectric response. With a considerable portion of Na on the cathode, before conversion to NaH there is a definite rise, suggestive of a γ_i at X/p of about 400, which rises to a maximum of about 0.035 at an X/p of 1,500.

These two studies essentially represent the only Townsend-method studies done under such conditions of variation of gas and cathode surface that by inference the effects of μ, γ_i, and $f\theta g$ can be separated in some measure. Actually, as noted, γ_i, $f\theta g$, and $f_m\theta_m g_m$ can act simultaneously, and unless some additional techniques are used, the processes cannot be distinguished. Virtually no further studies have been made for the purpose of observing the complete and systematic variation of the second coefficient in pure gases. Measurements were made by F. M. Penning and C. C. J. Addink (VIII.24) for γ for Ne and A mixtures, using the unsatisfactory evaluations from starting potentials of a glow discharge between parallel plates. The α/p values came from other work of Townsend and McCallum. These are of no great significance, as indicated before.

In the studies by A. A. Kruithoff and F. M. Penning (VIII.4) of α/p, or their η, in Ne and in Ne-A mixtures, γ could be derived from equations. The data obtained for Ne scatter badly, as shown in figure 9.23. γ seems to decrease at first as X/p increases, and then perhaps rises again, hinting at some photoelectric action. In these gases, metastable atoms of Ne, γ_m, are effective, as well as γ_i, since a Cu cathode of low ϕe was used in gases of high ionizing and excitation potentials. At low pressures in pure A (below 50 mm), Lauer (26) observed only a γ_i with an Ni cathode. However, L. Colli and U. Facchini (50) have shown that at above 140 m... in pure A, there is a photon γ_p that leads to self-sustaining discharge with time delay of some 4 μ secs. At 50 mm, working in the author's laboratory, they

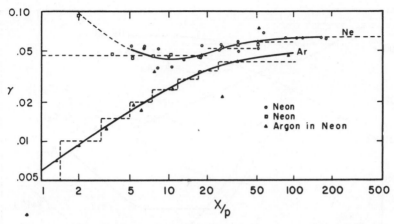

Fig. 9.23. Kruithoff and Penning's data for γ_c in pure Ne and Ne-A mixtures on Cu as a function of X/p.

showed that the effect was about half γ_i and half γ_p at threshold, with much more delay in γ_p. Below 50 mm, γ_i may have predominated. Here, ion energies at the cathode were about thermal. The least traces of impurity in the A, or a failure to outgas the cathode above 900° C., wiped out all γ_i effect at these energies.

It is interesting to note that in mixtures of Ne and A, with the most effective percentage of A, the curves for γ observed rise monotonically from low to higher values as X/p increases. In comparison with those for pure Ne, this could indicate an increasing effect of γ_i as X/p increases, with relative reduction in α'. At low X/p, the α' effect removes all metastables which produced the high values of γ_i and γ_p in pure Ne. At higher X/p, the γ_i increases, and γ_m, which in pure Ne caused the high γ values at low X/p, is now reduced through decrease in f_m, so that the two curves are the same.

It is not clear why better results were not obtained. The methods of calculation were not very precise, and usually included the sparking potential as one of the three values of potential used. It is possible that with the short gap used, the heavy currents j_0, and the many attendant corrections, measurements were not so propitious as those of Hale and Bowls. They were unable to get values of γ at low X/p, as sparks occurred before upcurving; again probably associated with the use of small α and heavy j_0. With the high values of γ and relatively low values of X/p in inert gases, it appears that α and γ are hard to evaluate with such measurements, according to Molnar.

Extensive data on γ for inert gases were reported in 1940 by A. A.

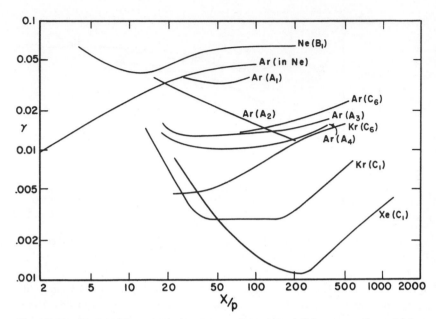

Fig. 9.24. Kruïthoff's values for γ_c as a function of X/p on six Cu cathodes subjected to different histories in Ne, A, Kr, and Xe, as indicated.

Kruithoff (VIII.4) in his concluding paper on the inert gas series. It must be remembered that the cathode used was Cu, and that j_0 was very heavy. Thus, the condition of the Cu cathode altered during the measurements. Work was done with three tubes, and with cathodes having six different histories in regard to treatment and outgassing.[10] The values for Ne, A, Kr, and Xe are shown in figure 9.24. The cathode tubes and states are shown, with A, B, or C referring to the tube used, and the numerals indicating the states used. Further data are shown in the curves of figure 9.25. Some of the curves came from values of γ computed from the sparking potential V_s, while others came from direct measurement. It is seen that the values of γ appear to be pressure-dependent in some measure. The three sets of data at A, B, and C apply to different cathode states. There appears to be some photoelectric or other effect at lower X/p, which decreases before $X/p = 30$ is reached. Thereafter, from an X/p of about 50 on

---

[10] A further complication in the studies of Kruithoff arose from the fact that as X/p and p change, the ratios of ion concentrations He^+ to He_2^+, Ne^+ to Ne_2^+, and A^+ to A_2^+ change. These two ion species can hardly be expected to give similar values of γ, the values for the monatomic ions being greater. This situation was unknown at the time of Kruithoff's work.

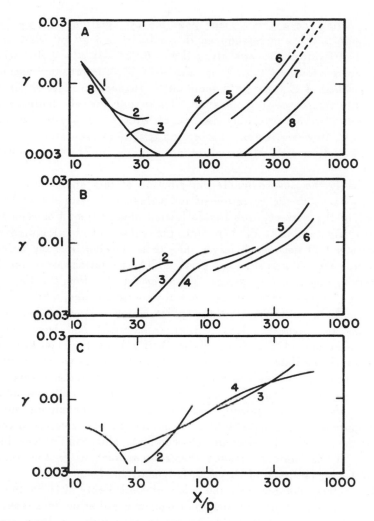

Fig. 9.25. Continuation of Kruithoff's data of figure 9.24, showing the effects of different cathode conditions. Values of γ appear to be pressure-dependent. They should vary as X/p. However, change of ions with pressure, e.g., from mostly He^+ to He_2^+, could well alter γ.

up, γ increases with X/p, and is perhaps caused partly by metastables and partly by positive ions.[11]

Calculations of the excitation relative to ionization as X/p decreases suggested to Kruithoff that photoelectric processes might be

[11]It is now recognized that in He, Ne, and A, the positive ions are partly monatomic and partly molecular. Ratios of the two ions vary over wide limits with X/p and p.

active. Using the analysis made possible by equation 9.44, he found that figure 9.25A was reproduced if $\gamma_i = 0.004$ and $g\theta = 0.0029$, while curve 4 of figure 9.25C was given· if $\gamma_i = 0.022$ and $g\theta = 0.001$, with g in the expression for ν taking the value of 0.72. The pressure variation was ascribed to changes in g incident to changes in plate separation with maintenance of X/p constant. These data merely indicate that the results were reasonably in accord with a composite action of γ_i and $gf\theta$. However, metastable action $g_m f_m \theta_m$ at the cathode is also possible.* It was doubtless absorbed in γ_i, as indicated in equation 9.48.

Probably the most valuable contribution of this study, beyond the indications as to the variation of the values of γ with the *state* and *history* of the surface, was the following observation: For tube C in state 1, figure 9.25A, at $X/p > 50$, the values of γ calculated from V_s (curves 1-7) were much larger than those coming from the calculation using the i-V curves, e.g., curve 8. The deviations were ascribed to *inhomogeneity of the surface*. Measurement of γ from the log i/i_0-x curves gives *an average value for a composite surface*, while V_s corresponds to a value for γ at the point which triggered a spark and thus has the highest value. Similar conclusions had been reached by Ehrenkrantz (47) and by Hale (VIII.11) in the correlation of Ehrenkrantz and Hale's V_s values with Hale's average values of γ (51).

It appears clear, beginning in 1923 and more particularly from 1930 on, when the existence of mechanisms alternate to Townsend's β first began to be recognized, that with improving techniques various investigators should have begun to gather direct evidence favoring one or the other of the alternate mechanisms. This can be seen in the studies of the basic processes themselves, such as in the work of James Taylor (48), and of Penning, Oliphant, and Moon (15).

Particularly notable was the work of Carl Kenty (24) on the diffusion of radiation and escape of resonance radiation in gases. He also studied the relative yields by action of metastable atoms and of photons of more and less than 1,500 Å wave length in photoelectric liberation from surfaces (24). He observed that photons of short wave length (around and below 500 Å) were very much more effective in liberating electrons from surfaces than were the longer ones, or even metastable atoms. He used surfaces of Ni, W, Mg, W-O, and constantan. The values of $\nu\psi = \theta$ at very low pressures (~ 0.1 mm) of Ne were about 0.11 for constantan, and went as low as 0.0014 for Mg. Yields were larger for "gassy" metals. Well-degassed Ni, with He, Ne, and A, using radiations of short wave length, gave values of θ of 0.044,

*See footnote 11 on preceding page.

0.016, and 0.006, respectively. Surfaces with O on W gave *greater* yields than pure W, except with A. Kenty found the relative emission from the same metal, using Ne, He, and A at low pressures (0.5 to 2 mm), to be in the ratios of 20:2:1. Addition of traces of impurities increased the currents, owing to metastable atoms acting on the impurities. The effect in Ne could be reduced by irradiation with Ne light, which reduced the metastable atoms by one-half. This did not affect the currents in pure gases appreciably, meaning that the currents in pure gases were largely photoelectric. In Ne, perhaps 10% or less of the currents were caused by metastable atoms. The fraction was smaller in A, but could be larger in He, for resonance radiation in He has exceptionally long free paths and escapes readily.

It is fitting to close this section with mention of studies of γ made on various surfaces by F. Llewellyn Jones and D. E. Davies (52). The technique used was the questionable one of measuring the sparking potential in plane parallel gaps with plates of 3 cm diameter and 2.5 mm separation of various materials as a function of pressure near the minimum value. The gases used were air and H_2, and the electrodes were given various treatments. The values of γ were inferred from the values of V_s, using the best values of α available. Some of the gases, notably air, were Hg-contaminated in certain studies. While much accuracy in evaluation of γ cannot be claimed, relative values are of interest. Sparking-potential curves with slightly oxidized surfaces in air indicated the following: V_s was highest with an Ni cathode in mercury-free air, and next highest in the same gas for an Al cathode. In the presence of Hg vapor, V_s was lower with Ni, and still lower with Cu and Hg. The extreme variation between Ni in pure air and Cu + Hg in contaminated air, at $pd = 20$ cm × mm Hg, was from 1,750 to 1,500 volts. At the minimum potential, the relative values changed. Electrodes of Cu + Hg in air showed a double minimum, but lay below Ni + Hg.

As the author has warned, the values of γ deduced from such data are *not* reliable, for α in Hg-contaminated air is higher by some tens of per cent than in pure air. As no data on α for uncontaminated air are at hand, the values of γ inferred by Jones and Davies may be completely in error. That the Hg altered α values is clearly demonstrated by the double minimum with Cu cathode. This, as Penning showed, is the direct consequence of two *primary* ionization processes in mixtures where excited N_2 can ionize Hg in air. The double minimum could, of course, also be caused by two different γ mechanisms; one of high value at low X/p, and one of high value at high X/p. Such action has not been reported before, but might occur in H_2. However,

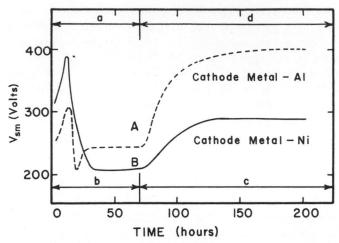

Fig. 9.26. Jones-Davies curves for variation of sparking potential V_{sm} of an Ni-Al electrode system in pure H_2 with time. For an Al cathode and Ni anode, curve A represents the cleaning of the cathode. Curve B shows the effect when Ni is the cathode and has had an Al film deposited on it which is later sputtered off by the discharge.

it is improper to draw conclusions as to γ from such data unless the values of α used are obtained under the same conditions. Thus, the author cannot feel that the data on γ for air with Hg are too significant.

Filling the tubes with pure H_2, the values of the minimum sparking potential V_{sm} were determined for a number of cathodes following cathode bombardment in pure H_2. Curves for V_{sm} as a function of clean-up time in hours are shown for an Al cathode opposite an Ni anode as it first cleans up under bombardment and then has Ni sputtered on it from an Ni anode used as cathode. This is shown in curve A of figure 9.26. The case when an Ni cathode has an Al film deposited on it and later has it sputtered off, is shown in curve B of figure 9.26. It is seen that initial bombardment with H_2^+ ions cleans the Al and increases V_{sm} as time goes on. Very clean Al has a low value of V_{sm}, and as Ni deposits on the cathode by sputtering, V_{sm} increases to a high value. As the Ni cathode cleans up, V_{sm} rises, but falls as Al sputters over it. As the bombardment removes the Al film, the value of V_{sm} rises. It should be noted that V_{sm} for an Al film on Ni is 30 volts lower than for a cleaned Al surface, and likewise, that a sputtered Ni film on Al has V_{sm} nearly 100 volts higher than the Ni metal. In this experiment, the values of γ computed are shown in table 9.5. Here pressures are low and X/p is high.

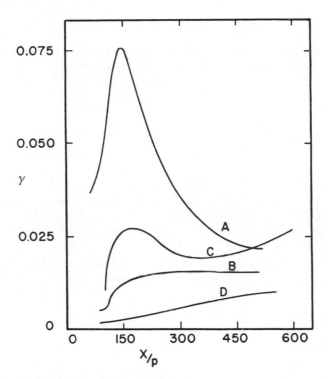

Fig. 9.27. Jones-Davies curves for γ on Cu in pure H_2, with various electrode conditions, as a function of X/p. Curve A, slightly oxidized Cu; curve B, after baking; curve C, after 10 hours' exposure to H_2; curve D, cleaned by ion bombardment and outgassed.

Further studies on various metals, using pure H_2 and the electrode systems cited, gave some curves for γ as a function of X/p. That for Cu is shown in figure 9.27. Here A is the curve for slightly oxidized Cu. It shows a strong photoelectric peak at $X/p \sim 150$, and is still falling at an X/p of 500. After bakeout at 400° C. with H_2 present, and then further bakeout in vacuum, the curve B was obtained. The strong photoelectric peak has disappeared, but some secondary action of a photoelectric nature is present. Exposure to H_2 for 10 hours gave curve C. Here again, a photoelectric peak is pronounced, but an increased sensitivity to a γ_i rising at an X/p of 300 appears. Cleaning by ion bombardment and outgassing yields a curve with very little photoelectric γ and a low but increasing γ_i, starting at an X/p of 150. This is shown as curve D. These results are in general agreement with Hale's observations on Pt in H_2. However, the influence of the

TABLE 9.5

Changes of Sparking Potential and γ on Various Cathodes
in H_2, as Reported by Jones and Davies

Cathode	V_{sm}	X/p	γ
Al	243	200	0.1
Al on Ni	212	200	0.15
Ni	289	180	0.075
Ni on Al	390	245	0.015

treatment on values of γ is striking indeed. In the region of $X/p \sim 150$, γ varies by a factor of 30, while at X/p around 500, the change is by a factor of 2 only. It is clear that at low X/p, H^+ and H_2^+ ions do not give an appreciable γ_i, but that this begins to be important certainly around an $X/p = 300$.

All these studies indicate the very variable, complex, and unpredictable behaviors of the mechanisms under varying conditions, and indicate that $f\theta g$, $f_m \theta_m g_m$, and γ_i are all active and important in varying degrees under different circumstances. It is also clear that the measurements of the Townsend type from the log i/i_0-x curves can yield indications as to which mechanisms are active only under the variations in gas content and cathode surface which Bowls and Hale used. Again, such values are average values for a composite surface, and different regions may have quite different characteristics. Thus, a few spots of high γ would cause a low V_s, but the γ measured would be high. Something more is obviously needed in technique to give the answers required.

§ 13. **The Beginning of Dynamic Studies.**

The missing method of attack was apparently first used by R. W. Engstrom and W. S. Huxford (31). The suggestion came from the study of the time for A-Cs photo tubes to reach current equilibrium after the light was flashed on them. The time delay was ascribed to the slow diffusion of metastable atoms. A. M. Skellett (54) interpreted a change in amplification occurring with a change in frequency as being caused by the delay of the *positive ions* in reaching the cathode after leaving the anode. This at once raised a question as to the time lags of different agencies. It thus occurred to Engstrom that if it were possible to make a time measurement of the secondary process, the various mechanisms active could be sorted out. Electrons move rapidly, and photoelectric effects at the cathode should occur in intervals of 10^{-7} second. The ions take some 10^{-5} second to cross the gap, and thus the γ_i action should move on a time scale of 10^{-5} sec. Finally, metastable atoms diffuse, and the time scale for the maximum of their action is some 10^{-4} to 10^{-3} sec, depending on pressure and tube dimensions. The long delay times indicated for metastable atoms had been noted in commercial gas photo tubes by F. Schröter and G. Lubszynski (54), K. H. Kingdon and H. E. Thompson (54), and by M. R. Campbell and R. S. Rivlin (54).

If metastable atoms cause the time lag, the lag should increase with gas pressure and discharge path, which will not occur for positive ions. In the work initiated by Engstrom and Huxford, a plane parallel gap was constructed with variable x. Dynamic studies of these actions could be made by a method developed by Engstrom and Huxford, and these could be combined in the same apparatus with the standard type of static measurements of Townsend. As indicated, the relation with positive ion liberation and metastable action is expressed by equation 9.44, which reads:

$$(9.44) \qquad i/i_0 = \frac{\epsilon^{ax}}{1 - (\gamma_i + f_m \theta_m g_m)(\epsilon^{ax} - 1)} .$$

The time analysis requires first, the probable time delay caused by diffusion of metastable atoms, and secondly, the effect of this on the measured current. For metastable atoms diffusing to the cathode, the statistical character of the diffusion process makes it possible to set the probability of arrival at a time t per unit time, as approximated by the expression:

$$(9.66) \qquad P(t) = \frac{1}{\tau_0} \epsilon^{-t/\tau_0},$$

when $t \overset{>}{-} 0$, and becomes 0 if $t < 0$, The time τ_0 is the *average* interval between creation and arrival for those metastables reaching the cathode. Setting the variable t equal to 0 denotes the time of creation of the metastables. In order to determine the value of τ_0, it is necessary to set up the equation for diffusion of metastable atoms [12] as applied to infinite plane parallel electrodes and solve the relation. Solution gives

$$\tau_0 = \frac{d^2}{12 D} \left[1 + \frac{2}{15} ad + \frac{1}{180} a^2 d^2 + \ldots \right]$$

$$+ (x_m/d) \left[2 - (2/5) ad - \frac{1}{45} a^2 d^2 + \ldots \right] (See \ next \ page)$$

---

[12] The theory, as more fully developed by Molnar, is given in section 15.

$$(9.67) \qquad + (x_m/d^2)^2 \left[-1 + (2/5) \, ad - \frac{1}{36} \, a^2 d^2 + \dots \right].$$

Here d is the gap length, x_m is the distance an electron must go to get the excitation energy, a is the first Townsend coefficient, and D is the coefficient of diffusion. This yields the form of the lagging current response to a constant photo current i_0 which is initiated at $t = 0$ as:

$$(9.68) \qquad i_{\text{rise}}(t) = 1 - (1 - i_a) \, \epsilon^{-(i_a/\tau_0)t}$$

Here the equilibrium current is referred to as unity. The quantity i_0 is the nonlagging fraction of the current for rise. If the photoelectric sources are cut off at $t = t$, $t' = 0$, when the rising current lacks saturation by an amount i_s, the falling characteristic may be represented by an equation:

$$(9.69) \qquad i_{\text{fall}}(t') = (1 - i_b - i_s) \, \epsilon^{-(i_b/\tau_0)t}.$$

Here i_b represents the nonlagging fraction of the current for fall of the characteristic. It can be shown that $i_a = i_b$. If it is experimentally possible to measure the exponential decay constant, $\tau = \tau_0/i_a$, and the nonlagging fraction of the current i_a from the amplification, τ_0 may be evaluated. The quantity τ_0 may be studied as a function of d and p where the variation is predicted by equation 9.67. Since a can be measured by static studies, the variation in D with p yields D_0. Thus, the value of D_0 for the metastable argon atoms in argon may be determined. From static measurements, not only a but γ may be evaluated for each time-lag curve. Finally, the current amplification is given by the expression:

$$(9.70) \qquad A = \frac{i_a}{i_0} = \epsilon^{ax} \Big/ \left[1 - \gamma \, (\epsilon^{ax} - 1) \right],$$

so that i_a can be evaluated. The value of the quantity γ_i can be inferred from the fact that the instantaneous amplification is independent of metastable atom contribution γ_m. Thus,

$$(9.71) \qquad i_a A = \frac{\epsilon^{ax}}{1 - \gamma_i (\epsilon^{ax} - 1)}.$$

Since at equilibrium the current ratio i/i_0 can be evaluated, then from equation 9.44 it is possible to determine $\gamma = \gamma_i + \gamma_m = \gamma_i + f_m \theta_m g_m$. From γ and γ_i, the value of γ_m can be found, as $\gamma_m = \gamma - \gamma_i$. Thus, from $\gamma_m = g_m f_m \theta_m = g_m (\omega_m/a) \theta_m$, with g_m known from geometry, $f_m \theta_m$ can be found. Engstrom preferred to evaluate a number proportional to the fractional electron energy being delivered to excitation of metastable states in place of $f_m \theta_m$. This quantity is

$$\theta_m \frac{\omega_m}{X} = \frac{a}{X} \frac{\gamma_m}{g_m} = \eta \ (\gamma_m/g_m).$$

This can be compared to $(\omega_m/X)_{max} = 1/E_m$, where E_m is the excitation potential of the metastable state, viz., 11.5 to 11.7 e.v. for A.

The experimental arrangements consisted in cutting off i_0 on the photo tube surface by a sectored disc on a commutator. Instantaneous values of current were measured by electrometer, using a null method with potentiometer. The usual procedure for log i/i_0-x curves was modified because of photoelectric fatigue effects. Current-voltage characteristics were determined at a number of plate separations, and from these the i-x data were computed by interpolation. Back diffusion, change of photosensitivity with X, and variation of scattered light with plate separation were corrected for. The photo current density j_0 was $j_0 = 1 \times 10^{-10}$ amp/cm^2. Pressures ran from 0.098 to 0.815 mm Hg. The values of a/p as a function of X/p observed ran from $X/p = 50$ to $X/p = 200$ with considerable spread, straddling the curve of Kruithoff and Penning (VIII.4). These data did not show the decrease of a/p at high X/p that was earlier observed by Huxford (VIII.5). The values of γ observed ranged from 0.32 to 0.43. They started from a low value at $X/p = 50$ and rose to a peak at $X/p = 150$, with a gradual decline thereafter. The points scattered badly for different pressures. The lowest pressures, both for a/p and γ, yielded the most data. It is clear that correction for terminal energies was needed, and that equilibrium with the field was not reached at the lowest pressure. The data from time lags showed the largest scatter. Current densities needed for time studies had to be high, but never exceeded 1×10^{-7} amp/cm^2. Currents ten or more times greater gave evidence of space-charge distortion.

The time-lag curve is shown in figure 9.28 on a millisecond time scale. The vacuum time-lag curve is the rectangular curve indicated. The curve with gas present is the one with the exponential rise and exponential decay. Rising and falling characteristics agree in general, and indicate that the effects produced by the individual electrons leaving the cathode are *not* affected by the previous discharge current. At the lowest pressure there was detected a time lag of the order of 0.01 sec, present to a few per cent. This was attributed to a slow change in the very sensitive cathode surface with bombardment. The quantity r_0 was determined, but did not vary perceptibly with amplification, so that average values were used. The values of r_0 did vary,

§ 13

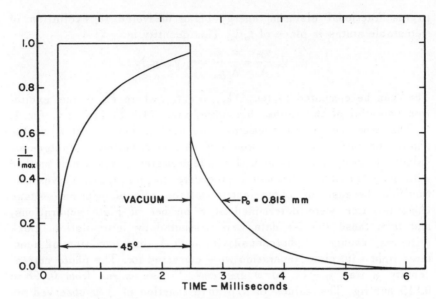

Fig. 9.28. Engstrom-Huxford time-lag curves for rise and fall of current with metastable action. The rectangular curve is the vacuum curve, while the curved rise and fall is in the presence of gas.

as metastable atom lags should, with pressure and gap length. The average values of r_0 should follow the rough relation $r_0 = 1.36$ $d^2/12D = kpd^2$, since $k = 1.36/12 \, D_1$, with D_1 the coefficient for A metastable atoms in A at 1 mm Hg pressure. The use of a gauze in the anode led to some difficulty with diffusion back and forth, and correction had to be made. Agreement with the theory above was remarkably good. This gave the value of D_0 for the argon metastables reduced to standard conditions as $D_0 = 0.084$ cm^2 sec^{-1}. This is slightly more than $1/2 \, D_0$ for A atoms in A, which is $D_0 = 0.157$. This is a reasonable agreement. The values of γ indicate, among other things, that the surface is more sensitive for greater bombarding currents.

The values of γ, corrected for back diffusion to yield *total* emission, are shown in figure 9.29. Those for γ_i are shown in figure 9.30. It is noted from figure 9.29 that while at low X/p the γ values showed no decrease with X/p, the values of γ_i, as drawn in figure 9.30, do show a strong variation, as should be the case. This means that metastable action is more important at low values of X/p, as might be expected. A plot of $\theta_m \omega_m/X$ against X/p for the best data is shown in figure 9.31. It runs from 0.022 to 0.002 in the range of measurement.

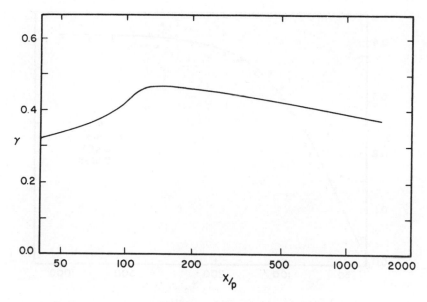

Fig. 9.29. Engstrom-Huxford curve for total γ corrected for back diffusion as a function of X/p, using Cs cathode in A.

The value of $\omega_m/X = 1/E_m = 0.086$. The minimum efficiency for liberation of electrons by metastable atoms from an activated Cs surface is $\theta_m = 0.4$ secondary electron per metastable atom.

In a previous study Engstrom (53) had studied A with a pure Ba cathode. He made time-lag measurements on this combination. There was no lag of the order found for Cs. The lag was approximately 7×10^{-5} second. This indicates the primary importance of γ_i for positive ions. Thus, θ_m must be small for A metastables on Ba. Ba was activated by exposure to H_2. Photoemission increased markedly. With this, an average lifetime of 0.17 millisecond with 62% lagging current was observed. This gave $\tau_0 = 0.067$ millisecond, which is in agreement with the 0.076 millisecond computed for metastable atoms.

This pioneering study led the way to the modern studies, in which the time resolution of the cathode ray oscilloscopes now available permits of scanning the lag curves directly and down to 10^{-7} sec and better. These techniques became possible only after World War II, and constitute the methods of today.

§ 14. Fast Oscillographic Analysis of γ_i and fθg by von Gugelberg.

The application of the fast oscillograph to the determination of secondary mechanisms was first made in 1947 by H. L. von Gugelberg

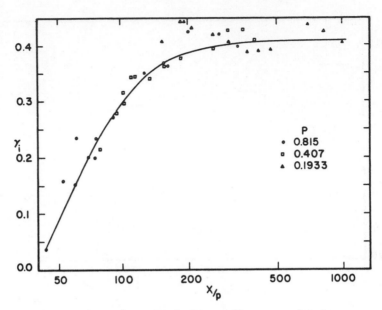

Fig. 9.30.   Engstrom-Huxford curves for γ_i as a function
of X/p, using a Cs cathode in A.

(25). In 1930, M. Steenbeck (55) had derived the equations for the growth of a Townsend glow discharge, using the first and second Townsend coefficients. Later, a more complete treatment was given in von Engel and Steenbeck's excellent book (55). The treatment was extended by W. Bartolomeyczyk (55) to include photoelectric action at the cathode. In 1937, an approximate solution to the same basic relations had been made by R. Schade (55), using γ_i and compared with experiment. It was satisfactory so far as it went, but it was incomplete. The relations of Steenbeck and Bartolomeyczyk were superior. A partial analysis to extend the previous treatments to include the effect of metastable atoms γ_m was developed by W. Rogowski (31). It was set up primarily for cylindrical geometry, and was applicable to a glow-discharge column but not to the Townsend gap.

Steenbeck and Bartolomeyczyk's Analysis of the Growth of a Townsend Discharge.

Let α be the first Townsend coefficient, and let $n+$ and $n-$ represent the concentrations of positive ions and electrons, while $j+$ and $j-$ represent the corresponding current densities. The drift velocities of the carriers are $v+ = Xk+$ and $v- = Xk-$, and initially the secondary process will be assumed to be the liberation of electrons by positive

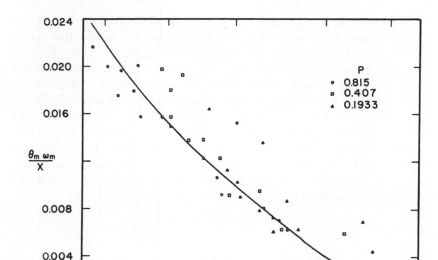

Fig. 9.31. Engstrom-Huxford curves for γ_m corrected for back diffusion against X/p, for Cs cathodes in A.

ion impact with coefficient γ. The basic relations may be written as:

$$\frac{\partial n_-}{\partial t} = - \frac{\partial}{\partial x} (v_- \, n_-) + a v_- n_-$$

and

(9.72)
$$\frac{\partial n_+}{\partial t} = \frac{\partial}{\partial x} (v_+ \, n_+) + a v_+ n_+ ,$$

leading to the current-density relations:

$$\frac{\partial}{\partial t} \left(\frac{i_-}{v_-} \right) = - \frac{\partial i}{\partial x} + a i_-$$

and

(9.73)
$$\frac{\partial}{\partial t} \left(\frac{i_+}{v_+} \right) = \frac{\partial i_+}{\partial x} + a i_- .$$

The integration for t requires an auxiliary assumption. This was first made by Steenbeck. He assumed that the current grew exponentially with time about a certain average buildup time τ, characteristic of the situations X/p, x, a, and γ. Such an assumption is justified, since the ionization and space-charge accumulation are cumulative exponentially. If this proceeds at a constant rate owing to relatively constant carrier velocities, and if secondary actions in a yield no temporal diffusion, the current increase would be expected to be exponential, with a sharply defined time. Such autoaccelerative creation of carriers exponentially reduces the time of growth steps. As developed by Steenbeck it was, however, an assumption. The quantity τ was set as the characteristic time constant of the process, and is thus associated with the *formative time lag* to be discussed later. Thus, Steenbeck, and later Bartolomeyczyk set the current-density function of x and t as a new current-density function of x alone, in the form:

$$j_-(x, t) = \epsilon^{t/\tau} j_-(x)$$

and

(9.74) $$j_+(x, t) = \epsilon^{t/\tau} j_+(x).$$

With this assumption, the expressions may be integrated to read:

$$j_-(x) = C\, \epsilon^{\int_0^x (a - 1/\tau v_-) dx}$$

and

(9.75) $$j_+(x) = \epsilon^{\int_0^x dx/\tau v_+} \left[C' - C \int_0^x a\, \epsilon^{\int_0^x (a - 1/v\tau) dx} dx \right].$$

In this integration, the quantity $1/v$ replaces the summation $(1/v_+) + (1/v_-)$ for convenience. The boundary conditions set $j_-(0) = \gamma j_+(0)$ and $j_+(d) = 0$ at the cathode and anode, respectively. At $x = 0$ the negative electron contribution, neglecting external ionization, is $\gamma j_+(0)$, as postulated for the γ process, and at the anode at $x = d$ cm, $j_+(d) = 0$. Introduction of these into the relations at 9.75 leads at once to the *generalized* sparking-threshold condition, which reads:

(9.76) $$1 = \gamma \int_0^d a\, \epsilon^{\int_0^x (a - 1/v\tau) dx} dx.$$

If, in addition to the secondary liberation by positive ion bombardment, the photoelectric liberation is included, H. L. von Gugelberg sets the boundary condition as:

(9.77) $$i_-(0) = i_0 + \gamma i_+(0) + g\theta \int_0^d i_-(x) f(x) \epsilon^{-\mu x} dx.$$

In this relation, i_0 is the externally induced photoelectric density at the cathode, g is the geometrical factor for photon arrival at the

cathode, and θ is the secondary electron liberation per photon, including the back-diffusion correction factor ν, $\theta = \psi\nu$. The quantity $f(x)$
is the photon-production ratio at (x) per electron produced, represented
by $f(x) = (\omega/a)_x$, and μ is the absorption coefficient, which must not
be too large. Actually, ω is the number of photons produced per cm
path electron advance in the field direction, so that $f(x) = (\omega/a)_x$
represents the efficiency of active photon production relative to
ionization at each point x. The relation can be thrown into the form
with $\epsilon^{t/\tau} j(x)$, reading:

$$(9.78) \qquad j_-(0) = \frac{i_0}{\epsilon^{t/\tau}} + \gamma j_+(0) + g\theta \int_0^d j_-(x) f(x)\, \epsilon^{-\mu x}\, dx.$$

At the anode, it is possible to set $i_+(d) = 0$ and $j_+(d) = 0$. The more
complete breakdown relation then becomes

$$1 = \frac{i_0}{i_-(0)} + \gamma \int_0^d a\, \epsilon^{\int_0^x (a - 1/v\tau)dx}$$

(9.79)

$$+ g\theta \int_0^d f(x)\, \epsilon^{\int_0^x (a - 1/\tau v)dx - \mu x}\, dx.$$

Near breakdown, $i_-(0)$ should be so much greater than i_0, the externally imposed current, that the first term may be neglected. If the
fields are uniform, as for plane parallel gaps, then the two relations
become respectively:

$$(9.80) \qquad 1 = \gamma a\, \frac{\epsilon^{(a - 1/\tau v)d} - 1}{a - 1/\tau v} \qquad \text{for ion action only,}$$

and

$$1 = \frac{a\gamma}{a - 1/\tau v} \left\{ \epsilon^{(a - 1/\tau v_+)d} - 1 \right\}$$

(9.81)

$$+ \frac{gf\theta}{a - \mu - 1/\tau v_-} \left\{ \epsilon^{(a - \mu - 1/\tau v_-)d} - 1 \right\},$$

if both actions are present.

Relation 9.80 was originally deduced by Steenbeck. Solution of
this relation for $1/\tau$, with some approximations to be discussed later,
yields the relation arrived at and tested experimentally by Schade.

For convenience, equation 9.80 may be regarded. It will be noted
that this relation *now defines the sparking threshold correctly and*

unambiguously from a dynamic study. If r is very large, so that $1/rv$ approaches 0, the relation reverts to

(9.80a) $1 = \gamma(\epsilon^{\alpha l} - 1)$.

This relation is the original Townsend sparking condition, which was reinterpreted by Holst and Oosterhuis (47). The relation indicates that when the condition is satisfied, the space-charge accumulation leading to a spark will take a very long time, but can occur. The shorter is r, the larger will be $1/rv$. This deducts from the value of α. Thus, $\gamma[\epsilon^{(\alpha-1/rv)d}]$ can remain greater than unity, and lead to breakdown only if α increases as rapidly or more rapidly than $1/rv$ increases. Since increase in α requires increase in X/p, this means that r will decrease only as X/p increases. Thus, the formative time lag and the time constant of the discharge will decrease rapidly with overvoltage.

In the original derivations, neither Steenbeck nor Bartolomeyczyk use $1/r$, but replace this by $\lambda = 1/r$. They then indicate that if $\lambda < 0$, the discharge does not materialize; if $\lambda = 0$, the threshold is reached and discharge takes a long time; and for $\lambda > 0$, the discharge will occur. The use of a pure symbol λ in this fashion is physically incorrect. Actually, the quantity λ is a reciprocal time, and a negative λ or a reciprocal negative time makes no sense. Dimensionally, $1/rv$ is a reciprocal distance characteristic of the discharge, as is α. Usually, v does not vary too rapidly with X/p, so that the behavior depends more or less critically on the characteristic time. For a discharge to materialize, the reciprocal characteristic time distance must be larger than the reciprocal distance represented by α, otherwise $\epsilon^{(\alpha-1/rv)d}$ can never permit the condition to be fulfilled. In fact, depending on γ and d, the reciprocal length α must be sufficiently large compared to $1/rv$ to permit the relation

(9.82) $$\frac{\alpha}{\alpha - 1/rv} \gamma \, \epsilon^{(\alpha - 1/rv)d} = 1$$

to be satisfied. This means merely that enough ionizing acts must occur in the characteristic length rv so that in a gap of length d the avalanche can be sufficiently large.

It must further be noted that no field distortion by space charge has been assumed in this deduction. As the space charges build up with increasing t, the relations and the threshold conditions will be altered, *insuring* consummation of the spark if α/p increases more rapidly than linearly with X/p. At the beginning, however, the initial idealized conditions apply, as outlined above.

The relations may be solved for the value of the reciprocal time $1/\tau$, or, if desired, for the time τ. If $1/\tau v$ is negligible compared to a, i.e., near the threshold, then expansion of the exponential in powers of $1/\tau v$ leads to the expression:

$$(9.83) \qquad \frac{1}{\tau v} = \frac{1}{d} \left(1 - \frac{1+\gamma}{\gamma \, \epsilon^{ad}} \right) .$$

This expression is not significantly different from the one deduced in another fashion by Schade and compared with experiment by him. Schade's expression reads:

$$(9.84) \qquad \frac{1}{\tau v_+} = \frac{1}{d} \left(1 - \frac{1}{\gamma \, \epsilon^{ad}} \right) .$$

However, it is better to solve retaining the exponential form. This leads to the solution:

$$(9.85) \qquad \frac{1}{\tau v} = a - \frac{1}{d} \log \left(\frac{1}{\gamma} + 1 \right) .$$

It is seen that as $1/\tau v$ increases and thus τ decreases, a and γ are larger and d is smaller. Thus, the shorter the gap, and the larger a and γ, the shorter will be τ. Since a and γ presumably increase with X/p over much of the region, this means that τ decreases with over-voltage.

Steenbeck has shown that as the gap length increases indefinitely, the value of $1/\tau v$ approaches a limiting value. This value is

$$\left(\frac{1}{\tau v} \right)_{d \, \cdot = \, \infty} = (1 + \gamma) \, a$$

or

$$(9.86) \qquad \tau_\infty = \frac{1}{v(1 + \gamma) \, a}$$

for very large d. Solution of the more complete equation, including photoelectric effect at the cathode for a uniform field for the value of $1/\tau$, with simplification of equation 9.81 yields

$$(9.87) \qquad 1 = \gamma \, \epsilon^{\left(a - \frac{1}{\tau v_+} \right) d} + \frac{g \theta \omega}{a - \mu} \, \epsilon^{\left(a - \mu - \frac{1}{\tau v_-} \right) d} .$$

This in turn leads to two expressions for the time constant, depending on whether ions alone act or whether photons alone act at the cathode. These are

$$(9.88) \qquad \frac{1}{\tau_i} = v_+ \left\{ a - \frac{1}{d_i} \log_e \left(\frac{1}{\gamma_i} \right) \left[1 - \frac{g\theta\omega}{a-\mu} \, \epsilon^{(a-\mu)d_i} \right] \right\}$$

for the ions, and

$$(9.89) \qquad \frac{1}{\tau_p} = v_- \left\{ a - \mu - \frac{1}{d_p} \log_e \frac{a-\mu}{g\theta\omega} \right\}$$

for the pure photon mechanism.

Introduction of the absorption increases the critical distance for spark-over caused by photoionization alone, which is

$$d_p = \frac{1}{a} \log_e \left(\frac{a}{g\theta\omega} + 1 \right),$$

to

$$(9.90) \qquad d_p' = \frac{1}{a-\mu} \log_e \left(\frac{a-\mu}{g\theta\omega} + 1 \right).$$

The time constant for very large d, when photons alone act, becomes

$$(9.91) \qquad \left(\frac{1}{\tau_p} \right)_{d \cdot = \infty} = v_- (a - \mu + g\theta\omega)$$

instead of

$$\left(\frac{1}{\tau_i} \right)_{d \cdot = \infty} = v_+ (1 + \gamma_i) a .$$

It is seen that for larger d, if μ is not too great, τ decreases from τ_i, which depends on ionic velocities v_+ and the product $\gamma_i a$, to τ_p, which depends on electron velocities v_-, a, and $g\theta\omega$.

It is of importance to note that equation 9.87 has a lower threshold of d when both γ_i and $g\theta\omega$ are active. Thus, by increasing d at constant X/p and holding the other factors constant, breakdown will first be caused by the combination of γ_i and $g\theta\omega$, beginning at a small distance d_{ip}, satisfying equation 9.87. Under these conditions, with shorter $d = d_{ip}$, the time of breakdown will primarily be set by the slowest agency involved, τ_i. At larger values of d, when $d = d_p$, the action of $g\theta\omega$ must alone be able to initiate the discharge. Thus, beyond a gap length d_p, the discharge is initiated by a photon-conditioned breakdown, and the time becomes characteristic of τ_p. Accordingly, the choice of an appropriately high value of X/p, beginning with a short gap length increase in d to d_{ip}, leads to a discharge with time constant τ. Further increase in d to d_p leads to a new breakdown, with a discharge time having the ultimately low value of

(9.91)
$$\tau_p = 1/[v_-(a - \mu + g\theta\omega)] \ .$$

The two values of d, i.e., d_{ip} and d_p, can be observed by changing the time τ of the applied potential pulse so as to cover τ_{ip} or τ_p.

If metastables are present in addition to γ_i and $g\omega\theta/a$, still another expression more complicated than equation 9.88 will apply. This effect will set in at a distance d_m, less than d_i. It will have a time constant τ_m that is characteristic of the diffusion of metastable atoms to the cathode. Unfortunately, this process with plane parallel plates was too complicated for computation in von Gugelberg's work. It was later solved approximately by the analysis of J. P. Molnar, as will be indicated. It must be noted that there is thus a still lower limiting value of d, and thus V, for breakdown where τ_m is still larger than τ_i.

It must now be recognized that according to this theory, in a plane parallel gap there are at a given X/p, at constant p and X, *three different thresholds for sparking*, i.e., V_m, V_i, and V_p, with corresponding critical gap lengths d_m, d_i, and d_p, and average time constants τ_m, τ_i, and τ_p, when all three secondary mechanisms are active at once. These thresholds correspond respectively to conditions where $\gamma_m + \gamma_i + (g\theta\omega)/(a-\mu)$, $\gamma_i + (g\theta\omega)/(a-\mu)$, and $(g\theta\omega)/(a-\mu)$ are active. The distances and voltages increase in sequence, following $V_m < V_i < V_p$, $d_m < d_i < d_p$, and the corresponding time constants follow the sequence $\tau_m > \tau_i > \tau_p$, with orders of magnitude for a 1-cm gap respectively 10^{-3}, 10^{-5}, and 10^{-7} sec.

By making various assumptions, it is possible, by means of equations, to plot a theoretical curve for the reciprocal of the time $1/t$ against the values of d, or better, V, observed with given p and fixed $X = V/d$, assuming the two mechanisms. In figure 9.32, curve 1 is that for a pure γ_i, and curve 2 is for a pure $(g\theta\omega)/(a-\mu)$. The combined action is shown in the full curve 3, assuming a photoelectric portion of 0.3%. The effect of the initial current i_0 with increasing d yields the composite curve 4.

The experimental procedure of von Gugelberg follows. He used some six sealed-off tubes with Townsend gaps, illuminating the cathode through the anode. Two of these had mobile electrodes for changing d. The fixed gaps had lengths d between 1.3 and 7.5 mm. The electrodes were clean Ni, or Ni coated with Ba and BaN_3 from the destruction of BaN_3. The currents i_0 were so heavy that at a potential within 0.8 of sparking, the currents could be measured on a sensitive galvanometer. The currents so measured as the discharge built up ranged from 10^{-11} to 10^{-4} amp. The oscillographic time resolution was of the

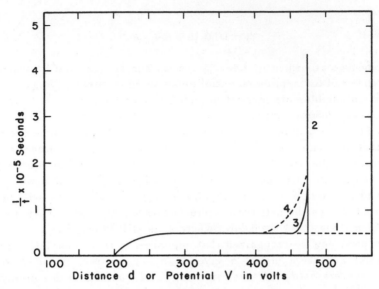

Fig. 9.32. Von Gugelberg's curves for the reciprocal of the characteristic breakdown times, plotted against gap length, or potential, at constant uniform field $X = V/d$, first with ions active and later with photons active at the cathode. Curve 1 is for a pure γ_i, curve 2 is for a pure γ_p (photons), with combined action shown by curve 3, photons being active to 0.3%. The effect of an initial i_0 from the cathode yields the dotted transition curve.

order of several tenths of a microsecond. Reproducibility was within 10% in a single series. The gases used were He, Ne, A, Kr, Xe, H$_2$, and N$_2$. Purification and outgassing were probably adequate.

Despite the fact that the theory was not worked up for γ_m, the action of the metastable atoms was noticeable in the measurements. Near and below the threshold for γ_i, very long buildup times were noted, setting in at a smaller value of V. Where these occurred, the $(1/t)$-V curves at onset showed a very steep rise. The long, nearly horizontal portion of the curves following later went through a point of inflection and reached the value of $1/t = 1/\tau_i$ characteristic of ions. The effectiveness of metastable atoms was largest in absolute value in He, and least for the heavier inert gases. In the steady state, the relative magnitude of the metastable action might have comprised from 5% to 25% of the total secondary action. In H$_2$, where metastables do not form, there was no initial rise and no long period. The actual values for the gases indicated showed τ_i to be in keeping with the best data on α and v_+.

The transitions to the photo effect were, in general, not so sharp as the calculated curves indicate. In a measure, this was caused by

the inertia of the electrical circuits used. This inertia rendered evaluation of $1/\tau_p$ uncertain, and made the estimates of the percentage par-
ticipation of the photo-effect term $(g\theta\omega)/(\alpha - \mu)$ inaccurate in the
stationary state. In the range of potentials used, running up to 630
volts, He, Ne-A mixtures, and N_2 showed no notable photoelectric
contribution to the spark, in agreement with later work. This would
make the photon action less than 0.1%. Even Ba electrodes gave no
photon transition in He. For A with Ni electrodes, the transition was
at almost the double voltage for ions. The stationary photoelectric
liberation must have been between 1.6% and 7%. Ba electrodes were
expected to give better photoelectric response, but actually gave less.
The author attaches no significance to this observation, owing to the
capricious nature of surfaces and the use of BaN_3. BaN_3 and all
nitrides come from diazotization, and such processes *never* yield pure
products.

§ 15. The Oscillographic Studies of Metastable Atoms by J. P. Molnar.

Quite independently of von Gugelberg's work, a group at the Bell
Laboratories in 1946 initiated a program of investigation of the second
coefficient mechanisms in Townsend discharges. Preliminary experiments confirmed generally the work of Engstrom and Huxford, in which
transient analyses of Townsend currents in argon showed a slow
component attributable to metastable atoms. In addition, a theoretical
study by R. R. Newton (56), then at the Bell Laboratories, showed
that the method could be extended to give useful results by increasing
the time resolution and thereby observing the ion-induced electron
emission. The remarkable facilities of the Bell Telephone Laboratories,
in personnel as well as equipment, led to a most complete exploitation
of this type of attack.

The problem was divided into two portions. The studies on the
very short time-lag effects, viz., the photoelectric and positive ion
movements, were undertaken by J. A. Hornbeck (58). The longer time-
interval studies, involving metastable atoms, were carried out by J. P.
Molnar (57). The author has had access to the full reports through the
courtesy of Messrs. Molnar[13] and Hornbeck and the Bell Telephone
Laboratories.

The problem of metastable action, so far treated in a general way

---

[13]In fact, the author's draft of this section, except for the first two paragraphs, was completely rewritten by Dr. J. P. Molnar, since he alone was in
a position to "boil down" his original seventy or more pages of reports into
an effective section that was much more compact.

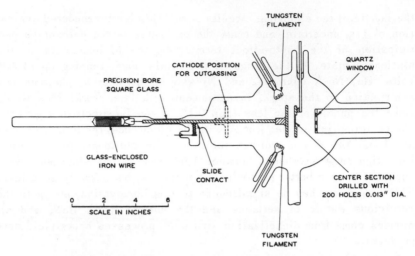

Fig. 9.33. Molnar's experimental tube for the dynamic study of
secondary actions owing to metastables at the cathode.

only, was worked up in detail theoretically by Molnar in such a fashion
as to make the experimental data on Townsend gaps yield the needed
information. A standard Townsend tube with plane parallel electrodes
illuminated through holes in the anode to yield a current i_0 was used,
as· illustrated in figure 9.33. Inert gases were investigated at roughly
1 mm pressure. The light giving i_0 was shuttered so as to produce a
flash of light lasting 5 milliseconds once every one-thirtieth of a
second. A potential could be applied to the electrodes. If the potential
was below that for ionization, the current consisted only of primary
photoelectrons, and thus followed the intensity of light with no delay
on this time scale. At higher potential there began the ionization by
electron impact to avalanches in the gas. This was followed by a
subsequent emission of current, caused by the action of ions, photons,
or metastables at the cathode.

On an observational time scale of milliseconds for the 0.1 to 1.0
cm gap length used, the ions and photons act essentially instantaneously. The lag in reaching the steady-state current resulting from
metastable atoms lasts about a millisecond and is clearly resolved
on the oscilloscope.

The basic analysis developed by Engstrom and Huxford, which
assumed the metastable emission to be produced only by metastable
impact on the cathode, was extended by Molnar to include consideration of metastables destroyed *in the gas*. These destroyed metastables

may lead to photons which can act on the cathode.[14] Thus, the theory must be extended to explain the more accurate modern observations.

Unfortunately, the wave form of the transient current produced is nearly the same for electrical effects arising from metastable action at either of these locations. This circumstance requires that second-order effects, as well as separate studies, be made to sort out the processes and locale of action observed. The theory, as will be developed, enables accurate predictions of the wave forms to be expected when a set of ionization and emission coefficients is assumed. The inverse problem of the analysis of an observed oscillograph pattern to sort out the basic data is more difficult, but some information can be obtained in this fashion. For example, the diffusion coefficients of metastable atoms are directly obtained. The basic assumption used is that the primary metastable atoms *are produced at once* by direct electron impact or decay of excited states of short life from electron impact. The experimental Townsend gap, as well as its method of employment, follows closely that of the Philips group (VIII.4).

Short plate distances were used. Currents were observed with increase in potential and distance keeping the field strength constant, using high initiating electron currents. Corrections were applied for the distance x_i or x_m ("lumped" usually as x_0) to get the ionizing or exciting energy E_i or E_m. The electron current increased as $\epsilon^{a(x-x_0)}$ The metastables were assumed to form at a rate proportional to the electron current arising from the avalanches. This is somewhat of an idealization, as electrons cannot form the metastables just where they are created. After creation the new electrons start from rest, so that first they must get the energy equivalent to x_m to create the metastables. However, with any given electron cloud ionizing at a given instant, metastables are produced in a certain ratio to the ions. There are also errors at low $x - x_0$, where a_i and ω_m are not constant. The metastables, once created, get thermal energy very rapidly and

---

[14]Metastables are, of course, also destroyed at the anode, and current forms can be readily calculated for electrical effects which might conceivably originate as a result of these destructions. There was no experimental evidence, however, to suggest that any such effect actually occurred. Also, the metastables can ionize impurity gas molecules (Penning effect), and the resulting transient current can also be calculated by the methods indicated above for the case of a small percentage of impurity (VIII.4). Care was taken in the experiments, however, to avoid the Penning effect, and no test was made of these calculations. Similarly, effects caused by metastable-metastable or metastable-electron collisions were avoided in the experiments, by keeping the primary current sufficiently small.

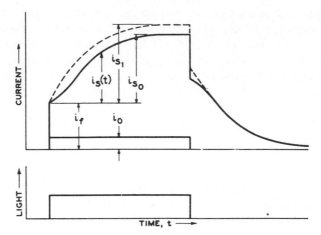

Fig. 9.34. Diagram illustrating the theoretical curve forms of current versus time to be expected from metastable action in the Townsend gap of figure 9.33, as observed oscilloscopically by Molnar.

then diffuse, colliding with atoms until they either reach the electrodes or are destroyed in the gas.

In pure gases such destruction is believed to be brought about by collisions between the metastables and neutral atoms, which excite or de-excite the metastable atoms into near-by radiating states. In all the rare gases except helium these states lie within about 0.1 e.v., and therefore such processes might be expected to be fairly likely. In helium the separation is 0.7 e.v., and here it seems more probable that the formation of molecules may be taking place. In all these experiments, however, impurities are an ever-present worry, and these can, of course, destroy metastables by accepting the energy either for ionization (Penning effect) or excitation (VIII.4).

The experimental procedure of interest in this analysis is one in which the light giving i_0 is suddenly flashed on and kept on until approximate equilibrium is reached, at which point it is cut off. The current will thus build up to a fixed value and then decay. The diagram of figure 9.34 illustrates the process. At $t = 0$ the light is flashed on. The current i_0 is indicated on the ordinate scale. In consequence of this, the electrons multiply in avalanches, giving $i_0 \left[\epsilon^{\alpha(d-x_0)} - 1 \right]$ positive ions and $i_0 \, \epsilon^{\alpha(d-x_0)}$ electrons. At the same time, excited atoms are also created.

The ions are drawn by the field to the cathode and a fraction of the photons emitted by excited atoms of short life reach the cathode, both giving rise to additional electron emission. These processes are *fast* on the time scale used by Molnar and give rise, therefore, to the fast component of current i_f, which is given by the Townsend equation:

(9.92)
$$i_f = \frac{i_0 \, \epsilon^{\,a(d - x_0)}}{1 - \gamma_f \left[\epsilon^{\,a(d - x_0)} - 1\right]}.$$

Here γ_f can be interpreted as the number of electrons which enter the discharge stream at the cathode as the result of one ion being created in the gas with the corresponding average number of excited atoms of short life.

The current of interest in this study is the one that rises as a result of metastable action, and is designated by $i_s(t)$ in figure 9.34. This rises with a form that is closely that of an inverted negative exponential, and when the light is cut off, decays in a form that is the inverse of the rising part.

The general approach to a theory follows Engstrom and Huxford, who assumed that a function $P_K(t)$ can be calculated which gives the rate of destruction of metastable atoms at the cathode at time t. These atoms are all products of the ionization and excitation in the avalanche started by a single electron leaving the cathode at $t = 0$. It thus includes the metastable atoms directly formed by the one primary electron plus those produced by the new electrons of that avalanche. It does *not* include any of the metastables formed by secondary electrons leaving the cathode as a result of gamma processes. Molnar sets the integral $\int_0^\infty P_K(t)dt$ equal to *the total number of metastables created by one electron leaving the cathode*.

Not all metastables created by that electron go to the cathode; some go to the anode, and some are destroyed in the gas. These anode- and gas-destroyed metastables call for two functions; $P_A(t)$ for the anode process, and $P_G(t)$ for the gas destruction. The total rate at which the metastables of the avalanche leave the space between the electrodes is the sum of $P_K(t)$, $P_A(t)$, and $P_G(t)$, and the time integral of this sum gives the total number of metastables produced in the avalanche. By including the loss of metastables in the gas, Molnar's treatment is more complete than Engstrom and Huxford's, as well as that of Newton, who assumed that the metastables were lost only by diffusion to the electrodes.

The calculation for $i_s(t)$ will first be made, assuming that electrical effects are caused only by the diffusion of metastables to the cathode. This has the coefficient $\nu\gamma_m = \theta_m = \psi_m\nu$, as used by Molnar. As used in the previous simplified considerations, γ_m was set equivalent to

(9.43)
$$g_m \frac{\omega_m}{a} \psi_m \nu = g_m f_m \theta_m$$

in analogy to γ_i. This study in effect is concerned with calculating g_m and f_m separately. Therefore, it is essential to define all *cathode* efficiencies as $\nu \gamma_i$, $\nu \gamma_r$, and $\nu \gamma_m$, making these quantities, without the back-diffusion factor, liberation efficiencies only. The products $\nu \gamma_i$, $\nu \gamma_r$, and $\nu \gamma_m$ are then equivalent to the previous ones, γ_i, θ, and θ_m.

The total delayed current $i_s(t)$ may be described in terms of a metastable-induced electron current at the cathode, analogous to i_0, enhanced by the same *fast* processes which increase i_0 to i_f. Thus,

(9.93)
$$i_s(t) = \frac{i_f}{i_0} \left(\begin{array}{c} \text{metastable-induced electron} \\ \text{current leaving cathode at time } t \end{array} \right).$$

The metastable-induced *electron* current at the cathode will in turn be given by the metastable particle current to the cathode at this time, multiplied by $\gamma_m \nu$. To evaluate this particle current we make use of the $P_K(t)$ function defined above, by writing

(9.94)
$$\left(\begin{array}{c} \text{Metastable particle} \\ \text{to cathode at time } t \end{array} \right) = \int_0^t P_K(t') \left(\begin{array}{c} \text{total electron current} \\ \text{leaving cathode at time } t' \end{array} \right) dt'.$$

Now the total electron current at the cathode in a Townsend discharge is always given ·by the total current, here given as $i_f + i_s(t)$, divided by the gas amplification factor $\epsilon^{a(d - x_0)}$. If these substitutions are made in equation 9.93, and equation 9.92 is used, it follows that

(9.95)
$$\frac{i_s(t)}{i_f} = \frac{\gamma_m \nu}{1 - \gamma_f [\epsilon^{a(d - x_0)} - 1]} \int_0^t P_K(t') \left[1 + \frac{i_s(t')}{i_f} \right] dt'.$$

This represents the fundamental integral equation, the solution of which is of interest.

If the fundamental process is one of photoelectric emission caused by photons generated as a result of metastables being destroyed in the gas, then, by analogous reasoning, the relation

(9.96)
$$\frac{i_s(t)}{i_f} = \frac{\psi \chi_G \nu}{1 - \gamma_f [\epsilon^{a(d - x_0)} - 1]} \int_0^t P_G(t') \left[1 + \frac{i_s(t')}{i_f} \right] dt'$$

is obtained. Here ψ is the photoelectric efficiency at the cathode, and χ_G is the fraction of photons from the metastables destroyed in the gas which get to the cathode. A similar equation can be set up for the case of metastables being destroyed at the anode in such a way as to emit photons, which can then go to the cathode and give photoelectric emission there. With slight additional complication it is also possible to describe the process in which the metastable atoms are assumed to be *ionized* on contact with the anode, much as cesium atoms are known to be ionized when striking hot tungsten filaments.[15] The Penning effect can be set up in this form as well. However, the experiments of Molnar showed no evidence for the anode effects being present, and care was taken to avoid the Penning effect.

More commonly, the two processes described by equations 9.95 and 9.96 were simultaneously present. To describe this situation a similar equation holds in which the right-hand side is given by the sum of the right-hand sides of equations 9.95 and 9.96. The result is not so formidable when use is made of the expressions for $P_K(t)$ and $P_G(t)$, as derived below, in which both are expressed as series of the same exponential function with different coefficients.

To evaluate the $P(t)$ functions, it is assumed that the metastables have a diffusive motion, expressed by the diffusion equation, written in the one-dimensional form as

$$(9.97) \qquad \frac{\partial \rho}{\partial t} = D \, \frac{\partial^2 \rho}{\partial x^2} - G\rho.$$

Here ρ is the linear density of metastables in the gap (a function of both x and t) created by a single electron leaving the cathode at $t = 0$. The quantity D is the diffusion constant, and G is the probability per second that a metastable atom will be destroyed in the gas. The solution must satisfy the boundary condition that $\rho = 0$ at $x = 0$ and $x = d$, which represent the cathode and anode positions.

The solution of equation 9.97 which satisfies these boundary conditions is

$$(9.98) \qquad \rho = \sum_n a_n \sin\left(\frac{n\pi x}{d}\right) \epsilon^{-\left(\frac{\pi^2 n^2 D}{d^2} + G\right)t}, \text{ with } n = 1, 2, 3 \ldots.$$

The a_n's are so chosen that ρ describes properly the metastable distribution at $t = 0$. Here the exponential terms are all unity, so that the a_n's are simply coefficients in the Fourier expansion of the initial

---

[15]In their classic investigations of the fine structure of the hydrogen energy states, W. E. Lamb and R. C. Retherford (59) have looked for this effect with metastable hydrogen atoms and obtained negative results. This may possibly be explained by the necessity of using *hot* filaments (which they apparently did not use) in order that the ionized atoms may break away from the surface forces.

distribution. With ρ thus known as a function of x and t, then the $P(t)$ functions are given by $P_K(t) \equiv$ particle current to cathode $= D(\partial\rho/\partial x)_{x=0}$; $P_A(t) \equiv$ particle current to anode $= -D(\partial\rho/\partial x)_{x=d}$; and $P_G(t) \equiv$ total rate of destruction in the gas $= G \int_0^d \rho dx$.

It is thus noted, without going into the detailed solutions, that $P_K(t)$, $P_A(t)$, and $P_G(t)$ can each be expressed by a sum of exponential functions, and the time constants of the exponentials are the same for each of the functions. Moreover, it turns out that in many situations the first term, i.e., the one with the longest time constant, describes a substantial part of the $P(t)$ function. Thus, a two-term description of $P_K(t)$ and $P_G(t)$ is adequate. $P_A(t)$ probably requires more terms.

The problem of evaluating $i_s(t)$ from equations 9.95 or 9.96 now becomes one of calculating the appropriate $P(t)$ functions and assuming suitable values for the various parameters. The solutions obviously present mathematical difficulties which it is not necessary to enter into here. Suffice it to say that $i_s(t)$ can be obtained in the form

$$(9.99) \qquad i_s(t) = i_{s0} - i_{s1}\, \epsilon^{-t/T_1} - i_{s2}\, \epsilon^{-t/T_2},$$

where the number of exponential terms is the same as that used to describe $P(t)$. If this is limited to two, then $i_s(t)$ is describable by two exponentials. Furthermore, the second term, i_{s2}, is generally appreciably smaller than the first, i_{s1}. For equation 9.95, i_{s2} is negative; while for equation 9.96, i_{s2} is extremely small, and positive. The form of $i_s(t)$, as shown schematically in figure 9.34, is drawn so as to illustrate the former case in exaggerated form, with the dashed line giving $i_s(t)$ when described by only one exponential term.

The inverse problem of evaluating the time constants of the $P(t)$ function from the experimental data is also presented. The accuracy of the data permit only the *first* time constant (i.e., T_1) to be measured. Together with this quantity, the primary current amplitude i_{s1} and the sum of the other current amplitudes i_{s2} can be determined, the latter having no well-defined time constant T_2 as a result of the "lumping." The analysis shows that if τ_1 is the time constant of the first term of the $P(t)$ function,

$$(9.100) \qquad \tau_1 = T_1\, \frac{i_f + 1.3\, i_{s2}}{i_f + i_{s1} + 1.3\, i_{s2}}.$$

This result is essentially a refinement of a relation developed and used by Engstrom and Huxford, in which i_{s2} was assumed to be zero. The relation given by equation 9.100 is especially useful, because $1/\tau_1$ is equal to $(\pi^2 D/d^2) + G$. Thus, if $1/\tau_1$ is evaluated as a function of $1/d^2$, one can obtain the quantities D and G.

In his detailed study, Molnar showed from theory how to evaluate $\omega_m \gamma_m$ from the data. The derivation is, however, too lengthy to include. As a possible source of error, Molnar studied the effect of radial diffusion, which in exact solution presents formidable mathematical difficulties. Simplified analysis showed that if the electrode spacing relative to diameter is kept below 0.2, the effects of radial diffusion on the time constant are quite small, as is the total number of metastables lost.

The experimental techniques were simple, perfected, and elegant. However, there are certain limitations on Molnar's technique and data, largely by the use of short gaps, fairly high i_0, and the general difficulty in the regions of X/p where much secondary action goes on. The limitations encountered resided largely in the necessity of having accurate values of a. These can be obtained only by judicious fitting of the log i/i_0-d curves to the Townsend equation, if data yielding sufficient accuracy are available. According to Molnar, his data did not yield reliable values in this fashion. Molnar used the Philips technique, and as indicated by the curves of figure 8.23, this would not yield good values of a. On the other hand, the techniques of the Berkeley group, using larger x and lower i_0, yielded accurate and consistent data on a. Where γ is relatively constant, a has been obtained with a fair degree of accuracy. For the fast γ_i and $f\theta g$ processes, it appears that γ_i is fairly constant with X/p, while $f\theta g$ changes rapidly with X/p.

Tests were made on the relative effectiveness of radiative photo effects by quenching of metastable action, using external quenching light and the photo effect in the slow component. It was found that at high X/p, the photon contribution, even to the fast component, was small when compared with earlier static observations. Thus, Molnar's study was limited to high X/p, where γ_f for the fast component was taken as constant.

The sum $\gamma = \gamma_s + \gamma_f$ of the slow and fast components was calculated, using this assumption from the total current and $\epsilon^{a(d-x_0)}$. This showed that γ_s varied with d.

Further to control the measurements of a, two gaps interconnected with the same gas filling were used, one with a Ni cathode of low γ, and the other of a standard type BaO surface on Ni of high γ. Later, four tubes were used, with surfaces of Ta, Mo, BaO on Ta, and a fourth intended to be Ba on Ta, but which ended up as Ta. Some adsorption of gases on the surfaces must have been present, despite all precautions. Values of X/p ranged from 50 to 200 volts/(cm × mm). The range could not be extended toward lower X/p, because at the

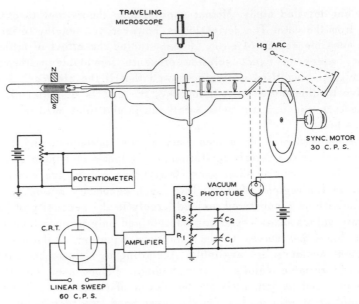

Fig. 9.35. Diagram of Molnar's device for analysis of metastable diffusion and γ_i in a Townsend gap, including the timing circuits for compensating the cathode ray signals and evaluating time constants.

higher pressures required for such measurements, the metastables were destroyed too rapidly. Extension to higher X/p involves lower pressures, which result in short time constants for $i_s(t)$ and consequent difficulties of separation from i_f.

Molnar's first tubes were large, and similar to those of Engstrom and Huxford. They were hard to outgas, though they had the advantage that the tube walls were quite distant. Later tubes were of smaller diameter, coated with aquadag, and maintained at a potential halfway between that of the anode and cathode. The electrodes had a diameter of 5 cm. Elaborate precautions were taken to maintain parallelism between plates on changing distance. The BaO surfaces were prepared by methods standard in practice. Purity of gases was achieved by flashed Ba from a batalum "getter" and liquid-nitrogen traps.

A high-pressure mercury lamp, operated on d.c., was used for i_0. The rise time of the shuttered light pulse was of the order of 30 μ sec. The current was measured by using a suitable resistor and placing the resulting potential difference iR across the sweep of a cathode ray oscillograph, as shown in figure 9.35. The amplifier noise was reduced to a minimum. To obtain 0.5% accuracy and still retain adequate time resolution, currents of at least 10^{-8} ampere were needed.

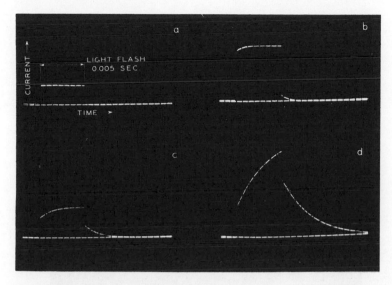

Fig. 9.36. Oscillographic curves observed by Molnar. Curve (a) shows the vacuum photo current from the cathode, curve (b) shows a low-voltage trace, while curves (c) and (d) show traces with increasing potential, compared with figure 9.34.

Space-charge distortion (and/or possible effects of metastable-metastable collisions) set in at 2×10^{-7} ampere, thus limiting the range of measurement.

Accurate current values were obtained by a null method. With a partially reflecting mirror some of the light was directed into a vacuum photo tube which generated a current pulse exactly in step with the primary current in the gap. This current flowed through two resistor-capacitor combinations $R_1 C_1$ and $R_2 C_2$. By means of these a voltage pulse was formed, having a shape and size very similar to that of the Townsend current but of opposite sign. This could be combined with the voltage generated by the Townsend current, thus bucking out the Townsend signal when R_1, C_1, R_2, and C_2 were properly adjusted. This treatment eliminated any variation in i_0 caused by variation in light intensity.

The time constant of the $R_1 C_1$ combination ranged from 0 to 30 μ sec to match the fast component i_f, while the time constants of the $R_2 C_2$ combination ranged from 0.1 to 30 milliseconds to match the slow component i_{sl} of equation 9.99. When the amplitudes and time constants were adjusted to give the best fit to the Townsend gap current, there remained nearly always a current intermediate in time

§ 15

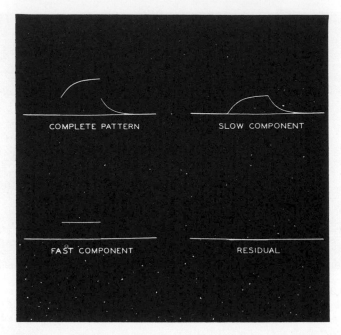

Fig. 9.37. Oscillograms of Molnar, showing the operation of the compensator. The legends under the curves show the effects.

constant and negative in amplitude. This component may be identified as i_{s2} in equation 9.99. Its amplitude could be measured by the decrease necessary in the fast component to bring the current trace up to base line.

It is seen that from the values of R_1, C_1, R_2, and C_2, the data are obtained quite "painlessly." This procedure, under favorable conditions, allows the amplitudes to be measured to 0.2% and the time constants to 2%. The operation of the system is shown in figure 9.36. There the oscillogram of i_0 is shown at (a). Trace (b) shows a low-voltage trace, while (c) and (d) show progressively traces of larger voltages V. For analysis, the effect of RC compensation is shown in figure 9.37. The complete pattern is shown, with successively the fast component taken out, the slow component removed, and the residual after full compensation.

This experimental arrangement provided a relatively simple and accurate means for obtaining the diffusion constant D and the volume-destruction probability G for metastables, by evaluating τ_1 at a series of different values of d. Measurements were made of i_f, i_{s1}, i_{s2}, and T_1 for various values of V. τ_1 was then computed, using equation

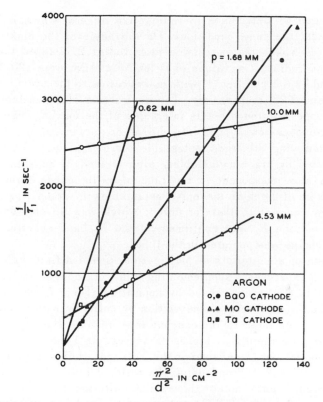

Fig. 9.38. Reciprocals of the time plotted against π^2/d^2 at different gas pressures in mm of Hg. Argon gas with different cathodes is used. Note the linear plots.

9.100. For a given value of d, η, as thus calculated, was found to be independent of V or the cathode surface, thus providing a gratifying check of the theory.[16]

Time-constant data are presented in figure 9.38 in the form of a plot of $1/\tau_1$ vs π^2/d^2 which yields a straight line for each pressure of gas, since, as shown earlier, $1/\eta = (\pi^2 D/d^2) + G$. The slope D fits a $1/p$ variation, as expected for diffusion. The value of D for argon metastables is 45 ± 4 cm^2 sec^{-1} at 1 mm pressure at 25° C. This may be compared to the self-diffusion coefficient of normal argon atoms,

[16]The theory, when developed for the case of ion formation by metastables destroyed at the anode, or ion formation by the Penning effect, yields a relation different from equation 9.100. The fact that equation 9.100 fitted the experimental data well is an indirect indication that these processes of ion formation were not active.

as measured by Hutchisson by radioactive tracers, which is 139 cm^2 sec^{-1} under the same conditions. On the basis of the elastic-sphere model, this makes the metastable atom radius 2.52 times the normal argon atom radius. The values of D for Ne and Xe were 120 $\pm$ 10 cm^2 sec^{-1} and 13 $\pm$ 1 cm^2 sec^{-1}, with radius ratios to the unexcited atoms of 2.45 and 2.22, respectively. The destruction of the metastables in the gas appears through y-axis intercepts of the curves, evaluating G.

On one occasion N_2 got into the argon to the extent of perhaps 0.1%, destroying all argon metastables in 100 μ sec. The N_2, when thus excited by argon metastables, also yielded N_2 metastables, producing a slow component in the tube of milliseconds duration. The diffusion coefficient of these N_2 metastables in argon was 157 cm^2 sec^{-1}, in contrast to that for argon, which was 45 cm^2 sec^{-1}. The presence of the N_2 was confirmed by the N_2 band spectrum when a glow discharge was operated in the tube.

In spite of all attempts at purification, G had a finite value. Light-absorption experiments supplementing this work convinced Molnar that most of this G was not caused by impurities. Thus, G must definitely be ascribed to a process of destruction by collision with neutral atoms of argon. G appeared to increase at low pressure linearly with pressure, and more rapidly at higher pressures. At 1 mm pressure it had a value of 80 sec^{-1}. Assuming the collision radius between normal argon atoms as 3.2 Å and using the ratio of radii of metastable and normal argon atoms noted above, the collision frequency of metastables at 1 mm and 25° C. comes out to be 1.6 $\times$ 10^7 sec^{-1}. The value of G observed thus indicates that the probability of the destruction of the argon metastables in impact with normal atoms is about one in 2 $\times$ 10^5 impacts, and yields excited A_2 molecules. See L. Colli (50).

The effect of irradiation of the metastables from an external argon discharge was investigated. The first excited configuration is $3p^54s$, which gives rise to $^1P_1$, $^3P_0$, $^3P_1$, and $^3P_2$ states. The $^1P_1$ and $^3P_1$ radiate, and $^3P_0$ and $^3P_2$ are metastable states. Irradiation with lines from transitions between $3p^54p$ and $3p^54s$ configurations is absorbed by atoms in states of $3p^54s$ configuration. Of the four, only the two metastable states are normally populated in appreciable density. Thus, the radiation raises the metastables to various states in the $3p^54p$ configuration, leading either to reversion to the metastable states by radiation or to the radiating states which decay by radiation to the ground state. The latter transitions give photons. The energies of the four states are 11.55, 11.62, 11.72, and 11.84 e.v., respectively, so that the photon and metastable energies are quite close.

The irradiation was achieved either by focusing light from a line

The Second Townsend Coefficient

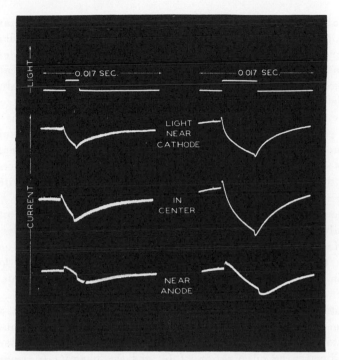

Fig. 9.39. Molnar's study of metastable action at the cathode included destruction of metastables by irradiation of the gas by its own light, using A gas. Here a destructive flash of light is on for 0.017 sec at the top level, synchronized by oscillograph response. The destructive flash at once raises a pip at the left edge of the oscillograph trace. This is greater if the anode or the center of the gap is illuminated, as most metastables are in those regions. The rise in current comes from photo effect at the cathode by quenching of metastables. The current falls, as there are no more metastables to diffuse. As the destructive light goes off, the second decrease pip appears. Metastables are no longer destroyed, and time must elapse before they reach the cathodes.

source on regions near the anode, in the middle, or near the cathode, or by surrounding the Townsend tube with a ring-shaped discharge tube. The latter was more effective, but could not be localized as to its action in the Townsend gap. The primary triggering Townsend gap illumination could be held steady, while the destructive argon illumination was varied, or vice versa. Pulsing the argon tube for two different time intervals irradiating three positions in the Townsend gap, starting at the cathode, yields the oscillograms shown in figure 9.39.

It is seen that application of the destructive flash at once increases the current slightly (the small positive pip). The action is somewhat greater in the center and near the anode, where metastable destruction affects a larger number of metastables. The sudden rise in current is caused by the photons from destroyed metastables producing an immediate release of secondary electrons from the cathode. The current accordingly decreases below its steady-state value because fewer metastables are now available to diffuse to the cathode and give rise to electron emission. When the destructive light is cut off the current decreases suddenly still more, since the emission of the photons from destroyed metastables is cut off. The current then recovers as the metastables build up and regain their normal rate of flow to the cathode. The slow decrease and recovery occur with less time lag when the destroying light is focused near the cathode.

In general, destructive illumination resulted in a lower steady-state value of the current, thus indicating that the metastables were more effective in producing electron emission by striking the cathode directly than in having the equivalent energy arrive in the form of radiation. With an Ni surface in an unknown state of contamination, the reverse was true, but this case was exceptional.

Quantitative analysis was made. G was measured for the normal discharge and yielded the natural loss G_c, caused by collisions with argon atoms. With the destructive illumination acting, the value of G observed gave the combination of G_c and the quantity G_s caused by the light. The maximum value attained for G_s was 1,500 sec^{-1}. Further analysis of the data and theory permitted the evaluation of the ratio ψ/γ_m, i.e., the ratio of the number of electrons emitted by the photoelectric action of a photon to that by direct collision of a metastable atom on the cathode. The average value of ψ/γ_m was 0.40 for Ta, 0.08 for Mo, and 0.10 for BaO. No quantitative data were available for the Ni surface mentioned above, but presumably the measurements would have yielded a value of $\psi/\gamma_m > 1$ for this case.

What Molnar termed "Townsend runs" were made, in which the amplitudes of the fast, slow, and medium components and the time constants of fast and slow components were made for twenty to fifty values of d. A typical set of i/i_0 values, plotted against d in cm, is shown in figure 9.40 for X/p of 117 volts/(cm × mm) for BaO, Mo, and Ta cathodes. The undulations of the Philips-type curves (VIII.4) are noted at low d. Difficulties of fitting the Townsend equation to obtain α under these conditions are to be noted. The light-intensity variations in the triggering source were canceled by the null method of measurement, but changes in photoemissivity of the surfaces with time required constant checking. To obtain large variations in i/i_0, i_0 had to be changed because of the limitations of the method when

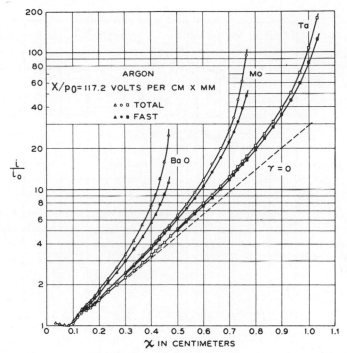

Fig. 9.40. Molnar's Townsend measurements of log i/i_0 plotted against plate separation x in cm. Note undulations of the Philips-type curves at low gap length.

i exceeded 10^{-7} ampere. Contact-potential differences were small. Computation was involved because of the many corrections, and there is no space for discussion of the details except to state that these all followed from the theory outlined.

Correction for back diffusion of electrons (Molnar's f_{esc}, or ν in this text) was made by studies of i_0 at low V. These were of course applied to conditions at high X/p. The theory for i with loss through back diffusion, determining ν, was originally derived by J. J. Thomson and tested by the author and Bradbury for plane parallel gaps, as well as by Rice and Johnson for coaxial cylinders at conditions mainly very different from those by Molnar. The theory and values studied by Bradbury largely apply to an X/p which is low, and values of d where loss at the cathode is confined to a layer very short compared to d, as the Thomson theory assumes.

Under the condition of Molnar's study, d varied from less than 0.1 cm to 1.0 cm at a pressure of 1.5 mm and fields X ranging from 15 to 500 volts/cm. The electron impacts in argon, being perfectly elastic

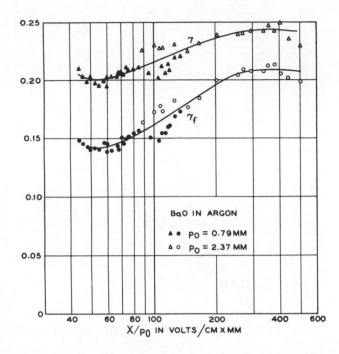

Fig. 9.41. Molnar's "Townsend run" values of total γ and the fast
component γ_f, plotted against X/p_0 for BaO cathodes in A gas.

below excitation, cause very little energy loss per impact. It is thus
improbable that the Thomson relation should accurately apply, and
C will lose its significance relative to the frequency of the light and
the work function of the surface. A new theory is required, involving
Ramsauer free paths and gain in energy in a step process. It is also
clear that the electron energies gained in the field within the back-
diffusion range of the cathode will wipe out the effects of the one-half
to one volt energy of photoelectric emergence. While the problem is
difficult, too little attention has been paid to back diffusion at low
p and high X/p, as the rather remarkable findings of Johnson and
Morton in nonuniform fields indicate.

In Molnar's work, cathode efficiency changed with pressure, so
that complete "Townsend run" data were incapable of yielding γ
values as a function of X/p. Resort to indirect methods gave γ_f as a
function of X/p for BaO, using for comparison an Ni electrode of low γ
in the same gas. The variation of γ_f with X/p in this case is shown
in figure 9.41. The variation of γ_f of figure 9.41, in comparison with
that of ν with X/p shown in figure 9.42, indicates that the observed

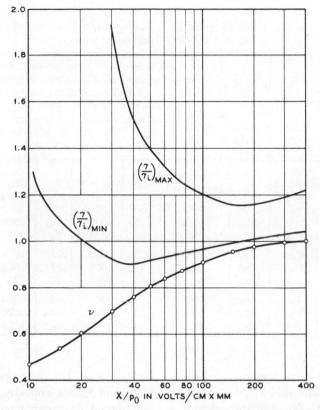

Fig. 9.42. Molnar's values for the back-diffusion loss factor ν in his studies relative to X/p_0. There are also shown the ratios of total γ to γ_i as a function of X/p.

variation of γ_f is largely caused by ν and not by ψ_f. This would in-,dicate that $\gamma_{ic} + \psi_{fg}$ is essentially constant between $X/p = 60$ and $X/p = 400$. Since f is decreasing as X/p increases, ψ must increase with decreasing f, which is likely, as Kenty has shown. It can also indicate a decrease in γ_{ic} with X/p, or else that θfg is negligible compared to γ_i in this region. The very low ratio of ψ/γ_m for BaO cathodes indicates the latter interpretation. It is suspected that except possibly at extremely high values of X/p, the value of γ_i in inert gases does not change very much with X/p, as recently shown by Hagstrum.

In the resulting summarizing tables for argon, Molnar gives ν, a, ω, and ω_m, from which f and f_m can be estimated. In addition, he gives values γ_f, γ_s, $\omega_m\gamma_m$, ν_{fg}, γ_{ic}, γ_{mc}, and θ for these values of X/p. Data on ω_m and ω could not be measured, so that calculated values of

§ 15

TABLE 9.6

Molnar's Values for ν, α, ω, ω_m, γ_f, γ_s, γ_i, γ_m, and θ, for Ta, Mo, and BaO Targets in Argon Gas

X/p volts/ (cm × mm)	ν	α cm^{-1}	ω, ω_m cm^{-1}	(Note: The data for the two higher values of X/p were obtained with $p = 1.535$ mm and the surfaces in the same condition. The data for the lowest value of X/p were obtained with $p = 4.135$ mm and the surfaces having a reduced efficiency.)		
195.4	0.97	6.63	2.6			
117.2	0.91	3.72	2.4			
72.6	0.86	5.10	7.0			

X/p	Cathode	γ_f	γ_s (near breakdown)	$\omega_m \gamma_m$	$(\omega_m/\alpha)f\theta$	γ_i	γ_m	θ
195.4	Ta	.026	.0025	.062	.0014	.026	.023	.009
195.4	Mo	.076	.0074	.160	.0008	.071	.060	.005
195.4	BaO	.23	.050	.83	.005	.23	.31	.031
117.2	Ta	.022	.0026	.056	.002	.022	.023	.009
117.2	Mo	.065	.011	.158	.001	.071	.065	.005
117.2	BaO	.21	.065	.65	.007	.22	.27	.027
72.6	Ta	.0060	.0009	.025	.0017	.0053	.0035	.0021
72.6	Mo	.030	.00025	.14	.001	.034	.020	.001
72.6	BaO	.073	.013	.54	—	.085	.078	—

Kruithoff were used, arbitrarily setting $\omega_m = \omega$. The γ_{mc} were calculated, using this ω_m. It is noted that γ_{mc} and γ_{ic} are about equal. Too much reliance probably should not be placed on these conclusions, which are shown in table 9.6.

These data are of interest as indicating conditions and behaviors in one gas, and within a limited range of fairly high-energy electrons, with metastables and ions of high potential energy. It is seen that here the values of α, ω, and ω_m are about commensurate. Accordingly, the effects of γ_i and γ_m would be expected to be of about the same order, since the energies E_i and E_m are large compared to ϕe. The BaO surfaces show far greater γ yields as well as photoelectric yields. The near equivalence of the metastable and ion yields may arise from the fact that a very similar physical process gives rise to electron emission in both cases. On the other hand, the photoelectric effect is a quite different mechanism, and the 11.5 e.v. photons involved probably penetrate the surface of the cathode to several atom layers. Hence, we might expect little correspondence between the efficiency of this process and that involved with the ions and metastables.

The results indicate the character of analysis and the accuracy which is to be anticipated. They also show the limitations of the method. It is seen that the secondary occurrences in a Townsend gap are involved indeed, and that the earlier simplifications require that caution be used in interpretation.

§ 16. The Dynamic Study of the Fast Components in Secondary Mechanisms by J. A. Hornbeck. [17]

As indicated, J. A. Hornbeck (58) carried out a study of the fast component of the secondary emission processes in a Townsend gap without space-charge distortion. This experiment corresponds to the time derivative of Molnar's experiment, since a very short, light pulse is used rather than a step-function light source. This work is an outgrowth of and was suggested by R. R. Newton's theoretical analysis of transient currents in a Townsend gap (56). The experimental results yielded the following information: A confirmation of Newton's theory, positive ion mobilities for both atomic and molecular rare gas ions, electron-drift velocities, and values of γ_i, the number of secondary electrons emitted from the cathode per positive ion arriving there.

The fast processes were studied by observing the transient current following illumination of the cathode of the Townsend gap for a short interval of 0.1μ sec with ultraviolet light. During the light pulse, a current i_0 of photoelectrons flows in the gap under the influence of a static field of value X and with a gas pressure p. These electrons in crossing the gap produce by electron impact with gas atoms, excited atoms, metastable atoms, and positive ions. On the time scale of this experiment (tens of microseconds), metastable atoms do not produce detectable currents by the θ_m effect because their rate of diffusion to the cathode is too slow. Radiation from excited atoms or molecules that does not involve a direct transition to the ground state was originally not considered important as a source of secondary electrons, because its wave length is, in general, too long.

Recent studies by L. Colli and U. Facchini (50) have shown delay processes in inert gases of the order of several electron-transit times to be of prime importance. These would be hard to detect in this geometry. In addition, the shorter wave-length radiations emitted in less than 10^{-7} sec would be a source of photoelectrons that are, for the purposes of this study, indistinguishable from the photoelectrons generated by the external light source. Radiation resulting from a

---

[17]The author originally wrote this summary of Hornbeck's work from collected but unpublished reports. In the interest of effectiveness and of a more recent summary, J. A. Hornbeck kindly rewrote this section, which is submitted with relatively little editing, done only for uniformity of style.

direct transition between an excited state and the ground state, i.e., resonance radiation, *may* be imprisoned and persist in its arrival at the cathode for some 10^{-4} or 10^{-5} sec. The radiation effects of this sort will, if large, contribute to the transient current studied. The positive ion current to the cathode will, however, furnish most of the secondary electrons.

Hornbeck, in his treatment (of which this is a part), gave a partial solution of R. R. Newton's (56) more general analysis for the fast component of the growth of a Townsend current. This problem has recently been exactly solved by R. N. Varney (60) at the Bell Laboratories. His solution is substituted for Hornbeck's, since it is more complete and generally useful. Simplifying assumptions follow. (1) The electrons cross the tube in relatively zero time compared to the positive ions, which move with speeds 0.005 of those of the electrons. (2) The initial distance traveled by the electrons to achieve ionization is negligible. (3) Diffusion and space-charge effects can be neglected. (4) There is a single coefficient[18] for ionization. (5) All ions of a given species have a unique drift velocity in the field. Hornbeck, in addition, assumed the n_0 triggering electrons to be liberated in a time too short to notice. Varney's more general solution omits this.

A complete integral equation treatment for the transient ion current, analogous to Molnar's treatment for diffusion is possible, and has been derived by Hornbeck. Since this treatment, rather than Newton's, lends itself more readily to illustrating the theory in a simplified fashion, it will be given here. The simplified version starts with four assumptions: (1) that the initiating photoelectric pulse consists of n_0 photoelectrons simultaneously leaving 1 cm^2 of cathode at $t = 0$;

---

[18]The subject of temporal and spatial liberation of electrons in an avalanche is now being closely scrutinized on the basis of new observations. Originally, it was assumed that in an avalanche, all electrons (a) and photons (ω) were created by impacts of electrons on atoms. This would make creation simultaneous at any distance x within 10^{-7} sec or better. However, if ionization is created in the gas by metastables (Penning effect), which on occasion may create most of the electrons in an avalanche; by photoionization in the gas (Hale effect), giving 25% of a statically measured; by collision of excited atoms with unexcited ones (Hornbeck-Molnar effect), creating 50% of a statically measured; and finally, by triple impact of two metastable states and an atom giving molecular ions—the liberation of electrons can be quite diffused in time and space. Similar actions, including the Colli-Facchini effect, which give photons that reach the cathode, and imprisonment of resonance radiation, will produce considerable delay in the γ process beyond the avalanche crossing time. Thus, a, as measured by static or Townsend techniques, may not be used correctly where time-dependent studies are made, the fast component of a being less than the slow one.

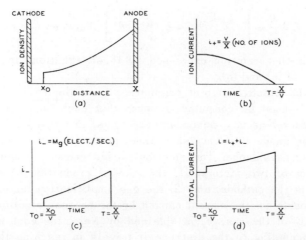

Fig. 9.43. This illustrates steps in the analysis of the impulses sensed by the cathode ray oscillograph for the fast components in a Townsend gap, as arranged by Hornbeck. Curves (a) and (b) represent equations 9.101 and 9.102. Curves (c) and (d) represent equations 9.105 and 9.106.

(2) that these electrons have nearly zero kinetic energy, and that their drift velocity in the gas is very fast compared to positive ion drift velocities; (3) that ionization by collision under constant field conditions may be characterized by a single coefficient α_i (even though some Penning effect, a slow process on this time scale, may be present); and (4) that all ions have a unique drift velocity in the field direction.

With these assumptions, and a plane parallel electrode geometry, the resulting density ρ_i of ions along the avalanche path at zero time is then zero from the cathode, $x = 0$, to $x = x_0$, where the first ionization can occur. Beyond x_0 to the anode, the ion density is $i = n_0$ $\epsilon^{(x-x_0)\alpha_i}$. Here $x_0 \simeq E_i d/V$, where d is the electrode separation, V is the applied potential, and E_i is the ionization potential of the gas. The density function ρ_i is plotted as a function of x in figure 9.43. The current that these ions contribute as a function of time is proportional to the number of ions and their velocity. Thus, i_+, the positive ion current in units of electronic charge per sec, is $i_+ = (v/d)n$, with n, the number of ions between the plates, given by $n = \int_{x_0}^d \rho_i(x)dx$ for $0 \lesssim t \lesssim x_0/v$, and $i_+ = v/d\int_{vt}^d \rho_i(x)dx$ for $x_0/v \lesssim t \lesssim d/v$. Here v is the ion-drift velocity. Thus, it is possible to write

$$(9.101) \qquad i_+ = \frac{v}{d} n_0 \left[\epsilon^{\alpha_i(d-x_0)} - 1 \right] \text{ between } 0 \lesssim t \lesssim \frac{x_0}{v}$$

and

$$(9.102) \qquad i_{+} = \frac{v}{d} n_0 \left[\epsilon^{a_i(d-x_0)} - \epsilon^{-a_i(vt-x_0)} \right] \quad \text{between} \quad \frac{x_0 -}{v} < t < \frac{- d}{v} .$$

The current-time relation expressed by these equations is shown in figure 9.43 at (a) and (b).

Next, the electric current originating from electrons released at the cathode must be computed. Assume that each ion neutralized at the cathode releases γ_i secondary electrons, and that each of these goes to the anode in a very short time, producing almost instantaneously a new avalanche. The electron-carried current component $i-$ is the product of two factors: (1) the rate of production of secondary electrons at the cathode, and (2) the gas amplification factor M_g. The latter accounts for the current carried by the progeny electrons formed in the body of the gas. M_g is obtained by weighting each avalanche electron according to the distance it travels in reaching the anode, i.e., for one electron leaving the cathode,

$$(9.103) \qquad M_g = 1 + \int_{x_0}^{d} \frac{d-x}{d} \rho_i(x)dx .$$

Here $\rho_i(x) = n_0 a_i \epsilon^{a_i(d-x_0)}$, with $n_0 = 1$. Integration yields

$$(9.104) \qquad M_g = \frac{1}{a_i d} \left[\epsilon^{a_i(d-x_0)} + a_i x_0 - 1 \right] .$$

The rate of production of secondary electrons is simply γ_i times the number of ions collected per second. Thus, in electronic units of current,

$$(9.105) \qquad \begin{cases} i_- = 0 & 0 \overline{<} t \overline{<} x_0/v \\ \\ i_- = n_0 M_g \gamma_i a_i v \, \epsilon^{a_i(vt-x_0)} & x_0/v \overline{<} t \overline{<} d/v \end{cases} .$$

The current $i-$ is plotted in figure 9.43 at (c).

The total current $i(t)$ as a function of time is

$$(9.106) \qquad i(t) = i_+(t) + i_-(t),$$

and is shown in figure 9.43 at (d).

There are two discontinuities; one of magnitude $n_0 M_g \gamma_i a_i v$ at $t = x_0/v$, and the other of magnitude $n_0 M_g \gamma_i a_i v \, \epsilon^{a_i(d-x_0)}$ at $t = d/v$. Both of these result from the discontinuous production of *secondary* electrons at the cathode on account of the discontinuous initial spatial formation of ions.

The tertiary ions produced by positive ions coming from the avalanches of the *secondary* electrons, and the higher-order production

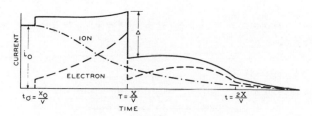

Fig. 9.44. Total current as a function of time for Hornbeck's fast components in the Townsend gap.

terms, have not been included. As Newton's more complete theory showed (56), these higher terms add little more than tails to the positive and negative current components shown. The two discontinuities persist, and their magnitudes are unchanged. There is in the more complete theory, however, a discontinuity in slope at twice $t = d/v$, i.e., at $t = 2d/v$. The total current and its two components from the complete theory are shown in figure 9.44.

The parameters a_i, γ_i, and v are obtained from experimentally observed quantities through the relations that follow. To be measured are the area A of the initial photo pulse, the magnitude i_{0+} of the initial positive ion current, the discontinuity in current Δ, and the transit time $T = d/v$. These are given by the relations:

$$(9.107) \qquad A = C M_g n_0 = \frac{C n_0}{a_i d} \left[\epsilon^{a_i(d - x_0)} + a_i x_0 - 1 \right] \quad \ldots \ldots ,$$

$$(9.108) \qquad i_{0+} = C n_0 \frac{v}{d} \left[\epsilon^{a_i(d - x_0)} - 1 \right] \quad \ldots \ldots ,$$

$$(9.109) \qquad \Delta = C n_0 M_g \gamma_i a_i v \, \epsilon^{a_i(d - x_0)} ,$$

and

$$(9.110) \qquad T = \frac{d}{v} .$$

The quantity C is a calibration constant of the measuring device. The quantity a_i is first obtained from the ratio,

$$(9.111) \qquad \frac{i_{0+} T}{A} = \frac{a_i d \left[\epsilon^{a_i(d - x_0)} - 1 \right]}{\left[\epsilon^{a_i(d - x_0)} + a_i x_0 - 1 \right]} \simeq a_i d ,$$

as follows: The coefficients B, D, etc., are defined by a series,

(9.112) $$a_i d = \frac{i_{0+} T}{A} \left(1 + B\sigma + D\sigma^2 + \ldots \right),$$

where

(9.113) $$\sigma = \frac{\dfrac{i_{0+} T}{A} \, x_0/d}{\left[\epsilon^{\frac{i_{0+} T}{A}\left(1 - \frac{x_0}{d}\right)} - 1 \right]}.$$

The quantity σ is at most about 0.20, and in many cases is negligible, since $a_i d \simeq i_{0+} T/A$.

Substitution of equation 9.113 in equation 9.112 evaluates the unknown coefficients B, D, etc.:

(9.113) $$B = 1, \quad D = 1 - \frac{\dfrac{i_{0+} T}{A}\left(1 - \dfrac{x_0}{d}\right) \, \epsilon^{\frac{i_{0+} T}{A}\left(1 - \frac{x_0}{d}\right)}}{\left[\epsilon^{\frac{i_{0+} T}{A}\left(1 - \frac{x_0}{d}\right)} - 1 \right]}.$$

$D\sigma^2$ is never more than 1%, so that well within experimental error, $a_i d$ is given by $a_i d = (i_{0+} T/A) (1 + \sigma)$.

To get γ_i,

(9.114) $$\gamma_i = \frac{\Delta}{i_{0+}} (1 + \sigma)^{-1} \, \epsilon^{\left[\frac{i_{0+} T}{A} (1 + \sigma)\left(1 - \frac{x_0}{d}\right) \right]}.$$

If i_{0+} is difficult to measure, γ_i can be found from the relation:

(9.115) $$\gamma_i = \left(\frac{T\Delta}{A} \right) \frac{\epsilon^{a_i(d - x_0)}}{a_i d}$$

if a_i is obtained independently, or from the literature.

Of all the quantities, v is most easily evaluated, through

(9.116) $$v = d/T.$$

The simple, idealized theory presented above neglects several physical effects that are observed experimentally. Actually, the ions do not have a single, unique velocity component (i.e., the drift velocity), but instead have a velocity distribution with random energy in all velocity components in space. At extremely low fields, the distribution is Maxwellian in a frame of reference moving with the drift velocity of the ions, for in this region thermal energy is much greater than the

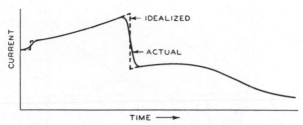

Fig. 9.45. Hornbeck's composite of fast components of current in the Townsend gap as a function of time. The dotted curve is the idealized solution; the full curve corresponds to reality as modified by diffusive action.

energy gained from the applied field. As the field is increased, the energy gained from the field becomes comparable with and subsequently greater than thermal energy. At very high fields, thermal effects can be ignored, and the randomness in the velocity distribution comes solely from energy gained in the applied field that is randomized by scattering collisions with neutral atoms.

Whether the velocity distribution is a displaced Maxwellian distribution, a high-field distribution, or a combination of these two, *the drift velocity can be defined as the mean velocity in the field direction*, and *a diffusion coefficient can be defined*, as Wannier has shown, *that represents the randomness in the ionic motions*. (See chapter I, part two, section 11.)

Diffusion will make the ions arrive at the cathode in a random manner about the mean transit time, and thus cause the large vertical discontinuity in figure 9.44 to slant and have rounded corners, as in figure 9.45. This may be expressed more exactly in terms of a diffusion coefficient D. If the ions move a distance d in average time $T = d/v$, and the root-mean-square deviation in their arrival time is Δt^2, the "definition" in the discontinuity is given by

$$\frac{\sqrt{\overline{\Delta t^2}}}{T} = \frac{2D}{vd} .$$

At low fields, D is the ordinary diffusion coefficient, defined in terms of the Maxwellian distribution. At high fields, Wannier has shown that this concept is replaced by a diffusion tensor, and the component that applies here is the diffusion coefficient in the field direction. Wannier has shown further that as a rule, the product of the diffusion coefficient and the gas density N is a function only of X/p and kT, i.e., $D \cdot N = f(X/p, kT)$, so that with increasing temperature and/or increasing field, D becomes larger at constant N. The definition of the small discontinuity occurring at $t = x_0/v$ will be poorer than that for the large discontinuity by $\sqrt{d/x_0}$.

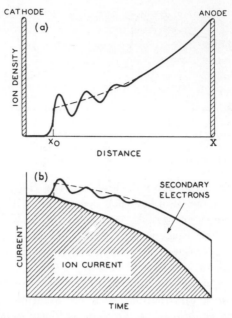

Fig. 9.46. Effects of bunching ions in the few ionizing distances x_0 for Hornbeck's short gaps, as modified by diffusion relative to ion current illustrated.

At the time this section was written, the discontinuity at $t = x_0/v$ was considered to be present, and certain oscillations noted in the oscillograms were assumed to be expressions of this sort of an action, as indicated in figure 9.46. Actually, this may have been the case in A or Ne at the lower pressures where x_0 can be large. In one set of Varney's observations (60) with a low γ and high X/p, where an x_0 might have been expected, there was obtained the dip indicated by Hornbeck to be caused by an x_0, but no oscillation. Thus, while the observations concerning oscillations in the oscilloscope traces made by Hornbeck fitted rather accurately with the assumption that a discontinuity occurred at $t = x_0/v$, and hence might generally be anticipated for the pressures and field strengths employed, Varney, using the same apparatus, had considerable difficulty in reproducing them. In fact, he only observed them under rare and not too clearly defined circumstances. Varney ultimately showed that when he obtained such oscillations, they were spurious, their origin lying in inadequate shielding of the spark source of illumination.

Actually, pressures and gap lengths d were generally of such magnitude as to make appreciable values of x_0 unlikely. If x_0 is the appreciable fraction of d assumed in the diagrams, it is not proper to assume values of α from previous studies, and the whole multiplication theory used is inexact, as α changes across the gap.

Figure 9.46 shows at (a) and (b) the effects to be expected from diffusion and from x_0 (if x_0 is important), respectively, as interpreted by Hornbeck. Actually, the effect of diffusion in figure 9.46(a) is observed, and was studied by Varney. The oscillations shown in figure 9.46(b) were observed by Hornbeck, but not exactly in the form shown, and were apparently instrumental. On one occasion Varney observed the initial dip caused by x_0, but no oscillation.

At this point it is of interest to give the more complete development of the theory by R. N. Varney (60) leading to evaluations of γ_i.

The standard equation for current density due to moving charges $j = \rho v$ may be rearranged in the form

$$(9.117) \qquad i = \frac{nev}{d},$$

where i is now the current itself, n is the total number of moving charges, v is the charge drift speed, and d is the anode-cathode separation. The symbol e is used for the electronic charge.

As the electrons drift through the gas under the influence of an applied electric field, they produce the well-known Townsend avalanche, or a total of

$$(9.118) \qquad n = n_0 \, \epsilon^{\alpha x}$$

electrons at any x for n_0 which start at one instant.

The average electron current which is observed when a burst of n_0 electrons is emitted from the cathode is calculated by averaging the instantaneous current,

$$(9.119) \qquad i_-(t) = n_0 \, \epsilon^{\alpha v_- t} \, \frac{ev_-}{d},$$

determined by combining equations 9.117 and 9.118 over the time the electrons flow, $0 < t < d/v_-$.

The averaging calculation gives

$$(9.120) \qquad \bar{i}_- = \frac{n_0 e v_-}{d} \, \frac{\displaystyle\int_0^{d/v_-} \epsilon^{\alpha v_- t} \, dt'}{\displaystyle\int_0^{d/v_-} dt} = \frac{n_0 e v_-}{d} \, \frac{(\epsilon^{\alpha d} - 1)}{\alpha d}.$$

The factor $(\epsilon^{\alpha d} - 1)/\alpha d$ is frequently called the "electron-current multiplication factor."

If the short burst of electrons is replaced by a continuous source of electrons giving out $n(t)$ electrons per sec, the resulting current is

(9.121)
$$\bar{i}_- = \frac{n(t)ev_-}{d} \frac{(\epsilon^{ad} - 1)}{ad}.$$

This result is suitable as long as $n(t)$ does not vary rapidly with t relative to the electron crossing time d/v_-.

The positive ion current as a function of time following a short photoelectric flash is next computed. Here the averaging process used for electrons is no longer appropriate, as the instantaneous current is desired. The current is obtained, as before, by the use of equation 9.117, with the proper value of n (the number of positive ions in the gap) inserted. The number n will be a function of time.

At the first instant after the flash, the ion avalanche has the form $n_0 \, (\epsilon^{ad} - 1)$, and hence,

(9.122)
$$i_+ = \frac{ev_+}{d} \, n_0 \, (\epsilon^{ad} - 1).$$

As this cloud of ions drifts in the electric field, ions are removed as they reach the cathode. At a time t after the pulse, a number of ions $n_0 \, (\epsilon^{av+t} - 1)$ have been removed, so that the positive ion current is

(9.123)
$$i_+ = \frac{n_0 ev_+}{d} \, (\epsilon^{ad} - \epsilon^{av+t}).$$

To this current must be added that caused by secondary electrons liberated from the cathode by the impact of the positive ions. For this calculation, some new symbols are introduced.

Let γ_i equal the number of electrons escaping from the cathode per incident positive ion. Let $n_+(t)$ equal the number of positive ions per second striking the cathode. $n_+(t)$ is a function of t.

The electron current arising from this secondary source is given by

(9.124)
$$i_- = n_+(t)e\gamma_i \frac{(\epsilon^{ad} - 1)}{ad}.$$

This equation is subject to a sharp discontinuity at $t = d/v_+$, as $n(t)$ is discontinuous at the instant the initial ion avalanche is finally swept out.

Returning to the positive ion current, the electrons $\gamma_i n_+(t)$ produce new positive ion avalanches, $\gamma_i n_+(t) \, (\epsilon^{ad} - 1)$. The sum of all these avalanches from 0 to t is needed to obtain the total number of new secondary ions. The positive ion current is therefore augmented by a term:

$$(9.125) \qquad i_+ = + \frac{ev_+}{d} \gamma_i \int_0^t n_+(t') \, (\epsilon^{\alpha d} - 1) \, dt'.$$

Again, at time t, these avalanches have been swept to varying degrees, so that the current should be diminished by a term:

$$(9.126) \qquad i_+ = - \frac{ev_+}{d} \gamma_i \int_0^t n_+(t') \, (\epsilon^{\alpha v_+(t-t')} - 1) \, dt'.$$

It may be noted that when t' is zero, the integrand describes the positive ions produced at $t' = 0$ and swept out at time t, while when $t' = t$, the integrand refers to the positive ions just produced at that instant, none of which have yet been swept out.

Combining equations 9.123, 9.125, and 9.126 gives the total positive ion current,

$$(9.127) \qquad i_+ = \frac{ev_+}{d} \left\{ n_0 \left(\epsilon^{\alpha d} - \epsilon^{\alpha v_+ t} \right) + \gamma_i \int_0^t n_+(t') \right.$$
$$\left. \left[\epsilon^{\alpha d} - \epsilon^{\alpha v_+(t-t')} \right] dt' \right\}.$$

At this point it will be assumed that $n_+(t')$ refers only to the time range $0 \lessgtr t' \lessgtr d/v_+$, and hence that i_+ is confined to this range too by the first term, which vanishes at $t = d/v_+$ and remains zero thereafter in the actual experiment. Finally, it may be pointed out about equation 9.127 that both i_+ and n_+ are unknown.

The two unknowns in equation 9.127 may be reduced to one by the following procedure: The ion current changes with time because (1) new ions are created, and (2) ions are swept out to the cathode. One may thus write

$$(9.128) \qquad \frac{di_+}{dt} = \frac{ev_+}{d} \left\{ \underset{(1)}{n_+(t) \gamma_i (\epsilon^{\alpha d} - 1)} - \underset{(2)}{n_+(t)} \right\} .$$

The numbers (1) and (2) under the two terms of equation 9.128 refer to the two sources of change of current described just above.

The derivative di_+/dt may also be found by direct differentiation of equation 9.127, noting that differentiation of a definite integral is called for in the process. The result is

$$(9.129) \qquad \frac{di_+}{dt} = \frac{ev_+}{d} \left\{ - n_0 \alpha v_+ \, \epsilon^{\alpha v_+ t} + \gamma_i n_+(t) (\epsilon^{\alpha d} - 1) \right.$$
$$\left. - \gamma_i \alpha v_+ \int_0^t n_+(t') \, \epsilon^{\alpha v_+(t-t')} dt' \right\} .$$

Equating the right sides of equations 9.128 and 9.129 gives

$$(9.130) \qquad n_+(t) = n_0 a v_+ \, \epsilon^{a v_+ t} + \gamma_i a v_+ \int_0^t n_+(t') \, \epsilon^{a v_+ (t - t')} \, dt'.$$

This is a linear integral equation of the second kind for $n_+(t)$ as a function of t. It may be solved as follows:

$$(9.131a) \qquad n_+ = n_0 a v_+ \, \epsilon^{a v_+ t} + \gamma_i a v_+ I(t)$$

and

$$(9.131b) \qquad \frac{dn_+}{dt} = n_0 a^2 v_+^2 \, \epsilon^{a v_+ t} + \gamma_i a v_+ \, \frac{dI}{dt}, \text{ but } \frac{dI}{dt} = n_+ + a v_+ I(t),$$

which has been used to derive equation 9.129.

From equation 9.131a, it follows that

$$(9.131c) \qquad \gamma_i \, \frac{dI}{dt} = \gamma_i \, n_+ + n_+ - n_0 a v_+ \, \epsilon^{a v_+ t}.$$

Combining equation 9.131c with equation 9.131b, there results

$$(9.132) \qquad \frac{dn_+}{dt} = n_0 a^2 v_+^2 \, \epsilon^{a v_+ t} + a v_+ n_+ \left(1 + \gamma_i - n_0 a^2 v_+^2 \, \epsilon^{a v_+ t} \right),$$

which integrates to

$$(9.133) \qquad n_+(t) = n_0 a v_+ \, \epsilon^{a v_+ (1 + \gamma_i) t}.$$

The correctness of the solution may be directly verified by substituting equation 9.133 into equation 9.130 and noting the resulting identity.

This solution may be substituted into equations 9.124 and 9.127, giving

$$(9.134) \qquad i_-(t) = \frac{n_0 e v_+}{d} \, \epsilon^{a v_+ (1 + \gamma_i) t} \, \gamma_i \, (\epsilon^{a d} - 1)$$

and

$$(9.135) \qquad i_+(t) = \frac{n e v_+}{d} \left\{ \epsilon^{a v_+ (1 + \gamma_i) t} \left(\frac{\gamma_i}{1 + \gamma_i} \, \epsilon^{a d} - 1 \right) + \frac{\epsilon^{a d}}{1 + \gamma_i} \right\}.$$

Equations 9.134 and 9.135 are valid in the range $0 \lessgtr t \lessgtr d/v_+$.

In the second cycle, i.e., for $d/v_+ \lessgtr t \lessgtr 2d/v_+$, all ions from the initial pulse have been swept out. There are terms in the basic equation for i_+ that are very similar to those in equation 9.127. All ions have their origin in the secondary processes occurring when positive ions strike the cathode. Not all of the ions produced by secondary processes in the first cycle $0 \lessgtr t \lessgtr d/v_+$ are swept out until $t = 2d/v_+$. In addition, new ions are created, and are partially swept out during the second cycle. One new symbol is needed:

Let $n_{1+}(t)$ equal the number of positive ions per second striking the cathode during the time interval $d/v_+ \lessgtr t \lessgtr 2d/v_+$. Then the current in this interval is given by

$$i_+ = \frac{ev_+\gamma_i}{d} \left\{ \int_0^t n_+(t') (\epsilon^{ad} - 1)\, dt' \right. \quad \text{(ions formed prior to } t=d/v_+\text{)}$$

$$+ \int_{d/v_+}^t n_{1+}(t')(\epsilon^{ad} - 1)\, dt' \qquad \text{(ions formed after } t=d/v_+\text{)}$$

(9.136)
$$- \int_0^{t-d/v_+} n_+(t')(\epsilon^{ad} - 1)\, dt' \qquad \begin{array}{l}\text{(ions of first term swept}\\ \text{out to } t-d/v_+\text{)}\end{array}$$

$$- \int_{t-d/v_+}^{d/v_+} n_+(t')(\epsilon^{av_+(t-t')} - 1)\, dt' \quad \text{(ions swept out to } t'=d/v_+\text{)}$$

$$\left. - \int_{d/v_+}^t n_{1+}(t')(\epsilon^{av_+(t-t')} - 1)\, dt' \right\}. \text{(ions swept out after } t'=d/v_+\text{)}$$

Proceeding, as before, to calculate di_+/dt, an integral equation in $n_{1+}(t)$ is formed, and is solved in the same way. The result is

(9.137) $\quad n_{1+}(t) = n_0 a v_+ \, \epsilon^{av_+(1+\gamma_i)t} \left\{ 1 - \epsilon^{-ad\gamma_i}\left[1 + av_+\gamma_i(t - d/v_+) \right] \right\}$.

From this result, the currents in the second cycle may be written as follows:

$$i_- = \frac{n_0 e v_+}{d} \, \epsilon^{av_+(1+\gamma_i)t} \, \gamma_i \, (\epsilon^{ad} - 1)$$

(9.138)
$$\left\{ 1 - \epsilon^{-ad\gamma_i} \left[1 + av_+\gamma_i\,(t - d/v_+) \right] \right\}$$

and

$$i_+ = \frac{n_0 e v_+}{d} \, \epsilon^{av_+(1+\gamma_i)t} \left(\frac{\gamma_i\,\epsilon^{ad}}{1 + \gamma_i} - 1 \right) \left\{ 1 - \epsilon^{-ad\gamma_i} \right.$$

(9.139)
$$\left. \left[1 + av_+\gamma_i\,(t - d/v_+) - \frac{\gamma_i}{1 + \gamma_i} \right] \right\} + \frac{n_0 e v_+}{d} \, \frac{\epsilon^{ad}}{1 + \gamma_i} \, \gamma_i \, \epsilon^{ad} .$$

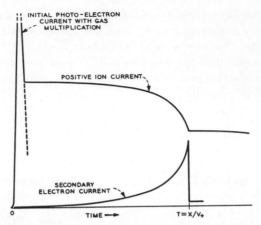

Fig. 9.47. Varney's schematic curves for current components to his exact solution of the fast-current equation in plane parallel geometry.

Comparison of equations 9.134 and 9.138 at $t = d/v_+$ shows that the results are not the same. The discontinuity may be computed by direct subtraction with this boundary value of t inserted, giving

$$(9.140) \qquad \Delta i_- = \frac{n_0 e v_+}{d} \, \epsilon^{ad} \, \gamma_i (\epsilon^{ad} - 1).$$

Equations 9.135 and 9.139 may be seen, on substitution of $t = d/v_+$, to give the same value of i_+. Hence, the positive ion current does not suffer a discontinuous change at the end of the first cycle. J. A. Hornbeck has given equation 9.140, obtained from other considerations.

For practical purposes, when $0 \lessgtr t \lessgtr d/v_+$, equations 9.138 and 9.139 take on the forms:

$$(9.141) \qquad i_- = \frac{n_0 e v_+}{d} \, \gamma_i (\epsilon^{ad} - 1) \, \epsilon^{av_+(1+\gamma_i)t}$$

and

$$(9.142) \quad i_+ = \frac{n_0 e v_+}{d} \left[\frac{\gamma_i}{1 + \gamma_i} \left(\epsilon^{ad} - 1 \right) \epsilon^{av_+(1+\gamma_i)t} + \frac{\epsilon^{ad}}{1 + \gamma_i} \right],$$

and the combined current measured becomes

$$(9.143) \quad i = \frac{n_0 e v_+}{d} \left\{ \left[\gamma_i (\epsilon^{ad} - 1) + \frac{\gamma_i}{1 + \gamma_i} \, \epsilon^{ad} - 1 \right] \epsilon^{av_+(1+\gamma_i)t} + \frac{\epsilon^{ad}}{1 + \gamma_i} \right\}.$$

Curves giving the components of equations 9.141 and 9.142 are shown schematically in figure 9.47.

Graphs of equation 9.143 are shown for ad, having values of 1, 3,

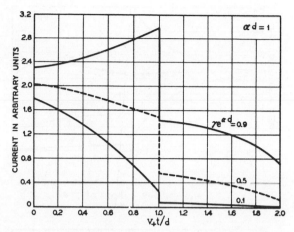

Fig. 9.48. Varney's solution of current equations for
$\alpha d = 1$ and various values of $\gamma_i\,\epsilon^{\alpha d}$.

and 5, in figures 9.48, 9.49, and 9.50, respectively. The horizontal
oscilloscope traces, appearing as dashed lines for two values of γ_i in
figures 9.49 and 9.50, have i constant with time, since v_+ and d are
constant. Thus, the time-dependent term in equation 9.143 vanishes
if the coefficient of the term is zero, or if

$$(9.144) \qquad \gamma_i\,(\epsilon^{\alpha d} - 1) + \frac{\gamma_i}{1 + \gamma_i}\ \epsilon^{\alpha d} - 1 = 0.$$

This relation may be solved for γ_i, giving

$$(9.145) \qquad \gamma_i = \left[\epsilon^{\alpha d}/(\epsilon^{\alpha d} - 1) \right]^{\frac{1}{2}} - 1.$$

Evaluation of γ_i in this fashion requires a knowledge of the time-
dependent α on this time scale. It would be desirable to evaluate α
from these data. An additional relation connecting αd and γ_i may be
found by comparing the height of the discontinuity at $t = d/v_+$ with the
current first, before or just after the jump. Simultaneous solution of
the resulting relation and equation 9.140 in principle evaluates γ_i and
αd. In practice, the fractional current change in discontinuity, as
depicted on the oscilloscope screen, is too insensitive to changes to
render this a practical method.

Hornbeck studied the value of α by measuring the area under the
initial peak of the oscillogram arising from the photo current. Other
methods could doubtless be found, but current precision is not adequate for such study except in order of magnitude.

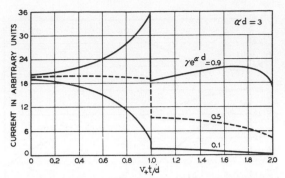

Fig. 9.49. Varney's solution of current equations for
$\alpha d = 3$ and various values of $\gamma_i \epsilon^{\alpha d}$.

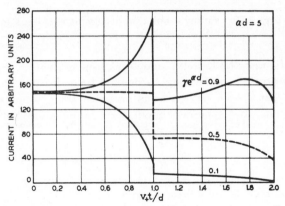

Fig. 9.50. Varney's solution of current equations for
$\alpha d = 5$ and various values of $\gamma_i \epsilon^{\alpha d}$.

Figure 9.51 shows three oscillograms of Varney for Kr^+ ions in pure Kr with Mo target. Potentials, reading upward, were 177, 182, and 187, respectively. Thus, potentials leading to the flat section can be made much finer than the ±5-volt range shown.

It is seen from the observed curves for i as a $f(t)$, that if v_+ is known, by arbitrarily fitting the data to the curve for various values of αd and of $\gamma_i \epsilon^{\alpha d}$, the quantity n_0 is evaluated. However, there should be more data available, and among other things, a/p is known as a function of X/p, so that under experimental conditions, αd can be assumed. Thus, with αd, more nearly complete evaluation of n_0 can be made, and from it, by matching curves, the value of $\gamma_i \epsilon^{\alpha d}$ and thus of γ_i can be derived. However, the value of the discontinuity Δi at $t = d/v_+$ at once gives γ_i from a knowledge of n_0 and $\epsilon^{\alpha d}$, using equation

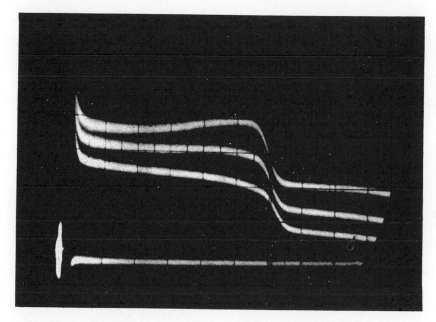

Fig. 9.51. Varney's oscillograms for current with Kr^+ ions on clean Mo for potentials 177, 182, and 187 volts, reading upward. Note that V can be chosen for i_+ constant with t to ± 1 volt.

9.140. It should be indicated that diffusion causes some rounding of corners, and introduces a little slope at the point where Δi_- occurs at $t = d/v_+$. This observed slope has been studied by Varney, and is caused by the holes in the anode which distort the field, and by diffusion. Correcting for the error caused by the holes, the value of the diffusion coefficient calculated is consistent with the value of mobility observed. Otherwise, observation and theory agree surprisingly well, and values of γ_i deduced are consistent with those expected from Hagstrum's work, if corrected for back diffusion.

With these comments, it is possible to leave Varney's discussion and return to the analysis of Hornbeck.

The finite time duration of the triggering light pulse does not alter the pattern of the i-t curves so long as it is short compared with ion transit times. Its diffusive influence is small compared with the real diffusion.

The photoelectrons from the cathode, liberated by the triggering light source with gas present, are reduced in number by back diffusion relative to those in vacuum. They travel with a uniform drift velocity, arriving at the anode in time intervals orders of magnitude greater than

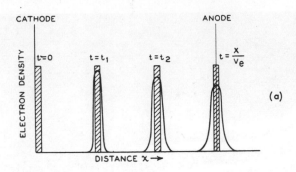

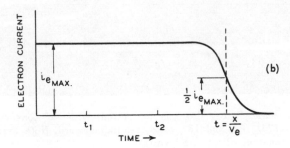

Fig. 9.52. The variation of the spatial electron-density curve with time, resulting from diffusion, in Hornbeck's study of fast components in a Townsend gap. The effect of this is indicated in the shape of the electron current-time curve shown at (b).

the transit time in vacuum. If the duration of the light pulse is short compared to the time of electron transit $t_e = d/v_-$, it is easy to measure v_-, as follows: The electron current is given by $i_- = v_-/d$ (number of electrons). With the sudden creation of electrons, the current rises abruptly from zero. It remains constant while the packet of n_0 photo-electrons traverses the distance d to the anode. As the first electrons reach the anode, i begins to fall, and with diffusion it drops off, as illustrated in figure 9.52. The time scale of the current is obviously much shorter than the currents caused by the Townsend processes.

The relation $t_- = d/v_-$ yields the electron-drift velocity. The value of t_- is taken from the point of inflection of the tail of the curve, as noted in figure 9.52 (b). If the duration of the light pulse t is not short compared to t_-, the theoretical expression for $i_-(t)$ is complicated, but has been derived by Hornbeck.

The experimental device for carrying out these studies is shown

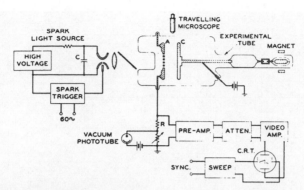

Fig. 9.53. Schematic diagram of Hornbeck and Varney's experimental arrangements for oscilloscopic study of the fast components of the Townsend gap and secondary mechanisms.

in figure 9.53. The Townsend gap was of conventional design, d being measured by a traveling microscope. The light impulse was produced by a triggered spark-gap source and circuit. The d.c. potential across the Townsend gap came from a battery of dry cells. The tube current flowed through the resistance R to ground. The iR drop was amplified and placed on the vertical deflection plates of a fast cathode ray oscillograph. To prevent blocking of the amplifiers by the large initial photo pulse, part of the incident light was reflected into a vacuum photo tube which developed current in phase with light. This current was introduced across a small resistor in the input of the amplifier, in order to develop a countervoltage to that from the tube current.

The light source had to give short, intense pulses, 0.1 μ sec long, and successive flashes had to be reproducible and equivalent. Used was a spark gap in air, triggered by an auxiliary spark from a third electrode, sparking through a hole in the cathode of the light-producing gap. The small capacity c discharged quickly across the gap. As there was a "time jitter," or lag, between trigger and main pulse, the time-axis sweep of the oscillograph was triggered by a pulse developed in a capacity pickup coupled to one of the main electrodes of the light gap.

The cleanup procedure was standard and adequate. The cathode was a standard BaO-coated nickel electrode, with a work function ϕe of slightly more than 2 volts. Shielding the circuits from the effects of the spark light source gave some concern, but was successfully achieved.

It is of interest to compare the observed oscillograph patterns with the predicted curves from theory, as shown in figures 9.44, 9.45, and

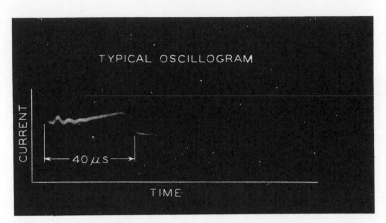

Fig. 9.54. Typical oscillogram observed by Hornbeck. Compare
this with figures 9.45 and 9.46 for interpretation.

9.46. Figure 9.54 is a typical oscillogram as observed in argon at
0.75 mm pressure with $X/p \simeq 75$ volts/cm × mm with $d = 1$ cm. The
large photoelectric pulse is not shown, as it was "bucked out." The
trace has all the anticipated qualitative features of figures 9.45 and
9.46. The initially constant current, followed by the ripples about
x_0 concealing it, the big discontinuity at $T = d/v$, followed by the
slope discontinuity at $T = 2d/v$, and the diffusive slopes and roundings
are clearly shown.

It should also be noted that Hornbeck's observations are quite
analogous to those of von Gugelberg (25), except that with Hornbeck's
superior facilities the accuracy and detail are far superior. Note that
von Gugelberg plotted the current against $1/t$ as d, and thus V increased. He observed three regions beginning at low d and V. If his
results had been plotted against t directly, he would have observed
the discontinuities caused by γ_i and γ_m, as observed in detail by
Hornbeck and Molnar. He also observed the spike caused by photo
effect and the electron current, which Hornbeck studied for his electron mobilities and which is shown in detail here. The theory used
by von Gugelberg is more complete than the elementary theory used
here, but is not graphically so descriptive, nor is it useful in evaluating γ, as are the procedures of Hornbeck and Varney.

In Hornbeck's report, some space is taken up in presenting his
ion-mobility data and their relation to other work and to Wannier's
theory. The results of this section of Hornbeck's study are presented
in detail in chapter I, as are those on ion-drift velocities by Varney.
However, it is of interest to note that the resolving power of this

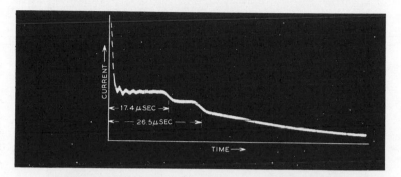

Fig. 9.55. Hornbeck's oscillogram in argon at $p_0 = 5.13$ mm, $X/p_0 = 36.6$ volts/cm-mm, showing *two* ions of different mobilities, later identified as A_2^+, fast ion, and A^+, slow ion.

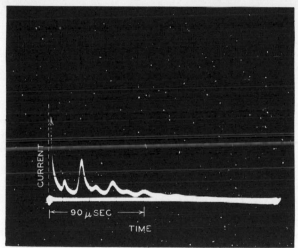

Fig. 9.56. Confirmation by Hornbeck of the two mobilities in A is shown in the oscillogram taken, using coaxial cylindrical geometry, where each ion mobility is characterized in its crossing time as a sharp peak. The resolution times are so good here that the successive peaks produced by γ_i at the outer cathode cylinder can be followed for four successive ionizing events. The two mobilities are clearly separated, and relative numbers of ions can be estimated.

method was sufficiently good to lead to very important new discoveries. Figure 9.55 shows Hornbeck's data in pure A at 5.13 mm pressure. Note the two breaks, indicating the presence of two drift velocities;

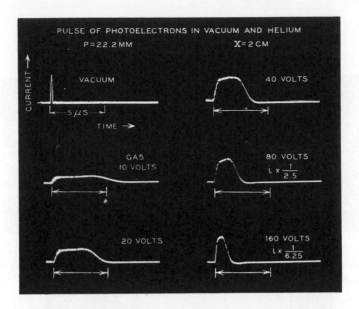

Fig. 9.57. Hornbeck's oscillograms for the fast photoelectric component in vacuum and in He gas. From the duration of these pulses, electron-drift velocities could be evaluated. Compare with theory, as shown in figure 9.52 (b).

the new one having twice the velocity of the other. In order further to confirm this, Hornbeck resorted to a coaxial cylindrical system in which the resolution was even sharper, and indeed confirmed the presence of two ionic carriers of widely different mobilities, as shown in the oscillogram of figure 9.56, taken for A gas. The second, fourth, and sixth peaks are for A^+ in A, while the first, third, and fifth correspond to A_2^+ ions. The relative areas under the curves give a measure of the relative numbers of ions in each class.

The appearance of two carriers within the short time of avalanche creation was indeed a surprise, especially when the two ions were present in commensurate amounts, as seen in the two oscillograms. While it was believed that He_2^+ ions of drift velocity about twice He^+ could be created from He^+ in triple impacts with He atoms, the creation in some 10^{-6} second by this process is impossible. Analysis by this technique, together with mass-spectrographic study, led Hornbeck and Molnar to discover that these He_2^+ ions were created from impact of excited atoms of the inert gases raised to levels within 3 volts or less of the ionizing potential with their own inert gas atoms. At times, 50% of the ions measured as α_i are created by this process, the other 50% being produced by direct electron impact.

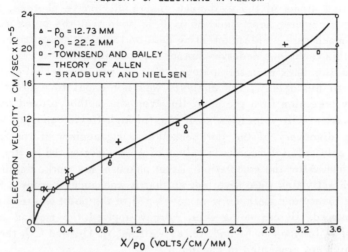

Fig. 9.58. Hornbeck's values of electron-drift velocities in He compared with the data of Townsend and Bailey and of Bradbury and Nielsen, as well as Harriet Allen's theory, at various values of X/p_0.

The study of the amplified photo current, as indicated, gives a means of measuring the electron velocities. In figure 9.57 the upper trace is the vacuum photo pulse as recorded by the oscillograph. Its very short duration should be noted. The subsequent pulses are those with gas filling of 22.2 mm and a 2-cm gap. The successive traces are for higher and higher potentials. The last two traces have been reduced in amplitude, as shown. It is clear that the traces conform with the theory of figure 9.52, and that the amplitude as well as the distance and time allow of evaluation of the electron-drift velocity. The area under the pulse should remain constant if n_0 is constant. Owing to decreasing loss through back diffusion, as the potential increases the area under the curve increases. In fact, the departure from constant n_0 can be determined by the increase in area.

Measured values of v for electrons in He are shown in figure 9.58, and compared with the data of Bradbury and Nielsen (III.3), Townsend and Bailey (III.4), and the theory of Harriet Allen (III.7), (III.21). Considering that the accuracy of pulse measurement is not much more than 10%, the agreement is remarkable. Hornbeck believes that the accuracy can readily be increased to 5%. In Ne and A, the form of the photoelectric pulse is not clear, since for both of these gases a sharp spike is observed at low X/p at the beginning of each pulse. Possibly this has to do with a photoelectric effect at the cathode which does not occur for He, or later in the phase for Ne and A, as the excited atoms of the avalanche absorb the active photons. However, no study has been made of it. It is seen that the pulse method without much care yields interesting data on the electron-drift velocity $v-$, and this technique deserves further exploitation.

While Hornbeck's initial purpose was to use the techniques described to evaluate γ_i, the analysis was not equal to evaluating γ with any precision from the data. However, the method proved fruitful in evaluating drift velocities $v+$ of ions in high fields, and led to the exciting discovery of the Hornbeck-Molnar mechanism of ionization, so that only order-of-magnitude values of γ_i were estimated by Hornbeck at the time. After the completion of that phase of his work, Hornbeck's research activities were diverted, so that it was under Varney's hands that the theory and methods were developed to the point where γ_i could be measured. Before doing this, Varney applied the method to the study of $v+$ for ions in Kr and Xe, as well as N_2, O_2, and CO, the data from which are presented in chapter I.

The techniques were of the best residual pressures, being kept down to 4×10^{-9} mm. The Mo electrodes were tested by mass spectrograph and had less than 0.01% impurity. The electrodes were induction-heated and then purified, and the cathode was stabilized by bombardment with currents up to perhaps 100 amperes, in bursts of short duration. When the sustaining voltage for the discharge reached the minimum values used in good tube manufacture, the surfaces were found to be gas-free and remarkably stable. They were again cleaned as needed. Cathode illumination giving i_0 was altered within limits by the use of screens. The plate separation d was reset, gas was admitted to pressure, and potential was raised by steps until patterns resembling the curves of figures 9.48 to 9.50, and such as those shown in the oscillogram of figure 9.51, were observed. The potential leading to an initial flat portion could be set to within ± 1 volt. The value of a for the pure gases used was taken for the values of X/p and p reduced to $0°$ C., as given by Kruithoff. Correction was made for using $a(d-x_0)$ in place of ad where needed. Data were calculated according to equation 9.140.

Values were obtained for γ_i for Ne, A, and Kr on Mo at various values of X/p. Some data were also obtained with A on BaO. The cathode was coated with $BaCO_3$, and activated by glow discharge in A. This surface was extremely sensitive to any gaseous conduction current through the tube, and was more strongly activated *or deactivated* in a short interval of measuring time. Changes in surface activity ran γ_i between the limits 0.5 and 10^{-3}. The curves for Ne^+, A^+, and Kr^+

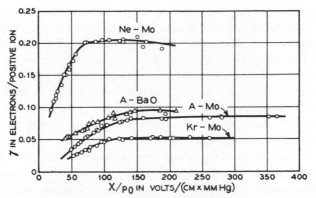

Fig. 9.59. Varney's values of γ_i for ions in Ne,
A, and Kr on clean Mo, and in A on BaO.

on clean Mo, and for A^+ on BaO, in a stable but intermediate state, are shown in figure 9.59. While the curves for Mo appeared to approach the origin as X/p was reduced, those for BaO in various stages of activation resembled those of figure 9.59 to different ordinate scales, but did not appear to approach 0 as X/p decreased. This difference is of importance, since the oscilloscope patterns fail to appear at $X/p \sim 40$ volts per cm times mm Hg for Mo, while they are observable to 22 for the coated cathode. As X/p is lowered, ad is also decreased. If proper oscillograms are to be observed, $\gamma_i \ \epsilon^{ad}$ must be near 0.5.

The behavior of γ_i with cathode surface is directly related to two effects in the presence of inert gases which could form second layers on Mo. As Parker's work (49) showed for A^+ ions on Ta and Pt covered with layers of gas, the value of γ_i rises from lower values of the order of 2 volts to near the value for clean Ta, and not quite as high as for clean Pt, when the ion energy gets to about 100 e.v. These changes were great compared to those observed by Varney. The energies of these ions observed by Varney at $X/p = 200$ ranged from a volt down. Thus, their γ_i values were in the most sensitive part of their range. The other phenomenon affecting the values of γ_i observed was the loss of electrons emitted by potential liberation through back diffusion to the cathode. This loss should not be very great at an X/p greater than 50. It would be larger for electrons emitted with higher energies at the lower X/p. There are not enough data on controls possible to yield a satisfactory explanation of the trend of Varney's curves with X/p, especially since his ion energies are indeed very low. Possibly at 0 ion energy with gas monolayers on Mo, γ_i should go to 0, while with BaO, which is a good secondary emitter of low ϕe, γ_i may not be 0 at $X/p = 0$.

The absolute values of γ_i observed by Varney for Ne^+, A^+, and Kr^+ ions on clean Mo at $X/p = 200$ were 0.2, 0.083, and 0.053, respectively. Values observed by Hagstrum (15) of γ_i for 10-volt He^+ ions on pure Mo were 10% less than on pure W. For pure W, Hagstrum observed values of 0.24, 0.094, and 0.047 for 10-e.v. Ne^+, A^+, and Kr^+ ions on clean W. Thus, the values for γ_i obtained by Varney's measurements are probably reasonably correct values. Varney's values of γ_i represent γ_i with no action of γ_m. If radiation from excited states should occur in the range of 10^{-8} sec, Molnar has stated that it could account for 7% of γ_i in his own studies, which were similar to Varney's. Possibly, then, there may be a correction to γ so that γ_i will be less than observed. However, the author is not inclined to agree with this. Any γ_p in the inert gases will be very much delayed and diffused as a result of imprisonment of resonance radiation, and the photon γ_p from excited molecules occurs only at higher pressures and in intervals of the order of a few microseconds only. Thus, in the crossing times of 10^{-5} sec, the secondary γ_p processes in inert gases will act to add and round or diffuse the corners, especially at the beginning and just after an ion crossing time. Since there is no indication of excessive action of this sort, the γ_p processes can be considered unimportant in Varney's study, and the γ observed is probably largely γ_i. The rapid aging of clean Mo surfaces reported by Molnar (57) did not influence Varney's results. γ_i was constant over several hours. After twenty-four hours with pumping, values of γ_i were usually some 10% below previous values. Any number of seemingly trivial abuses of the tube appeared to decrease the value of γ_i to 10^{-3} or 10^{-4}, as might be expected.

Again, as in all this work, the accuracy of the values of a of Kruithoff, as applied to this study, become of import, since the changes in the exponential function with small changes in a can so overshadow the values of γ_i. As indicated by Hornbeck, the relation connecting ad and γ by comparing the height of the discontinuity, at $t = d/v_+$, with the current just before the jump, gives a second equation which, combined with equation 9.140, can yield a and γ. This change, as noted on the screen, is not too accurate, and is insensitive to changes in ad and γ, thereby proving to be of little value for the purpose for which it is meant.

Enough has been given to show the value of these techniques. It is now of interest to describe recent applications to studies in other than plane parallel geometry, where very interesting data on γ are being obtained because of the high resolving power of these techniques.

§ 17. The Method of E. J. Lauer and of L. Colli and U. Facchini in Coaxial Cylindrical Geometry with Low X/p at the Cathode.

The time-resolution analyses of secondary mechanisms may fittingly be closed with a variant of the uniform-field study having a higher resolving power. Using a coaxial cylindrical Geiger counter tube with positive wire and brass cylindrical cathode. L. Colli, E. Gatti, and U. Facchini (50) triggered avalanches by means of α particles and β rays. The α particles came from a thin layer of uranium on the outer cathode cylinder, which emitted particles at a rate slow compared to the time scale of the oscilloscope sweep. The triggering electrons were created at random in the cylinder, yet with adequate amplification yielded pulses which were highly resolved. From the nature of the pulses, the workers concluded that the secondary mechanism in this system was a γ_p at the cathode and that there was no photoionization *in the gas* in this tube.

The advantages of such triggering appealed to E. J. Lauer (26), then working on a similar geometry in the author's laboratory. Lauer therefore made an alpha-particle source, consisting of some polonium at the tip of a wire inserted into a capillary tube of which the axis was closely parallel to the anode wire. This tube constituted an α-particle gun, emitting one α particle per second along a trajectory parallel to and close to the cathode cylinder. The source could be closed off by a shutter when not in use. Such an α-particle track of some 3.4 cm length in A at 760 mm pressure generates some ten thousands of electrons along a path about 0.01 or less cm in diameter in some 10^{-8} sec. These electrons form avalanches very close to the anode wire. When the avalanche electrons are engulfed in the anode, the positive ion space charge is disclosed out in the gap. This induces a current pulse from ground to cathode cylinder through a suitable resistance, from which an amplified signal can be observed in the oscilloscope. As time goes on, the ions move toward the cathode cylinder. If they produce no secondary electrons, the current terminates as the last ions reach the cathode.

Unlike the case for uniform field geometry, the shape of the current pulse has not been computed for this geometry, but this is not necessary. However, the shape of the current pulse is nicely observed in figure 9.60, which shows the pulse observed in H_2 gas at various pressures and potentials on the platinum anode wire. It is clear that by measuring the length of the pulse, the transit time τ_i of the positive ions can be determined. With a cylinder of radius b and anode wire of radius a at an applied potential V, the drift velocity of the ions per unit electrical field, or the mobility k_+, can be evaluated by

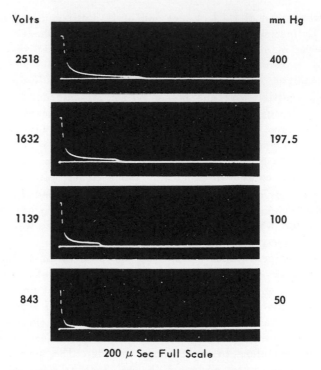

Volts

2518   400

1632   197.5

1139   100

843   50

mm Hg

200 μ Sec Full Scale

Fig. 9.60. Lauer's current oscillograms in pure H_2 in coaxial cylindrical geometry with slow sweep.

$$(9.146) \qquad k_+ = \frac{b^2 \log_e b/a}{2\tau V}$$

in the absence of space charge. If space charge is present to any extent, then

$$(9.147) \qquad k_+ = \frac{b^2 \log_e b/a}{2\tau (V + q_1 \log_e b/a)} \, ,$$

with q_1 the space charge per unit length of anode wire, and r the time for half the ions to be collected. The quantity q_1 can be determined from the area under the oscillograms for a given pulse by dividing it by the resistance across which the signal was generated. The space-charge corrected equation given was derived by H. den Hartog and F. H. Muller (61). For most investigations cited here the correction is of the order of 0.1%.

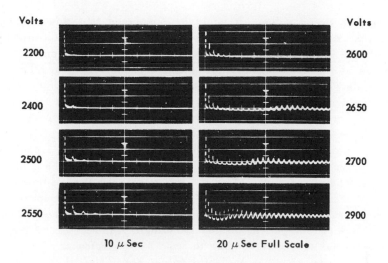

Fig. 9.61. Lauer's oscillograms in pure H_2 with fast sweep.
Timing marks are 2 microseconds.

Owing to the geometry, in which the field is high at the anode, the fraction of τ_i spent in transit near the wire is so small that the value of k_+ represents the value of k_+ at the X/p corresponding to that from the cathode up to two-thirds the gap length. The plots for k_+ against pressure were strictly linear, and yielded a drift velocity for pure H_2 gas of 13.4 cm^2/volt sec, probably corresponding to that for the H_3^+ ion. There was no γ_i visible for this ion in the X/p region of low values extending from 0.66 to 1.43 for the clean, H_2-coated Ni cathode used in this study. This indicated that γ_i in H_2 was of the order of 1×10^{-5} or less, in conformity with Hale's data for Pt.

Observing the initial portion of the pulse with a faster sweep rate on the oscilloscope, the sequence of events noted in figure 9.61 was observed. Here it is seen that as V and consequently X was raised at constant p, a series of small, sharply defined secondary pulses appeared, separated by about 1 microsecond in time after the first alpha-particle avalanche pulse. As potential increases the sequence of these secondary pulses increases. It is noted that following the α-particle avalanche, the amplitude of the successive pulses decreases down to a standard value as the sequence lengthens. Ignoring, for the moment, smaller fluctuations in amplitude, it is noted that the sequence becomes continuous and self-sustaining at a potential inter-mediate between 2,600 and 2,700 volts on the anode. From the time interval between pulses, it might be suspected that this represents the time required for a photon from the avalanche at the anode to reach the cathode and liberate a secondary photoelectron, which arrives at the anode with a new avalanche some 10^{-6} sec later. To test this, Lauer took the electron-drift velocities of Bradbury and Nielsen and integrated them across the gap. This gave a transit time agreeing within 2% with the interval between the sharp secondary peaks.

The value of γ can be computed from the relative areas under successive peaks, once the amplification factor $\epsilon^{\int a dx}$ can be evaluated. If n_0 ion pairs are produced by the α particle, the first avalanche has $n_0 \; \epsilon^{\int a dx}$ ion pairs. If associated with the production of these ions, γ electrons are liberated from the cathode by one of the secondary processes per ion pair produced, then there will be $\gamma n_0 \; \epsilon^{\int a dx}$ secondary electrons produced, leading to $\gamma n_0 \; \epsilon^{2 \int a dx}$ electrons in the second pulse and $\gamma^2 n_0 \; \epsilon^{3 \int a dx}$ in the third pulse, etc. Thus, if the ratio r is the observed

$$\frac{\text{area under } n\text{th pulse}}{\text{area under } (n-1)\text{th pulse}} \; ,$$

then, since $r = \gamma \; \epsilon^{\int a dx}$, it follows that $\gamma = r / \epsilon^{\int a dx}$.

In the later techniques, Colli and Facchini so amplified their α-particle pulse that n_0 could be evaluated, and then $n = n_0 \; \epsilon^{\int a dx}$ yielded $\epsilon^{\int a dx}$ at once when n was measured with an amplifying field active. There is some error here, as the field causing multiplication probably extracts more electrons from the α-ray track than does the sweeping field used to give n_0. It is possible to evaluate n_0 directly from the range-energy curves for α-particle ionization. Such calculation cannot be too far wrong, but could vary with traces of impurity in the inert gas used. It is also possible to calculate $\epsilon^{\int a dx}$ from the known field variation with x and known values of a if the value of X/p is such that the $a/X = \eta_-(X/p)$ curve has not reached its peak, as indicated in chapter VIII. If X/p is higher than this at the anode, $\epsilon^{\int a dx}$ is lower than the true multiplication factor, possibly by a factor of 2 to 6.

Of course, it is always possible to measure n_0 and n in a separate tube of the same design, in which the current giving n_0 is caused by a photo current from the Ni cylinder and can be measured, and then applying the various fields used, yielding n. This is the manner in which Morton and Johnson proceeded, and yields the best results. The methods tried by Lauer and Huber also used a current n_0 produced by external γ rays and measured n. Huber's data in N_2 gave γ_i computed from $\epsilon^{\int a dx}$ and from the α-particle range energy curves within

TABLE 9.7

Lauer's values for γ_i and γ_p on outgassed Ni for pure A and H_2 at values of X/p indicated. The values for γ_c are those at the cathode, corrected for back diffusion by Theobald

Argon p (mm)	X/p^*	γ_i	γ_c
25	3.12	7.8×10^{-4}	0.035
50	1.92	7.0×10^{-4}	0.051
100	1.18	4.0×10^{-4}	0.040
200	0.79	0.6×10^{-4}	0.006
400	0.52	0.2×10^{-4}	0.002
Hydrogen	X/p	γ_p	γ_c
100	1.43	6.9×10^{-4}	0.014
200	1.04	1.5×10^{-4}	0.004
400	0.79	0.74×10^{-4}	0.002
650	0.66	0.49×10^{-4}	0.0015

*X/p is the value at the cathode.

20% up to the point where Morton and Johnson indicate deviations. Underestimate of $\epsilon^{\int \alpha dx}$ would give γ too large, and this appears to be so above $X/p > 450$ in Huber's work in N_2. Lauer also estimated his γ_i values to be good to ± 20%. It is believed that improvements in the values of γ obtained from such studies are possible, if desired.

The values observed by Lauer for γ_i in A and for γ_p in H_2 as a function of X/p are given in table 9.7 as γ_i or γ_p. Since there is much back diffusion at the cathode for the low X/p active, the results must be corrected for this factor. The values for the γ corrected for back diffusion by Theobald's relations are also shown in the table in the last column as γ_c.

Again regarding the pulses for H_2: When the self-sustaining corona appears above $V = 2,650$ volts, it is noted that there is a slow-amplitude oscillation of the γ_p peaks. This can be attributed to the accumulation of positive space charge from previous pulses near the anode. This reduces the effective field X_m at the anode, and somewhat reduces amplification $\epsilon^{\int \alpha dx}$. With reduced γ_p pulses, the space charge accumulates more slowly, and as the more intense charge from the initial avalanches drifts away some mm from the anode region, the pulses recover in amplitude, only again to build up a space charge. This action is clearly noted in the oscillograms, and it is gratifying to get such clean-cut visual verification of the space-charge action, which was indicated as far back as 1937 by the author in Trichel and

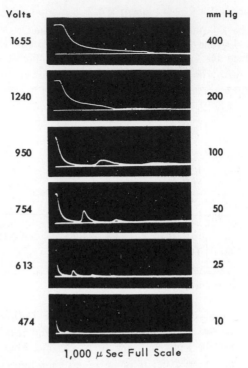

Volts   mm Hg

1655   400

1240   200

950   100

754   50

613   25

474   10

1,000 μ Sec Full Scale

Fig. 9.62. Lauer's oscillograms at slow sweep
in pure A, at various pressures.

Kip's point to plane corona studies. It is seen that the values of γ_p
in H_2 are small, even when corrected for back diffusion. Their variation with pressure indicates possible absorption of the radiations in
the gas on their way to the cathode. The values of γ_p in H_2 cannot be
compared with any known values, since the value of X/p where photons
are generated is very high, and the photons act on Ni at a point where
X/p is low. It is seen, however, that under these conditions γ is at
least 90% a γ_p in H_2 with Ni cathode, and it alone yields a self-
sustaining discharge in the form of an obviously low-order current.

In argon gas the situation is quite different. Figure 9.62 shows
Lauer's observations in argon at various pressures with slow sweep.
It is seen that at lower p and higher X/p there appears a clean-cut
γ_i at the point where the positive ions strike the cathode. It is noted
that at higher pressures only a small pip is observed, and at lower
p (50 mm) and higher X a sequence of a few pips follows. However,
at no point does a sequence of continuous γ_i pips indicating a self-
sustaining discharge occur. Actually, as later indicated, at ~ 50 mm

Colli and Facchini (50), on Lauer's tube, found the self-sustaining corona to be caused by 50% γ_i and 50% delayed γ_p.

Lauer was able to measure the ion-transit time, and found that the ions were largely A_2^+ ions of a mobility 1.94 cm²/volt sec. At 50 mm, Colli and Facchini, on Lauer's tube, later observed pulses of A_2^+ and A^+ that were about commensurate. The values of γ_i computed by Lauer are shown in table 9.7. It is seen that even corrected for back diffusion, the values are low compared to those observed by Parker on clean Ta or Pt by A^+ ions. While γ_i for A_2^+ and A^+ ions does differ somewhat, the differences in values observed at low and high pressures cannot be ascribed to this effect. It is possible that the high work function of Ni and layers of impurity gases condensed on the Ni cylinder were largely responsible. This is made plausible, since while Lauer had reasonably clean techniques, they could not compare with those of Parker and Hagstrum in studies of this sort, and background impurities from the A could deposit on the Ni.

In Lauer's published paper (26) he stated that he observed no γ_p in A, although at his highest pressure of 400 mm he observed a single weak γ pip, possibly attributable to γ_p. Judged by the standards established by the γ_p in H_2, the uncertainty as to the pip being a γ_p in A was logical. As his cylinders were of relatively smaller radius and his study was confined to pressures below 400 mm for A, he was only able to observe that with fast sweep his initial pulse was followed by a second pip, displaced toward the longer time intervals by somewhat *more* than an electron crossing time and of considerably greater duration, and he could not observe a sequence as in H_2.

Quite independently, L. Colli and U. Facchini (50) had studied supposedly pure A, at first with a brass cathode cylinder and later with one of Ni. Their cathodes had a larger radius than Lauer's, and they worked up to 1,000 mm of A. In consequence, at higher potentials they observed γ_p sequences of several pulses that were broadened and separated by more than the electron-transit times.

That a γ_p should appear in A at all was unexpected, so that Lauer's neglect of his peculiar pip can readily be understood. It may be added that at somewhat lower pressures (140 mm) Colli and Facchini, with their larger cylinder, also observed the same smeared-out single pulse seen by Lauer. Actually, in the inert gases and especially in A, the excited states are the metastable levels $^3P_2$ at 11.49 e.v. and $^3P_0$ at 11.61 e.v., with the $^3P_1$ resonance state at 11.58 e.v. Above this lie the higher excited levels, converging to the ionization limit at 15.86 e.v. Now the lifetimes of $^3P_2$ and $^3P_0$ are very long, and the resonance radiation of $^3P_1$ to the ground state is imprisoned for indefinite periods in the gas before reaching the cathode. With this imprisonment there is a good chance that most of these levels will go to the lower $^3P_2$ state by impacts with A atoms before reaching the cathode. All other electron transitions are of less than 4 e.v. energy, and thus emit light in the visible and near ultraviolet. They can yield no γ_i from Ni, the work function of which is 4.5 to 5 e.v. The delayed action and correspondence with the author concerning Lauer's work led Colli and Facchini to look for some secondary action in A that might lead to this process.

It was believed that ultraviolet photons of energy greater than 5 e.v. were being produced. To detect these, the cylindrical cathode was replaced by a set of Ni rods set on a circular frame coaxial with the anode wire. The rods were surrounded by a glass sleeve, coated inside with Apiezon L, a substance of low vapor pressure known to fluoresce brightly in the visible under ultraviolet radiation. The outside glass container was painted with a white diffusing material and the whole tube was viewed by a photomultiplier. The Apiezon L was tested and shown to fluoresce for no more than 5×10^{-7} sec, and the electrical α-particle avalanche was shown to last no more than 5×10^{-7} sec. The luminous pulses in the· tube were then studied at low multiplication (10-50) to avoid secondary effects for different pressures of A, ranging from 70 and 700 mm. Analysis of the pulse slopes indicated that they were given by an equation of the form $\epsilon^{-t/\tau_A} - \epsilon^{-t/\tau_m}$. Decay time τ_m was independent of pressure, and had a value of roughly 3.4 microseconds. The time τ_A, however, was pressure-dependent, and was found to vary as $1/9p^2$ with pressure.

These relations indicate that the radiation is created by a sequence of two reactions; one pressure-dependent and forming a radiating structure by triple impact, the other an emission act of long duration, possibly from a *quasi*-metastable state. The pressure-dependent reaction is of the same form as that observed by Molnar and Phelps (62) for the destruction of the $^3P_2$ metastable state of A by triple impacts to form an excited A_2^* molecule between 1 and 10 mm A pressure. The reactions assumed are:

$$A^m + 2A \rightarrow A_2^* + A$$

$$A_2^* \rightarrow A_2 + h\nu \rightarrow 2A.$$

The molecular state of A_2 is possibly slightly metastable, lifetime $\sim 3.5 \times 10^{-6}$ sec instead of 10^{-8} sec, and the photons $h\nu$ emitted must be of an energy greater than 5 volts and are not absorbed by the A gas, so that they liberate photoelectrons from the cathode yielding a γ_p. A further study of the photons emitted, using various absorbing screens of LiF, quartz, etc., led to the conclusion that the more lengthy of the photons emitted were around 1,250 Å, equivalent to 10.1 e.v. This roughly gives the heat of dissociation of A_2 plus the energy going to Coulomb separation as about 2 e.v.

Colli and Facchini observed that as pressure and potential were raised, the succession of γ_p pulses increased, and proved that the self-sustaining discharge threshold $\gamma_p \, \epsilon^{\int a dx} = 1$ in A at pressures above 200 mm was one due to a γ_p action, the γ_i action observed by Lauer no doubt slightly aiding. At pressures from 50 mm down, the situation is altered. Resonance radiation may begin to get through to trigger photons directly. Fewer will degrade to $^3P_2$ states, and these will lead to increased molecular photon delay times and less effective cathode action. The value of X/p at the cathode increases and γ_i action relatively increases. Self-sustaining discharge below 50 mm will then be largely by γ_i with some help from γ_p.

Colli and Facchini originally reported that they observed no γ_i action. Their A was initially not very pure, but was cleaned by circulation over hot Ca and Mg during observation. Their cathodes were outgassed at only 350° C. In the author's laboratory, with Lauer's techniques, Colli and Facchini observed γ_i pulses. If only 99.5% pure A was used, or on short exposure to air, with subsequent evacuation and use of *pure* A, no γ_i pulses were revealed. Outgassing to 900° C. or more for hours restored γ_i pulse with pure A gas.

Before going on to other gases, it is to be noted that Lauer examined H_2 with 0.1% and 1% of O_2 gas added. He did not push his investigations with these gases very far. Addition of the O_2 acted to damp and possibly diffuse the pulses due to γ_p in H_2. Thus, at a point near but below self-sustaining corona in pure H_2, the 0.1% O_2 caused the sequence to interrupt after some 9 pulses, and with 1% O_2 after only 4 γ_p peaks were discernible. This does not mean that the photon action ceased, but that owing to dispersion of ionizing events by other actions, such as photoelectric ionization in the gas (at 1% O_2 certainly), as well as by negative ion formation, the regularity of the pulses was interrupted by diffusely delayed ionizing events coming from electrons produced at random in the gas or by negative ions coming in at irregular intervals. The diffuse currents caused by such dispersion of the otherwise regular sequences triggered by the a particle would not contribute to the fast-sweep oscilloscope pattern.

Figure 9.63 illustrates the effect of O_2 on the regular *ion pulses*, with slower sweep in pure H_2 when 0.1% (top trace) and 1% of O_2 (bottom trace) were added to pure H_2. It is noted that the amplitude

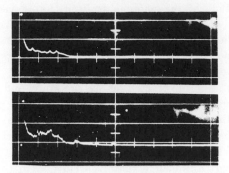

Fig. 9.63. Lauer's oscillograms, showing effect of 0.1% and 1% of O_2 on
the traces with slow sweep in pure H_2 owing to negative ion formation.

of the initial peaks is reduced, while the area under the curve caused
by ion movement in pure H_2 is enhanced. In fact, irregular pulses are
discernible, superposed on the otherwise smooth curves in pure H_2.
This stems from delay effects caused by attachment of the α-particle
avalanche electrons to make O_2^- ions on their way to the anode. The
electrons attach largely in the low-field regions and traverse only
part of the gap as ions, thus arriving at the anode at times intermediate
between zero and positive ion crossing time as negative and positive
ion-drift velocities are commensurate, though the O_2^- ions in H_2 should
be somewhat slower than H_3^+ ions. Such attaching electrons fail to
register in the current, owing to the initial α-particle avalanche. Thus,
they reduce the initial avalanche peak. As they lose their electrons
in the high-field region near the anode, they yield delayed avalanches
which register as current later in the cycle on the slow sweep and
thus increase the area under the tail of the curves, owing to ion movement. If there were very many electrons attaching, so that the delayed
ionization was continuous along the ion-movement curve, all that
would appear would be a decrease in the initial height of the pulse
with increased area under the ion-movement curve. There would probably be some slight total loss of ions, since some of these ions do
not make avalanches as large as those of the free electrons.

With the relatively slight attachment of electrons occurring in H_2
that has only 0.1% O_2 at say 400 mm pressure, the effect will be that
statistical fluctuations in the location of attachment will lead to the
arrival of small groups of ions at different times, yielding their own
pulses above the current due to ion movement. Lauer, using statistical
considerations and his amplification factor, was in fact able to determine the probability of electron attachment from the fluctuations

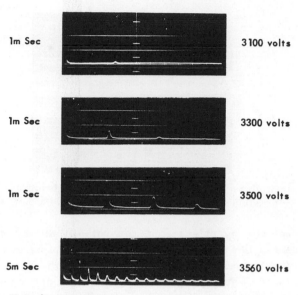

Fig. 9.64. Huber's oscillograms in pure N_2, outgassed Ni cathode, with coaxial cylindrical geometry, showing γ_i pulses at various slow sweep rates and potentials.

observed with 0.1% O_2. These values agreed in order of magnitude with known attachment probabilities. It is to be noted that with 1% O_2, the effect of the secondary peaks superposed on ion movement is much increased.

It is now of interest to turn to the observations of E. Huber (49), who carried over the studies of Lauer to N_2 and O_2. In very pure N_2, the studies from 25 to 600 mm revealed that with increasing potential on the anode wire, the initial α-particle pulse was followed by first one, then two, then three clearly defined pulses after an ion crossing time. Such pulses are shown for N_2 at 400 mm in figure 9.64. When the potential reached a proper value, a self-sustaining discharge set in, with initially regularly spaced, self-sustaining secondary pulses of constant amplitude following the triggering. In a few milliseconds these regular pulses washed out, leaving an irregular, continuous corona with minor fluctuations above the steady current value shown in the lower trace of figure 9.65. The top trace in figure 9.65 was taken at 10 volts below onset. The onset was characterized by a discontinuous rise in current to a few microamperes.

The clearly defined spacing between secondary γ_i pulses corresponds to one ion crossing time. With faster sweep there was no in-

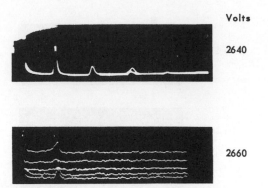

Fig. 9.65. Huber's oscillograms in pure N_2, just below and just above self-sustaining corona at 200 mm pressure, with slow sweep.

dication of any γ_p pulses from the cathode at any pressure. The smoothness of the γ_i pulses precludes any photoionization in the gas, or electron attachment, as might be expected for N_2.

That the self-sustaining corona current did not show a series of ion pulses spaced at uniform time intervals, is to be expected. Even if triggered by a single α-particle pulse, it is highly improbable that a regular sequence would continue indefinitely. The initial sequence started in a thin sheet of ionization processes, going radially from the anode wire to the cathode cylinder and passing through the initial track of the α-particle. With enough repetition, the successive diffusion of electron avalanches in space and time and the diffusion of the succeeding ion groups by self-repulsion must broaden the width of the peaks in time and spread the discharge into increasingly larger-angled, wedge-shaped sections, extending from cathode to anode until it completely fills the cylinder. Thus, after some thousands of self-sustaining sequences, the 0.1 mm radial diffusion of each electron avalanche will have spread the discharge radially all around the wire, with ionizing acts at different points no longer synchronized, and therefore almost continuous in time. It is also certain that delayed emission from the many forbidden transitions at higher energy from N_2 states must have acted to diffuse and spread the discharge in space and time about the anode, through delayed and feeble γ_i action. Again, localized sequences of pulses will build up space charges which may extinguish the discharge locally, while it spreads to other nonfouled regions. Such choking action will cause the current fluctuations. As potential increases above threshold, these fluctuations will reduce in magnitude and relatively to the current.

TABLE 9.8

Huber's values for γ_i for N_4^+ ions in pure N_2, with amplification factor measured and calculated in columns (a) and (b), while γ_i', corrected for back diffusion, is shown in column (e)

p (mm Hg)	(a) γ_i (M meas.)	(b) γ_i (M calc.)	(c) $(X/p)_{max}$	(d) j/j_0	(e) γ_i'
600	0.6×10^{-3}	0.7×10^{-3}	220	3.0×10^{-2}	2.0×10^{-2}
500	0.7×10^{-3}	1.0×10^{-3}	230	3.1×10^{-2}	2.3×10^{-2}
400	1.1×10^{-3}	1.2×10^{-3}	250	3.4×10^{-2}	3.2×10^{-2}
300	1.0×10^{-3}	1.3×10^{-3}	290	3.7×10^{-2}	2.7×10^{-2}
200	1.2×10^{-3}	1.5×10^{-3}	360	4.1×10^{-2}	2.9×10^{-2}
100	1.5×10^{-3}	2.4×10^{-3}	530	5.9×10^{-2}	2.5×10^{-2}
50	1.4×10^{-3}	3.4×10^{-3}	780	6.9×10^{-2}	2.0×10^{-2}

The drift velocities and mobilities of the positive ions in N_2 were calculated from the observed intervals, and gave a nice linear plot for the mobilities between pressures of 25 and 600 mm. This led to a value of the reduced mobility of 2.53 ± 0.08 cm²/volt sec at 760 mm and 20° C. Correction for the time spent by the ions in the high-field region indicates that only at 25 and 50 mm does the fraction of the time spent at high fields, and thus altered mobilities, exceed 1%. Mitchell and Ridler (I.19), at low X/p, reported a value of 2.67 cm²/volt sec at 20° C. Varney's recent data, from $X/p = 38$ to 1,000; extrapolate to good agreement with Mitchell and Ridler's values at low X/p. At low X/p Varney found one ion, and at high X/p he found another ion. These he identified as N_4^+ and N_2^+ ions, respectively, in conformity with Luhr's mass-spectrographic data. Thus, it is fairly safe to identify the present ion as N_4^+. The value of $K = 2.53$ observed here will place this ion exactly on Mitchell and Ridler's mass-dispersion curve for ions in N_2 gas if its mass corresponds to N_4^+.

The values of γ_i were computed from the areas under successive peaks divided by the amplification factor computed from the range of α particles and their specific ionization, and calculated by the integral of αdx. The results are shown in table 9.8, in columns (a) and (b), respectively. Column (c) gives the maximum values of X/p at the anode wire, which indicate that the multiplication factor M, as calculated from $\epsilon^{\int \alpha dx}$, should underestimate the ionization and overestimate γ_i for the data at 100 and at 50 mm, since $(X/p)_{max} > 450$ for these two cases. Using Theobald's data for correction for back diffusion j/j_0, assuming the average energy of electron emission as 3 e.v., it is seen that in column (e) the values of γ_i' for N_4^+ ions on clean but N_2-coated Ni at low X/p, amounting to at best 0.6 e.v. ion energy, are surprisingly constant, and equal to 2×10^{-2}, or 2%. For a mixture of N_2^+ and N^+ ions on N_2-coated, clean Pt and Ta, Parker (49) reports that $\gamma_i = 0.01$. Since the Theobald corrections for back diffusion could be off by a factor of 2, the agreement here is good.

While the actions induced by O_2 in N_2 end primarily with anode actions resulting from photoionization in the gas, it is of value to report Huber's observations briefly, as these actions are likely to be encountered by others in fast-sweep analysis, and must be differentiated from the more conventional secondary behavior. By accidental contamination caused by flashing supposedly clean W filaments as getters, as revealed by mass-spectroscopic analysis, from 0.2% to 2% of O_2 was introduced into the gas. In this case the value of γ_i was reduced, and a γ_p pulse appeared, which was neither strong nor sharply defined. Considerable study was therefore carried out in O_2-N_2 mixtures. The results are best summarized by reference to figure 9.66. The uppermost trace shows the pulses of figure 9.64 at 2,640 volts and 200 mm of pure N_2. The succeeding traces show pulses observed with 5% O_2 in N_2 at 200 mm, beginning with 2,640 volts potential.

It is at once noted that O_2 introduced certain changes.

1. The pulse sequence in pure N_2 was very much shortened by the O_2 at the same potential.

2. The amplitude of the one γ_i peak observed with O_2 was about one-fifth that in pure N_2.

3. The initial peak resulting from the α-particle avalanche was materially reduced in height by the O_2.

4. The rate of fall of current during ion crossing was delayed with O_2, and the area under the section of the trace caused by ion movement was much enhanced.

5. With increasing potential, secondary pulses of an irregular nature and short duration were superposed on the γ_i pulses, making them irregular.

6. At threshold at 2,960 volts, except perhaps for one or two γ_i sequences following the triggering α-particle pulse, all regularity ceased, and an irregular discharge appeared, interrupting itself for major fluctuations in fractions from one-half to one-third the ion crossing time.

7. Figure 9.67 shows the nature of the γ_p secondary pulses with fast sweep, occurring in the first few microseconds at 200 mm pressure near the onset of steady corona. It is seen that the photon pulses are irregular, diffuse, quickly attenuate, and at threshold do not yield a self-sustaining sequence as in H_2.

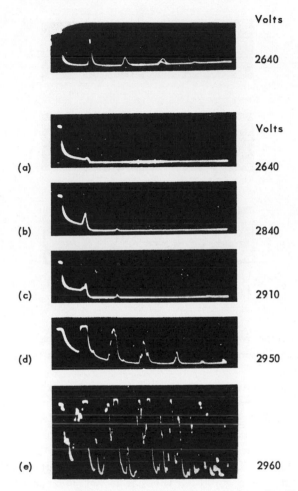

Fig. 9.66. Huber's oscillograms in pure N_2 (top trace), and in N_2 with 5% O_2 at various potentials to onset at constant slow sweep rate.

The results in pure N_2 and $N_2 + O_2$ need some further interpretation. While it was clear that in pure N_2 there was a strong γ_i which ultimately led to a self-sustaining corona, there was no γ_p. In pure N_2 the states largely excited are those giving rise to the second positive bands. While the energy of the upper excited states is about 12 volts, the greater proportion of the emission comes from transitions having less than 4 volts energy. It also appears that excited states of N are not usually seen in discharges. They can usually only be awakened by impacts with inert gas ions. In fact, the discharge spectrum in pure N_2 reveals largely bands of wave length more than 2,500 Å.

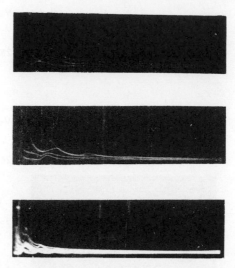

Fig. 9.67. Huber's fast oscilloscope sweep with N_2 and 5% O_2, showing weak photon pulses near threshold.

While transitions to ground states of much more energy are possible and do occur, these are mostly from forbidden transitions, i.e., having a long lifetime.

In the glow-discharge spectra of air, most of the light intensity in the visible comes from the N_2 second positive group, and the radiations below 2,500 Å come largely from the NO molecules. Theobald, in his study of back diffusion with clean but N_2-coated Ni, observed that his photoelectric emission did not come to any great extent from the 2,537 Å line of his Hg arc, but that most of it came from wave lengths shorter than 2,300 Å. Thus, it is not unexpected that Huber, with her N_2-coated Ni, detected no fast component γ_p in pure N_2 from her α-particle avalanches, especially at such high pressures of N_2 gas as used here. On the other hand, once threshold was reached, so that many accumulated states occurred with ample time, some photons from the less likely transitions helped spread the discharge avalanches all over the cylinder, leading to the general, statistically fluctuating, steady corona, devoid of the regularity observed in H_2.

It is not surprising that the addition of as little as 0.1% O_2 to N_2 should cause the appearance of a photon γ_p. Aside from the creation of NO molecules, excited states of O_2 could well have energy enough to produce photoelectrons from the Ni above some 5 e.v. The O_2 excited states will be created by impact of excited N_2 states with the few O_2 molecules. Photons from these will not be absorbed by the sparse O_2 molecules. They will lead to a small and diffused photon γ_p pulse. That the pulses were indeed γ_p pulses in N_2, contaminated by less than 1% O_2, could be proved by integrating the drift velocities of Bradbury and Nielsen in pure N_2 across the tube and comparing them with the pulse interval. The value of τ_e measured agreed with that calculated from 600 mm to 50 mm within 5%, ranging from 0.96 microsec at 600 mm to 0.38 microsec at 50 mm. Calculated values ran slightly high. The small amount of O_2 in N_2 would not cause much deviation from values in pure N_2.

There is some chance that with O_2 the photosensitivity of the cathode is increased, but in an ill-defined and unstable fashion, as observed by Theobald with Ni. R. Geballe (24) found an order-of-magnitude increase in γ_p from the cathode with $N_2 + 4\%$ O_2 over that in pure O_2 or N_2. In any event, the γ_p effect was too small to lead to any self-sustaining discharge, as noted in the oscillograms, since at potentials below that at which enough photon action can occur, a self-sustaining discharge by other mechanisms intervenes.

Returning now to the observations of the γ_i peak: It is noted that with the O_2, the γ_i peak at 2,640 volts is about one-fifth that for pure N_2. This is to be expected, for addition of O_2 to the gas gives an O_2 coating on the Ni cathode which was observed by J. H. Parker, Jr. (49), to decrease γ_i for N_2^+ by a factor of 10 when an all-O_2 coating replaced an N_2 coating on Pt or Ta cathodes. Here the coating was a mixed one of N_2 and O_2, on which γ_i could have been larger. Huber noted that the mere addition of O_2 to the N_2 did not at first alter γ_i, but that γ_i was quickly altered if the W filaments were heated up for some time, warming the Ni cylinder and thus accelerating the oxidation of the Ni. Once the Ni was contaminated with $O_2 + N_2$, it did not recover on evacuating the system. Heating and flushing with clean N_2 speeded recovery, but more thorough outgassing, such as heating to bright-red heat in vacuum, was needed to restore γ_i completely.

The decreased amplitude of the initial peak caused by the α-particle avalanche, and the increased area under the curve owing to ion motion, observed at 2,640 to 2,910 volts on slow sweep, can in part be accounted for by negative ion formation for electrons from the first α-particle avalanche in mid-gap. These, arriving later at the anode, add their secondaries later in the pulse period. Since with 5% O_2 in the low-field region, attachment is rather frequent, the oscillations observed by Lauer in H_2 with 1% and less of O_2 are smoothed out.

It is not likely that this action is alone responsible, since even with 5% of O_2 the attachment should not be so rapid. There is, however, a very interesting phenomenon to be noted, beginning at 2,840 volts and becoming more pronounced at 2,910 volts and higher potentials about the second γ_i pulse, and at 2,950 and 2,960 volts on all pulses. This is, that some irregular pulses appear to set in shortly before or simultaneously with the arrival of the first of the ions across the gap, and at higher potentials clearly before the ion cloud has completely crossed the gap. In fact, at 2,950 volts, before the ion cloud from the first α-particle avalanche has crossed more than two-thirds of the way to the cathode, a new pulse starts, and burns for some time. This irregularity is not seen during the first α-particle avalanche, but at higher potentials appears more and more prominently.

This phenomenon is caused by photoionization in the gas by photons created near the anode. With 5% O_2 the free path for photoionization in the gas is about 4 mm. Thus, with 5% O_2, as the electrons of the first α-particle avalanche cross, photoionization is extended through the gas to near the cathode. Then electrons can start new avalanches within electron-transit times. Such a discharge spreads rapidly along the whole anode wire, and at adequate potentials creates a space-charge sheath which terminates ionization until the space charge clears from near the anode. With the delayed avalanches from electron attachment, such photoionizing processes at lower potentials are propogated during the whole ion crossing time without choking off discharge. This results in a smoothing and increase of the current during ion transit.

As potentials get higher, the tendency to a discharge by photoionization in the gas through increase of $\epsilon^{\int \alpha dx}$ increases, and such discharge becomes self-quenching. Thus, while the initial α-particle triggered pulse is smoothed and prolonged by photoionization in the gas, it will not be possible for the new photoionizing-type pulse to appear until the space charge has cleared sufficiently from the anode. At 2,910 volts this occurs before the initial ion pulse crosses, and one sees a photon-produced, Geiger counter-like pulse, triggered by a belated ion arrival, in the cleared gap preceding the peak of the first γ_i pulse. At 2,950 volts this pulse is strong enough to build up a discharge that masks γ_i and chokes by space charge. After it has cleared slightly, a new secondary Geiger pulse appears, such as that first reported by Stever (63), followed after a clearing time by more such pulses. At 2,960 volts the spread of self-sustaining Geiger counter pulses by photoionization along the wire with self-extinction by space charge is as dominant a process as γ_i, if not more so. Thus, two secondary Geiger pulses are seen to follow on the first avalanche pulse, followed in turn by a primary and secondary Geiger pulse at two-thirds an ion crossing time. Then there is a γ_i triggered pulse followed by a secondary Geiger pulse after half an ion transit time, and one again at three-fourths an ion transit time and the second γ pulse. Soon thereafter the irregularly spaced Geiger pulses take command, and nearly smother the sequence of regular γ_i pulses that would normally give the self-sustaining corona.

It should be noted that with these mechanisms, even with the Geiger pulse mechanism, the threshold for self-sustaining corona in pure N_2 of about 2,650 volts is raised to 2,960 volts by 5% O_2. This arises largely through the lowering of γ_i by the O_2 on the Ni, since γ_i still figures strongly with 5% O_2. With increased O_2 concentration there will ultimately be a Geiger counter threshold at potentials below that for self-sustaining γ_i corona. This will lower the threshold for steady corona relative to 5% O_2.

The discovery by Huber of an *increase* of breakdown potential with addition of O_2 is contrary to the observations reported by C. G. Miller and the author (64). The explanation of this apparent contradiction is that Miller measured thresholds in what he believed to be pure N_2. He obtained this "pure" N_2 by flashing his W filament. The work of Huber shows that the flashing introduced above 1% O_2 into the N_2, so that Miller's N_2 was *not* pure. At these low percentages of O_2, photoionization in the gas was meager, and Miller was measuring a threshold with inactive cathode in $N_2 + 1\%$ O_2. Increasing the amount of O_2 beyond this then lowered the threshold for Miller, which was high for very slightly contaminated O_2 because of decrease in γ_i. Thus, while Miller observed a monotonic decrease of threshold from pure N_2 to air (20% O_2), Huber observed an increase in threshold from that in pure N_2. up to concentrations in O_2 somewhat below 20%; and then a decrease (as observed by Miller) beyond that for air with a subsequent rise as the value for pure O_2 was approached, as noted by Miller.

It appears that a γ_i in pure N_2 with clean Ni gives a low threshold, which *increases* as the cathode is made *insensitive* by O_2, but *decreases* as photoionization in the gas and Geiger counter action become more efficient. The subsequent rise in threshold is caused by the change from the Geiger counter pulse to the streamer action as the photoionizing free path decreases with the partial pressure of O_2. Streamers require slightly higher potentials than the Geiger counter-like burst pulses.

It should be remarked that the presence of O_2 impurity in Miller's supposedly pure N_2 that was introduced by flashing the W wire also accounts for his fluctuations in current of 10^{-3} sec duration, which

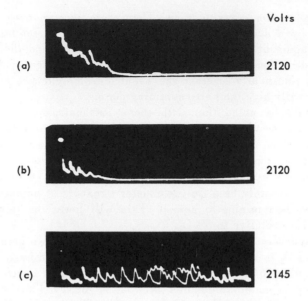

Fig. 9.68. Huber's oscillograms of pulses in air at various potentials on slow sweep. These are characteristically burst pulses.

were not noted by Huber for nearly pure N_2. Such fluctuations may have been associated with some cleanup of the cathode by ion action in Miller's case, whereas Huber's cathode in pure N_2 did not suffer much cleanup.

The addition of O_2 up to 20%, as in air produced the α-particle triggered pulses shown in figure 9.68, which resemble single burst pulses as reported by many observers in point to plane corona. At threshold the process became self-sustaining, as shown in the figure. There were no indications of any γ_i or γ_p, which is not strange, for the photons were strongly absorbed, ionizing the gas and propagating a discharge by anode action. The threshold potential for air is 2,145 volts, which is appreciably lower than for either pure N_2 or N_2 with less O_2. Despite fluctuation, duration of the quenched period of the burst pulses was about a quarter of an ion crossing time. This period would indicate that the innermost edge of the space-charge sheath had to travel roughly $\sqrt{1/4}$, or halfway across the gap, so that a new discharge could initiate. Initiation after adequate clearing was always assured by delayed arrival of negative O_2^- ions.

To prove that this discharge was actually one involving the anode wire and not any other action, Huber performed the following experiment: The α particles were fired either parallel, as in the previous

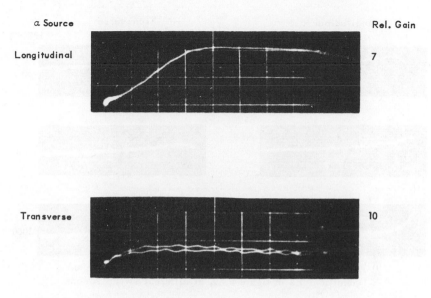

α Source   Rel. Gain

Longitudinal   7

Transverse   10

Fig. 9.69. Huber's pulses, triggered by longitudinal (upper trace) and
transverse (lower trace) particle tracks in pure N_2 with fast sweep.

work, or normal to the Ni cylinder radius and the cylinder axis along
a chord of the cylinder one-half the distance from Ni cylinder to anode
wire. The α particles thus produced an ionizing track along a chord
of the cylinder and of relatively short length in the gas, compared
to the particles fired parallel to the axis. The pulses in *pure* N_2 are
shown in figure 9.69 for the two sources, at relative gains 7 and 10
for 300 mm at 3,000 volts, with a sweep rate of 2×10^{-8} sec/cm. The
time taken for the rise of the pulse of the parallel α ray shown is the
time of travel of the α particle plus the time of formation of the electron avalanche.

With the transverse pulse, the time of α-particle traverse and
avalanche time are included, but now if the avalanche starts a pulse
spread down the wire in pure N_2, this time will be added. It is at
once seen that the rise of the longitudinal pulse is a bit slower than
that of the transverse pulse, as electron avalanches must all travel
practically the radius of the tube to the anode. In addition, the shape
of the pulse may indicate that this track was not too well collimated
parallel to the axis. The area under it is proportional to the avalanche
size, as no secondary actions occur in this time scale. The transverse
pulse rises slightly faster, since its nearest avalanche electrons have
only a half radius to traverse. Others arrive later, since they come

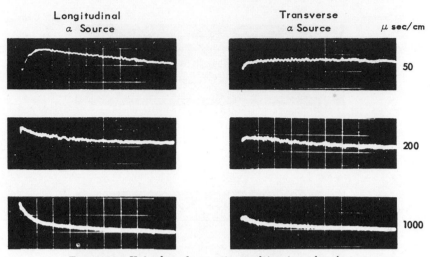

Fig. 9.70. Huber's pulses, triggered in air under the same
conditions as in figure 9.69, at different sweep speeds.

from the cylinder. The transverse pulse is more rounded because some
electrons come from the cylinder wall area as well. The areas under
such curves, when extended to full pulse duration, were observed to
be in the ratio of the length of the parallel and transverse α-particle
tracks in the cylinder, i.e., in the ratio of the primary ionization.
There is no indication of a spread of the pulse down the tube in pure
N_2.

Figure 9.70, on the contrary, shows the longitudinal and transverse
pulses in air at 300 mm and 2,770 volts at three sweep rates. At the
fastest sweep rate it is seen that the rise of the pulse with parallel
α-particle tracks is faster than the transverse pulse, the first reaching
a peak in 1.5 scale divisions, the latter reaching its peak in about
3.5 scale divisions. At decreasing sweep rates it is noted that the
area under both pulses is about the same. That is, despite the fewer
electrons in the transverse pulse, the total currents in both pulses
were equal and definitely larger than under the pure N_2 curves, indicating that the pulses were not proportional to primary ionization,
but depended on the duration of a self-quenching discharge, triggered
by the pulses only and independent of pulse size in charge generation.
Thus, it is clear that in air there is a new mechanism, the *burst pulse*,
observed by Trichel with positive point in 1937, and attributed by
the author to photoionization in the gas, which is synonymous with
the mechanism later found for the fast Geiger counter pulse.

TABLE 9.9a

Huber's Velocity of Geiger Pulse Propagation
Down the Wire at Different Potentials
and Pressures in Air

p	V	v
100 mm	1,580 volts	3×10^7 cm/sec
200 mm	2,190 volts	3×10^7 cm/sec
300 mm	2,720 volts	4×10^7 cm/sec
400 mm	3,240 volts	6×10^7 cm/sec

TABLE 9.9b

Huber's Velocity of Geiger Pulse
Propagation at Constant Potential
with Different Concentrations
of O_2 in N_2

(V = 2,720 volts; p = 300 mm)

Per cent O_2	v
0	No spread
5	9×10^7 cm/sec
10	6
21	4
40	No α pulses

Huber measured the velocity of the propagation of the ionization along the wire by analysis of transverse and parallel α-track pulses for air at different potentials and pressures, and at different O_2 concentrations, at 2,720 volts and 300 mm pressure. These are shown in tables 9.9a and 9.9b, respectively. While the velocity of spread v shows decrease as the absorbing free path $1/\mu$ decreases (i.e., as the pressure of O_2 increases), the increase in potential in table 9.9a masks this. From table 9.9b, it is clear, however, that the velocity decreases as the photoionizing path $1/\mu$, with absorption coefficient μ, decreases. It has been estimated that for these pulses $\mu \sim 10$ cm^{-1} in air ($1/\mu = 0.1$ cm), so that at 5% O_2 $1/\mu = 0.4$ cm, and at 40% O_2 it is 0.05 cm. At 0% O_2 there was no spread, and at 40% O_2 there were no α pulses, so that the spread could not be measured, if present. It is seen, however, that as $1/\mu$ decreases at nearly constant conditions, the velocity of spread does indeed decrease, as noted for Geiger counters.

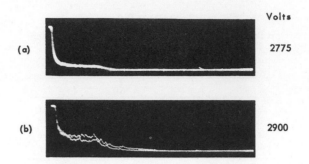

Fig. 9.71. Huber's α-particle triggered pulse in pure O_2 at 300 mm pressure at slow sweep rate. Upper trace (a) at 2,775 volts; lower trace (b) at 2,900 volts.

The cessation of the α-particle pulse at this pressure was owing to the fact that at the degree of multiplication required to observe details of the α-particle pulse, the discharge became self-sustaining. It was also clear that at higher O_2 concentrations the burst pulses were giving way to a new discharge form. These are best studied for pure O_2. For this gas, a low-amplification pulse is shown in figure 9.71(a) at 300 mm pressure, with 2,775 volts and a sweep rate of 1,000 μ sec per cm, with an increased oscilloscope sensitivity at RC = 3 microseconds, which can be used here, since slow sweeps only are needed. The drift velocities in O_2 could be measured with such pulses (though inaccurately), for if the end of the pulses was to be seen, then potential had to be increased, so that some secondary processes occurred. The value of the reduced mobility K_+ for O_2 at 20° C. and 760 mm was 2.2 ± 0.1 cm²/volt sec. This agrees quite well with Varney's value of 2.25 ± 0.1 cm²/volt sec at 0° C. and 760 mm, extrapolated from high field values. This ion he identified as O_2^+, in conformity with Luhr's mass-spectrographic study. It suffers retardation by charge-exchange reaction.

Figure 9.71(b), at 300 mm of O_2 at 2,900 volts and a sweep rate of 1,000 μ sec/cm, shows the appearance of some secondary mechanism. The pulses are of the burst-pulse variety, but of short duration, and are like those seen by Miller in pure O_2 at 200 mm. Note the greater amplitude and longer duration compared to the pulses at 2,775 volts. Part of this is caused by negative O_2^- ion formation, but some of it is akin to burst pulses, for it is like the pulses that at 200 mm and below lead to a self-sustaining burst-pulse corona. Apparently, at the short, absorbing free path here of less than 1 mm, the pulses do not quite propagate down the whole wire to give the full burst pulse

Fig. 9.72. Huber's α-particle triggered pulses in pure O_2 under the conditions of figure 9.71, but at 3,050 volts. The amplitude of these pulses is very great and the duration is short on the slow sweep rate used.

Fig. 9.73. Huber's large pulse in pure O_2 at 3,050 volts, as in figure 9.72, with fast sweep rate. The pulse shape is partly of instrumental origin.

noted at 200 mm. Finally, at the same pressure and sweep rate, the pulses appearing at 3,050 volts took on the very regular form of figure 9.72. These began to appear at 200 mm, and were more persistent above this pressure. (These, and *not* γ_i pulses.) They were regular. Their amplitude exceeded burst-pulse amplitudes by a factor of 200, relative to figure 9.68. At a given potential and pressure they had a constant amplitude. With faster sweep speed, their form is shown in figure 9.73. Here RC is 0.003 microseconds and the sweep rate is 1 microsecond per cm. The duration is less than 10^{-7} sec. The instantaneous currents were as high as 10^{-4} amp, and they contained on the order of 10^8 electrons.

The characteristics of these pulses are very similar to streamers propagating radially from the anode toward the cathode, studied in detail in positive point to plane geometry by M. R. Amin (65). They propagate in O_2 with $\mu > 100$ cm^{-1}, since the intense local photo-ionization leads to positive ion space-charge accumulation at the anode, the radial field of which, with highly absorbed ionizing photons, propagates into the gap as a preonset streamer. Amin, in point to plane geometry, has shown that they create about 8×10^9 ions per cm length in the gap. The velocity is initially high, of the order of 6×10^7 cm/sec, but slows down to 2×10^7 cm/sec as they run into the space charge of the preceding streamer. In the case of Huber's streamers, they must have been but some 2 mm long at threshold in O_2. The distance between streamers corresponds to two-thirds the positive ion transit time. Thus, the new streamer can start when the anode end of the old one has progressed 82% the distance to the cathode. Actually, since V is 3,050 volts instead of the 2,775 volts at which ion-transit times were measured, the streamers must actually clear to even closer to the cathode before the next streamer. These streamers start with or without α-particle triggering, once ionizing events in the tube start an avalanche.

The regularity of the sequence suggests that the streamer process is confined to one spot on the anode. Since the streamer length is some one-tenth the distance to the anode, the triggering of the next pulse arises from the γ_i electrons created by the tip of the streamer as it arrives at the cathode. This type of pulse does not continue indefinitely at any one point, for near threshold, by just statistical fluctuation, one fails to trigger its successor. Then the sequence breaks off, awaiting a new ionizing event. As potential is increased much above the threshold, streamers occur at random at several points on the wire so that the discharge becomes continuous with considerable fluctuation. At this point the anode is surrounded by a glow, as noted by Miller. With the high absorption coefficient for photons in O_2 at 760 mm, it is difficult to see how the discharge can diffuse around the whole wire and tube. However, gradual radial diffusion around the wire can take place, and no doubt there are always sufficient impurities present to disperse a few photons active at the cathode that are not absorbed along the tube, for with 10^{19} molecules/cm^3 it would take but few NO molecules and photons to diffuse the streamers well above threshold.

§ 18. Amin's Fast Oscilloscopic Studies of Point to Plane Corona.

It is of importance at this point to include the substantiation of these various secondary mechanisms that come from the fast-sweep oscillograms taken by M. R. Amin (65) in the author's laboratory for point to plane geometry. This geometry is not too serviceable for quantitative study, but it is especially adapted for the analyses of anode and some cathode processes, in virtue of the concentration of the luminous and other phenomena in an easily observable region. The apparatus used by Amin in the study of point to plane corona is shown in figure 9.74, which is largely self-explanatory. The points used varied from 0.1 to 0.25 cm diameter, with a 4-cm gap. The screen shown over the plate followed a device by A. F. Kip, which was on occasion used with an auxiliary field to record the current due to ion arrival without having it distorted by ion movement in the gap. By slightly displacing the screen relative to the plate, the ionizing pulse at the anode point showed a pip, and the current loop due to the

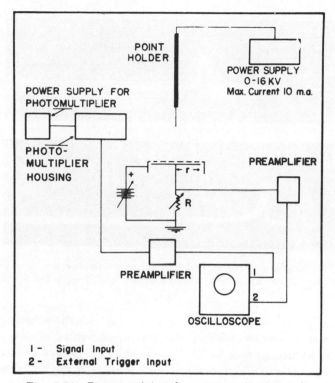

Fig. 9.74. Diagram of Amin's apparatus for the study
of point to plane corona.

arrival of ions on the screen could be observed and compared to
measured ion pulses. Usually, studies were made without the screen.
The photomultiplier arrangements for viewing luminosities in the gap
which could not be observed with coaxial cylindrical geometry are
also shown.

Before proceeding to the burst-pulse and streamer studies, there
is a relevant series of observations made by Amin, using a negative
Pt point and positive plane, which is again illustrative of a few
features of the Townsend-like breakdown. Figure 9.75 shows a 1×10^{-8}
sec timing pulse above, and below, the luminosity as viewed by the
photomultiplier for the negative Trichel pulse corona in air at 760
mm. This discharge is an intermittent miniature glow discharge, complete with Crookes dark space of 5×10^{-4} cm, a negative glow 2×10^{-2}
cm in diameter and 5×10^{-3} cm long, a Faraday dark space, and a
faint, fanlike positive column extending some 0.15 cm into the gap.
At threshold, single pulses like those shown in figure 9.75 occur

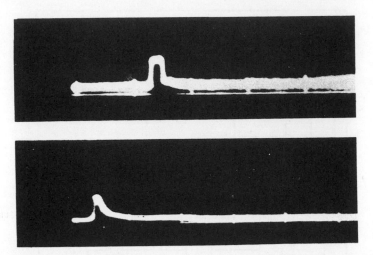

Fig. 9.75. Amin's oscillogram of a Trichel pulse discharge with negative point. Upper trace, 1×10^{-8} sec timing pulse; lower trace, Trichel pulse.

occasionally and at random. As potential is raised, a sequence of such pulses follows in regular succession, beginning at about 1,000 c.p.s. and extending to near 10^6 c.p.s. before a change occurs. It is seen that at threshold, this discharge rises to a current density of 70 amps/cm² and extinguishes by negative ion space-charge formation in 10^{-8} sec. Analysis shows that the rise of this pulse owing to high fields and short distances traversed can occur only by a photon γ_p from the cathode with a value of the order of 5×10^{-5}. The rapid extinction comes from the dissociative attachment of perhaps 60% of the electrons in the pulse to yield a negative ion space charge within perhaps 1 mm of the point (66). When this space charge clears to perhaps a few mm a new pulse occurs, triggered by impact of a belated positive ion on the cathode.

If the pressure is reduced so that the negative ion space charge forms more sparsely and farther out in the gap, more total ions are needed and the choking time is prolonged. This gives time for the many positive ions created out in the gap to reach the cathode, and the pulse initiated by a γ_p and sustained until quenching by a very efficient γ_i mechanism is clearly seen in figure 9.76. At 400 mm the photon pulse shows just a trace of the γ_i shoulder, while the effect of γ_i is seen in increasing amount as pressure goes down. Note that the electrical pulse is essentially the same as the photon pulse, except for the effect of ion movement in the high-field region. The

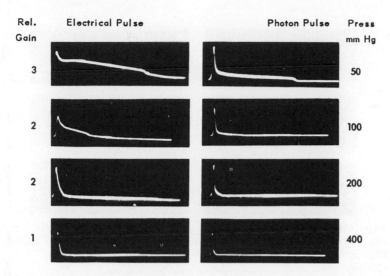

Fig. 9.76. Amin's oscillograms of Trichel pulses with fast sweep at different pressures. Electrical pulses (left) differ from photon pulses (right) only in the prolonged tails owing to ion movement in the high-field region.

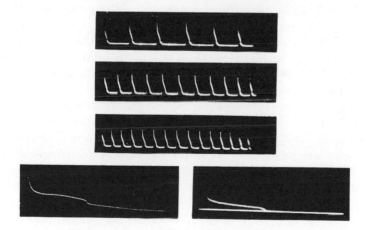

Fig. 9.77. Amin's Trichel pulses at 100 mm with slower sweep, showing the regular succession at 100, 200, and 250 kilocycles. Lower traces clearly show differences between electrical and photon pulses, at left and right, respectively. If slope owing to ion movement is removed from the ion pulse, then ion pulse and photon pulse are similar.

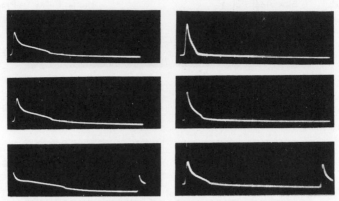

Fig. 9.78. Amin's oscillograms of photon pulses at high frequency and current density. "Unconditioned" point (left), "conditioned" point (right), at various pressures.

duration of the γ_i shoulder following the γ_p peak in the top trace is 4 microseconds, unlike the whole pulse at 400 mm pressure, which lasts around 1.5×10^{-7} sec. Figure 9.77 (top) gives a series of pulses at 100 mm pressure, showing frequencies of 100, 200, and 250 kilocycles. The lower traces show electrical (left) and photon (right) pulses at 50 mm and 10 kilocycles. The photon pulse terminates with the end of the γ_i shoulder process, while the ion-drift motion continues the current in the electrical pulse. This clearly differentiates γ_i action from ion movement.

Perhaps the most interesting oscillograms in relation to γ processes are those shown in figure 9.78. It had repeatedly been observed that as pulse frequency and current density increased with increasing potential, there was a point at which the current *decreased*, the pulse interval slightly *increased*, and the single-pulse amplitude, or better, current per pulse, *decreased*. This occurred irreversibly as a function of current-density duration, and perhaps pressure. The phenomenon was identified as some sort of a "conditioning" of the point associated with ion bombardment at high current density. The point was not altered in shape, nor was its surface visibly changed. It usually regained its normal condition after standing in the air for some hours. It was suspected that with heavy continued current densities, the oxide and other gas film layers were removed by ion bombardment as fast as they formed. Since such cleansing of the surface was normally supposed to *lower* the work function and *increase* secondary emission, the *reduction* of current and pulse size presented a paradox.

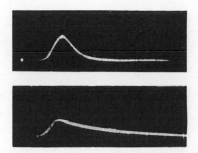

Fig. 9.79. Amin's oscillograms at fast sweep for the single burst pulse near positive point corona threshold. Top trace, photon pulse; lower trace, electrical pulse. Duration and shape are instrumental, and the pulses may well be less than the indicated 0.1 microsecond per scale division.

Reference to figure 9.78, showing pulses for the unconditioned surface (left) and conditioned surface (right), clarifies the picture. The traces, reading from top to bottom, are for 10^4, 10^5, and 2×10^5 cycles with increasing potential, respectively. The traces for the unconditioned point have had the oscilloscope gain *increased* by a factor of 1.5 relative to the conditioned traces. It is thus clear that "conditioning," or clearing. up, of the point does increase the yield, such that the initial γ_p and γ_i for the clean point are 50% greater than for the unconditioned point. Thus, the initial rate of production of electrons in the pulse is so high that the space charge is effectively built up in a very short interval of time and nearer the point, relative to the case for the lower γ_p on the unconditioned point. Hence, with both γ_p and γ_i increased, efficient choking shortens the pulse, fewer ions are needed to quench it, and *the ions per pulse are decreased*. The space charge from γ_p near the point clears more slowly, and it is seen on the lower trace that with the conditioned point the pulse interval is indeed somewhat longer. It is interesting to note that raising the potential for either point and increasing the repeat rate also reduces the effectiveness of γ_p relative to γ_i by bringing ions in sooner. It increases the duration of γ_i needed to quench, as the point fields are higher and take more space charge to quench. It is particularly important, however, to note the effects of cleanup, and the danger of drawing inferences from such phenomena as reduction in current without careful study.

Returning now to a positive point: Figure 9.79 shows the initial pulse with fast sweep owing to the burst pulse, or photoelectric Geiger counter pulse, with point to plane at threshold in air at 760 mm. The

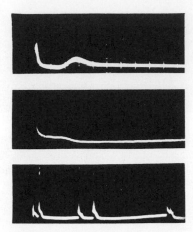

Fig. 9.80. Amin's oscillograms of burst pulses with slow sweep. Top trace used the screen and the delayed pip after 2 milliseconds denotes the arrival of the ion pulse. The area indicates 10^7 ions per pulse. Second trace is the pulse without screen. It shows that the pip at the end corresponds to ion crossing time. Lower trace shows a succession of pulses at slow sweep. Note that second pulse at right rises before the preceding one has crossed the gap.

upper trace is the photomultiplier measure of luminosity as a function of time, with 0.1 microsecond per scale division. The actual duration of light emission might have been less, but could not be resolved, as the 10^7 electrons per pulse did not allow a signal to be seen with faster sweep rate. The lower trace is the induced electrical pulse across the resistor. Note the slower decline owing to ion movement near the point.

Figure 9.80 shows slower sweep rates. The upper trace with screen in place shows the pip followed by the ion pulse. The second trace is the same pulse with the screen removed. Note that the decline of the pulse coincides with the arrival of the ion cloud at the screen in the upper trace. The bottom trace shows a succession of burst pulses above threshold at slow sweep. Note that the two pulses to the right are slightly superposed, indicating that in this gap the clearing time of the pulse is less than the crossing time. In fact, again about 80% of the gap length is required.

Amin noted that at threshold he observed a few pulses at random, separated by about an ion crossing time or longer, e.g., ~ 3 milliseconds. As potential was raised the succession of pulses increased in frequency, and the pulses increased in size and complexity, as

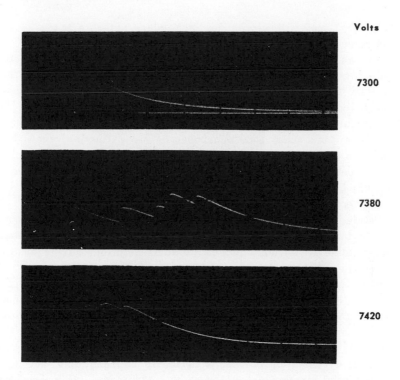

Volts

7300

7380

7420

Fig. 9.81. Amin's oscillograms of burst pulses above threshold with increasing potentials at moderately fast sweep rate. Note secondary pulses riding up on initial pulses. At highest sweep speed (which cannot be photographed), the secondary pulses can be *seen* clearly separated from the primary pulses.

shown by the three traces of figure 9.81, at 7,300, 7,380, and 7,420 volts, respectively. At first a primary pulse of 10^7 ions was occasionally followed by a secondary pulse of about 10^6 ions. At higher potentials the secondary pulses became successively more frequent, following each primary to give the typical burst-pulse profile shown at 7,420 volts. On fast sweep the secondary pulses were separated from the primary pulse and from each other by intervals of some 5 to 10 microseconds. While the appearance of the pulses shown in figure 9.81 was at slow sweep rate (the photographs requiring lower sweep rate, since single burst pulses are not reproducible), the fast sweeps could visually indicate the secondary pulses as separated from the primary pulses in time. Thus, the dead time between secondary pulses, which decreases with increased potential, is of the order of 10 microseconds and represents a partial clearing of space charge near the point ($\sim$ 1 mm), allowing a new secondary pulse to start, as earlier indicated by Stever (63) for Geiger counters.

At any given potential the succession of primary and secondary pulses builds up such a space charge out in mid-gap that the pulses entirely cease, and the ion cloud must move within 80% across the gap before a new burst sequence can follow. As potentials are raised higher and higher the secondaries in the pulse increase slightly in frequency and much more in number before extinction, such that the duration of bursts extends to longer and larger times. The clearing times between bursts decrease in duration, and eventually the intermittent burst-pulse corona gives way to a steady but slightly fluctuating corona at the *onset* of steady corona.

Under some conditions of geometry and with moist air somewhat above burst-pulse threshold, but below onset of steady corona, the burst pulse will trigger pulses of short duration, having amplitudes indicating that there are of the order of 10^9 ions involved. These appear interspersed with the bursts, and full bursts never precede them without a clearing interval; but the large pulses do trigger bursts before the oscilloscope sweep has completely recovered when sweep is slow.

While bursts only are active, the luminosity is spread over the high-field region of the hemispherically capped point, and in fact, as potential increases above onset of steady corona, this glow spreads over the shank of the point. When the large pulses appear, however, the luminosity projects into the gap along the axis, showing a narrow central core near the point and a radial outward flare some centimeter away from the point. Since burst pulses are interspersed with streamers, the tightly adhering glow over the hemispherical point will also usually persist. Amin proceeded to study these streamer pulses, such as reported by Huber, by observing the whole gap with photomultiplier and by current pulse, and then in detail by triggering the sweep with current pulse and observing the luminosity as a function of time by a slit 0.5 mm wide placed transverse to the point axis at various distances from the point. The flaring portion could also be studied by an off-axis vertical slit, viewing the region of the flare.

Figure 9.82 shows the fast oscilloscope sweep of the whole gap in the preonset streamer region. Since streamers, unlike burst pulses, repeat quite exactly, many streamer pulses can be superposed and high sweep speeds are applicable. The upper trace is a 2×10^{-8} sec square wave test pulse. The central trace is the photomultiplier trace, and the lower one is the electrical pulse across the resistance in series with the plate. Under other conditions where amplitudes are

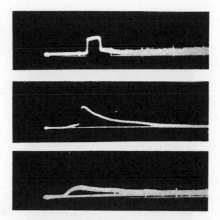

Fig. 9.82. Amin's oscillograms of streamers, viewing the whole gap with photomultiplier. Top trace, a 2×10^{-8} sec timing pulse; second trace, photon pulse; lower trace, electrical pulse.

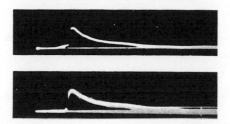

Fig. 9.83. Amin's oscillograms of streamers from positive point, showing that the rise is that of the luminosity from the triggering burst pulse *on the point surface*. Upper trace includes point; lower trace views streamer, but not point.

comparable, it can be shown that by and large the photomultiplier pulses pretty well duplicate the ionization pulses, i.e., ionization and luminosity are fairly proportional, except for the portion of the electrical pulse trace due to ion motion in the high-field region. It is seen that the whole pulse lasts a microsecond or more. The small rise, seen just before the steep rise resulting from the streamer formation in the photomultiplier trace, is real.

As indicated by figure 9.83, which represents photomultiplier traces taken including the tip of the point in the upper trace and excluding it in the lower trace, the initial rise is associated with luminosity at the surface of the tip, leading to streamer formation. It is, in fact,

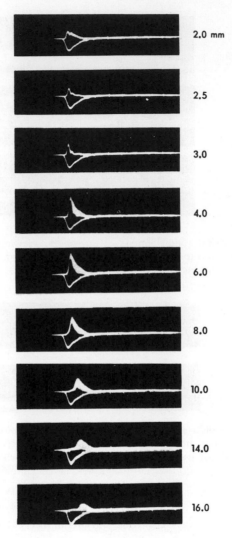

2.0 mm

2.5

3.0

4.0

6.0

8.0

10.0

14.0

16.0

Fig. 9.84. Amin's oscillograms, with triggering electrical pulse below and photomultiplier pulse above, for various positions of the viewing slit below the point.

the primary burst pulse that initiates the streamer. This shows the relative intensity of a primary burst pulse at the surface, and the intensity and thus relative ion production (ratio ~ 1:100) of the burst pulse and streamer.

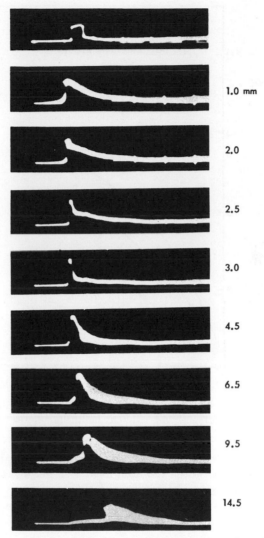

1.0 mm

2.0

2.5

3.0

4.5

6.5

9.5

14.5

Fig. 9.85. Same as figure 9.84, except that while beginning of the electrical pulse triggered the sweep, only the photomultiplier pulse is sho.n at different distances below point.

More interesting are the oscillograms observing the gap with the slit perpendicular to the axis, placed at various distances from the tip of the point. Figure 9.84 shows the electrical pulse below with the photomultiplier pulse superposed above for the indicated distances

§ 18

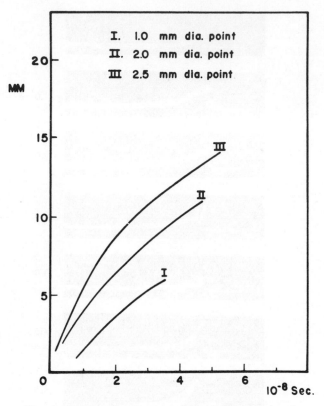

Fig. 9.86. Amin's distance-time curves for tip of
streamer for different point diameters.

from the tip of the point in mm. The delay in arrival of the streamer
tip is clearly seen on the oscillograms. For purposes of measurement
the oscilloscope sweep was triggered by the rise of the electrical
pulse, and the arrival of luminosity at the slit at various distances
was recorded on the oscillograms of figure 9.85. It is seen that the
luminosity rises with extreme sharpness as the tip arrives at the
slit, and that after the tip passes there is continued luminosity in
the form of a sort of shoulder, extending for longer and longer times,
of the order of magnitude of 2×10^{-8} sec and up, behind the tip. The
irregular features, broadening of the traces, etc., after the streamer
advances some 6 mm from the point, may in part be ascribed to the
fact that the streamer path is deflected radially from the axis as it
approaches the positive ion space charge of the preceding extinct
streamer. That this is the case can be shown by placing the slit

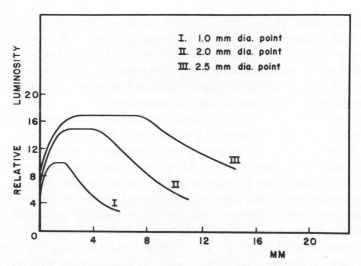

Fig. 9.87. Amin's curves of relative tip luminosity as a function
of distance from the point in positive streamers.

vertically, parallel to the axis, at various points *off the axis*, and
displaced downward different distances from the tip. The diverted
streamer tips can then be recorded as occasional light pulses that
pass the slit as a result of being diverted. This radial motion also
causes some apparent decrease in tip velocity. Near the point a
parallel slit 0.5 mm wide and 0.5 mm from the axis sees no luminosity,
indicating that the undeflected streamer width is less than 0.5 mm.

From oscillograms such as those described above, distance-time
curves can be made of streamer tip advance. Such curves are seen
for three point diameters in the preonset streamer range in figure
9.86. Tip velocities begin at high values near the point, of the order
of 6×10^7 cm/sec, and slow to about 2×10^7 cm/sec as the streamer
runs into space charge and declines.

Figure 9.87 shows the relative tip *luminosity* as a function of
distance from the point for three diameters of point. Except for an
initial very short time, and the period after the streamer has been
diverted by space charge, it is seen that the intensity is nearly constant during active advance; and this constancy also applies to ionization. By measuring the number of ions in the streamer by using the
gauze, or calibrating the oscilloscope to indicate ions, Amin was
able to show that the number of positive ions left behind per cm length
in the streamer channel was nearly constant for these streamers, and
of the order of 8×10^9 ions per cm. This is in good agreement with
earlier estimates of A. F. Kip and W. N. English (67).

The shoulder of luminosity behind the advancing tip is caused by the radial expansion of the positive space charge left behind in the streamer channel in consequence of radial fields about the axis, which draw in avalanches, feeding electrons into the streamer. This gives a transient luminosity, as the author has shown. In some cases, it may progress more slowly than the streamer tip.

At the onset of steady burst-pulse corona, streamers disappear because of the space charge. At much higher fields, the space charge near the point from burst pulses is too attenuated to prevent streamers. Thus, again streamers appear. These are more vigorous, and cross the gap, leading to an ultimate return stroke of ionization and a spark or arc breakdown. If the point radius is small compared to gap length, the prebreakdown streamers can be seen visually and studied by oscilloscope for some range of potential before they cross the gap and cause a spark. With points of larger diameter and with shorter gaps, the streamers may cross and lead to sparks without being visually manifest. Recent studies by Amin and later by Hudson, in the author's laboratory, indicate that owing to the continuous corona and space charge present, as well as to the drain of current from the point just at breakdown by the incipient streamers, the situation is very complex. This is further complicated by the type of geometry needed to get a few prebreakdown streamers before a successful one crosses. The "noise" of the spark is also troublesome where a repeated sequence of events must be scanned. Using two photomultipliers, one at the point to trigger the sweep for each streamer and a second one to scan the gap, it appears that some 100 microseconds before the breakdown streamer a weak streamer occurs. It appears that this is needed with the large points to liberate a large enough burst of electrons from the plate to start a breakdown streamer sequence from the point. This streamer, starting near the point, has a considerable duration or shoulder. As the streamer moves some mm and from the point, a very fast streamer tip separates, with a more prolonged, intense, and slowly moving luminosity following. The fast tip reaches the point with velocities near 10^8 cm/sec, while the long, intense luminosity follows after with a speed of 4×10^7 cm/sec and less. In some instances, when this reaches the cathode the bright return stroke follows at once. On other occasions, the slower process appears to drain so much charge from the tip that it is only some 10^{-7} sec later that a third fast streamer advances over the same path and triggers the return stroke. The velocity of the return stroke is exceedingly high, and its exact behavior cannot be resolved.

It is seen that the two anode processes that are dependent on photoionization in the gas under different conditions of photoionizing free paths are now no longer the basis of any conjecture, speculation, or hypothesis, but are directly observable realities which can be studied and measured at will. It is to be noted that the earlier hypotheses as to their nature and qualities were not too far wrong. It is finally seen that the streamers and burst pulses definitely figure in breakdown of gases, as either discharges or sparks.

§ 19. Derivation of Expressions for Burst-Pulse, Geiger Counter Spread, and Streamer Thresholds.

A. *The Burst-Pulse Threshold* (68).

If a potential V is applied to a point of radius a, in the rapidly declining field beyond a the electron will be able to ionize out to some distance r_0 from the point surface, such that the Townsend function a is so low that adr is of negligible value, r being the distance from the point *surface*. Thus, electrons entering the field from outside will create avalanches of magnitude $\epsilon \int_a^{a+r_0} a dr$. The value of the integral can readily be calculated if the field X_r as a function of V and r or $a + r$ is known, and if the quantity $a/p = f(X/p)$ is known. The evaluation of this integral may in some cases be simplified, as shown by E. E. Dodd (70). Now accompanying the avalanche of $\epsilon \int adr$ electrons and ions, there will be created $f\epsilon \int adr$ photons of wave lengths capable of photoionizing the gas and with a chance f_1 of ionizing it when absorbed. If β is the chance that one of these photoelectrons is produced at a distance in excess of r_{0g}, then the threshold V_g for a self-sustaining burst-pulse corona may be set as

$$(9.148) \qquad \beta f \; \epsilon^{\int_a^{a+r_{0g}} a dr} \; = 1$$

The quantity β may be roughly set as $\beta = 0.5 \; f_1 \; \epsilon^{-\bar{r}_{0g} \mu}$, on the simplifying assumption that there is one single photoionizing type of absorption coefficient μ active, with a chance f_1 of photoionizing on absorption. The factor 0.5 comes from the fact that half the photons emitted in the avalanche will be directed toward the surface of the point, and not out into the gas, as r_{0g} is usually less than a. The quantity $\bar{r}_{0g}$ is an average path for photons between a and $r_{0g} + a$ from the head of the avalanche at the anode surface which achieve a length r_{0g}. It can roughly be computed as $\bar{r}_{0g} = r_{0g}/\cos \bar{\theta}$, where $\cos \bar{\theta}$ is the average angle of photoemission, with the normal to the point surface given by $\bar{\theta} = \int_0^{\pi/2} \theta \sin \theta \, d\theta / \int_0^{\pi/2} \sin \theta \, d\theta = 1$ radian.

A rigorous calculation of β has been carried out by R. J. Wijsman (68), and differs little numerically from the approximate value. Thus, $\beta = 0.5 \hat{} f_1 \, \epsilon^{-1.86 \mu r_{0g}}$. The values of μ in the burst-pulse regime may range from 2.5 cm^{-1} at 5% O_2, 10 cm^{-1} for air, and perhaps 20 cm^{-1} where burst pulses cease. For air at 760 mm pressure at threshold, for a hemispherically capped cylindrical point of $a = 0.019$ cm, and plane 3 cm distant, $V_g = 5,050$ volts, $r_{0g} = 0.04$ cm, and $\epsilon^{\int \alpha dr} = 6 \times 10^4$ ions. Taking μ as 10 cm^{-1}, as observed by Cravath, $\beta = 0.238$, which makes $f f_1 = 7 \times 10^{-5}$. With variations in the percentage of O_2, the changes in V_g for the same point will not materially affect r_{0g}. However, the values of the amplification factor $\epsilon^{\int \alpha dr}$ will vary with V, and will be higher at 5% O_2 and perhaps a bit higher at 40% O_2 than for air. The value of β will range roughly from 0.5 to 0.1, so that $f f_1$ will remain in the neighborhood of 10^{-5}, and unless β is very great, will not exceed 10^{-4}.

Cravath estimated the active photons per ion from a steady corona as 10^{-4} in air at 760 mm. However, if $\mu = 100$ cm^{-1} without material change in r_{0g} and $\epsilon^{\int \alpha dr}$, the value of $f f_1$ will have to be around 5×10^{-2}, and it is clear that burst pulses cannot propagate in agreement with observation in O_2. It may be at once remarked that the type of relation for self-sustaining discharge and thus for current amplification with these anode processes is not very different for those with cathode γ processes, and observed values at threshold are in fact of the same order of magnitude.

B. The Geiger Counter Spread.

Somewhat earlier than the author, and unknown to him, F. Alder, E. Baldinger, P. Huber, and F. Metzger (69) had derived a threshold relation for the *spread* of a Geiger counter pulse by photoionizing action in the gas. This derivation, from a gaseous electronic viewpoint, was rather poor, though correct in principle. As altered by the author in terms of good gaseous electronic practice, it is here reproduced.

Consider a coaxial cylindrical Geiger counter system, with central anode wire and outer cathode cylinder of radii a and b cm, respectively. At a potential V on the anode the field X at a distance r from the cylinder axis is $X = V/(r \log b/a)$. The discharge will spread along the wire if the last quanta from the first avalanche are produced on the average a distance z_0 from it. The electron starting from z_0 initiates a new avalanche and spreads the discharge. The average time of the light-emitting process is designated as θ. The projection of the step z_0 along the wire is x_0, and the velocity of spread of the pulse along the wire is $v = (x_0/\theta)$. The electrons and photons are generated largely in the last ionizing free paths near the wire after the avalanche has progressed from a distance out in the gap r_0 at which appreciable ionization begins. The time of flight of the photons is negligible, and the time of emission of the photoionizing radiations is presumed to be about 2×10^{-10} sec. If it is longer, it can last a time τ_f. The largest time-consuming component is the time taken for the electron to proceed from r_{0g} to a, where r_{0g} is the edge of the ionizing zone with the threshold potential V_g applied. Thus, θ will be calculable from $v(r)$, the drift velocity, as a function of X/p, taken from observed or computed data, and the variation of X with r at constant p, giving $v(r)$ as a function of r. This makes

$$(9.149) \qquad \theta = \int_{r_{0g}}^{a} \frac{dr}{v(r)} + \tau_f ,$$

if τ_f is not negligible.

The quantity x_0 is obtained by calculating the flux of photons from a point A on the wire that are emitted in a cone of aperture ϕ intercepting a plane B normal to the wire between ϕ and $\phi + d\phi$. Calling n_0 the photons created in the avalanche, the number dn of photons reaching the plane within the solid angle designated may be written as

$$(9.150) \qquad dn = n_0 \, \epsilon^{-\mu s} \frac{2\pi s \sin \phi}{4\pi s^2} \, d\phi = \frac{n_0}{2} \, \epsilon^{-\frac{\mu x}{\cos \phi}} \sin \phi \, d\phi .$$

Here μ is the absorption coefficient of the photoionizing radiation and s is the distance along the cone. In the notation of this chapter, $n_0 = f \epsilon \int_{r_{0g}}^{a} \alpha \, dr$, where f is the photons per ion and $\epsilon \int_{r_{0g}}^{a} \alpha \, dr$ is the Townsend integral, when $\alpha/p = f(X/p)$ and X/p is a function of r. Since r_0 is small compared to b, integration limits can be set between 0 and $\pi/2$ in ϕ. Thus,

$$(9.151) \qquad n(x) = \frac{n_0}{2} \int_0^{\pi/2} \epsilon^{-\frac{\mu x}{\cos \phi}} \sin \phi \, d\phi .$$

On integration by parts, this leads to

$$(9.152) \qquad n(x) = \frac{n_0}{2} \left[\epsilon^{-\mu x} + \mu x \, Ei \, (-\mu x) \right] ,$$

with

$$Ei\,(-\mu x) \;=\; \int_{\mu x}^{\infty} \frac{\epsilon^{-y}}{y}\, dy \,.$$

Let f_1 be the chance that a photon of coefficient μ on absorption yields a photoelectron. Thus, $n f_1$ electrons result from n photons. The front of the discharge will propagate a distance x_0, defined in such a way that the n quanta give exactly 1 electron. Thus, x_0 is defined by the relation $f n(x_0) = 1$. The propagating threshold for the pulse is therefore:

$$(9.153) \qquad \frac{n_0 f_1}{2}\,[\,\epsilon^{-\mu x_0} + \mu x_0 Ei\,(-\mu x_0)\,] = 1 \,.$$

This yields the threshold, as given by

$$(9.154) \qquad 0.5\, f f_1\; \epsilon^{\int_{r_{0g}}^{a} a\,dr}\,[\,\epsilon^{-\mu x_0} + \mu x_0 Ei\,(-\mu x_0)\,] = 1 \,.$$

If the partial pressure p_a of the gas yielding f is present in a mixture, such as in counters, to a total pressure p, the exponential in equation must be multiplied by p_a/p. The quantity r_{0g} is determined from the limiting value of X_0 for ionization in the scale of distances used, and is defined by $r_{0g} = V_g/(X_0 \log b/a)$.

The expression $\int_{r_{0g}}^{a} a\,dr$ can be replaced by a general expression for coaxial cylinders, derived by E. E. Dodd (70), as

$$(9.155) \qquad \int_{r_{0g}}^{a} a\,dr = \left(\frac{V_g}{\log b/a}\right) \int_{0}^{\frac{V_g/p}{a\,\log b/a}} \left(\frac{X}{p}\right)^{-2} f\left(\frac{X}{p}\right)\, d\left(\frac{X}{p}\right),$$

with $a/p = f(X/p)$.

Further changes are the replacement of x_0 by θv and reduction of μ in terms of the partial pressure p_i of the photoionizable gas present, thus, $\mu = \mu_0\, p_i/p$, with p the total gas pressure present. Then the expression for the threshold reads

$$(9.156)\; 0.5\, f f_1\; \frac{p_a}{p}\, \epsilon^{\int_{r_{0g}}^{a} a\,dr}\left[\,\epsilon^{-\mu_0 \frac{p_i}{p} v \theta} + \mu_0 \frac{p_i}{p}\, v\theta Ei\left(-\mu_0 \frac{p_i}{p} v\theta\right)\right] = 1.$$

This expression is now open to discussion. It differs from the author's expression 9.148, setting V_g the threshold for a localized burst-pulse corona, in that it sets a threshold for the Geiger counter pulse that propagates along the anode with a **velocity** v. If the additive term containing the exponential integral (which can under normal conditions be neglected, and comes from the averaging over ϕ) be omitted, the two expressions differ superficially in the inclusion of the ratios p_a/p and p_i/p in the propagation equation, which are implicitly contained in the definition of f and μ in equation 9.148. There is a real difference between the two, however, in that the burst-pulse threshold expression 9.148 uses an $\epsilon^{-1.86\mu r_{0g}}$, while the pulse-spread threshold expression 9.156 contains a term, $\epsilon^{-\mu_0(p_i/p)v\theta}$. Now the relation for the spread defines a minimum distance of spread $x_0 = v\theta$, where v is the velocity of spread. Actually, x_0 has a significance only as a distance needed if with θ fixed a pulse is to spread with velocity v. Neither x_0 nor v are fixed by any physically determined quantity, but their ratio x_0/v equals a time θ which is predetermined by conditions, for θ is fixed by the value of r_0 at threshold, by the electron-drift velocity, and possibly by τ_f. While θ can be calculated or measured, and v is observed, x_0 is a convenient length, defined only by $v\theta$.

It now happens that v, as observed, is confined between rather narrow limits. It is possible to account for these limiting values. The upper limit is fixed by the expression for the corona threshold set by the author, and the lower limit of v is set by the condition that the spread may not be so slow that the corona is extinguished by space-charge accumulation locally before it advances very far. The limit for any self-sustaining discharge, whether it spreads or not, is set by equation 9.148, and it fixes the minimum avalanche length at V_g as r_{0g}. Now this avalanche is executed in a time θ. Since the self-sustaining condition implies that all

$$(9.148) \qquad 0.5\ f_1 f\ \epsilon^{\int_{r_{0g}}^{a}\alpha\,dr}\ \epsilon^{-1.86\,\mu r_{0g}}$$

photoelectrons must have been created in θ, the velocity of the creation of the active photons of the avalanche is fixed as r_{0g}/θ. The value of v obviously cannot exceed r_{0g}/θ, or their propagation would occur with partial avalanches. It is thus possible to write $(r_{0g}/\theta) \gtrless v$, therefore v_m, the maximum value of v, is fixed by $v_m = r_{0g}/\theta$. It follows that $r_{0g} \gtrless v\theta = x_0$. Thus, x_0 is less than r_{0g}, and at a maximum velocity v_m, $x_0 = r_{0g}$.

The minimum value of v may be calculated on the assumption that a sequence of n avalanches will create a space charge of positive ions near the anode that will choke off the discharge. Since near V_g for burst-pulse corona, the discharge is easily extinguished by space-charge accumulation, n need not be very large. Since the time of each successive avalanche sequence is θ, the n successive avalanches take $n\theta$. As r_{0g} represents the distances the avalanche travels, if the velocity of propagation is v_l, v_l is equal to $r_{0g}/n\theta$. This should represent the lower limit to the velocity of spread. Hence,

$$v_l = r_{0g}/n\theta \text{ and } x_{0l} = v_l\theta = r_{0g}/n,$$

with

$$(9.157) \quad r_{0g}/n\theta \overset{<}{} v, \ r_{0g}/n \overset{<}{} v_l\theta = x_{0l}, \ v_l = r_{0g}/n\theta \overset{<}{} v \overset{<}{} r_{0g}/\theta = v_m.$$

It should be added that these limits were not considered by counter investigators, since most studies were made above threshold because of the nature of instrumentation used.

The question next arises as to what produces these limits and the variation of v and x_0. Obviously, these limits are determined by the complex interrelationships of equation 9.156. That is, the threshold potential, the geometry, and the variation of a/p with X/p primarily determine the value of r_{0g}. These in turn, especially the value of V_g for propagation, must as well depend on f_1f, p_a, p_i, p, and μ_0. If conditions could be arranged so that V_g and r_{0g} were essentially constant, then the value of $\mu_0 p_i/p$ would largely govern the conditions. That is, as in O_2-N_2 mixtures, the value of V_g is not materially altered, for as p_i for O_2 is changed, the value of $\mu = \mu_0 p_i/p$ will change. Then, if the threshold is to be maintained, increase in μ requires a decrease in $v\theta = x_0$. Hence, at constant θ, increase in μ implies a decrease in x_0 and thus in v.

This has been observed in counter pulse behavior, and has also directly been observed in O_2-N_2 mixtures by Elsa Huber (49). Here v goes from 9×10^7 cm/sec to 4×10^7 cm/sec for a change in p_i of O_2 from that corresponding to 5% O_2 to 20% O_2 in N_2. Above 40% O_2, no more pulses spreading down the wire are observed. Instead, at threshold, smaller pulses that go on and off, as x_0 is presumably too small to propagate because of the large μ, are observed; i.e., a local burst-pulse corona. If potential is raised, the streamers appear.

It is likely that the counter pulses can propagate down the wire at less than 5% O_2. However, it appears that higher potentials are required, increasing r_{0g} and perhaps r_{0g}/θ, to get pulses at 1% O_2. The actual change in x_0 and v observed for the range open to study is one-half that to be expected from the variation of μ with p_i. This lack of proportionality reflects the changes in V_g and r_{0g} with percentages of O_2 which, while small, are not negligible. If the value of μ is varied, say in pure O_2, by changing p, the value of V increases with increasing O_2 and increasing μ because of the changes produced in r_{0g}, θ, and V_g.

C. *The Threshold for Streamer Formation in Uniform Field Geometry,*
Including Photoionization in the Gas.

The semiempirical theories of J. M. Meek (71) and H. Raether (72)
for the threshold of streamer formation in plane parallel geometry were
based primarily on the space-charge field distortion, and, while recognizing the necessity of adequate photoionization in the gas, did
not include this factor. In 1948, the author and R. J. Wijsman (68)
succeeded in formulating a more complete theory, including photoionization. This contained no arbitrary assumptions and was based
solely on the condition that the space-charge field, through photoionization and enhanced avalanches, had to be self-sustaining. Plane
parallel geometry was used for calculation to simplify the equations.
The same sort of approximations used by Meek and Raether in calculating fields were employed again for the sake of simplicity. A single
photoionizing wave length of absorption coefficient μ was assumed.
More elaborate calculations by W. B. Kunkel (73), R. C. Fletcher
(73), and E. E. Dodd (73), reported elsewhere, have shown that the
approximations of the simple, crude equations to be used are not
seriously wrong, and that image fields in the anode or of the bipolar
mid-gap avalanches produce only trivial corrections.

For simplicity, a uniform-field gap was considered, with uniform
field X at a pressure p, despite the fact that few streamer thresholds
occur in such fields. Adaptation to the nonuniform-field case can be
made with relatively little difficulty, but the derivation is clarified
by use of the uniform-field picture. An electron leaving the cathode
and advancing a distance x in the field *has* created ϵ^{ax} new electrons
where the quantity a/p is a function of X/p. In so doing it has left
behind ϵ^{ax} nearly immobile positive ions. The positive ions created
in any distance dx after a path of length x in the field is $a\,\epsilon^{ax}dx$. In
advancing a distance x in the field the electron cloud has expanded
radially to a distance from the avalanche axis, given by

$$(9.158) \quad \rho = (6Dt)^{\frac{1}{2}} = \left(6D\,\frac{x}{v}\right)^{\frac{1}{2}} = \sqrt{6\frac{2}{3}\,u_+\,\frac{x}{X}} = \sqrt{\frac{4}{3}\,\frac{\lambda_0^2\,eXx}{p^2v^2m}}\,,$$

where v is the drift velocity of the electrons in the field and D is
the coefficient of diffusion. The quantity D/v can be computed if the
Ramsauer free path λ of the electrons at 760 mm pressure, the drift
velocity v, and the field X at the pressure p, are known.

Now in traversing a distance dx after an avalanche length x with
diffusion radius ρ, the number n of ions contained in a small cylindrical element of height dx, radius ρ, and volume $\pi\rho^2dx$, at a point M

located at x on the axis, is $n = a\ \epsilon^{ax}dx$, and yields a concentration of ions,

$$(9.159) \qquad N = \frac{a\ \epsilon^{ax}dx}{\pi\rho^2 dx} = \frac{a\ \epsilon^{ax}}{\pi\rho^2},$$

about M.

A quantity q of positive ion space charge at M will create a space-charge field at some distance r from M, given by $4\pi q/4\pi r^2$. Since it is inconvenient to compute the space-charge field owing to the ions in the cone, say ρ cm high and $\pi\rho^2$ cm^2 in area about M, it will be more convenient to compute q as if the ions were distributed in a spherical volume of radius ρ with its center at M. Thus, the quantity of charge q will be set as $q = (4/3)\pi\rho^3 Ne$. This calculated charge and field will differ only by some unimportant constant factor from that owing to the slightly conical volume of height ρ with a gradual increase of density due to the difference $\epsilon^{-a(x+\rho)} - \epsilon^{ax}$, as ρ is not too large compared to x. Thus, the charge involved is $(4/3)\pi\rho^3 Ne$, and the space-charge field X' at r cm will be given by

$$(9.160)\ X' = \frac{4}{3}\ \pi\rho^3\ \frac{Ne}{r^2} = \frac{4}{3}\ \pi\rho Ne = \frac{4}{3}\ \frac{\pi\rho^3 ea\ \epsilon^{ax}}{\pi\rho^2 r^2} = \frac{4}{3}\ e\rho a\ \epsilon^{ax}/r^2 = E/r^2.$$

Hence, the total field along the axis of the initial avalanche on the side toward the cathode will be

$$(9.161) \qquad X_1 = X + X' = X + E/r^2.$$

The condition to be set for the extension of the positive space charge and its conducting plasma of transient electrons toward the cathode is that when q/e has reached an appropriate magnitude in the imposed field X, also of suitable magnitude, the photoelectrically initiated avalanches feeding into the positive space-charge tip T at q/e produce enough positive ions to maintain q/e and advance the tip.

Accompanying the ionization yielding the q/e ions, there were produced a number of $f_1\ q/e$ photons. The factor f_1 may be taken as essentially constant. Some of these photons will liberate electrons in the surrounding gas by photoionization. Of these, some electrons will be created within a region R so close to the first avalanche axis that their avalanches feed into T. It seems a fair approximation to take for this region R the space inside a coaxial cylinder about the first avalanche axis, with cross-sectional radius ρ. The electric field at any point is $\vec{X}_1 = \vec{X} + \vec{X}'$, the vector sum of X and X'. For most of the points within R, the direction of $\vec{X}'$ is so close to $\vec{X}$ that $\vec{X}_1$ can be taken, as shown in equation 9.161.

If μ is the absorption coefficient of the photon, then in a region between r and $r + dr$, lying entirely in R, the number of absorbed photons is approximately $f_1(q/e)(\rho^2/4r^2)\,\epsilon^{-\mu r}\mu dr$. A fraction f_2 of these absorbed photons will lead to ionization, creating

$$(9.162) \qquad f_2 f_1 (q/e)(\rho^2/4r^2)\,\epsilon^{-\mu r}\mu dr$$

electrons between r and $r + dr$. Each of these electrons causes an avalanche, of which the tip, at $r = \rho$, contains a number of ions equal to

$$(9.163) \qquad (4/3)\,\bar{a}'\rho'\,\epsilon^{\int_\rho^r a' dr'} ,$$

in analogy to equation 9.159. Here a' is the first Townsend ionization coefficient in the field $X_1 = X + [E/(r')^2]$. Use of r' in this integral instead of r is to indicate that this integration may be performed separately and preceding later integration. The quantity $\bar{a}'$ is the value of a' in X_1 when $r = \rho$.

The symbol ρ' represents the radius of the new avalanche tip, which is smaller than ρ, as the electron travels a distance less than x in the enhanced field X_1. If the drift velocity is taken as approximately constant for small field changes, equation 9.158 fixes ρ' as

$$(9.164) \qquad \rho' = \rho \left(\frac{r}{x}\right)^{\frac{1}{2}} .$$

Combining equations 9.162 and 9.163, and integrating from ρ to x, gives the total number of ions created by all avalanches near the tip T as

$$(9.165) \qquad \int_\rho^x f_1 f_2 (q/e) \left(\frac{\rho^2}{4r^2}\right) \epsilon^{-\mu r} \mu dr \frac{4}{3}\bar{a}' \left(\frac{r}{x}\right)^{\frac{1}{2}} \epsilon^{\int_\rho^r a' dr'} .$$

This approximation is invalid if $1/\mu$ is not appreciably greater than ρ. The condition for streamer propagation is now clearly that the number of ions given by equation 9.165 be set equal to q/e, the number in the initial avalanche, so that on eliminating q/e, the equation for the threshold of streamer propagation reads

$$(9.166) \qquad \frac{1}{3} f_1 f_2 \frac{\bar{a}'\rho^3}{x^{\frac{1}{2}}} \mu \int_\rho^x r^{-3/2} \epsilon^{-\mu r} \epsilon^{\int_\rho^r a' dr'} dr = 1 .$$

This relation is seen to be of a type analogous to equation 9.80a. It contains all the important factors, though some are in averaged form. It now sets a threshold devoid of arbitrary assumptions, in contrast to Meek's equation. It should show, through the variation of μ

with ρ, greater departures from Paschen's law. Solution of this relation for the sparking field strength X_s will follow the procedure pattern set by all previous theories, beginning with that of Townsend's equation 9.7. Given are the stated values of p and x and gas for the gap in question. Required are the experimental values of the functions $\alpha/p = f(X/p)$ for the gas, together with values of the quantities f_1, f_2, μ, v, and D, which in function now replace the quantity γ of the condition $\gamma \, \epsilon^{\int x dr} = 1$. In the small range of X/p covered in such a calculation, α/p as a $f(X/p)$ can closely be approximated by a simple, empirical, analytical expression, derived from observation, permitting of integration in equation 9.166. A value of X is chosen by guess, and through equation 9.158, ρ is evaluated. The value of α is then found from X, p, and the table of α/p as a function of X/p, and X' is determined from equations 9.160 and 9.158. This yields the value of $\overline{\alpha}'$, and when placed in the empirical form of $\alpha/p = f(X/p)$, allows integration of the quantity 9.166. The evaluation of the left-hand side of equation 9.166 is then possible. If this is different from unity, judicious new choices in X are made, which permit the value of X_s for the solution of equation 9.166 to be accomplished by graphical means.

Such an equation should be applicable for the calculation of the streamer sparking threshold if the variables are known. In uniform field geometry, the threshold so calculated will lie above that for low-order self-sustaining Townsend discharges by about 6% in air and perhaps 100% in A. Thus, it will be of little value in calculating breakdown thresholds in any gases. The Townsend predischarge setting the real threshold will obey Paschen's law. However, if nonuniform fields with highly stressed anode occur, the modification of this theory for nonuniform field geometry will lead to correct calculation for streamer onset in the absence of space-charge disturbance.

BIBLIOGRAPHY TO CHAPTER IX

(1) L. B. Loeb and J. M. Meek, *Mechanism of the Electric Spark*, Stanford University Press, 1941, p. 29. Also, H. Raether, Zeits. f. Phys. *117*, 375, 524, 1941; Erg. d. Exakt. Naturwiss. *22*, 73, 1949.

(2) C. G. Miller and L. B. Loeb, Jour. App. Phys. *22*, 494, 614, 1951; L. B. Loeb, Phys. Rev. *76*, 255, 1949.

(3) L. H. Fisher and B. Bederson, Phys. Rev. *78*, 331, 1950; *81*, 109, 1951; L. H. Fisher and G. A. Kachickas, Phys. Rev. *79*, 232, 1950; *88*, 878, 1952; *91*, 775, 1953.

(4) L. B. Loeb, Phys. Rev. *81*, 287, 1951.

(5) A. von Engel and M. Steenbeck, *Elektrische Gasentladungen*, Julius Springer, Berlin, 1934, vol. 2, p. 52.

(6) R. N. Varney, H. J. White, L. B. Loeb, and D. Q. Posin, Phys. Rev. *48*, 818, 1935.

(7) H. W. Bandel, Phys. Rev. *95*, 1117, 1954.

(8) F. Llewellyn Jones and A. B. Parker, Proc. Roy. Soc. *A213*, 185, 1952; J. Dutton, S. C. Haydon, and F. Llewellyn Jones, Proc. Roy. Soc. *A213*, 203, 1952.

(9) R. W. Crowe, J. K. Bragg, and V. G. Thomas, Phys. Rev. *96*, 10, 1954.

(10) J. Franck and E. von Bahr, Verh. d. Deutsch. Phys. Gesell. *16*, 57, 1914; W. F. Horton and A. C. Davies, Proc. Roy. Soc. *A95*, 333, 1919.

(11) For extended discussion of this see L. B. Loeb, *Fundamental Processes of Electrical Discharge in Gases*, John Wiley & Sons, New York, 1939, chap. IX, sec. 3, pp. 374 ff., and R. N. Varney, L. B. Loeb, and W. R. Haseltine, Phil. Mag. *29*, 379, 1940.

(12) O. Beeck, Ann. d. Physik *6*, 1001, 1930; Phys. Zeits. *35*, 36, 1934; R. M. Sutton, Phys. Rev. *33*, 364, 1929; R. M. Sutton and J. C. Mouzon, Phys. Rev. *35*, 694, 1930; *37*, 310, 1931; O. Beeck and J. C. Mouzon, Ann. d. Physik *11*, 737, 858, 1931; J. C. Mouzon, Phys. Rev. *41*, 605, 1932; R. N. Varney, Phys. Rev. *47*, 483, 1935; *50*, 159, 1936; *53*, 732, 1938; A. Rostagni, Nuovo Cimento *11*, 34, 1934; Phys. Rev. *53*, 729, 1938; N. Wayland, Phys. Rev. *52*, 31, 1937; R. N. Varney and W. C. Cole, Phys. Rev. *50*, 261, 1936; R. N. Varney, W. C. Cole, and M. E. Gardner, Phys. Rev. *52*, 526, 1937; O. Beeck and N. Wayland, Ann. d. Physik *19*, 129, 1934.

(13) A. M. Cravath, Phys. Rev. *47*, 254, 1935; C. Dechene, Le Radium 7, 533, 1936; H. Greiner, Zeits. f. Phys. *81*, 593, 1933; R. Geballe, Phys. Rev. *66*, 316, 1944; H. Costa, Zeits. f. Phys. *113*, 531, 1939; *116*, 508, 1940; H. Schwiecker, Zeits. f. Phys. *116*, 562, 1940; H. Raether, Zeits. f. Phys. *110*, 611, 1938; L. B. Loeb, Brit. Jour. App. Phys. *3*, 341, 1952.

(14) J. S. Townsend, *Electricity in Gases*, Oxford University Press, 1914.

(15) M. L. E. Oliphant, Proc. Roy. Soc. *A124*, 228, 1929; M. L. E. Oliphant and P. B. Moon, Proc. Roy. Soc. *A127*, 373, 388, 1930; H. S. W. Massey, Proc. Camb. Phil. Soc. *26*, 386, 1930; *27*, 460, 1931; F. M. Penning, Proc. Koenigl. Akad. v. Weetens, Amsterdam *31*, 14, 1928; *33*, 841, 1930; Physica *8*, 13, 1928; W. J. Jackson, Phys. Rev. *28*, 254, 1926; *30*, 473, 1927; H. Paetow and W. Walcher, Zeits. f. Phys. *110*, 174, 1951; M. Helea and E. L. Chaffee, Phys. Rev. *49*, 925, 1936; S. S. Shekhter, Jour. Exp. Theor. Phys. U.S.S.R. 7, 750, 1937; A. Rostagni, Ricerca Sci. *9*, 663, 1938; M. Helea and C. Houtermans, Phys. Rev. *58*, 608, 1940; R. M. Chaudhri and A. W. Kahn, Proc. Phys. Soc. Lon. *61*, 526, 1948; A. Cobas and W. E. Lamb, Phys. Rev. *65*, 827, 1944; D. Greene, Proc. Phys. Soc. Lon. *63*, 876, 1950; W. Ploch and W. Walcher, Zeits. f. Phys. *130*, 174, 1951; L. J. Varnerin, Jr., Phys. Rev. *91*, 859, 1953; I. Okano, Jour. Phys. Soc. Japan *8*, 362, 1953. Especially, H. D. Hagstrum, Phys. Rev. *89*, 338, 1953; *91*, 541, 1953; and two subsequent papers in Phys. Rev.: *96*, 325, 1954, and *96*, 336, 1954. Also, J. H. Parker, Jr., Phys. Rev. *93*, 1148, 1954. Many recent papers on coronas in coaxial cylindrical geometry, by E. J. Lauer, Elsa Huber, L. Colli and U. Facchini, as well as R. N. Varney, in plane parallel geometry with fast oscilloscopic analysis (see *infra*), bear on this in practice.

(16) C. W. Oatley, Proc. Phys. Soc. Lon. *51*, 318, 1939; G. L. Weissler and G. Kotter, Phys. Rev. *73*, 538, 1948; G. L. Weissler and T. N. Wilson, Phys. Rev. *76*, 591, 1949; G. L. Weissler, Jour. App. Phys. *24*, 472, 1953; R. C. L. Bosworth and E. K. Rideal, Proc. Roy. Soc. *A162*, 1, 1937; Proc. Camb. Phil. Soc. *33*, 394, 1937.

(17) G. K. Wehner, Jour. App. Phys. *25*, 270, 1954; Phys. Rev. *93*, 653A, 1954.

(18) D. Alpert, Jour. App. Phys. *24*, 860, 1953; D. Alpert and R. S. Buritz, Jour. App. Phys. *25*, 202, 1954.

(19) O. Luhr, Phys. Rev. *44*, 459, 1933.

(20) J. K. Theobald, Jour. App. Phys. *24*, 123, 1953.

(21) J. W. Peterson, Jour. App. Phys. *25*, 907, 1954.

(22) J. S. Townsend, *Electricity in Gases*, Oxford University Press, 1915, p. 331; *Electrons in Gases*, Hutchinson's, London, 1947, pp. 98 ff.

(23) M. W. Zemansky, Phys. Rev. *29*, 513, 1927; C. Kenty, Phys. Rev. *42*, 823, 1923; H. W. Webb and H. A. Messenger, Phys. Rev. *33*, 319, 1929; T. Holstein, D. Alpert, and A. O. McCoubrey, Phys. Rev. *76*, 1257, 1949; *85*, 985, 1952; T. Holstein, Phys. Rev. *72*, 1212, 1947; *83*, 1159, 1951.

(24) Bergen Davis and F. S. Goucher, Phys. Rev. *10*, 101, 1917; J. T. Tate, Phys. Rev. *8*, 680, 1916; C. Kenty, Phys. Rev. *44*, 891, 1933; *43*, 181, 1933; *38*, 2079, 1931; E. G. Schneider, Jour. Opt. Soc. Am. *30*, 128, 1940; G. L. Weissler and Po Lee, Jour. Opt. Soc. Am. *42*, 84, 200, 1952; Proc. Roy. Soc. *A219*, 71, 1953; N. Wainfan, W. C. Walker, and G. L. Weissler, Jour. App. Phys. *24*, 1318, 1953; Phys. Rev. *93*, 651A, 1954; W. Oblensky, Ann. d. Physik *36*, 961, 1912; D. S. Burch, R. C. Irick, and R. Geballe, Phys. Rev. *93*, 650A, 1954.

(25) H. L. von Gugelberg, Helv. Phys. Acta *20*, 307, 1947.

(26) E. J. Lauer, Jour. App. Phys. *23*, 300, 1952; L. Colli, Phys. Rev. *95*, 892, 1954; L. Colli and U. Facchini, Phys. Rev. *96*, 1, 1954; H. W. Bandel, Phys. Rev. *95*, 1117, 1954.

(27) C. G. Miller and L. B. Loeb, Jour. App. Phys. *22*, 494, 614, 1951; M. R. Amin, Jour. App. Phys. *25*, 627, 1954; H. W. Bandel, Phys. Rev. *95*, 1117, 1954.

(28) For references and discussion of this early work, see A. L. Hughes and L. A. DuBridge, *Photoelectric Phenomena*, McGraw-Hill, New York, 1932. See also, L. B. Loeb, *Atomic Structure*, John Wiley & Sons, New York, 1938, p. 266.

(29) C. Kenty, Phys. Rev. *80*, 95, 1950; Jour. App. Phys. *21*, 1309, 1950.

(30) E. Flegler and H. Raether, Zeits. f. Phys. *99*, 635, 1936; *103*, 315, 1936; Zeits. f. Tech. Phys. *16*, 435, 1935; A. M. Cravath, Phys. Rev. *47*, 254, 1935; L. B. Loeb, Rev. Mod. Phys. *8*, 267, 1936; R. R. Wilson, Phys. Rev. *50*, 1082, 1936.

(31) R. W. Engstrom and W. S. Huxford, Phys. Rev. *58*, 67, 1940; W. Rogowski, Zeits. f. Phys. *115*, 257, 1940.

(32) L. Malter, Phys. Rev. *49*, 879, 1936; H. Paetow, Zeits. f. Phys. *111*, 770, 1939; H. Jacobs, Phys. Rev. *84*, 877, 1951; H. Jacobs, J. Freely, and F. A. Brand, Phys. Rev. *88*, 492, 1952; D. Dobischek, H. Jacobs, and J. Freely, Phys. Rev. *91*, 804, 1953.

(33) W. Schottky, Zeits. f. Phys. *14*, 63, 80, 1923; O. W. Richardson, Proc. Roy. Soc. *A117*, 719, 1928; W. S. Pforte, Zeits. f. Phys. *49*, 46, 1928; N. A. de Bruyne, Phil. Mag. *5*, 574, 1928; Proc. Roy. Soc. *A120*, 428, 1928; Phys. Rev. *35*, 172, 1930; E. O. Lawrence and L. B. Linford, Phys. Rev. *36*, 482, 1930.

(34) R. Holm, in a report entitled, "Remarks on the Theory of the Arc," Stackpole Carbon Co., St. Marys, Pa., 1949. Also, Conference on Gaseous Electronics, Brookhaven, New York, October 27-29, 1948, paper G2.

(35) J. E. Lilienfeld, Phys. Zeits. *23*, 506, 1922; R. A. Millikan and C. F. Eyring, Phys. Rev. *27*, 51, 1926; R. A. Millikan, C. F. Eyring, and S. S. Mackeown, Phys. Rev. *31*, 900, 1928; R. A. Millikan and C. C. Lauritsen, Phys. Rev. *33*, 598, 1929; F. Roether, Ann. d. Physik *81*, 317, 1926; B. S. Gosling, Phil. Mag. *1*, 609, 1926; T. E. Stern, B. S. Gosling, and R. H. Fowler, Proc. Roy. Soc. *A124*, 699, 1929.

(36) W. V. Houston, Zeits. f. Phys. *47*, 33, 1928; J. R. Oppenheimer, Phys. Rev. *31*, 66, 1928; L. Nordheim, Proc. Roy. Soc. *A119*, 173, 689, 1928; Phys. Zeits. *30*, 177, 1929; R. H. Fowler and L. Nordheim, Proc. Roy. Soc. *A118*, 229, 1928.

(37) C. del Rosario, Jour. Franklin Inst. *103*, 205, 1928; C. C. Chambers, Jour. Franklin Inst. *218*, 463, 1934; A. J. Ahearn, Phys. Rev. *50*, 238, 1936.

(38) E. W. Müller, Zeits. f. Phys. *102*, 734, 1936; Phys. Zeits. *37*, 828, 1936; Zeits. f. Tech. Phys. *17*, 412, 1936; Zeits. f. Phys. *106*, 132, 541, 1937; *108*, 668, 1938; Naturwissenschaften *49*, 820, 1939.

(39) J. E. Henderson and R. E. Badgley, Phys. Rev. *38*, 540, 1931; J. E. Henderson and R. K. Dahlstrom, Phys. Rev. *55*, 473, 1939; F. R. Abbott and J. E. Henderson, Phys. Rev. *56*, 113, 1939.

(40) W. Shockley and R. P. Johnson, Phys. Rev. *49*, 436, 1936.

(41) R. H. Haefer, Zeits. f. Phys. *116*, 604, 1940. An excellent summary is found in R. O. Jenkins, "Reports on Progress in Physics," Phys. Soc. Lon. *9*, 177, 1943.

(42) W. P. Dyke and J. K. Trolan, Phys. Rev. *89*, 799, 1953; W. P. Dyke, W. W. Dolan, and G. Barnes, Jour. App. Phys. *24*, 570, 1953; W. P. Dyke, E. E. Martin, and J. P. Barbour, Phys. Rev. *91*, 1043, 1953; W. W. Dolan, W. P. Dyke, and J. K. Trolan, Phys. Rev. *91*, 1054, 1953; J. P. Barbour, W. W. Dolan, E. E. Martin, and W. P. Dyke, Phys. Rev. *92*, 45, 1953; W. P. Dyke, W. W. Dolan, J. K. Trolan, and F. J. Grundhauser, Jour. App. Phys. *25*, 106, 1954.

(43) J. C. Trump and R. J. van de Graaf, Jour. App. Phys. *18*, 327, 1947.

(44) W. H. Bennett, Phys. Rev. *37*, 582, 1931; *40*, 416, 1932; *44*, 859(L), 1933; *45*, 890, 1934; Phys. Rev. (to be published in 1955). See also, Naval Research Laboratory, Memorandum Report 203, August 12, 1953.

(45) E. W. Haworth, Phys. Rev. *80*, 223, 1950; E. W. Haworth and L. H. Germer, Phys. Rev. *73*, 1121, 1948; Jour. App. Phys. *20*, 1085, 1949; L. H. Germer, Jour. App. Phys. *22*, 958, 1133, 1951; L. H. Germer and J. L. Smith, Jour. App. Phys. *23*, 553, 1952.

(46) L. B. Loeb, G. G. Hudson, A. F. Kip, and W. H. Bennett, Phys. Rev. *60*, 714, 1941; W. N. English, Phys. Rev. *74*, 173, 1948.

(47) G. Holst and E. Oosterhuis, Phil. Mag. *46*, 1117, 1923; L. J. Neuman, Proc. Nat. Acad. Sci. *15*, 259, 1929; F. Ehrenkrantz, Phys. Rev. *55*, 219, 1939.

(48) J. Taylor, Phil. Mag. *3*, 753, 1927; *4*, 405, 1927; Proc. Roy. Soc. *A114*, 73, 1927.

(49) E. Huber, Phys. Rev., January 15, 1955; J. H. Parker, Jr., Phys. Rev. *93*, 1148, 1954.

(50) L. Colli, E. Gatti, and U. Facchini, Phys. Rev. *80*, 92, 1950; *84*, 606, 1951; L. Colli, Phys. Rev. *95*, 892, 1954; L. Colli and U. Facchini Phys. Rev. *96*, 1, 1954.

(51) L. B. Loeb, *Fundamental Processes of Electrical Discharge in Gases*, John Wiley & Sons, New York, 1939, chap. X, sec. 7, pp. 417 ff.

(52) F. Llewellyn Jones and D. E. Davies, Proc. Phys. Soc. Lon. *B64*, 397, 519, 1951.

(53) R. W. Engstrom, Phys. Rev. *55*, 239(A), 1939

(54) A. M. Skellett, Jour. App. Phys. *9*, 631, 1938; F. Schröter and G. Lubszynski, Phys. Zeits. *31*, 897, 1930; K. H. Kingdon and H. E. Thompson, Jour. App. Phys. *1*, 343, 1931; M. R. Campbell and R. S. Rivlin, Proc. Phys. Soc. Lon. *49*, 12, 1937.

(55) A. von Engel and M. Steenbeck, *Elektrische Gasentladungen*, Julius Springer, Berlin, 1934, vol. 2, p. 178; M. Steenbeck, Wiss. Veröff. a. d. Siemens Werken, *9*, 43, 1930; W. Bartolomeyczyk, Zeits. f. Phys. *116*, 235, 1940; R. Schade, Zeits. f. Phys. *104*, 487, 1937.

(56) R. R. Newton, Phys. Rev. *73*, 570, 1948.

(57) J. P. Molnar, Phys. Rev. *83*, 933, 940, 1951.

(58) J. A. Hornbeck, Phys. Rev. *80*, 297, 1950; with G. H. Wannier in Phys. Rev. *82*, 458, 1951; *83*, 374, 1951; *84*, 615, 1951.

(59) W. E. Lamb and R. C. Retherford, Phys. Rev. *79*, 549, 1950.

(60) R. N. Varney, Phys. Rev. *93*, 1156, 1954.

(61) H. den Hartog and F. H. Muller, Physica *15*, 789, 1949.

(62) J. P. Molnar and A. V. Phelps, Phys. Rev. *89*, 1202, 1953.

(63) H. G. Stever, Phys. Rev. *61*, 38, 1942.

(64) C. G. Miller and L. B. Loeb, Jour. App. Phys. *22*, 740, 1951.

(65) M. R. Amin, Jour. App. Phys. *25*, 210, 358, 1954.

(66) L. B. Loeb, Phys. Rev. *86*, 256, 1952.

(67) A. F. Kip, Phys. Rev. *55*, 549, 1939; W. N. English, Phys. Rev. *71*, 638, 1947; *74*, 170, 1948.

(68) L. B. Loeb, Phys. Rev. *73*, 798, 1948; L. B. Loeb and R. J. Wijsman, Jour. App. Phys. *19*, 797, 1948.

(69) F. Alder, E. Baldinger, P. Huber, and F. Metzger, Helv. Phys. Acta *20*, 73, 1947.

(70) E. E. Dodd, Phys. Rev. *78*, 620, 1950.

(71) J. M. Meek, Phys. Rev. *57*, 722, 1940; L. B. Loeb and J. M. Meek, *Mechanism of the Electric Spark*, Stanford University Press, 1941.

(72) H. Raether, Zeits. f. Phys. *117*, 375, 524, 1941; Arch. f. Elektrotech. *34*, 49, 1940.

(73) R. C. Fletcher, Phys. Rev. *76*, 1501, 1949. See also, L. B. Loeb, ONR report, *Electrical Breakdown in Uniform Fields*. (In press. To appear early in 1955.)

APPENDIX I

NOTES COVERING ADVANCES, 1955-1959

Since the spring of 1955 when this book was published, there appeared in 1956 volumes xxi and xxii of the *Encyclopedia of Physics* from the press of Springer Verlag, West Berlin, Heidelberg, and Göttingen, edited by S. Flügge. Volume xxi contains chapters on (1) Thermionic Emission, by Wayne B. Nottingham; (2) Field Emission, by R. H. Good, Jr., and Erwin W. Müller; (3) Secondary Emission of Solids Under Electron Impact, by R. Kollath (in German); (4) Photoionization in Gases, by C. L. Weissler; (5) Motions of Ions and Electrons in Gases (comprehensive theory only, with no experimental data on ions, their nature, and formation), by W. P. Allis; (6) Formation of Negative Ions and (7) Recombinations of Ions, by L. B. Loeb; (8) Ionization by Electrons in Electrical Fields, by A. von Engel; (9) Secondary Effects, by P. F. Little. All these chapters except (3) are in English. Chapters (1), (2), (3), and (4) are excellent and cover basic atomic processes that are not found in this book. (5) is a very valuable comprehensive summary of the advanced theory of chapters i, ii, iii, and iv of this book but omits all experimental data and theory of ionic composition. The other chapters cover in less detail the content of other chapters of this book. Volume xxii deals with discharge forms and applies basic processes to these manifestation. Chapter (1), by F. Llewellyn Jones, deals with Ionization Growth and Breakdown from the viewpoint of Townsend's school and data from that writer's laboratory. Chapter (2) dealing with the Glow Discharge, by G. Francis, is a very complete comprehensive treatment of the subject. Chapter (3) deals with Radiation from Low Pressure Discharges. It is an excellent treatment by R. G. Fowler which, by content, belongs properly in volume xxi. Chapter (4), in German, is a most outstanding contribution on Arc Discharge, by H. Maecker and W. Finkelnburg. Chapter (5) deals with Electrical Breakdown with Steady or D.C. Impulse Potentials, by L. B. Loeb. Chapter (6), by S. C. Brown, deals with Alternating Potential Breakdown including Microwave Breakdown. Chapter (7), deals with Lightning Discharge by the world's leading authority, B. F. J. Schonland. Except (4), all chapters are in English.

The material in these two volumes supplement and augment the present book.

Beyond the data mentioned above, some important advances since the present volume went to press merit presentation. These are presented in order of the chapters to which they belong.

Chapter 1

IONIC MOBILITIES

Most notable is the discovery of new ion species in the inert gases. H. J. Oskam (1) in a microwave study of decaying plasmas in Ne-He mixtures inferred the creation of $NeHe^+$ ions as a dominating structure from Ne^+ ions These new species were independently and simultaneously verified by M. Pahl and U. Weimer (2), using an effusion mass spectrograph. The latter investigators also observed a predominating formation of AH^+ ions, with only 1% of H_2 in A at pressures below 3 mm Hg replacing the prevalent A_2^+ ions. These ions had long been known to exist from early mass spectrographic studies at very low pressures but were not known to be a predominating species in breakdown studies. More work on ions in discharges using effusion type mass spectrographs on N_2, by H. Dreeskamp (3) and O. M. Saproschenko (4) in Varney's laboratory, reveals the presence of N^+, N_2^+, N_3^+, and N_4^+ ions. The N_4^+ ions are unstable with heat of formation of < 0.2 e.v. and are formed by the reaction $N_3^+ + N_2 \rightarrow N_4^{+*}$. N_3^+ appears at 22.1 ± 0.5 e.v. which is an appearance potential greater than that for N_2^+ but less than that for N^+ and thus comes from a reaction $N_2^{+*} + N_2 \rightarrow N_3^+ + N$. Dreeskamp did not observe N_4^+, but his conditions were not such as to observe so unstable an ion. Of value also are measurements of the mobilities of Hg ions in the inert gas series by Channin and Biondi (5), since these ions figure in ion cataphoresis and other studies. Later work on temperature variation of mobilities in A and the inert gases, by E. C. Beaty (6), and by L. M. Channin and M. A. Biondi (6), led to assumption of the possible existence not only of A^+ and A_2^+ but of an A_2^+ ion in an excited state having a different collision cross section from that of A_2^+. Uncertainty still exists as to the low X/p values for the He_2^+ ions. The temperature variation was compared with theory. R. N. Varney, F. R. Kovar, and E. C. Beaty (7) also measured the temperature variation of the ions in N_2^+. L. S. Frost (8) investigated the influence of a variable ion mobility on the ambipolar diffusion coefficient such as might be caused by the variation of K with X/p. He showed that the diffusion coefficient can be lowered by a factor of three in such action, although the magnitude of the effect in the column of a glow discharge where K does not vary by a large factor alters D by no more than 10%. D. S. Burch and R. Geballe (9) evaluated negative and positive ion mobilities and electron attachment coefficients in O_2. This very important paper assigns proper roles to the formation of O_2^- and O^- ions. It also indicates the existence of three positive ions O^+, $K \sim 3.38$, O_2^+, $K \sim 2.2\text{-}1.95$ and O_3^+, $K \sim 2.5$, and three negative ions including the O_3^- ion beyond the two mentioned. Probable modes of formation are indicated.

M. A. Biondi points out that Blanc's law for carrier mobilities in gaseous mixtures requires broader interpretation than the simple statement that the law holds as long as the nature of the ion remains invariant in both gases. This law derives from the assumption that the collision cross section σ_{AA} and σ_{AB} of ions of gas A in gases A and B in the two component mixtures are independent of the composition of the gas so that mobility varies in proportion to the relative numbers of A and B atoms, respectively. Since drift velocities and cross sections derive from force laws rather than from solid elastic type impacts between ion and molecule, it follows that action leading to the cross section σ_{AA} of A ions in A gas follows one law, whereas σ_{AB}, those of ions A in gas B, follow another law. Thus collision cross sections will no longer necessarily vary in proportion to the concentrations of A and B molecules. Thus if ions A interact by charge exchange forces with atoms A and thus have solid elastic impacts whereas polarization forces with atoms B determine σ_{AB}, the values of σ_{AB} will vary with composition. It can be shown that in such cases a much more rigorous derivation is required which leads to deviations in the $1/K_{AB}$ plot against mole fraction similar in shape to those created by cluster formation. The situation is much more pronounced for electron mobilities in mixtures where energy distribution laws at the X/p values are different for gases A and B, as Ramsauer free paths vary differently with velocity. This may account for the results of W. N. English with drift velocities of electrons in counter gas mixtures.

A very complete paper by E. A. Mason, H. W. Schamp, Jr., and J. T. Vanderslice (10) coördinates on ion mobility theory the Muschlitz and other interaction cross sections with the polarization and repulsive force terms for ions in gases. They further reëxamine the theory of mobilities of Li^+ ions in He with relatively no more success than the earlier study of Geltman. A very important paper by Mason and Vanderslice on mobilities of hydrogen ions in H_2 yields values of 13.9, 17, and 22 cm^2/volt sec to H_2^+, H^+, and H_3^+, respectively, in H_2 identifying the commonly observed ion as H_2^+, H^+ observed only by Persson; H_3^+ not observed. Rose (11) has recently reported mobilities in very pure H_2 at high X/p, using Hornbeck's technique. Uninterpreted data indicate two mobilities may be involved (13.4 and 17) with complex transition curves akin to those of Varney in N_2. More work using mass spectrograph is needed.

Electron Interactions in a Gas

Here little that is startling has emerged. Of note are papers with the following titles: A Microwave Study of Excitation Probability in Ne, by A. L. Gilardini and S. C. Brown (12) in 1957 and Evaluation of Electron Mobility in Geiger Counter Gases, by T. E. Bortner, G. S. Hurst, and G. W. Stone (13), using a new method. R. Haas made studies of the energy loss of slow electrons in N_2. A. H. Dougal and L. Goldstein (14) evaluated energy exchange through Coulomb collisions between ions and electrons. L. Goldstein, J. Sekiguchi, and H. Fletcher (15) determined electron interaction and heat conduction in gases. Some of these data do not agree with earlier and later microwave studies. H. Margenau (16) developed a cyclotron resonance method for evaluating collision cross sections of low energy electrons. L. G. H. Huxley (17) has extended his free path formulae for the coefficient of diffusion and electron drift velocity in gases. M. P. Madan, E. I. Gordon, and S. J. Buchsbaum (18) determined the frequency of ionization in a microwave breakdown.

Probe Techniques

Outstanding in this direction is a microwave study by G. Schultz and S. C. Brown (20) of positive ion collection by probes. L. S. Frost and A. V. Phelps (19) computed energy distribution functions in H_2 at 77 K at X/p values so that rotational excitation predominates. Deduced values of K and D/K are compared with experimental values. Excitational cross sections are 2.5 times those of Gerjuoy and Stein with a momentum transfer cross section in agreement with Bekefi and Brown. T. H. Yeung and J. Sayers (21) developed a radio frequency probe technique for the measurement of plasma electron concentrations in the presence of negative ions. Further work on the collection of positive ions by a probe in a plasma, correcting and extending the conclusions of Boyd reported earlier in this book, was carried on by R. L. F. Boyd, P. Reynolds, and J. E. Allen (22). T. Okada and K. Yamamoto (23) report studies on the disturbance phenomena in probe studies of ionized gases. However, this material represents very little new in critique of probe studies not previously collected in this book. G. Medicus (24) extended the earlier developments and techniques on automatic plotting of probe curves developed jointly with Wehner as previously reported; he indicates a simple way of obtaining electron velocity distributions of electrons in discharge plasmas from probe curves. He also obtained diffusion and elastic collision losses of fast electrons in plasmas. In principle he reapplies the Sloane and McGregor weak superposed A. C. method to probes to obtain the form of the distribution law. He justifies his procedure on application of what he calls "the simplest form of the diffusion law." Using a ball of fire mode of glow discharge, he delineated the presence of a low energy distribution and another group of electrons with an independent and high energy. These curves recall the earlier two component curves of Druyvesteyn which had been shown to be spurious. Whether the present analysis of Medicus is justified remains for the future to determine.

Negative Ions

The development of the retarding potential method coupled with mass spectrograph studies have led to significant advances in this field of study. These are reported by W. M. Hickam and R. E. Fox (25) for electron attachment in SF_6. The curves for the probability of attachment as a function of energy indicate attachment as peaking at zero electron energy. This gas can be used for correcting for contact potentials and calibrating curves for other processes. R. E. Fox (26) next investigated negative ion formation in HCl as a function of electron energy. He confirms the dissociative process and finds about the same energy as inferred in Bradbury's earlier work. As energy increases, other processes occur at certain critical potentials, whose investigation corrects and reinterprets earlier conclusions of Neuert (27) on HCl. A sequence of three papers by M. A. Biondi and R. E. Fox (28) reports results on the application of their new techniques to the dissociative attachment of electrons in I_2. Cross sections as a function of energy are obtained and discrepancies with other work are much clarified. Fox (28) also studied electron attachment in NO_2.

G. J. Schulz (29) investigated the formation of H^- by electron impact on H_2. Appearance potentials indicate energies in these processes to be much higher than those active in most gaseous breakdown studies. Three different processes are observed at different energies. The study of negative ions in oxygen has been investigated by several observers. As indicated, D. S. Burch and R. Geballe find three different negative ions which they identify as O^-, O_2^-, and O_3^- in terms of the drift velocities in comparison to those of O^+, O_2^+, and O_3^+. The mechanism of formation is analyzed relative to changes with pressure and X/p ratios. J. D. Craggs, A. Thorborn, and B. A. Toze (30) studied ions in O_2, their study dealing primarily with dissociative attachment.

Using very intense localized ionization of short duration from a high energy electron accelerator beam and measuring electron densities as a function of time with a weak microwave probing signal, V. A. I. Van Lint, E. G. Wikner, and D. L. Trueblood (31) studied attachment in O_2, O_2-N_2, and O_2-He mixtures over an extended low temperature range. From 1 to 150 mm Hg negative ion formation was a three-body process with a minimum at 170°K. At 300° N_2 molecules act as 5.3% effective third bodies. Addition of He showed electrons to be at the low temperature. The three-body reaction of O_2 is given by $-dn/dt = \text{Kn } N^2$, with n electron and N molecule densities and $K = 2.1 \times 10^{-30}$ cm^6 sec^{-1}. An extensive investigation of negative ion formation in O_2 by L. M. Channin and Biondi (32), using the Loeb electron filter adapted by Bradbury and Nielsen as an electrical shutter with superb techniques, clearly delineates the attachment to form O_2^- and its decline with energy. They note, however, a large increase in attachment when dissociative attachment forming O^- sets in at an average swarm energy of about 1.62 e.v. as indicated in this text. The sensitivity of the method is such that the pressure dependence of the O_2^- process, long sought without success, is observed and can be followed up to 46 mm pressure. Later study presented by Phelps (33) indicated that the course of the Bradbury-Bloch theory is followed. However, the data indicate that the binding energy of 0.15 e.v. ascribed to it by Branscomb would make the ion quite unstable at 300°K and may be more nearly 0.30 e.v. Another outstanding series of contributions are those of D. S. Burch, S. J. Smith, and L. M. Branscomb and S. Geltman (34) at the Bureau of Standards on the photo detachment of electrons from O^- with accompanying theory, and a second by the first three authors in which photodetachment of the O_2^- ion is at last observed. From the theory of S. Geltman (35) their data evaluate the attachment energy of O_2^- as 0.15 ± 0.05 e.v., disproving the value of 0.9 volt assigned by Massey. This confirms the lower value assumed by Bradbury and Bloch and that inferred from the writer's impact detachment study as < 0.37 e.v. Cross sections for photodetachment of O_2^- at 3 e.v. are 2.4×10^{-18} cm^2 whereas those for O^- at 3 e.v. are 7×10^{-18} cm^2. The heat of formation of O^- is set as 1.465 ± 0.005 e.v. One more outstanding contribution in this period by P. M. Waters (36) in the writer's laboratory was the observation that the notorious mechanism first reported by F. Arnott that positive ions, atoms, or molecules, of such nature as to have a positive electron affinity, could neutralize themselves and add an electron on impact with metal surfaces at impact energies above some 100 volts, with a probability of the order of 10^{-3} or 10^{-4}, does *not* occur for Li^+ in impact with atomically clean W to more than one part in 10^8. If the W is soiled by exposure to air, Li^+ ions of some hundred volts *sputter off* negative ions, presumably of O^-, to the extent of one in 10^3. Thus the Arnott process is not a basic mechanism of neutralization and charge exchange from atomically clean metal surfaces but probably a sputtering off of adsorbed negative ions as the author predicted in volume xxi of the *Encyclopedia of Physics*.

Recombination of Ions

In this field rather extensive progress has been made. The observation of large recombination rates assumed to occur for electrons in inert gases from microwave data was after 1950, associated with molecular ion formation and dissociative recombination. However, as data in chapter vi indicate, pressure variations and other unorthodox behavior of the observed coefficients made most of the data suspect.

Earlier workers with the microwave techniques were aware of the sources of errors inherent in a method which observes only electron loss and attempted to avoid them. They were, however, not aware of the nonlinearity of $1/n - t$ plots with disparate electron-molecular-ion densities that occur under most conditions of their observations and of other inherent errors such that they applied oversimplified analyses to data of a temporally inadequate range. Thus they ascribed too much accuracy to their data and drew unwarranted conclusions as will now appear.

The first clarifying contribution was that of K. B. Persson (37) in 1957 on limitations of microwave methods in the measurement of electron densities in H_2. Here it was shown that unless great care was used, higher modes of ambipolar diffusion, the appearance of trace electron attaching impurities from the cleanest cell walls, etc., can lead to false apparent values of recombination coefficients. He then showed that with great care observations of electron loss in pure H_2 gas *do not indicate a dissociative recombination to occur,* contrary to the earlier results reported by Biondi and Brown and by L. J. Varnerin before 1955. The ambipolar diffusion coefficient for ions in H_2 gas, assumed to be exceptionally pure and devoid of higher diffusion modes as inferred by Persson, corresponds to a new mobility of 17 $cm^2/volt$ sec. This value is definitely higher than that of the other investigators, is a value new to the literature, and is indicated by Vanderslice and Mason (10) to be that of H^+ which has a very small recombination cross section. The whole matter merits further studies including mass spectrographic analysis. Whether dissociative recombination occurs in the supposedly less pure H_2 of the earlier studies is still an open question. The work of Persson was followed by studies in He, Ne, A, and other inert gases and in mixtures of Ne and He, He and A, Ne and A, Kr, etc., after a very careful review and analysis of past theory and experiment in a thesis by H. J. Oskam (1). He studied the electron loss in the older plasmas at 5 and 30 mm pressure with increased sensitivity, avoiding many pitfalls in technique of the past using older plasmas, e.g., in excess of 1 m sec old. Besides discovering the $NeHe^+$ ions and observing dissociative recombination in Ne_2^+ in agreement with Biondi, as well as for the $NeHe^+$ ion, he failed to observe any recombination loss of note in He. Loss of electrons and He_2^+ ions was largely by ambipolar diffusion. This seemed contrary to the 1948 observations of Biondi which Biondi also now repudiates.

The values of He_2^+ mobilities derived from ambipolar diffusion in He by Oskam were 17.3 $cm^3/volt$ sec, which agrees with Hornbeck's extrapolated values from direct measurement but disagrees with Tyndall and Powell's value of 21.6 as well as the value of 20 by Biondi and Channin and Kerr's (38) recently corrected value of 18.5 from diffusion. Oskam's values for Ne^+ in He are around 24, and for A^+ in He are about 23. Kerr ascribes the low value of Oskam for He in this time interval to neglect of correction for the generation of He^+ ions and electrons from metastable atoms. Oskam ascribes the formation of Ne He^+, in He with small amounts of Ne to the reaction $He_2^+ + Ne \rightarrow Ne^+ + 2He$, as ionization potentials are close and cross sections are large. Then $Ne^+ + 2He \rightarrow NeHe^+ + He$, and $Ne^+ + Ne + He \rightarrow NeHe^+ + Ne$ at an appreciably lower rate depending on relative pressures. A does not form an He^+ ion. Recent careful analysis of the limits of applicability and reliability of the microwave method for α from the slope of the $1/n - t$ plot have been made by E. P. Gray and Kerr (38). Solutions were achieved with only one ion over a wide range of $\beta = \alpha n_0 \Lambda^2/D_a$ of the diffusion equation. It was concluded that linear $1/\bar{n} - t$ plots do not prove recombination to control $\bar{n}$ unless $\bar{n}$ changes by a factor of 5 or more over the linear portion (2). The method is valid, i.e., the slope of the $1/n - t$ plot is close to α only for large β.

The work of D. E. Kerr (38) and his group at Johns Hopkins, using both microwave and optical observations, extended studies in pure He from 2 m secs out to 70 and later to early times and low pressures. Increased sensitivity of detection permitted studies out to these long time intervals at 50 to 30 mm pressure. In his studies with 10- to 100-fold greater sensitivity, carried out over long time intervals with very pure gases including simultaneous spectral analyses, he was able to avoid the pitfalls indicated above but they cover a different time range from those of others to be reported. His initial electron loss, as with Oskam, was largely by ambipolar diffusion of He_2^+ out to 30 m secs. There is a parallel loss of intensity of a molecular band spectrum of He_2^* over the same time interval. This decline Kerr ascribes to a slow triple impact reaction of He_2^+ electron and an He atom leading to the excited He_2^* molecules. Being slow it naturally parallels the rapid decline of He_2^+ by diffusion and becomes too faint to see through decrease in He_2^+ after 30 m secs. It plays only a minor role in loss of He_2^+ ions and electrons. The decay of electrons from 30 to 70 m secs is ascribed by Kerr to an effective reduced ambipolar diffusion of He_2^+ ions leading to an apparent mobility of 17.3 cm^2/volt sec as also observed by Oskam in this period. The decrease in diffusive loss results from the simultaneous formation of He^+ ions and electrons by interaction of two He^m metastable atoms. Metastable atoms are created to the extent of 10^{14} per cm^3 by the discharge. They diffuse very slowly compared to He_2^+. Thus the ultimate long time loss of the carriers in this reaction is determined by the loss of the He^m by diffusion. The small He^+ formation and recreation of electrons reducing the observed loss of electrons leads obviously to the lowered ambipolar diffusion loss of the faster He_2^+ created in triple impacts of He^+ with He atoms. In the longer time intervals this loss of He_2^+ becomes very slow compared to diffusion losses of He^m, because of slowing of He_2^+ formation at the very low concentrations compared to the residual He^m. This study confirms Oskam's failure to observe recombination electron loss in the *later* afterglow of He, and may account for Oskam's low value of mobility of He_2^+.

In the meanwhile W. A. Rogers (39) in a doctoral dissertation under Biondi made an intensive study of the electron loss, spectral light distribution, and Doppler shift of lines in the He afterglow from the time of microwave breakdown on out to $\sim$ 2 m sec in continuation of Bondi's earlier studies reported in this book. During breakdown the light is the directly radiated light of excited atomic He states created by electron impact including the cascading of electrons from higher levels down. Many He_2^+ ions and electrons are initially formed by the Hornbeck-Molnar process. Once breakdown terminates, all ionization drops to a minimum near zero as does the light intensity as a result of fast ambipolar diffusion of He_2^+ the electrons and the radiation within $\sim$ 10^{-6} sec. Thereafter the light intensity of helium atomic lines and electron density builds up to a peak at about 1 m sec. The atomic lines observed are very little broadened by Doppler shift in this period. After breakdown the metastable, He^m, concentration is probably of the order of 10^{14} per cm^3 and thus so exceedingly high as to dominate the whole afterglow period. This follows from the low diffusion coefficient of He^m and the tendency of higher states, including resonant states by imprisonment of resonance radiation, to end as He^m. Thus, while at 5 mm pressure the He_2^+ and electrons are rapidly lost by diffusion, the metastable actions persist. The interaction of two He^m atoms in the period of rise of intensity creates He^+ ions and free electrons having 16 volts energy. These electrons in turn excite the other He^m atoms to higher excited atomic states, which return by cascading to the ground state and emit the line spectrum showing for example the lines $4,472A^\circ$ and $5,876A^\circ$. The He^+ ions at a slower rate undergo triple impacts with He atoms yielding He_2^+ ions in high vibrational states. These reactions take time so that as the electrons degrade from 16 volts energy by collisions, the high rate of ionization of He^m declines. Thus there is a decrease in light from He^*, a decrease in He^+ while He_2^+ ions are created and electrons slow down. These electrons and the He_2^+ ions are chiefly lost by ambipolar diffusion in the later afterglow period as Kerr and Oskam show. However, in the earlier period after rise in luminosity and during the decline of the peak, at $\sim$ 1 m sec some of these molecular ions recombine dissociatively, leading to an excited He^* atom and unexcited ones in sufficient number for the light radiated to be visible. These excited He^* atoms have rather high energies in consequence of the high state of excitation of freshly created He_2^+. Thus they yield the prominent atomic lines $4,472A^\circ$ and $5,876A^\circ$ in that period of the afterglow. These lines, in contrast to the same lines seen during the rise period, appear to be appreciably Doppler broadened. Investigation of the unexpected changes in relative intensities between the Doppler-broadened and nonbroadened lines in the decline part of the afterglow with pressure show that some of the highly excited states produced cascade down and emit light that is not appreciably broadened, whereas other lines emitted show broadening, indicating that they come from states freshly created by dissociation. The variation of the line intensities as observed at two different pressures leaves no great doubt about what is occurring. These studies were not extended to longer periods as observed by Oskam and Kerr, nor did they use as sensitive detection devices for this was not necessary. However, they prove the presence of dissociative recombination of He_2^+ during the first m sec of afterglow. The effect of this process on electron decline is, however, never the dominant loss process, as assumed from earlier data in this book in agreement with the observations of Oskam and Kerr. Evidence is at hand that by the time the He_2^+ ion decline is observed by Oskam and by Kerr the He_2^+ ions have lost most of their vibrational energy and are thus incapable of yielding dissociative recombination. The electrons also have cooled to thermal values.

The very important contribution of these investigations is that in He_2^+ only in the relatively long-lived highly vibrational excited state of newly created He_2^+ can appreciable dissociative recombination loss occur and, as is to be expected from theory, this leads to excited Doppler broadened atomic lines. It seems likely as well that a small fraction of the He_2^+ ions can undergo a three-body recombination process yielding He_2^* by triple impacts with an electron and an atom of He leading to a band spectrum of He_2^*. *Neither proc-*

ess, *each of which is confined to a relatively limited* time interval, *contributes markedly to loss of electrons from the plasma.* It is also clear that though He_2^+ exists in the later periods beyond 2 m secs, this He_2^+ seems not to be able to recombine appreciably dissociatively to give $He^* + He$. This can only be ascribed to the loss of the vibrational excitation needed for recombination through impacts with He atoms as time goes on. It is thus clear that electron loss in the later afterglow is largely by ambipolar diffusion of He_2^+ and that recreation of electrons and He_2^+ by He^m complicates the loss rate. Thus the first observed difference in disappearance rates of electrons from those assumed to occur for He_2^+ by ambipolar diffusion loss alone were erroneously ascribed to a recombination loss. Actually the loss was probably caused by spurious processes such as higher modes of diffusion, possible contamination, etc., and did not represent true phenomena attributable to He. In Ne, however, Oskam's critical methods do verify Biondi's observations of a loss of Ne_2^+ and $NeHe^+$ as well by dissociative recombination. However, in this case the energy relations of the molecular ions are different from those in He. Still later studies of Kerr (40) at low pressures in short time intervals indicate that there is still much to be learned despite these revealing data. The conclusions to be drawn from these investigations indicate that in the first place the reactions taking place in decaying plasmas are much more complex than was originally suspected. This situation, together with the nonlinearity of the $1/n - t$ plots for recombination, unless electron and ion concentrations are closely commensurate, the action of higher diffusion modes and of trace impurities as well as secondary electron generation from metastable interaction, etc., make it very doubtful if any conclusions concerning recombination loss in competition with ambipolar diffusion can *safely be drawn on the basis of temporal declines in average electron density alone.* Thus the data on dissociative electron-ion recombination reported in chapter vi needs reassessment and careful checking, especially where pressure dependence is observed. There is no doubt, however, that dissociative recombination physically occurs with large coefficients following reversal of reactions of the Hornbeck-Molnar type. On the principle of detailed balancing, the cross sections for such recombination should be correspondingly large, leading to rapid loss. What, however, most workers lost sight of in their early enthusiasm is that the large cross sections apply to the *exact reversal* of the process as would be expected in a *plasma in thermal equilibrium.* That is the reaction

$$H^* + He \leftrightarrows He_2^{+v} + e + 1/2 \, mv^2$$

as written will apply *only when* in the gas He_2^{+v} and $(e + 1/2 \, mv^2)$ *have the appropriate values of the* $^{+v}$ *and of* $1/2 \, mv^2$. Such a condition may only occur during limited time intervals in the afterglow since vibrational deëxcitation of He_2^{+v} must occur in time and since the electrons must be in the correct phase of their cooling down period after receiving energy. In the case of Ne_2^+ and $NeHe^+$ there seems to be a rather large loss of electrons by dissociative recombination between 0.25 and 2.5 m sec relative to ambipolar diffusion according to Oskam. Whether it leads to line emission open to experimental observation remains to be seen. Biondi also observed electron-ion loss in pure Ne with nearly the same coefficient α of 2.3×10^{-7} cm^3/sec whereas for $NeHe^+$ the value of α is 4.1×10^{-7} cm^3/sec. That this loss should so far exceed the ambipolar diffusion loss of Ne^+ and $NeHe^+$ in He when the mo-bilities of Ne^+ are $\sim$ 24 cm^2 volt and those of $NeHe^+$ presumably equally high is not clear. That Ne_2^+ formation differs from that of He_2^+ in that the Ne_2^+ does not seem to require high vibrational excitation so that recombination may only require electrons of near thermal energy has earlier been indicated by Biondi and Holstein as stated in this book. However, too little is known about the energies involved to make predictions. Much more work needs to be done combining electron decay with spectroscopic and mass spectroscopic tech-niques during long time intervals with proper precautions.

Only one more paper on recombination is that of T. H. Y. Yeung (41) who studied the ion-ion recombination coefficient in Br_2 and I_2. He studied the change in dielectric constant of the highly electronegative gas discharge plasma caused by the loss of electrons through attachment to yield negative ions with subsequent ion-ion recombination. Even at 10^{13} electron/cm^3 at 0.05 mm Hg pressure the electrons disappear by attachment within 300μ secs after the discharge. Thereafter, any change in dielectric constant yields ion densities. Using pulsed radio frequency discharges the ion-ion recombination coefficients of 1.47×10^{-8} and 1.85×10^{-8} cm^3/sec were found for I_2 and Br_2. respectively. The recombination process does not seem to follow the Thomson mechanism, the cross section for the process decreasing by a factor of $\sim$ 3 as temperature increases from $293°$ to $380°$ K. The coefficient is *independent of pressure* from $\sim$ 0.07 to 1 mm Hg. The value of the cross section is 8.7×10^{-13} cm^2 at $293°$ K. The temperature variation of the process is larger than the Thomson theory leads one to expect, and independence of pressure is not in conformity with the Thomson mechanism. The cross section of $\sim 10^{-12}$ cm^2 is materially smaller than that of Thomson's sphere of active attraction at $293°$ K which is $\sim 10^{-11}$ cm^2. The author ascribes the recombina-tion to molecular ions I_2^- and Br_2^-. Since the molecules of I_2 and Br_2 are in the 1Σ type of ground states they should have no electron affinity and Cl_2^- and Br_2^- should not form. The negative ions in these gases have *repeatedly* been identified mass spectrographically as I^- and Br^-, and this is recently con-firmed by the excellent work of Fox and Biondi for I_2. However, more com-plicated reactions could set in at higher densities. The low cross section for recombination could well be expected as charge transfer for the very strongly bound I^- and Br^- ions will give a very small value to the Thomson factor, and lack of pressure dependence implies that the triple collisions removing energy of thermal motion within the sphere of active attraction are not important in the charge transfer process in these gases. This action may be associated with large mass, strong polarization forces, and large radii of such molecules. This unorthodox ion-ion recombination behavior requires much more extensive investigation. Atom ion-electron recombination of H^+ ions has been observed by Fowler and Atkinson (42) in the intense ionization in shock waves.

The First Townsend Coefficient

New and more accurate data for H_2 have been obtained for very pure H_2 and D_2 under Alpert cleanliness conditions by D. J. Rose (43) at Bell Laboratories. His data fit well on a smooth α/X curve. At low X/p they lie below Ayers values and not far from Hales though they are more consistent. They show Hales data to be quite low and erratic at intermediate X/p. Similar measure-ments were made by L. H. Fisher and D. J. Debitetto (44) for both N_2 and H_2

using an all metal chamber, not outgassed. The contamination was not such as to affect seriously α in H_2. How good the data in N_2 are is not determinable since O_2, the most common contaminent next to H_2O, has a first coefficient not far different. Second coefficients in this study are, however, completely in error for N_2. In H_2 the second coefficients are not badly affected because of the reducing and gettering action of H^+ ions. W. Hopwood, N. J. Peacock, and D. Wilkes (45) in 1956 also measured coefficients for H_2 in all metal chambers that were not outgassed, using contaminated electrodes and relatively impure gas. In general, impurities can seriously alter values of α as witness the extreme case of traces of A in Ne, or of Hg in A. In H_2 gas J. M. Somerville, H. A. Blevin, and S. C. Haydon (46) in a note to *Nature* indicate the peculiar insensitivity of α values in H_2 to impurities. Second coefficients under unclean conditions are usually meaningless except as applied to that experiment. M. A. Harrison (47) in 1957 observed the first coefficient in N_2 for an X/p of 24 to 82. The chamber was the relatively clean glass chamber used by Geballe and Harrison for evaluation of the effect of attachment on the first coefficient. The N_2 used was pure to 0.01% by mass spectroscopic measurement, that from NaN_3 being purest. The values agreed very well with Bowles but extended to much lower X/p in virtue of the long range of variation of gap length possible. The data of Ayers lay far above these data at low X/p and Posin's impure N_2 lay well below. Harrison's values of impure N_2 with some O_2 and A lay below the curve. The data agree quite well with those of Crompton, Dutton, Hayden, and Lewellyn Jones (48). In the work of Crompton, Dutton, Hayden, and Lewellyn Jones (48) the gas was not so pure since the metal chamber and other electrodes were not outgassed.

Very important in recent advances are the studies of single avalanches and the avalanche statistics since the significant applications of the first coefficient lie primarily in the evaluation of avalanche sequences. The static methods of investigation of the first coefficient reveal only average values of α where the process is one depending on different mechanisms of ionization beyond direct impact, some of which involve temporal delays. Modern techniques involving fast oscilloscope studies require knowledge not only of the average static values but of the temporal factors in the behavior of α and the statistical fluctuations of the resulting successive avalanche sequences.

In the matter of avalanche statistics a major advance was made by W. Legler (49) in Raether's laboratory; he extended the work of Wijsman to successions of avalanches and the development of a chain of generations of avalanches from a γ and $e^{\alpha x}$ sequence. This leads to predictions concerning the build-up of a breakdown initiated by single electron avalanches. The basic equations of Legler had earlier been foreshadowed and were later extended and applied to different geometries as well as tested experimentally in the work of K. J. Schmidt (50) on electron avalanches in uniform fields and in counters. Later studies by L. Frommhold (51) in "Statistics of Avalanches in Uniform and Other Fields, I, II, and III" extended and corroborated the theory. This work extends observations from Geiger-counter gases to air and studies secondary actions in relation to the succession of generations. K. J. Schmidt-Tiedemann (52) developed a broad band noise-suppressing amplifier that extended oscilloscopic detection and measurement of single avalanches from 10^7 down to nearly 10^3 electrons per avalanche. J. K. Vogel and H. Raether (53) observed single avalanches at high $p\,d$ values and inferred the secondary mechanism observing that γ_p is the predominating action in air.

More details are given by Vogel (53) in a later paper in which he observes ion drift velocities and negative ion formation in O_2. In N_2 and air a notably delayed ionization is observed which confirms Bandel's (IX 7) data in air and indicates secondary ionizing mechanisms in α. A further investigation of Legler (54) studied the ultraviolet radiation from avalanches in the hope of observing photons of wave lengths greater than 2,000 A°. From 20-120 cm × mm Hg pressure of air between 3,300 and 3,600 A°, about 0.4 photons per electron were observed. This alone enables an avalanche series triggered by a photo-electric γ to be observed. Frommhold (55) also investigated the potential change produced by a charge between plates of a parallel plate condenser system including the edge effects. He considered a single charge as well as a cloud of charges. This led to the conclusion that irregularities in avalanche profiles previously attributed to negative ions in such gaps are in reality caused by avalanches near the plate edges. In consequence A-C_2H_5OH mixtures were shown to have less than 5% negative ions. Further papers in this area belong properly to the study of second coefficients. This applies to papers by R. Kluckow and K. J. Schmidt-Tiedemann mentioned later.

Secondary Processes Active in Discharges

Here some important advances have also been made. Studies of secondary emission on positive ion bombardment were extended by H. D. Hagstrum (56) for effects of metastable ions of the inert gases from which increased γ_i coefficients in the inert gases were obtained. Hagstrum also studied the effects of monolayer absorption times on γ_i. H. W. Berry (57) finally published his excellent paper on kinetic emission of secondary electrons by impact of fast neutral He atoms from 1,000 to 4,000 volts on clean surfaces. Perhaps the most interesting contribution was the direct verification of the *kinetic emission* γ_i process for C_s^+ and Li^+ on atomically clean W surfaces by P. M. Waters (58). Data for Li^+ were closely parallel to and just below those computed for kinetic emission on W by He^+ ions by Hagstrum through deducting his theoretically computed potential emission from the observed total emission by He^+ as a function of energy. The values ranged from $\sim 10^{-6}$ at 150 e.v. to 6.2×10^{-2} and 1.2×10^{-2} at 1,500 volts for Li^+ and C_s^+ respectively. Below 350 e.v. the secondary kinetic value of γ_i was increased by a factor of ~ 10 and by 2-3 at 350 e.v. through addition of a monolayer of adsorbed N_2 or O_2 on the W.

In a private communication R. N. Varney (59) reports that, owing to the large cross section for charge exchange ~ 300 cm^2/cm^3 mm Hg at energies of 200 to 4,000 e.v., many neutral Hg atoms strike graphite or pure Fe which are not atomically clean. These neutrals liberate secondary electrons with a $\gamma_n = 0.50 \pm 0.25$ independent of energy. γ_i for Hg ions from these surfaces are ~ 0.04 at 3,000 volts. This action is not a kinetic ejection process and the ionization potential of Hg precludes potential liberation. It is not a γ_p from photons created in the gas. It could come from a photo effect of excited atoms on the Hg coated surface. Further study is needed.

D. J. Rose (60, 43) in a report and in a paper together with Eisinger discusses the secondary emission processes in a glow discharge in H_2. Using a clever device the actions of ion impact and photo effect on W cathodes in H_2 and Ne can be segregated. In H_2 at an $X/p = 600$, $\gamma_i = 0.07$, and the photo electric $\gamma_p = 0.035$. For Ne $\gamma_i = 0.20$ while $\gamma_p = 0.02$. In H_2 γ_i drops rapidly as X/p is reduced, which Rose ascribes to gas layers on the cathode that the light atoms cannot penetrate at low energies.

Very important in view of many breakdown studies now in progress, with alternating potentials at lower frequencies using glass cells with external electrodes, are the measurements of V. K. Rohatgi (61) on the photoelectric efficiencies for secondary electron liberation from glass, e.g., γ_p. Contrary to papers of V. Engel and Harries, the values of γ_p are 10^{-4} for 2,537 A° on borosilicate and on soda glass and $\sim 10^{-3}$ for radiations from a Ne glow discharge. The volume conductivity of the glass is such as to complicate the phenomena associated with low frequency breakdown with external electrodes.

In the laboratory of R. N. Varney (62) further studies have been made on the ionization of Hg atoms by fast Na^+ and K^+ ions. Although in the past Na^+ ions were observed to excite and ionize Hg and Ne at relatively low energies as reported in the book, K^+ did not seem to do so. From a recent private communication it seems that K^+ does ionize Ne at appropriate energies (> 60 volts). The electrons emitted in this case have ~ 20 e.v. energy. They are emitted highly directionally and thus escaped previous detection.

Several studies of radiations producing photo-ionization in the gas have appeared, W. H. Prowse and G. R. Bainbridge (63) report on such radiations from spark discharge. The paper cited extends earlier observations of Dechene and of Cravath. W. Bemerl and H. Fetz (64) report on photoelectrically active ultraviolet radiations in H_2 and O_2 discharges. The work is of doubtful value because of the unorthodox techniques used, which are replete with various potential sources of error. Probably the most striking and important investigation is that of A. Przybylski and H. Raether (65) and by Przybylski in studies of the gas-ionizing radiations in air and O_2. Two groups of wave lengths were found, one of $\sim 1,000$ A° with an absorption coefficient of 34 cm^{-1} and another with one $\sim > 100$ cm^{-1}. There is evidence for the former in some recent work by R. J. Westberg (66). Further data on the wave lengths, coefficients, and nature of such radiations come from the studies of G. L. Weissler (67) and his group, using vacuum spectrometers.

In connection with studies of the first coefficient cited, the papers of D. J. Rose (43) and of L. H. Fisher and D. J. Debitetto (44, 68), and W. Hopwood and N. J. Peacock in J. D. Cragg's (45) laboratory in Liverpool yield values for γ_p and γ_i for H_2, N_2, and O_2. The lack of physical cleanliness which is critical for γ_i and γ_p studies in all but those of Rose (43) renders the data of value only in relation to their experimental conditions. Electrodes must be atomically clean or coated with monolayers of known gases before such data have *general* significance. The peculiar behavior of γ_i in N_2 and H_2 with minute traces of O_2 reported by E. Huber and by L. Colli and U. Facchini indicate why such data are valueless.

K. J. Schmidt-Tiedemann (69) observed secondary electron yields in N_2, H_2, and O_2 at low pressures with clean electrodes, using single avalanche techniques. He observed a γ_i with N_2 gas, a γ_p with H_2, and a γ_p in O_2. He also noted an unexplained temporal delay in the yields of γ_i in N_2 of great significance in breakdown. In an earlier paper W. Kluge (70) observed secondary mechanisms in low-pressure discharges. Here gases and electrodes again were not clean.

R. Kluckow (71) measured current growth in static breakdown, observing the current rise using initial single as well as multiple avalanches. He verified the statistics of Legler, confirmed the observations of Bandel (IX 7) in air, and, perhaps more important, proved that *a single avalanche can start a breakdown sequence of the Townsend discharge.* His conditions permitted him to observe what seem to be anode streamer pulses.

Other Investigations on Processes of Atomic Physics
Bearing on Basic Processes

These contributions comprise: G. J. Schulz (72), "Measurement of Atomic and Molecular Excitation by a Trapped Electron Method," a most effective and sensitive *new method* for determining cross sections; G. J. Schulz and R. E. Fox (73), "Excitation of A and of He Metastables Near Threshold"; and J. F. Waymouth and F. Bitter (74), "Analysis of Plasmas of Flourescent Lamps" which yields data on concentrations of metastable atoms and interactions in inert gas Hg mixtures.

A. V. Phelps (75) in the Westinghouse Research Laboratories, using the most modern techniques, has collected a number of very important data concerning the destruction of metastable and other resonant states in He, Ne, and Hg. These are contained in a series of papers extending from 1953 on. The work is summarized in several more recent articles, namely, "Absorption Studies of He Metastable Atoms and Molecules" (1955), "Production and Destruction of Excited Atoms and Molecules" given as a paper at the Third International Congress on Gaseous Electronics (Venice, 1957), and finally in a Westinghouse Research Scientific Paper (December, 1958), entitled "Diffusion, Deëxcitation and Three Body Collision Coefficients for Excited Ne Atoms." These processes have such an important bearing on gaseous discharge plasma studies that they merit being read by all in this field. Proper presentation is too lengthy for inclusion in this section. The neon paper has the most complete data on any gas. Basically, measurements depend on optical absorption studies of known lines and bands with gated photomultiplier following a pulsed discharge. A very recent addition to this field of study is an article entitled "Current Dependence of Decay of Metastable Hg Atoms in Hg-A Discharge Afterglows," by M. Yokoyama (76). Here the destructive influence is by electron impacts. However, the behavior is quite involved.

Another study of great importance for basic process affecting breakdown thresholds revealing a new mechanism akin to the Penning effect is that of T. Nakaya (77). This deals with the influence of light on the starting potentials of a breakdown in glow discharge tubes containing fair pressures of A (from 4 to 15 mm of Hg), and relatively high pressures of Hg, e.g., such that there are densities of Hg starting at 10^{13} per cm^3 and extending to 3×10^{16} Hg atoms/cm^3. This requires wall temperatures of the discharge tube from $10°C$ to $90°C$. If the starting potentials of the DC discharge with gap length 30 cm and electrode diameter 2.3 cm are taken beginning at $10°C$ the starting potential $V_s \sim 700$ volts falls abruptly to a minimum of 500 volts near $18°C$ with 3×10^{13} atoms Hg/cm^3. Thereafter, the value of V_s rises rapidly to a flat maximum of 850 volts between $30°$ and $40°C$ at which point with 10^{14} Hg atoms/cm^3 there is a new decline to a flat minimum of $V_s = 650$ volts lying between $55°$ and $70°$ with between 5×10^{15} and 1×10^{16} atoms/cm^3. Thereafter, the potential V_s again rises to its former value of 900 volts. If the tube is illuminated with light the breakdown potential beyond 1×10^{15} Hg atoms and $40°C$ temperature remains around 850 volts and rises to 1,400 volts at 3×10^{16}

Hg atoms/cm^3. There is no light effect below 10^{14} atoms/cm^3. The most effective light is Hg arc light through glass, transmitting down to 2,537 A$^\circ$. The effect is most intense near the anode. H$_2$ gas quenches the action. At 0.7 mm A gas, visible light lowers the starting potential a little. The effect of illumination in raising V_s in some instances persists for some time with steady potential and is the more effective the more the electrodes are separated. This effect depends on the intensity of illumination, its duration, and the potential across the tube. The concentrations of Hg relative to A involved in the first drop of V_s are those characteristic of the Penning effect. This is only affected by destruction of the argon metastables, A^m, which create the Hg$^+$ ions with high efficiency. The A metastables are destroyed by A light but not appreciably by white light nor by 2,537. At low A densities, the reactions needed for lowering V_s in the higher pressure region are prevented by an inadequate supply and short diffusive loss lifetime of Hg^m metastable atoms. Here 2,537 may increase the amount of $^3P_1$ states and these give more Hg^m by impacts thus lowering the threshold slightly.

The very large rise in V_s at Hg pressures, well in excess of the ideal Penning effect concentrations, may be ascribed to the fact that in the predischarge period the currents build up a very high concentration of Hg$_2^*$ ($^3\Sigma_{ou}^-$) molecules from ^3P_o and $^3P_2$ Hg metastables, by Hg^m 6^3Po and 2 Hg (6^1S_o) $\rightarrow$ Hg$_2^m$ ($^3\Sigma_{ou}^-$) and more frequently by Hg^m 6^3P_0 and Hg^1 S$_0$ + A $\rightarrow$ Hg$_2^m$ ($^3\Sigma_{ou}^-$) + A with a conversion coefficient 10^{-30} n_{Hg} n_A. Here the A atoms as a vehicular gas assist in creation of the metastable molecule and reduce its loss by diffusion to the wall. As Kenty and Larson have shown with small current ($\sim$ 0.5 mA) and high argon pressure ($\sim$ 50 mm) with wall temperatures of 60°, the ionization of the Hg molecules is the predominant mechanism in a glow discharge column. Thus V_s is lowered by this action for it gives a gas of low ionizing potential. Any agent destroying the Hg$_2^m$ states or their generating agency, the Hg metastable atoms, will influence V_s. Thus light that destroys the Hg$_2^m$ will raise V_s. The 2,537 line or parts of it that are broad and self-reversed are close to the energy that converts Hg$_2$ (6^3P_o + 6^1S_o) to Hg (7^3S_0 + 6^1S_0) and so may destroy this vital molecule. Other light may affect the molecule but will also destroy Hg$_2^m$ $^3P_0$ and Hg^m $^3P_2$ by raising them to radiating states. This also raises V_s. All trace impurities such as H$_2$, N$_2$, O$_2$, CO$_2$, and CO destroy Hg^m. In time these are cleaned up by gas cataphoresis and so the tube becomes more sensitive as these impurities are cleaned by the discharge. H$_2$ deliberately added is very destructive of Hg^m for it is dissociated by the Hg^m and thus destroys the action of light and raises V_s. That the region near the anode is most sensitive to illumination follows from the fact that in the initial breakdown process the cumulative ionization and excitation are greatest in the anode region. What the effect of the prolonged illumination is and how it produces a prolonged increase in potential after the light has been cut off and how this is affected by the potential is not yet proven. The recent advances in understanding the mechanisms active in gas cataphoresis in glow discharge tubes coming from the work of C. Kenty and analysis by L. B. Loeb (78) may furnish a clue. This action causes segregation of gases at one end of the tube, e.g., for some discharge conditions Hg at the cathode in an A filled tube. Thus such segregation by changing concentrations in the anode region could easily account for such long recovery time actions if return diffusion is slow. This very important adjunct to the influence of current created entities on the breakdown mechanism leading to a photosensitive tube is a striking illustration of the complexities appearing when dealing with gaseous plasmas.

Further contributions have been made to the study of breakdown criteria. A. L. Ward (79), using the computers at the Bureau of Standards, has extended the calculations of the effect of space charge in a cold cathode discharge in pure A at low pressures. The calculation is quite complete and supplements earlier work going close up to the glow discharge condition.

P. L. Auer (80) has extended his analysis of the growth of a Townsend Discharge in a handier and more rigorous fashion. This, together with a further amplification of Davidson's (81) methods, leaves this problem in fairly good shape. A somewhat more fallible calculation carried out by Miyoshi (82) appeared somewhat earlier and has been criticized by Davidson.

Probably more important relative to the question of the mechanism of the of the filamentary spark breakdown in air and the streamer theory are two papers by W. Köhrmann (83) in Raether's laboratory. These papers locate the point in dry and moist air at which the transition from a streamer spark resulting from space change distortion by an antecedent Townsend discharge goes over to a streamer spark starting from a single avalanche. This transition region has been sought by L. H. Fisher and by B. Gänger and others but with no success. This point gives the critical avalanche size needed to launch a streamer spark from the anode in air at atmospheric pressure. It is somewhat dependent on moisture content. For dry air it occurs at 6.5% over voltage and at 3% over voltage at 14 mm H_2O vapor. Further light on the mechanism of streamer breakdown in air comes from the dissertation of G. G. Hudson, University of California, June, 1957, and in a paper by the author at the III International Conference of Gaseous Electronics (84). Here by fast photomultiplier techniques using two photomultipliers scanning gaps extending from the point to plane types to 30 cm diameter spheres to planes, the primary and secondary streamers going from anode to cathode were observed as well as some evidence of branching. Cross plots of luminosity across the gap at various times points toward the action of ionizing potential space waves of high speed in building the arc channel.

Very recently E. Nasser (84) at the Technical University of Berlin has adroitly applied the Lichtenberg figure technique to the analysis of streamer breakdown in air at atmospheric pressure. Using a photographic film normal to the axis in point to plane corona below and above spark breakdown potentials, at various distances from the point and pulsed square potential impulses, many data are obtained. At points of impact of streamer channels on the film the length of the Lichtenberg traces gives streamer tip potentials. The multiplicity of streamers by branching is observed and studied. The photoelectric effect in advance of the tips is observed. Velocities of streamer tips can be measured and avalanche size needed for streamer initiation are estimated in agreement with estimates by the author and Raether.

In connection with the behavior of O_2 in which streamer formation is most common, F. Kaufman and J. R. Kelso (85) report on the dissociation of O_2 molecules in electrical discharges. Using a microwave breakdown technique, dissociation of very pure O_2 is observed to be less than 1%. Small amounts of N_2 (0.01%) and up raises the output of O atoms to nearly 80 for every N_2 molecule added. Walls are of no influence and electron concentrations are little changed by N_2. The effect is a catalytic one involving formation of NO. This alters all previous theories of the dissociation of O_2 in discharges.

Other advances of interest have been made in the study of sputtering mechanisms especially by G. Wehner (86). These include not only comprehensive data on mercury ions of low energy but a new measurement and analysis of forces active on bombardment of electrodes by ions. Considerable progress has been made on the study of the pumping action of the Alpert-Bayard ion gauge and the trapping and reëmission of trapped He atoms from glass and Mo surfaces. This work was done by L. J. Varnerin (87) and J. H. Carmichael who measure trapping efficiency (atoms removed/atoms collected) from 150 to 2,600 e.v. The trapping is in all cases associated with metal surfaces, or with sputtered or evaporated metals on glass. In all cases penetration of He atoms and others seems to be confined to within a few Å of the surface. The efficiency of the process is limited by reëmission rather than by a saturation of trapping sites and is unaffected by the surface occupation up to a monolayer. The impact of ions does not release important quantities of trapped atoms. The reëmission plays an important role and depends on the past history of the surface. The gas reëvolved on a time scale short compared to observation times results in an apparent trapping efficiency less than unity. The long time reëmission of gas gives rise to the saturation effect. These observations go far to clarifying a hitherto baffling phenomenon but one having no relation to chemical clean-up of gases termed "gettering."

BIBLIOGRAPHY TO APPENDIX I

(1) H. J. Oskam, Jour. Appl. Phys. 27, 848, 1956. Microwave Investigation of Disintegrating Gaseous Discharge Plasmas, Thesis Univ. of Utrecht. November, 1957.
(2) M. Pahl and U. Weimer, Naturwissenschaften, 44, 487, 1957. Zeits. f. Naturforschung, 12A, 926, 1957; 13A, 50, 743, 1958. U. Weimer, Zeits. f. Naturforschung, 13A, No. 4, 1958, 14A, 239, 1959.
(3) H. Dreeskamp, Zeits. f. Naturforschung, 12A, 876, 1957.
(4) O. M. Saproschenko, Phys. Rev. 111, 1550, 1958.
(5) L. M. Channin and M. A. Biondi, Phys. Rev. 107, 1219, 1957.
(6) E. C. Beaty, Phys. Rev. 104, 17, 1956. L. M. Channin and M. A. Biondi, Phys. Rev. 106, 473, 1957.
(7) R. N. Varney, F. R. Kovar, and E. C. Beaty, Phys. Rev. 107, 1490, 1957.
(8) L. S. Frost, Phys. Rev. 105, 354, 1957.
(9) D. S. Burch and R. Geballe, Phys. Rev. 106, 183, 188, 1957.
(10) E. A. Mason, H. W. Schamp, Jr., and J. T. Vanderslice, Annals of Physics, 4, 233, 1958. E. A. Mason and J. T. Vanderslice, Phys. Rev. 114, 497, 1959.
(11) D. J. Rose, 12th Ann. Gaseous Electronics Conf. Washington, D.C., October 15, 1959, Paper D-2.
(12) A. L. Gilardini and S. C. Brown, Phys. Rev. 105, 31, 1957.
(13) T. E. Bortner, G. S. Hurst, and G. W. Stone, Rev. Sci. Inst. 28, 103, 1957.
(14) A. H. Dougal and L. Goldstein, Phys. Rev. 109, 615, 1957.

(15) L. Goldstein, J. Sekiguchi, and H. Fletcher, Phys. Rev. *109*, 625, 1958.

(16) H. Margenau, Phys. Rev. *108*, 1367, 1957.

(17) L. G. H. Huxley, Austral. Jour. Res. *10*, 118, 1957.

(18) M. P. Madan, E. I. Godon, and S. J. Buchsbaum, Phys. Rev. *106*, 839, 1957.

(19) L. S. Frost and A. V. Phelps, 12th Ann. Gaseous Electronics Conf. Washington, D. C., October 15, 1959, Paper D-3.

(20) G. J. Schultz and S. C. Brown, Phys. Rev. *98*, 1642, 1955.

(21) T. H. Yeung and J. Sayers, Proc. Phys. Soc. Lon. *70B*, 663, 1957.

(22) R. L. F. Boyd, P. Reynolds, and J. E. Allen, Proc. Phys. Soc. Lon. *70B*, 297, 1957.

(23) T. Okada and K. Yamamoto, Jour. Phys. Soc. Japan, *13*, 1212, 1958.

(24) G. Medicus, Rev. Sci. Inst. *28*, 822, 1957, Jour. Appl. Phys. 27, 1242, 1956, Phys. Rev. *29*, 903, 1958.

(25) W. M. Hickam and R. E. Fox, Jour. Chem. Phys. *25*, 642, 1956.

(26) R. E. Fox, Jour. Chem. Phys. *26*, 1281, 1957.

(27) H. Neuert, Zeits. f. Naturforschung, *8a*, 459, 1953.

(28) M. A. Biondi and R. E. Fox, or Biondi, or Fox, Phys. Rev. *109*, 2005, 1958; *109*, 2008, 2012, 1958. Biondi, Westinghouse Paper 403 FD, 310 p-3 June, 1959, Fox, Westinghouse Sci. Paper 6-40306-1-Pl, July 15, 1959.

(29) G. J. Schulz, Westinghouse Research, Scientific Paper 6-94439-4 P 12, July 21, 1958.

(30) J. D. Craggs, A. Thorborn, and B. A. Toze, Proc. Roy. Soc. *A* 240, 473, 1957.

(31) V. A. J. Van Lint, E. J. Wikner, D. L. Trueblood, 12th Ann. Gaseous Electronics Conf. Washington, D.C., October 15, 1959, Paper F-1.

(32) L. M. Channin and M. A. Biondi, Westinghouse Research Report 6-94439-7R5 October, 1957.

(33) A. V. Phelps, 12th Ann. Gaseous Electronics Conf. Washington, D.C., October 15, 1959, Paper E-5.

(34) D. S. Burch, S. J. Smith, L. M. Branscomb, Phys. Rev. *112*, 171, 1958. L. M. Branscomb, D. S. Burch, S. J. Smith, and S. Geltman, Phys. Rev. *111*, 504, 1958.

(35) S. Geltman, Phys. Rev. *112*, 176, 1958.

(36) P. M. Waters, Phys. Rev. *111*, 1053, 1958.

(37) K. B. Persson and S. C. Brown, Phys. Rev. *106*, 1915, 1957.

(38) D. E. Kerr, and M. N. Hirsh, Bull. Am. Phys. Soc. *3*, 228, 1958. Also 11 Annual Conf. on Gaseous Electronics, D.E.P. of Am. Phys. Soc. New York, October 22-25, 1958, paper C-6, p. 30. E. P. Gray and D. E. Kerr 12th Ann. Gaseous Electronics Conf. Washington, D.C., October 15, 1959, Paper E-4.

(39) W. A. Rogers, Westinghouse Research Report 6-94439-7R6, December 18, 1957. Also 11 Conf. Gaseous Electronics, New York, October 22-25, 1958, Paper C7, p. 31.

(40) D. E. Kerr, personal communication, October 15, 1959.

(41) T. H. Yeung, Proc. Phys. Soc. Lon. *71*, 341, 1958.

(42) R. G. Fowler and W. R. Atkinson, Phys. Rev. *113*, 1268, 1959.

(43) D. J. Rose, Phys. Rev. *104*, 273, 1956.

(44) L. H. Fisher and D. J. Debitetto, Phys. Rev. *104*, 1212, 1956.

(45) W. Hopwood, N. J. Peacock, and D. Wilkes, Proc. Roy. Soc. *A235*, 339, 1956.

(46) J. M. Somerville, H. A. Blevin and S. C. Haydon, Nature, *179*, 38, 1957.

(47) M. A. Harrison, Phys. Rev., *105*, 366, 1957.

(48) R. W. Crompton, J. Dutton, S. C. Haydon, and Llewellyn Jones, Proc. Phys. Soc. Lon. *69B*, 2, 1956.

(49) W. Legler, Zeits. f. Phys. *140*, 221, 1955; Ann der Phys. *18*, 374, 1956.

(50) K. J. Schmidt, Zeits. f. Phys. *139*, 251, 1954, *139*, 266, 1954.

(51) L. Frommhold, Zeits. f. Phys. *144*, 396, 1956, *150*, 172, 1958.

(52) K. J. Schmidt-Tiedemann, Zeits. f. Angew, Physik, *9*, 454, 1957.

(53) J. K. Vogel and H. Raether, Zeits. f. Phys. *147*, 141, 1957; J. K. Vogel, Zeits. f. Phys. *148*, 355, 1957.

(54) W. Legler, Zeits. f. Phys. *143*, 173, 1955.

(55) L. Frommhold, Zeits. f. Phys. *145*, 324, 1956.

(56) H. D. Hagstrum, Phys. Rev. *104*, 301, 317, 1956, Phys. Rev. *104*, 1516, 1956.

(57) H. W. Berry, Jour. App. Phys. *24*, 1219, 1958.

(58) P. M. Waters, Phys. Rev. *121*, 1053, 1958.

(59) R. N. Varney, personal communication, August, 1959.

(60) D. J. Rose and J. Eisinger, Bull. Am. Phys. Soc. 2, 84, 1957. Also Bell Laboratories Technical Report, 1957.

(61) V. K. Rohatgi, Jour. Appl. Phys. *28*, 951, 1957.

(62) R. N. Varney, private communication, December, 1958.

(63) W. N. Prowse and G. R. Bainbridge, Can. Jour. Res. *35*, 324, 1957.

(64) W. Bemerl and H. Fetz, Zeits. Angew. Phys. *8*, 424, 1956.

(65) A. Przybylski and H. Raether, Zeits. f. Naturforschung, *13a*, 234, 1958; A. Przybylski, Zeits. f. Phys. *151*, 264, 1958. Office of Naval Research Technical Report No. 21 Contract Nonx 228 (11) Proj. Desig. NR-017-505, August 11, 1958.

(66) R. J. Westberg, Phys. Rev. *114*, 1, 1959.

(67) G. L. Weissler and Associates, Encyclopedia of Physics, Vol. XXI, Chap. 4, pp. 304-382, Springer Verlag, Berlin, 1956.

(68) D. J. Debitetto and L. H. Fisher, Phys. Rev. *111*, 390, 1958.

(69) K. J. Schmidt-Tiedemann, Zeits. f. Phys. *150*, 299, 1958.

(70) W. Kluge, Zeits. f. Phys. *146*, 314, 1956.

(71) R. Kluckow, Zeits. F. Phys. *148*, 564, 1957.

(72) G. J. Schulz, Phys. Rev. Let. *1*, 223, 1958, To appear Phys. Rev. 1959.

(73) G. J. Schulz and R. E. Fox, Phys. Rev. *106*, 1179, 1957.

(74) J. F. Waymouth and F. Bitter, Jour. App. Phys. *27*, 122, 1956.

(75) A. V. Phelps and J. P. Molnar, Phys. Rev. *89*, 1202, 1953 and A. V. Phelps, Phys. Rev. *99*, 1307, 1955; *110*, 1362, 1958, Paper, 3d Int. Conf. Gaseous Electronics Venice, 1957, Westinghouse Research Scientific Paper No. 6-94439-6-P3, May 8, 1957, and for Neon Scientific Paper No. 6-94439-6-P5, December 15, 1958.

(76) M. Yokoyama, Science of Light, Japan, 7, 42, 1958.

(77) T. Nakaya, Proc. Phys. Soc. Japan, *11*, 1264, 1956.

(78) C. Kenty, Bull. Am. Phys. Soc. Ser. II, 3, 82, 1958, L. B. Loeb, Jour. Appl. Phys. *29*, 1368, 1958.

(79) A. L. Ward, Phys. Rev. Ltrs. *1*, 475, 1958, to appear Phys. Rev. 1959.

(80) P. L. Auer, Phys. Rev. *111*, 671, 1958.

(81) P. M. Davidson, Phys. Rev. *106*, 1, 1957.

(82) N. Miyoshi, Phys. Rev. *103*, 1609, 1956.

(83) W. Köhrmann, Zeits. f. Angew. Phys. 7, 183, 1955; Ann. der Phys. *18*, 379, 1956.

(84) L. B. Loeb, Italian Phys. Soc. Report on III Int. Conf. on Phenomena in Ionized gases, Venice 11-15, June, 1957, Publ. Milan, October, 1957 p. 646. E. Nasser, Archiv f. Elektrotechnik, *44*, 157, 168, 1959.

(85) F. Kaufman and J. R. Kelso, 12th Ann. Conf. on Gaseous Electronics, Washington, D.C., October 15, 1959, Paper F-5.

(86) G. Wehner, Phys. Rev. *102*, 690, 1956, Phys. Rev. *108*, 35, 1957. General Mills Scientific Report, 1847, April 30, 1958.

(87) L. J. Varnerin and J. H. Carmichael, Jour. Appl. Phys. *28*, 913, 1957.

APPENDIX II

STANDARD REFERENCE DATA

LIST OF FUNDAMENTAL CONSTANTS
After J. W. DuMond and E. R. Cohen, 1952, as reported in *Reviews of Modern Physics*, volume 25, page 691, 1953.

Not correlated with variables of least square adjustment

Standard volume of a perfect gas (physical scale)
$V_0 = 22420.7 \pm 0.6$ cm^3 atm mole^{-1}

Gas constant per mole (physical scale)
$R_0 = (8.31662 \pm 0.00038) \times 10^7$ erg mole^{-1} deg^{-1} C.

Atomic mass of hydrogen
H = 1.008142 $\pm$ 0.000003

Rydberg wave number for infinite mass H and He
$R_\infty = 109737.309 \pm 0.012$ cm^{-1}
$R_H = 109677.576 \pm 0.012$ cm^{-1}
$R_{He4} = 109722.267 \pm 0.012$ cm^{-1}

Least square adjusted output values. The quantities following the ± sign show the standard error by external consistency

Velocity of light
$C = 299792.9 \pm 0.8$ km sec^{-1}

Avogadro number (physical scale)
$N = (6.02472 \pm 0.00036) \times 10^{23}$ (g mole)$^{-1}$

Loschmidt number (physical scale)
$L_0 = N/V_0 = (2.68713 \pm 0.00016) \times 10^{19}$ cm^{-3}

Electronic charge
$e = (4.80288 \pm 0.00021) \times 10^{-10}$ e.s.u.

$e' = e/c = (1.60207 \pm 0.00007) \times 10^{-20}$ e.m.u.

Electron rest mass
$m = (9.1085 \pm 0.0006) \times 10^{-28}$ g

Proton rest mass
$m_p = (1.67243 \pm 0.00010) \times 10^{-24}$ g

Neutron rest mass
$m_n = (1.67474 \pm 0.00010) \times 10^{-24}$ g

Planck constant
$h = (6.6252 \pm 0.0005) \times 10^{-27}$ erg sec
$\hbar = h/2\pi = (1.05444 \pm 0.00009) \times 10^{-27}$ erg sec

Faraday constant (physical scale)
$F = Ne = (2.89360 \pm 0.00007) \times 10^{14}$ e.s.u. (g mole)$^{-1}$
$F' = Ne/c = (9652.01 \pm 0.25)$ e.m.u. (g mole)$^{-1}$

Charge to mass ratio of electron
$e/m = (5.27299 \pm 0.00016) \times 10^{17}$ e.s.u. g^{-1}
$e'/m = e/mc = (1.75888 \pm 0.00005) \times 10^7$ e.m.u. g^{-1}

Ratio h/e
$h/e = (1.37943 \pm 0.00005) \times 10^{-17}$ erg sec (e.s.u.)$^{-1}$

Fine structure constant $\alpha = e^2/\hbar c$
$\alpha = (7.29726 \pm 0.00008) \times 10^{-3}$

Atomic mass of proton
$H^+ = 1.007593 \pm 0.000003$

Ratio of proton mass to electron mass
1836.13 ± 0.04

First Bohr radius
$a_0 = \hbar^2/me^2 = (5.29171 \pm 0.00006) \times 10^{-9}$ cm

Classical electron radius
$r_0 = e^2/mc^2 = (2.81784 \pm 0.00010) \times 10^{-13}$ cm
$r_0^2 = (7.9402 \pm 0.005) \times 10^{-26}$ cm^2

Compton wave length of the electron
$\lambda_{ce} = h/mc = (24.2625 \pm 0.0006) \times 10^{-11}$ cm

Fine structure doublet separation in H
$\Delta E_H = 0.365969 \pm 0.000008$ cm^{-1}

Boltzmann constant
$k = R_0/N = (1.38042 \pm 0.00010) \times 10^{-16}$ erg deg^{-1}
$k = (8.6164 \pm 0.0004) \times 10^{-5}$ e.v. deg^{-1}

First radiation constant
$C_1 = 8\pi hc = (4.9919 \pm 0.0004) \times 10^{15}$ erg cm

Second radiation constant
$C_2 = hc/k = (1.43884 \pm 0.00008)$ cm deg

Atomic specific heat constant
$C_2/c = (4.79946 \pm 0.00027) \times 10^{-11}$ sec deg

Wien displacement law constant
$\lambda_m T = 0.28979 \pm 0.00005$ cm deg

Stefan Boltzmann constant
$\sigma = (\pi^2/60) \cdot (k^4/\hbar c^2) = (0.56686 \pm 0.00005) \times 10^{-4}$ erg cm^{-2} deg^{-4} sec^{-1}

Bohr magneton
$\mu_0 = he/(4\pi mc) = (0.92732 \pm 0.00006) \times 10^{-20}$ erg gauss^{-1}

Magnetic moment of the electron
$\mu_e = (0.92838 \pm 0.0006) \times 10^{-20}$ erg gauss^{-1}

Nuclear magneton
$\mu_n = \mu_0 \; Nm/H^+ = (0.505038 \pm 0.000036) \times 10^{-23}$ erg gauss^{-1}

Proton moment
$\mu_p = 2.79277 \pm 0.00006$ nuclear magnetons

Mass energy conversion factors
1 g = $(5.60999 \pm 0.00025) \times 10^{26}$ m.e.v.
1 electron mass = 0.510984 ± 0.000016 m.e.v.
1 atomic mass unit = 931.162 ± 0.024 m.e.v.
1 proton mass = 938.232 ± 0.024 m.e.v.
1 neutron mass = 939.526 ± 0.024 m.e.v.

Quantum energy conversion factors
1 e.v. = $(1.60207 \pm 0.00007) \times 10^{-12}$ erg

Wave length associated with 1 abs e.v.
$E\lambda_g = (12397.8 \pm 0.5) \times 10^{-8}$ e.v.-cm

Wave number associated with 1 abs volt
$\bar{\nu}/E = (8065.98 \pm 0.30)$ cm^{-1} e.v.$^{-1}$

Ionization potential of hydrogen
$E_{iH} = 13.5978 \pm 0.0005$ e.v.

De Broglie wave length of the electron
$\lambda_{De} = 7.27373 \pm 0.00016$ cm^2 sec^{-1}/v
$= (1.226377 \pm 0.000032) \times 10^{-7}$ cm (e.v.)$^{1/2}$/$E^{1/2}$

Other useful constants taken from R. T. Birge of 1941

Gravitational constant
$G = (6.670 \pm 0.005) \times 10^{-8}$ dyne cm^2 gram^2

Standard liter
$1 = 1000.028 \pm 0.001$ cm^3

International ohm = p absolute ohm
$p = 1.00048 \pm 0.00002$

International ampere = q absolute ampere
$q = 0.99986 \pm 0.00002$

International volt = pq absolute volt
$pq = 1.00034 \pm 0.00003$

International joule = pq^2 absolute joule
$pq^2 = 1.00020 \pm 0.000045$

Pressure atmosphere at 45° lat A_{45}
$A_{45} = (1.013199 \pm 0.000003) \times 10^6$
dyne/cm^2

Mechanical equivalent of heat
$J = (4.1847 \pm 0.0008) \times 10^7$ erg per
cal 15

Absolute temperature melting ice above absolute 0 in °K
$T_0 = 273.15 \pm 0.01$ °K

Acceleration gravity at 45° lat
$g_{45} = 980.616$ cm per sec^2

ATOMIC CRITICAL POTENTIALS OF CERTAIN ELEMENTS IN E.V.

Data largely from C. Moore, "Atomic Energy Levels," U. S. Bureau of
Standards Circular No. 467, vols. I and II, 1949, 1952

Element	First Electronic Potential		Metastable Levels			Ionization Potential
H	10.16 $^3S_1$	— $^3P_1$	— $^3P_2$	— $^3P_0$	— $^1S_0$	13.595
He^4	19.81	20.96	20.96	20.96	20.62	24.580
Ne	—	16.53	16.62	16.72	—	21.559
A	—	11.62	11.53	11.72	—	15.755
Kr	—	9.98	9.82	10.51	—	13.996
Xe	—	8.39	8.28	9.4	—	12.127
Mg	—	2.71	2.715	2.705	—	7.644
Cu	—	1.882	1.895	1.879	—	6.111
Ba	—	1.115	1.138	1.185	—	5.210
Hg	—	4.89	5.47	4.67	—	10.434
Element	First Excitation Potential					Ionization Potential
Li	1.845					5.390
Na	2.11					5.138
K	1.61					4.339
Rb	1.56					4.176
Cs	1.38					3.893
O	1.967 9.15					13.614
N	2.382 3.576 10.33					14.54
C	1.263					11.264
F	12.71					17.418
Cl	0.109 8.825					13.01
Br	—					11.84
I	2.34					10.44

MOLECULAR CRITICAL POTENTIALS IN E.V.

From Herzberg and other sources. Dissociation data after Leo Brewer.

Gas	First Electronic Excitation Potential	Energy of Dissociation	Ionization Potential
H_2	11.47	4.477	15.422
O_2	1.635	5.115	12.2
N_2	5.23	9.762	15.576
O_3	—	6.17	—
NO	5.38	6.507	9.25
CO	6.04	11.111	14.00
CO_2	10.0	16.562	13.7
H_2O	7.6	9.511	12.6
Cl_2	2.27	2.481	13.2
Br_2	1.71	1.97	13.3
I_2	1.472	1.542	9.0
N_2O	—	11.439	11.0
OH	4.06	4.45	12.9
HCl	9.62	4.40	—
He_2	—	—	4.251
SO_2	—	—	12.1

INDEX TO AUTHORS *

*Lightface page references will be found in text.
Boldface references occur in bibliographies.

INDEX TO SUBJECTS